JANE'S
FIGHTING SHIPS
1919

JANE'S FIGHTING SHIPS 1919

A Reprint of the 1919 Edition of Fighting Ships

Founded by

FRED T. JANE

Edited by
Surgeon-Lieut O. PARKES, RN
and MAURICE PRENDERGAST

ARCO PUBLISHING COMPANY, INC.
New York

First published by Sampson Low Marston in 1919

This edition published 1969 by ARCO PUBLISHING COMPANY, INC.
219 Park Avenue South, New York, N.Y. 10003

Library of Congress Catalog Number 69-14519
ARCO Book Number 668-02018-0

Printed in Great Britain

ALPHABETICAL LIST OF ADVERTISERS.

CLASSIFIED LIST OF ADVERTISERS.—Continued.

15 adv.

VICKERS LIMITED.

ALL TYPES OF WARSHIPS DESIGNED, BUILT, ENGINED, ARMED, AND ARMOURED READY FOR SERVICE.

COMMERCIAL SHIPS.

MAIL and PASSENGER STEAMERS.

Icebreakers, Dredgers, and other Special Craft.

Turbines.

Steam, Oil, and Gas Engines.

Floating Docks and Cranes.

AIRCRAFT.

Small Tools.

Manufacturers of the Single Collar Thrust, Bearings of the Michell Oil Film type for any power of Reciprocating Engines, Turbines, or other Machinery. These Bearings are particularly suitable for heavy loads at high speeds with oil bath or forced lubrication. Single Collar Thrust Blocks are now fitted to shafts transmitting 20,000 Shaft Horse Power.

Locomotive Crank Axles.

High Tensile Steel Tyres. ("Australia Brand.")

Stampings and Forgings of all kinds.

Bevel Gears.

Train Lighting by Electricity.

Electrical Equipment of every description.

Motor Cars.

"DURALUMIN" (Regd. Trade Mark.)

High Efficiency Vacuum Plants, Contraflo Condensers, Kinetic Reciprocating Air Pumps, Cascade Filters, Winch Condensers, Feed Heaters, and Evaporators for Land and Marine Installations.

HEAD OFFICES:
Vickers House, Broadway, LONDON, S.W. I.
WORKS:
Barrow-in-Furness, Sheffield, Birmingham, Erith, Dartford, Crayford, Ipswich, Weybridge.

JOHN BROWN & COMPANY Limited.

Head Office:—ATLAS WORKS, SHEFFIELD.

Telegrams:—"ATLAS, SHEFFIELD"

Shipyard and Engine Works:—CLYDEBANK, near GLASGOW.

Telegrams:—"SHIPYARD, CLYDEBANK"

Foundry:—SCUNTHORPE, LINCS.   Telegrams:—"ATLAS, SCUNTHORPE."

London Office:—8, THE SANCTUARY, WESTMINSTER, S.W.

Builders of **WARSHIPS** of the greatest dimensions and power.

BATTLESHIPS, CRUISERS, TORPEDO BOATS, DESTROYERS

FIRST-CLASS HIGH-SPEED OCEAN STEAMERS,

OF THE LARGEST SIZE AND POWER.

MANUFACTURERS OF

ARMOUR PLATES.

Hollow Rolled TURBINE DRUMS.

FORGED WHEELS AND SPINDLES FOR TURBINE ENGINES.

GUN FORGINGS.

LARGEST SIZES OF CRANK & STRAIGHT SHAFTING.

MARINE BOILER FURNACES.

Railway and Tram Tyres, Axles, Springs, Buffers, Steel Castings, etc.

Steam Yacht "MAYFLOWER."

"AQUITANIA."

SHIPYARD & ENGINE WORKS, CLYDEBANK, near GLASGOW.

MERRYWEATHERS'
FIRE & SALVAGE BOATS

For SEA, HARBOUR & RIVER USE.

SPECIALLY DESIGNED TO SUIT LOCAL REQUIREMENTS.

Merryweathers' Fire and Salvage Tug for Naples.

MERRYWEATHER Electric Sanitary Pumps for Warships, Steamships, etc.

MERRYWEATHER Fresh Water Electric Pumps { for Warships, Steamships, etc.

MERRYWEATHER Electric Submersible Pumps and Ship Salvage Plant.

MERRYWEATHER Light portable "VALIANT" Steam Pump and Fire Engine for Warships, Steamships, etc.

MERRYWEATHER "HATFIELD" Pump, { driven by petrol, electricity, steam or other motive power.

MERRYWEATHER Light portable Pumps and Boilers { for Salvage use on existing tugs.

MERRYWEATHER High-class Hose Piping { for Fire, Sea Salvage and other uses.

Illustrated Catalogues and Estimates on application.

MERRYWEATHER & SONS Ld.,
Greenwich, LONDON, S.E.10.

Contractors to the British and Foreign Admiralties.

MOTOR LAUNCHES

Our Motor Boat and Launch shops in continuation of pre-war practices have been very considerably enlarged and extended and equipped on the most modern lines, enabling us to offer the best in design and construction. The activities of our Flying Boat and Seaplane enterprise, have resulted in the inauguration of the first Flying Boat passenger service in the world, on which is used The Supermarine Four Seater Channel Type. We have similar machines ready to supply to any company or corporation desiring to establish a similar service in any part of the world.

The same high class standard of design and excellence of workmanship and materials are embodied in our Motor Launches. The model illustrated can be used for sea or river work, and is fitted with electric self-starter and all the latest and most up-to-date improvements, full details of these are given in our Motor Launch Brochure, which contains a complete specification, a copy of this will be sent upon application. Quotations sent on application, and immediate delivery can be given.

No. 1792

LONDON OFFICE }	DONINGTON HOUSE, NORFOLK STREET, STRAND, W.C.2.	TELEPHONE CENTRAL 7770.
TELEPHONE TELEGRAMS and CABLES }	37 WOOLSTON, 2 lines. "SUPERMARIN," SOUTHAMPTON.	CABLE CODES } WESTERN UNION. A.B.C. 5th EDN. MARCONI INTERNATIONAL.

SUPERMARINE AVIATION WORKS, Lᵀᴰ
SOUTHAMPTON, ENGLAND.

Chantier et Ateliers de St. Nazaire (Penhoët.)

SOCIÉTÉ ANONYME AU CAPITAL DE 12 MILLIONS SIÉGE SOCIAL: 6 BIS RUE AUBER PARIS.

Chantier de PENHOËT a Saint-Nazaire
Chantier de Normandie à Grand Ouevilly près Rouen) France

NAVIRES DE GUERRE.   NAVIRES DE COMMERCE.

Cuirassé "LORRAINE"
de la Marine Nationale Française.

CUIRASSÉS,   CROISEURS-CUIRASSÉS
CONTRE-TORPILLEURS, TORPILLEURS
CANONNIÈRES.

Paquebot "FRANCE"
de la Cie Générale Transatlantique.

PAQUEBOTS DE LUXE ET MIXTES,
YACHTS, CARGO-BOATS, PÉTROLIERS
REMORQUEURS.

MACHINES ET CHAUDIERES MARINES DE TOUS SYSTÈMES.   **TURBINES MARINES "PARSONS"**

CHANTIERS
ET
ATELIERS
Augustin Normand
LE HAVRE

—

DESTROYERS = TORPEDO BOATS = SUBMARINE AND SUBMERSIBLE BOATS

YACHTS AND FAST BOATS —— MERCHANT AND FISHING VESSELS

40 advt.

MARINE GEARED STEAM TURBINES.

De Laval Geared Marine Turbine for Cargo Boat;
3000 h.p.

The De Laval Marine Turbine is of the pressure stage impulse type. The expansion of steam is accomplished entirely in the nozzle and the same pressure exists on both sides of each wheel, so that theoretically no end thrust exists and close clearances are unnecessary. The wheels are forged steel discs, and proportioned to withstand high rotating speeds. The shafts are so proportioned that the critical speed is much higher than the normal running speed. Ample reversing power is provided by a special reversing element on the rotor.

The wheel case is so supported that it is free to expand in all directions without changing the position of the centre line and it is, therefore, possible to start the turbine quickly and safely without danger of rubbing, vibration and other troubles due to distortion.

THE DE LAVAL DOUBLE HELICAL SPEED REDUCING GEAR,

De Laval Gear for Destroyer; 13,500 h.p.

Upon which the success of the modern marine turbine depends, was introduced by the De Laval Company in 1889, since which time thousands of De Laval gears have been placed in successful operation. They are cut on special machines, developed, designed and built for the purpose by the De Laval Steam Turbine Company, and each gear after cutting is carefully tested for correct angle, correct shape of tooth and correct pitch.

The gear case is of rigid design, holding both gear and pinions in correct alignment. The bearing seats are carefully scraped to standard size to insure interchangeability of the bearings, which can be removed without disturbing the main parts. The bearings consist of shells split horizontally, lined with babbitt and ground on all contact surfaces to standard dimensions.

The gear has either a cast iron or cast steel centre upon which are shrunk seamless rolled steel bands, specially treated to secure uniform hardness of the teeth.

The shaft is of hammer forged open hearth steel, ground on all surfaces to standard dimensions. The pinions are cut directly on the pinion shafts, which are chrome nickel steel forgings of greater hardness than that of the gear bands.

All De Laval Marine Turbines and Gears are designed for forced feed lubrication.

According to the size and speed of the boat, single-pinion, single reduction, two-pinion, double-reduction, and double reductions with either one or two turbine shafts are supplied.

All turbines and gears are built according to the requirements of Lloyd's Register of Shipping.

DE LAVAL STEAM TURBINE DRIVEN AUXILIARIES include Circulating, Boiler Feed, Bilge, Cargo and Fire Pumps, also Turbo-Generators and Blowers.

The organization and the equipment of the De Laval shops have been developed during the past twenty years in the manufacture of Steam Turbines, Speed-reducing Gears, Centrifugal Pumps, and other special centrifugal equipment. Only high-grade work is turned out. Parts are standardized and are built and inspected by means of limit gauges to insure accurate dimensions and perfect interchangeability. Capacities and efficiencies are guaranteed and equipment carefully tested at the works before shipment.

ASK FOR OUR LITERATURE ON MARINE EQUIPMENT.

DE LAVAL STEAM TURBINE CO., Trenton, N.J., U.S.A.

De Laval Two-pinion Speed-reducing Gear for
17½ knot Passenger Boat.

Two-pinion Double-helical Gear for Destroyer;
13,500 h.p.

De Laval Double-pinion Speed-reducing Gear for
Destroyer; 6500 h.p.; 3600 to 450 r.p.m.

De Laval Compound Marine Turbine; 2500 h.p.

BAUSCH & LOMB OPTICAL CO.,

Range Finder
(20-foot Base)

Range Finders for Coast Defense up to 50-foot Base } with absolute internal

Range Finders for Turrets up to 35-foot Base } adjustment for infinity

Submarine Periscopes Instantly Convertible into Range Finder or a Vertical Telescope with 100° Field for Observing Aeroplanes

Searchlights

Gun Sight Telescopes

Field Glasses (Stereo Prism Binocular).

Stereo Prism Binocular.

Bausch & Lomb Optical Co.,

Rochester, N. Y., U. S. A.
37-38 Hatton Garden, London, E. C.

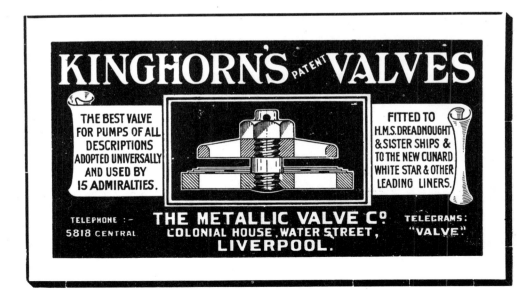

The "DOG-WATCH" Nautical Binocular.

(Specially designed for Marine use at night.)

Height when closed, 3¾ inches.   Magnifying power, 3 diameters.

Diameter of object lenses, **2 inches.**   Field of View at 1,000 yds. 180 yds.

The "Dog-Watch" Binocular has been specially designed with a view to making it as efficient as possible for use at sea under *unfavourable* conditions of *light* and *atmosphere*. Having the moderately low magnifying power of 3 diameters it will be found of great utility when the conditions are not favourable and will clearly define objects when glasses of higher power will fail to do so. The object lenses are extra large, thus admitting the greatest possible amount of light, and giving an extraordinarily brilliant image.

The "Dog-Watch," therefore, is pre-eminently suitable for night use and in unfavourable weather, and in use under these conditions, it has been pronounced by Pilots and Naval Men generally to be unsurpassed.

The body of the "Dog-Watch" is constructed of hard metal specially designed to withstand rough usage. The eye-pieces are curved to the shape of the eye, to obscure the side light, and fixed sun and spray shades are fitted to the object lenses. Loops are provided at the sides for sling or lanyard.

Captain W. JOLLIFFE, S.Y. "Queen Mab," writing for a Binocular suitable for night use said, "I have got several glasses on my Ship but not one of them is the slightest use at night."

A "Dog-Watch" Binocular having been sent to him we received the following letter: "I enclose cheque for 'Dog-Watch.' I consider it a very good glass for night work."

Price, complete in Solid Leather Case with Shoulder Straps, £4 15s.

Code Word for Telegrams—"VIBRATOR."

The "FLASHLIGHT" Naval Telescope.

AS LARGELY USED IN THE BRITISH

NAVY AND MERCANTILE MARINE.

The **"Flashlight"** Telescope is eminently suitable for naval purposes, the body and tube being constructed of hard drawn German Silver and, although light in weight, is exceedingly strong and is able to withstand a great amount of hard wear and rough handling.

The lenses are of the finest quality, giving a remarkably brilliant and well-defined image and a wide field of view.

For Yachting, general Marine and look-out purposes, the "Flashlight" Telescope can be strongly recommended.

The body is covered with brown leather and fitted with a Strap and solid leather protecting cap, as illustrated, to protect object lens when not in use. Diameter of object lens 1¾ inches; Magnification 18 diameters, length when closed 17½ inches; when extended to full length 22½ inches.

Price, **£4 10s.**   Code Word for Telegrams—"VULCANISM."

LAWRENCE & MAYO, LTD.,

Manufacturing Opticians, Admiralty Chart Agents for Eastern Ports,

Head Office: 19, NEW OXFORD STREET, LONDON.

Branches in the East: CAIRO, ALEXANDRIA, DELHI, BOMBAY, CALCUTTA, MADRAS, LUCKNOW, SIMLA and RANGOON.

Code Address for Telegrams—"STOCKADE, LONDON."

'A1' AT KEW.

Highest Award Class "A" Kew Certificate.   *Highest Award Class "A" Kew Certificate.*

The "White Star" Sextant

(Latest Model)

Specification.—8 in. Special design, extra rigid club pattern, bridge handle Sextant, with Spring tangent, divided on Silver to 10 seconds, best large fixed Horizon with Capped adjustment **and improved horizontal adjustment by means of a key, thus avoiding all strain on the glass.** Seven neutral shades, Blank, Prospect, and Inverting Telescopes, with extra power and fitted with outside object cells, also Star Binocular, two dark heads, refractor to Vernier, fitted in polished Mahogany case with flush handle, lock and key, and fastening hooks. Kew "A" Certificate. Highest Class Workmanship throughout.

Price, **£22 10s. 0d.**   Code Word for Telegrams—"STARBEAM."

ROBINSONS' BOAT-RELEASING GEAR

IS FITTED

IN ALL SHIPS OF THE BRITISH NAVY AND IN MANY FOREIGN NAVIES.

CHAIN SLING FITTING. (Hooks held in position by Steadying-lines.)

KEEL-BOLT FITTING.

FREQUENTLY USED FOR SLIPPING IN ROUGH WATER AND WITH SHIP UNDER WAY.

COMPLIES WITH THE FOLLOWING REQUIREMENTS SPECIALLY INSISTED UPON IN THE NAVY:—

BOTH ENDS RELEASE AT ONCE, whether before or after becoming water-borne; therefore no inducement to slip too soon.

RELEASES BY LETTING GO A LINE, held with a turn round a thwart or cleat, **not** by pulling a line or lever (which in a crowded boat may be pulled or pushed accidentally.)

IS A PLAIN TUMBLING HOOK with **no** obstruction to hooking-on or to unhooking by hand; yet is

PERFECTLY "MOUSED" against accidental unhooking.

VISIBLE CONNECTION BETWEEN HOOKS entirely above thwart level (a point particularly insisted on in the Navy).

Not a single complaint of failure or of accident in many hundreds of cases of sudden lowering to pick up men overboard, in all kinds of weather and frequently or generally with considerable way still on the ship.

Note that Robinson's is a true **releasing gear,** and **not** merely a fixed hook with or without a mousing. Without simultaneous slipping gear there is no guarantee against one end being unhooked or unhooking itself before the other.

RING-SHACKLE
ATTACHED TO
LOWER BLOCK
OF FALLS.

EYE ON EACH
SIDE FOR
STEADYING
LINES.

MOUSING

TO STEM OR STERN.

TO KEEL.

CHAIN-SLING FITTING.

ROBINSON'S COMMON HOOKS,

FOR BOAT SLINGS.

NOW FITTED TO ALL BOATS IN THE BRITISH NAVY NOT FITTED WITH ROBINSON'S RELEASING GEAR.

SIMPLE, HANDY, SAFE.

THWART

KEEL-BOLT FITTING.

PATENTEES AND SOLE MAKERS:

H. E. C. ROBINSON & Co., Ltd.,

STRAND-ON-THE-GREEN, CHISWICK, LONDON, W.

The BLACKBURN AEROPLANE and MOTOR CO., LTD., LEEDS.

Works: LEEDS and BROUGH.

London Offices: Donnington House, Norfolk Steet, W.C. 2.

Designers and Constructors of Aircraft.

Specialists in
TORPEDO
AIRCRAFT
as supplied to the
BRITISH ADMIRALTY.

SDEB 14. GENERAL UTILITY TYPE.

(DESIGNED BY SERGE DE BOLOTOFF.)

DE BOLOTOFF, LTD., ENGINEERS.

76 adv.

Plant of 145 m/m.

Starting Car.

Plant of 240 m/m.

Steel Ingot of 100 tons.

Cross Bars of Turbine.

Driving Shaft with 4 Bends.

Petrol Electric Motor.

Plant of 305 m/m.

Plant of 400 m/m.

Plant of 340 m/m.

Cⁱᵉ ᴅᴇꜱ Fᴏʀɢᴇꜱ ꜱ Aᴄɪᴇ́ʀɪᴇꜱ

ᴅᴇ ʟᴀ

MARINE ᴇᴛᴅ HOMÉCOURT

(COMPAGNIE ᴅᴇ SAINT-CHAMOND)

Sᴏᴄɪᴇ́ᴛᴇ́ Aɴᴏɴʏᴍᴇ - ᴄᴀᴘɪᴛᴀʟ : 70 Mɪʟʟɪᴏɴꜱ

DIRECTION GÉNÉRALE
12, RUE DE LA ROCHEFOUCAULD - Paris (IXᵉ)

ADMINISTRATEUR - DIRECTEUR - GÉNÉRAL : THÉODORE LAURENT

Telephone TRUDAINE 51 99 § 56 88

Télégrammes : FORGACIER - PARIS

WORKS ESTABLISHED 1823.   London Office: 38, VICTORIA STREET, WESTMINSTER, LONDON, S.W.1.

Brand
PARK GATE
YORKSHIRE STEEL.

THE PARK GATE IRON & STEEL CO.

LIMITED,

ROTHERHAM, ENGLAND.

Manufacturers of High-class Steel by Siemens' Process only.

STEEL PLATES,

FOR MARINE, LANCASHIRE, LOCOMOTIVE, LAND, AND OTHER BOILERS.

Also BRIDGE & TANK PLATES, SHEETS, & CHEQUERED PLATES to Admiralty Pattern

STEEL SUPPLIED TO THE **BRITISH ADMIRALTY** FOR MARINE AND OTHER BOILERS.

Also **HIGH TENSILE STEEL** (in Plates, Sheets & Bars),

FOR BATTLESHIPS, TORPEDO BOATS, AND DESTROYERS.

STEEL BARS in rounds, squares, flats, angles, tees & sectional bars of all descriptions.

WELDING AND CASEHARDENING STEEL.

Steel supplied to British Admiralty, War Office, Board of Trade, Lloyds, English & Foreign Railways.

82 adv.

85 adv.

HEAP'S Patent Screwing Machines

Patent Automatic Bolt Screwing Machine.

are made in all sizes and suitable for dealing with all classes of work. The illustration opposite shows our 3″ Patent Automatic Bolt Screwing Machine, which is one of a complete line of Single and Multiple Head Machines specially designed for use wherever large quantities of Bolts have to be screwed in the most expeditious and economical manner. As shown, it is fitted with Lead Screw, which makes it very suitable for screwing Boiler Stays and other work in which accuracy of pitch is essential.

The illustration opposite shows our Patent Bent Tube Screwing Machine which has been specially designed for screwing the long bent tubes, largely used by Shipbuilders. The Vice is of unique design. It is simple in construction and yet by single lever movements can be moved above or below the centre line of the Screwing Dies, from back to front, or swivelled, thus enabling the most awkwardly bent tubes to be dealt with. As the various motions can be locked the machine will also screw straight tubes. :: :: :: :: Made in sizes up to 10″.

COMPLETE CATALOGUE POSTED FREE ON REQUEST.

JOSHUA HEAP & Co. Ltd.,
ASHTON-UNDER-LYNE, ENGLAND.

Patent Bent Tube Screwing Machine.

97 adv.

250-TON STEAM FLOATING CRANE.
Crane designed and constructed by Cowans, Sheldon & Co. Ld.
Pontoon designed and constructed by Sir W. G. Armstrong, Whitworth & Co. Ld.
Fitted with 5,865 feet of Thos. & Wm. Smith's High-class Crane Rope varying from 2½ in. to 5½ in. circ.

The Electric Ship!

ELECTRIC drive for great ships became a fact with the successful trials of the U. S. S. New Mexico, flagship of the Pacific Fleet, the first battleship to be propelled by electricity.

"This," says Secretary Daniels, "marks an epoch in naval progress."

Ten years ago electric propulsion for vessels was being discussed. But it remained for W. L. R. Emmet, consulting engineer of the General Electric Company, in co-operation with the Bureau of Steam Engineering, U. S. Navy, to apply it to large ships.

Five years ago electric drive was installed on the collier Jupiter—one of her sister ships was equipped with geared steam-turbine drive—another with direct-connected reciprocating engines. Results proved the unquestionable superiority of electric drive.

And so electric drive was adopted for the super-dreadnaught New Mexico. Steam from her oil-burning boilers drives two Curtis turbo-generators, which generate electric current, and feed it through a central control to four 7,000 h.p. motors,

30-12

each coupled to a propeller. Two thousand additional horsepower is generated for lighting, steering, turret machinery and other auxiliary lines—making the New Mexico an electric ship indeed!

One of the four 7,000 h.p. electric motors—each on the end of a propeller shaft. They drive the New Mexico up to 21 knots, and can be reversed in thirty seconds.

The chief advantages of electric drive are:

1. Economy—At the varying speeds required in naval maneuver electric drive is more economical than any other type of propulsion. As compared with the U. S. S. Pennsylvania—driven by direct-connected turbines—the New Mexico uses from 20 to 30% less fuel at speeds above 15 knots.

2. Reliability—Electric propelling machinery has no motion other than simple rotation. In five years, the Jupiter has been held up only once by trouble with her electrical equipment; the repairs were made by her own crew in a few hours.

3. Flexibility of Installation—Electric motors

may be placed far aft, making the propeller shafts shorter and therefore less liable to injury. The turbines can be near the boilers, eliminating many feet of steam piping. Power is transmitted through small cables; the control can be in any convenient place.

The operator of this control board—in the center of ship—controls the speed and power of the turbo-generators and propelling motors, in response to telegraphic orders from the bridge.

4. Protection—Electric drive gives vastly greater safety than the old types, because each unit can be isolated in its own watertight compartment. A shell explosion in one place would neither sink nor stop the ship. The throwing of a switch disconnects a damaged motor or shaft and the others go on propelling. One of the two main turbo-generators of the New Mexico could be destroyed, and the compartments flooded; yet the ship could go on at three-fourths of her maximum speed, with the other generator driving all four motors.

The New Mexico is the first of thirteen new dread-

naughts and six battle cruisers, all to be electrically driven.

And she forecasts the coming of faster, safer, more economical merchant vessels.

Admiral Benson, Chief of Naval Operations, U. S. N., says " . . . . . . as soon as the merits of this system become known commercially, electric propulsion will prove its practical value in the merchant marine just as thoroughly as it has to the Navy."

Two of these 14,000 h.p. Curtis turbo-generators, singly or together, produce current for any or all of the four motors.

The building of electric propulsion machinery for ships of the U. S. Navy and Merchant Marine is but one of the many activities of the General Electric Company in its service to the Government, to transportation, to industries, to science, to cities, and to the home.

* * *

An illustrated booklet describing the New Mexico, entitled, "The Electric Ship", will be sent upon request. Address General Electric Company, Desk 33, Schenectady, N. Y., U. S. A.

GENERAL ELECTRIC

KERR STUART'S

5, Broad Street Place, London, E.C. 2.

129 adv.

131 adv.

The Pease Blue Print Paper Sensitizing Machines

(Ferro Prussiate).

Are so compact and simple in operation that no large user of ferro-prussiate paper and cloth should be without one. With one of these machines there is no occasion for loss through deterioration or spoiled paper—no waiting for fresh supply. These are especially valuable for humid climates and for places distant from the source of supply. They are in successful operation in twenty foreign countries.

The DUPLEX Machine (here illustrated) for paper 42in. or 54in. wide, occupies a floor space of only $6\frac{1}{2} \times 8$ft. maximum, and has an over-all length of $9\frac{1}{2}$ft. It has an output of 300 to 600 linear yards of sensitized paper per hour, dependent upon quality of the paper and atmospheric conditions. Machines of smaller capacity are also manufactured. It is constructed entirely of metal and is self-contained; all parts are readily accessible for cleaning, adjustment and repairs. All rolls either have ball-bearings or are positively driven. Only one employee is required. We send full directions for installing and operating.

The paper or cloth is automatically rolled up into measured rolls any length desired as it comes out of the drying oven. It is super-dried by means of an air drying heater and a motor-driven circulating fan, thus insuring absolutely dry paper, coated in any condition of atmosphere. The paper may be singly or doubly coated as desired. Gas or electricity may be used for drying.

The entire equipment is operated by a $\frac{1}{4}$-horse-power motor and the speed regulated by our specially designed rheostat, which allows a wide range of speeds to accommodate various grades of paper and conditions of atmosphere.

The Pease Sensitizing Chemicals.

We have greatly simplified the process of sensitizing paper by means of our mixed chemicals which are compounded in dry form, any printing speed desired, and packed in 5-pound air-tight cans ready for use. It is only necessary to dissolve the contents of one of these cans in water. The dry compound, if kept according to our instructions, will retain its properties indefineitly. One can of the prepared chemical will make sufficient solution to coat sixteen to twenty-four 50-yards rolls of paper.

These chemicals are being shipped to all parts of the world with excellent success, and two 10-gallon mixing jars and stand are furnished with each machine.

The Pease Unsensitized Papers.

We are prepared to furnish unsensitized paper, any width, thickness or grade desired, of quality and surface especially adapted for use on the PEASE Sensitizing Machines. Ask for samples and prices. Write for Catalogue 28.

THE C. F. PEASE COMPANY

246, Institute Place, Chicago, U. S. A.

Cable Address, " Peaseco, Chicago."   *Codes, A. B. C. 5th Edition, Private.*

Ready Mixed Chemicals.

Unsensitized Paper.

DRYING OVEN

SENSITIZED

MEASURING DEVICE

MEASURED ROLL

SPEED CONTROL

SOLUTION TRAYS COATING ROLLS

ORIGINAL ROLL UNSENSITIZED

136 adv.

138 adv.

A-WHEELING WE WILL GO

Rudge it,

Don't Trudge it.

on a Rudge·Whitworth Bicycle. No other machine is so easy-going, so comfortable, so trusty. Built on the substantial basis of years of skilled engineering and scientific experience, and undergoing the most stringent of tests in our Chemical and Physical Reseach Laboratories, the Rudge·Whitworth is the most popular mount on the road.

Write for Catalogue, post free from nearest agent or direct from

Rudge-Whitworth, Ltd.,
(Dept. 706), COVENTRY.

London Depot: 230, Tottenham Court Road, (Oxford Street End), W. 1.

R. 417

By Appointment
Cycle Makers to
H M KING GEORGE.

A ROVING COMMISSION.

Nothing can better "Clear the cobwebs" from a tired brain than a rousing Multi tour by the quiet shores and through the pleasant country·side of Old England. Town, country, seaside—the convenience of city travelling, the joy of pleasure riding are all open to the happy possessor of a RUDGE MULTI. The embodiment of Freedom and enduring reliability, the Rudge Multi is unequalled in excellence. *Write for Illustrated Catalogue to—*

Rudge-Whitworth, Ltd.,
(Dept. 706), COVENTRY.

London Depot: 230, Tottenham Court Road, (Oxford Street End). W.1.

R 407.

THOS. W. WARD LIMITED,

H.M.S. "HOOD."

The above Illustration is from a Photograph of the Official Model, kindly furnished by the Builders, Messrs. J. Brown & Co., Ltd., of Clydebank. N.B.—For plan and description of "Hood" see page 61.

Frontispiece.

JANE'S FIGHTING SHIPS
1919

FOUNDED IN **1896** BY FRED T. JANE.

XXII YEAR OF ISSUE.

JOINT EDITORS:
SURGEON–LIEUT. O. PARKES, R.N.
AND MAURICE PRENDERGAST.

SAMPSON LOW, MARSTON
& CO., LTD: LONDON AND
EDINBURGH, MCMXIX.

PREFACE.

PREFACE.

WORK on the present Edition of " FIGHTING SHIPS " was begun in December, 1918, and was pushed on without intermission during the succeeding months. The results now presented, although a little delayed, will, we feel sure, be satisfactory to our readers.

The labour incurred in preparing this Edition has been exceptionally heavy; we doubt if any issue of our Annual has occasioned so much anxiety. The Editors have had to deal with large masses of information, withheld from publication by the belligerent Naval Powers since 1914. They have also had to investigate the demobilisation of the War Fleets to a peace footing. The indeterminate state of the late Enemy Navies, and the chaotic conditions of the Russian Fleet, have presented very perplexing problems.

Dealing, as is our custom, with the various sections of this book in sequence, we offer the following comments on the present Edition.

GLOSSARY.

The glossary of technical terms was overhauled thoroughly last year, and brought up-to-date. This year, our lists of foreign naval expressions have been completed by the addition of French and Swedish terms.

BRITISH NAVY.

Various new Maps have been added, and the Gunnery Tables have been renovated by Captain R V. Walling, R. G. A. (retired). Mr. E. L. King has kindly allowed us to make use of his " Silhouettes of Effective British Warships." These drawings depart very largely from the usual scale and form of " FIGHTING SHIPS " Silhouettes. We should be glad to have our readers' opinions, whether Mr. King's form of drawings should be generally adopted for all Navy sections. The British Ship Pages have been entirely renovated this year. Plans and illustrations of British Warship types have been prepared on a lavish scale. Since the signing of the Armistice, the Admiralty have been able to release much information which, undoubtedly, has raised the standard of accuracy in British Warship data. All textual details are founded on the latest and most reliable information that can be secured. One of the most interesting features added is Aircraft recognition views, presenting British Warships from a new angle of vision. We tender our grateful thanks to British Shipbuilders, for the very large amount of information they have kindly placed at our disposal. Exigencies of space have prevented us from using all the excellent photographs furnished to us by British Shipbuilders. The views which we could not use have been presented to the Imperial War Museum, where they will form a permanent record of the magnificent output of British shipyards during the war.

UNITED STATES.

This section has been revised from the latest official data, placed at our disposal by the U.S. Naval Headquarters in London. We are happy to say that we have, once more, the valuable services of Lieut. Henry Reuterdahl, U.S. N.R.F., the distinguished naval artist and critic. It is largely through his kind assistance that we are able to publish so many new and up-to-date illustrations of U.S. Warships.

JAPAN.

The Navy Department, Tokyo, has once again verified all the technical details of this section. A considerable number of Japanese Minelayers and Fleet Auxiliaries, hitherto unheard of, have been added. Some very valuable notes, received shortly before publication, are given on an Addenda page.

FRANCE.

During his attendance at the Versailles Peace Conference, Capt. R. V. Walling, R.G.A., approached Mons. Leygues (the Minister of Marine) and Admiral le Bon (then Chief of Staff) on our behalf, with a view to the French Navy Section being officially revised. M. Leygues and Admiral le Bon readily assented to the proposals made, and authoritative details of French warships are now given. We may add that very cordial relations have been established between " FIGHTING SHIPS " and Capitane le Marquis de Balincourt, Editor of our esteemed contemporary " Flottes de Combat." We are indebted to Capitane le Marquis de Balincourt for a large series of very useful notes, dealing with the World's Navies.

ITALY.

Pressure of work again prevents Mr. Charles de Grave Sells from preparing his Engineering Article, but it was largely through his kind interest that we secured an official revision of our Italian Navy Section. Attention is called to that extraordinary creation, the Monitor *Faa' de Bruno*—a vessel which approaches the future naval " hippopotami," as defined by Admiral of the Fleet, Lord Fisher of Kilverstone.

MINOR NAVIES.

During the war, the edicts of the Allied Censors debarred us from paying too close attention to the Allied Navies. The barriers erected by our late Enemies also made it very difficult—at times— to secure information regarding

3

their Fleets. Attention was therefore concentrated on the field of the Neutral Navies and these were put in a satisfactory condition. This year the Minor Navies have not been neglected, but have been checked from the latest official information. Among the new Navy Sections will be found the Belgian and Esthonian Navies. Details were specially prepared for us by the Naval Staff at Reval at the request of Mr. John Piitka, the Marine Agent of Estonia in London. The Hellenic Naval Section has been revised by command of Admiral Condouriotis, the Minister of Marine. The Chinese and Siamese pages, although they occupy but a small space, have given a considerable amount of trouble during the past four years. It was found extremely difficult to secure reliable details of these Navies. Thanks to the kindness of Correspondents, they have both been brought up-to-date.

Late Enemy and Russian Navies.

The treatment of these Sections has been the subject of much anxious thought. No steps have yet been taken to dispose of the German ships salved at Scapa Flow. Although the future establishment of the German Navy is strictly laid down in the Peace Treaty, Germany has (as yet) taken no steps to reduce her Navy to the status required by the Allies. The Austrian Fleet, the Hungarian Danube Flotilla, the Bulgarian and Turkish Fleets are all interned under Allied and U.S. supervision. The disposal of the warships belonging to these Powers is still a matter of pure speculation. The Russian Fleet is rent between contending factions, and various units of the Russian Navy have been temporarily added to the Allied Navies. All these Navies have been relegated to the end of this Edition, on the ground that they cannot be considered as effective fighting forces at the present moment.

Special Article.

Five years have elapsed since Illustrations of British Warships have been allowed to appear in "Fighting Ships." British Illustrations have been re-instated, but H.M. Ships appear in so altered a guise, compared with their 1914 build, that some lay and foreign readers may be perplexed by the changes carried out between 1914 and 1919. A short and non-technical article has been prepared by the Editors, dealing with the War's influence on British Naval Construction. It consists largely of notes, generally covering all British Warship types, which could not be accommodated in the British Navy section without an undue degree of repetition.

War Loss Section.

Mr. Francis E. McMurtrie has prepared a Final Summary of the naval casualties of the late War, based on official and authoritative information. The lists given afford the most complete compendium of information on this subject ever presented; they are the outcome of the perseverance and care of Mr. McMurtrie in collecting information. The long tables detailing the circumstances and dates of destruction of German Submarines will be scanned with interest.

Conclusion.

It may be finally said that, in this Edition, there is only one page which was transferred in unaltered form from 1918 "Fighting Ships." Particulars of the world's warships now given are based on highly reliable information. The number of illustrations added or renovated this year runs to nearly eight hundred.

Shortly before his lamented death, the late Mr. Fred T. Jane made arrangements that this annual should be edited in conjunction by Dr. Oscar Parkes and Mr. Maurice Prendergast.

These plans have been held in abeyance. Dr. Oscar Parkes joined H.M. Navy in 1916, as Surgeon-Lieutenant, R.N. Being stationed in the Mediterranean, he was unable to give the degree of assistance planned by the late Mr. Jane. Mr. Maurice Prendergast therefore carried on the work of Editorship up to the date of the Armistice. Surgeon-Lieut. Oscar Parkes, O.B.E., R.N. has now joined Mr. Prendergast as Joint Editor, and is largely responsible for the splendid series of British Warship Photographs added to this Edition. To them, our Editors, we offer our cordial thanks for their labours in preparing our present Edition—an Edition which we know has been anxiously awaited by our patrons. Under the control of Surgeon-Lieut. Parkes, R.N. and Mr. Prendergast —and through the assistance of our innumerable correspondents throughout the world — future Editions of " Fighting Ships " will not fall below the high standard of the Edition we now issue.

THE PUBLISHERS.

" Overy House,"
100, Southwark Street,
London, S.E. 1.

CONTENTS.

CONTENTS—*continued.*

ABBREVIATIONS, MAJORITY INTRODUCED IN THIS EDITION.

AA.	Anti-Aircraft.
C.M.B.	Coastal Motor Boat.
D.A.M.S.	Defensively Armed Merchant Ship.
D.C.	Depth Charge
Dir. Con.	Director Controlled.
M.L	Motor Launch
PV.	Paravane
R.F.	Range Finder
R.F.A.	Royal Fleet Auxiliary
S.D.V.	Submarine Decoy Vessel
SL.	Searchlight
S/M.	Submarine

GENERAL INDEX, *continued.*

GENERAL INDEX, *continued.*

12

GENERAL INDEX, *continued.*

GLOSSARY OF TECHNICAL TERMS.

ENGLISH.	GERMAN.	FRENCH.	ITALIAN.	RUSSIAN.	SPANISH.	SWEDISH	DUTCH.
1 Abaft	1 Achtern (adv) hinter (prep); achterlicher als quer ab (abaft the beam)	1 Sur l'arrière	1 A poppa	1 Korma	1 A popa	1 Akterligt	1 Achterlijker dan dwars
2 Abeam	2 dwars ab, quer ab	2 Par le travers	2 Per traverso	2 Poperek	2 Por el través	2 Tvärs ut /direction/	2 Dwars
3 Above water	3 Ober wasser	3 Au dessus de l'eau	3 Sopracqua	3 Nadvodnie	3 Sobre el agua	3 Ofvervattens	3 Boven water
4 Accommodation hulk	4 Wohnschiff	4 Caserne flottant 4 Ponton	4 Pontone d'accomodamento		4 Ponton de comodidad	4 Logementsfartyg	4 Accomodatie legger
5 Ahead	5 Vorwärts	5 Avant	5 A prora (davanti)	5 Vpered	5 A proa	5 Förut /direction/ Framat /movement/	5 Vooruit
6 Air lock	6 Luftverschluss (?)	6 Ecluse de chauffe/sas	6 Serratura d'aria		6 Cerradura de aire	6 Luftsluss	
7 Amidships	7 Mittschiffs	7 Au milieu	7 Al centro	7 Vseredinu	7 Al centro	7 Midskepps	7 Midscheeps
8 Ammunition ship	8 Munitionsschiff	8 Porte-munitions	8 Nave di munizioni	8 Soodno s ammunicziei ; boevimi pripasami	8 Buque de municiónes	8 Ammunitionsfartyg	8 Ammunitie schip
9 Anti-aircraft (gun)	9 Fliegerabwehrgeschütz kanone (abbrev. Flak)	9 Canon contre-aeriens	9 Cannone anti-aeroplani	9 Protivo-aeroplanniya	9 Cañon antiaeroplanos	9 Luftförsvarskanon /generally "Luftkanon"/	9 Anti-luchtschip (kanon)
10 A.P. (projectile)	10 Panzersprenggranate	10 Projectil de rupture	10 Proiettile	10 Probivanshii-bronu	10 Proyectil	10 Halvpansargranat	
11 Armament	11 Armierung		11 Armamento	11 Vo-oroojenie	11 Armamento	11 Bestyckning	11 Bewapening
12 Armed liner, or Auxiliary cruiser	12 Hilfskreuzer	12 Croiseur auxiliaire	12 Nave armata / incrociatore ausilare	12 Vo-oroojeunii passajirskii-parokhod ; Vspomogatelnii krieser	12 Buque armado/o crucero auxiliar	12 Hjälpkryssare	12 Gewapende lyner of hulp kruiser
13 Armour	13 Panzer	13 Cuirasse	13 Corazzato	13 Bronia	13 Coraza Blindage	13 Pansar	13 Pantser
14 Armoured cruiser	14 Panzerkreuzer	14 Croiseur cuirassé	14 Incrociatore corazzati	14 Bronenosnii-kreiser	14 Crucero acorazado	14 Pansarkryssare	14 Gepantserde Kruiser
15 Astern	15 Rückwärts	15 Arrière	15 A poppa	15 Nazad	15 A popa	15 Back	15 Achteruit
16 Athwartship	16 dwarsschiffs	16 Par le travers (d'un navire)	16 Atraverso il bastimento	16 Soodno-na-traverze	16 Por el través del buque	16 Tvärskepps	
17 Awash	17 im uberflüten Zustand		17 A fior d'acqua	17 Vroven-s-vodoi	17 A flor de agua	17 I övervattensläge	
18 Barbettes	18 Barbetten	18 Barbettes	18 Barbette	18 Barbeti	18 Torres-barbetas	18 Barbettorn	18 Barbette
19 Bases (of barbettes)	19 Trunk (Schacht)	19 Au dessous la tourelle	19 Piattoforme	19 Vnizu	19 Plataformas	19 Fasta torn	19 Torenwal
20 Battery	20 Batterie	20 Batterie	20 Batteria	20 Battereya	20 Bateria	20 Batteri	20 Battery
21 Battle-cruiser	21 Panzerkreuzer	21 Cuirassé rapide. 21 Croiseur de bataille.	21 Incrociatore di battaglia	21 Boevoi kreiser	21 Crucero de batalla	21 Slagkryssare	21 Slag kruiser
22 Battleship	22 Linienschiff	22 Cuirassé d'escadre	22 Nave da battaglia	22 Bronosets	22 Acorazado	22 Slagskepp	22 Slagschip
23 Beam	23 Breite	23 Largeur	23 Larghezza	23 Shirina	23 Manga	23 Bredd	23 Breedte
24 Before	24 vorn ; vor (prep.) vorlicher als quer ab (before the beam)	24 Avant.	24 Avanti	24 Pered ; pred	24 A proa	24 Förut	24 Voor
25 Belt	25 Gürtel	25 Ceinture	25 Cintura	25 Poyass	25 Faja	25 Gördelpansar	25 Gordel
26 Bilge keel	26 Schlingerkiel	26 Quille de roulis	26 Chiglia di rollio	26 Bokovoi keel	26 Quilla de pantoque	26 Slingerköl	26 Kimkiel
27 Binnacle	27 Kompassgehäuse	27 Boussole	27 Abitacolo		27 Bitácora	27 Nakterhus	27 Nachthuis

JAPANESE

(pronounce as French).

Fighting tops {Shento-Shorou}	Ends {Hashi}	Draught {Kisswi}	Displacement {Hai-sui-Tonsu}	Destroyer {Kuchiku-tei}	Deck {Kanpan}	Cruiser {Junyo-Kan}	C. T. (Conning tower) {Shireito}	Complement {Teiin}	c/m (Centi metre)	Casemates {Kuku-Hodai}	Capacity {Yorio}	Bunkers {Shekitanko}	Bulkheads {Kakuheki}	Bridge {Kankio}	Boilers {Kikan}	Bow {Kanshu}	Belt {Kotai}	Beam {Haba}	Battleship {Shento-Kan}	Battery {Hodai}	Bases (of Barbettes, etc.) {Hoto-no-Kibu}	Barbettes {Tototo}	Astern {Tomo}
79	77	70	65	62	51	50	46	45	41	38	36	34	33	32	29	31	25	23	22	20	19	18	15
戰鬪檣樓	両端	吃水	排水噸數	驅逐艦	甲板	巡洋艦	司令塔	定員	センチメートル	穹窖砲臺	容量	石炭庫	隔壁	艦橋	汽罐	艦首	甲帶	巾	戰鬪艦	砲臺	砲塔の基部	露砲塔	艦後

Armoured Cruiser {Kotetsu-Junyo-Kan}	Armour {Kotetsu}	Amidships {Chuō}	Ahead {Omote}	Above water
14	13	7	5	3
甲鐵巡洋艦	甲鐵	中央	艦前	水上

ENGLISH.	GERMAN.	FRENCH.	ITALIAN.	RUSSIAN.	SPANISH	SWEDISH.	DUTCH.
28 B.L. (gun)	28 Hinterlader	28 Canon culasse	28 Cannone a retrocarica	28 Zaryajansheesyas kazennoi chasti	28 Cañón de retrocarga	28 Bakladdningskanon	
29 Boilers	29 Kessel	29 Generateurs	29 Caldaie	29 Kotli	29 Calderas	29 Angpannor	2 Ketels
30 Boom (port defence)	30 Hafensperre	30 Estacade	30 Asta da bome (per difesa portuale)		30 Cadena de troncos (para defensa de puerto)	30 Bomstängsel	30 Sluitboom
31 Bow	31 Bug	31 Avant	31 Prora	31 Noss	31 Proa	31 Bog	31 Boeg
32 Bridge	32 Kommando-Brücke	32 Pont	32 Ponte di comando	32 Most	32 Puente	32 Brygga	32 Brug
33 Bulkheads	33 Schötten	33 Traverses	33 Paratie	33 Pereborki	33 Manpanos	33 Skott	33 Schot
34 Bunker (coal)	34 Kohlenbunker	34 Soute à charbon	34 Carbone per carboniere	34 Oogolnaya yama. To bunker, groozitsya ooglem	34 Carbón de las carboneras	34 Kolboxar	34 Bunker (Kolen)
35 Camouflage	35 Unsichtbarmalen	35 Camouflage	35 Camuffamento or " Camouflage "	35 Iskoostvennoe prikpitie	35 " Camouflage "	35 Maskering	35 Identiteits verberging
36 Capacity	36 Capacität	36 Enposant de charge	36 Capacita	36 Poinyestchenie	36 Capacidad	36 Kapacitet	36 Vermogen
37 Capstan	37 Ankerspill, Ankerwinde	37 Cabestan	37 Argano		37 Cabrestante	37 Ankarspel, Spel	37 Spil
38 Casemates	38 Casematten	38 Casemates	38 Casamette	38 Kazemat	38 Casamatas	38 Kasematter	38 Kazemat
39 Centre-, (keel-) line	39 Kiellinie	39 Quille centrale/mediane	39 Paramezzale centrale	39 Srednyaya liniya ; diametralnaya ploskost	39 Sobrequilla central	39 Midskeppslinje	39 Midden (kiel) lijn
40 Chart house	40 Kartenhaus		40 Sala nautica	40 Shtoormanskaya roobka	40 Caseta de derrota	40 Styrhytt	40 Kaarthuis
41 Coal	41 Kohlenvorrat	41 Charbon	41 Carbone	41 Ugol	41 Carbon	41 Kol	41 Steenkolen
42 Coast defence ship	42 Küstenpanzerschiff	42 Garde-côtes.	42 Nave per difesa della costa	42 Soodno beregovoi oboroni	42 Buque para defensa de costas	42 Kustförsvarsfartyg	42 Kust verdedigings schip
43 Coastguard vessel	43 Küstenschutzschiff	43 Navire garde-côtes	43 Nave guarda costas	43 Soodno beregovoi okhrani	43 Buque guarda costa	43 Kustbevakningsfartyg	43 Kust bewakings schip
44 Compass	44 Kompass		44 Bussola		44 Brújula	44 Kompass	44 Kompass
45 Complement	45 Besatzung	45 Équipage	45 Equipaggio	45 Kompleki	45 Dotacion	45 Besättning	45 Bemanning
46 C.T. (conning tower)	46 Kommando Turm	46 Block-haus (C.T.)	46 Torre di comando	46 Roolevaia bashnia	46 Torre de mando	46 Stridstorn	46 Commando-toren
47 Crane	47 Kran	47 Grue	47 Grua	47 Kran	47 Grua	47 Kran	47 Kraan
48 " Creep " (anti-submarine)	48 U – drache (?)	48 Gerbe sousmarine	48 " Serpeggiare " (anti-sommergibile)	48 Tral	48 Arrastramiento (anti-submarino)		
49 Crow's nest	49 Krähennest	49 Nid de pie	49 Gabbia di crocetta		49 Garita para el vijía	49 Utkikskorg	49 Kraaie nest
50 Cruiser	50 Kreuzer	50 Croiseur	50 Incrociatore	50 Kreïser	50 Crucero	50 Kryssare	50 Kruiser
51 Deck	51 Deck	51 Pont	51 Ponte	51 Palooba	51 Cubierta	51 Däck	51 Dek
52 Depôt ship	52 Stammschiff, Mutterschiff	52 Soutien/Convoyeur de	52 Nave di deposito/Nave appoggio	52 Soodno sklad ; soodno baza	52 Buque de depósito	52 Depotfartyg	52 Depot schips
53 „ (torpedo craft)	53 „ (für Torpedofahrzeuge)	53 „ (Torpilleurs).	53 „ Siluranti		53 „ (torpederos)	53 „ för torpedbåtar	53 Depot (torpedo vaartuig)
54 „ (destroyers)	54 „ („ Zerstörer)	54 „ (Destroyers).	54 „ Cacciatorpediniere	54 Soodno-matka dlya kontr-minonosetzev	54 „ (cazatorpederos)	54 „ „ jagare	54 „ (torpedo jagers)

JAPANESE.
(pronounce as French.)

Term	Japanese
Water line {Suishen} 216	水線
Upper deck {Jokanpan} 213	上甲板
Turrets {Yihoto} 212	圍砲塔
Trials {Shi Unten (Kokoromi Unten)} 206	試運轉
Tons 194	噸
Torpedo tubes {Suirai Hatsushahuan} 193	水雷發射管
Torpedo boat {Suirai-Tei} 192	水雷艇
Torpedo {Suirai} 191	水雷
Submerged {Suichu} 182	水中
Submarine {Shen-sui} 180	潜水
Stern {Kanbi} 179	艦尾
Starboard (side) {Ugen} 178	右舷
Speed {Sokurioku} 176	速力
Shields {Tate} 173	楯
Screens {Kukusho} 167	スクルー
Ram {Shoto} 155	撞頭
Protection to vitals {Yobu-Bogio} 150	要部防禦
Port (side) {Sagen} 147	左舷
Normal displacement {Kitei} 135	規定
m/m (Millimetre)	ミリメークー
M. (Metre)	メークー
Masts {Hobashira} 123	檣
Main (-deck) {Chukan-pan} 121	中甲板
Machinery 119	機械
Lower (-deck) {Gekan-pan} 118	下甲板
Liquid fuel {Yakitai-Nenrio} 117	液体燃料
L. (Length) {Nagasa} 113	長
Kts. (Knots) 112	節
Hoods {Hogai} 101	砲�íí
Guns {Hiwo} 95	砲
Funnels {Yentotsu or Entotsu} 92	烟突

ENGLISH.	GERMAN.	FRENCH.	ITALIAN.	RUSSIAN.	SPANISH.	SWEDISH.	DUTCH.
55 Depôt ship (T.B.)	55 Stammschiff (für Torpedoboote)	55 Soutien de (Torpilleurs)	55 Nave appoggio (torpedine)		55 Buque de depósito (torpederos)	55 Depotfartyg för torpedbåtar	55 Depôt (T.B.)
56 „ (M.L.)	56 „ („ Motorboote)	56 „ (Vedettes).	56 „ (moto-scafo)		56 „ (lancha de motor)	56 „ „ motorbåtar	56 „ (M.L.)
57 „ (submarines)	57 Mutterschiff (für Unterseeboote)	57 „ (Sous-marins).	57 „ (sommergibili)	57 Soodno-matka dlya podvodnikh lodok	57 „ (submarinos)	57 „ förundervattensbåtar	57 „ (onderseeërs)
58 Depression (of guns)	58 Senkung	58 Angle negatif de pointage	58 Depressione (cannone)	58 Oogol snijeniya	58 Puntería baja (de las piezas)	58 Dumpning	
59 Depth charge	59 Wasserbombe	59 Charge de fond	59 Carica di fondo (esplosivo)	59 Bomba dlya vzriva pod vodoi	59 Carga de fondo (explosiva)	59 Vattenbomb	59 Diepte lading
60 Derrick	60 Ladebaum	60 Mât de charge	60 Albero da carico	60 Nod-emnaya strela	60 Pescante de carga	60 Bom	60 Laadboom
61 Despatch vessel	61 Aviso	61 Aviso	61 Nave per dispacci	61 Posilnoe soodno	61 Buque de aviso	61 Avisofartyg	61 Koerier schip
62 Destroyer	62 Zerstörer	62 Contre-torpilleur	62 Caccia-torpediniere	62 Kontr-minonosets	62 Cazatorpederos	62 Jagare	62 Torpedobootjager
63 Diesel engine	63 Dieselmaschine, Ölmaschine, Ölmotor	63 Moteur Diesel	63 Macchina "Diesel"	63 Dizel-motor	63 Máquina "Diesel"	63 Dieselmotor	63 Diesel machine
64 Dirigible	64 Lenkbares Luftschiff	64 Dirigeable.	64 Dirigibile	64 Derijabl	64 Dirigible	64 Luftskepp	64 Bestuurbare
65 Displacement	65 Deplacement	65 Déplacement	65 Dislocamento	65 Vodoizmiestchenie	65 Desplazamiento	65 Deplacement	65 Waterverplaatsing
66 Division (of fleet)	66 Division	66 Division	66 Divisione (di una flotta)	66 Deviziya; devizion	66 División (de una flota)	66 Division	66 Eskader
67 Dock (floating)	67 Schwimmdock	67 Dock (flottant).	67 Bacino (galleggianto)	67 Dok (plavoochii)	67 Dique flotante	67 Flytdocka	67 Dok (drijvend)
68 „ (graving)	68 Trockendock	68 Cale sèche	68 Bacino (di carenaggio)	68 Dok (sookhoi)	68 Dique seco	68 Torrdocka	68 „ (droog)
69 Dockyard (D.Y.)	69 Werft	69 Arsenal	69 Arsenale	69 Shipyard, Verv.	69 Arsenal	69 Varv	69 „ werf
70 Draught (mean)	70 mittlerer Tiefgang	70 Tirant d'eau	70 Immersione media		70 Calado medio	70 Djupgående, medel—	70 Diepang (gemiddeld)
71 „ (max.)	71 grösster Tiefgang	71 Tirant d'eau maximum	71 Immersione massima		71 Calado máximo	71 „ maximi—	71 „ (grootste)
72 Dreadnought	72 Dreadnought	72 Dreadnought	72 Dreadnought	72 Drednaoot	72 Dreadnought	72 Dreadnought	
73 Drifter	73 Drifter, Dampflogger	73 Chalutier	73 Nave di pesca ("Drifter")	73 Maloe soodno	73 Vapor de pesca ("Drifter")		73 Smak
74 Echelon	74 Staffellinie	74 Echelon. / 74 En quinconce.	74 Linea in "Echelon"	74 Eshelon	74 Linea en escalones	74 Flankformering	
75 "Electric drive"	75 elektrische Antrieb	75 Commande electrique	75 Comando elettrico		75 Impulsión electrica	75 Elektrisk drift	
76 Elevation (of guns)	76 Höhewichtung, Elevation	76 Angle de pointage positif	76 Elevazione (cannone)	76 Oogol vozvosheniya	76 Elevación (tiro de cañón)	76 Elevation	
77 Ends	77 Enden	77 Extrémités	77 Estremita	77 Krai	77 Extremos	77 Stävar	77 Einden
78 Examination Vessel	78 Untersuchungschiff	78 Arraisonneur	78 Nave d'ispezione		78 Buque de inspección	78 Undersökningsfartyg	78 Onderzoekings schip
79 Fighting tops	79 Marsen	79 Hunes	79 Coffe militari	79 Poostchechnii mars	79 Cofas militares	79 Stridsmärsar	79 Gevechtsmars
80 Fire Control	80 Feuerleitung	80 Direction de tir	80 Controllo del tiro	80 Kontrol ognya	80 Regulator de tiro	80 Eldledning	80 Controle by het vuren
81 „ top	81 Artilleriestand im Topp	81 Hune télémètrique.	81 „ (coffa)		81 „ „ (cofa)	81 Eldledningsmärs	
82 Fire director	82 Zentralabfeuerung	82 Direction du feu	82 Direttore de tiro	82 Mekhanizm oopot reblyaemii pri strelbl zalpom	82 Director de tiro	82 Centralavfyrning	
83 Fisheries vessel	83 Fischerieschutzboot	83 Garde-pêche. / 84 Navire amiral	83 Nave peschiera	83 Maloe voennoe soodno dlya ohhrani ribnikh promislov	83 Buque de pesquería	83 Fiskeri-inspektionsfartyg	83 Controle schip (visschery)
84 Flagship	84 Flaggschiff		84 Nave ammiraglia	84 Flagmanskii korabl	84 Buque almirante	84 Flaggskepp	84 Vlagschip
85 Fleet	85 Flotte	85 Flotte.	85 Flotta		85 Flota	85 Flotta	85 Vloot
86 Flotilla	86 Flotille	86 Flotille.	86 Flottiglia	86 Flotiliya	86 Esquadrilla	86 Flottilj	86 Flotilje
87 „ leader	87 Führerschiff	87 Conducteur de flotille.	87 Nave capofilo	87 Soodno vedooshii flotiliu	87 Buque cabo de fila	87 Flottiljchefsfartyg	87 „ leider
88 Forecastle	88 Back	88 Gaillard d'avant.	86 Castello di prua	88 Bak	88 Castillo	88 Back	88 Logies
89 Foremast	89 Fockmast	89 Mât de nusaine	89 Albero di trinchetto		89 Palo trinquete	89 Fockmast, Förligmast	89 Fokkemast
90 Freeboard	90 Freibord	90 Franc-bord	90 Bordo libero	90 Zapas plavoochesti soodna	90 Obra muerta	90 Fribord	90 Uitwatering
91 Full load displ't	91 Gesamte Wasserverdrängung	91 Deplacement en plein charge	91 Carico completo (dislocamento)	91 Vodvizmeshenie v polnom groozoo	91 Cargamento completo (desplazamiento)	91 Deplacement, fullt rustad	91 Volle lading merk
92 Funnels	92 Schornsteine	92 Cheminées	92 Fumaioli	92 Trubi	92 Chimeneas	92 Skorstenar	92 Schoorsteen
93 Fuze	93 Zünder	93 Amorce	93 Spoletta	93 Vzrivatel	93 Espoleta	93 Tändrör	93 Grut
94 Gunboat	94 Kanonenboot	94 Cannonière	94 Cannoniera	94 Kanonerskaya lodka	94 Lancha cañonera	94 Kanonbåt	94 Kanonneerboot
95 Guns	95 Geschütze	95 Artillerie	95 Cannoni	95 Orudiia	95 Cañones	95 Kanoner	95 Kanonnen
96 Gyroscopic compass	96 Kreiselkompass	96 Compas gyroscopique	96 Busola giroscopica	96 Jiroskop	96 Brújula giroscópica	96 Gyroskopkompass	96 Gyroskoop kompas
97 Hawse	97 Klüse	97 Crussiere	97 "Hawse" (apertura per la catena dell'ancora)	97 Kluz	97 Escobén	97 Klys	97 Slang
98 H.E. (bursting charge)	98 Sprengladung	98 Haut explosif	98 Alto esplosivo (carica di scoppio)	98 Silno-vzrivchatii	98 Fuérte explosivo (carga estelladora)	98 Sprängladdning	

	ENGLISH.	GERMAN.	FRENCH.	ITALIAN.	RUSSIAN.	SPANISH.	SWEDISH.	DUTCH.
99	H.E. (shell)	Sprenggeschoss, Sprenggranate	Obu à grande capacité	Granata di alto esplosivo	Silno-vzrivchatii snaryud	Granada de fuerte explosivo	Spränggranat	
100	Hoist (ammunition)	Munitionsaufzug	Monte-charges.	Elevatore di munizioni	Podem (in full, podemnaya mashina)	Ascensor para municiónes	Ammunitionshiss	Hysche (ammunitie)
101	Hoods	Kuppel	Carapaces	Scudi	Pokrishki	Carapachos	Kåpor	Pantserkoepel
102	"Horns" (of mine)	Kontakte, Fühlhörner (?)	Antennes	Corna (di una mina)		Conteras (de una mina)	Horn	"Hoorns" (van mijn?)
103	Hospital ship	Hospitalschiff, Lazarettschiff	Navire-hôpital	Nave ospedale	Gospitalnoe soodno	Buque-hospital	Lasarettsfartyg	Hospitaal schip
104	Hull	Rumpf	Coque	Scafo	Korpoos; koozov soodna	Casco	Skrov	Hol
105	Hulk	Hulk	Ponton	Pontone	Blokshiv	Pontón	Pram	Legger
106	Hydroplane (boat)	Gleitboot	Hydroplane (bateau)	Idroplano (battello)	gidroplane	Hidroplane (buque)	Hydroplan	
107	„ (in subs.)	Tiefenruder					Djuproder	
108	Ice-breaker	Eisbrecher	Brise-glace.	Rompighiaccio	Ledokol	Rompehielos	Isbrytare	Ysbreeker
109	Jumping wire	Minenabweiser, Minendraht	Orin.	Salto del filo (?)		Paso del alambre	Avledarewire	
110	Kite-balloon	Drache	Saucisse /"Captif"	Pallone a cervo-volante	Zmeikovii aerostat	Globo-cometa cautivo	Ballong	Kabel ballon
111	Kite-balloon ship	Drachenschiff	Navire porte ballon captif	„ id (nave d'appoggio)	Soodno-matkadlya zmeikovikh aerostatov	„ (buque portador)	Ballongfartyg	„ „ schip
112	Kts. (Knots)	See-meilen (or knotten)	Noeuds	Nodi	Uzell	Millas	Knop	Knoopen (mylen)
113	Length (*p.p.*)	Länge zwischen den Perpendikeln	Longueur (entre perpendiculaires)	Lunghezza tra le perpendicolari		Eslora entre perpendiculares	Längd mellan perpendiklarne	Lengte (p.p)
114	„ (*w.l.*)	Länge auf der Wasserlinie (?)	„ (à la flottaison)	Lunghezza alla linea di carico		Eslora en la linen de ague, máxima	„ i vattenlinjen	„ (w.l.)
115	„ (*o.a.*)	Länge uber alles	„ (totale)	Lunghezza massima		Eslora de fuera a fuera de miembros	„ överallt	„ (grooste)
116	Light cruiser	kleiner Kreuzer	Croiseur léger	Incrociatore leggiera	Legdii kreiser	Crucero ligero	Lätt kryssare	
117	Liquid Fuel	Heizoil	Combustile liquide	Combustibile liquido	Jhidkoe toplivo	Combustibele liquido	Brännolja	Vloeibare brandstof
118	Lower deck	Zwischen-deck	Faux pont	Ponte inferiore	Nijhniaia paluba	Cubierta baja	Mellandäck, Trossdäck	Tusschendeks
119	Machinery	Maschinen	Machines	Machinaria	Mekhanizm	Máquinas	Maskineri	Werktuigen (machines)
120	Magazine	Munitionskammer	Soute.	Magazino-deposito munizioni	Sklad; magazin	Pañol de municiónes	Ammunitionsdurk	Magazyn
121	Main-deck	Batterie deck	Pont de batterie	Ponte principale	Glavnaia paluba	Cubierta principal	Huvuddäck	Kuildek
122	Mainmast	Grossmast		Albero di maestra		Palo mayor	Stormast	Groote mast
123	Mast	Mast	Mât.	Albero		„ macho	Mast	Mast
124	„ (tripod)	Dreibein, Dreifussmast	„ (tripode).	„ (treppiedi)	Machta trepojnaya	„ trípode	Tripodmast	
125	„ (lattice)	Gittermast	„ (en treillis)	„ (graticcio)	Reshetchataya machta	„ de celosía	Gallermast	
126	Microphone	Geräuschempfänger	Microphone	Microfono	Mikrofon	Micrófono	Mikrofon	Microphone
127	Mine	Mine	Mine	Mina	Mina	Mina	Mina	Mijn
128	Mine-layer	Minenleger	Mouilleurs de mines / Pose-mines	Posa-mina	Minnii zagraditel	Colocador de minas	Minutläggningsfartyg	Mijn legger
129	Mine-sweeper	Minensucher	Dragueurs de mines	Draga-mina	Minnii tralshik	Rastreador de minas	Minsvepningsfartyg	Mijn veeger
130	Mizzen-mast	Besanmast	Mât de artimon.	Albero di mezzana		Palo mesana	Mesanmast	Bezaans mast
131	M.L. (motor launch)	Motorboot	Vedette	Lancia a motore	Motornoe patrolnoe soodno (literally, motor patrol vessel)	Lancha de motor	Motorbat	M.L. motor launch
132	M. S. (motor ship)	Motorschiff	Bateau automobile	Nave a motore	Motornoe soodna	Buque de motor	Motorfartyg	M.S. motor schip
133	Monitor	Monitor	Monitor	Monitor	Monitor	Monitor	Monitor	Monitor
134	Navy yard	Marinewerft	Arsenal	Cantiere dello stato	Admiralteistve	Arsenal del estado	Orlogsvarv	Marine werf
135	Normal displ't	Normale Wasserdrängung	Deplacement normal	Dislocamento normale	Normalnoe vodoizmeshenie	Desplazamiento normal	Normal deplacement	Normale water verplaatsing
136	Net Cutter	Netzschere	Coupe-filets	Taglia-rete		Cortador de redes	Nätsax	Net breeker
137	Net layer	Netzleger	Mouilleur de filets	Posa-rete		Colocador de redes	Nätutläggningsfartyg	Net legger
138	Oil tanker	Öldampfer, Tankdampfer	Pétrolier	Nave petroliera a cisterna	Nalivnoe soodno	Buque de cisterna petrolero	Oljetankfartyg	Olie tankship.
139	Paddle-wheel	Rad	Roue	Ruote a palette	Grebnoe parokhodnoe koleso	Rueda de paletas	Skovelhjul	Wiel (raderboot)
140	„ steamer	Raddampfer	Navire à roues.	Piroscafo a ruote		Vapor de ruedas	Hjulångare	Raderboot

GLOSSARY OF TECHNICAL TERMS.—*Continued.*

	ENGLISH.	GERMAN.	FRENCH.	ITALIAN.	RUSSIAN.	SPANISH.	SWEDISH.	DUTCH.
141	Patrol boat/vessel	Vorpostenboot, Fahrzeug	Patrouilleur	Battelo / nave di pattuglia	Patrolnoe soodno	Buque de patrulla/ Lancha de patrulla	Bevakningsbåt	Patrouille boot
142	Periscope	Sehrohr	Periscope.	Periscopio	Periskop	Periscopio	Periskop	Periskoop
143	Pilot vessel	Lotsenboot	Bateau pilote	Battello pilota		Bote de práctico	Lotsbåt	Loods boot
144	Pinnace (steam)	Dampfpinasse	Chaloupe à vapeur	Canotto a vapore	Kater	Pinaza de vapor	Ångslup	Stoom barkes
145	Pole mast	Stangenmast	Mât gaule.	Albero a palo		Palo enterizo ó tiple	Palmast	
146	Poop	Poop, Hinterschiff	Dunette.	Cassero di poppa	Korma ; oot	Toldilla	Poop, Hytta	Poep
147	Port (side)	Backbord	Babord	Sinistra	Lievii	Babor	Babord	Bakboord
148	Powder (propellant)		Charge d'explosion	Polvere impellente	Porokhovoi	Pólvora impelente	Krut	Poeder
149	Propeller	Schraube, Propeller	Helice	Elica	Grebnoi vint	Hélice	Propeller	Schroef
150	Protection to vitals	Schutz an vitalen stellen	Protection des machines	Protezione delle parti vitali	Zastchita	Protection de las partes vitales	Skydd för vitala delar	Bescherming der vitale deelen
151	Protective deck	Schutzdeck	Pont cuirassé.	Coperta proteggente	Bronevaya palooba	Cubierta de protección	Pansardäck	Beschermings dek
152	Q.F.(=R.F. in U.S.)	Schnell Feuer Geschutz	à tir rapide.	Tiro rapido	Skorostrelnii	Tiro rápido	Snabbskjutande kanon	Snelvuur
153	Radius of action	Fahrbereich, Aktionsradius	Rayon d'action.	Raggio d'azione	Radius deistviya	Radio de acción	Aktionsradie	Straal van actie
154	Rake (of masts, &c.)	Rak	Incliné/e/s sur l'arriere	Inclinazione (di nu albero)	Ooklon	Inclinación (de un palo)	Fall /på master, etc./	Hang (van masten)
155	Ram	Ramsporn	Eperon	Sperone	Tarann	Espolon	Ramm	Ram
156	Range yds./metres	Entfernung, Schlussweite	Portée	Portate—yarde/metri	Dalnost boya	Alcance yardas/metros	Avstånd	Afstand (yds./meters)
157	Range-finder	Entfernungsmesse	Télémètre.	Telemetro	Dalnomer	Telémetro	Avståndsmätare	Afstand zoeker
158	Repair ship	Reparaturschiff	Transport/Navire-atelier.	Nave per riparazione	Plavoochaya masterskaija	Buque de reparaciones	Verkstadsfartyg	Reparatie schip
159	River gunboat	Flusskanonenboot	Cannonière de riviere	Cannoniera da fiume	Rechnaya kanonerskaya lodka	Lancha cañónera de río	Flodkanonbåt	Rivier kanonneerboot
160	River monitor	Flussmonitor	Monitor de riviere	Monitor da fiume		Monitor de río	Flodmonitor	Rivier monitor
161	Royal yacht	Königliche Yacht	Yacht royal/impérial/présidentiel	Yacht reale	Korolevskaya yakhta	Yate real	Kunglig yacht	Koninklijk yacht
162	Rudder	Ruder, Steuerruder, Seitenruder, Ventikalruder	Gouvernail.	Timone	Rool	Timón	Roder	Roer
163	Salvage ship	Bergungsschiff	Navire releveur	Nave di salvataggio	Spasatelnoe soodno	Buque de salvamento	Bärgningsfartyg	Bergings schip
164	S. S. (steamship)	Dampfer	Navire à vapeur	Vapore		Buque de vapor	Ångfartyg	S.S. (stoomschip)
165	S. V. (sailing vessel)	Segler	Voilier	Bastimento a vela		Buque de vela	Segelfartyg	Z.S. (zeilschip)
166	Scout	Aufklärungskreuzer	Eclaireur/Estafette	Nave esploratrice	Raabedchik	Buque explorador	Spaningsfartyg	Verkenaer
167	Screens	Splitter-traversen	Écrans	Schermi	Shirmi	Pantallas	Splintskärmar	Splinterschilden Schermen
168	Seaplane	Wasserflugzeug	Hydravion.	Idrovolante	Gidroaeroplan	Hidrovolante	Hydroaeroplan	Water vliegtuig
169	Seaplane-carrier	Flugzeugmutterschiff	Porte-avions.	,, (nave appoggio)	Soodno-matka dlya gidroaeroplanov	,, (buque portador)	Flygmaskins—depotfartyg	Watervliegtuig drager
170	Searchlight	Scheinwerfer	Projecteur.	Proiettore	Projektor	Proyector	Strålkastare	Zoeklicht
171	Searchlight-top	Scheinwerfertopp	Hune à projecteurs	,, (coffa)		,, (cofa)	Strålkastaremast	Controle top zoeklicht
172	Sheer (of hull)	Sprung		Cervatura dello scafo		Arrufo del casco	Sprang	Geer (van hol)
173	Shields	Schützschildern	Boucliers.	Scudi	Stchit	Mantelete	Sköldar	Schilden
174	Sloop	Sloop, U–bootsabwehrkreuzer	Aviso(?)	Scialuppa	Shlup	Balandra		Sloep
175	Sounding machine	Lotmaschine	Sonde/Appareil	Macchina da scandaglio		Aparato para sondar		Diepte peiling machine
176	Speed	Geschwindigkeit	Vitesse	Velocita	Skorost khoda	Velocidad	Fart	Vaart, Snelheid
177	Squadron (of fleet)	Geschwader	Escadre	Squadra (di una flotta)	Eskadra ; brigada	Escuadra de una flota	Eskader	Eskader (van vloot)
178	Starboard	Steuerbord	Tribord	Dritta	Pravaia storona	Estribor	Styrbord	Stuurboord
179	Stern	Heck	Arrière	Poppa	Korma	Popa	Akter	Hek
180	Submarine	Untersee-Boote	Sousmarin	Sottomarino	Podvodnaia lodka	Submarino	Undervattensbat	Onderzeetorpedoboot
181	Submarine-chaser	U–bootsjäger	Contre-sousmarins	Cacciasommergibili		Caza-submarino	U-batsjagare	Onderzeër jager
182	Submerged	Unterwasser	Submergé	Subacqueo	Podvodnii	Sumergido	Under vattnet	Onderwater
183	Submersible	Tauchboot	Submersible	Sommergibile	Opooskanshiisya pod vodoo ; mogooshii opooskatsya	Sumergible	Dykbåt	Duikboot
184	Super-firing (guns)	Übereinandergestellt	Superposé/e/s (canons.)		Strelba s visshei pozitsii cherez nizshoon		Överhöjda kanoner	

ENGLISH.	GERMAN.	FRENCH.	ITALIAN.	RUSSIAN.	SPANISH.	SWEDISH.	DUTCH.
185 Supply ship	185 Proviantschiff	185 Ravitailleur/Transport vivres	185 Nave di provviste		185 Buque de abastecimiento	185 Provianfartyg	185 Toever schip
186 Surveying ship	186 Vermessungsschiff	186 Navire pour Service Hydrographique	186 Nave idrografica	186 Opisnoe soodno	186 Buque hidrográfico	186 Sjömätningsfartyg	186 Controle schip
187 Tank vessel (for water)	187 Wasserfahrzeug	187 Citerne	187 Nave-cisterna (acqua)	187 Nalivnoe soodno	187 Buque de cisterna (agua)	187 Vattenbåt	187 Tank schip (voor water)
188 Tender	188 Beiboot, Tender	188 Annexe	188 Battello d'avviso	188 Tender	188 Bote-aviso	188 Hjälpfartyg	188 Lichter
189 Topmast	189 Marsstänge	189 Mât de hune	189 Albero de freccia	189 Stenga	189 Mastelero de galope	189 Stang	189 Steng
190 Top gallant mast	190 Bramstänge	190 Mât de perroquet	190 Albero de velaccio	190 Bram-stenga	190 Mastelero de juanete	190 Bramstang	190 Bovenbram steng
191 Torpedo	191 Torpedo	191 Torpille	191 Siluro	191 Mina	191 Torpedo	191 Torped	191 Torpedo
192 Torpedo boat	192 Torpedo boot	192 Torpilleur	192 Torpediniera	192 Minonosets	192 Torpedero	192 Torpedbåt	192 Torpedoboot
193 Torpedo tubes	193 Torpedo lancier-röhre	193 Tubes lance torpille	193 Tubi lancia siluri	193 Minnie aparati	193 Tubos lanza torpedos	193 Torpedtub	193 Lanceerinridiling (Cuis
194 Tons	194 Tonnen	194 Tonnes	194 Tonnelate	194 Tonni	194 Toneladas	194 Ton	194 Tonnen of Kanon)
195 Training ship	195 Schulschiff	195 Navire-Ecole	195 Nave scuola di marina	195 Oochebnoe soodno	195 Buque escuela de marina	195 Övningsfartyg	195 Opleidings schip
196 „ (boys)	196 Schiffsjungen-schulsschiff	196 „ mousses	196 „ (ragazzi)		196 „ (muchachos)	196 Skeppsgossefartyg	196 „ (jongens)
197 „ (engineers)	197 Maschinenschulschiff	197 „ mecaniciens	197 „ (macchinisti)		197 „ (máquinistas)	197 Maskinistskolfartyg	197 „ (machinisten)
198 „ (gunnery)	198 Artillerieschulschiff	198 „ de cannonage	198 „ (artiglieria)		198 „ (artilleria)	198 Artilleriskolfartyg	198 „ (kanonneers)
199 Training ship (midshipmen, &c.)	199 Kadettenschulschiff	199 „ d'application	199 „ (guardie-marine)		199 „ (guardia-marinas)	199 Kadettfartyg	199 „ (adelborsten, etc.)
200 Training ship (navigation)	200 Navigationsschulschiff	200 „ navigation	200 „ (navigazione)		200 „ (navegación)	200 Skolfartyg	200 „ (navigatie)
201 „ (mine)	201 Minenschulschiff	201 „ de torpilles	201 „ (mina)		201 „ (minas)	201 Minskolfartyg	201 „ (mijn)
202 „ (stokers)	202 Heizerschulschiff	202 „ de chauffe	202 „ (fuochisti)		202 „ (fogoneros)	202 Eldareskolfartyg	202 „ (stokers)
203 „ (torpedo)	203 Torpedoschulschiff	203 „ de torpilles automobils	203 „ (siluri)		203 „ (torpedos)	203 Torpedskolfartyg	203 „ (torpedo)
204 Transport	204 Transporten, Transportdampfer	204 Transport	204 Trasporto	204 Transport; transportnoe soodno	204 Buque transporte	204 Transport	204 Transport
205 Trawler	205 Fischdampfer	205 Chalutier	205 "Trawler"	205 Traooler	205 "Trawler" (Buque de pesca)	205 Trawlare, Fiskeångare	205 Stoom visscherman
206 Trials	206 Probefahrten	206 Essais	206 Prove	206 Ispitaniia	206 Pruebas	206 Provturer	206 Proeftocht
207 Trimming tank	207 Trimmtank		207 "Trimming tank" (cisterna di assetamento)	207 Ooravnitelnaya sisterna	207 "Trimming tank" (cisterna de equilibración)	207 Trimtank	207 Ballast tank
208 Tug	208 Schleppdampfer	208 Remorqueur	208 Rimorchiatore	208 Booksir; booksirnoe soodno	208 Remolcador	208 Bogserbat	208 Sleep boot
209 Turbo-generator	209 Turbogenerator	209 Turbo-moteur	209 Turbo-generatore		209 Turbo-generador	209 Turbingenerator	
210 Turbine	210 Turbine	210 Turbine	210 Turbina	210 Turbina	210 Turbina	210 Turbin	210 Turbine
211 „ (geared)	211 Turbine mit Reduziervorrichtung, Turbine mit mehrfacher Übersetzung	211 Turbines à engrenages	211 Turbina ad ingranaggio		211 Turbina con engranaje	211 Utväxlad turbin	
212 Turrets	212 Türme	212 Tourelles	212 Torri	212 Bashnia	212 Torres	212 Torn	212 Torens
213 Upper deck	213 Oberdeck	213 Pont de gaillards	213 Ponte superiore	213 Verkhniaia paluba	213 Cubierta alta	213 Övre däck	213 Opperdek
214 Uptake (to funnels)	214 Rauchfang, Exhaustor	214 Base de cheminées	214 Cassa a fumo (nel fumaiolo)	214 Naroojnaya dimovaya trooba	214 Flus de reunión de chimenea	214 Rökupptag	
215 Ventilator	215 Ventilator, Lüfter	215 Ventilateur	215 Ventilatore	215 Ventilyator	215 Ventilador	215 Ventilator	215 Luchtkoker
216 Water line	216 Wasserlinie	216 Flottaison	216 Linea d'acqua	216 Vaterliniia	216 La linea de flotacion	216 Vattenlinje	216 Waterlyn
217 Wireless telegraphy (W/T)	217 Funkentelegraphie (F.T.); drachtlose Telegraphie	217 Telegraphie sans fils (T.S.F.)	217 Radiotelegrafia	217 Bezprovolornoe telegrafirovanie	217 Radio-telegrafia	217 Gnisttelegrafi, Radiotelegrafi	217 Telegraphie zonder draad
218 „ „ aerials	218 Antennen, Luftdrähte	218 Antennes de T.S.F.	218 „ (antenne)	218 Anteni	218 „ (antenas)	218 Antenner, Luftnät	
219 „ „ spreaders	219 Antennen spr (?)	219 Deflecteurs de T.S.F.	219 „ (Stendadori ærei)		219 (Extendedores aéreos)	219 Spröt för gnistnät	
220 Watertight door	220 Wasserdichte Tür	220 Porte de cloison etanche	220 Porta stagna	220 Vodonepronicziaemaya dver	220 Puerta estanca	220 Vattentät dörr	220 Waterdichte deur
221 „ compartment	221 Wasserdichte Abteilung	221 Cloison etanche	221 Compartimento stagno	221 Vodonepronicziaemoe otdelenie	221 Compartimiento estanco	221 Vattentät avdelning	221 Waterdichte afdeeling
222 Yacht (steam)	222 Dampfyacht	222 Yacht (à vapeur)	222 Yacht a vapore	222 Yakhta (parovaya)	222 Yate de vapor	222 Ångyacht	222 Yacht (stoom)

(ROYAL) BRITISH NAVY.

LIMITS OF BRITISH NAVAL STATIONS, 1919.

From Chart furnished by courtesy of the Hydrographic Department, Admiralty.

SEAPLANES.

ENSIGN

JACK

ADMIRAL

VICE ADMIRAL

REAR ADMIRAL

ROYAL STANDARD

NAVAL RESERVE (BLUE ENSIGN)

MERCANTILE ENSIGN (RED ENSIGN)

Red
White
Blue
Yellow

(In 2000 yard squares. Soundings in fathoms. Heights in feet.)

ROSYTH

to	knots.
Aberdeen	95
Dover	473
Helder	360
Hull	260
Kronstadt ...	1345
Newcastle	130
Portsmouth ...	570
Sheerness... ...	458
Wilhelmshaven	445

SHEERNESS

to	knots.
Dover...	45
Dunkirk	70
Helder	190
Hull	200
Kronstadt ...	1200
Newcastle	328
Portsmouth ...	150
Wilhelmshaven	270

PORTSMOUTH

to	knots.
Barbados ...	3600
Berehaven ...	375
Brest	226
Cherbourg ...	72
Devonport ...	155
Gibraltar	1200
Lorient	331
New York... ...	3080
Pernambuco ...	3900

Portland	55
Wilhelmshaven	620

DEVONPORT

to	knots.
Berehaven ...	375
Brest	140
Cape of Good Hope	5890
Cherbourg ...	110
Gibraltar	1050
Lorient	233
New York... ...	2905
Portland	100
Queenstown ...	292
Rochefort... ...	370
Toulon	1764

GIBRALTAR

to	knots.
Ajaccio	1000
Algiers	420
Berehaven ...	1170
Bizerta	875
Brest	953
Devonport ...	1050
Malta	980
Oran	225
Toulon	713

MALTA

to	knots.
Aden	2320
Ajaccio	450
Bizerta	240

Constantinople...	702
Port Said... ...	920
Sevastopol ...	1000
Spezia	580
Suda Bay... ...	575
Suez	1010
Toulon	612

ADEN

to	knots.
Batavia	3950
Beira	2824
Bombay	1652
Cape Town ...	4450
Colombo	2100
Delagoa Bay ...	3340
Devonport... ...	4350
Durban	3650
Karachi	1470
Mauritius... ...	2600
Suez	1310
Tamatave ...	2290
Zanzibar	1770

COLOMBO

to	knots.
Bombay	900
Calcutta	1240
Devonport... ...	6450
Fremantle (W.A.)	3105
Karachi	1400
Penang	1280
Rangoon	1207

Singapore... ...	1600
Sydney(N.S.W.)	5450

SINGAPORE

to	knots.
Bangkok	820
Batavia	500
Devonport... ...	8020
Hong Kong ...	1430
Manila	1320
Saigon	648

HONG-KONG

to	knots.
Devonport... ...	9450
Kiao-chau ...	1270
Manila	650
Nagasaki	1067
Port Arthur ...	1415
Saigon	930
Shanghai	870
Ta-kau(Formosa)	340
Vladivostock...	1927
Wei-hai-wei ...	1470
Yokosuka... ...	1620

CAPE OF GOOD HOPE

to	knots.
Ascension... ...	2395
Durban	812
Falkland Isles	4800
Fremantle (W.A.)	4850
Hobart	5527

Madagascar ...	1800
Port Elizabeth	428
Portsmouth ...	5960
St. Helena ...	1710
Teneriffe	4470

ESQUIMAULT

to	knots.
Honolulu	2410
San Francisco ...	750
Seattle	76
Yokosuka... ...	4300

SYDNEY (N.S.W.)

to	knots.
Adelaide	1076
Auckland... ...	1280
Batavia	4476
Brisbane	510
Cape of Good Hope	6157
Colombo	5450
Devonport (via Cape)...	12,047
Hobart	630
Melbourne ...	570
Singapore ...	4980
Wellington, (N.Z.)	1234

24

1. DEVONPORT and **KEYHAM.** At *Devonport* (South Yard)—two big slips, three small. Dry docks :—No. 3, could just take *Duncan* class, size 430 × 93 × 34¾ feet, and three others, of which one (No. 2 Dock) can take a second class cruiser; other two suitable for small craft only. At *Keyham* (North Yard)—No slips. New basin, 35½ acres, depth, 32¾ft. Tidal basin, 10 acres, depth, 32ft.

Dry Docks in New Extension:—
Entrance lock, 730＊ × 95 × 44 feet.
No. 9 (double) 745 × 95 × 32 ,,
Keyham (North Yard) No. 10 (double) 741 × 95 × 44 feet.
,, 8 659 × 95 × 32 ,,
＊ Can be lengthened 86 feet.

In the old part of the yard there are three docks, of which one (No. 7) can take a second class cruiser; the others small craft only. Total employees for the two yards, 14,000–15,000.

Admiralty Chart No. 1267. Rise of Spring Tide 15½ feet (Dockyard).

BRITISH NAVY.

ADDENDA AND CORRECTIONS:—1.

NAVAL ORDNANCE : MEDIUM B.L.   Following are correct details of 5.5 inch.   Length, 50 cals.   Weight of gun, 6 tons 4 cwt.   Weight of projectile, 82 lbs.   M. V., 2950 ft.-secs.   M. E., 4520 ft.-tons.   Weight of charge, 23½ lbs.   Rounds per minute : 12.   *Remarks.*—Mounted in *Hood.*   Range, at 30° elevation : 12,000 yards.

The Russian (Black Sea) Dreadnought, **VOLYA** was temporarily taken over by the British Navy during 1919 ; reported to have joined Gen. Denikin's Naval Forces in the Black Sea and to have been re-named **GENERAL ALEXEIEFF.**

INDOMITABLE to be sold.

CAPETOWN to be towed to Pembroke D.Y. for completion.

Unofficially reported that *EFFINGHAM* will be built as an Aircraft carrier.

CALLIOPE (and other Light Cruisers) no longer have searchlight and control tower amidships.

FOX for disposal.

Monitors—*continued.*

ROBERTS.   *Official R.A.F. Photo.*

Note.—*Roberts* is not included in the Post-War Fleet Organization.   The above photograph has, however, been selected as an illustration, because it gives, by far, the best impression of the box-like hull and huge beam of the big Monitors.   The projection of the " bulges " is also very clear in the above view.   The formation and throwing-off of the coarse bow-wave are also worth noting.

Monitors.

MARSHAL SOULT.

Monitors—*Continued.*

HUMBER, M 33 for sale, **M 31** to be converted for Minelaying.

M 19 (of M 19—27 class). **M 23** for sale.

M 16 (of M 16—18 class).

Destroyers.

Russian (Black Sea) Destroyer **Derski** has been temporarily taken over by British Navy.

Tryphon (Yarrow "S" Type) did not go aground on Danish Coast, as stated. She went aground at Tenedos about last June and lay there on her beam-ends for three weeks. She was salved and brought to Pera for temporary repairs. She was then towed to Malta but nearly sank on passage. She is said to be too badly damaged for any further use, but an H.M.S. *Triton*—perhaps *Tryphon*—was recently reported as repairing by Yarrows.

Illustration of **Taurus** (Thornycroft "R") is really **Patriot** (Thornycroft "M").

TRIDENT.   *Photo, Cribb, Southsea.*

Nizam to be sold.

D.C.B. (*Depth Charge Boats*).

These are a modified type of C.M.B. without torpedoes in troughs but carrying Thornycroft Depth Charge Throwers or U. S. type Y-guns and special load of Depth Charges.

About 100 M.L. (Motor Launches) have been sold.

Submarines.

Delete: **F** Class Submarines and **E 54**; all are for sale.   *Delete:* **L 55,** lost 1919.

Aircraft Carriers.

VINDICTIVE reported very badly damaged by grounding in the Baltic. **NAIRANA** re-conditioned for mercantile service. **EAGLE** to be towed to Portsmouth D.Y. for completion.

Minesweepers.

Delete: **KINROSS** (of later "Hunt" Class), lost in Ægean, 1919. **FANDANGO** (not listed) of "Dance" Class, armed with 1—6 pdr. AA. gun, lost 1919.

Salvage Vessel.

MELITA for sale.

WESTERN ENTRANCE.

EASTERN ENTRANCE.

2. PORTSMOUTH. One slip for building battleships or cruisers up to 750 feet.

Three large and one small basins.

Dry docks :—No. 15, 563 × 94 × 33½ feet.
,, 14, 770 × 100 × 33½ ,,
,, 13, 560 × 82 × 33½ ,,
,, 12, 485 × 80 × 33½ ,,

Lock A. 461 × 80 × 33⅓ feet.
,, B, 461 × 81¾ × 34 ,,
,, C, 850 × 110 × 40 ,,
,, D, 850 × 110 × 40 ,,

and ten smaller docks. Total employees, about 8000 normally, probably 16,000 now.

Admiralty Chart No. 2631-2045. Rise of Spring Tide, 13½ feet (Dockyard).

Note.—Breakwater from Lumps Fort due south about 2 miles. Aircraft base at Calshot, Southampton, before the war. By the end of 1913, 17 oil fuel reservoirs were built.

(All maps divided into 2000 yard squares. Soundings in fathoms. Heights in feet).

PORTLAND. 1500 acres of enclosed harbour; minimum depth, 30 feet. Floating dock suitable for destroyers. Coaling station. N. and E. entrances 700 feet wide. Strongly fortified. Admiralty Chart No. 2255. Rise of Spring Tide, 9 feet (Bill of Portland); 6¾ feet (Breakwater).

Other Naval Harbours and Stations in Home Waters.

BEREHAVEN. Good anchorage. **SCILLY.** The anchorage is moderately good. The entrance is very narrow, difficult and dangerous. **LOUGH SWILLY & BUNCRANA.** Very moderately fortified. Good anchorage. **KINGSTOWN** (DUBLIN), **TORBAY, FALMOUTH, CROMARTY FIRTH, MORAY FIRTH,** (SCOTLAND, E. COAST), **SCAPA FLOW, LOCH EWE, LAMLASH,** &c. **CAMPBELTOWN.** Submarine Training Station. **SHANDON, GARELOCH.** Anti-Submarine Station, for Experiments and Training.

DOVER. New harbour, 610 acres; depth of 30 feet at low water over half the area. E. entrance, 1 cable; W. entrance, 800 feet. Coaling station. Well fortified. Floating dock for Destroyers.

Moorings for 16 battleships, 5 large cruisers, 7 *Counties*, 4 small cruisers, and for destroyers.

(The tide at entrance is very strong, making ingress difficult).

Admiralty Chart No. 1698-1828.

Rise of Spring Tide, 18¾ feet.

West Coast (Wales).

PEMBROKE. Building yard. Two large slips. Dry docks:—One, 404 × 75 × 24¾ feet (high water). About 2500 employees.

Admiralty Chart No. 915-2393.

Rise of Spring Tide, 22½ feet (Dockyard).

(All maps divided into 2000 yard squares. Soundings in fathoms. Heights in feet.)

HARWICH.

HARWICH. Base for Torpedo Craft, Submarines, &c. Admiralty Chart No. 2693.

IMMINGHAM. For Repairs.

OSEA ISLAND. River Blackwater. C.M.B. Base.

HAULBOWLINE. Dockyard. No slips. Dry docks :—
(a) Entrance, size 720 × 94 × 32½ feet.
(b) No. 1 „ 608 × 94 × 32½ „ (lengthened 1911). Employees 1000 (now more).
Admiralty Chart No. 1765. Rise of Spring Tide 11¾ feet.

ROSYTH (and PORT EDGAR). Three docks 850 × 110 × 36 feet. Entrance lock 850 × 110 × 36 feet. Also Floating Docks.
Admiralty Chart No. 114 B. Rise of Spring Tide, 16½ feet.
Aircraft Base at Carlinghouse before War.

BRITISH DOCKYARDS—THE NORE (Home Station).

(In squares of 2000 yards. Soundings in fathoms. Heights in feet).

CHATHAM. Three building slips. Three large closed basins. Dry docks :—

No. 9,	650 × 84 × 33 feet.
„ 8,	456 × 82 × 33 „
„ 7,	456 × 82 × 32½ „
„ 6,	456 × 80 × 32½ „
„ 5,	460 × 80 × 32½ „

Also floating docks.

There are four other docks suitable only for small craft (Nos. 1, 2, 3, 4). Total employees, 12,000.

Admiralty Chart No. 1834-1607-1185. Rise of Spring Tide, 18¼ feet.

SHEERNESS. No slips. One small basin. Dry docks :—Five, all small, and able to take small craft only. Also floating docks. Destroyer base. Flying school and aircraft base at Isle of Grain, before the war. Floating dock, 680 × 113 × 36 feet (33,000 tons). Employees, 2,500.

Admiralty Chart No. 1833. Rise of Spring Tide 16 feet.

Errata : East Sutor now *North Sutor.*
West Sutor now *South Sutor.*

Cromarty Firth. Fleet Anchorage. **INVERGORDON.** Dockyard. Floating Docks, one, 680 × 113 × 36 feet (33,000 tons *Dreadnought*), another *Dreadnought* Floating Dock, third Floating Dock for Light Cruisers, T.B.D. and S/M.

SCAPA FLOW. Fleet Anchorage only, 1919. Admiralty Chart Nos. 2180, 2581, 3729.

(Maps to Uniform Scale. Divided in 2000 yard squares. Soundings in fathoms).

BERMUDA.

N. America and West Indies.

BERMUDA. Naval Dockyard. Fortified. Large floating dock, $545 \times 92\frac{3}{4} \times 33$ feet (*Dreadnought*, 17,500 tons). Shallow harbour. Admiralty Chart No. **360.**

BRIDGETOWN (Barbados). Coaling. Open roadstead. There is a small dock here, able to take vessels drawing up to 14 feet.

ST. JOHN'S (Newfoundland). There is a private dock here, $569\frac{1}{2} \times 85 \times 24$ feet. (*Dreadnought, if lightened.*)

TRINIDAD. 4,000 tons floating dock, $365 \times 65 \times 18$ feet.

Note : ESQUIMAULT and Docks in the Dominion of Canada transferred to Royal Canadian Navy Section.

Cape Station.

CAPE COAST CASTLE (British Gold Coast, W. Africa). Fortified coaling station. Anchorage average 28 feet.

PORT STANLEY (Falkland Is.) Good deep harbour. Fortified coaling station.

ST. HELENA. Fortified coaling station. 10-fathom harbour.

SIERRA LEONE (W. Africa). Fortified coaling station. Anchorage, 6-16 fathoms.

SIMON'S BAY (Cape of Good Hope). Naval dockyard. Selborne Dock, $750 \times 95 \times 36$ feet. (*Dreadnought.*) Tidal basin, 28 acres, 30 feet deep. Fortified moderately. Admiralty Chart No. **1849.** There is a dock at Capetown, $500 \times 66 \times 24\frac{1}{2}$ feet, and a floating one at Durban, $425 \times 70 \times 23$ feet.

Australia.

(See Royal Australian Navy Section).

New Zealand.

(See New Zealand Section).

BRITISH COMMERCIAL HARBOURS AND IMPORTANT SHIPPING PORTS.

British Private Docks, at Home, able to take Dreadnoughts.

There are 235 dry docks of considerable size in U.K outside Royal Yards.

HEBBURN (Graving),	...	...	...	size,	$700 \times 90 \times 28\frac{1}{2}$ feet.
BRISTOL (Avonmouth)	...	...	...	,,	$855 \times 100 \times 34$,,
SOUTHAMPTON (No. 5)	...	...	...	,,	$745 \times 91 \times 28\frac{1}{2}$,,
,, (No. 6)	...	...	...	,,	$782 \times 100 \times 31$,,
LIVERPOOL (Canada Graving)	...	...	,,	$925 \times 94 \times 32$,,
,, (Brocklebank Graving)	...	...	,,	$800 \times 93 \times 31\frac{1}{2}$,,
,, (Gladstone)	...	...	...	,,	$1020 \times 120 \times 47$,,
BIRKENHEAD (No. 3)	...	...	...	,,	$750 \times 85\frac{1}{4} \times 26$,,
,, (No. 6)	...	...	...	,,	$730 \times 82 \times 30$,,
,, (No. 7)	...	...	...	,,	$880 \times 92 \times 33$,,
GLASGOW (No. 4)	...	...	...	,,	$1020 \times 110 \times 40$,,
RENFREW	...	...	...	..	$1020 \times 100 \times 36$,,
BELFAST (No. 1)	...	...	...	,,	$850 \times 96 \times 35\frac{1}{4}$,,
,, (No. 2)	...	...	...	,,	$750 \times 96 \times 33$,,

Principal Commercial Harbours (1914).

(In order of importance, with approximate tons of shipping clearing annually).

London (9 million) ; Liverpool (7 million) ; Cardiff ($6\frac{3}{4}$ million) ; Newcastle and district ($4\frac{1}{2}$ million) ; Hull ($2\frac{1}{4}$ million) ; Glasgow (2 million) ; Southampton ($1\frac{1}{2}$ million) ; and Newport, Blyth, Swansea, Sunderland, Leith, Dover, Kirkcaldy, Grimsby, Middlesbrough, Grangemouth (all doing about 1 million) ; Harwich, Manchester, Bristol, Goole, Hartlepool, Belfast, and Folkestone (all doing from $\frac{3}{4}$ to $\frac{1}{4}$ million).

Mercantile Marine (British and Colonial).

Lloyds Return, June 1919, as follows:—

				Tons *Gross.*
United Kingdom	...	...	...	16,345,000
British Dominions	...	...	...	1,863,000
			Total	18,208,000

BRITISH WARSHIP BUILDERS.

Note.—The headings give the abbreviated titles by which builders are mentioned on later Ship Pages. With a few exceptions, all details given below were kindly approved or furnished in 1919 by the firms mentioned.

Armstrong.

Note.—Hitherto it has been the custom to refer to this firm as " Elswick." The Elswick Shipyard has practically ceased naval construction. From now onwards, the firm will be mentioned as " Armstrongs " or " Armstrong Whitworth."

SIR W. G. ARMSTRONG, WHITWORTH & CO., Ltd. (Newcastle-on-Tyne). *Armstrong Naval Yard.* 70 acres. Frontage about a mile. Nine slips, 1000 to 500 ft. long. *Walker Shipyard.* Area 30 acres. Frontage 317 yards. Six slips from 650 to 450 ft. long. Total employees, including ordnance, armour plate, marine engine and steel works, about 31,000.

Beardmore.

WM. BEARDMORE & CO., Ltd. (Naval Construction Works, Dalmuir, nr. Glasgow). All classes of ships, naval and mercantile, up to largest size and highest speed. Engines of all types and sizes. Six big slips, four smaller. Employees *circa* 10,000. This yard is designed for vessels up to 900 ft. long. 220-ton crane. Fitting basin of 8 acres, 28 ft. at low water. Patent slip 460 ft. long.

Cammell Laird.

CAMMELL LAIRD & CO. (BIRKENHEAD AND TRANMERE). Area of yard, 108 acres. Six slips (longest 1000 ft.), six small slips. Seven graving docks, five small and No. 6, 708 × 80 × 12 ft.; No. 7, 861 × 90 × 15 ft. Outer basin, 14½ acres; inner basin, 2¾ acres. Annual capacity, 100,000 tons *gross* and 400,000 H.P. output. Establishment consists of North (Old) Yard, where destroyers, submarines and passenger steamers of cross-channel type can be built up to 375 ft. long. At the South (New) Yard, warships and mercantile vessels of the largest dimensions can be built. Builders of light cruisers, flotilla leaders (speciality), submarines, &c. Patentees of Camellaird-Fullager Diesel Engines. Equipment of yard thoroughly up-to-date. Employees, 12,000 to 15,000.

Clydebank.

JOHN BROWN & CO. (SHIPBUILDING & ENGINEERING WORKS, CLYDEBANK, GLASGOW). Area, 80 acres. River frontage, 1050 yards. Building berths : Five of 950 to 600 ft. in length, and three 600 to 450 ft. in length. Building berths are commanded by derricks, tower and gantry cranes ; two of berths are covered. Tidal basin : 5¼ acres in area, 30 ft. depth, L.W.O.S.T. with two entrances of 130 and 180 ft. width respectively. Basin commanded by two 150-ton cranes ; also four wharf cranes of 5 to 30 tons capacity. Builders of war and mercantile vessels of all types and the largest dimensions, inclusive of machinery and equipment. Brown-Curtis turbines, direct-drive, geared-cruising and all-geared types. Output in 1918 : 22,196 tons (exclusive of launch of H.M.S. *Hood*), 313,600 H.P. (exclusive of machinery for H.M.S. *Hood*). Total employees, shipyard and engine works, 8500 to 10,000.

Denny.

WM. DENNY & BROS. (LEVEN SHIPYARD, DUMBARTON, N.B.). Area : 60 acres. Building berths : 10 up to 550 ft. in length. Two wet basins, one 475 ft., one 910 ft. Numerous cranes with lifts up to 110 tons. Employees : 3800. Destroyers, torpedo boats, submarines and mercantile vessels built, with necessary machinery, &c.

Doxford.

WM. DOXFORD & SONS, LTD. (PALLION YARD, SUNDERLAND). Builders of vessels up to 20,000 tons dead-weight. Also reciprocating, turbine and Diesel marine engines up to any size. Also special self-discharging colliers and bunkering craft. Output over 100,000 tons *gross* per annum.

Fairfield.

THE FAIRFIELD SHIPBUILDING & ENGINEERING CO. (GOVAN, GLASGOW). Area : 70 acres. Water front : 2600 ft. 11 slips to build ships up to 900 ft. in length. Dock : six acres with 270 ft. entrance. 250-ton crane. Wet basin : 900 ft. long and ten docks up to 900 ft. Employees : 8500. Naval and mercantile ships, engines, boilers, &c., of all types. Associated with Northumberland S.B. Co.

Harland & Wolff.

HARLAND & WOLFF, LTD. (BELFAST). Eight large slips in main yard (two 860 × 99 ft.). Six large slips completed or in course of completion in new yard. Two large docks and three smaller in the vicinity of the works. Employees : 20,000. Also at Govan, Glasgow, 7 large slips ; Greenock, 6 large slips. Exceptional facilities at Bootle, Liverpool, and at Southampton, for the repair of ships and machinery.

Hawthorn Leslie.

R. & W. HAWTHORN, LESLIE & CO., LTD. (HEBBURN YARD, HEBBURN-ON-TYNE). Twelve slips up to 700 ft. long. One dock : 460 × 68 × 21 ft. on blocks ; 26 ft. draught at quay at low water. Engine department of 150,000 I.H.P. per annum. Designers and builders of cruisers, destroyers and other warship types. Engine every type of war vessel. Builders of locomotives for main line service and works. Employees : 6-7000.

Palmers.

PALMERS SHIPBUILDING & IRON CO., LTD. (HEBBURN-ON-TYNE). All classes of war and mercantile vessels. Build turbine and reciprocating engines, water-tube and Scotch boilers. Fully equipped for all classes of repairs to hulls and machinery. Fourteen slips. Employees : 9000. Has two docks : Hebburn, 700 × 90 × 29 ft. ; Jarrow, 440 × 70 × 18 ft. ; also patent slipway (Jarrow)—all used for warships. Employees : 9000.

Scott's.

SCOTT'S SHIPBUILDING & ENGINEERING CO., LTD. (GREENOCK, N.B.). Slips for six large and four small vessels ; fitting-out basin ; graving dock. Employees : 6000. Makers of heavy oil engines and licensees for Laurenti type of submarines.

Stephen.

ALEX. STEPHEN & CO., LTD. (LINTHOUSE, GOVAN, NEAR GLASGOW). Build destroyers and torpedo craft ; also mail, passenger and cargo steamers. Machinery : all types, 40,000 H.P. output per annum. Boilers : Scotch, cylindrical and all water-tube types. Seven building berths for building ships up to 700 ft. long. Water front : 1500 ft. Area of yard : 52 acres. Repairs of all classes to hulls and machinery at firm's Govan graving dock. Works adjacent to Glasgow Docks. Employees : 3500.

Swan Hunter.

SWAN, HUNTER & WIGHAM RICHARDSON, LTD. (WALLSEND-ON-TYNE). Twenty-one building berths, fifteen of which are served by overhead electric cranes. Four berths covered in. Employees : about 8000. Annual *gross* shipbuilding capacity (1918) : 150,000 tons. Engine works : 100,000 H.P. output per year.
The dry docks dept. includes a large repairing yard with two graving docks and two floating docks. Engine works have developed the Neptune and Polar marine oil engines. Total area of works : 78 acres. Water frontage : 4000 ft. Shipyard also at Southwick-on-Wear, with three building berths. Allied firms are the Wallsend Slipway & Engineering Co., Ltd., Wallsend ; Barclay, Curle & Co., Ltd., of Whiteinch, Govan, Elderslie and Glasgow.

Thornycrott.

JOHN I. THORNYCROFT & CO., LTD. (WOOLSTON, SOUTHAMPTON). Builders of torpedo boats, destroyers, light cruisers, merchant vessels up to 400 ft. Thirteen building berths, including three covered in. One hauling-up slip for ships up to 170 ft. long. Machinery output for 1918 was 211,843 H.P. Employees : about 5,000. Water frontage : 2000 ft. Opposite Southampton Docks. Specialities : Turbines, water-tube boilers, oil fuel gear. Workshops in Southampton Docks, adjacent to fitting-out dock for hull and machinery repairs. Total floor area : 25,000 sq. ft.

Vickers.

VICKERS, LTD. (BARROW-IN-FURNESS). Area of shipbuilding department only : about 50 acres. Thirteen building berths, viz., one, 520 ft. long ; two (covered-in), 420 and 330 ft. long ; three, 450 to 350 ft. long ; five (covered-in), 330 ft. long ; all berths served by electric or steam travelling cranes, lattice work derricks and electric winches. Fitting-out basin equipped with two 150-ton Giant Hammerhead cranes, 30-ton electric jib crane, two 10-ton steam derrick cranes, one 18-ton steam travelling crane, and numerous other cranes, winches and capstans ; also 20-ton floating crane. One floating dock, 2000 tons lift ; new floating dock, 420 × 59½ (clear) ft., to lift 5200 tons. One graving dock, 500 × 60 × 22 ft. Shops for building boilers, engines, electric equipment, shells, &c. Employees (engineering and shipbuilding) : about 30,000. (Overseas Branch : Canadian Vickers Co., Montreal.)

White.

J. SAMUEL WHITE & CO., LTD. (COWES). The oldest shipyard on the Admiralty List. Light cruisers, gunboats, flotilla leaders, destroyers, submarines, minelayers, patrol boats, turbine pinnaces, and small naval craft of every kind. Seven building berths. Engine works for reciprocating and turbine engines of highest powers, "White-Forster" water-tube boilers, "White" Diesel engines, and "White" patent oil fuel installations. Hammer-head 80-ton crane. Employees : 4500.

Yarrow.

YARROW & CO., LTD. (SCOTSTOUN, GLASGOW). Area of yard : 12 acres. Water frontage : 750 ft. Nine building berths, for ships up to 400 ft. long. Wet basin for fitting-out, 350 × 85 ft., served by 50-ton crane. Specialities are destroyers, fast yachts, vessels for shallow river navigation, both of stern-wheel type and of type propelled by screws working in tunnels. Yarrow water-tube boilers and Yarrow superheater, both for land and marine use. Also vessels propelled by internal-combustion motors. Employees : about 2000. (Overseas Branch : Yarrows, Ltd., Victoria, B.C.—see Canadian Navy Section.)

Majority built engines, &c.   Those whose names are in heavy type built Monitors, Sloops, Minesweepers, Patrol Gunboats, Patrol Boats, &c. during the War.

Shipbuilders.

ABDELA, Isaac J. & Mitchell, Ltd., Queen's Ferry, Chester.
AILSA Shipbuilding Co., Ltd., Troon.
ALLEY & McLellan, Ltd., Polmadie, Glasgow.
ARDROSSAN Dry Dock and Shipbuilding Co., Ltd., Ardrossan.
AUSTIN, S. P. & Sons, Ltd., Sunderland.
AYRSHIRE Dockyard Co., Irvine, N.B.
BAIRD Bros., North Shields.
BARCLAY CURLE & Co., Ltd., Whiteinch, Elderslie, Stobcross, Kelvin-
    haugh, Govan, all near Glasgow.
BARTRAM & Sons, Ltd., Sunderland.
BEACHING Bros., Ltd., Great Yarmouth.
BLUMER, John & Co., Sunderland.
BLYTH Shipbuilding and Dry Docks Co., Ltd., Blyth.
BOW, McLachlan & Co., Paisley.
BROOK & Co., Lowestoft.
BROWN, George & Co., Greenock.
BURNTISLAND Shipbuilding Co., Burntisland (near Rosyth, N.B.)
CAIRD & Co., Ltd., Greenock, N.B.
CALEDON Shipbuilding and Engineering Co., Ltd., Dundee & Stannergate.
CAMPBELTOWN Shipbuilding Co., Campbeltown.
CAMPER & NICHOLSON, Ltd., Gosport.
CHALMERS, W. & Co., Ltd., Rutherglen, Glasgow.
CHAMBERS, J., Lowestoft.
CLYDE Shipbuilding and Engineering Co., Ltd., Port Glasgow
COCHRANE & Sons, Ltd., Selby.
COLBY Bros., Lowestoft.
CONNELL, Charles & Co., Ltd., Scotstoun.
COOK, Welton & Gemmell, Ltd., Thornaby Yard, Beverley.
COX & Co., Engineers, Ltd., Falmouth.
CRABTREE & Co., Ltd., Great Yarmouth.
CRAIG, Taylor & Co., Ltd., Stockton-on-Tees.
CRAN & SOMERVILLE, Leith.
CRICHTON & Co., South Saltney, Chester.
CROWN, John & Sons, Ltd., Sunderland.
CUMMING, D. M., Ltd., Blackhill Yard, Glasgow.
DAY, Summers & Co., Southampton.
DIXON, Sir Raylton & Co., Ltd., Cleveland Yard, Middlesbrough-on-Tees.
DOBSON, William & Co., Newcastle-on-Tyne.
DUBLIN Dockyard Co., Ltd. Dublin.
DUNCAN, R. & Co., Ltd., Port Glasgow.
DUNDEE Shipbuilding Co., Ltd., Dundee.
DUNLOP, Bremner & Co., Ltd., Port Glasgow.
DUTHIE Torry Shipbuilding Co., Aberdeen.
EARLE'S Shipbuilding and Engineering Co., Hull.
EDWARDS & Co., Ltd., Milwall.
ELTRINGHAM, Jos. T. & Co., Wallington Quay, South Shields.
FAY, J. G. & Co., Ltd., Southampton.
FELLOWS & Co., Ltd., South Town Dry Docks, Great Yarmouth.
FERGUSON Bros., Port Glasgow.
FIFE, W. & Sons, Fairlie.
FINCH, E. & Co., Ltd., Chepstow.
FLEMING & Ferguson, Ltd., Paisley.
FORBES, J. & G., Sandhaven, Fraserburgh.
FORTH SHIPBUILDING Co., Alloa.
FULLERTON, J. & Co., Paisley.
FURNESS Shipbuilding Co., Haverton Hill-on-Tees.
GOOLE Shipbuilding & Repairing Co., Ltd., Hull, and Associated Firm,
    The Dundee Shipbuilding Co., Ltd., Dundee.
GRANGEMOUTH Dockyard Co., Grangemouth.
GRAY, W. & Co., Ltd., West Hartlepool and Seaton, Teesmouth.
GREENOCK Dockyard Co., Ltd., Greenock.
HALL, A. & Co., Ltd., Aberdeen.

HALL, Russell & Co., Ltd., Aberdeen.
HAMILTON, William & Co., Ltd., Port Glasgow.
HARKESS, W. & Sons, Ltd., Middlesbrough.
HAWTHORNS & Co., Ltd., Leith.
HENDERSON, D. & W. & Co., Ltd., Partick, Glasgow.
HEPPLE (1919), Ltd., South Shields.
HILL & Sons, Chas., Bristol.
HILL, Richard & Co., Poole, Dorset.
INGLIS, A. & J., Glasgow.
IRVINE'S Shipbuilding & Dry Docks Co., Ltd., Middleton Yd., Hartlepool.
LAING, Sir James & Sons, Ltd., Sunderland.
LARNE Shipbuilding Co., Larne Harbour.
LEWIS, J. & SONS, Aberdeen.
LITHGOW'S Ltd. (late Russell & Co.), Port Glasgow.
LIVINGSTONE & COOPER, Hessle, Hull.
LLOYD ROYAL BELGE (late Brys & Gylsen), Whiteinch, Glasgow.
LOBNITZ & Co., Ltd., Renfrew.
LYTHAM Shipbuilding & Engineering Co., Lytham, Lancs.
MACKIE & Thomson, Ltd., Govan.
MANCHESTER Dry Dock Co., Ltd., Manchester.
McALLISTER. R. & Sons, Dumbarton.
MacCOLL & Thomson, Ltd., Govan.
MacCOLL, A., Abercorn Basin, Belfast.
McGREGOR & Sons, Kirkintilloch.
McMILLAN, A. & Sons, Ltd., Dumbarton.
McMILLAN & Bremner, Scotstoun.
MENZIES & Co., Leith.
MERSEY Engineering Works Co., Ltd., Liverpool.
MONTROSE Shipbuilding Co., Ltd., Montrose.
MORRIS, J. & D., Pelaw Main (Tyne District).
MUNRO, A., Ardrishaig.
MURDOCH & Murray, Ltd., Port Glasgow.
NAPIER & Miller, Ltd., Old Kilpatrick.
NORTH OF IRELAND Shipbuilding Co., Londonderry.
NORTHUMBERLAND Shipbuilding Co., Ltd., Howdon-on-Tyne.
OSBOURNE Graham & Co., Ltd., Sunderland.
OUSE Shipbuilding Co., Hook, near Goole.
PHILIP & Son, Ltd., Dartmouth.
PICKERSGILL, Wm. & Sons, Ltd., Sunderland.
PIMBLOTT, I. & Sons, Ltd., Northwich.
PRIESTMAN, J. & Co., Sunderland.
RAMAGE & Ferguson, Leith.
READHEAD, J. & Sons, Ltd., South Shields.
RENNIE FORRESTT Shipbuilding, Engineering and Dry Dock Co., Ltd.,
    Wivenhoe, Essex.
RENNOLDSON, Chas. & Co., South Shields.
RENNOLDSON, J. P. & Sons, South Shields.
RICHARDSON, DUCK & Co., Ltd., Stockton-on-Tees.
RITCHIE, Graham & Milne, Whiteinch, Glasgow.
ROBERTSON, A. & Co., Sandbank, Argyllshire.
ROBERTSON, A. W. & Co., Canning Town.
RODGERS, A. & Co., Port Glasgow.
ROPNER & Sons, Ltd., Stockton-on-Tees.
ROSE Street Foundry and Engineering Co., Inverness.
SCARR, Henry, Hessle.
SCARR, T. H., Howden.
SCOTT & Sons, Bowling, nr. Glasgow.
SHORT Bros., Ltd., Pallion, Sunderland.
SHRUBSALL, H., E. Greenwich.
SIMONS, Wm. & Co., Ltd., Renfrew.
SIMPSON, Strickland & Co., Ltd., Dartmouth.
SMITH'S Dock Co., Ltd., Middlesbrough-on-Tees.
STOTHERT & Co., Ltd., Bristol.

SUNDERLAND Shipbuilding Co., Ltd., Sunderland.
THOMAS, W. & Sons, Amlwich, N. Wales.
THOMPSON, J. L. & Sons, Ltd., Sunderland
THOMPSON, R. & Sons, Ltd., Sunderland.
TYNE Iron Shipbuilding Co., Ltd., Willington-Quay-on-Tyne.
WALKER, C. H. & Co., Ltd., Sudbrook, nr. Chepstow, Mon.
WALKER, R. C., Grimsby.
WARREN, W. H., New Holland, Lincs.
WATSON, J. S., Gainsborough.
WHITE Bros., Itchen, Southampton.
WHITE, Wm. & Sons, Cowes, I.W.
WILLIAMSON, R. & Sons, Workington.
WILLOUGHBY Bros., Ltd., Plymouth.
WOOD, SKINNER & Co., Ltd., Newcastle-on-Tyne.
WORKMAN, CLARK & Co., Ltd., Belfast.
YARWOOD, W. J. & Sons, Castle Dock, Northwich, Cheshire.

Marine Engine Builders (*Exclusive of Diesel Engine builders*).

ABERNETHY, J. & Co., Aberdeen.
AITCHISON, Blair & Co., Clydebank.
ALLEN, W. H., Sons & Co.
AMOS & Smith, Ltd., Hull.
BELL, HEMSLEY, Ltd., Southampton.
BLAIR & Co., Ltd., Stockton-on-Tees.
BRITISH Westinghouse Co., Ltd., Trafford Park, Manchester, Rateau
    Turbines.
CAMPBELL & Caldermoore, Paisley.
CENTRAL Marine Engine Works, West Hartlepool.
CLARK, G., Ltd., Sunderland.
COOPER & Greig, Dundee.
DICKINSON, J. & Sons, Ltd., Sunderland.
DUNSMUIR & Jackson, Ltd., Govan.
ELLIOTT & Garrood. Ltd., Beccles.
FISHERS, Ltd., Paisley.
GAUDLIE, Gillespie & Co., Glasgow.
GREY, G. T., South Shields.
HOLMES, C. D. & Co., Ltd., Hull.
HUTSONS, Ltd., Kelvinhaugh, Glasgow.
HOSKING, T. J., Ltd., London.
KINCAID, J. G. & Co., Ltd., Greenock.
LEWIS, J. & SONS, Aberdeen.
LIDGERWOOD, W. V. V., Speedwell Ironworks, Coatbridge.
McCOLL & Pollock, Ltd., Sunderland and Belfast.
McKIE & Baxter, Glasgow.
MILLER & Macfie, Ltd., Glasgow.
MUIR & Houston, Ltd., Glasgow.
MUMFORD & Co., Colchester.
NORTH-EASTERN Marine Engineering Co., Ltd., Wallsend-on-Tyne,
    and Sunderland.
PARSON'S Marine Steam Turbine Co., Ltd., Wallsend.
PLENTY & Son, Ltd., Newbury.
RANKIN & Blackmore, Greenock.
RICHARDSONS, WESTGARTH & Co., Ltd., Hartlepool.
RITCHIE, J., Partick.
ROWAN, David & Co., Glasgow.
ROSS & Duncan, Glasgow.
RUSSEL & Co., Glasgow.
SHIELDS Engineering and Dry Dock Co., Ltd., North Shields.
SISSON, W. & Co., Ltd., Gloucester.
VAUXHALL and West Hydraulic Engineering Co., Ltd., Luton, Bedford.
WALLSEND Slipway and Engineering Co., Ltd., Wallsend (Dock 540 ft.
    long).
WILLANS & ROBINSON, & Co., Rugby.

BRITISH NAVY.

Diesel Engine Builders.

(From " The Motorship," New York.)

	Type of Engine.
Cammell Laird & Co., Birkenhead	Fullagar (2-cycle)
North British Diesel Engine Co., Glasgow	——?—— (4-cycle)
Clyde Shipbuilding & Engineering Co., Govan, Glasgow ..	Carels (2-cycle)
Harland & Wolff Diesel Dept., Glasgow	Burmeister & Wain (4-cycle)
Wm. Doxford & Sons (Northumberland Shipbuilding Co., Ltd.), Sunderland	Junkers (2-cycle, Solid-injection)
Wallsend Slipway, Wallsend-on-Tyne	——?——?——
North Eastern Marine Engineering Co., Wallsend-on-Tyne	Werkspoor (4-cycle)
John I. Thornycroft & Co., London	Carels (2-cycle)
Wm. Denny Bros. & Co., Ltd., Dumbarton	Sulzer (2-cycle)
J. Samuel White & Co., East Cowes	White M.A.N. (2-cycle)
*Vickers Limited, Barrow-in-Furness	Vickers (4-cycle)
Mirrlees, Bickerton & Day, Stockton-on-Tees	Mirrlees (4-cycle)
Willans, Robinson & Co., Rugby	Willans (4-cycle)
Yarrows Limited, Scotstoun	M .A .N. (2-cycle)
Fairfield Shipbuilding & Engineering Co., Port Glasgow ..	M. A. N. (2-cycle)
Scotts Shipbuilding & Engineering Co., Greenock	Ansaldo-Fiat (2-cycle)
Alex. Stephen & Sons, Linthouse (Glasgow)	——?——?——
Sir W. G. Armstrong, Whitworth & Co., Newcastle-on-Tyne	Armstrong-Whitworth (2 & 4-cycle)
Richardsons Westgarth, Middlesborough	Carels (2-cycle)
Wm. Beardmore & Co., Ltd., Dalmuir	Beardmore & Tosi (4-cycle)
Swan, Hunter & Wigham Richardsons Ltd., Newcastle-on-Tyne	Neptune & Polar (2-cycle)
Palmers Shipbuilding & Engineering Co., Jarrow-on-Tyne	——?——?——
Barclay, Curle & Co., Glasgow	Burmeister & Wain (4-cycle)
Norris, Henty & Gardners Ltd., Patricroft	Gardner (4-cycle)
Union Ship Engineering Co. Ltd., Montrose	——?—— (4-cycle)
Ruston & Hornsby, Lincoln	Nelseco† (4-cycle)

* Also building engines in association with Messrs. Petters, Yeovil.

† Several other British engineering companies also built the Nelseco (American) marine Diesel engine during the war.

Uniforms.

| Admiral | Vice-Admiral | Rear-Admiral | Commodore | Captain | Commander | Lieutenant-Commander | Lieutenant (under 8 years) | Sub-Lieutenant |

Admiral of the fleet one stripe more than a full Admiral.

In relative ranks, Engineers have the same *with the curl*, and with purple between the stripes (1915 change).
" " Surgeons " " " red " (1918 change).
" " Paymasters " " " white " (" ").
" " Naval Instructors " " " blue " (" ").

Note.—On the right sleeve only, inverted chevrons are worn for every year of War Service since August 5th, 1914. The first and lowest chevron in silver is for War Service up to Dec. 31st, 1914. The upper gold chevrons are for each year's service from Jan. 1st. 1915. Also worn by the Royal Marines, R.A.N., R.C.N., R.N.R., R.F.R., R.N.V.R., R.N. Sick Berth Reserve and officers of the Mercantile Marine serving in H.M. Ships and Auxiliaries.

Personnel and Navy Estimates. 1919-20.

Provisional Estimates have only been presented to Parliament, for the sum of £149,200,000, but it is noted that revised and detailed Estimates will be presented at a later date in the Financial Year. Personnel is estimated at 280,000 officers, seamen, boys, coastguards and Royal Marines, but this total is being rapidly decreased by demobilisation and discharges. It was 180,000 in August, 1919, and will be about 147,000 in Jan., 1920.

Admiralty (October, 1919).

Maintenance Operations.		
First Lord	The Right Hon. Walter Long, M.P.
First Lord and Chief of Staff ..	Admiral Earl Beatty, G.C.B., D.S.O., &c.
Deputy First Sea Lord	
Deputy Chief of Staff	
Assistant Chief of Staff	
Second Sea Lord	
Third Sea Lord and Controller ..	
Fourth Sea Lord	
Civil Lord	
Chief Constructor	Sir Eustace H. Tennyson D'Eyncourt, K.C.B.

BRITISH NAVAL ORDNANCE, HEAVY, B.L. (Capt. R. V. WALLING, R.G.A., retired).

NOTE.—All details are unofficial, but believed to be approximately correct. Particulars given, for reference purposes, of some older marks of guns, now dismounted from H.M. Ships.

Designation, Calibre, ins.	Mark.	Length.	Weight of piece without B.M.	Weight of Projectile.	M.V.	M.E.	Weight of Charge.	Max. R.P.M.	REMARKS.
		cals.	tons cwts. qrs.	lbs.	f. s.	f. t.	lbs.		
18	I	35 ?	150 0 0 ?	3,600 ?	?	?	?	?	Monitors and "Furious" originally mounted these pieces, but they have been removed.
15	"B"	45	96 0 0	1950	2500	84,500	450	1.2	Particulars doubtful. Mk. I also reported to be 42 cals. long.
	I	45	96 0 0	1920	2655	84,070	428	1.2	
13.5	V	45	74 18 1	1250	2700	63,190	296	1.5	With tapered inner "A" tube, without forward step, weighs 1 cwt. more. Obsolete Marks: I; II; III; IIIa, b, c, d, e, and f; IV.
12	XII	50	65 13 1	850	3010	53,400	307	2	} Dreadnoughts and Battle Cruisers.
	XI / XI*	50	65 13 1	850	3010	53,046	307	2	
	X	45	56 16 1	850	2800	47,800	258	2	
	X*	45	56 12 1						
	IX	40	50 0 0	850	2650	39,200	246	2	Mk. IX guns in "King Edward" class only:—Wt. of Charge, 254 lbs. Marks: VI, IV, V, Vw, VIII. VIIIe, VIIIv, IX, IXe, IXv, IXw, X, X*, XI, XI* and XII have been introduced into the Naval Service.
10	VII	45	30 4 2	500	2850	26,945	146⅔	3	Only mounted in "Triumph," now sunk.
	VI / VI*	45	36 10 0	500	2800	27,181	146⅔	3	Only mounted in "Swiftsure." Mk. VI*, land guns. Wt. given is that without "Ring, connecting hydraulic buffer." A Mk. V pattern was sealed, but the gun was never made.
9.2	XI	50	28 0 0	380	3000	23,700	128½	4	
	XI*	50	27 15 2	380	3000	22,930	128½	4	
	Xv	46	27 19 0	380	2800	20,685	120	4	Only two Mk. Xv guns in the Service.
	X	46	27 19 0	380	2800	20,685	120	4	There is one Mk. $\frac{X}{IX}$ gun for Naval Service.
	VIII	40	24 6 3	380	2347	14,520	66	4	"Terrible" only; two guns from "Powerful" mounted in R.G.A. Battery at Scapa Flow. Twenty different Marks have been made and fourteen introduced in Naval Service.
14	I	45	85 0 0	1400	2700	70,770	324	2	Elswick Ordnance Co., "Armstrong" design. H.M.S. "Canada" only.
	?	45	70 6 0	1400	2600	65,700	?	?	Bethlehem guns, mounted in monitors only ("Abercrombie" class).

MEDIUM, B.L.

Designation, Calibre, ins.	Mark.	Length.	Weight of piece without B.M.	Weight of Projectile.	M.V.	M.E.	Weight of Charge.	Max. R.P.M.	REMARKS.
7.5	III / III*	50	15 9 3	200	3000	12,481	54¼	5	Monitors, removed from "Swiftsure," Mks. IV and IV* were for "Triumph," sunk. New Mark in "Hawkins" and "Raleigh," of which no details available.
	II** / V	50	14 16 2	200	2800	12,500	61	5	
	I	45	13 9 2	200	2600	9340	61	5	"Devonshire" class only. Other Marks in Naval Service: I* and I** of 45 cal./L; II and II* of 50 cal./L.
6	XVIII	50	?	100	?	?	?	7	New ships.
	XIV	50	?	100	3100	6665	?	7	"Cleopatra" class.
	XI* / XI	50	8 8 2	100	3000	6240	32 1/12	7	
	VIII / VII	45	7 7 2	100	2750	5250	23	7	Mk. VIII left hand guns for "T" mounting in "County" class. Many new Marks of 6 in. introduced during the War, including a short Mk. XIX for L.S. (Travelling Carriage.)
5.5	I	50	6 10 0	115	2870	6000 (?)	?	8	Woolwich Arsenal. Details doubtful. Mounted in "Furious" and "Hood," "Birkenhead" and "Chester" 5.5 guns and mountings by Coventry Ordnance Co.
4.7	I	50	3 14 0	45	3000	2800	14	12	Woolwich Arsenal. Modified 4.7 inch Q.F. V (L.S.). New T.B.D's.

Also :—
Q.F. 6 in., many marks } quite obsolete, but were mounted in D.A.M.S. and S.D.V.
Q.F.C. 6 in., „ „ } during the War.
Q.F. 4.7 in. Mk. V, Land Service only.

Mk. IV, three-motion B.M., Mk. IV "B," same, converted to single-motion.
Mk. III, „ Mk. III "B" „ „
Mk. II, „ Mk. II "B" „ „
Mk. I, „ Mk. I "B" „ „

LIGHT GUNS.—(See Note on previous page).

Designation, Calibre, ins.	Mark.	Length.	Weight of piece without B.M.	Weight of Projectile.	M.V.	M.E.	Weight of Charge.	Max. R.P.M.	REMARKS.
		cals.	tons cwts. qrs.	lbs.	f. s.	f. t.	lbs.		
4	IX	50	?	31	3000	1934	$11\frac{1}{4}$	?	B.L.
	VIII	50	2 2 0	31	3000	?	$5\frac{3}{8}$	12	B.L.
	VII	40	1 6 0	31	3000	?	$9\frac{15}{16}$	12	B.L.
	V	45	2 2 $3\frac{3}{4}$	31	3000	1934	$7\frac{11}{16}$	20	Semi-automatic ; extensively used on AA. mountings.
	IV	40	1 3 0	31	2300	1137	?	20	Semi-automatic ; lighter model of Mk. V. Obsolete Marks : I, II and III Q.F. and four marks of Q.F.C.
3	III	50	1 3 0	$14\frac{1}{2}$	3050	992	$5\frac{3}{4}$	30	Semi-automatic ; for AA. mountings.
	II	40	1 0 0	$12\frac{1}{2}$	?	?	?	?	Q.F. ; for submarines.
	I	30	19 0	$12\frac{1}{4}$	?	?	?	25	Q.F. ; for A.A.C. mountings.

Torpedoes.

No official details available. Various Marks of 21 inch, 18 inch and 14 inch torpedoes said to be in service ; the first two with heaters, the third without. Also a specially light 14 inch mark for use by " Cuckoo " type Torpedo-dropping Seaplanes and C.M.B.

Mines.

No official figures available. Among the various Marks of mines produced during the War, the following are said to exist : (a) Spherical types with swinging-bar contact, either above or below mine ; (b) " British Elia " type—may be the same as (a) just described ; (c) Pear-shaped and spherical types with horn contacts ; reported to be very like German mines ; (d) Special types for laying by Destroyers, Submarines and C.M.B.

Aircraft Bombs.

There are only vague and unofficial references to these types : Experimental 3300 lb. type ; 1650 lb. type (with bursting charge of 1100 lbs. T.N.T.), 530 lb., 230 lb. (with A.P. nose ?), 112 lb. and 100 lb. Fuzes said to be impact, delay action and special types for use against submarines.

Depth Charges.

Only mark reported is 300 lb. type.

Searchlights.

36 inch, 24 inch, 20 inch (all controlled in latest ships). About 8—36 inch and 2—24 inch (Signalling) in Dreadnoughts and Battle Cruisers ; 4—36 inch in Light Cruisers ; 1—24 inch or 20 inch in T.B.D. Twin 24 inch mountings were used in *Iron Duke, King George, Orion, Colossus, Neptune, Lion* and *New Zealand* Classes, but these are said to have been replaced by single 36 inch controlled S.L.

Paravanes (PVs.)

No official details available. Reported that there are about twenty marks, roughly divided into " M," " B " and " C " patterns. " M " type said to be " otter gear " of simple design for use by mercantile craft up to 18 kts. speed, keeping depth by ordinary form of hydrostatic valve. " B " type said to be for Battleships and older Cruisers up to 22 kts. speed ; " C " pattern for Light Cruisers, &c., up to 28 kts. speed. Depth kept in these by hydrostatic valves, plus " mercury oscillators," the hydrostatic valve by itself being too sluggish to prevent the PVs. "porpoising." Length about 12 feet, breadth about 7 feet across spread of 'planes. Destroyers reported to use special types of PVs., viz., H.S.S.S. and H.S.M.S. PVs. towed in large ships by chains from skeg (or PV. plate) attached to forefoot, under stem ; also by sliding bar shoes at stem. Destroyers and vessels of light draught can tow their PVs. from stern.

Naval Ordnance.—*continued.*

Also (for Anti-Submarine purposes) :—

11 inch howitzer mounted in some ships of " Devonshire " and " County Classes."
200 lb. stick bomb howitzer in some Special Service Vessels.
Thornycroft Depth Charge Thrower in Destroyers, P-boats, some Sloops and Special Service Vessels.

Also :—

Q.F., 12 pr. 12 cwt. Mk. I.
    ,,   ,,   Mk. II (war model) ; mostly for merchantmen.
    ,, 12 pr. 18 cwt. Mk. I, for " G," " H " and " I " classes of T.B.D.
    ,, 12 pr. 8 cwt. Mk. I (boat gun).
    ,, 14 pr. Mk. I (H.M.S. " Swiftsure "—now removed).
    ,, 6 pr.
    ,, 3 pr.   have been used as AA. guns.
    ,, 3 pr. (semi-automatic, Vickers design)   Saluting guns in big ships.
    ,, $2\frac{1}{4}$ pdr. (automatic) modified " pom-pom " for AA. work.
    ,, 77 mm.—captured German field guns, adapted for use in some submarines.

Machine Guns :—

  .303 inch Vickers.
  .303 inch Maxim.
  .303 inch Lewis.

Rifles :—

  .303 inch Lee-Enfield (Long).

Pistols :—

  .45 inch Webley automatic (H.V.).

Scale : 125 feet to 1 inch.

"DANCE" *class.*

"HUNT" *class.*
BELVOIR, BICESTER, &C.

Later "HUNT" *class.*
ABERDARE, ABINGDON, &C.

(Minesweepers.)

"KIL" *class.*
(Patrol Gunboats.)

BEND OR	ORMONDE		ARD PATRICK	ROCK SAND
HARVESTER	SEFTON		DONOVAN	SANFOIN
IROQUOIS	SILVIO		FLYING FOX	SIR HUGO
LADAS	SIR BEVIS		MINORU	SPEARMINT
			ORBY	

And others, with mast
abaft funnel.

And others, with mast
before funnel.

"24" *class (Sloops).*

These ships were built to resemble Merchant Ships for Convoy
and Submarine Decoy purposes.   Cannot be distinguished
from Mercantile Vessels, and therefore omitted.

PC-boats.   ANCHUSA & AUBRIETIA *classes.*
(Later "Flower" Class Fleet Sweeping Vessels/Sloops.)

Scale : 250 feet to 1 inch.

ARGUS.
*(Aircraft Carrier.   No funnels.   2 telescopic masts
abeam amidships.   Chart-house disappears.)*

M 16—M 22
M 23—27*
M 29—33
Gun forward on raised deck.

HUMBER.

GORGON.

GEN. CRAUFURD.
SIR J. MOORE

MARSHAL SOULT
MARSHAL NEY*
Has no barbette:

EREBUS
TERROR

FURIOUS.
(Aircraft Carrier.)

ROYAL SOVEREIGN *class.*

COURAGEOUS
GLORIOUS.

**(One Funnel types continued
on next page.)**

39

TWO FUNNELS.

ONE & TWO FUNNELS.

Scale : 125 feet to 1 inch.

Scale : 250 feet to 1 inch.

AZALEA   CORNFLOWER
BUTTERCUP   GODETIA
CAMPANULA   HYDRANGEA
CELANDINE   LILY

Other Ships.

"FLOWER" class (*Acacia, Arabis, Azalea* types).
Are Fleet Sweeping Vessels (Sloops). Some now have no mainmast.

ATHERSTONE, CHELMSFORD, &C.
(*First type built.*)

BANBURY, HARPENDEN, &C.
(*Second type built.*)

"RACECOURSE" class.
(*Paddle Minesweepers.*)

MAIDSTONE.   WOOLWICH.   LUCIA.

(*Submarine Depot Ships.*)

GREENWICH.   SANDHURST.

(*T.B.D. Depot Ships.*)

CYCLOPS   ASSISTANCE   ARK ROYAL.
(*Aircraft Carrier.*)

(*Repair Ships.*)

PEGASUS.   MANXMAN.   NAIRANA.

(*Aircraft Carriers*).

DILIGENCE.
(*T.B.D. Depot Ship*).

BRITISH WARSHIPS.—RECOGNITION SILHOUETTES.
(E. L. KING).

Scale of all : 250 feet to 1 inch.

CHAMPION *class* (2)

CAMBRIAN *class* (4).

CENTAUR *class* (2).

CALEDON *class* (3).

CERES *class* (5).

CARLISLE *class* (5).*

A :—"D" *classes.*

B :—"D" *classes.*

VINDICTIVE.

* Some have (*a*) hangar and chart house combined (*b*) "trawler bows."

DREADNOUGHT.

ORION *class* (4).

COLOSSUS.
HERCULES.

HAWKINS *class* (2 or 4).

BELLEROPHON *class* (3).

COLLINGWOOD.
ST. VINCENT.

NEPTUNE

AGINCOURT.

ERIN.

IRON DUKE *class* (3).

KING GEORGE V *class* (4).

CANADA.

Scale of all : 250 feet to 1 inch.

COMMONWEALTH.

QUEEN ELIZABETH *class* (5).

RENOWN.
REPULSE.

ARETHUSA *class* (7).

CAROLINE *class* (6).

" COUNTY " *class*.

PRINCESS MARGARET.
(*Minelayer.*)

TIGER.
(*Now has topmast to derrick mast, no topmast to foremast.*)

LION, PRINCESS ROYAL.

INFLEXIBLE.
INDOMITABLE.

NEW ZEALAND.

FOUR FUNNELS.   FOUR FUNNELS.

ADVENTURE.

BOADICEA, BLANCHE,
BLONDE.

ACTIVE, FEARLESS.

BRISTOL *class*.

WEYMOUTH *class*.

BIRKENHEAD.
(*Straight mainmast*)

CHESTER.
(*Raking mainmast.*)

BIRMINGHAM.
LOWESTOFT.

CHATHAM *class*.

DEVONSHIRE *class*.

EURYALUS.

AMPHITRITE.

(*Mine Layers.*)

P 14—P 64.

P 11, P 21, P 24, P 49.

P 17.

"I" class.

Lurcher, Firedrake.
(Oak, *with short mainmast*.)

"L" *class* (2-funnel).

Yarrow "M."

Yarrow "Later M."
(*Note sloping stern*.)

Admiralty "Modified R."

All "S" names & *Trinidad*.

All "T" names & *Shark*.

Admiralty "S."

Yarrow "S."

Thornycroft "S."

Admiralty "V" *class*.

Admiralty "V" *class*.
(*Appearance when Minelaying*.)

"V" *class*. (*Leaders*.)
(*High foremast. Vampire has triple tubes*.)

Thornycroft "V" *class*.

Spencer, Shakespeare,
Wallace. (*Leaders*.)

Bruce, Douglas, &c.
"Large Admiralty type." (*Leaders*.)

Scale of all : 125 feet to 1 inch.

" G " class.

SWIFT. (Leader.)

" L " class (3 funnels).
(Legion : Minelaying screens.)

Thornycroft ",M "* & " R " classes.
* After gun not on platform.

Admiralty " M's "

Admiralty " R's " (A).
(Tarpon, Telemachus : Minelaying screens.)

Admiralty " R's " (B).

Talisman, Termagant, Trident.

" H " class.

" K " class.

Medea, Melampus, Melpomene.

Grenville, Parker, Seymour, Saumarez.
(Leaders.)

Abdiel (Minelayer).

Gabriel & Marksman type (Leaders).

Botha, Broke, Faulknor. (Leaders.)

Mansfield, Mentor.

BRITISH SUBMARINES.—RECOGNITION SILHOUETTES.

(E. L. KING.)

Scale of all : 125 feet to 1 inch.

"F" class.   "H 21—32 & Later" *class.*   "E 7—20 & Later" *class.*   "G" *class.*

L 4 (and with 2 masts), L 5, 15 & 16.   L 1, 2, 7, 9.   "M" *class.*

L 3.   L 6, 10, 12, 14, 17.   "K" *class.*

"R" *class.*

(ROYAL SOVEREIGN CLASS.)

ROYAL SOVEREIGN (29th April, 1915), **ROYAL OAK** (17th Nov., 1914),
RESOLUTION (14th Jan., 1916), **RAMILLIES** (12th Sept., 1916),
REVENGE (29th May, 1915).

Normal displacement, 25,750 tons (about 31,250-33,500 tons *full load*). Complement, 937-997.
Length (*over all*), 624¼ feet. Beam, 88½ feet.* *Mean* draught, 27 feet. Length (*p.p.*), 580 feet.
*For *R.S.* and *R.O.* With bulge protection, *Revenge* and *Resolution* 101' 5", *Ramillies* 102½ feet.

Guns :
  8—15 inch, 42 cal. ⎫ **Dir. Con.**
  14—6 inch, 50 cal. ⎭
  2—3 inch (anti-aircraft)
  4—3 pdr.
  5 M.G.
Torpedo tubes (21 inch) :
  4 *submerged*

Armour (K.C.) : (Vertical.)
  13" Belt . . . .
  6"—4" Belt (ends) . . . .
  1" Belt (bow) . . . .
  6", 4" Bulkheads (f. & a.)
  6" Battery . . . .
  10"—7" Barbettes . . . . .
  13"— " Gunhouses . . . . .
  1½" Funnel uptakes . . .
  6"—3" C.T. Base . . . . .
  11" C.T. (6"—3" Hood) .
  6" Fore Com. Tube . . .
  6" Torp. Con. Tower . .
  4" Tube (T.C. Tower) .

Armour (H.T.) : (Deck.)
  1" Fo'xle over Battery
  1½"—1½" Upper . . . . . .
  2", 1½", 1" Main . . . . . .
  2½", 1" (forw'd) ⎫ Lower
  4", 3", 2½" (aft) ⎭
Special Protection :
  1¾"—1" Internal citadel
    between end barbettes

ROYAL SOVEREIGN.   *Photo, Cribb, Southsea.*

Ahead :
4—15 in.
2 to 4—6 in.

Astern :
4—15 in.
2 to 4—6 in.

Broadside : 8—15 in., 7—6 in., 2—21 in. tubes.

Machinery : Turbine, Parsons. Boilers : (see *Notes*). 4 screws. Designed H.P. 40,000 =
23 kts. *without* bulges, about 21½-22 *with* bulges. Fuel : Oil only, *normal*, 900 tons ; *maximum*,
about 3400 tons. Coal : 140 tons (only for " domestic " use).

Gunnery Notes.—Much as *Queen Elizabeth* class. Battery differently disposed in these ships. 6 inch batteries are wet
in head seas, but dwarf walls in battery retain water and it is rapidly drained away.
Armour Notes.—Thicknesses much as *Queen Elizabeth* class, but armour differently distributed. Barbettes 6"—4" as
they descend behind belt. Gunhouses, 13" face, 11" sides and rear ; crowns specially heavy. In these ships 2"
protective deck has a high 2" slope behind belt, so that flat part of protection can be put on main deck and at top
of belt, instead of a deck lower. Internal protection is very good, and with bulge protection, these ships are heavily
defended against underwater attack. *Royal Sovereign* and *Royal Oak* have yet to be fitted with bulges.
Engineering Notes.—Designed to burn coal, but while building " all oil fuel " was adopted, and it was hoped that 23 kts.
would be secured without increase of H.P. Addition of bulges has brought speed down again to about 21 kts. On
deep load, the bulge protected ships cannot get much above 19.5 kts. till they have burnt off fuel.

47

RAMILLIES. Aircraft View.   *Official R.A.F. Photo.*

Name	Builder	Machinery	Laid down	Completed	Trials :—	Boilers	Best recent speed
Royal Sovereign	Portsmouth Y.	Parsons	Jan.'14	May, '16	41,115 = 21·6	18 Babcock	
Royal Oak	Devonport Y.	Hawthorn	Jan.'14	May, '16	40,360 =	18 Yarrow	
Resolution	Palmer	Palmer	Nov.'13	Dec., '16	41,106 =	18 Yarrow	
Ramillies	Beardmore	Beardmore	Nov.'13	Sept. '17	42,356 = 21·5	18 Babcock	
Revenge	Vickers	Vickers	Dec.'13	Mar.'16	42,962 = 21·9	18 Babcock	

General Notes.—Begun under 1914-15 Estimates. *Revenge* first named *Renown*. *Ramillies* injured herself at launch
and was delayed in completion. They are fine ships, but suffer rather from reduced freeboard. They are steady
ships, those with bulge protection being splendid gun platforms. With bulges, *normal* displacement is really about
29,350 tons (33,500 *full load*).

1912-13 BRITISH DREADNOUGHTS. ("Fast Division.")

(QUEEN ELIZABETH CLASS.)

QUEEN ELIZABETH (Oct., 1913), **WARSPITE** (Nov., 1913), **VALIANT** (4th Nov., 1914),
BARHAM (31st Dec., 1914), **MALAYA** (18th Mar., 1915).

Normal displacement, 27,500 tons (about 31,000-33,000 *full load*).   Complement, 955-1016.

Length (*p.p.*), 600 feet.   Beam, 90½ feet. $\left\{\begin{array}{l}\textit{Mean draught, }30\frac{2}{3}\textit{ feet.}\\\textit{Max. \quad\,,\quad\quad }33\frac{1}{2}\textit{ \,,}\end{array}\right\}$ Length (*over all*) $\left\{\begin{array}{l}\textit{Q.E. }643\frac{3}{4}\textit{ ft.}\\\textit{Rest }639\frac{3}{4}\textit{ ,,}\end{array}\right.$

Guns :
  8—15 inch 42 cal. } **Dir. Con.**
  12—6 inch, 50 cal. }
  2—3 inch (anti-aircraft)
  4—3 pdr.
  5 M.G.
Torpedo tubes (21 inch) :
  4 *submerged* (broadside).

Armour (K.C.) :
  13″ Lower belt . . . .
  6″—4″ Upper belt . . . .
  6″—4″ Belt (ends) . . . . .
  6″, 4″ Bulkheads(f. & a.)
  6″ Battery . . . .
  10″—7″ Barbettes . . . . .
  11″ Gunhouses . . . .
  1½″ Funnel uptakes . . .
  6″—3″ C.T. base . . . . .
  11″ C.T. (6″—2″ Hood) . .
  4″ Fore com. tube . . . . .
  6″ Torpedo C.T. . . . . . .
  4″ Tube (T.C. tower) . .

Armour (H.T.) :
  1″ Fo'xle (over battery) . .
  2″—1¼″ Upper . . . .
  1¼″ Main . . . .
  1″ Middle . . . .
  3″ (ends) . . . . }
  1″ (amidships) } Lower
Special Protec. :
  2″—1″ Internal citadel
  between end barbettes

Vertical. / *Deck.*

Ahead :
4—15 in.
3 to 6—6 in.

Astern :
4—15 in.

Broadside : 8—15 in., 6—6 in., 2—21 in. tubes.

Machinery : Parsons turbine, but *Barham* has Brown-Curtis. Geared cruising turbines in
all ships.   Boilers : 24 (see *Notes*).   Designed H.P. 75,000 = 25 kts.   Fuel : Only oil, 550 tons
normal, 3400 tons *max*.   Coal : 100 tons. for starting boilers and "domestic" purposes.

Gunnery Notes.—Range of 15 inch only limited by *max.* visibility. Elevation of these guns has been enlarged. 6-inch controlled in two groups from director towers on middle bridges. *Queen Elizabeth* completed with four extra 6-inch at stern ; these were found useless, guns removed and ports plated over. *Barham* came into service with 2—6 inch in shields on fo'xle deck amidships ; these, too, have been removed, but in a head sea they were said to have been equal to whole main deck battery.

Armour Notes.—Belt is 13″ at w.l. only, 6″ on upper edge, 8″ on lower, and applied in vertical strakes. Barbettes, 6′ and 4″ within belt. 1½″ traverses to battery, but no rear screens—only dwarf walls to retain and drain away water admitted to battery. Rear bulkhead to battery is 6″ diagonal and 4″ where it crosses centre line. Internal protection of these ships is very fine.

Engineering Notes.—"All oil" installation very successful. These ships steam splendidly, and can maintain a high average speed for long periods. H.P. turbines on wing shafts, with cruising turbines geared at forward end ; L.P. turbines on inner shafts.

QUEEN ELIZABETH.*

*Other ships without fore topmast, as *Warspite* view.

Photo, Graphic Union.

WARSPITE.

Photo, Cribb, Southsea.

Name.	Builder.	Machinery.	Laid down.	Com- pleted.	Trials.	Boilers.	Best recent speed.
Queen Elizabeth	Portsmouth	Wallsend	Oct. '12	Jan., '15	57,130 =	24 Babcock	
Warspite	Devonport	Hawthorn	Oct. '12	Mar., '15	77,510 =	24 Yarrow	
Valiant	Fairfield	Fairfield	Jan. '13	Feb., '16	71.112 =	24 Babcock	
Barham	Clydebank	Clydebank	Feb. '13	Oct., '15	76.575 =	24 Yarrow	
Malaya	Elswick	Wallsend	Oct. '13	Feb., '16	76,074 =	24 Babcock	

Note.—First four begun under 1912 Estimates. *Malaya*, extra ship, gift of Federated Malay States. Estimated cost (average), £2,500,000 per ship = £90 per ton. At the Battle of Jutland, *Warspite, Valiant, Burham* and *Malaya* supported the First Battle-Cruiser Squadron. *Queen Elizabeth*, Flagship, C.-in C., Grand Fleet, 1917-18. *Barham* grounded on May Island during War and badly injured herself, but was salved and repaired. In appearance and general design, these five ships are the finest in the British Navy. Their decks are remarkably clear, and internal arrangements are very spacious. Taken all round, they present the most successful type of capital ship yet designed.

MALAYA (Aircraft view).

Official R.A.F. Photo.

(IRON DUKE CLASS.)

BENBOW (Nov., 1913), **EMPEROR OF INDIA** (ex-*Delhi*, Nov., 1913),
IRON DUKE (Oct., 1912), **MARLBOROUGH** (Nov., 1912).

Normal displacement, 25,000 tons. *Full load,* 28,800 tons. Complement, 995 to 1022.

Length (*o.a.*), $622\frac{3}{4}$ feet. Beam, $89\frac{1}{2}$ feet. $\begin{cases} \textit{Mean draught, } 28\frac{1}{2} \text{ feet.} \\ \text{,, } \text{Max. } \text{,, } 32\frac{3}{4} \text{ ,,} \end{cases}$ Length (*p.p.*), 580 feet

Guns :
10—13·5 inch (M.V.) } **Dir. Con.**
12—6 inch, 50 cal.
2—3 inch (anti-aircraft)
4—3 pdr.
5 M.G.
(1 landing)
Torpedo tubes (21 inch) :
4 *submerged* (broadside)

Armour (K.C.) :
12″-8″ Lower belt ......
9″ Middle belt ....
8″ Upper belt ....
6″—4″ Belt (ends) ....
8″, 6″, 4″ Bulkheads
(f. & a.) ....
6″ Battery* ....
10″—7″ Barbettes .....
11″— ″ Gunhouses....
1½″ Funnel uptakes ...
6″—3″ C.T. base ....
11″ C.T. (4″—3″ hood)..
6″ Fore com. tube ....
6″ Torpedo C.T. ......
4″ After com. tube ...

Armour (H.T.) :
1″ Fo'xle (over battery)
2″—1¼″ Upper ....
1″ (amidships) }
2½″—1½″ (aft) } middle
2½″—1″ Lower ....
Special Protection :
1½″—1″ Screens to Mags,
shell and engine rooms

Vertical.
Deck.

* *See* Notes.

IRON DUKE.

Ahead:
4—13·5 in.
5—6 in.

Astern :
4—13·5 in
4—6 in.

Broadside : 10—13.5 in., 6—6 in., 2—21 in. tubes.

Machinery : Turbine (Parsons). Boilers : (see *Notes*). Designed H.P. 29,000 = 21 kts.
Coal : *normal,* 1000 tons ; *maximum,* 3250 tons. Oil : *normal,* 1050 tons ; *max.,* 1600 tons.

Gunnery Notes.—Originally had 2—6 inch in casemates at stern, but these were found utterly useless. Ports we[re]
sealed up and guns re-mounted on forecastle deck. Forward 6-inch battery used to be swamped out in head sea[s]
Rubber sealing joints for gun-ports were designed and added at Scapa Flow.

Armour Notes.—Belt is 12″ at w.l. only and 8″ on lower edge. Barbettes, 6″ and 3″ as they descend through deck[s]
behind belt. Battery has 1″ traverses and 4″ bulkhead completely athwartships, just before fore funnel. Interna[l]
protection more complete than in *King George V* class, but, all the same, screens do not completely extend betwee[n]
end barbettes. At Jutland, *Marlborough* was torpedoed over boiler rooms, where there is *no* internal protectio[n]
Lord Jellicoe is therefore in error when he says that the torpedo struck " at about one of the most favourable spo[ts]
for the ship."

Name.	Builder.	Machinery.	Laid down.	Com- pleted.	Trials.		Boilers.	Best recen[t] speed
					30 hrs.	Full power.		
Benbow	Beardmore	Beardmore	May '12	Oct. '14		32530 = 21·5	18 Babcock	
E. of India	Vickers	Vickers	May '12	Nov '14		29654 =	Yarrow	
Iron Duke	Portsmouth Y	Laird	Jan.'12	Mar.''14	20,875 = 19	30010 = 21·6	18 Babcock	
Marlborough	Devonport Y	Hawthorn	Jan.'12	June '14		32013 = 21·6	Yarrow	

Note.—Begun under the 1911 Estimates. Derived from *Orion* class through *King George* type. Average cost abo[ut]
£1,891,600. *Emperor of India* was originally named *Delhi*. *Iron Duke,* Flagship, C.-in-C., Grand Fleet. 1914-

CANADA (ex *Almirante Latorre*), (Nov., 1913.)
Displacement, 28,000 tons (about 32,000 *full load*).   Complement (1176).

Length (*p.p.*), 625 feet.   Beam, 92½ feet. {*Mean* draught, 29 feet.} Length (*over all*), 661 feet.
{*Max.*   „   32   „ }

Guns (Elswick) :
  10—14 inch, 45 cal. }
  12—6 inch 50 cal.   } **Dir. Con.**
  2—3 inch (anti-aircraft)
  4—3 pdr.
  (2 landing)
  4"M.G.
Torpedo tubes (21 inch) :
  4 *submerged*

Armour : (Vertical.)
  9" Lower belt ....
  7" Middle belt ....
  4½" Upper belt ....
  6"—4" Belt (ends) ....
  4½", 4" B'lkh'ds (f. & a.)
  6" Batteries ....
  10" Barbettes ....
  10"— 6" Gunhouses.....
  3" C.T. base* ....
  11" C.T. (6"—3" hood)..
  6" Fore com. tube ....
  6" Torpedo C.T. ......
  6" Aft com. tube .....
  *Not shown on plans.

Armour : (Decks.)
  1" Shelter (over case-
    mates) ....
  1" Fo'xle (over battery)
  1½" Upper (outside
    battery) ....
  1½" Main (aft) ....
  1" Protective ....
  2" (forward) } lower ...
  4" (aft) ... }
Special Protec. :
  2"—1½" Internal screens
    (mags., &c.) ......

CANADA.   *Photo, Cribb, Southsea.*

6" DIRECTOR TOWER.

Ahead :
4—14 in
4 to 8-4 in.

Broadside : 10—14 in., 6 or 7—6 in., 2—2 in. tubes.

Astern :
4—14 in.
3 to 6-4 in.

Machinery : Turbine, 4-shaft : (L.P.) Parsons ; (H.P.) Brown-Curtis. Boilers : 21 Yarrow.
Designed H.P. 37,000 = 22.75 kts.   Coal : *normal*, 1150 tons ; *maximum*, 3300 tons. Oil : 520
tons.

Gunnery Notes.—14-inch have a range only limited by *max.* visibility. Originally had 16—6 inch, but the 2—6 inch on
  upper deck, abeam of after funnel, were removed and ports plated over. Reason for removal was because guns
  were only a few feet from muzzle of "Q" turret 14-inch guns on extreme bearing and were damaged by blast.
  Fourteen 6-inch are shown on plans ; two more 6-inch have been removed, but from which positions is not yet
  known.
Armour Notes.—Barbettes, 6" and 4" as they descend behind belts.

CANADA : Aircraft View.   *Official R.A.F. Photo.*

Engineering Notes.—Reported that the Chilean Ministry of Marine stipulated, at the last moment, that full speed
  should be attained without using forced draught. Funnels were accordingly raised to increase natural
  draught. Reported to have made 23-24 kts. in service.
Torpedo Notes.—Tubes are 21 inch Elswick side-loading, worked by hydraulic power.

Name	Builder	Machinery	Laid down	Completed	Trials	Boilers	Best recent speed
Canada	Elswick	Clydebank	Nov.'11	Sep.'15	39247 =	Yarrow	

General Notes.—Laid down for Chile as the *Valparaiso*, her name being altered afterwards to *Almirante Latorre*.
  Purchased for British Navy on outbreak of War. Additional protection, &c., added during War is said
  to have raised her *normal* displacement to over 30,000 tons. First designed with secondary battery of
  22—4.7 inch, and 2 stump masts abeam aft. Her sister ship, *Almirante Cochrane*, also taken over for British
  Navy, re-named *Eagle* and modified for service as an Aircraft Carrier.

ERIN (ex *Reshadieh*), (Sept., 1913).

Normal displacement, 23,000 tons; 25,250 *full load.* Complement, 1130.

Length (*o.a.*,) 559½ feet. Beam, 91 ft. 7¼ in. { *Max.* draught, 30 ft. 11 in. } Length (*p.p.*), 525 feet.
{ *Mean* ,, 28 ft. 5 in. }

Guns (Vickers) :
10—13.5 inch, 45 cal. } **Dir.**
16—6 inch, 50 cal. } **Con.**
2—3 inch (anti-aircraft)
Torpedo tubes (21 inch) :
4 *submerged*

Armour (K.C.) :
12″—9″ Lower belt ....
8″ Upper belt ....
8″—5″, 4″ B'lkh'ds (f.&a.)
5″ Battery ....
1″ Battery traverses ..
10″—8″ Barbettes .....
11″ Gunhouses ....
1″ Funnel uptakes ....
12″ C.T. (6″ tube) .....
4″ Torpedo C.T. (3″ tube)

Armour (H.T.) :
1½″ Fo'xle (over battery)
1½″ Upper (beyond battery)
1½″ Main ....
3″ (ends) }
1″ (amidships) } middle
Special Protection :
1½″ internal citadel ...

ERIN.

Photo, Topical.

Broadside : 10—13.5 in., 8—6 in., 2—21 in. tubes.

Machinery : Parsons turbines. 4 screws. Designed H.P. 26,500 = 21 kts. Boilers : 15
Babcock. Coal : *normal,* 900 tons ; *maximum,* 2120 tons + 710 tons oil.

Gunnery Notes.—On plan 6—6 pdr. of original design shown ; these guns not mounted now.

Armour Notes.—12″ belt at w.l. with very narrow strap of 9″ over. Barbettes 5″ and 3″ within belt. 1″ battery traverses divide 6-inch guns by pairs.

Special Protection (correction to plans).—Internal screens (shown by dot shading in sections 9-15 on profile) should really extend to end barbettes over sections 6-18.

Torpedo Notes.—Elswick side-loading tubes. Stern tube removed during War.

Name.	Builder.	Machinery.	Laid down.	Completed	Trials.	Boilers.	Turbines.	Best recent speed.
Erin	Vickers	Vickers	Feb. '11	Aug. '14		Babcock	Parsons	

General Notes.—Designed by Armstrong, Vickers and Brown, in conjunction with Turkish Ministry of Marine. Purchased for British Navy, August, 1914. Designed with after tripod mast ; had tall pole mast stepped when completing, but this was cut down when ship was taken over for British Navy. The design forms an interesting comparison with *King George V* class of same displacement. *Erin* has, in comparison, 16—6 inch guns in 5″ battery added and better internal protection. But her scantlings are lighter than those ruling in British Navy ; her fuel supply is about 1000 tons less than in British Dreadnoughts, and her ammunition supply is below the average. Steams well, is a good sea-boat, and remarkably handy. Internal accommodation is rather cramped.

AGINCOURT (ex *Sultan Osman I*, ex *Rio de Janeiro*), (January, 1913).

Normal displacement, 27,500 tons (30,250 tons *full load*). Complement, 1267.

Length *over all*, 671½ feet.   Beam, 89 feet. $\begin{cases} Mean \text{ draught, 27 feet.} \\ Max. \quad ,, \quad 30\frac{1}{2} \text{ ft.} \end{cases}$ Length, (*p.p.*) 632 feet, (*waterline*) 668 feet.

Guns (Elswick) :
14—12 inch, 50 cal. } **Dir. Con.**
20—6 inch, 50 cal. }
8—3 inch
2—3 inch (anti-aircraft)
4—3 pdr.
1—3 pdr. (anti-aircraft)
Torpedo tubes (21 inch) :
2 *submerged* (Elswick side-loading)

Armour :
Vertical. {
9″ Lower belt . . . .
6″Upper belt . . . .
6″—4″ Ends . . . .
6″—3″ Bulkh'ds (f. & a.)
6″ Battery . . . .
6″ Battery bulkheads
1″ Battery traverses . .
9″ Barbettes . . . .
12″—8″ Gunhouses . . . . .
12″ C.T. (6″—4″ hoods)
8″ Fore com. tube . . . .
9″ Torpedo C.T. . . . . . .
6″ After com. tube . . .
}

Armour :
Decks : {
1½″ Fo'xle (over battery)
1½″ Upper (outside battery) . . . .
1½″—1″ Main . . . .
}
2½″ Lower cover rudder
Special Protection :
1½″ & 1″ double screens (end barbettes).
1½″ single sceens ('midships barbettes).

AGINCOURT.

Name	Builder	Machinery	Begun	Completed	Trials H.P. kts.
Agincourt	Armstrong	Vickers	Sept.,1911	Aug.,1914	40,279 = 22.42

Ahead :
4—12 in.
6—6 in.

Astern :
4—12 in.
6—6 in.

Broadside : 14—12 in., 10—6 in., 1—21 in. tube.

Machinery : Parsons 4-shaft turbine.   Boilers : 22 Babcock.   Designed H.P. 34,000 = 22 kts.   Coal : *normal*, 1500 tons ; *maximum*, 3200 tons + 620 tons oil.

Gunnery Notes.—Barbettes are a special Elswick design, all operations of loading and firing being controlled by a single lever, working in a quadrant very like the change-speed " gate " of a motor car.

Armour Notes.—Internal protection as stipple shading on numbered sections in profile.   Barbettes 3″ within belt.

Torpedo Notes.—Stern tube removed during War.   Owing to limited space athwartships, 21-inch torpedoes have small war heads.   Water from tubes pumped out into flat, to re-load ; when rapid firing of torpedoes is required, there is 3 feet of water in flat.

General Notes.—The history of this ship merits recording with some detail.   Four designs were drafted at first for her. That accepted was for a battleship of 32,000 tons, armed with 12—14 inch, 16—6 inch and 14—4 inch guns.   The Brazilian Government then considered her too large and expensive a unit, and her construction was stopped. A special mission was went by Armstrongs to Rio de Janeiro, and new outline scheme was prepared in one night. This was the Elswick " Design 690A," as given on this page.   In January, 1914, she was sold to Turkey by Brazil for £2,725,000, and became the *Sultan Osman I*.   In July, 1914, she docked at Devonport for trials, and, on the outbreak of war, whe was appropriated by the British Navy, being named *Agincourt*.   Alterations were begun, including the removal of the big flying-boat deck joining the two superstructures.   She joined the Grand Fleet in 1915.   In 1916, the after tripod mast was removed and replaced by a pole mast.   In 1918, the pole mainmast was removed, and she attained present rig.   With extra protection and other war additions, she displaces about 29,500 tons now.   A good steamer, a good sea-boat, and a steady gun platform.   Handles very well, considering her length.   In Reserve, 1919.   Proposed to give her bulge protection, but nothing has been done in this matter. A full and interesting history of this ship appeared in " The Marine Engineer," May, 1919.

(KING GEORGE CLASS.)

KING GEORGE V (Oct., 1911), **CENTURION** (Nov., 1911), **AJAX** (March, 1912).

Normal displacement, 23,000 tons (about 25,500 *full load*). Complement, 812 to 849.

Length *over all*, 597⅔ feet. Beam, 89 feet. { *Mean* draught, 27½ ft. / *Max.* „ 30 ft. 10 in. } Length (*p.p.*), 555 feet.

KING GEORGE V.

Photo, Topical.

Guns :
10—13.5 inch (M.V.) } **Dir.**
16—4 inch   } **Con.**
2—4 inch (anti-aircraft *Cent.*)
2—3 inch (anti-aircraft *Ajax, K.G.V.*)
4—3 pdr
5 M.G.
(1 landing)
Torpedo tubes (21 inch) :
2 *submerged* (broadside)

Armour (K.C.) :
Vertical. {
12″ Lower belt . . . .
9″ Middle belt . . . .
8″ Upper belt . . . .
4″, 6″, 8″ B'lkh'ds (fore)
2″ 10″ 8″ B'lkh'ds (aft)
6″—4″ Belt (bow) . . . . .
2½″ Belt (stern) . . . . . .
10″—7″ Barbettes . . . . .
11″—″ Gunhouses. . . . .
1½″ Funnel uptakes . . .
3½″—1″ Battery (4 inch guns) . . . .
1″ C.T. base (5″ tube within) . . . .
11″ C.T. (4″ hood) . . . . .
6″ Torpedo C.T. (4″ tube)
}

Armour (H.T.) :
Deck. {
1¾″, 1½″ Upper . . . .
1½″ Main . . . .
1″ Middle . . . .
2½″—1″ (bow). .
3″ (stern) . . . . . . } lower
4″ (over rudder)
}
Special Protec. . . . .
—″ Internal screens to magazines, &c. . . . . . .

KING GEORGE V

Ahead :
4—13·5 in.

Astern :
4—13·5 in.

Broadside : 10—13·5 in., 1—21 in. tube.

Machinery : Turbine (Parsons). Boilers : 18 Babcock or Yarrow. Designed H.P. 27,000 = 21 kts. . Coal : *normal*, 900 tons ; *maximum* (*A. & C.*) 3150 tons, (*K. G. V.*) 2870 tons + 850 tons oil in all three.

Note to Plans.—These require revision, but new plans cannot be put in hand until definite information is secured, describing present positions of 4 inch guns, AA. guns and searchlights. "Coffee box." S.L. towers added to after funnel and extra tops to mast.

Gunnery Notes.—Heavier projectile said to be fired by 13.5 inch in these ships.

Armour Notes.—As *Orion* class ; internal protection is more extensive in these ships, but internal screens are not continuous between end barbettes. Battery for 4-inch guns on forecastle, 3″ face, 3½″ ports, 1″ rear screen thwartships. Deck armour more extensive in these ships.

Torpedo Notes.—Stern tube removed during War.

Name	Builder.	Machinery.	Laid down	Completed	Trials : 30 hours.	Full power.	Boilers	Best recent speed
King George V	Portsmouth Y.	Parsons	Jan. '11	Nov. '13	19,808 =	28,005 = 21·4	Babcock	. . .
Centurion	Devonport Y.	Hawthorn	Jan. '11	May '13		28,235 = 21·88	Yarrow	22·47
Ajax	Scotts	Scotts	Feb. '11	Oct. '13	19,830 =	28,090 = 21·66	Babcock	. . .

General Notes.—Begun under 1910 Estimates. Are generally similar to *Orion* class. Average cost, £1,945,200 = about £85 per ton. On first commission, *Centurion* had experimental form of fire-control for 4-inch guns and 2 searchlights, centrally controlled.* *King George V*, also an experimental form of coaling gear. *Audacious* los during the War. *King George V* has anti-rolling tanks.

NOTE.

*These remarks *re Centurion* have appeared in previous editions, but their importance is not realised. The addition made to *Centurion* in 1913 show that the need for controlled secondary guns and searchlights for night actions wa realised *three years before Jutland.*

(ORION CLASS.)

ORION (Aug., 1910). **THUNDERER** (Jan., 1911), **MONARCH** (March, 1911),
CONQUEROR (May, 1911).

Normal displacement, 22,500 tons (about 25,000 *full load.*) Complement, 806 to 828.

Length (p p.), 545 feet. Beam, 88½ feet. $\left\{ \begin{array}{l} \textit{Mean draught, } 26\frac{5}{8} \textit{ feet} \\ \textit{Max. } \text{,,} \quad 30\frac{3}{4} \textit{ feet} \end{array} \right\}$ *Length over all*, 581 feet.

Guns :
10—13.5 inch (M.V.) **) Dir.**
16—4 inch **) Con.**
1—4 inch (anti-aircraft)
1—3 inch (anti-aircraft)
4—3 pdr.
5 M.G.
(1 landing)
Torpedo tubes (21 inch) :
2 *submerged* (broadside)

Armour (K.C.) :
Vertical.
{ 12″ Lower belt ....
9″ Middle belt ....
8″ Upper belt ....
4″, 6″, 8″ B'lkh'ds (fore) .
6″—4″ Belt (bow) ....
2½″ Belt (stern) ......
2½″, 8″, 10″ B'lkh'ds (aft)
10″—7″ Barbettes .....
11″— ″ Gunhouses....
1½″ Funnel uptakes ...
11″ C.T. (6″, 3″ hoods)..
5″ Fore com. tube ....
3″ Torpedo C.T. & tube

Armour (Nickel) :
Decks.
{ 1½″ Upper ....
1½″ Main ....
1″ Middle ....
2½″ Lower ....
4″ over rudder ....
Special protection :
—″ Internal screens to
magazines, &c. .....

head :
4—13.5 in.

ORION.

Astern :
4—13.5 in.

Broadside : 10—13.5 in., 1—21 in. tube.

Machinery : Parsons turbine. Designed H.P. 27,000 = 21 kts. 4 screws. Boilers : 18
(see *Notes*). Coal : *normal*, 900 tons ; *maximum*, 3300 tons coal + 800 tons oil.

Armour Notes.—12″ belt very narrow and submerged at deep load. Barbette bases, 6″—3″ within belt. Internal
vertical screens to magazines, &c., not continuous between end barbettes.

Torpedo Notes.—Stern tube removed during War.

| Name | Builder | Machinery | Laid down | Completed | Trials:— | | Boilers | Best recent speed |
					30 hrs.	8 hrs. full power (mean)		
Orion	Portsmouth Y.	Wallsend	Nov.'09	Jan.'12	18,966=19·5	29,108=21·02	Babcock	22·3
Conqueror	Beardmore	Beardmore	Apl. '10	Nov.'12	19,100=19·5	28,400=22 13	Babcock	23·1
Thunderer	Thames I.W.	Thames I.W.	Apl. '10	June'12	18,927=18·8	27,416=20·8	Babcock	21·45
Monarch	Elswick	Hawthorn	Apl. '10	Apl. '12	19,128=	28,555=21·88	Yarrow	...

ORION.

Photo, C. N.

General Notes.—*Orion* begun under 1909 Estimates ; the others are ships which were known as "Conditional *Dread-noughts*," laid down under the same Estimates. Average cost, £1,887,870. In these ships, protection is given to the boats for the first time. On her first cruise the *Orion* in the Bay of Biscay rolled 21°. This rolling was attributed to her small bilge keels, 6 feet only. During 1912, improved bilge keels were fitted and the ships roll far less. On trials, *Conqueror* made a *maximum* of over 23 kts. *Monarch* was originally named *King George V.* The general design for these ships was considered for the *Dreadnought*, but rejected on the score of size and cost.

Note to Plans.—Require revision, but new plans cannot be drafted until reliable information is secured describing present positions of 4-inch guns, AA. guns and searchlights. "Coffee-box" S.L. towers added to second funnel. 4-inch on shelter deck now housed in.

(COLOSSUS CLASS).

COLOSSUS (April, 1910) & HERCULES (May, 1910).

Normal displacement, 20,000 tons (about 22,250 *full load*).   Complement, 831 and 845.

Length (*waterline*), 540 feet.   Beam, 85 feet.   Draught $\begin{cases} (normal), & 27 \text{ feet.} \\ (max.), & 31 \text{ feet.} \end{cases}$ Length *over all*, 546 feet.
Length, (*p.p.*) 510 feet.

Guns :
10—12 inch, 50 cal. } Dir. Con.
12—4 inch
1—4 inch (anti-aircraft) (*Col.*)
1—3 inch (anti-aircrcft) (*Herc.*)
4—3 pdr.
5 M.G.
(1 landing)
Torpedo tubes (21 inch) :
 2 *submerged*

Armour (K.C.) :
Vertical. {
11″ Lower belt . . . .
8″ Upper belt . . . .
1½″, 2″, 5″ & 8″ Bulk-
 heads . . . .
7″—2½″ Belt (bow) . . .
2½″ Belt (stern) . . . . . .
10″—7″ Barbettes . . . . .
11″— ″ Gunhouses. . . . .
1″ Funnel uptakes . . . .
11″ C.T. (6″ & 3″ hoods) .
5″ Fore com. tube . . . .
3″ Torpedo C.T. . . . . .
3″ Tube, T.C.T. . . . . . .
}

Armour (Nickel) :
Decks. {
1¼″ Main . . . .
1¾″ Middle . . . .
2¼″—1¾″ (bow) } Lower
3″ (stern)
4″ (over rudder) }
Special Protection : . . . . .
—″ Screens to magazines
 &c. . . . .
}

Ahead :
4 to 6—12 in.

Broadside : 8 to 10—12 in., 1—21 in. tube.

Astern :
6 to 8—12 in.

  Machinery : Parsons turbine.   Designed H.P. 25,000 = 21 kts.   Boilers : Yarrow or Babcock.
Coal : *normal*, 900 tons ; *maximum*, 2900 tons + 800 tons oil.

Gunnery Notes.—Broadside of 10—12 inch not often used, as decks are badly stressed by firing over them.

Armour Notes.—Armouring different to *Neptune*. These ships are "soft enders." On plan, belt forward should stop at Section 2, and belt at stern at Section 20. Beam barbettes, 11″ on exposed faces, 6″ within belt ; other barbettes, 4″ inside belt. *Neptune's* internal protection not used in these ships, internal screens not being continuous between end barbettes. Weights of armour : 4560 tons vertical + 2010 tons decks = 6570 tons.

Torpedo Notes.—Stern tube removed during War. 21-inch tubes introduced in these ships.

Engineering Notes.—Much as *Neptune*.

Name	Builder	Machinery	Laid down	Completed	Trials		Boilers	Best recent speed
					30 hours.	8 hours f.p.		
Colossus	Scott S.& E.Co.	Scott	July,'09	July '11	18,000 = 19·6	27.334 = 21·3	18 Babcock	
Hercules	Palmer	Palmer	July,'09	Aug. '11	18,000 = 19·6	26,559 = 21·5	Yarrow	

COLOSSUS.

Photo, Topical.

HERCULES.

General Notes.—These ships are similar to the *Neptune*, differing mainly in disposition of anti-torpedo armaments, size of tubes, armouring and internal protection. Begun under the 1909 Estimates, but they were laid down earlier than is usually the case. Average cost, £1,730,000 = *about* £87 per ton. Placed in Reserve, 1919.

Note to Plans.—These require revision, but new plans cannot be prepared till definite information is secured describing present positions of 4-inch guns, AA. guns, and searchlights. After half of flying boat deck removed 1914-15. "Coffee-box" S.L. towers round 2nd funnel. All 4-inch guns decked in.

NEPTUNE (Sept., 1909).

Normal displacement, 19,900 tons (about 22,000 *full load*).   Complement, 813.

Length (*waterline*), 540 feet.   Beam, 85 feet. { Draught (*normal*), 27 feet. } Length *over all*, 546 feet (*p.p.* 510 feet).
{ „   (*max.*)   30   „ }

Guns :
10—12 inch, 50 cal. } **Dir.**
12—4 inch   } **Con.**
2—3 inch (anti-aircraft)
4—3 pdr.
5 M.G.
(1 landing)
Torpdedo tubes (18 inch) :
2 *submerged*

Armour (K.C.) :
Vertical {
10″ Lower belt ....
8″ Upper belt ....
5″ & 8″ Bulkheads ....
7″—2½″ Belt (bow) ...
2½″ Belt (stern) ......
9″ Barbettes ....
11″— ″ Gunhouses.....
11″ C.T. (5″ tube) ....
1½″ Torpedo C.T.....
1″ Funnel uptakes ....
}

Armour (Nickel) :
Decks. {
1¼″ Main ....
1¾″ Middle ....
1½″ (bow) } lower
3″ (stern) }
}
Special protection :
″— ″ Internal screens
over magazines and
machinery spaces ...
″ Bulkheads to keel....

Ahead :
4 to 6—12 in.

NEPTUNE.

Astern:
6 to 8—12 in.

Broadside : 8—12 in., 1—18 in. tube.

Machinery : Parsons turbine. Designed H.P. 25,000 = 21 k ts. Boilers : Yarrow. Coal : *normal* 900 tons ; *maximum* 2710 tons + 790 tons oil fuel.

Armour Notes.—Armouring generally as *St. Vincent* class, but further internal sub-division. Internal screens are continuous between end barbettes and well inboard. Beam barbettes 10″ on exposed faces. On plan, Sections 1-3, 2½″ belt should be shown rising nearly to upper deck.

Gunnery Notes.—Firing of beam barbettes over decks (to get 10—12 inch broadside) not often resorted to, as decks get badly stressed by blast.

Torpedo Notes.—*Submerged* tube removed during War.

Engineering Notes.—Consumption on trial was 1.46 lbs. per h.p. at full power. Turbines : H.P. rotor diameter, 82 inch ; L.P. rotor diameter, 109 inch. R.P.M. 332. Boiler pressure : 235 lbs. per square inch. Heating surface : 63,630 square feet. Total weight of machinery with auxiliaries : 1109 tons + water to working level, 2036½ tons. Engine room complement, 231.

Name	Builder	Machinery	Laid down	Completed	First Trials :		Boilers	Best recent speed
					30 hrs.	8 hrs f.p.		
Neptune	Portsmouth	Clydebank	Jan. '09	Jan. '11	18,373 = 19	27,721 = 21	Yarrow	22·7

NEPTUNE.   *Photo, Sadler & Renouf.*

General Notes.—Begun under 1908 Estimates. Cost to build, £86.8 per ton. Cost of machinery, £258,000. Fore funnel heightened 1912. Forward half of flying decks removed, 1914-15. Has the best internal protection of all the 12-inch Dreadnoughts—in fact her internal protection was not equalled in later Battleships till the *Queen Elizabeth* and *Royal Sovereign* classes came into service. Placed in Reserve, 1919.

Note to Plans.—These require revision, but new plans cannot be prepared till definite information is secured regarding present positions of 4-inch guns, AA. guns and searchlights. Fore half of flying boat deck removed, 1914-15. "Coffee-box" S.L. towers added to 2nd funnel and mainmast, director top to foremast and "clinker screen" to fore funnel. All 4-inch guns decked in.

(ST. VINCENT CLASS).

ST. VINCENT (Sept., 1908), & **COLLINGWOOD** (Nov., 1908).

Normal displacement, 19,250 tons.　*Full load*, about 22,900 tons.　Complement, 813 and 823.

Length (*waterline*), 530 feet.　Beam, 84 feet. { Mean draught, 27 feet. / Max.   „ $31\frac{1}{4}$ feet. } Length *over all*, 536 feet (*p.p.* 500 feet).

Guns :
- 10—12 inch, — cal. } **Dir. Con.**
- 12—4 inch
- 2—3 inch (anti-aircraft)
- 4—3 pdr.
- 5 M.G.
- (1 landing)

Torpedo tubes (18 inch) :
- 2 *submerged* (broadside)

Armour (K.C.) : *(Vertical.)*
- 10″ Lower belt ....
- 8″ Upper belt ....
- 7″ & 2″ Belt (bow) ...
- 2″ Belt (stern) ......
- 8″—5″ Bulkheads ....
- 9″ Barbettes ....
- 11″— ″ Gunhouses.....
- 11″ Fore C.T. (5″ tube)
- 8″ After C.T. (4″ tube)

Armour (K.N.C.) : *(Decks.)*
- $1\frac{1}{2}$″, $\frac{3}{4}$″ Main ....
- $1\frac{3}{4}$″ Middle ....
- $1\frac{1}{2}$″, 3″ Lower ......
- Special Protec. ......
- —″ Internal screens to magazines, boilers and engine rooms ......
- —″ Bulkheads to keel ..

ST. VINCENT (1). ✳

Ahead :
4 to 6
12 in.

Astern :
6 to 8
12 in.

Broadside 8—12 inch, 1—18″ tube.

ST. VINCENT (2). ✳

✳ After Control Top removed since above photographs were taken.

Note to Plans.—These require revision, but new plans cannot be prepared till definite information is secured describing present positions of 4-inch guns, AA. guns and searchlights.

Machinery : Parsons turbine (as *Dreadnought*). 4 screws. Boilers : Yarrow or Babcock. Designed H.P. 24,500 = 21 kts.　Coal : *normal*, 900 tons ; *maximum*, 2,800 tons + 940 tons oil + 190 tons patent fuel.

Torpedo Notes.—Stern tube removed during War.

Armour Notes.—Armour generally as *Bellerophon* class, but thinner belt at bow and stern. On plans, bow belt in Sections 1-3 should be shown rising almost to upper deck. Internal screens are continuous between end barbettes and set well inboard. Barbette bases, 5″ within belt. Exposed faces of beam barbettes, 10″.

Engineering Notes.—In this class (and all later Dreadnoughts up to *Iron Duke* class), no cruising turbines. An extra stage at forward end of H.P. turbine is used when running at cruising speed. For full speed, bye-pass valves used. H.P. rotor diameter, 68 inch. L.P. rotor diameter, 92 inch. 324 R.P.M. Pressure, 235 lbs. Heating surface : 63,414 square feet. Weight of main and auxiliary engines : $1072\frac{1}{2}$ tons + water to working level = $1983\frac{1}{4}$ tons. Average consumption on trials : 1.8 lbs. per H.P.

Name.	*Builder.*	*Machinery and Boilers by.*	*Laid down.*	*Com- pleted.*	*Trials : 8 hrs. full power.*	*Boilers.*	*Best recent speed.*
St. Vincent	Portsmouth	Scott Eng. & S. Co.	Dec.'07	May, '10	25878 = 21·2	Babcock	
Collingwood	Devonport	Hawthorn L.	Feb.'08	April '10	26319 = 20·4	Yarrow	

General Notes.—Begun under 1907 Estimates. These ships are simply enlarged *Bellerophons* and second improvements on original *Dreadnought* design. *Collingwood* did not reach designed speed on first trials. Internal protection is very complete. Underwent large refit in 1912-13. *Vanguard* lost by explosion during the War. *St. Vincent* and *Collingwood* in Reserve or employed as Gunnery Training Ships in 1919.

(Bellerophon Class).

BELLEROPHON (July, 1907), **TÉMÉRAIRE** (Aug., 1907), **SUPERB** (Nov., 1907).

Normal displacement, 18,600 tons (about 22,000 *full load*). Complement, 733 to 793.

Length (*waterline*), 520 feet. Beam, 82½ feet. $\begin{cases} Max. & \text{draught, } 30' 11'' \\ Mean & ,, & 27\frac{1}{4} \text{ feet.} \end{cases}$ Length *over all*, 526 feet (*p.p.* 490 feet).

Guns :
10—12 inch, 45 cal.
11—4 inch (*Tem. & Superb*) } Dir.
10—4 inch (*Bell'n*) } Con.
2—4 inch (anti-aircraft *B. & T.*)
2—3 inch (anti-aircraft *Sup.*)
4—3 pdr.
5 M.G.
1 (landing)
Torpedo tubes (18 inch, M. '04) :
2 *submerged* (broadside)

Armour (K.C.) : } Vertical
10"—9" Lower belt ....
8" Upper belt ....
7"—6" Lower & upper belts (bow) ....
5" Belt (stern) ....
8" After bulkhead ....
10"—9" Barbettes .....
11"— " Gunhouses ....
11" Fore C.T. (4" tube)
8" After C.T. (4" tube)

Armour (K.N.C.) : } Decks
{ 1¾"—¾" Main ....
{ 3"—1¾" Middle ......
{ 4"—1½" Lower ....
Special protec. ......
—" Screens to magazines, boiler and engine rooms

BELLEROPHON. (Marksman Type Leader alongside).   *Official R.A.F. Photo.*

Ahead :
4 to 6—12 in.

Astern :
4 to 6—12 in.

Broadside : 8—12 in., 2—18 in. tubes.

BELLEROPHON.

Machinery : Parsons turbine. 4 screws. Details as *Dreadnought*. Boilers : 18 Babcock or Yarrow. Designed H.P. 23,000 = 20.75 kts. Coal : *normal*, 900 tons ; *maximum*, 2648 tons + 842 tons oil + 170 tons patent fuel.

Armour Notes.—Armouring is well planned. Internal screens in these ships run between end turrets and are set well inboard. Exposed faces of beam barbettes, 10".

Engineering Notes.—H.P. rotor diameter, 68 inch. L.P. rotor diameter, 92 inch. 324 R.P.M. Pressure : 235 lbs. Heating surface : 55,530 square feet. Weight of main and auxiliary engines : 1014½ tons. Water to working level, total weight = *about* 1936 tons. Trial consumption averaged 1.55 lbs.

Torpedo Notes.—Stern tube removed during War.

Name.	Built at.	Machinery by.	Laid down.	Completed.	Trials. 8 hrs. full power.	Boilers.	Best recent speed.
Bellerophon	Portsmouth	Fairfield	Dec., '06	Feb., '09	24090=21	Babcock	
Témeraire	Devonport	Hawthorn Leslie	Jan., '07	May, '09	24619=21	Yarrow	
Superb	Elswick	Wallsend Co.	Feb., '07	May, '09	25375=21	Babcock	

Note to Plans.—These require revision, but new plans cannot be prepared till definite information is secured describing present positions of 4-inch guns, AA. guns and searchlights.

General Notes.—Begun under 1906 Estimates. Average cost of machinery, about £285,000. Underwent large refit in 1913-14. Design is generally as *Dreadnought*, but with larger degree of internal sub-division and protection against torpedo attack ; also better anti-torpedo attack battery. All largely refitted in 1912-14, before outbreak of war. The internal protection of these ships is very complete. *Bellerophon* and *Superb* used as Gunnery Schools (Turret Drill), 1919. *Temeraire*, Cadets' Training Ship (sea-going).

DREADNOUGHT (February, 1906).

Normal displacement, 17,900 tons. *Full load, about* 20,700 tons. Complement, 862.

Length (*w.l*), 520 feet. Beam, 82 feet. $\left\{\begin{array}{l}\textit{Maximum} \text{ draught, 31 feet.} \\ \textit{Mean} \quad ,, \quad 26\frac{1}{2} \quad ,,\end{array}\right\}$ Length, (*o.a.*) 526 feet (*p.p.* 490 feet).

Guns :
10—12 inch, 45 cal. } Dir. Con.
10—12 pdr.
2—3 inch (anti-aircraft, 13 pdr.)
2—12 pdr. (anti-aircraft)
4—3 pdr.
5 M.G.
(1 landing)
Torpedo tubes (18 inch) :
4 *submerged* (broadside)

Armour (K.C.) :
Vertical.
{ 11″—9″ Lower belt ....
8″ Upper belt ....
11″ Bulkhead (aft) ....
6″ Belt (bow) ....
4″ Belt (stern) ....
11″—8″ Barbettes ....
12″ Gunhouses ....
11″ Fore C.T. ....
5″ Fore com. tube ....
8″ After C.T. ....
4″ After com. tube ...

Armour (K.N.C.) :
Decks.
{ ¾″ Main (forward).....
1¾″ (flat) Middle .....
2¾″ (slope) (amidships)
4″ at ends (Middle) ...
3″—1″ Lower ....
Special protection.....
″ Screens to Mags., &c.

DREADNOUGHT

Ahead :
4 to 6—
12 in.

Broadside : 8—12 in., 1—18 in. tube.

Astern :
4 to 6—
12 in.

DREADNOUGHT.   *Photo, Cribb.*

Machinery : Parsons turbine. 4 screws. Boilers : 18 Babcock & Wilcox in 3 groups. Designed H.P. 23,000 = 21 kts. Coal : *normal*, 900 tons ; *maximum*, 2900 tons + 1120 tons oil + 120 tons patent fuel. Nominal radius : 6600 at 10 kts. ; 5000 at 19 kts.

Torpedo Notes.—Stern tube removed during War.

Engineering Notes.—Full power, 400 revolutions. One H.P. ahead, one H.P. astern turbine on each wing shaft; inner shafts, 3 turbines each (cruising L.P. ahead ; L.P. astern). 1 astern turbine on each. Boiler pressure : 250 lbs., reduced slightly at the turbines. Each turbine has 39,600 blades. Main condensers : 26,000 square feet ; auxiliary : 6000. Grate surface : 1599 square feet. Heating surface : 55,400 square feet. On trials she exceeded her speed for short spurts (best mile at 21.78), but barely averaged it on her eight hours' run. Very free from vibration. Weight of machinery : main and auxiliary, 973½ tons + water = 1897¾ tons.

Coal consumption.—Very economical at full speed, *about* 340 tons per day for full power. At slow speed consumption is heavy. At 4600 H.P. (13 kts.) it averages nearly 160 tons a day. At 10,000 H.P., *about* 250 tons per day.

Armour Notes.—Base of amidships barbettes is 8″ only and all barbette bases 3″ behind belt. Protective deck aft is 2″ flat, 3″ on slopes and over steering gear. Internal screens to magazines, &c., are not continuous between end barbettes.

Name.	Built at	Machinery by	Laid down	Completed	Trials (mean). 30 hrs. at 16,250. 8 hrs. full.		Boilers.	Best recent speed
Dreadnought	Portsmouth	Vickers	Dec., '05	*Oct. '06	16,930 = 19·3	24,712 = 20·9†	Babcock	...

* Was not really complete at this date. First commission began Dec., 1906. £262,500 was spent in finishing her and £60,400 of this sum was voted in 1907-8. †Maximum attained 27,518 = 21.6 kts.

Note to Plans.—These require revision, but new plans cannot be prepared till information is received giving present positions of 12-pdr. and AA. guns and searchlights.

General Notes.—Freeboard forward : 28 feet. Cost £1,797,497. Begun under 1905 Estimates. In this ship the officers' quarters are forward, crew aft. The ship is very steady, and consequently extremely wet and uncomfortable. She has a remarkably steady gun platform. Draws 2½ feet more than designed, with normal coal. She was very quickly built. All material used is extremely strong. Tactical diameter, extreme helm : 865 yards at 19 kts. ; 825 yards at 12 kts. The ship can stop in 1025 yards at 20 kts. (3 minutes), in 725 yards at 12 kts. Re-fitted 1916. Rammed and sank *U 29*, commanded by Kap. Leut. Otto Weddigen. Placed in Reserve, 1919.

Historical Notes.—When Lord Fisher went to the Admiralty, as First Sea Lord, in October, 1904, he brought with him, from the Mediterranean, plans for various new types of warships. Among these was a design for a battleship with 12—12 inch guns arranged in pairs along centre line ; three pairs of guns at bows, three at stern, the inner barbettes rising in tiers, so that six guns could fire ahead, six astern, and all twelve on broadside. The Special Commission on Designs very much liked this plan, but it had to be rejected on the score of size and cost, and the risk of the superfiring system, on which no practical experience was then available. Lord Fisher's design was modified to an *Orion* plan, but this too had to be rejected on the score of cost and size. The penultimate design with 8—12 inch (two forward, two aft, two on each beam) turned out to be akin to a plan, evolved by Sir Philip Watts and Lord Fisher in the 'eighties, for combining the gun plans of the old *Inflexible* and *Devastation*. The fifth amidship turret of the final Dreadnought design was added, because it happened to fit in.

1916 BRITISH BATTLE CRUISERS

(ANSON TYPE.—1 SHIP).

HOOD (22nd August, 1918).

Normal displacement, 41,200 tons (up to 45,000 tons *full load*).   Complement

Length {p.p. 810* ft.}   Beam {w.l.}   Draught {mean 28½ ft.
       {o.a. 860 ft.}   {outside bulges 104 ft.}   {max.
                         *Approximate

See Frontispiece for Illustration of Official Model.

Guns :
  8—15 inch, 42 cal.
  12—5·5 inch, 50 cal. } **Dir. Con.**
    4—4 inch (anti-aircraft)
    4—3 pdr.
    5 M.G.
    (1 landing)
  Torpedo tubes (21 inch) :
    Not known.

Armour (K.C.) :
  12″ Lower belt ....
  5″, 6″ Lower belt
    (bow and stern) ......
  7″ Middle belt ....
  5″ Middle belt (bow)......
  5″ Upper belt ....
  —″ Bulkheads ....
  12″ Barbettes ....
  15″—11″ Gunhouses .....
  —″ C.T. base (—″ tube) ..
  11″—9″ C.T. (6″ hood over)
  —″ Torpedo C.T. (—″ tube) ..
  —″ R.F. Towers ....
  —″ Funnel uptakes ......

Armour (H.T.) :
  2″ Fo'xle (amids.)......
  Decks { 1½″ flat
        { 2″ slopes } main
        { 1″ bow
        { 3″ stern } lower

Special protection :
  Improved bulges and double
    internal H.T. screens.

Ahead :
  4—15 inch
  6—5·5 inch

Astern :
  4—15 inch

Broadside : 8—15 inch, 6—5·5 inch, —— 21 inch tubes.

Machinery : Brown-Curtis (geared) turbines.   4 screws.   Boilers : Yarrow.   Designed S.H.P.
144,000 = 31 kts.   Fuel : Oil only.   tons *normal*, 4,000 tons *maximum*.

Gunnery Notes.—15 inch guns have large degree of elevation ; director controls similar to *Renown* and *Repulse* ;
  special long-base R.F. in gunhouses. Originally designed to mount 16—5·5 inch, but the four after 5·5 inch shown
  in illustration of Official Model are not mounted.

Armour Notes.—Area covered by 12″ lower belt, *about* 550 × 10 ft. General scheme of armouring and framing is
  extremely massive and strong. Barbette shields have heavy crowns and are of a new design, giving high-angle
  fire to 15 guns.

P.V. Notes.—New type of sliding shoe at stem adopted.

General Notes.—Begun under Emergency War Programme. Originally, there were four ships in this class, *Anson, Hood,
Howe, Rodney.* They were begun in the autumn of 1916 (*a*) to replace Battle Cruisers lost at Jutland, (*b*) to meet
the German Battle Cruisers, *Graf Spee, Prinz Eitel Friedrich* and *Ersatz Hansa*, which were laid down in 1916.
Contractors were : *Anson* (Armstrong), *Howe* (Cammell Laird), *Rodney* (Fairfield), *Hood* (as Table). The enemy
having ceased work on all his large ships, in 1917, *Anson, Howe* and *Rodney* were stopped in March, 1917, and dismantled to clear slips after the Armistice, but not before £1,634,000 had been expended on them. These ships
were designed to meet the lessons of Jutland. In *Hood*, the outstanding feature is the huge areas covered by heavy
armour, strong framing, &c.—in fact, the general scheme of protection is on the lines of German Battle Cruisers.
Since November, 1916, *Hood* has been proceeding very slowly. Her estimated cost is six to six **and**
two-thirds millions, but may be seven millions before she is finished. Her size is colossal, and she will be the largest
warship in the world, until the U.S. *Massachusetts* class of Dreadnoughts comes into service in 1921-22.

Name	Builder	Machinery	Begun	Completed	Trials
Hood	Clydebank	Clydebank	{ 31 May, '16 * { 1 Sept., '16 }	Nov., '19†	

*Laid down a few hours before the Battle of Jutland began.   Original design modified after this battle ; work to
    modified design begun 1st Sept., 1916.
†Projected date ; will probably be exceeded.

1915 BRITISH BATTLE CRUISERS

(RENOWN CLASS.)
REPULSE (8th January, 1916), RENOWN (4th March, 1916).

Normal displacement, 26,500 tons (about 32,000-32,700 *full load*).   Complement, *Renown*, 999 ; *Repulse* 1016.

Length (*p.p.*), 750 feet. { o.a. 794 feet *Repulse* / o.a. 794 feet 1½in. *Renown* } Beam { *Repulse* 90 feet* / *Renown* 90 feet 2 in.* } Draught { *Repulse* 26¼ feet (*mean*), 30¼ feet (*max.*) / *Renown* 26⅔ feet (*mean*), 30 feet (*max.*) }

*Outside bulges.

Guns :
6—15 inch, 42 cal. } **Dir.**
17—4 inch, 50 cal. } **Con.**
2—3 inch (anti-aircraft)
4—3 pdr.
5 M.G.
(1 landing)
Torpedo tubes (21 inch) :
2 *submerged**
*See Torpedo Notes.

Armour (K.C.) :
6″ (amidships)
4″ (within bow) } Lower belt
3″ (stern)
4″ Fore b'lkhead
3″ After b'lkh'd
1½″ Upper belt ....
7″—4″ Barbettes ....
11″—7″ Gunhouses .....
1½″ Funnel uptakes ...
2″ C.T. base (3″ tube within) ....
10″ C.T.
6″ Sighting hood over C.T. ....
3″ Torpedo C.T. ......

(Vertical.)

Armour (H.T.) :
{ 1½″—½″ Fo'xle ....
{ 1⁷⁄₁₆″—1½″ Upper ......
{ 3″—¾″ Main (2″ slopes)
2½″ Bow
3½″—3″ Stern } Lower
—″ Barbettes ....
3″ C.T. and hood ....
1½″ Torpedo C.T. ....

(Crowns / Decks)

Special protection :
Modified bulges about 20 ft. deep, filled with oil ....

Ahead :
4—15 in.
8—4 in.

Astern :
2—15 in.
12—4 in.

Broadside : 6—15 in., 13—4 in., 1—21 in. tube.

Machinery : Brown-Curtis (direct drive) turbines.   4 screws.   Boilers : 42 Babcock & Wilcox. Designed H.P. not exactly specified, but expected to be 110,000 to 120,000 S.H.P. for 30 kts. In service, S.H.P. 112,000 = about 31.5 kts.   Fuel (oil only) : 1000 tons *normal* ; *Repulse* 4243 tons *maximum* ; *Renown* 4289 tons *maximum*.

Gunnery Notes.—15-inch have range only limited by maximum visibility.   Director tower under control tower on foremast.   4-inch triples have 2 director towers, and all guns can be worked from either tower or half the 4-inch from one tower.   If towers are destroyed, 4-inch can work independently.   4-inch triples are clumsy and not liked. They are not mounted in one sleeve ; have separate breech mechanism ; gun crew of 23 to each triple.   First salvo fired by forward 15-inch of *Renown* did considerable damage forward, and she had to be docked for repairs.

Torpedo Notes.—*Submerged* tubes a failure.   *Renown*, on 1919 re-fit, reported to have had *submerged* tubes removed and replaced by 8 *above water* tubes in 4 twin mountings on main deck.

Armour Notes.—Armouring adapted from *Invincible* and *Indefatigable* classes.   Belt about 9½ ft. deep.   *Special Protection.*—Projected that bulges be deepened.   *Renown* may have had bulges enlarged on her 1919 re-fit, and her beam may be larger now.

Engineering Notes.—Turbines similar to *Tiger*.   For full description, *v.* "Engineering," April 11th, 1919.   Boilers : 250 lbs. per sq. in.   Heating surface : 157,206 sq. ft.   Consumption at full speed : *about* 1400 tons oil fuel per day.

Aircraft Notes.—Two aeroplanes carried on flying-off platforms on crowns of "B" and "Y" turrets.

Name	Builder	Machinery	Begun*	Completed	Trials : H.P. kts.	Where run
Repulse	Clydebank	Clydebank	Jan.25,'15	Aug.,1916	119,025=31.7	Skelmorlie (deep load)
Renown	Fairfield	Fairfield	Jan.25,'15	Sept.,1916	126,300=32.68	Arran (normal load)

*To Battle Cruiser design.

General Notes.—Provided for by 1914-15 Navy Estimates ; first designed as slightly modified *Royal Sovereigns*, contracted for on that basis, and begun 1914, but building was not pushed on actively after the outbreak of War.   After the Falklands Battle it was decided that these two ships should be re-designed as Battle Cruisers.   Outline design was prepared in ten days, and builders received sufficient details by January 21st, 1915, to begin building, but full designs were not finished and approved till April, 1915.   Intended that they should be completely built in fifteen months, but this time was somewhat exceeded.   Both ships have turned out remarkably well and reflect great credit on their designers and builders.   Internally, they are most spacious, but they are lightly built, and their guns "shake them up" considerably.   Remarkable speeds have been claimed for these ships.   When attempting to intercept enemy warships in November, 1917, *Renown* is said to have touched 41 kts.   Be this as it may, they have certainly done 33-34 kts. in service.   Reported to have cost about three to four millions each.

RENOWN.

RENOWN.

REPULSE.

Photo, Sub-Lieut Vickers, R.N.

TIGER (Dec., 1913).

Normal displacement, 28,500 tons.   Full load, about 35,000 tons.   Complement 1185.

Length (waterline), 675 feet.   Beam, 90½ feet. { Mean draught, 28⅓ feet. { Length (o.a.) 704 feet.
                                                 { Max.   „   34   „   { Length (p.p.) 660 feet.

Guns :

8—13.5 inch (M.V.) } **Dir.**
12—6 inch (M. XII) } **Con.**
2—3 inch (anti-aircraft)
4—3 pdr.
5 M.G.
(1 landing)
Torpedo tubes (21 inch) :
4 submerged (broadside)

Armour (K.C.) :

Vertical.

{ 9″ Lower belt . . . .
{ 6″ Upper belt . . . .
{ 3″ Under lower belt . .
{ 4″ Bulkheads . . . .
{ 6″ Battery (1″ traverses)
{ 5″, 4″ Battery Bulk'ds)
{ 6″ Casemates (2″ rear)
{ 9″—8″ Barbettes . . . . . .
{ 9″ Gunhouses . . . .
{ 2″ C.T. base . . . .
{ 4″ Com. tube . . . .
{ 10″ C.T. . . . .
{ 6″—3″ hood over C.T.
{ 6″ Torpedo · C.T. (4″
{   tube) . . . .

Armour (H.T.) :

Deck.

{ 1½″—1″ Fo'xle . . . .
{ 1½″—1″ Upper . . . .
{ 1″ Amidships } Lower
{ 3″ Bow   }
Special protection :
2½″—1″ H.T. magazine
screens . . . .

Ahead :	Astern :
4—13.5 in.	2 or 4—13.5 in.
4—6 in.	2—6 in.

Broadside: 8—13.5 in., 6—6 in., 2—21 in. tubes.

Machinery : Turbines (Brown-Curtis direct drive). 4 screws. Boilers : 39 Babcock. Designed H.P. 85,000 = 28 kts. (108,000 = 30 attained). Coal: *normal* 1000 tons, *maximum* 3320 tons coal and 3480 tons oil fuel.

Name	Builder	Machinery	Begun	Completed	Trials : H.P. kts.
Tiger	Clydebank	Clydebank	June, 1912	Oct., 1914	87,500 = 28 104,635 = 29

Armour Notes.—Armour as *Lion* Class, but 6″ battery and extra H.T. decks added.   Barbettes, 4″, 3″, 1″, as they descend through decks behind belts. ¾″ rear screen to 6″ battery. Internal magazine protection is not continuous between barbettes.

Engineering Notes.—4-shaft turbines in 2 sets, each set has H.P. ahead and H.P. astern turbine on wing shaft, one L.P. ahead and one L.P. astern, in same casing on inner shaft. Boilers in 5 rooms. The enormous fuel capacity (6800 tons coal and oil) does not give this ship any exceptional radius of action, for she burns about 1200 tons of fuel per day at 60,000 S.H.P.

General Notes.—Begun under 1911 Estimates by J. Brown & Co., Clydebank ; machinery by builders. Completed October, 1914. Estimated cost was £2,593,095, but this was exceeded. As first designed, this ship was to have been very much like the *Lion* class. A year after the *Tiger* was laid down the Japanese battle-cruiser *Kongo* was completed and passed her trials. Comparison between the *Lion* and *Kongo* designs showed the Japanese ship to be superior in armament and protection. Work was suspended on the *Tiger*, and her design was altered to embody certain improvements displayed by the *Kongo*. These alterations resulted in the *Tiger* being one and a half years on the stocks before launching. Until *Hood* was launched in 1918, *Tiger* was the largest ship in H.M. Navy. She was also a remarkably handsome ship until the present hideous rig was adopted in 1918.

TIGER.

For Plan and description, v. opposite page.

TIGER (present appearance).   *Photo, Renouf.*

TIGER (Aircraft Recognition View).   *Official R.A.F. photo.*

LION and **PRINCESS ROYAL.**

For Plan and description, see next page.

PRINCESS ROYAL (Aircraft Recognition View).   *Official R.A.F. photo.*

(LION CLASS.)

LION (August, 1910), PRINCESS ROYAL (April, 1911).

Normal displacement, 26,350 tons. *Full load,* 29,700 tons. Complement, 1085 & 1061.

Length (*w.l.*), 675 feet. Beam, 88½ feet. { *Mean* draught, 27⅔ feet. } { *Length over all,* 700 feet.
                                         { *Max.* draught, 31⅓ feet. } { Length *p.p.,* 660 feet.

Guns :
8—13.5 inch (M.V.) } **Dir. Con.**
16—4 inch, 50 cal. }
2—3 inch (anti-aircraft)
4—3 pdr.
(*P.R.* 2—2 pdr. pom-pom)
5 M.G.
(1 landing)

Torpedo tubes (21 inch) :
2 *submerged* (broadside)

Armour :
Decks { 1″ Upper ....
       { 1½″—1″ Amidships } Lower
       { 2¼″ Ends }

Special protection :
—″ Magazine screens

PRINCESS ROYAL.   *Photo Topical.*

Ahead:
4—13.5 in.

LION.

Astern:
2—13.5 in.

Broadside : 8—13.5 in., 1—21 in. tube.

Armour (K.C.) :

Vertical. { 9″, 6″, 5″ Lower belt ..
          { 6″, 5″, 4″ Upper belt ..
          { 4″ Bulkheads ....
          { 9″—8″ Barbettes .....
          { 9″ Gunhouses ......
          { 1½″ Funnel uptakes ...
          { 10″ C.T. (4″ tube K.N.C.)
          { 6″—3″ Sighting hood .
          { 1″ Torpedo C.T. ......

Machinery : Parsons turbine. 4 screws. Boilers : 42 Yarrow. Designed H.P. 70,000 = 28 kts. Coal : *normal* 1,000 tons ; *maximum,* 3500 tons + 1135 tons oil.

Armour Notes.—Barbettes are 3″ and 1″ below upper and main deck. Magazine screens not continuous between end barbettes. 2,900 tons vertical + 2,300 tons deck armour = 5,200 tons.

Engineering Notes.—*Lion* on trials used coal only. No attempt was made on builders' trials to force these ships up to a phenomenal speed. In service, they have attained 30 kts., developing rather more than 100,000 H.P. Coal consumption : 950 tons a day at full power. *P. Royal* on 2/3 trial burned only 1·16 lbs. per h.p. per hour.

Name	Builder	Machinery	Laid down	Completed	Trials (mean)		Boilers	Best recent speed
					At 3/4 power	Full power		
Lion	Devonport Y.	Vickers	Nov.'09	Jun. '12	54,763 = 24·5	73,802 = 27	Yarrow	
Princess Royal	Vickers	Vickers	May, '10	Nov.'12	53,315 =	76,510 = 28·52	Yarrow	

General Notes.—The *Lion* begun under the 1909 Estimates ; the *Princess Royal* is one of the "contingent Dreadnoughts" of the same year's estimates. On trials, flames from the fore funnel rendered the fire control station then over fore funnel on tripod, almost untenable. Alterations were consequently made. Average cost per ship, £2,087,000 = about £73¼ per ton. About £60,000 was spent on altering each. *Lion* was disabled in the Dogger Bank action. A similar but slightly larger ship of this type, *Queen Mary,* was sunk in the Battle of Jutland.

LION.   *Photo, Topical.*

Note to Plans.—These require revision, but new plans cannot be prepared till information is received giving position of 4 inch and AA. guns and searchlights.

(Presented to the British Navy by the Dominion of New Zealand.)

(INDEFATIGABLE TYPE.)

NEW ZEALAND (July, 1911).

Note.—For AUSTRALIA, a sister ship, see Royal Australian Navy Section.

Normal displacement, 18,800 tons ; about 20,000 tons, *full load.*   Complement, 853.

Length (*waterline*),　　feet.   Beam, 80 feet. $\left\{\begin{array}{l}\textit{Mean} \text{ draught, } 26\tfrac{1}{2} \text{ feet.} \\ \textit{Max.} \quad\text{,,} \quad 30 \text{ feet.}\end{array}\right\}$ Length *over all*, 590 feet (*p.p.*, 555 feet).

Guns :
8—12 inch, 50 cal. **Dir. Con.**
10—4 inch
1—4 inch (anti-aircraft)
4—3 pdr.
2—2 pdr. pom-pom
5 M.G.
(1 landing)
Torpedo tubes (18 inch) :
2 *submerged* (broadside)

Armour (K.C.) :
Vertical
6″ Belt (amidships) ...
5″—4″ Belt (forward)
4″ Bulkheads.........
7″, 4″, 3″ Barbettes ...
7″ Gunhouses ....
$1\tfrac{1}{2}$″—1″ Funnel uptakes
(Nickel) ....
10″ C.T. ....
6″—3″ Hood over C.T.
4″ Com. tube ....
1″ Torpedo Director
Tower ....

Armour—*continued.*
Decks
1″ Main ....
2″—1″ Amidships ⎱ Lower
$2\tfrac{1}{2}$″ Fore and aft ⎰ Deck
Special protection :
—″ Screens to Magazines

Photo wanted.

Resembles *Australia* in Australian
Navy Section.

Ahead :
4 to 6—12 in.

Astern :
4 to 6—12 in.

Broadside : 8—12 in., 2—18 in. tubes.

Machinery : Parsons turbine.   4 screws.   Designed H.P. 44,000 = 25 kts.   Boilers : Babcock.
Coal : *normal*, 1000 tons ; *maximum*, 3170 tons coal + 840 tons oil.

Armour Notes.—On plans, belt should not extend to stem or stern.   6″ belt from lower to middle deck, Sections 7-17 ;
5″ belt, Sections 5. 6 and 18, 19 ; 4″ belt, Sections 3, 4 and 20-21 ; $2\tfrac{1}{2}$″ deck, Sections 1, 2 and 22, 23.   Armour for
funnel uptakes not shown.   Magazine screens not continuous between end barbettes.

Torpedo Notes.—Stern tube removed during War.

Name	Builder	Machinery	Laid down	Completed	Trials (mean) 30 hours 3/4	8 hours full	Boilers	Best recent speed
New Zealand	Fairfield	Fairfield	June,'10	Nov. '12	31,794 = 24·72	46,894 = 26·38	Babcock	

General Notes.—Design is generally an enlarged *Invincible*.   Special feature is that the amidship guns are further apart
in order to permit of fairly free use on either broadside.   She is a better sea-boat than the *Invincibles*.   This ship
was originally laid down for the Dominion of New Zealand, but finally presented to the British Navy.   *Indefatigable*,
the original ship of this type, was sunk in the Battle of Jutland.

Note to Plans.—These require revision, but new plans cannot be prepared till information is received giving present
disposition of 4-inch guns, AA. guns and searchlights.   Chart-house and forebridges have been moved back to leave
C.T. unobstructed.   For other corrections, see *Armour Notes.*

E 2

(INVINCIBLE CLASS).
INFLEXIBLE (June, 1907) & **INDOMITABLE** (March, 1907).
Normal Displacement, 17,250 tons (about 20,000 *full load.* Complement, 837.
Length (*waterline*), 560 feet. Beam, 78ft. 10 in. { Mean draught, 26 feet. } Length *over all*, 567 feet (p.p. 530).
{ Max. " 29¾ feet. }

Guns :
  8—12 inch, XI, 45 cal. } **Dir.**
  12—4 inch } **Con.**
  1—4 inch (anti-aircraft)
  1—3 inch (anti-aircraft)
  4—3 pdr.
  5 M.G.
  (1 landing)
Torpedo tubes (18 inch) :
  4 *submerged*

Armour (K.C.) :
Vertical. {
  6″ Belt (amidships) ...
  4″ Belt (bow) ....
  7″—6″ Bulkheads ....
  7″ Barbettes ....
  7″ Gunhouses ....
  10″ C.T. (fore) ....
  4″ Tube (fore) ......
  6″ C.T. (aft)..........
  3″ Com. tube (aft) ....
}

Armour—continued.
Decks. {
  1″—¾″ Main ....
  1½″ Middle ....
  2½″ Lower (aft) ......
  2″ Slopes } Lower (amidships)
  1½″ Flat }
}
Special protection :
  —″ Screens to magazines

INDEFATIGABLE

Ahead :
4 or 6—
12 in.

Broadside : 6—12 in., 2—18 in. tubes.

Astern :
4 to 6—
12 in.

Machinery : Parsons turbines. 4 screw. Boilers : Yarrow or Babcock. Designed H.P.
41,000 = 25 kts. Coal : *normal*, 1000 tons ; *maximum*, 3080 tons + 710·725 tons oil fuel.

Gunnery Notes.—Amidship turrets are very cramped together, and broadside of 8—12 inch can only be rarely fired.
Armour Notes.—Internal magazine screens not continuous between end barbettes.
Torpedo Notes.—Stern tube removed during War.

Name	Builder.	Machinery, etc.	Laid down.	Completed.	Trials (mean). Full power.	Boilers.	Best recent speed.
Inflexible	Clydebank	Clydebank	Feb., '06	Oct., '08	43,391 = 25·5	Yarrow	...
Indomitable	Fairfield	Fairfield	March, '06	June, '08	43,780 = 25·3	Babcock	...

General Notes.—Begun under 1905-6 Estimates. Average cost of each, *about* £1,752,000 = £101·6 per ton. These
ships at full speed burn *about* 500 tons of coal a day, plus about 125 tons of oil. They are not very steady gun
platforms. Average cost of machinery, *about* £472,000. *Invincible* of this class lost in Battle of Jutland. *Inflexible*
severely damaged by a mine in the bombardment of the Dardanelles, March 18th, 1915. Placed in Reserve, 1919.

Notes to Plans.—These require revision, but new plans cannot be prepared till information is received giving present
distribution of 4-inch guns, AA. guns and searchlights. Stern tube removed. Chart-house and forebridges re-built
to leave C.T. clear. 4-inch guns now in unarmoured casemates.

INDOMITABLE

Photo, Topical.

AIRCRAFT VIEW.

Official R.A.F. photo.

COMMONWEALTH, as re-built 1918.

(KING EDWARD CLASS).

COMMONWEALTH (May, 1903). (Re-built 1918).

Normal displacement, 16350 tons. *Full load*, 17,050 tons. Complement, 753.

Length { *waterline*, 439 feet. } Beam { at *w. l.*, 78 feet. } { *Mean* draught, 26¾ feet. }
{ *over all*, 457 feet. } { outside bulges, feet. } { *Max.* ,, 28 feet. }

Guns :
4—12 in., IX, 40 cal. { **Dir.**
4—9·2 in., IX, 45 cal. { **Con.**
4—6 inch, VII
8—12 pdr.
2—3 inch (anti-aircraft)
6—3 pdr.
2—3 pdr. (anti-aircraft)
5 M.G.
(1 landing)
Torpedo tubes (18 inch) :
4 *submerged* (broadside)

Armour (Krupp) :
9″ Belt (amidships) ...
7″—3″ Belt (forward) .
2½″ Belt (aft)........
2″—1″ Main, middle,
lower decks ....
12″—6″ Barbettes (N.C.)
12″—8″ Gunhouses (K.C.)
8″ Lower deck side....
7″ Battery (2″ traverses)
4″ Secondary turrets ..
12″ C.T. (6″ tube) .....
Special protection :
Bulges, — ft. deep ...

Machinery : 2 sets 4-cylinder triple expansion. 2 screws. Boilers : 16 Babcock. Designed H.P. 17,500 (*n.d.*), 18,000 (*f.d.*) = 18·5 kts. (15 since bulge protection was added ?). Coal : *normal*, 950 tons ; *maximum*, 2194 tons + 380 tons oil fuel.

Name.	Builder.	Machinery	Laid down	Completed.	30 hours ¼ power.	8 hours full power.	Boilers.	Best recent speed.
Commonwealth	Vickers	Fairfield	June '02	1905	12,769 = 17·9	18,538 = 19·01	16 Babcock	18·7

General Notes.—Built under 1901-2 Estimates. Rebuilt 1918, when bulge protection, director controls, extra searchlights and fore tripod mast were added. Note that all 6-inch guns have been removed from battery ; 4—6 inch are mounted on upper deck in shields. Serves as sea-going Gunnery Ship for qualifying gunlayers.
Removals.—Africa, Zealandia, for Disposal ; will not be required for War Fleet. Dominion, Hibernia, Hindustan, for sale.

NOTE.—Disposal of other Pre-Dreadnoughts as follows :

LORD NELSON Class :—

Lord Nelson for Sale. *Agamemnon*, for Fleet Firing Service and in Reserve. Will probably be Target Ship.

SWIFTSURE Class :—

Swiftsure. Target Ship.

DUNCAN Class :—

Albemarle, Duncan, Exmouth, all for Sale.

FORMIDABLE Class :—

Prince of Wales, Venerable, Implacable, for Special Service (Harbour Duties only). *Queen*, disarmed and Accommodation Ship only. *London*, Minelayer and listed on later page.

CANOPUS Class :—

Albion, Canopus, for Sale ; *Vengeance,** for Special Service (probably only Harbour Duty as Hulk). *Glory*, Harbour Depot Ship, Rosyth.

MAJESTIC Class :—

Cæsar, Hannibal, Illustrious,* Magnificent, Mars,* Victorious,** for Special Service, mostly as Harbour Depot Ships. *Prince George,** Harbour Depot Ship for Destroyers in Reserve. *Jupiter* for Sale.

Old ROYAL SOVEREIGN Class :—

Redoubtable (ex *Revenge*) for Sale.

*These Ships have been completely disarmed or mount only a few light guns.

(COURAGEOUS CLASS—2 Ships).

COURAGEOUS (5th February, 1916), **GLORIOUS** (20th April, 1916).

Normal displacement, *about* 18,600 tons (*about* 22,700 tons *full load*).   Complements C. 842. G. 829.

Length $\begin{cases} p.p. & 735 \text{ ft.} \\ o.a. & 786\frac{1}{2} \text{ ft.} \end{cases}$ Beam (outside bulges), 81 ft.   Draughts $\begin{cases} mean & 22\frac{1}{4} \text{ ft.} \\ max. & 26 \text{ ft.} \end{cases}$

Guns :
4—15 inch, 42 cal. } **Dir. Con.**
18—4 inch
2—3 inch (anti-aircraft)
4—3 pdr.
5 M.G.
(1 landing)
Torpedo tubes (21 in.) :
2 *submerged*
12 *above water* (4 triple deck)

Armour :
Vertical.		
3″ Belt (amidships) ...
2″ Belt (within bow) ..
2″ (H.T.) Fore bulkhead
3″—1″ (H.T.) After Bulkhead ....
1½″ Side over belt.....
7″—3″ Barbettes .....
9″—7″ Gunhouses.....
1″—1½″ Funnel uptakes
2″ C.T. base..........
3″ Tube ....
10″ C.T. ....
6″ Sighting hood......
3″ Torpedo C.T. (2″ tube)

Armour—*continued.*
Decks (H.T.)	
1″ Forecastle ....
1″ Upper ....
1¾″—¾″ Main (between barbettes) ....
1½″ Lower (stern, flat)
3″ Lower (stern, over rudder) ....
2″ Lower (on slopes) ..

Crowns.	
4¼″ Barbettes (since increased) ....
3″ C.T. and sighting hd.
1¾″—¾″ Torpedo C.T. .

Torpedo protection (H.T.) :
Modified bulges 25 ft. deep filled with oil fuel
1½″—1″ Outer internal screens between barbettes
¾″ Inner screen to boiler and engine room vents

Ahead :
2—15 in.
6—4 in.

Broadside : 4—15 in. 12—4 in. 7—21 in. tubes.

Astern :
2—15 in.
9—4 in.

Machinery : Parsons (all-geared) turbines. 4 screws. Boilers : 18 Yarrow (small tube). Designed H.P. 90,000 = *about* 31 kts. Fuel (oil only) : *normal*, 750 tons ; *maximum*, 3160 tons.

Gunnery Notes.—Range of 15-inch only limited by maximum visibility. 15-inch director tower on foremast under control tower. Arcs as plans : 20° elevation, 5° depression. 4-inch director tower on each mast, all 4-inch can be controlled from either tower, or half of 4-inch from one tower. Triple 4-inch guns are reported to be an indifferent type of mounting and rate of fire, singly or in salvo, is not good, as loaders are liable to obstruct one another. Arcs for 4-inch : 155° fore guns, 180° amidships guns, 120° for forward centre-line triple, 150° after C.L. triple.

Torpedo Notes.—*Submerged* tubes not successful, as bars bend when attempting to fire torpedoes at speeds over 22-23 kts.

Armour Notes.—General scheme of armouring on Light Cruiser lines, the 3″ belt being built up of 2″ plating on 1″ shell plating. Decks round magazines thickened during completion. Gunhouses : 13″ face, 7″ sides, 11″ rear, 4¼″ roof (now thicker), 5″ overhang. Barbettes : 7″—6″ above upper deck, 6″—4″ above main deck, 3″ below main deck.

Engineering Notes.—General arrangement of machinery as in Light Cruiser *Champion*. 4-shaft geared turbines and double helical gearing. Have done 32-33 kts. in service. A rather singular point is that these ships are 1½ kts. faster on *deep load* draught than when in normal trim.

Aircraft Notes.—Flying-off platforms on barbette crowns ; 2 aeroplanes carried.

GLORIOUS. Aircraft Recognition View.

Official R.A.F. Photo.

For Plans and Description, see opposite page.

GLORIOUS.

Photo, Cribb, Southsea.

Name	Builder	Machinery	Begun	Completed	Trials
Courageous	Armstrong	Parsons	May, 1915	Dec., 1916	93,780 = 31·58
Glorious	Harland & Wolff, Belfast	Harland & Wolff	Mar., 1915	Nov., 1916	91,165 = 31·6

General Notes.—Emergency War Programme ships. Design of these ships is said to have been formulated by Admiral of the Fleet Lord Fisher, when First Sea Lord, 1914-15. Their shallow draught is said to have been planned with a view to future operations in the Baltic. In 1915, credits could not be secured for commencing extra Battle Cruisers, taking two years to build. But additional Light Cruisers had been approved, and the opportunity was taken to design these two ships as " Large Light Cruisers." They were designed about January, 1915, and it was intended that they should be finished in a year. Accordingly, the number of big guns and mountings available had to be taken into consideration in planning armament. The twelve months' projected building time was exceeded by six months, as these ships were not commissioned till October, 1916.

The intended Baltic operations having been negatived, a tactical role as " Light Cruiser Destroyers " was assigned to these vessels. The objection is, their end-on fire of two 15-inch guns (when in chase), is too heavy and slow-firing. Against a small and rapidly-moving target, like an enemy Light Cruiser (continually altering her course), two 15-inch guns have only a fair chance of securing hits—but one salvo on the target would probably be decisive.

The lines of these vessels are remarkably fine, the beam at fore barbette being only 71 feet. On her acceptance trials, *Courageous* met heavy weather and was driven hard into a head sea. Her hull became badly strained just before the fore barbette. She was docked and doubling plates added here; subsequent trials showing that the defect had been overcome. *Glorious* did not develop this weakness, but after twelve months' service she was strengthened in the same way, as a precautionary measure. When running into a head sea, these two ships can easily outstrip destroyers. They are said to have done 35 kts. in service.

These vessels are abnormal in type—so abnormal, they have been dubbed the " Outrageous Class." In 1919, they were laid up in reserve, as their cost of maintenance is very high. It does not appear that they will have a very long life. No figures are available for cost, but they are said to have run to three millions each. A third unit, *Furious*, of slightly modified *Courageous* design, was converted for service as an Aircraft Carrier.

OLD BRITISH CRUISERS.

Note.

In 1919, *Minotaur, Shannon, Duke of Edinburgh,* placed on Disposal List as not required for further duty with War Fleet. All to be sold at first convenient moment. *Achilles* reported to be Stokers' Training Ship (Harbour Duty only). During the Armistice period, *Cochrane* stranded in the Mersey and broke in two. She was not worth salvage, and abandoned as a total wreck.

SUFFOLK.

CARNARVON.

(DEVONSHIRE CLASS.)
CARNARVON (Oct., 1903), **ANTRIM** (Oct., 1903), **DEVONSHIRE** (April, 1904).

Displacement, 10,850 tons. Complement, 653.

Length (*over all*), 473½ feet. Beam, 68½ feet. *Maximum* draught, 25½ feet.
Guns (2—11 inch anti-submarine howitzers may still be mounted in some ships): 4—7·5 inch I, 6—6 inch VII, 8—3 pdr., 5 machine, (1 landing). Torpedo tubes (18 inch): 2 *submerged.* Armour (Krupp): 6″—4½″ Belt (amidships), 2⅝″ Belt (forward), 2″ Deck (aft), 4½″ Bulkheads (aft), 6″ Barbettes, 7½″—4½″ Hoods to these, 6″ Casemates, 10″ Conning tower (fore). Machinery: 2 sets vertical triple expansion. 2 screws. Boilers, various: 17-15 water-tube and 6 cylindrical. Designed H.P. 20,500 (*n.d.*), 21,000 (*f.d.*)=22.25 kts. Coal: *normal* 800 tons; *maximum* 1,750 tons (*Carnarvon* + 250 tons oil).

Name.	Built at	Laid down.	Completed.	Trials:—30 hours at 4/5.	8 hrs. full power.	Boilers 4/5.	Last best speed.
Devonshire Antrim	Chatham Clydebank	March, '02 Aug., '02	Aug., '05 July, '05	14,830=21·0 14,628=21·21	21,475=23·17 21,604=23·20	15 Niclausse 17 Yarrow	23·1 22·4
Carnarvon	Beardmore	Oct., '02	May, '05	15,212=21·43	21,460=23·1	17 Niclausse	22·1

(Engines by builders, except for *Devonshire*, which are by Thames Ironworks.)
General Notes.—Cost, per ship, about £850,000. Built under 1901 Estimates. *Argyll* and *Hampshire* of this class lost during the war. 1919: *Devonshire* in Reserve; *Antrim* for Signals and W/T. experiments. Some of these three ships partially dismantled. *Carnarvon,* sea-going Training Ship for Cadets. *Roxburgh* for sale.

LANCASTER (Mar., 1902), **BERWICK** (Sept., 1902), **DONEGAL** (Sept., 1902), **CORNWALL** (Oct., 1902), **CUMBERLAND** (Dec., 1902), and **SUFFOLK** (Jan., 1903). *Normal* displacement, 9,800 tons. Complement, 690. Length *over all,* 463½ feet. Beam, 66 feet. *Max.* draught, 25½ feet. Guns (2—11 inch howitzers may still be in some ships): 6 in., 45 cal., as follows : 4 in *Cornwall* and *Cumberland,* 8 in *Donegal* and *Berwick,* 10 in *Lancaster,* 14 in *Suffolk,* and (in all ships) 4—12 pdr., 2—3 pdr. (anti-aircraft), 2 or 1 machine, (1 landing). Torpedo tubes (18 inch): 2 *submerged.* Armour (Krupp): 4″ Belt (amidships), 2″ Belt (bow), 5″ Bulkhead (aft), 2″ Deck (aft), 4″ Barbettes (H.N.), 5″ Turrets to these (H.N.), 4″ Casemates (10), 10″ Conning tower. Machinery: 2 sets 4 cylinder vertical triple expansion. 2 screws. Boilers: Various—see *Notes.* Designed H.P. 22,000=23 kts. Coal: *normal* 800 tons; *maximum* 1,730 tons.

Name.	Built at	Machinery	Laid down.	Completed	30 hrs. 4/5.	8 hours full power.	Boilers.	Last recorded best speed.
Essex	Pembroke	Clydebank	Jan., '00	1904	16,132=19·6	22,219=22·8	Belleville	22
Lancaster	Elswick	Hawthorn L.	Mar., '01	1904	16,004=22·0	22,881=24	Belleville	24·1
Berwick	Beardmore	Humphrys	Apl., '01	1903	16,554=21·7	22,680=23·7	Niclausse	24·4
Donegal	Fairfield	Fairfield	Feb., '01	1903	16,333=22·3	22,154=23·7	Belleville	24·3
Cornwall	Pembroke	Hawthorn	Mar., '01	1904	16,487=21·8	22,694=23·6	Babcock	24·0
Cumberland	L. & Glasgow	L. & Glasgow	Feb., '01	1904	16,472=22·1	22,784=23·7	Belleville	24·4
Suffolk	Portsmouth	Humphrys & T.	Mar., '02	1904	16,350=21·2	22,645=23·7	Niclausse	23·7

General Notes.—1900 Estimates. Cost about £775,000 each. *Bedford,* of this class, was wrecked 1910 on the China Station, *Monmouth* sunk in battle, off Chile, *Essex,* in 1919, only Harbour Depot and Accommodation Ship for Destroyers in Reserve.

Note.

Following old Cruisers for disposal (will not be required for War Fleet): *Leviathan, Edgar.** Following assigned to Special Service (Harbour Duties only): *Sutlej, Diadem, Europa, Terrible, Theseus*, Grafton,* Crescent.* For sale: *King Alfred, Kent, Argonaut, Bacchante, Endymion.** Both *Amphitrite* and *Euryalus* converted to Minelayers.

* Fitted with bulge protection.

("E" CLASS—1, 2 OR 3 SHIPS ?)

EMERALD (building ?)* *ENTERPRISE* (building),* *EUPHRATES* (building ?).*

* Reported September, 1919, that one ship had been stopped, other two to proceed.

Displacement,   tons.   Complement,

Length $\begin{cases} p.p. & \text{feet} \\ o\,a. & \text{feet} \end{cases}$ Beam $\begin{cases} w.l. & \text{feet} \\ \text{outside bulges} & \text{feet} \end{cases}$ Draught $\begin{cases} mean & \text{feet.} \\ max. & \text{feet.} \end{cases}$

Guns :
  7—6 inch, 50 cal. (**Dir. Con.**)
  3—3 inch AA. ?
  4—3 pdr.
  (Some M.G.)
Torpedo tubes (21 inch) :
  12, in four triple deck mount-
    ings, *above water*

Armour :
  No details.

Reported to have 3 funnels, raking, arranged as in *Lion*, with tower for S.L. and AA. guns between 2nd and 3rd funnels. Tripod foremast and stump mainmast. 6 inch guns disposed in same way as 7.5's of *Hawkins*, but third centre line gun between 3rd funnel and mainmast and 4th centre line superfires over 5th centre-line (quarter deck) gun

Building ?

Machinery : Turbines (all-geared) Brown-Curtis or Parsons. 2 screws. Designed S.H.P. 60,000 ?=32 to 35 ? kts. Boilers : 12 Yarrow. Fuel (oil only) : *normal,*   tons ; *maximum,* *about* 1000 tons.

Name	Builder	Machinery	Begun	Completed	Trials H.P. kts.	Turbines
Emerald	Armstrong		1918			
Enterprise	Clydebank	Clydebank	June 28/18			
Euphrates	Fairfield	Fairfield	1918			Brown-Curtis

General Notes.—Begun under Emergency War Programme. All details given are unofficial. Reported that these are a modified *Chatham* type of *about* 5000 tons, with same machinery as *Hawkins* type, but "all-geared" turbines and oil-burning boilers only.

(CARLISLE CLASS—5 SHIPS.)

CAIRO (19th Nov., 1918), **CALCUTTA** (——, 1919), **CARLISLE** (9th July, 1918), **CAPETOWN** (28th June, 1919), **COLOMBO** (18th Dec., 1918).

Displacement, 4190 tons. Complement, *about* 330-350.

Length $\begin{cases} p.p. & 425 \text{ feet} \\ o.a. & 451\frac{1}{2} \text{ ,,} \end{cases}$ Beam, $43\frac{1}{2}$ feet. Draught $\begin{cases} mean & 14 \text{ feet} \\ max. & 16\frac{1}{3} \text{ ,,} \end{cases}$

Guns :
5—6 inch, 50 cal. (**Dir. Con.**)
2—3 inch AA.
4—3 pdr.
2—2 pdr. pom-pom
1 M.G.
Torpedo tubes (21 inch) :
  8 *above water*, in 4 double
    mountings

Armour (H.T.) :
3" Side (amidships) ...
$2\frac{1}{4}$"—$1\frac{1}{2}$" Side (bow) ..
2" Side (stern) ....
1" Upper deck (amids.)
1" Deck over rudder ..
(No C.T. or tube)

Ahead :
2—6 inch.

Broadside : 5—6 in., 4—21 in. tubes.

Astern :
2—6 inch.

Machinery : Turbines (all-geared), Brown-Curtis or Parsons types. Designed S.H.P. 40,000 = 29 kts. 2 screws. Boilers : — Yarrow. Fuel (oil only) : *normal*, 300 tons ; *maximum*, 950 tons.

Name	Builder	Machinery	Begun	Completed	Trials : H.P. kts.	Turbines
Cairo	Cammell Laird	Cammell Laird	Nov.28,'17	Sep.23,'19		
Calcutta	Vickers	Vickers	1917 ?	Nov.11,'18	40,930 = 28·45	
Carlisle	Fairfield	Fairfield	1917	1919		
Capetown	Cammell Laird	Cammell Laird	Feb.23,'18	June, '19		
Colombo	Fairfield	Fairfield	1917 ?			

General Notes.—Emergency War Programme ships, ordered June-July, 1917, that is, *after* the first three units of " D Class " (*Danae, Dragon, Dauntless*) were ordered. In these ships, " trawler bows " were added, to remedy defects shown by *Ceres* and *Calypso* classes. Conning tower also abolished, and hangar for aeroplanes combined with chart-house. Unofficially referred to as " Repeat C Class."

To distinguish.—From *Danae* and other *D* Cruisers—no 6-inch gun between foremast and first funnel. From *Ceres* class, by " trawler bows " and aeroplane hangar before tripod mast.

CARLISLE. (*Capetown* same.)

" Trawler bow," large forebridges, but *no* hangar.

CAIRO.

74

("D CLASS," THIRD GROUP— SHIPS.)
DESPATCH (24th Sept., 1919), **DIOMEDE** (29th April, 1919) —For others see *Cancelled Ships.*

Length $\begin{cases} p.p. & \text{feet} \\ o.a. & ,, \end{cases}$ Beam, feet. Draught $\begin{cases} mean & \text{feet.} \\ max. & ,, \end{cases}$

("D CLASS," SECOND GROUP—3 SHIPS.)
DELHI (23rd Aug., 1918), **DUNEDIN** (1919), **DURBAN** (29th May, 1919).

Length $\begin{cases} p.p. & 445 \text{ feet} \\ o.a. & 472\frac{1}{2} \text{ ,,} \end{cases}$ Beam, $46\frac{1}{2}$ feet. Draught $\begin{cases} mean & 14 \text{ feet.} \\ max. & 16\frac{1}{4} \text{ ,,} \end{cases}$

("D CLASS," FIRST GROUP—3 SHIPS.)
DANAE (26th Jan., 1918), **DAUNTLESS** (10th April, 1918), **DRAGON** (29th Dec., 1917).

Length $\begin{cases} p.p. & 445 \text{ feet} \\ o.a. & 471 \text{ ,,} \end{cases}$ Beam, 46 feet. Draught $\begin{cases} mean & 14\frac{1}{4} \text{ feet.} \\ max. & 16\frac{1}{2} \text{ ,,} \end{cases}$

Displacement (of all above), 4,650 tons. Complement, *about* 350.

Guns :
6—6 inch, 50 cal. (**Dir. Con.**)
2—3 inch AA.
4—3 pdr.
2—2 pdr. pom-pom.
1 M.G.
Torpdeo tubes (21 inch) :
12 in 4 triple deck mountings.

Armour (H.T.) :
3" Side (amidships) ...
2", $1\frac{3}{4}$", $1\frac{1}{2}$" Side (bow
and stern) ....
1" Upper deck (amids.)
1" Deck over rudder ..

Ahead :
2—6 in.

Astern
2—6 in.

Broadside : 6—6 in., 6—21 in. tubes.

Machinery : Turbines (all-geared), Brown-Curtis or Parsons types. Designed S.H.P. 40,000
= 29 kts. 2 screws. Boilers : Yarrow (small tube). Oil fuel only : *normal*, 300 tons ; *maximum*,
1050 tons.

Name	Builder	Machinery	Ordered	Begun	Completed	Trials H.P. kts.	Turbines
Despatch	Fairfield*	Fairfield	Mar., 1918	1918			
Diomede	Vickers*	Vickers	Mar., 1918	1918			
Delhi	Armstrong		Sept., 1917	29 Oct., '17	June, 1919	41,000 = 28·5†	
Dunedin	Armstrong		Sept., 1917				
Durban	Scotts*	Scotts	Sept., 1917				Brown-Curtis
Danae	Armstrong	Wallsend	Sept., 1916	Dec., 1916	July, 1918	40,463 =	
Dauntless	Palmer		Sept., 1916		Dec., 1918		
Dragon	Scott	Scott	Sept., 1916	Jan., 1917	Aug., 1918	40,035 =	Brown-Curtis

*Towed to following Dockyards for completion : *Diomede* to Portsmouth, *Despatch* to Chatham, *Durban* to Devonport.
† With PVs. out, and on deep draught.

DANAE.

Photo, Seward, Weymouth.

Hangar forward, as *Carlisle*. Bows as *Danae* above.

DRAGON, DAUNTLESS.

No hangar, " trawler " bows, high bridges, revolving
launching platform for aeroplane abaft
fourth 6-inch gun.

DELHI.

General Notes.—Emergency War Programme ships. Note that first three were ordered *before Carlisle* class. Design
generally as *Ceres* class, but lengthened *about 20 feet,* to add a sixth 6-inch between foremast and first funnel ; also
triple tubes. Completion of *Despatch* and *Diomede* may be indefinitely postponed.

Cancelled Ships (Third Group).—*Daedalus* (Armstrong), *Daring* (Beardmore), *Desperate* (———), *Dryad* (Vickers).
All ordered March, 1918, with *Diomede* and *Despatch.* Cancelled 1918. Possible that *Desperate* may proceed,
so as to complete three ships in third group, as in other two groups. Contractor for *Desperate* not known ; may
be Palmer.

(CERES CLASS—5 SHIPS.)

CARDIFF (ex *Caprice*, 12th May, 1917), **CERES** (24th March, 1917), **COVENTRY** (ex *Corsair*, 6th July, 1917), **CURACOA** (5th May, 1917), **CURLEW** (5th July, 1917).

Displacement, 4190 tons.   Complement, 327.

Length $\begin{Bmatrix} p.p. & 425 \text{ feet} \\ o.a. & 450 \quad ,, \end{Bmatrix}$ Beam, 43½ feet.   Draught $\begin{cases} mean & 14 \text{ feet.} \\ max. & 16\frac{1}{4} \quad ,, \end{cases}$

CURLEW.   *Photo, Seward, Weymouth.*

Guns :
5—6 inch, 50 cal. (**Dir. Con.**)
2—3 inch AA.
4—3 pdr.
1 M.G.
Torpedo tubes (21 inch) :
8 *above water*, in 4 *double*
   mountings

Armour (H.T.) :
3″ Side (amidships) ...
2¼″—1½″ Side (bow) ..
2″ Side (stern) ......
1″ Upper deck (amids.)
1″ Deck over rudder ..
(Harvey or Hadfield)
3″ C.T. ....
— Tube ....

Ahead :
2—6 in.

Broadside : 5—6 in., 4—21 in. tubes.

Astern :
2—6 in.

Machinery : Turbines (all-geared), see Table.   2 screws in all.   Designed S.H.P. 40,000 =
29 kts.   Boilers : Yarrow.   Fuel (oil only) : 300 tons, *normal ; maximum,* 950 tons.

Name	Builder	Machinery	Begun	Completed	Trials H.P. kts.	Turbines
Cardiff	Fairfield	Fairfield	July, 1916	July, 1917	41,450 = 28·96	B.-Curtis A.G.
Ceres	Clydebank	Clydebank	Apl.26,'16	June, 1917	39,425 = 29·1	B.-Curtis A.G.
Coventry	Swan Hunter	Wallsend	Aug., 1916	Feb., 1918	39,967 =	B.-Curtis A.G.
Curacoa	Pembroke D.Y.	Harland & Wolff	July, 1916	Feb., 1918	40,428 =	B.-Curtis A.G.
Curlew	Vickers	Vickers	Aug., 1916	Dec., 1917	40,240 = 28·07	Parsons A.G.

General Notes.—All Emergency War Programme ships, ordered April, 1916.   Very wet forward, to remedy which
defect the later *Carlisle* and *Dragon* classes were given " trawler " bows.

To distinguish : From *Dragon* and " D " Cruisers.—No 6 inch between foremast and first funnel.   The same point
separates this class from the *Caledon* class.

COVENTRY   *Photo, Messrs. Swan Hunter & Wigham Richardson, Builders.*

(IMPROVED BIRMINGHAM CLASS—2 or 4 SHIPS.)

EFFINGHAM (building), *FROBISHER* (building), **HAWKINS** (Oct., 1917), **RALEIGH** (29th Aug., 1919).

Displacement, 9750 tons.   Complement,   —

Length $\begin{cases} p.p.\ 565\ feet \\ o.a.\ 605\ ,, \end{cases}$ Beam $\begin{cases} w.l. & 58^*\ feet. \\ outside\ bulges\ 65\ ,, \end{cases}$ Draught $\begin{cases} mean\ 17\frac{1}{4}\ feet. \\ max.\ 20\frac{1}{2}\ ,, \end{cases}$

*Approximate.

HAWKINS.   Port quarter view.

Photo, Cribb, Southsea.

Guns :
7—7·5 inch, 50 cal. (**Dir. Con.**)
8—12 pdr.
4—3 inch AA.
4—3 pdr.
2—2 pdr. pom-pom
- M.G.
Torpedo tubes (21 inch) :
4 *above water*
2 *submerged*

Armour (H.T. or Nickel) :
3″—2″ Side (amidships)
2½″—1½″ Side (bow) ..
2½″—2¼″ Side (stern)
1″ Upper deck (amids.)
1½″—1″ Deck over
  rudder (Hadfield) ..
3″ C.T. ....
Anti-Torpedo Protection :
Bulges, 10 ft. deep ...
Unpierced Bulkheads,
  below lower deck ...

Ahead :
2 to 4—7·5 in.

Astern :
2 to 4—7·5 in.

Broadside: 6—7·5 in., 3—21 in. tubes.

General Notes.—Begun under Emergency War Programme. These ships were designed in the summer of 1915 and ordered December, 1915. They were planned to meet possible improvements in German Light Cruiser types, and also for hunting enemy commerce raiders in the Atlantic—hence their big fuel capacities. Since oil fuel might not be obtainable at distant naval stations and ports, they were given some coal and 4 small coal-burning boilers arranged to provide sufficient steam for cruising speeds. In the post-war era, they will prove excellent Flagships to Light Cruiser Squadrons. Internally, design is very spacious, and *Hawkins* has proved a very good sea-boat. One unit of this class, *Cavendish* (Harland & Wolff), was accelerated in building, and completed as the Aircraft Carrier *Vindictive* (q.v.).

Machinery : Turbines, Brown-Curtis or Parsons (geared cruising). Designed S.H.P. in *Hawkins*, 60,000 = 30 kts. (other 3 ships, with oil fuel only, expected to develop 70,000 S.H.P. and about 31 kts.). 4 screws. Boilers : 12 Yarrow (small tube). Fuel : *As originally designed.* Coal: *normal*, 800 tons ; *maximum*, 1000 tons + 1600 tons oil. *Hawkins* reported to have these proportions of fuel, but other three ships may be modified to take about 3000 tons oil only, *max.* capacity.

Gunnery Notes.—7·5's are a new semi-auto. B.L. mark on centre-pivot mountings and with H.A. elevation. Unofficially stated that projectile is light and muzzle velocity high, so that guns have practically a range only limited by *maximum* visibility. Armaments originally projected for this class were (*a*) mixed battery of 9·2 inch and 6 inch, (*b*) 14—6 inch.

Torpedo Notes.—Above water tubes are single (side-loading ?), mounted athwartships on upper deck below mainmast. In *Repulse* class, *Glorious* class and *Centaur* class, *submerged* tubes have proved very satisfactory, as bars bend when attempting to fire torpedoes over 20 kts. Possible that *submerged* tubes have not been mounted in *Hawkins*.

Armour and Protection Notes.—Armour on Light Cruiser lines. Estimated that bulges and sub-division will keep ship afloat, even if all three boiler-rooms and both engine-rooms are flooded.

Name	Builder	Machinery	Begun	Completed	Trials H.P. kts.	Turbines
Effingham	Portsmouth D.Y.		1916 ?	No.		
Frobisher	Devonport D.Y.		1916 ?	No.		
Hawkins	Chatham D.Y.	Beardmore	1916 ?	July25, '19		Brown-Curtis
Raleigh	Beardmore		Dec.9, '15	No.		

Cancelled Ships.—Building of *Effingham* and *Frobisher* has been proceeding intermittently for the past three years, and, in the spring of 1919, *Effingham* was only in frame, and *Frobisher* little advanced. Possible that these two ships may be stopped. *Raleigh* is launched, but her completion is being delayed indefinitely.

HAWKINS.   Port bow view.

Photo, Cribb, Southsea.

(CALEDON CLASS—3 SHIPS.)

CALEDON (25th Nov., 1916), **CALYPSO** (24th Jan., 1917), **CARADOC** (23rd Dec., 1916).

Displacement, 4120 tons. Complement, 344.

Length $\begin{cases} p.p. \ 425 \ \text{feet} \\ o.a. \ 450 \quad \text{,,} \end{cases}$ Beam, $42\frac{3}{4}$ feet. Draught $\begin{cases} mean \ 14\frac{1}{4} \ \text{feet.} \\ max. \ 16\frac{1}{4} \quad \text{,,} \end{cases}$

Guns :
5—6 inch, 50 cal. (**Dir. Con.**)
2—3 inch AA.
4—3 pdr.
1 M.G.
Torpedo tube (21 inch) :
  8 *above water*, in 4 double
    mountings

Armour (H.T.) :
  3″ Side (amidships) ...
  $2\frac{1}{4}″-1\frac{1}{4}″$ Side (bow) ..
  $2\frac{1}{2}″-2″$ Side (stern) ..
  1″ Upper deck (amids.)
  1″ Deck over rudder ..
  (Harvey or Hadfield)
  6″ C.T. } probably
  4″ Tube } removed

CALYPSO.

Photo, by courtesy of Messrs. Hawthorn Leslie & Co. (Builders).

Ahead :
1—6 in.
      Broadside : 5—6 in., 4—21 in. tubes.
Astern :
2—6 in.

Machinery : Turbines (all-geared), Parsons. 2 screws. Designed S.H.P. 40,000 = 29 kts.
Boilers : 8 Yarrow. Fuel (oil only) : *normal*, 300 tons ; *maximum*, 935 tons.

Gunnery Notes.—Mark of 6-inch gun introduced in this class and mounted in later Light Cruisers has about 40° elevation.

Name	Builder	Machinery	Begun	Completed	Trials : H.P. kts.
Caledon	Cammell Laird	Cammell Laird	Mar.17,'16	Mar., '17	47,887 =
Calypso	Hawthorn Leslie	Hawthorn Leslie	Feb.7, '16	June 21,'17	43,312 =
Caradoc	Scott S.B. Co.	Scotts	Feb., '16	June, '17	41,196 =

General Notes.—Emergency War Programme. Were known as "Tyrwhitt's Dreadnoughts," as they were units of Harwich Force, under Vice-Admiral Sir Reginald Tyrwhitt. When new, they could make 29-30 kts. Are very wet forward, the fo'xle 6-inch being almost unfightable in a head sea. *Cassandra*, of this class, built by Messrs. Vickers Ltd., lost in Baltic by mine, soon after Armistice was signed.

To distinguish

Caledon class	from	*Centaur* class
1. *Three* yards on foremast.		1. *Two* yards on foremast.
2. AA. guns abeam *between* funnels.		2. AA. guns on centre line *before and abaft* S.L. tower.
3. Deck tubes.		3. Tubes *submerged*.
4. *Raking* stem.		4. "Yacht" stems.
Note.—Searchlight bridge before forefunnel not fitted in *Caledon*.		*Note.*—S.L. bridge before forefunnel not fitted in *Centaur*.

Very like *Calypso* on preceding page.

(Centaur Class—2 Ships.)

CENTAUR (6th Jan., 1916), **CONCORD** (1st April, 1916).

Displacement, 3750 tons. Complement, 336-329.

Length, (*p.p.*) 420, (*o.a.*) 446 feet. Beam, 42 feet. Draught $\begin{cases} \textit{mean } 14\frac{1}{2} \text{ feet.} \\ \textit{max. } 16\frac{1}{3} \text{ ,,} \end{cases}$

Guns :
5—6 inch, 50 cal. (**Dir. Con.**)
2—3 inch AA.
2—2 pdr. pom-pom
1 M.G.
Torpedo tubes (21 inch) :
2 *submerged*

Plans :—Generally same as *Caledon* class.

Armour (H.T.) :
3″ Side (amidships) ...
2¼″—1¼″ Side (bow) ..
2½″—2″ Side (stern) ..
1″ Deck (amidships)...
1″ Deck over rudder ..

Ahead :
1—6 in.

Astern :
2—6 in.

Broadside : 5—6 in., 1—21 in. tube.

Machinery : Parsons I. R. turbines. 4 screws. Boilers : 8 Yarrow. Designed S.H.P. 40,000 = 28·5 kts. Fuel (oil only) : *normal*, 300 tons ; *full load*, 824 tons.

Name	Builder	Machinery	Begun	Completed	Trials : H.P. kts.
Centaur	Armstrong	Vickers	Jan., 1915	Aug., 1916	31,679 = 26·8
Concord	Armstrong	Vickers	Feb., 1915	Dec., 1916	40,908 =

General Notes.—Emergency War Programme ships. When new, could make 30-32 kts. Specially well sub-divided. *Submerged* tubes unsatisfactory ; may be replaced by twin or triple deck tubes in the future. *Centaur* had her bow and stern blown off by mines during War.

Very like *Champion* and *Calliope*, *v.* illustration of *Calliope* on a later page.

(Cambrian Class—Later 4 Ships.)

CAMBRIAN (3rd March, 1916), **CANTERBURY** (21st Dec., 1915), **CASTOR** (28th July, 1915), **CONSTANCE** 12th Sept., 1915).

Displacement, 3750 tons. Complement, 323.

Length, (*p.p.*) 420, (*o.a.*) 446 feet. Beam, 41½ feet. Draught, 16¼ feet *max*, 14⅝ *mean*.

Guns :
4—6 inch, 50 cal. (**Dir. Con.**)
1—4 inch AA. (*Canterbury*)
2—3 inch AA. (other ships)
2—2 pdr. pom-poms
Torpedo tubes (21 inch) :
6 *above water* (*Canterbury*)
4 *above water* (other ships)

Armour (H.T. and Harvey) :
3″ side (amidships) ...
2¼″—1½″ Side (bow) ..
2½″—2″ Side (aft) ....
1″ Deck (amidships)...
1″ Deck over rudder ..
6″ C.T.) Removed
4″ Tube ʃ from some

Ahead :
1—6 in.

Broadside : 4—6 in. (2 or 3—21 in T.T. ?).

Astern :
2—6 in.

Machinery : Turbines, as *Notes*. 4 screws. Boilers : 8 Yarrow in all. Designed S.H.P. 40,000 = 28.5 kts. Fuel (oil only) : *normal*, 420 tons ; *maximum*, 841 tons.

Name	Builder	Machinery	Begun	Completed	Trials : H.P. kts.	Turbines
Cambrian	Pembroke	Cammell Laird	Dec., 1914	May, 1916	40,100=	Parsons I.R.
Canterbury	Clydebank	Clydebank	Oct.14,'14	May, 1916		Brown-Curtis
Castor	Cammell Laird	Cammell Laird	Oct.28,'14	Nov., 1915	42,337=	Parsons I.R.
Constance	Cammell Laird	Cammell Laird	Jan.25,'15	Jan., 1916	41,892=	Parsons I.R.

General Notes.—Begun under 1914-15 Estimates. Design generally same as *Champion* and *Calliope*. *Castor* flies broad pennant of Commodore (*D*).

BIRKENHEAD (ex *Antinauarkos Condouriotis*, 18th Jan., 1915), **CHESTER** (8th Dec., 1915).

		Length (feet).		Beam.	Draught (feet).		Displace-	Comple-
		(*p.p.*)	(*o.a.*)	(ft.)	*mean*	*max.*	ment (tons)	ment.
Birkenhead	.. ..	430	446	49⅚	15½	17	5235	452
Chester	.. ..	430	456½	49⅚	15¼	17¼	5185	402

Guns :
10—5·5 inch (**Dir. Con.**)
1—3 inch AA.
2 or 1—3 pdr. AA.
1 M.G.
Torpedo tubes (21 inch) :
2 *submerged*

Armour :
″ Belt ....
″ Ends ....
″ Deck ....
″ Shields ....
″ C.T. ....

No plans available.

BIRKENHEAD.

To distinguish.—*Birkenhead* has *straight* pole mainmast, as above view ; *Chester's* pole mainmast is *raked aft*.

Ahead :
3—5·5 inch.

Astern :
5—5·5 inch.

Broadside : 6—5·5 in., 1—21 in. tube.

Machinery : Turbines : Parsons (compound ré-action). 4 screws. Boilers : 12 Yarrow. Designed S.H.P. : *Birkenhead*, 25,000 = 25 kts. ; *Chester*, 31,000 = 26·5 kts. Fuel : *Birkenhead*, 1070 tons coal + 352 tons oil, both *max.* ; *Chester*, 1172 tons *max.* oil only.

Gunnery Notes.—5·5 inch guns and mountings by Coventry Ordnance Co. They are said to have proved so successful that it was decided to introduce this calibre into the Navy as an official mark of gun.

Name	Builder	Machinery	Begun	Completed	Trials*	
					H.P.	kts.
Birkenhead	Cammell Laird	Cammell Laird	Mar. 21, '14	May, 1915	26,767 =	
Chester	Cammell Laird	Cammell Laird	Oct. 7, '14	May, 1916	31,423 =	

*S.H.P. only ; no speeds taken.

General Notes.—Begun for Greek Navy ; purchased for British Navy under the War Emergency Programme. These ships have been very well reported on. They are good sea-boats, and the majority of their guns are mounted well above waterline. Steam well and are good for 23 kts. continuous, except in bad head seas. Designed by Messrs. Cammell Laird & Co. as an improvement on the British *Chatham* and Australian *Melbourne* classes.

(Cambrian Class—First Two Ships.)

CALLIOPE (Dec. 17th, 1914), **CHAMPION** (May 29th, 1915).

Displacement, 3750 tons.   Complement, 324.

Length, 420 (*p.p.*), 446 (*o.a.*) feet.   Beam, 41½ feet.   Draught $\begin{cases} mean\ 14\frac{1}{2}\ feet. \\ max.\ 16\quad ,, \end{cases}$

Calliope

Guns :
4—6 inch (**Dir Con.**)
2—3 inch AA.
1 M.G.
Torpedo tubes (2—21 inch*):
submerged
*4—21 inch *above water* reported added 1919.

Champion

4—6 inch (**Dir Con.**)
1—4 inch AA.
1—3 pdr. AA.
Torpedo tubes (6—21 inch):
above water

Armour (H.T.)
4″ Side (amidships) ...
2¼″—1½″ Forward ....
2½″—2″ Aft ....
1″ Deck (amidships)...
1″ Deck over rudder hd.
(Hadfield)
6″ C.T. } removed ? ..
2″ Tube }

Calliope.

Photo, Topical.

Plans generally same as *Cambrian* class on a preceding page.

Note.

Calliope very badly damaged by oil fuel fire at sea, November, 1919. If not scrapped, she will require extensive re-construction before she can return to service.

Ahead :
1—6 inch.

Astern :
2—6 inch.

Broadside : 4—6 in., —21 in. tubes.

Machinery : Turbines (all-geared), Parsons.   Screws : 4 in *Calliope*, 2 in *Champion*.   Designed S.H.P. in *Calliope*, 37,500 ; in *Champion*, 40,000 = 28·5 kts. in both ships.   Boilers : 8 Yarrow. Fuel (oil only) : 405 tons, *normal* ; maximum, 772 tons.

Name	Builder	Machinery	Laid down	Com-pleted	First trials :	Turbines	Boilers	Best recent speed
Calliope	Chatham	Parsons	Jan.'14	June '15	30,917=28	Parsons A.G.	Yarrow	
Champion	Hawthorn	Hawthorn	Mar., 9 '14	Dec. 20, '15	{30,290 = {41,000=29			

General Notes.—Begun under 1913-14 Estimates, with 6 *Caroline* class, on next page.   Same hull, &c., but all-geared turbines adopted.   Also carry less oil fuel, have thicker side plating, and—of course—one funnel less.

(CAROLINE CLASS—6 SHIPS.)

CAROLINE (Sept. 29th, 1914), **CARYSFORT** (Nov. 14th, 1914), **CLEOPATRA** (Jan. 14th, 1915), **COMUS** (16th Dec., 1914), *also* **CONQUEST** (20th Jan., 1915), **CORDELIA** (Feb. 23rd, 1914).

Displacement, 3750 tons. Complement, 325.

Length (*p.p.*), 420 feet. Beam, 41½ feet. Draught, (*max.*) 16, (*mean*) 14½ feet. Length *over all*, 446 feet.

CAROLINE (and *Carysfort, Comus*).   *Photo, Topical.*

Guns : *(Caroline, Carysfort, Comus)*
- 4—6 inch (**Dir. Con.**)
- 2—3 inch AA.
- 1 M.G.

Tubes :
- 4—21 inch *above water* in 2 pairs

Armour (H.T.) :
- 3″ Side (amidships), 2¼″—1½″ forward, 2½″—2″ aft, 1″ Deck (amidships), 1″ Deck over rudder head. (Hadfield), 6″ C.T. and 4″ tube, but removed from some.

Guns : *(Conquest)*
- 4—6 inch (**Dir. Con.**)
- 1—4 inch AA.
- 2—2 pdr. pom-poms
- 1 M.G.

Tubes :
- As *Cleopatra*

Guns : *(Cleopatra)*
- 4—6 inch (**Dir. Con.**)
- 2—4 inch AA.
- 2—2 pdr. pom-poms
- 1 M.G.

Tubes :
- 8—21 inch *above water* in 4 pairs

Guns : *(Cordelia)*
- 4—6 inch (**Dir. Con.**)
- 1—4 inch AA.
- 1 M.G.

Tubes :
- As *Cleopatra*

Ahead :
1—6 in.

Broadside : 4—6 in., 2 or 4—21 in. tubes.

Astern :
2—6 in.

Machinery : Turbine : Parsons or Brown-Curtis. Boilers : 8 Yarrow. Designed H.P. 40,000 = 28·5 kts. Fuel (oil only) : *normal*, 482 tons ; *maximum*, 917 tons.

Name	Builder	Machinery	Laid down	Completed	Trials	Turbines	Boilers	Best recent speed
Caroline	Cammell-Laird	Cammell-Laird	Jan. '14	Dec. '14	30,735 = 27	Parsons I R.	Yarrow in all.	
Carysfort	Pembroke	Hawthorn	Feb. '14	June,'15	32,573 = 28·4	Brown-Curtis		
Cleopatra	Devonport	Cammell-Laird	Feb. '14	June,'15	31,280 =	Parsons		
Comus	Swan, Hunter	Wallsend	Nov. '13	May, '15	32,736 =	Parsons I.R.		
Conquest	Chatham	Scotts	Mar '14	June,'15	31,825 =	Parsons I.R.		
Cordelia	Pembroke	Hawthorn	July, '13	Jan. '15	30,716 =	Parsons I.R.		

General Notes.—Caroline of this class was built within twelve months. Belong to the 1913-14 Estimates. Originally had 2—6 inch and 8—4 inch ; re-armed during War.

CLEOPATRA.

CONQUEST.

CORDELIA.

(ARETHUSA CLASS—7 Ships).

AURORA (30th Sept., 1913), **GALATEA** (May 14th, 1914), **INCONSTANT** (July 6th, 1914),

ROYALIST (Jan. 14th, 1915), **PENELOPE** (Aug. 25th, 1915), **PHAETON** (Oct. 21st, 1914),

UNDAUNTED (April 28th, 1914).

Displacement, 3500 tons.   Complement, 318.

Length (p.p.), 410 feet.   Beam, 39 feet.   { Mean Draught, 13½ feet. }   Length over all, 436 feet.
{ Max.   „   15½ „ }

Guns :
Galatea, Inconstant, Phaeton,
Royalist :—
　3—6 inch } **Dir.**
　4—4 inch { **Con.**
　2—3 inch AA.
Penelope as above, but 1—4 inch
　AA. in place of 2—3 inch AA.

Guns :
Undaunted, Aurora :—
　2—6 inch } **Dir.**
　6—4 inch { **Con.**
　1—4 inch AA. } Undaunted
　2—2 pdr. AA.
　2—3 inch AA.—Aurora

Armour (H.T.) :
　3″ Amidships.........
　2¼—1½″ Forward .....
　2½—2″ Aft ....
　1″ Deck (amidships)...
　1″ Deck over rudder hd.
　　(Hadfield)
　6″ C.T. } Removed from
　4″ Tube } some ships

and—in all—
Torpedo tubes : 8—21 inch above water

Photo wanted.

Galatea, Inconstant, Penelope, Phaeton, Royalist.

Note :—Ships fitted to tow Kite Balloons have aftermast before S. L. tower.

Ahead :
1—6 inch.
　　Broadside : 2 or 3—6 in., 3 or 2—4 in., 4—21 in. tubes.

Astern :
1—6 inch.
2—4 inch.

Machinery : Turbine (see Notes).   Boilers : 8 Yarrow in all.   Designed H.P. 40,000 = 28.5
kts.   Fuel : Oil only, 482 tons normal ; 810 tons maximum.

Armour Notes.—C.T. removed and replaced by revolving launching platform for a seaplane or aeroplane.   Side armour
serves dual purpose of providing protection and giving skin plating.

Gunnery Notes.—Beam 4-inch forward very wet and cannot be fought in a head sea.   Accordingly, 2—4 inch right
forward have been taken out of five ships and a third 6-inch mounted on centre-line between 3rd funnel and S.L.
tower.

Name	Builder	Machinery	Laid down	Com-pleted	Trials	Turbines	Boilers	Best recent speed
Aurora	Devonport	Parsons	Oct. '12	Oct. '14	30,417 = 27·4	Parsons I. R.	Yarrow small tube in all	
Galatea	Beardmore	Beardmore	Jan. '13	Dec.'14	30,796 =	Parsons I. R.		
Inconstant	Beardmore	Beardmore	April '13	Jan. '15	30,357 =	Parsons I. R.		
Royalist	Beardmore	Beardmore	June '13	Mar.'15	31,034 =	Parsons I. R.		
Penelope	Vickers	Vickers	Feb. '13	Dec. '14	32,052 =	Parsons I. R.		
Phaeton	Vickers	Vickers	Mar.'13	Feb. '15	34,595 =	Parsons I. R.		
Undaunted	Fairfield	Fairfield	Dec. '12	Sep.'14	32,161 = 27·5	Brown-Curtis		

General Notes.—Built under 1912 Estimates.   Arethusa of this class lost in the War.   All have tripod masts.   Very
cramped internally.

F 2

(CHATHAM CLASS—LATER SHIPS.)

BIRMINGHAM (May, 1913), **LOWESTOFT** (April, 1913).

Displacement, 5440 tons.   Complement, 433.

Length (*p.p.*), 430 feet.   Beam, $49\frac{5}{8}$ feet. $\left\{ \begin{array}{l} \textit{Mean draught, } 15\frac{3}{4} \text{ feet.} \\ \textit{Max. } \quad \text{,, } \quad 17\frac{1}{2} \text{ ,,} \end{array} \right\}$ Length *over all*, 457 feet.

Guns :
9—6 inch (**Dir. Con.**)
1—3 inch anti-aircraft
4—3 pdr.
2 machine
Torpedo tubes (21 inch) :
2 submerged

Armour (Nickel and H.T.) :
3″ Side (amidships) ....
$1\frac{1}{2}$″ Side (forward) ....
$1\frac{3}{4}$″ Side (aft) ....

(C.T. removed).

BIRMINGHAM.

Photo, Dr. B. H. Pidcock.

Ahead :
2 to 4—6 in.

Broadside, 5—6 in., 1—21 in. tube.

Astern :
3 to 5—6 in.

Machinery : Parsons turbine. Boilers : 12 Yarrow. Designed H.P. 25,000 = 25·5 kts.
Coal : *normal,*   tons ; *maximum,* 1165 tons + 235 tons oil = 4680 miles at 10 kts.

Name	Builder	Machinery	Laid down	Com-pleted	Trials : Full power.	Boilers	Best recent speed
Birmingham	Elswick	Hawthorn	June'12	Jan. '14	26,519 = 25·5	Yarrow	23
Lowestoft	Chatham Y.	Fairfield	July, '12	Apl., '14	26,350 = 25·6	Yarrow	24

Belong to 1911 Estimates.   Average cost of above two ships £356,768.   *Nottingham* of this class sunk in the War.

LOWESTOFT.

Following Notes also for *Southampton, Dublin* and *Chatham* (next page) :—

Armour Notes.—Vertical side plating from 2 ft. 7 in. below w.l. to (*a*) upper deck amidships, (*b*) 3 ft. below upper deck fore and aft.   Armour is really 2″ nickel amidships, 1″ forward and aft, but side plating is added for total thicknesses given.

Machinery Notes.—Impulse reaction turbines, viz., on each shaft, one ahead impulse turbine plus an ahead reaction turbine, an impulse astern turbine and an astern reaction turbine.

(CHATHAM CLASS—EARLIER SHIPS.)

SOUTHAMPTON (May, 1912), **DUBLIN** (April, 1912), **CHATHAM** (Nov., 1911).

Displacement, 5400 tons.   Complement, 429-440.

Length (*p.p.*), 430 feet.   Beam, 49⅚ feet. {Mean draught, 15¾ feet. / Max. „ 17' 8"} Length *over all*, 457 feet.

Guns :
8—6 inch (M. XI)
1—3 inch anti-aircraft
4—3 pdr.
4 or 2 machine
(1 landing).
Torpedo tubes (21 inch) :
2 submerged

Armour :
2" Deck on slopes ....
3" Side (amidships).........

C.T. may have been re-placed by aeroplane plat-form.

Ahead :
3—6 in.

Broadside: 5—6 inch, 1—21 inch tube.

Astern :
3—6 in.

Machinery : Curtis turbine in *Southampton*, 2 screws ; others Parsons, 4 screws. Boilers : Yarrow. Designed H.P. 25,000 = 25·5 kts. Coal : *normal* 750 tons ; *maximum* 1240 tons + 260 tons oil.

Name	Builder	Machinery	Laid down	Completed	Trials ⅘ power.	Full power.	Boilers	Best recent speed
Southampton	Clydebank	Clydebank	Apl. '11	Feb. '13	23,607 =	26,006 = 26·5	Yarrow in all.	24
Dublin	Beardmore	Beardmore	Apl. '11	Mar. '13	22,606 =	26,041 = 25·7		
Chatham	Chatham	Thames I.W.	Jan. '11	Dec. '12	23,127 =	25,901 = 25·7		

Belong to 1910 Estimates. Average cost £334,053. Tripod masts fitted to all. Australian *Melbourne, Sydney, Brisbane* and *Adelaide* are similar ships.

WEYMOUTH.   (WEYMOUTH CLASS.)
WEYMOUTH (Nov., 1910), **YARMOUTH** (April, 1911), **DARTMOUTH** (Feb., 1911).

Displacement, 5250 tons.   Complement, 433.

Length (*p.p.*), 430 feet.   Beam, 48½ feet. {Mean draught, 15 feet. / Max. „ 17½ „} Length *over all*, 453 feet.

Guns (**Dir. Con.**) :
8—6 inch (M. XI)
1—3 inch anti-aircraft
4—3 pdr.
4 machine
(1 landing)
Torpedo tubes (21 inch) :
2 submerged.

Armour : (Nickel)
2" Deck Amidships ..
1"—¾ Deck (ends) ...
(C.T. removed).. ....

Ahead :
3—6 in.

Broadside: 5—6 inch, 1—21 inch tube.

Astern :
3—6 in.

Machinery : Parsons turbine (compound re-action), 4 screws, except *Yarmouth*, Curtis, 2 screws. Boilers : 12 Yarrow. Designed H.P. 22,000 = 25 kts. Coal : *normal* 750 tons ; *maximum* 1290 tons + 260 tons oil = 5600 miles at 10 kts.

Name	Builder	Machinery	Laid down	Completed	Trials 30 hrs. at 3/4	8 hrs. full power	Boilers	Best recent speed
Dartmouth	Vickers	Vickers	Feb. '10	Oct. '11	18,839 = 24·95	23,467 = 25·90	Yarrow	23·24
Weymouth	Elswick	Parsons Tur. Co.	Jan. '10	Oct. '11	18,076 =	23,532 = 25·60		
Yarmouth	London & Glas. Co.	L. & G. Co.	Jan. '10	Apl. '12	=	24,000 = 26·00		

General Notes.—These three belong to the 1909 Estimates. Average cost £393,363. *Falmouth* of this class sunk in the war.

LIVERPOOL.   (Pre-War Photo, but shows S.L. on Foremast.)   *Photo, Symonds & Co.*

(BRISTOL OR "TOWN" CLASS.)

BRISTOL (Feb., 1910), **GLASGOW** (Sept., 1909), **GLOUCESTER** (Oct., 1909),
LIVERPOOL (Oct., 1909), and **NEWCASTLE** (Nov., 1909).

Displacement, 4800 tons. Complement, 411.

Length (*p.p.*), 430 feet. Beam, 47 feet. $\left\{\begin{array}{l}\textit{Mean draught, } 15\frac{1}{4}\textit{ feet.}\\ \textit{Max. ,, } 17\frac{3}{4}\textit{ ,,}\end{array}\right\}$ Length *over all*, 453 feet.

Guns (**Dir. Con.**) :
  2—6 inch (M. XI)
  10—4 inch (M. VIII)
  1—3 inch (anti-aircraft)
  4—3 pdr.
  4 (or 2) machine
  (1 landing).
Torpedo tubes (18 inch) :
  2 *submerged.*

Armour (Cast or Nickel) :
  2″ 1¾″ ¾″ Deck..............
  6″ Conning tower ....
  4″ Tube ....

Ahead :
1—6 in.
2—4 in.

Astern :
1—6 in.
2—4 in.

Broadside: 2—6 in., 5—4 in., 1—18 in., tube.

Machinery: Turbine, Parsons in all, 4 screws; except Curtis in *Bristol*, 2 screws. Boilers: 12 Yarrow, small tube. Designed H.P. 22,000 = 25 kts. Coal: *normal* 600 tons; *maximum* 1353 tons + 260 tons oil. Built under 1908 Estimates.

NEWCASTLE.   (No topmast to mainmast.)

BRISTOL.   (Big top to foremast.)

Name	Builder	Machinery	Laid down	Com-pleted	Trials: ⅘ power.	Full power.	Boilers
Bristol	Brown	Brown	Mar.'09	Feb.'11	14,300 = 24·06	24,227 = 26·84	Yarrow
Glasgow	Fairfield	Fairfield	Mar.'09	Jan.'11	14,055 = 23·7	22,472 = 25·8	in
Gloucester	Beardmore	Beardmore	Apl.'09	Jan.'11	13,968 = 23·447	24,335 = 26·296	all.
Liverpool	Vickers	Vickers	Feb.'09	Oct.'10	13,970 = 23·883	24,718 = 26·171	
Newcastle	Elswick	Wallsend Co.	Mar.'09	Oct.'10	14,038 = 23·342	24,669 = 26·266	

FEARLESS.

BLANCHE.

(BOADICEA TYPE—LAST TWO.)

ACTIVE (March, 1911), **FEARLESS** (June, 1912).

Displacement, 3440 tons. Complement, 325-321.

Length, (*p.p.*) 385, (*o.a.*) 406 feet. Beam, 41½ feet. *Max.* draught, 15 feet 7 ins.

Guns :
Fearless 8— } 4 inch M. VII.
Active 10—
1—3 inch anti-aircraft
4—3 pdr.
1 machine gun
Torpedo tubes (21 inch) :
  2 *above water*

Armour (Hadfield) :
1″ Deck ....
4″ Conning tower......
2½″ Tube ....

" Fearless " attached to Submarines.

(Plan as *Blanche* and *Blonde*).

(BOADICEA TYPE).

BLANCHE (November, 1909), **BLONDE** (July, 1910).

Normal displacement, 3350 tons. Complement, 314.

Length, (*p.p.*) 385, (*o.a.*) 405 feet. Beam, 41½ feet. *Max.* draught, 15½ feet.

Guns :
  8—4 inch (M. VII)
  1—4 inch anti-aircraft
  4— 3 pdr.
  1 machine.
Torpedo tubes (18 inch) :
  2 *above water*

Armour (Hadfield) :
1½″ Deck ....
4″ Conning tower
2½″ Tube..... ......

Machinery : Parsons turbine. Boilers : 12 Yarrow (small tube). Designed H.P. 18,000 = 25 kts. Coal : *normal* 350 tons ; *maximum* 780 tons. Also 190 tons oil. Built under 1911 Estimates. *Amphion* of this class sunk, August, 1914.

Name	Builder	Machinery	Laid down	Completed	Trials Full power.		Boilers	Best recent speed
Active	Pembroke	Hawthorn	July, '10	Dec. '11		19,803=25·1	} Yarrow in both	—
Fearless	Pembroke	Beardmore	Nov., '11	Oct. '13	19,697=25·4 &	19,489=25·9		—

Machinery : Parsons turbine. Boilers : 12 Yarrow. Designed H.P. 18,000 = 24-25 kts. Coal : *normal*, 450 tons ; *maximum*, 780 tons coal + 190 tons oil. Both built under 1909 Estimates.

Name	Builder	Machinery	Laid down	Completed	Trials		Boilers	Best recent speed
					30 hrs.	8 hrs.		
Blanche	Pembroke, Y.	Hawthorn	Ap. '09	1910	15,000=22·3	18,542=25·67	} Yarrow small tube	26·1
Blonde	Pembroke, Y.	Laird	Dec. '09	1911		18,772=25·3		

Note to Plans.—2—4 inch removed, but from which positions is not yet known.

(BOADICEA TYPE.)

BOADICEA (May, 1908).

Normal displacement, 3300 tons. Complement, 317.

Length (*p.p.*), 385 feet. (*o.a.* 405). Beam, 41 feet. *Mean* draught, 13½ feet (14⅝ *max.*).

Guns:
  10—4 inch (M. VII.)
  1—4 inch anti-aircraft
  4—3 pdr.
  1 machine.
Torpedo tubes (18 inch):
  2 *above water*

Armour: (Hadfield).
  1″ Deck ....
  4″ C.T. ....
  2½″ Tube ......

Machinery: Parsons turbine   Boilers: 12 Yarrow.   Designed H.P. 18,000 = 25 kts.   Coal: *normal*, 450 tons; *maximum*, 855 tons coal + 200 tons oil.

Name	Builder	Machinery	Laid down	Completed	Trials (mean) Full power.	Boilers	Best recent speed
Boadicea	Pembroke Y	Clydebank	July'07	1909	18,536 = 25·5	Yarrow	27·9

1907 Estimates; *Bellona*, (1908 Estimates.) for sale 1919.

NOTE.—All the old Light Cruisers of "Sentinel" type given below will not be used again for Fleet Service except in emergency.

ADVENTURE (Sept., 1904). By Elswick. Displacement, 2670 tons. Dimensions: 374 × 38¼ × 13½ feet (*maximum* draught). Complement, 301. Guns: 2—6 inch, 6—4 inch, 1—3 inch AA., 1—6 pdr., 2—2 pdr. AA. Torpedo tubes (14 inch): 2 *above water*. Armour: 2″ Deck. Machinery: 2 sets 6 cylinder. 2 screws. Boilers: ⅘ Yarrow curved, ⅕ cylindrical. *About* H.P. 16,000 = 25·5 kts. Coal: *normal*, 150 tons; *maximum*, 455 tons. *Attentive* for Sale.

FORESIGHT (Oct., 1904). By Fairfield. Displacement, 2850 tons. Dimensions: 360 × 39¼ × 15⅓ feet (*maximum* draught). Complement, 298. Guns: 9—4 inch (M. VII), 1—3 inch AA. Torpedo tubes (14 inch): 2 *above water*. Armour: 2″ Belt amidships, 1½″—⅝″ Deck. Machinery: 2 sets 6 cylinder. 2 screws. *About* H.P. 15,000 = 25¼ kts. Coal: *normal*, 150 tons; *maximum*, 500 tons. *Forward* for Sale.

SENTINEL (April, 1904) and **SKIRMISHER** (Feb., 1905). Both by Vickers, Ltd. Displacement, 2895 tons. Dimensions: 360 × 40 × 14¾ feet (*maximum* draught). Complement, 298. Guns (M. VII): 9—4 inch and (in *Sentinel*) 1—3 inch AA., 1—6 pdr. AA., 1—3 pdr. AA., (in *Skirmisher*) 1—3 inch AA., 1—6 pdr. Torpedo tubes (14 inch): 2 *above water*. Armour: 1½″—⅝″ Deck. Machinery: 2 sets 4 cylinder. 2 screws. H.P. *about* 17,000 = 25 kts. Coal: *normal*, 160 tons; *maximum*, 410 tons.

HIGHFLYER (June, 1898). Large re-fit, 1919. 5600 tons. Complement, 450. Dimensions: 350 (p.p.) × 54 × 22 feet (*max.* draught). Guns : 11—6 inch wire (M. VII, VIII), 6—12 pdr., 4—3 pdr., 4 Maxims, 1 landing. Torpedo tubes (18 inch) : 2 *submerged.* Armour : 3″ Armour deck, Protection to vitals, 5″ Engine hatches, 6″ Conning tower. Machinery : 2 sets 4 cylinder triple expansion. 2 screws. Boilers : Belleville. Designed H.P. 10,000 = 19·5 kts. Coal : *normal,* 500 tons ; *maximum,* 1120 tons. Complement, 481.

Photo, N. O'Toole, Esq.

(ASTRÆA CLASS.)

FOX (— 1893). 4360 tons (sheathed and coppered). Complement, 318. Dimensions : (p.p.) 320 × 49½ × 21½ feet (*max.* draught). Armament : 2—6 inch, 8—4·7 inch, 1—12 pdr., 2—6 pdr., 1—3 pdr., 4 M.G., 1 landing. Torpedo tubes (18 inch) : 3 *above water* (*may be removed*). Armour : 2″ Deck, 5″ Engine hatches, 3″ Conning tower. Designed H.P. (*f.d.*) 9000 = 19·5 kts. Coal : *maximum,* 1000 tons. Built under Naval Defence Act, 1889. *Hermione,* Depot Ship at Southampton.

OLD BRITISH LIGHT CRUISERS.

NOTE:—All old Light Cruisers given below assigned to Special Service, 1919, but will only serve for Harbour Duties. Fighting value nil. Ships deleted since last Edition are for sale.

(TOPAZE CLASS.)

TOPAZE (July, 1903), **AMETHYST** (Nov., 1903). Displacement, 3000 tons. Complement, 290-300. Dimensions : 360 × 40 × 14½ feet (*mean* draught). Guns : *Topaze,* 12—4 inch, 1—6 pdr. AA., 2—3 pdr. AA., 1—6 pdr., 3 M.G. ; *Amethyst,* 2—6 inch, 8—4 inch, 2—3 pdr., 3 M.G. Torpedo tubes (18 inch) : 2 *above water.* Armour (steel) : 2″ Deck. Machinery : 2 sets triple expansion, except *Amethyst,* Parsons turbine. 2 screws. Boilers : Normand-Laird in *Topaze,* Yarrow in *Amethyst.* Max. H.P. *Topaze,* 9800 = 22·2 kts. ; *Amethyst,* 12,000 = 23·4 kts. nominal. Coal : *normal,* 300 tons ; *maximum,* 750 tons. Built under 1902-3 Estimates.

HYACINTH. As *Highflyer* opposite.

(TALBOT CLASS.)

TALBOT (April, 1895), **VENUS** (Sept., 1895), **DORIS** (March, 1896). Displacement, 5600 tons. Complement, 393. Dimensions : 364 (*w.l.*) × 54 × 23 feet (*max.* draught). Length over all, 370⅓ feet. Guns : 9—6 inch, 45 cal. M. VII, 4—12 pdr., 12 cwt., 1—3 pdr., 2 M.G. Torpedo tubes (18 inch) : 2 *submerged,* 1 *above water* (stern). Armour : 2½″ Armour deck, Protection to vitals, 6″ Engine hatches, 6″ Conning tower (Harvey). Machinery : 2 sets inverted triple expansion. 2 screws. Boilers : 8 single-ended cylindrical. Designed H.P. *natural* 8000 = 18·5 kts. ; *forced* 9600 = 19·5 kts. Coal : *normal,* 550 tons ; *maximum,* 1065 tons.

ASTRÆA. As *Fox* opposite.

(APOLLO CLASS.)

ANDROMACHE (1890), **LATONA** (1890), **NAIAD** (1890). 3400 tons. Complement, 273. Dimensions : (p.p.) 300 × 43⅔ × 18 feet. Guns : 1 small. Armour : 2″ Deck. Designed H.P. 7000 = 18·5 kts. (nat.) ; 9000 = 20 kts. (f.d.). Coal : *maximum,* 560 tons. Built under Naval Defence Act, 1889. Converted to Minelayers about 1910, but not so used now.

Coast Defence Vessel.

GORGON (ex *Nidaros*, 9th June, 1914).

Displacement, 5700 tons. Complement, 303.
Length (*o.a.*), 310 feet. Beam, 73¾ feet. *Max.* Draught, 16½ feet.

Guns (Elswick) :
2—9·2 inch
6—6 inch
2—3 inch anti-aircraft.
4—2 pdr. pom-poms.

Armour :
*7″ Belt ....
*4″ Ends ....
2″ Deck ....
4″ Citadel ....
8″ Turrets ....
6″ Secondary guns ....
8″ Fore C.T. ....
6″ Aft C.T. ....
* Not fitted ?

Machinery : Triple expansion. 2 screws. Boilers : Yarrow. Designed H.P. 4000 = 13 kts.
Coal : *maximum* 364 tons + 170 tons oil.

Name	Builder	Machinery	Begun	Completed	Trials.
Gorgon	Armstrong	H. Leslie	June, 1913	June, 1918	

Notes.—There were originally two ships in this class, begun at Elswick in May-June, 1913, for the Norwegian Navy, as the Coast Service Battleships *Bjoergvin* and *Nidaros*. Construction was stopped when war began, and they lay in the Tyne in an incomplete condition until 1915, when they were taken over for the British Navy and named *Glatton* (ex *Bjoergvin*) and *Gorgon* (ex *Nidaros*). *Glatton* blew up at Dover during September, 1918. As originally designed, this ship had a beam of 55¾ feet and a speed of 15 kts. Beam has been increased and speed reduced by the addition of "blisters" to the hull. The belt may never have been fitted.

Monitors

 EREBUS.

EREBUS (19th June, 1916), TERROR (18th May, 1916).

Displacement, 8000 tons. Complements, 226 and 223.
Length, (*p.p.*) 380, (*o.a.*) 405 feet. Beam, 88 feet. *Mean* Draught, 11 feet.

Guns :
2—15 inch, 42 cal. (**Dir. Con.**)
8—4 inch
2—12 pdr.
2—3 inch (anti-aircraft)
2—2 pdr. (anti-aircraft)
4 M.G.

Armour :
4″ Bulkheads, F. & A.
8″ Barbettes ....
13″-4¼″ Gunhouses ....

4″ Box Citadel (over magazines) ......
6″ C.T. ....
1″ Fo'xle & Upper D'ks
4″ Main Deck (Slopes)
2″ Main Deck ......
1½″-¾″ Lower Deck ..
Anti-torpedo Pro.
Bulges

Machinery : Triple expansion. 2 screws. Boilers : Babcock. Designed H.P. 6000 = 12 kts.
Fuel : 650 tons *normal*, 750 tons, *maximum*, oil only.

Gunnery Notes.—15 inch are high angle and can range up to 40,000 yards. Smoke screen apparatus fitted. *Erebus* has 15 inch removed from *M. Ney.*
Special Protection.—Bulges about 15 feet deep, sub-divided into 50 w.t.c. *Erebus* hit full amidships by distance-controlled boat, carrying heavy charge. Was repaired in a fortnight and rails were fitted to "blisters" of both ships to prevent distance-controlled boats riding up blisters. *Terror* hit by three torpedoes in succession—2 right forward beyond bulge protection inflicted heavy damage. The third torpedo hit the bulge and did no harm at all.

Name	Builder and Machinery	Begun	Completed	Trials
Erebus	Harland & Wolff (Govan)	Oct., 1915	Sept., 1916	7244 H.P. = 14·1 kts.
Terror	Harland & Wolff (Belfast)	Oct., 1915	Aug., 1916	6235 H.P. = 13·1 kts.

General Notes.—Both Emergency War Programme. Designed as an improved "Abercrombie" type to outrange the 15 and 11 inch guns mounted by Germans on Belgian Coast. Their speed, considering their great beam, is remarkable. Were the "crack" monitors of the famous Dover Patrol.
Cancelled 1918.—Large monitor (unnamed) by Messrs. Wm. Hamilton.

M. Ney.
Guns : Has only 6—6 inch, 2—3 inch AA., 2—3 pdr. AA.

See Addenda pages.

M. Soult.
Guns : 2—15 inch (Dir. Con., H. A. elevation), 8—4 inch, 2—12 pdr., 2—3 inch AA., 2—2 pdr. AA.

MARSHAL NEY (24th August, 1915), MARSHAL SOULT (17th June, 1915).

Displacement, 6670 tons. Complements, *M. Ney* 186, *M. Soult*, 228.

Length, 340 (*p.p.*), 355⅔ (*o.a.*) feet. Beam, 90¼ feet. Draught, 10½ feet.

Guns : As noted above. Armour : in *Soult* only, 8″ Barbette, 13″—4¼″ Gunhouse : in both, 4″ Bulkheads fore and aft, 6″ C.T., 4″—1″ Box Citadel over Magazine, 1″ Fo'xle Deck, 2″—1½″ Upper Deck, Lower Deck 3″ at bow, 1½″ at stern, 1″ Navig. Position. Deep Bulge Protection.

Machinery : 2 sets Diesel. 2 screws. Designed H.P 1500 = 6-7 kts. Fuel : 235 tons, *maximum* oil only.

Name	Builder	Machinery	Begun	Completed	Trials
M. Ney	Palmer	White	Jan., 1915	Aug., 1915	2309 H.P. = 6·3 kts.
M. Soult	Palmer	Vickers	Jan., 1915	Nov., 1915	1898 H.P. = 6·6 kts.

General Notes.—Emergency War Programme. *M. Ney* practically a failure, on account of her engines being highly unreliable. 15 inch guns and barbette removed from her about 1917, and she was moored as Guard-Ship in the Downs.

Sir John Moore.

GENERAL CRAUFURD (8th July, 1915), SIR JOHN MOORE (31st May, 1915).

Displacement, 5900 tons. Complements, 237.

Length, 320 (*p.p.*), 335½ (*o.a.*) feet. Beam, 87¼ feet. Draught, 10½ feet.

Guns :
2—12 inch, M. VIII, 25 cal.
4 to 2—6 inch
2—12 pdr.
2—3 inch AA.
2—2 pdr. anti-aircraft.
4 M.G.

Armour (Krupp) :
6″ Bulkheads F. & A..
8″—2″ Barbettes ......
10½″—2″ Gunhouse...
6″ Conning tower ...
1″ Foxle deck ....
6″ Upper deck (slopes)
2″ Upper deck ....
1½″ Main deck ....
Anti-torpedo protection :
Deep bulges.

Machinery : Triple expansion. 2 screws. Boilers : Babcock & Wilcox. Designed H.P. 2310 (?) = 6-7 kts. 2 screws. Coal : 350 tons, *maximum*.

General Notes.—Emergency War Programme. Armed with 12 inch from old *Majestics*. These Monitors are extremely slow and unwieldy—in fact against a strong head wind and sea, they can only make 1 or 2 kts. But most remarkably steady gun platforms, on account of their huge beam and bulges.

Name	Builder and Machinery	Begun	Completed	Trials
Gen. Craufurd	Harland & Wolff (Belfast)	Jan., 1915	Aug., 1915	2523 H.P. = 7·4 kts.
Sir Jno. Moore	Scotts S.B. Co.	Jan., 1915	July, 1915	2500 H.P. = 7·75 kts.

Special Note.—All other Monitors of *Abercrombie* (14 inch) type and *Earl of Peterborough* (12 inch) type on Disposal List, 1919—not required for War Fleet and will be broken up soon.

Monitors.

M 29, M 31 (Workman Clark), **M 32, M 33** (Harland & Wolff, Belfast). All launched and completed during 1915. 535 tons. Complement, 75. Dimensions : 170 × 31 × 6¾ feet. Guns : 2—6 inch (1—3 inch AA. in *M 31, M 33*), 1—6 pdr. AA., 4 or 2 M.G. Designed H.P. 400 = 10 kts. Machinery : Triple expansion. 2 screws. Boilers : Yarrow. Oil fuel : 45 tons. *M 30* lost during the War.

Notes.—All Emergency War Programme.

M 23 (with 7·5 inch gun).

For description, v. next column.

Monitors--*continued.*

For photo, see Addenda pages.

M 19, M 20, M 22, M 23, M 24, M 25, M 26, M 27. All built by Sir Raylton Dixon & Co. Launched May-September, 1915. Completed May-October, 1915. 540 tons. Complement, 67-82. Dimensions : 170 × 31 × 6 feet. Guns : *M 19—20* as *M 16—18* below, *M 22* also as those below, but 1—12 pdr. and 1—3 pdr. extra. *M 23—26*, 1—7·5 inch, 1 or 2—3 inch AA., 1—12 pdr. and (in some) 1—6 pdr. or 2—2 pdr. AA., or pom-pom, 2 M.G. *M 27*, 1—4.7 inch, 2—3 inch AA., 2—2 pdr. pom-pom, 2 M.G. Machinery : *M 19—20, 23—27*. Bolinders oil engines, 640 B.H.P. *M 22*, triple expansion engines and White-Forster boilers. I.H.P. 650. 4 screws in *M 24, 26, 27*, 2 in others. Speed : 12 kts. in all. Oil : 25-28 tons. *M 22* and *M 28* of this class lost during the War.

For photo, see Addenda pages.

M 16, M 17, M 18. Built by Messrs. Gray & Co. Launched April-May, 1915, completed June-July, 1915 Guns : 1—9·2 inch, 1—3 inch AA., 2 M.G. I.H.P. 800 = 12 kts. Triple expansion engines. 2 screws. Boilers : Loco. Oil : 32 tons. All other details as *M 19—27* above, from which they differ in appearance. *M 15* lost during the War.

General Notes.—All Emergency War Programme.

Armoured Gunboat.

Photo, Abrahams, Devonport.

HUMBER (ex *Jarary*, Vickers, 1913). 1260 tons. Dimensions : 261 (*p.p.*), 266¾ (*o.a.*) × 49 × 5⅔ feet. Guns : 3—6 inch, 2—4·7 inch howitzers, 4—3 pdr., 1—3 pdr. AA. Armour : 2″ sides, ″ Barbette, ″ C.T. Upper deck is protective. H.P. 1450 = 12 kts. Boilers : Yarrow. Coal : 187 tons + 90 tons oil fuel.

General Notes.—Brazilian River Monitor *Jarary*. Purchased 1914. 1—6 inch gun (salved from old wrecked *Montagu*) was added, mounted on quarter deck. Purchased for British Navy on outbreak of war. Designed for service on the Amazon, S. America, but has actually taken part in several coastal bombardments and other operations entailing long sea voyages. Sister ships, *Mersey* (ex *Madera*), *Severn* (ex *Solimoes*), on Sale List, 1919.

Large China Gunboats.

LADYBIRD.   (INSECT CLASS—12 BOATS.)

APHIS (1915), **BEE** (1916), **CICALA** (December, 1915), **COCKCHAFER** (December, 1915), **CRICKET** (December, 1915), **GLOWWORM** (February, 1916). All by Barclay Curle.

GNAT (1915), **LADYBIRD** (1915). Both by Messrs. Lobnitz.

MANTIS (1915), **MOTH** (1915). Both by Sunderland S.B. Co.

SCARAB (1915), **TARANTULA** (1915). Both by Wood, Skinner & Co.

645 tons. Complement, 53. Dimensions : 230 (*p.p.*), 237½ (*o.a.*) × 36 × 4 feet. Guns : 2—6 inch, 2—12 pdr., 6 M.G. ; also 2—3 inch AA. in a few. Machinery : Triple expansion. Twin screws in tunnels fitted with Messrs. Yarrow's patent balanced flap. Boilers : Yarrow. Designed H.P. 2000 = 14 kts. Fuel (coal or oil) : 35 tons coal + 65 tons oil.

Notes.—Emergency War Programme. Ordered February, 1915. Completed November, 1915-April, 1916. Built to Yarrow design under Messrs. Yarrow's supervision. Originally intended that these boats should proceed to Salonika, be dismantled, transported in sections overland and be re-erected and re-floated on a tributary of the Danube, to fight the Austro-Hungarian Danube Flotilla. To conceal their objective, they were ordered as River Gunboats for the Chinese Rivers—hence their name of " China Gunboats." Several were towed out to Malta, but the great " drive " by the enemy armies through Serbia stopped these plans. These ships then proceeded to the Tigris and Euphrates. *Glowworm* badly injured by explosion, 1919, on Dvina River.

Small China Gunboats.

SEDGEFLY.   (FLY CLASS—16 BOATS.)

BLACKFLY, BUTTERFLY, CADDISFLY, CRANEFLY, DRAGONFLY, FIREFLY, GADFLY, GRAYFLY, GREENFLY, HOVERFLY, MAYFLY, SAWFLY, SEDGEFLY, SNAKEFLY, STONEFLY, WATERFLY. Built by Messrs. Yarrow, Ltd., in sections, shipped out to Mesopotamia and erected at Abadan, 1915-6—See *Notes* below. 98 tons. Complement, 22. Dimensions : 120 (*p.p.*), 126 (*o.a.*) × 20 × 2 feet. Guns : 1—4 inch, 1—12 pdr., 1—6 pdr. (not in all), 1—3 pdr. AA., 1—2 pdr. pom-pom, 5 or 4 M.G. Machinery : 1 set triple expansion engines. Single screw in tunnel fitted with Messrs. Yarrow's patent balanced flap. Boilers : 1 Yarrow, burning coal or oil. Designed H.P. 175 = 9·5 kts. Fuel : 5 tons coal + 10 tons oil.

Notes.—Twelve of these craft are said to have been ordered by the Admiralty in February, 1915, from Messrs. Yarrow, Ltd. They were intended to police the Tigris against Arab guerillas. After capture of *Firefly* by Turks, the number was increased to 16. *Firefly* was re-captured in the British advance from Kut-el-Amara to Bagdad. They were built in sections and shipped out, the port and starboard sections being numbered and painted red and green, to facilitate erection by native labour at Abadan. *Firefly* began to be erected August, 1915, and entered service in November of the same year. The last of the original twelve were shipped out in August, 1915, and were in service by March, 1916, the extra four (*Blackfly, Caddisfly, Hoverfly, Sedgefly*) following them later. All Emergency War Programme. Eight of these transferred to War Office.

			Begun.	Sent out.					Begun.	Sent out.
Blackfly	..	..	12/15	4/16	*Greenfly*	..	..	..	2/15	9/15
Butterfly	..	..	2/15	7/15	*Hoverfly*	..	..	..	11/15	4/16
Caddisfly	..	..	12/15	4/16	*Mayfly*	..	..	..	2/15	8/15
Cranefly	..	..		7/15	*Sawfly*	..	..	..	2/15	8/15
Dragonfly	..	..		7/15	*Sedgfley*	..	...	...	11/15	9/16
Firefly	..	..	2/15	7/15	*Snakefly*	..	..	..		
Gadfly	..	..		8/15	*Stonefly*	..	..	..	2/15	9/15
Grayfly	..	..		8/15	*Waterfly*	..	..	..		

River Gunboats.

WIDGEON (1904). 180 tons. Dimensions: $165 \times 24\frac{1}{2} \times 2\frac{1}{2}$ feet. Also **TEAL** (1901) & **MOORHEN** (1901). 180 tons. Dimensions: $165 \times 24\frac{1}{2} \times 2\frac{1}{4}$ feet. Armament: 2—6 pdr. and 4 M.G. Bullet-proof hull, &c. H.P. 670 = 13 kts. Complement, 37—31. Coal: 39—36 tons.

KINSHA (bought 1900). 616 tons. $192\frac{1}{4} \times 30 \times 6\frac{3}{4}$ feet. Guns: 2—12 pdr., 7 Maxims. H.P. 1200 = 14 kts. Coal: 65 tons. Complement, 58.

WOODCOCK (1897) & **WOODLARK** (1897). 150 tons. Dimensions: $148\frac{1}{2} \times 24 \times 2$ feet. Armament: 2—6 pdr., 4 M.G. Bullet-proof hull, etc. H.P. 550 = 13 kts. Coal: 28 tons. Complement, 26.

Photo by favour of Lt. Com. Hutton.

NIGHTINGALE, ROBIN, SANDPIPER, SNIPE (all 1897). 85 tons. $107\frac{3}{4} \times 20 \times 2$ feet. Guns: 2—6 pdr., 4 M.G. H.P. 240 = 9 kts. Coal: 11 tons. Complement, 25.

Gunboats : 1st Class.

HUSSAR (1894), ex-Torpedo Gunboat. Serves as Yacht and Despatch Vessel, C-in-C., Mediterranean. 1070 tons. Guns: 1—4·7 inch, 2—12 pdr., 1—6 pdr. AA. I.H.P. 2500 = 17·5 kts. Coal : 190 tons. Complement, 190.

Note.— Similar vessels, *Circe, Gossamer, Speedwell, Skipjack, Spanker, Seda,* are on Disposal List, 1919. *Halcyon* on Sale List.

BRAMBLE, BRITOMART, DWARF, THISTLE (1898-99). 710 tons. Complement, 90. Dimensions : $187\frac{1}{2} \times 33 \times 9\frac{3}{4}$ feet. Guns : 2—4 inch, 4—12 pdr., 4 or 6 machine. Designed H.P. 1300 = 13·9 kts. Yarrow boilers. Coal : 145 tons.

Gunboat **SPHINX** given as Despatch Vessel among miscellaneous pages at end of British Navy Section.

Gunboats : 3rd Class.

Old *Blazer, Bloodhound, Banterer* (ex *Plucky*), *Bustard, Kite,* &c., still exist, but are only used for subsidiary duties.

Old Sloops.

Note.—Fleet Sweeping Vessels (Sloops are listed after the Submarine Section on later pages).

Photo, G. M. Carter, Esq.

CADMUS, CLIO, ESPIEGLE, ODIN (1900-03). 1070 tons. Complement, 121—112. 6—4 inch, 4—3 pdr. (*Espiegle* and *Odin* 4—4 inch *only*), 2 or 3 M.G. I.H.P. 1400 = 13¼ kts. Boilers: first two, Niclausse; other two, Babcock. Coal: 195—225 tons.

Photo, Symonds.

VESTAL & **RINALDO** (1890-1898). 980 tons. 4—4 inch, 4—3 pdr., 1 M.G. I.H.P. 1400 = 13·5 kts. Belleville boilers. Coal : 160 tons. Complement, 40.

No photo available.

ALERT (1893-95). 960 tons. 4—4 inch, 4—3 pdr., 3 M.G. I.H.P. 1400 = 13·5 kts. Coal : 156 tons. Complement, 107.

(KIL CLASS—81 BOATS.)

4 *G. Brown & Co.:* **KILBERRY** (July, 1918), **KILBEGGAN** (September, 1918), **KILBIRNIE** (————), **KILBRACHAN.**

21 *Cochrane:* **KILDALKEY** (March, 1918), **KILDARE** (April, 1918), **KILDANGAN** (March, 1918), **KILDONAN** (April, 1918), **KILDRESS** (April, 1918), **KILDWICK** (April, 1918), **KILFINNY** May, (1918), **KILFREE** (————), **KILGOWAN** (————), **KILKEE** (————), **KILKENNY** (————), **KILKENZIE** (————), **KILKERRIN** (————), **KILHAMPTON** (————), **KILLADOON** (————), **KILLIGAN** (————), **KILLALOO** (————), **KILLANE** **KILLARNEY** (————), **KILLARY** (————), **KILLEGAN** (————).

14 *Cook, Welton & Gemmell:* **KILCHATTAN** (April, 1918), **KILCHVAN** (————), **KILCLIEF** (May, 1919), **KILCLOGHER** (————), **KILCOLGAN**(————), **KILCOMMON** (————), **KILCONNELL** (————), **KILCOOLE** (————), **KILCORNEY** (————), **KILCOT** (————), **KILCREGGAN** (————), **KILCULLEN** (————), **KILCURRIG** (————), **KILDALE** (————).

4 *Hall Russell:* **KILBRIDE** (May, 1918), **KILBURN** (May, 1918), **KILBY** (————), **KILCAVAN** (————),

30 *Smith's Dock Co.:* **KILCHRENAN** (January, 1918), **KILCHREEST** (June, 1918), **KILCLARE** (January, 1918), **KILCOCK** (April, 1918), **KILDARY** (November, 1917), **KILDAVIN** (February, 1918), **KILDIMO** (April, 1918), **KILDORRY** (February, 1918), **KILDOROUGH** (November, 1917), **KILDYSART** (May, 1918), **KILFENORA** (December, 1917), **KILFULLERT** (March, 1918), **KILGARVAN** (May, 1918), **KILGOBNET** (December, 1917), **KILHAM** (June, 1918), **KILKEEL** (March, 1918), **KILLERIG** (July, 1918), **KILLINEY** (July, 1918), **KILLOUR** (August, 1918), **KILMALLOCK** (December, 1918), **KILMANAHAN** (December, 1918), **KILMARNOCK** (March, 1919), **KILMARTEN** (March, 1919), **KILMEAD** (May, 1919), **KILMELFORD** (————, 1919), **KILMERSDON** (————, 1919), **KILMINGTON** (————), **KILMORE** (————), **KILMUCKRIDGE** (————, 1919), **KILMUN** (————, 1919).

8 (*Builders unknown*) **KILDPART** (————), **KILLENA** (July, 1918), **KILLOWEN** (September, 1918), **KILLYBEGS** (September, 1918), **KILLYGORDON** (————), **KILMACRENNAN** (November, 1918), **KILMAINE** (November, 1918), **KILMALCOLM** (October, 1918).

KILDWICK.   *Photo by courtesy of Messrs. Cochrane & Co. (Builders).*

890-893 tons. Complements, 39. Dimensions: 170 (*p.p.*), 182 (*o.a.*) × 30-30¼ × 11¾ feet. Guns: 1—4 inch (1—4·7 inch in a few). Designed H.P. 1400 = 13 kts. Machinery: 1 set inverted triple expansion. 1 screw. Boilers: Cylindrical return tube. Coal: 330 tons.

General Notes.—All Emergency War Programme. Many completed after end of War without armament. Some now serving as Tenders to Training Ships, Schools, &c.; others laid up.

Cancelled boats.—*Kilglass* (Brown), *Kilbrittan, Kilcar, Kilbane, Kilbarchan* (all Hall Russell). Others listed above may have been stopped, September, 1918, but no list available.

N o. in Cla ss.	Class Letter or Type.	First begun.	Last com-pleted.	Displacements. tons.	Dimensions. Length × Beam × Dr'ft. (*o.a.*) (*Max.*)	Designed } =kts. S.H.P. } speed.	Fuel. tons.	Guns. (*aa* = Anti-aircraft.)	Torpedo Tubes. No. and size.	Com-plement.
	Flotilla Leaders :—									
7	*Admiralty " Large Design"*	1917	1919	1801	332½ × 31¾ × —	40,000＝36·5	505/480 *oil*	All 5—4·7 inch 1—3 inch *aa*	All 6—21 inch	All 164
5—3 ?	*Thornycroft (Spenser)*	1916 {	1919 *Bldg ?* }	1740	329 × 31¾ × —	40,000＝36	500/400 *oil*			
6	*Admiralty V*	1916	1917	1316—1339	312 × 29½ × 11¾	27,000＝34	370/320 *oil*	4—4 inch 1—3 inch *aa*	4—21 inch (*Vampire*, 6—21 inch)	115
4	*Marksman (Later)*	1915	1916	1666—1673	325 × 31¾ × 11¾	36,000＝34	510/413 *oil*	4—4 inch 2—2 pdr.	(*Abdiel :* none) 4—21 inch	116
7	*Marksman*	1914	1916	1604—1687						104
3	*Broke (Purchased)*	1912	1915	1694—1742	331¼ × 32¼ × 11½	30,000＝31·32	{ 403 coal 83 *oil*	2—4·7 inch 2—4 inch 2—2 pdr.	4—21 inch	205
1	*Swift*	1907	1910	2207	353 × 34¼ × 13	30,000＝36	385/280 oil	1—6 inch 2—4 inch 1—2 pdr.	2—18 inch	138
	Destroyers :—									
21 ?	*Admiralty (V 4·7 inch)*	1918 {	1919 *Bldg.* }	1300 (average)	312 × 29½ × —	27,000＝34	350/320 *oil*	4—4·7 inch 2—2 pdr.	6—21 inch	127
7	*Yarrow S*	1917	1919	930	269½ × 25¾ × —	23,000＝36	255/215 *oil*	All 3—4 inch 1—2 pdr.	All 4—21 inch	All 90
5	*Thornycroft S*	1917	1919	1087	275¾ × 27⅓ × —	29,000＝36	300/250 *oil*			
50	*Admiralty S*	1917	1919	1075	276 × 26⅔ × —	27,000＝36	300/250 *oil*			
2	*Thornycroft V (six tube)*	1917	1918	1315	312 × 29½ × —	30,000＝35	370/320 *oil*		6—21 inch	127
16	*Admiralty V (six tube)*	1917	1918	1280—1316	312 × 29 × 11¼	27,000＝34	370/320 *oil*	All 4—4 inch 1—3 inch *aa*	6—21 inch	127
2	*Thornycroft V*	1916	1918	1325	312 × 30⅔ × 11¾	30,000＝35	375/325 *oil*		4—21 inch	110
21	*Admiralty V*	1916	1918	1272—1339	312 × 29½ × 11¼	27,000＝34	370/320 *oil*		4—21 inch	110
10	*Admiralty Modified R*	1916	1917	1076—1091	276 × 26¾ × 11¾	27,000＝36	300/250 *oil*			
4	*Yarrow M (Later)*	1915	1917	897—923	271½ × 25¾ × 10½	23,000＝36		All 3—4 inch 1—2 pdr.	All 4—21 inch	All 82
5	*Thornycroft R*	1915	1917	1035	274 × 27⅓ × 11	29,000＝35	285/220 *oil*			
34	*Admiralty R*	1915	1917	1036—1096	275 × 26½ × 11¾	27,000＝36	290/240 *oil*			82
74	*Admiralty M*	1914	1916	994—1042	275 × 26½ × 10½	25,000＝34	265/220 *oil*			80

No. in Class.	Class Letter or Type.	First begun.	Last completed.	Displacements. tons.	Dimensions. Length × Beam × Dr'ft. (o.a.) (max.)			Designed S.H.P. } = kts. speed.	Fuel. tons.	Guns. (aa = Anti-aircraft.)	Torpedo Tubes. No. and size.	Complement.
	Destroyers—continued.											
6	*Thornycroft M*	1913	1916	985—1070	273	× 27½ ×	11	27,500 = 35	275/210 *oil*	All 3—4 inch 1—2 pdr.	All 4—21 inch	82
10	*Yarrow M*	1912	1916	879—898	270	× 26⅓ ×	10⅓	23,000 = 35-36	228/202 *oil*			79
2	*Hawthorn M*	1914	1915	1055	271	× 27 ×	10¾	27,000 = 35	290/220 *oil*			76
3	*Talisman* (ex *Turk*)	1914	1916	1098	309	× 28⅔ ×	9½	25,000 = 32	237 *oil*	5—4 inch	4—21 inch	102
3	*Medea* (ex *Greek*)	1914	1915	1007—1040	273⅓	× 26¼ ×	10¼	25,000 = 32	276/225 *oil*	3—4 inch 1—2 pdr.	4—21 inch	80
17	L (*Lochinvar* L	1915 1912	1915 1914	965—1010	269	× 27½ ×	10½	24,500 = 29	235/270 *oil*	3—4 inch 1—2 pdr. *aa*	4—21 inch	73
13	K { 5 *Special* 9 *Admiralty*	1911 1911	1913 1913	898—996	267½	× 27 ×	10½	22,500 = 31 24,500 = 29	260/196 *oil*	3—4 inch 1—2 pdr.	4—21 inch	73
21	I { 3 *Special* 6 *Builders* 14 *Admiralty*	1910 1910 1910	1912 1912 1912	745—810	262 × 27⅔ × 9½ 246¼ × 25½ × 9			20,000 = 32 16,000 = 29 13,500 = 27	180/140 *oil*	2—4 inch, 2—12 pdr. 1—3 pdr. *aa*	2—21 inch	70
17	H	1909	1911	720—780	246½	× 25⅓ ×	8⅔	13,500 = 27	170/140 *oil*	2—4 inch, 2—12 pdr. 1—3 pdr. *aa*	2—21 inch	72
13	G	1908	1910	897—995	274⅛	× 28 ×	10	12,500 = 27	200-241 *coal*	1—4 inch, 3—12 pdr. 1—3 pdr. *aa*	2—21 inch	96

Notes.

Total over Table is composed thus :—31 Leaders (+ 2 *building?*), 339 Destroyers (+ 17 *building and completing?*) = 370. In the above Table, dimensions and H.P. in some classes have been simplified to an average for the class. Dates refer to the time the first boat was laid down and the last boat completed. Launching dates are given in description by classes on subsequent pages.

The following Notes are for Flotilla Leaders and Destroyers from *M* up to *V* and *S* Classes :—Searchlights, 1—20 or 24 inch, and 2—10 inch signalling. In the War Leaders, *V* and *S* boats, 20—24 inch searchlights are controlled on target in conjunction with guns. Also directors for tubes.

Nearly all boats (inclusive of some pre-war boats) carry 2 depth charge throwers, depth charges and PVs. of H.S. types. *Abdiel*, some *V* and *R* boats used as Minelayers.

Features which help in picking out War Design boats are thus :—Admiralty boats have round and slightly hollowed sterns (except *Warwick*, mined and re-built with straight stern). Thornycroft boats have straight stern. Yarrow boats (from Later Yarrow M's) have strongly sloping sterns. White boats sometimes have strongly ribbed funnels ; Hawthorn Leslie boats caged tops to funnels *without* caps ; Thornycroft boats have usually one big flat-sided funnel, and *all* funnels have caged caps. Thornycroft boats stand high out of water and look big. Yarrow boats have very sharp bows. When towing Kite Balloons, after mast is removed and W/T. aerials are spread to two poles abeam and between tubes.

7 Admiralty Large Design.

DOUGLAS.

5 *Cammell Laird*: **Bruce, Campbell, Douglas, Mackay** (ex *Claverhouse*), **Malcolm.**

2 *Hawthorn Leslie*: **Montrose, Stuart.**

Displacement: 1801 tons. Dimensions: 320 (*p.p.*), 332½ (*o.a.*) × 31¾ × 10½ feet (*mean*) draught. Guns: 5—4·7 inch (DIR. CON.), 1—3 inch AA. (*Stuart*, also 2—2 pdr. AA). Tubes: 6—21 inch in two triple mountings. Machinery: Parsons (all-geared) turbines. Designed S.H.P. 40,000 = 36·5 kts. Boilers: Yarrow. Oil: *about* 505/480 tons. Complement, 164.

General Notes.—Emergency War Programme boats. *War Losses: Scott* (Cammell Laird). *Cancelled* 1918: *Barrington, Hughes* (both Cammell Laird).

		Begun.	Launch.	Comp.				Begun.	Launch.	Comp
Bruce	..	12/5/17	26/2/18	30/5/18		Mackay	..	5/3/18	21/12/18	/6/19
Campbell	..	10/11/17	21/9/18	21/12/18		Malcolm	..	27/3/18	29/5/18	20/5/19
Douglas	..	30/6/17	8/6/18	2/9/18		Montrose	..	4/10/17	10/6/18	14/9/18
						Stuart	..	18/10/17	22/8/18	21/12/18

3 + 2? Thornycroft Type.

As *Douglas*, but Thornycroft funnels.

5 *or* 3 Thornycroft: *Keppel, Rooke* (both building 1919, but may be stopped), **Shakespeare, Spencer, Wallace.** 1740 tons. Dimensions: 318¼ (*p.p.*), 329 (*o.a.*) × 31¾ × 10½ feet (*mean*) draught. Guns: 5—4·7 inch (DIR. CON.),* 1—3 inch AA., 1—2 pdr. pom-pom. Tubes: 6—21 inch in 2 triple deck mountings.

Machinery: Brown-Curtis all-geared turbines. Designed S.H.P. 40,000 = 36 kts. 2 screws. Boilers: Yarrow. Oil: *about* 550/400 tons.

General Notes.—Built under War Emergency Programme. Appearance almost exactly same as *Bruce, Campbell, &c.,* but these boats have the usual big, flat-sided Thornycroft funnels with caged caps. Complement, 164. No War Losses. *Cancelled* 1918: *Saunders, Spragge* (*Keppel* and *Rooke* may have been stopped in Sept., 1919).

*Unofficial and unverified reports credit *Keppel* and *Rooke* with 4—5·5 inch (DIR. CON.), 1—3 inch AA. *or* 2—2 pdr. AA.

		Begun.	Launch.	Comp.	Trials.
Keppel	..	10/18	....	....	....
Rooke	..	11/18	....	....	....
Shakespeare	..	10/16	7/7/17	10/17	38.74
Spencer	..	10/16	22/9/17	12/17	37.76
Wallace	..	8/17	26/10/18	2/19	37.72

5 "Admiralty V" Leaders.

VALENTINE.

Photo, Seward, Weymouth.

2 *Cammell Laird :* **Valentine, Valhalla :** 1339 tons.
2 *Denny :* **Valkyrie, Valorous :** 1325 tons.
1 *White :* **Vampire :** 1316 tons.

Dimensions : 300 (*p.p.*), 312 (*o.a.*) × 29½ × 9 feet (*mean*). 11¾ (*max.*) draught. Guns : 4—4 inch (Mk. V. DIR. CON.), 1—3 inch A.A. Tubes : 4—21 inch in pairs, but *Vampire* only has 6—21 inch in two triples. Machinery : Turbines, all geared-types. *Valentine* and *Valhalla* Parsons, others Brown-Curtis. Designed S.H.P. 27,000 = 34 kts. 2 screws. Boilers : Yarrow, except *Vampire* with White-Forster. Oil : *about* 370/320 tons. Complement, 115.

General Notes.—Emergency War Programme boats. Are exactly the same as the Admiralty V Destroyers, but specially fitted as Leaders. No War Losses.

To distinguish : From Admiralty and Thornycroft V's : *high* foremast, bridges rather larger, more boats carried abeam of 2nd funnel ; searchlight platform between tubes extended to take standard compass. After mast stands *against* after superstructure.

	Begun.	Launch.	Comp.			Begun.	Launch.	Comp.
Valentine	7/8/16	24/3/17	27/6/17	Valorous	..	25/5/16	8/5/17	21/8/17
Valhalla	8/8/16	22/5/17	31/7/17	Vampire	..	10/10/16	21/5/17	22/9/17
Valkyrie	25/5/16	13/3/17	16/6/17					

4 Marksman (later) Type.

SEYMOUR.

Photo, C.N.

4 *Cammell-Laird :* **Grenville, Parker** (ex *Frobisher*), **Saumarez, Seymour.** First two 1,666 tons, last two 1673 tons. Dimensions : 315 (*p.p.*), 325 (*o.a.*) × 31¾ × 10 feet (*mean*), 12¼ (*max.*) draught. Guns : 4— 4 inch (DIR. CON.), 2—2 pdr. pom-pom, 1 M.G. Tubes : 4—21 inch in pairs. Machinery : Parsons turbines. 3 screws. Designed S.H.P. 36,000 = 34 kts. Boilers : Yarrow. Oil : *about* 510/420 tons. Complement, 116.

General Notes.—All Emergency War Programme. Same design as *Gabriel, Marksman*, &c., but have only three funnels.

War Losses.—*Hoste* (Cammell Laird). *Removals.*—*Anzac* (Denny) presented to Australia, 1919.

		Begun.	Launch.	Comp.			Begun.	Launch.	Comp.
Grenville	..	19/6/15	17/6/16	11/10/16	Saumarez	..	2/3/16	14/10/16	21/12/16
Parker	..	19/6/15	16/8/16	13/11/16	Seymour	..	23/11/15	31/8/16	30/11/16

7 Marksman Type.

1 *Cammell Laird* : **Abdiel.** 1687 tons. Parsons turbines. Armament : 3—4 inch, 2—2 pdr. Tubes : None. This boat is a Minelayer carrying *about* 60-70 mines behind screens from fourth funnel to stern. Complement, 110. Dimensions, H.P., speed, etc., as *Gabriel*, &c., below.

LIGHTFOOT.

3 *Cammell Laird* : **Gabriel, Ithuriel,** 1655 tons, **Kempenfelt,** 1607 tons.
1 *White* : **Lightfoot,** 1607 tons.
1 *Hawthorn Leslie* : **Marksman,** 1604 tons.
1 *Denny* : **Nimrod,** 1608 tons.
Dimensions : 325 × 31¾ × 11¾ feet. Armament : 4—4 inch (DIR. CON.), 2—2 pdr. AA.* 4—21 inch tubes in pairs. Machinery : Turbines, Brown-Curtis in *Marksman* and *Nimrod*, Parsons in rest. All 3 screws. Boilers : White-Forster in *Lightfoot*, Yarrow in others. Designed H.P. 36,000 = 34 kts. Fuel : 510/413 tons oil. Complements, 106-116.
*Nimrod 1—3 inch AA., 1—2 pdr. pom-pom, *Kempenfelt* 1—3 inch AA., 2—2 pdr. pom-poms.
Notes.—*Abdiel*, *Gabriel*, and *Ithuriel*, Emergency War Programme. *Nimrod* and *Kempenfelt*, 1914-15 Programme. *Marksman* and *Lightfoot*, 1913-14 Programme.

	Begun.	Launch.	Comp.			Begun.	Launch.	Comp.
Abdiel	6/5/15	12/10/15	26/3/16		Lightfoot	9/6/14	28/5/15	29/5/15
Gabriel	12/1/15	23/12/15	1/7/16		Marksman	20/7/14	28/4/15	18/11/15
Ithuriel	14/1/15	18/3/16	2/8/16		Nimrod	9/10/14	12/4/15	25/8/15
Kempenfelt	2/10/14	1/5/15	20/8/15					

3 White Boats (ex-Chilean).

FAULKNOR.

3 *White* : **Botha** (ex *Almirante Williams Rebolledo*, 1911), 1742 tons ; **Broke** (ex *Almirante Goni*, 1913), 1704 tons : **Faulknor** (ex *Almirante Simpson*, 1913), 1694 tons. Dimensions : 331¼ × 32½ × 11 ft. 7 in. Armament : 2—4·7 inch, 2—4 inch, 2—2 pdr. pom-poms. 4—21 inch tubes.* Designed H.P. 30,000 = 31 kts. in *Botha*, = 32 kts. in *Broke* and *Faulknor*. Machinery : Turbines. Boilers : White-Forster. 3 screws. Fuel : (*max.*) 403 coal + 83 oil. Complement, 205.

Note.—Another of the class, *Tipperary*, ex *Almirante Riveros*, sunk in Battle of Jutland. Purchased, August, 1914, on outbreak of war, from Chile. Re-armed 1918-19.

*Tubes singly mounted in *Botha*, in pairs in *Broke* and *Faulknor*.

1 Special Boat.

1 *Cammell Laird* : **Swift** (1907). 2207 tons. Dimensions : 353 × 34¼ × 13 feet. Oil : 385/280 tons. H.P. 30,000 = 35 kts. Parsons turbines. 4 screws. Yarrow boilers. Armament : 1—6 inch, 2—4 inch, 1—2 pdr. pom-pom. 2—18 inch tubes. Complement, 138. Cost about £280,500.

Notes.—Although 12 years old, still the biggest Leader in British Navy. Extensively rebuilt after action in Dover Straits, 1918.

4 + 17 ? "Admiralty V" (with 4·7 inch guns).

		Begun.	Launch.	Comp.
Vansittart	..	1/7/18	17/4/19	....
Vimy ..	..	16/9/18	1919	....
*Warren**	..	....	....	....
Venomous	..	31/5/18	21/12/18	6/19
Verity	..	17/5/18	19/3/19	....
Veteran	..	30/8/18	26/4/19	....
Volunteer	..	16/4/18	17/4/19	6/19
*Watson**	..	....	....	....
Wanderer	..	1918	1/5/19	1919
*Whelp**	..	....	....	....

		Begun.	Launch.	Comp.
Whitehall	..	6/18	1919	....
Whitshed	..	6/18	1/19	7/19
Wild Swan	..	7/18	10/5/18	....
*Werewolf**	..	1918	17/7/19	....
Witherington	..	27/9/18	16/1/19	10/19
Wivern	..	19/8/18	15/4/19	....
Wolverine	..	8/10/18	17/7/19	....
*Worcester**	..	20/12/18	....	....
*Wrangler**	..	3/2/19	....	....
*Wren**	..	1/18	....	....
*Wye**	..	1/18	....	....

*Probably cancelled with some other boats (names unknown) on above List.

Boats cancelled 1918.—*Vashon, Vengeful* (Beardmore), *Vigo, Vigorous, Virulent, Volage, Volcano, Wistful* (Clydebank), *Votary, Wager, Wake, Waldegrave, Walton, Whitaker* (Denny), *Wave, Weazel, White Bear* (Fairfield), *Welcome, Welfare, Wellesley* (Hawthorn Leslie), *Wheler, Whip, Whippet* (Scott), *Whitehead, Willoughby, Winter* (Swan Hunter), *Wishart, Witch* (Thornycroft), *Westphal, Westward Ho!* (White), *Wayfarer, Woodpecker, Yeoman, Zealous, Zebra, Zodiac* (Yarrow).

WHITSHED.

Photo, Messrs. Swan Hunter (Builders).

2 Beardmore : **Vansittart, Vimy** (ex *Vantage*).

1 Chatham D. Y. : Warren.*

3 Clydebank : **Venomous** (ex *Venom*), **Verity, Veteran.**

1 Denny : **Volunteer.**

1 Devonport D.Y. : Watson.*

1 Fairfield : **Wanderer.**

1 Pembroke D.Y. : Whelp.*

3 Swan Hunter : **Whitehall, Whitshed, Wild Swan.**

6 White : **Werewolf,* Witherington, Wivern, Wolverine,*** Worcester,* Wrangler.*

2 Yarrow : Wren,* Wye.*

*Probably cancelled, Sept., 1919.

Displacement : 1300 tons *average*. Dimensions : 300 (*p.p.*), 312 (*o.a.*) × 29½ × 9 feet (*mean*) draught. Guns : 4—4·7 inch (*Dir. Con.*), 2—2 pdr. pom-poms. Tubes : 6, in two triple mountings. Machinery : Turbines (all-geared type)—all above probably Brown-Curtis, but *Whitehall* (and perhaps one or two others) Parsons. Designed S.H.P. 27,000 = 34 kts. 2 screws. Boilers : Yarrow, except *White* boats with White-Forster. Oil : *about* 350/320 tons. Complement, 127.

General Notes.—Begun under War Emergency Programme, but cost of completion of many may come under post-war Estimates. The position regarding these boats is as follows :—56 were ordered, out of which 35 were stopped in Nov.-Dec., 1918, as list opposite. 21 were proceeding up to Sept., 1919, when further boats (number uncertain) were stopped. Completion of boats launched may be postponed indefinitely. Differ from preceding V's in armament. Sometimes—but unofficially—referred to as " Repeat W Class." No War Losses, none of these boats being finished till 1919.

To distinguish.—Proportions of funnels reversed compared with other V's. These boats have *thick* fore funnel and *thin* after funnel. No 3 inch AA. abaft 2nd funnel. 2 pdr. pom-poms abeam between funnels.

7 "Yarrow S."

Photo wanted.

5 "Thornycroft S."

SPEEDY.   *Photo, Messrs. Thornycroft (Builders).*

7 *Yarrow :* **Tomahawk, Torch, Tumult, Tryphon,* Turquoise, Tuscan, Tyrian.** Displacement, 930 tons. Dimensions : 260¼ (*p.p.*), 269½ (*o.a.*) × 25¾ × 9 feet (*mean*) draught. Guns : 3—4 inch (Mk. IV with 30° elevation), 1—2 pdr. pom-pom. Tubes : 4—21 inch in pairs. Machinery : Brown-Curtis (direct drive) turbines. Designed S.H.P. 23,000 = 36 kts. Boilers : Yarrow. Oil : *about* 255/215 tons. Complement, 90.

General Notes.—Emergency War Programme boats. Otherwise as " General Notes " to Admiralty S boats.

To distinguish.—From Admiralty and Yarrow S : shorter fo'xle, sloping Yarrow stern. From other types : as Distinction Notes for Admiralty S boats. No War Losses.

	Begun.	Launch.	Comp.	Trials.		Begun.	Launch.	Comp.	Trials.
Tomahawk ..	4/17	16/5/18	7/18	35.15	Turquoise ..	6/17	9/11/18	3/19	39.6
Torch ..	4/17	16/3/18	5/18	39.19	Tuscan ..	6/17	1/3/19	6/19	....
Tryphon ..	4/17	22/6/18	9/18	35.37	Tyrian ..	6/17	5/19	1919	....
Tumult ..	6/17	17/9/18	12/18	35.70					

***Tryphon** injured by grounding on Danish Coast. Salved and reported to be re-fitting, 1919.*

5 *Thornycroft :* **Speedy, Tobago, Torbay, Toreador. Tourmaline.** 1087 tons. Length : 266¾ (*p.p.*), 275¾ (*o.a.*) × 27¼ × 9 feet (*mean*) draught. Guns : 3—4 inch (Mk. IV with 30° elevation), 1—2 pdr. pom-pom. Tubes : 4—21 inch in pairs. Machinery : Brown-Curtis (all-geared) turbines. 2 screws. Designed S.H.P. 29,000 = 36 kts. Boilers : Yarrow. Oil : *about* 300/250 tons. Complement, 90.

General Notes.—Emergency War Programme boats ; otherwise as " General Notes " to Admiralty S Class. No War Losses.

To distinguish.—From Admiralty S and Yarrow S : note that fo'xle 4 inch is *raised* : big funnels ; stand higher out of water. From other classes, distinction notes as for Admiralty S boats.

	Begun.	Launch.	Comp.	Trials.		Begun.	Launch.	Comp.	Trials.
Speedy ..	5/17	1/6/18	8/18	38.51	Toreador ..	11/17	7/12/18	4/19	36.40
Tobago ..	7/17	15/7/18	10/18	38.21	Tourmaline ..	1/18	4/19	1919	....
Torbay ..	11/17	6/3/19	7/19	......					

50 "Admiralty S."

2 *Beardmore* : **Tactician, Tara.**

9 *Clydebank* : **Scimitar, Scotsman, Scout, Scythe, Seabear, Seafire, Searcher, Seawolf, Simoom.**

6 *Denny* : **Senator, Sepoy, Seraph, Serapis, Serene, Sesame.**

2 *Doxford* : **Shamrock, Shikari.**

5 *Fairfield* : **Sikh, Sirdar, Somme, Spear, Spindrift.**

4 *Hawthorn Leslie* : **Tenedos, Thanet, Thracian, Turbulent.**

4 *Palmer* : **Steadfast, Sterling, Stonehenge, Stormcloud.**

4 *Scott* : **Strenuous, Stronghold, Sturdy, Swallow.**

3 *Stephen* : **Sabre, Saladin. Sardonyx.**

6 *Swan Hunter* : **Shark, Sparrowhawk, Splendid, Sportive, Tilbury, Tintagel.**

5 *White* : **Tribune, Trinidad, Trojan, Truant, Trusty.**

TILBURY.   *Photo, Messrs. Swan Hunter (Builders).*

1075 tons. Dimensions : 265 (*p.p.*), 275-277 (*o.a.*) × 26⅜ × 9 feet (*mean*) draught. Guns : 3—4 inch (Mk. IV with 30° elevation), 1—2 pdr. pom-pom. Tubes : 4—21 inch in pairs. Machinery : Turbines (all-geared type). Brown Curtis (A.G.) in all except following :—Palmer boats, Parsons (A.G.); *Tilbury, Tintagel,* Parsons (A.G.). Designed S.H.P. 27,000 = 36 kts. 2 screws. Yarrow boilers in all, except White boats with White-Forster. Oil : *about* 300/250 tons. Complement, 90.

General Notes.—Emergency War Programme boats, but cost of completion of about 40 boats may come under post-war Estimates. Design derived from "Admiralty Modified R" boats. Came into service with a single 14 inch tube on each beam (mounted on turntables or racks) at break of fo'xle, making six tubes in all. These 14 inch have now been removed. Reported to be not quite so successful as the Admiralty M's and R's. No War Losses. *Saturn, Sycamore* (both Stephen) cancelled. *Stalwart, Success, Swordsman, Tattoo, Tasmania,* presented to Royal Australian Navy, 1918.

To distinguish.—Long fo'xle. sheered and slightly turtle-backed. Funnels about equal in size, the extra height of fore funnel not being very prominent. Wedge-shaped bridges built off fo'xle, and open underneath. Features in these boats which also appear in the R and Modified R types are :—Mounting of searchlight on after pair of tubes ; pom-pom on platform just before mainmast ; after 4 inch in bandstand ; boats abeam of 2nd funnel.

		Begun.	Launch.	Comp.
2 B'more	Tactician ..	21/11/17	7/8/18	23/10/18
	Tara ..	21/11/17	12/10/18	9/12/18
9 Clydebank	Scimitar ..	30/5/17	27/2/18	4/18
	Scotsman ..	10/12/17	30/3/18	6/18
	Scout ..	25/10/17	27/4/18	6/18
	Scythe ..	14/1/18	25/5/18	7/18
	Seabear ..	13/12/17	6/7/18	9/18
	Seafire ..	27/2/18	10/8/18	11/18
	Searcher ..	30/3/18	11/9/18	11/18
	Seawolf ..	30/4/18	2/11/18	1/19
	Simoom ..	30/5/17	26/1/18	3/18
6 Denny	Senator ..	10/7/17	2/4/18	7/6/18
	Sepoy ..	6/8/17	22/5/18	6/8/18
	Seraph ..	4/10/17	8/7/18	25/12/18
	Serapis ..	4/12/17	17/9/18	21/3/19
	Serene ..	2/2/18	30/11/18	30/4/19
	Sesame ..	13/3/18	30/12/18	28/3/19
2 Doxf'd	Shamrock ..	....	8/18	1919
	Shikari ..	....	14/7/19	1919
5 Fair'd	Sikh ..	....	7/5/18	29/6/18
	Sirdar ..	....	6/7/18	6/9/18
	Somme ..	....	10/9/18	4/11/18
	Spear ..	....	9/11/18	17/12/18
	Spindrift ..	....	30/12/18	2/4/19

		Begun.	Launch.	Comp.
4 H.L.	Tenedos ..	6/12/17	21/10/18	6/19
	Thanet ..	13/12/17	5/11/18	1919
	Thracian ..	17/1/18	......	....
	Turbulent ..	14/11/17	1919	....
4 Palmer	Steadfast ..	....	8/8/18	3/19
	Sterling ..	....	8/10/18	3/19
	Stonehenge ..		1919	9/19
	Stormcloud ..		30/5/19	......
4 Scott	Strenuous ..	....	9/11/18	1/19
	Stronghold ..	....	5/18	1919
	Sturdy ..	....	......	.....
	Swallow ..	....	1/8/18	9/18
3 Stephen	Sabre ..	10/9/17	23/9/18	9/11/18
	Saladin ..	10/9/17	17/2/19	11/4/19
	Sardonyx ..	25/3/18	27/5/19	1919
6 S.H.	Shark ..	....	9/4/18	7/18
	Sparrowhawk ..	....	14/5/18	9/18
	Splendid ..	....	10/7/18	10/18
	Sportive ..	....	19/9/18	12/18
	Tilbury ..	....	13/6/18	9/18
	Tintagel ..	....	9/8/18	12/18
5 White	Tribune ..	21/8/17	28/3/18	16/7/18
	Trinidad ..	15/9/17	8/5/18	9/9/18
	Trojan ..	3/1/18	20/7/18	6/12/18
	Truant ..	14/2/18	18/9/18	17/3/19
	Trusty ..	11/4/18	6/11/18	9/5/19

2 Thornycroft "V" (Later Six-tube Boats).

WOOLSTON.

Photo, Messrs. Thornycroft (Builders).

2 *Thornycroft:* **Wolsey, Woolston.** 1315 tons. Dimensions : 300 (*p.p.*), 312 (*o.a.*) × 29½ × 9 feet (*mean* draught). Guns : 3—4 inch (Mk. V. DIR. CON.), 1—3 inch AA. Tubes : 6—21 inch in two triple deck mountings. Machinery : Brown Curtis turbines (all-geared type). 2 screws. Designed S.H.P. 30,000 = 35 kts. Yarrow boilers. Oil : *about* 370/320 tons. Complement, 127.

General Notes.—Emergency War Programme. Differ from other Admiralty Later V's in H.P., speed, and a few other particulars. No War Losses.

To distinguish.—Big flat-sided funnels with caged caps. Divide from *Viceroy* and *Viscount* by the triple tubes in these boats.

	Begun.	Launch.	Comp.	Trials.			Begun.	Launch.	Comp.	Trials.
Wolsey	3/17	16/3/18	14/5/18	36.64		Woolston	4/17	27/14/18	28/6/18	37.11

18 Admiralty "V" (Later Six-tube Boats).

Appearance generally same as *Woolston*, but funnels as Admiralty "V" boats.

2 *Beardmore :* **Wakeful, Watchman.**
2 *Denny :* **Walker, Westcott.**
2 *Doxford :* **Walpole, Whitley.**
2 *Fairfield :* **Walrus, Wolfhound.**
2 *Hawthorn Leslie :* **Warwick, Wessex.**
2 *Palmer :* **Waterhen, Wryneck.**
2 *Scott :* **Westminster, Windsor.**
2 *Swan Hunter :* **Whirlwind, Wrestler.**
2 *White :* **Winchester, Winchelsea.**

Displacement : 1280-1316 tons (1300 *average*). Dimensions : 300 (*p.p.*), 312 (*o.a.*) × 29 × 9 feet (*mean*), 11¼ (*max.*) draught. Guns : 3—4 inch (Mk V DIR. CON.), 1—3 inch AA. Torpedo tubes : 6—21 inch in two triple deck mountings. Machinery : "All-Geared" turbines, Brown-Curtis in all except Palmer boats with Parsons. 2 screws. Designed S.H.P. 27,000 = 34 kts. Boilers : Yarrow, except White boats with White-Forster. Oil : *about* 370/320 tons. Complement, 127.

General Notes.—All Emergency War Programme. The Notes to the Admiralty V's also apply to these boats, the only difference being in the increased number of tubes in above. The triple tubes are actually lighter than the " Admiralty M " Mark of twin tubes mounted in all preceding classes back to the M's. No War Losses.

To distinguish.—From Modified V's : 3 inch AA. gun in bandstand abaft second funnel ; from first V's : by shorter mainmast ; from *Vampire* : by shorter foremast, no extension to S.L. platform for standard compass, after mast stands away from after superstructure.

	Begun	Launch.	Comp			Begun.	Launch.	Comp.
Wakeful	17/1/17	6/10/17	11/17		Wessex	23/5/17	12/3/18	11/5/18
Watchman	17/1/17	2/12/17	1/18		Waterhen	......	26/3/18	17/7/18
Walker	26/3/17	29/11/17	12/2/18		Wryneck	......	13/5/18	11/18
Westcott	30/3/17	14/2/18	12/4/18		Westminster	......	24/2/18	18/4/18
Walpole	......	12/2/18	7/8/18		Windsor	......	21/6/18	28/8/18
Whitley	......	13/4/18	10/18		Whirlwind	......	21/6/18	28/8/18
Walrus	......	27/12/17	8/3/18		Wrestler	......	15/12/17	3/18
Wolfhound	......	14/3/18	27/3/18		Winchester	24/5/17	15/12/17	15/3/18
Warwick	10/3/17	28/12/17	18/3/18		Winchelsea	12/6/17	1/2/18	20/4/18

2 "Thornycroft V."

VICEROY.   *Photo, Messrs. Thornycroft (Builders).*

2 *Thornycroft*: **Viceroy, Viscount.** 1325 tons. Dimensions: 300 (*p.p.*), 312 (*o.a.*) × 30′ 7″ × 9½ feet (*mean*) 11¾ feet (*max.*) draught. Guns: 3—4 inch (Mk. V DIR. CON.), 1—3 inch AA. Tubes: 4—21 inch in pairs. Machinery: Brown Curtis (all-geared) turbines. 2 screws. Designed S.H.P. 30,000 = 35 kts. Boilers: Yarrow. Oil fuel: *about* 375/320 tons. Complement, 110.

General Notes—Emergency War Programme boats. Differ from Admiralty V design in dimensions, H.P. and speed. No War Losses.

To distinguish.—Have big, flat-sided funnels with caged caps. The fore funnel not being so prominently raised as in other " V " boats. Other distinctive features as Admiralty V's.

	Begun.	Launch.	Comp.	Trials.
Viscount	12/16	29/12/17	3/18	37.69
Viceroy	12/16	17/11/17	1/18	36.5

21 "Admiralty V."

————————as Minelayer.

3 *Beardmore*: **Vancouver, Vanessa, Vanity.**
2 *Clydebank*: **Vanoc,* Vanquisher.***
1 *Denny*: **Venturous.***
2 *Doxford*: **Vega, Velox.**
2 *Fairfield*: **Vendetta, Venetia.**
2 *Hawthorn Leslie*: **Verdun, Versatile.**
3 *Stephen*: **Vesper, Vidette, Voyager.**
2 *Swan Hunter*: **Violent, Vimiera.**
2 *White*: **Vectis, Vortigern.**
2 *Yarrow*: **Vivacious, Vivien.**

* Minelayers.

Displacements: 1272-1339 tons (1300 *average*). Dimensions: 300 (*p.p.*), 312 (*o.a.*) × 29¼ × 9 feet (*mean*), 11¾ (*max.*) draught. Guns: 4—4 inch (Mk. V. DIR. CON.), 1—3 inch AA. Torpedo tubes: 4—21 inch in pairs. Machinery: " All-Geared " turbines: Brown-Curtis in all, except Doxford and Swan Hunter boats with Parsons. 2 screws. Designed S.H.P. 27,000 = 34 kts. Boilers: Yarrow in all, except White boats with White-Forster. Oil: *about* 370/320 tons. Complement, 110. Trials: *Vivacious* 33·01, *Vivien* 36.79.

General Notes.—All Emergency War Programme. These boats are of remarkable size and power for Destroyers; in fact, five of them, with slight modifications, have been converted to Flotilla Leaders.

To distinguish.—From " W " type, *no triple tubes*; mainmast *short*. From " V Leaders," foremast shorter, forebridges different, no extension to S.L. platform for standard compass, mainmast *away* from after superstructure, fewer boats.

		Begun.	Launch.	Comp.			Begun.	Launch.	Comp.
Vancouver	..	15/3/17	28/12/17	9/3/18	*Vendetta*	..	....	3/9/17	17/10/17
Vanessa	..	16/5/17	16/3/18	27/4/18	*Venetia*	..	....	29/10/17	19/12/17
Vanity	..	28/7/18	3/5/18	21/6/18	*Verdun*	..	13/1/17	21/8/17	3/11/17
Vanoc	..	20/9/16	14/6/17	8/17	*Versatile*	..	31/1/17	31/10/17	11/2/18
Vanquisher	..	27/9/16	18/8/17	9/17	*Vesper*	..	27/12/16	15/12/17	20/2/18
Venturous	..	9/10/16	21/9/17	29/11/17	*Vidette*	..	1/2/17	28/2/18	27/4/18
Vega	..	....	1/9/17	12/17	*Voyager*	..	17/5/17	24/6/18	24/6/18
Velox	..	....	17/11/17	1/4/18	*Violent*	..	11/16	1/9/17	11/17
					Vimiera	..	10/16	22/6/17	9/17
					Vectis	..	7/12/17	4/9/17	5/12/17
					Vortigern	..	17/1/16	15/10/17	25/1/18
					Vivacious	..	7/16	3/11/17	12/17
					Vivien	..	7/16	16/2/18	28/5/18

War Losses.—*Vehement* (Denny). *Verulam* (Hawthorn Leslie) and *Vittoria* (Swan Hunter) lost 1919 in Baltic operations.

4 Yarrow "Later M."

Photo wanted.

As Illustration of *Mounsey* on later page,
but with sloping stern.

5 "Thornycroft R."

TAURUS.   *Photo, Messrs. Thornycroft (Builders).*

4 *Yarrow* : **Sabrina, Sybille, Truculent, Tyrant.** Displacements : 897-923 tons. Dimensions : 269¼ (*p.p.*),
271½ (*o.a.*) × 25¾ × 8½ feet (*mean*), 10½ (*max.*) draught.   Guns : 3—4 inch, 1—2 pdr. pom-pom, 1 M.G.   Torpedo
tubes : 4—21 inch in pairs. Machinery : Brown-Curtis turbines. 2 screws. Designed S.H.P. 23,000 = 36 kts.
Boilers : 3 Yarrow. Oil fuel : 256-213/215-200 tons. Complement, 82.

General Notes.—All Emergency War Programme. Generally same as the first group of " Yarrow M's " (*Miranda,
Mounsey, Nerissa, Rival, &c.*), but the above boats have the Yarrow form of strongly sloping stern. Note that
these have *no* geared turbines, nor is the after 4 inch in a bandstand. Accordingly, there is *no* Yarrow " R "
design.

War Losses.—*Strongbow, Surprise, Ulleswater* (all Yarrow).

	Begun.	Launch.	Comp.	Trials.		Begun.	Launch.	Comp.	Trials.
Sabrina	8/15	24/7/16	9/16	36.96	Truculent	3/16	24/3/17	5/17	38.27
Sybille	8/15	5/2/17	2/17	39.11	Tyrant	3/16	19/5/17	7/17	37.37

5 *Thornycroft* : **Radiant, Retriever, Rosalind.** 1034-7 tons.   Dimensions : 274 (*o.a.*) × 27¼ × 11 feet
(*max.*) draught. Also **Taurus, Teaser.** 1064 tons.   Dimensions : 274½ (*o.a.*) × 27 × 11 feet (*max.*)
draught.   Following details for all six boats : Length (*p.p.*), 265 feet.   Mean draught, 8½ feet.   Guns : 3—4 inch,
1—2 pdr. pom-pom, 1 M.G.   Tubes : 4—21 inch in pairs. Machinery : Brown-Curtis (all-geared) turbines. 2
screws. Designed S.H.P. 29,000 = 35 kts. Boilers : 3 Yarrow. Oil fuel : *about* 285/220 tons. Complement, 82.

General Notes.—All War Emergency Programme. Are separated from the " Thornycroft M's " in the same way as the
" Admiralty R's " are divided from the " Admiralty M's," viz., by after 4 inch guns being in bandstand and machinery
being " all-geared " turbines. No War Losses.

	Begun.	Launch.	Comp.	Trials.		Begun.	Launch.	Comp.	Trials.
Radiant	12/15	5/11/16	2/17	39.67	Taurus	3/16	10/3/17	5/17	39.27
Retriever	1/16	15/1/17	3/17	36.8	Teazer	3/16	21/4/17	7/17	40.22
Rosalind	10/15	14/10/16	12/16	37.09					

10 "Admiralty Modified R."

1 *Beardmore* : **Ulster.** 1086 tons. Brown-Curtis A.G. turbines.

1 *Doxford* : **Umpire.** 1091 tons. Brown-Curtis A.G. turbines.

1 *Fairfield* : **Undine.** 1090 tons. Brown-Curtis A.G. turbines.

2 *Palmer* : **Urchin, Ursa.** 1085 tons. Parsons A.G. turbines.

2 *Scott* : **Tirade, Ursula.** 1076 tons. Brown-Curtis A.G. turbines.

1 *Swan Hunter* : **Tower.** 1087 tons. Brown-Curtis A.G. turbines.

2 *White* : **Trenchant, Tristrum.** 1085 tons. Brown-Curtis A.G. turbines.

Dimensions : 265 (*p.p.*), 275½-276 (*o.a.*) × *about* 26¾ × 10½ feet (*mean*), 11¾ (*max.*) draught. Guns : 3—4 inch (Mk. IV with 30° elevation in *Ulster* and *Ursa*), 1—2 pdr. pom-pom. Tubes : 4—21 inch in pairs. Machinery : " All-Geared " (A.G.) turbines as noted above. 2 screws. Designed S.H.P. 27,000 = 36 kts. Boilers : 3 Yarrow in all except *Trenchant* and *Tristram* by White with 3 White-Forster. Oil : *about* 300/250 tons. Complement, 82.

General Notes.—All Emergency War Programme. These boats are said to be an attempt by the Admiralty to combine the " Admiralty R " design with that of the Yarrow " Later M's." They are said to be not quite so satisfactory as the Admiralty M's and R's, but good sea-boats.

To distinguish.—Very long and high fo'xle, which is *not* sheered or turtle-backed as in " S " boats. Charthouse built on fo'xle. Fore funnel *very close* to foremast. Funnels nearly equal in size with boats in davits abeam of after funnel. Quarter-deck abaft of mainmast is shorter than in " Yarrow M " boats, and has 4 inch in bandstand.

War Losses.—*Ulysses* (Doxford).

	Begun.	Launch.	Comp.			Begun.	Launch.	Comp.
Ulster	19/9/16	10/10/17	21/11/17	*Tirade* ..	....	21/4/17	6/17
Umpire ..	....	9/6/17	8/17	*Ursula* ..	....	8/17	9/17
Undine ..	....	22/3/17	26/5/17	*Tower* ..	9/16	5/4/17	8/17
Urchin ..	....	7/6/17	8/17	*Trenchant* ..	17/7/16	23/12/16	30/4/17
Ursa	....	23/7/17	10/17	*Tristram* ..	23/9/16	24/2/17	30/6/17

TOWER. *Photo by courtesy of Messrs. Swan Hunter (Builders).*

URCHIN. Some boats have platform on after pair of tubes, as above. *Photo, Topical.*

34 "Admiralty R."

THISBE. *Photo by courtesy of Messrs. Hawthorn Leslie (Builders).*

TELEMACHUS as Minelayer. After-pair of tubes and 4 inch gun are dummies painted on screens. *Photo, Lt. C. de Brock, R.N.*

STARFISH. *Note.*—Satyr, Skate, Sharpshooter, Starfish, Stork only, have mainmast as above illustration.

3 *Beardmore:* **Satyr, Sharpshooter,** Parsons A.G. turbines, **Tancred,** Brown-Curtis A.G. turbines.

7 *Clydebank:* **Restless, Rigorous, Romola, Rowena, Skate, Tarpon,* Telemachus.***

3 *Denny:* **Rob Roy, Rocket, Redgauntlet.**

1 *Doxford:* **Redoubt.**

1 *Fairfield:* **Tempest.**

6 *Harland & Wolff* (Goran): **Salmon, Skilful, Springbok, Sylph, Tenacious, Tetrarch.**

5 *Hawthorn Leslie:* **Sarpedon, Stork, Starfish, Thisbe, Thruster.**

3 *Stephen:* **Sceptre, Sturgeon, Tormentor.**

4 *Swan Hunter:* **Radstock, Raider, Sorceress, Torrid.**

1 *White:* **Sable.**

**Tarpon, Telemachus,* Minelayers.

Displacements vary from 1096 to 1036 tons (1065 *average*). Length, (*p.p.*) 265 feet (*o.a.* varies from 274 to 276 feet). Beam, 26¾ feet. *Mean* draught, 9 feet. *Max.* draughts, 11¼ to 12 feet. Guns: 3—4 inch, 1—2 pdr. pom-pom (1 M.G., but not in all). Torpedo tubes: 4—21 inch in pairs. Machinery: Turbines—"all-geared" types. Clydebank, Denny, Fairfield, Harland & Wolff, Stephen, Swan Hunter and White boats, Brown-Curtis A.G. turbines; Doxford and Hawthorn Leslie boats, Parsons A.G. turbines: Beardmore boats as separately noted. Designed S.H.P. 27,000 = 36 kts. 2 screws in all. Boilers: 3 Yarrow or Modified Yarrow, except *Sable* by White, with White-Forster boilers. Oil fuel: 295-285/250-243 tons. Complement, 82.

		Begun.	Launch.	Comp.				Begun.	Launch.	Comp.
3 B'd-more.	Satyr ..	15/4/16	27/12/16	2/2/17	6 H. & W.	Salmon ..	27/8/15	7/10/16	20/12/16
	Sharpshooter	23/5/16	27/2/17	2/4/17		Skilful ..	20/1/16	3/2/17	26/3/17
	Tancred ..	6/7/16	30/6/17	1/9/17		Springbok	27/1/16	9/3/17	30/4/17
						Sylph ..	30/8/16	15/11/16	10/2/17
7 Clydebank.	Restless ..	22/9/15	12/8/16	10/16		Tenacious ..	25/7/16	21/5/17	12/8/17
	Rigorous	22/9/15	30/9/16	11/16		Tetrarch ..	26/7/16	20/4/17	2/6/17
	Romola	25/8/15	14/5/16	8/16					
	Rowena	25/8/15	1/7/16	9/16	6 H. L.	Sarpedon	27/9/15	1/6/16	2/9/16
	Skate ..	12/1/16	11/1/17	2/17		Stork ..	10/4/16	25/11/16	1/2/17
	Tarpon	12/4/16	10/3/17	4/17		Starfish	26/1/16	27/9/16	16/12/16
	Telemachus	12/4/16	21/4/17	6/17		Thisbe ..	13/6/16	8/3/17	6/6/17
						Thruster ..	2/6/16	10/1/17	30/3/17
3 D'y	Rob Roy ..	15/10/15	29/8/16	15/12/16					
	Rocket ..	28/9/15	2/7/16	7/10/16	3 Stn.	Sceptre..	10/11/15	18/4/17	26/5/17
	Redgauntlet ..	30/9/15	23/11/16	7/2/17		Sturgeon ..	10/11/15	11/1/17	26/2/17
						Tormentor ..	1/5/16	22/5/17	22/8/17
(Doxf'd) Redoubt	..	......	28/10/16	3/17					
					4 S.H.	Radstock	9/15	3/6/16	9/16
(F'field) Tempest	..	......	26/1/17	20/3/17		Raider ..	9/15	17/7/16	10/16
						Sorceress	11/15	29/8/16	12/16
						Torrid ..	7/16	10/2/17	5/17
					(White) Sable ..		20/12/15	18/6/16	30/11/16

General Notes.—All Emergency War Programme boats. General design is as the "Admiralty M's" but these boats have geared turbines and 2 screws, and are rather faster than the "Admiralty M's."

To distinguish.—Note that the after 4 inch is mounted in a bandstand.

War Losses.—Simoon (Clydebank), Recruit (Doxford), Tornado (Stephen), Torrent (Swan Hunter), Setter (White).

74 "Admiralty M."

(23 " Repeat M " + 45 " M " + 6 " Pre-War M.")

PYLADES (" Repeat M ").

2 *Beardmore* : * **Pelican, Pellew.** (Repeat M.)

10 *Clydebank* : **Napier, Penn, Peregrine.** (Repeat M.) **Ossory, Mameluke, Marne, Mons**—also **Milne, Morris, Moorsom.** (Pre-War.)

7 *Denny* : **Petard, Peyton.** (Repeat M.) **Maenad, Marvel, Mystic, Narwhal, Nicator.**

9 *Doxford* : **Norseman, Oberon.** (Repeat M.) **Octavia, Ophelia, Opportune, Oracle, Orestes, Orford, Orpheus.**

11 *Fairfield* : **Observer. Offa, Phœbe.** (Repeat M.) **Mandate, Manners, Mindful, Mischief, Onslaught, Onslow, Orcadia, Oriana.**

3 *Hawthorn Leslie* : **Pigeon, Plover.** (Repeat M.)

8 *Palmer* : **Oriole, Osiris.** (Repeat M.) **Nonsuch, Norman, Northesk, Nugent**—also **Murray, Myngs.** (Pre-War).

6 *Scott* : **Plucky, Portia.** (Repeat M.) **Obdurate, Obedient, Paladin, Parthian.**

5 *Stephen* : **Prince, Pylades.*** (Repeat M.) **Nizam,* Noble** (ex *Nisus*), **Nonpareil.**

4 *Swan Hunter* : **Pasley.** (Repeat M.) Brown-Curtis turbines. **Martial,** Parsons turbines, **Menace,** Brown-Curtis turbines—also **Matchless.** (Pre-War) Parsons turbines.

6 *Thornycroft* : **Michael, Milbrook, Minion, Munster, Nepean, Nereus.**

4 *White* : **Medina** (ex-*Redmill*), **Medway** (ex*Redwing*), (both Repeat M). **Magic, Moresby.**

Nizam and *Pylades* were launched by Messrs. Stephen and completed by Messrs. Beardmore.

Displacements vary from 994 to 1042 tons (1025 *average*). Length : 265 feet (*p.p.*) (*o.a.* varies from 271½ to 276½ feet). Beam : 26⅝ to 26¾ feet. *Mean* draught : 8⅜ feet. *Max.* draught : *about* 10¼ feet. Guns : 3—4 inch, 1—2 pdr. pom-pom., 1 M.G. Tubes : 4—21 inch in pairs. Machinery : Clydebank, Fairfield and Stephen boats, Brown-Curtis turbines ; Beardmore, Denny, Doxford, Hawthorn Leslie, Palmer, Scott, Thornycroft, White boats, all Parsons turbines ; Swan Hunter boats as specially noted above. Designed S.H.P. 25,000 = 34 kts. 3 screws in all. Boilers : 3 Yarrow in all, except White boats with White-Forster. Oil fuel : 298-237/243-202 tons. Complement, 80.

General Notes.—Boats with " N," " O " and " P " names, all Emergency War Programme ; the War boats with " M " names, Emergency War Programme, but part of their cost was met by the provision in 1914-15 Navy Estimates for ten destroyers. The Pre-War M's, 1913-14 Programme. Proved a remarkably successful type of Destroyer, although not so fast as the Thornycroft and Yarrow " M's."

To distinguish.—Easily distinguished by their three, small round funnels, with 4 inch mounted between second and third funnels. Can be separated from the Admiralty R's by the after 4 inch *not* being mounted in " bandstand." The Repeat M's have *raking* stems ; the Pre-War M's have rather shorter funnels.

War Losses.—Repeat M's : *Pheasant* (Fairfield), *Partridge* (Swan Hunter). War M's : *Narborough* (Clydebank), *Opal* (Doxford), *Mary Rose, Negro, North Star* (all Palmer), *Nomad* (Stephen), *Marmion, Nessus, Nestor* (all Swan Hunter). Pre-War M's : No losses.

		Begun.	Launch.	Comp.
2 B'dmore.	Pelican	25/6/15	18/3/16	1/5/16
	Pellew	28/6/15	18/5/16	30/6/16
10 Clydebank.	Napier	24/3/15	27/11/16	1/16
	Penn	9/6/15	8/4/16	5/16
	Peregrine	9/6/15	29/5/16	7/16
	Ossory	23/12/14	9/10/16	11/15
	Mameluke	23/12/14	14/8/15	10/15
	Marne	30/9/14	29/5/15	8/15
	Mons	30/9/14	1/5/15	7/15
	Milne	1914	5/10/14	12/14
	Morris	1914	19/11/14	12/14
	Moorsom	1914	21/12/14	2/15
7 Denny.	Petard	5/7/15	24/3/16	23/5/16
	Peyton	12/7/15	2/5/16	29/6/16
	Maenad	10/11/14	10/8/15	12/11/15
	Marvel	11/1/15	7/10/15	28/12/15
	Mystic	27/10/14	26/6/16	11/11/15
	Narwhal	21/4/15	3/12/15	3/3/16
	Nicator	21/4/15	3/2/16	15/4/16
9 Doxford.	Norseman	....	15/8/16	11/16
	Oberon	....	29/9/16	12/16
	Octavia	....	21/6/16	11/16
	Ophelia	....	13/10/15	5/16
	Opportune	....	20/11/16	6/16
	Oracle	....	23/12/15	8/16
	Orestes	....	21/3/16	6/16
	Orford	....	19/4/16	12/16
	Orpheus	....	17/6/16	9/16
11 Fairfield.	Observer	....	1/5/16	15/6/16
	Offa	....	7/6/16	31/7/16
	Phoebe	....	20/11/16	28/12/16
	Mandate	....	27/4/15	13/8/15
	Manners	....	15/6/15	21/9/15
	Mindful	....	24/8/15	10/11/15
	Mischief	....	12/10/15	16/12/15
	Onslaught	....	4/12/15	3/3/16
	Onslow	....	15/2/16	15/4/16
	Orcadia	....	26/7/16	29/9/16
	Oriana	....	23/9/16	4/11/16

		Begun.	Launch.	Comp.
2 H. Leslie.	Pigeon	14/7/15	3/3/16	2/6/16
	Plover	30/7/15	3/3/16	30/6/16
8 Palmer.	Oriole	....	31/7/16	11,16
	Osiris	....	26/9/16	12/16
	Nonsuch	....	8/12/15	2/16
	Norman	....	20/3/16	8/16
	Northesk	....	5/7/16	10/16
	Nugent	....	23/1/17	4/17
	Murray	....	6/8/14	12/14
	Myngs	....	24/9/14	2/15
6 Scott.	Plucky	....	21/4/16	7/16
	Portia	....	10/8/16	10/16
	Obdurate	....	21/1/16	3/16
	Obedient	....	16/11/16	2/16
	Paladin	....	27/3/16	5/16
	Parthian	....	3/7/16	9/16
5 Stephen.	Prince	27/7/15	26/7/16	21/9/16
	Pylades*	27/7/15	28/9/16	30/12/16*
	Nizam*	11/2/15	6/4/16	29/6/16*
	Noble	6/2/15	25/11/15	15/2/16
	Nonpareil	24/2/15	16/5/16	28/6/15
			*Completed by Messrs. Beardmore.	
4 Swan Hunter.	Pasley	7/15	15/4/16	7/16
	Martial	10/14	1/7/15	10/15
	Menace	9/14	9/11/15	4/16
	Matchless	11/13	5/10/14	12/14
6 Thornycroft.	Michael	10/14	19/5/15	8/15
	Milbrook	11/14	12/7/15	10/15
	Minion	11/14	11/9/15	11/15
	Munster	11/14	24/11/15	1/16
	Nepean	2/15	21/1/16	3/16
	Nereus	3/15	24/2/16	5/16
4 White.	Medina	22/9/15	8/3/16	30/6/16
	Medway	2/11/15	19/4/16	2/8/16
	Magic	1/1/15	10/9/15	8/1/16
	Moresby	14/1/15	20/11/15	7/4/16

OBDURATE (War M's)   *Official R.A.F. Photo.*

6 "Thornycroft M."

READY.   *Photo, Messrs. Thornycroft.*

6 *Thornycroft*: **Rapid, Ready,** 1033 tons. **Patriot, Patrician,** 1004 tons. **Meteor,** 1070 tons. **Mastiff,** 985 tons. Dimensions : 265 (*p.p.*), 271-274 (*o.a.*) × 27½ × 10½-11 feet. Guns : 3—4 inch, 1—2 pdr. pom-pom, 1 M.G. Tubes : 4—21 inch in pairs. Machinery : *Meteor* and *Mastiff*, Parsons turbines, 26,500 S.H.P. = 35 kts. ; other Brown-Curtis turbines, 27,500 S.H.P. = 35 kts. 3 Yarrow boilers. Oil : *about* 285-250/220-200 tons. Complement, 82.

Note.—*Meteor* and *Mastiff* 1913-14 Programme ; rest Emergency War Programme. Proved very successful boats.

10 "Yarrow M."

MOUNSEY.   *Photo, Messrs. Yarrow, Ltd.*

10 *Yarrow* : **Relentless, Rival, Nerissa. Moon, Morning Star, Mounsey, Musketeer, Miranda, Minos, Manley.** Displace 879-898 tons. Dimensions : 260¼ (*p.p.*), 269½-271½ (*o.a.*) × 25⅔-27 × 10½ feet. Guns : 3—4 inch, 1—2 pdr. pom-pom. Torpedo tubes : 4—21 inch in pairs. Brown-Curtis turbines. 3 Yarrow boilers. Designed S.H.P. 23,000 = 35-36 kts. Oil fuel : 228/202 tons. Complement, 79.

Notes.—*Miranda, Minos, Manley,* 1913-14 Programme ; *Morning Star, Mounsey, Musketeer,* part Emergency War Programme, plus sum voted for ten boats in 1914-15 Estimates ; *Relentless, Rival, Nerissa,* Emergency War Programme. Very successful boats. Design by Messrs. Yarrow, Ltd. These boats have *straight* sterns.

6 THORNYCROFT.

	Begun.	Launch.	Comp.	Trials.		Begun.	Launch.	Comp.	Trials.
Rapid ..	8/15	7/16	8/16	35.45	Meteor ..	5/13	7/14	9/14	34.85
Ready ..	9/15	8/16	10/16	34.36	Mastiff ..	7/13	10/14	11/14	37.52
Patriot ..	7/15	4/16	6/16	37.34					
Patrician..	6/15	6/16	7/16	35.6					

10 YARROW.

	Begun.	Launch.	Comp.	Trials.		Begun.	Launch.	Comp.	Trials.
Relentless	....	4/16	5/16	37.69	Miranda	10/12	5/14	8/14	33.53
Rival	5/15	6/16	9/16	36.83	Minos	10/12	8/14	10/14	36.73
Nerissa ..	11/14	2/16	3/16	36.74	Manley	10/12	10/14	11/14	33.88
Moon	9/14	4/15	6/15	37.86					
Morning Star	9/14	6/15	8/15	36.92					
Mounsey	9/14	9/15	11/15	39.02					
Musketeer	9/14	11/15	12/15	35.6					

2 "Hawthorn M."

MANSFIELD.   *Photo, Sub-Lt. H. Lawrence, R.N.R.*

2 *Hawthorn* : **Mansfield, Mentor.** Launched 1914. 1057 and 1053 tons. Dimensions : 265 (*p.p.*), 271 (*o.a.*) × 27 × 10¾ feet. Guns : 3—4 inch, 1—2 pdr. AA., 1 M.G. Tubes : 4—21 inch in pairs. Parsons turbines. 3 screws. Yarrow boilers. Designed S.H.P. 27 000 = 35 kts. Oil : 290/220 tons. Complement, 76.

Notes.—1913-14 Programme boats.

TRIDENT.   *Photo by courtesy of Messrs. H. Leslie.*

3 *Hawthorn Leslie* : **Talisman, Termagant, Trident.** 1098 tons. Complement, 102. Dimensions : 309 ft.
× 28 ft. 7 in. × 9 ft. 6 in. Guns : 5—4 inch. Torpedo tubes : 4—21 inch in pairs (very light type). Carry D.C.
Machinery : Parsons turbines and Yarrow boilers. 3 screws. Designed H.P. 25,000 = 32 kts. Fuel : 237 tons
oil. *Turbulent* lost during War. All begun for Turkish Navy, but taken over by Admiralty. Proved so successful,
their design formed basis for the later Admiralty V's and W's.

	Begun.	Launch.	Comp.		Begun.	Launch.	Comp.
Talisman	7/12/14	15/7/15	19/1/16	Trident	7/1/15	20/11/15	24/3/16
Termagant	17/12/14	26/8/15	18/3/16				

3 ex-Greek.

MEDEA.

1 *Clydebank* : **Medea** (ex *Kriti*). 1007 tons.
2 *Fairfield* : **Melpomene** (ex *Samos*), **Melampus** (ex *Chios*). 1040 tons. Complement, 80.
Dimensions : 273½ × 26¾ × 10¼ feet. Guns : 3—4 inch, 1—2 pdr. pom-pom, 1 M.G. Torpedo tubes : 4—21 inch in
twin deck mountings. Also usual D.C. Machinery : Brown-Curtis turbines and Yarrow boilers. 3 screws.
Designed H.P. 25,000 = 32 kts. Fuel : 276/225 tons.
Notes.—Ordered for Greek Navy, and taken over for British Navy, 1914. *Medusa* (ex Greek *Lesvos*), built by Clydebank,
lost during War.

	Begun.	Launch.	Comp.		Begun.	Launch.	Comp.
Medea	8/4/14	30/1/15	5/15	Melampus	....	16/12/14	29/6/15
Melpomene	....	1/2/15	16/8/15				

17 L Class (16 Pre-War + 1 War.)

LEGION, as Minelayer. After 4 inch and tubes are dummies painted on screens.
(ALL 3 FUNNELS.)

1 *Beardmore* : **Lochinvar** (Oct., 1915). 1010 tons. Brown-Curtis turbines.
2 *Beardmore* : **Llewellyn** (1913), **Lennox** (1914). 996 tons. Parsons turbines.
2 *Fairfield* : **Lawford** (1913), **Lydiard** (1914). 1003 tons. Trials : *Laforey* 29·9 kts.
2 *Parsons* (*Hawthorn*) : **Leonidas** (1913), **Lucifer** (1913). 987 tons.
2 *Swan, Hunter & W. Richardson* : **Laertes** (1913). 982 tons. **Lysander** (1913). 976 tons. Trials : *Laertes*
31·2, *Lysander* 29·9.
2 *Thornycroft* : **Lance** (1914). 997 tons. **Lookout** (1914). 1002 tons.
2 *Denny* : **Loyal** (1913), 995 tons, **Legion** (1914), 1072 tons.
War Losses in above : *Laforey, ~~Lennox~~ Lassoo.*
Lovis

LAUREL.   *Photo, Symonds.*
(ALL 2 FUNNELS.)

2 *White* : **Laurel** (1913), **Liberty** (1913). 965-975 tons.
4 *Yarrow* : **Lark** (1913), 968 tons. **Landrail** (1914), 983 tons. **Laverock** (1914), 994 tons. **Linnet** (1913).
970 tons. All Brown-Curtis turbines.

All to Admiralty design. Armament : 3—4 inch, 1—2 pdr. pom-pom, 1 M.G. 4—21 inch tubes in pairs. Machinery :
Parsons turbines in all, except where otherwise noted. Designed H.P. 24,500 = 29 kts. ; *Leonidas* and *Lucifer*
only, 22,500 = 29 kts. Dimensions : 269 × 27½ × 10½ feet. Fuel : 290-270/230-200 tons oil. Complement, 77.
Lochinvar (and lost *Lassoo*), Emergency War Programme ; rest 1912-13 Programme.

13 K Class.

"K CLASS" SPECIAL BOATS. Amidships 4 inch *abaft* funnel and *before* after tube. After S.L. or AA. gun platform *before* mainmast. *Garland* has cut-away stern.

"K CLASS" ADMIRALTY BOATS. S.L. or AA. gun platform *abaft* 3rd funnel, amidships 4 inch *between* after tubes and mainmast. Forefunnel close to foremast.

Special Boats.

3 *Thornycroft*: **Porpoise,** 934 tons, **Unity, Victor,** 954 tons (1913). Designed H.P. 22,500 = 31 kts. All made about 30.3 on trials.

1 *Thornycroft*: **Hardy** (1912). 898 tons. H.P. 21,000 = 32 kts.

1 *Parsons* (hull sub-contracted to Cammell Laird): **Garland** (1913). 984 tons. Dimensions as Admiralty boats. Designed H.P. 24,500 = 30 kts. *Trials,* 31 kts.

Notes to above.—Dimensions (except *Garland*): 265½ × 26½ × 9½-10¼ feet. All Parsons turbines. 2 screws. Yarrow boilers. Oil: 250-260/200-220 tons. *Hardy* said to have Diesel engine for cruising speeds; she was so designed, but it is uncertain if this Diesel engine was ever installed or not.

War Losses.—*Paragon, Fortune.*

Admiralty Design Boats.

3 *Clydebank*: **Acasta,** 996 tons, **Achates,** 982 tons (1912), **Ambuscade,** 935 tons (1913). *Trials*: *Acasta* 29 kts. *Achates* 32·3 kts. *Ambuscade* 30·4 kts. *Acasta* practically destroyed at Jutland and rebuilt. Brown-Curtis turbines in these boats.

2 *Hawthorn Leslie*: **Christopher,** 938 tons, **Cockatrice,** 951 tons (1912). *Trials*: *Christopher* 30.9 kts. *Cockatrice* 29·7 kts.

2 *London and Glasgow*: **Midge, Owl,** 936 tons. (1913) *Trials*: *Midge* 32·9 kts. *Owl* 32·7 kts.

1 *Swan Hunter*: **Spitfire** (1913). 935 tons. *Trials*: 30·3 kts.

Notes to above boats.—Dimensions: 267½ × 27 × 10½ feet. Designed H.P. 24,500 = 29 kts. All Parsons turbines, except Clydebank boats. 2 screws. Yarrow boilers. Oil: 260/200 tons.

War Losses.—*Ardent, Contest, Sparrowhawk, Shark.*

General Notes.—All 1911-12 Programme. Guns: 3—4 inch (1—4 inch on AA. mounting in some boats), 1—2 pdr. pom-pom in nearly all, 1 M.G. Tubes: 2—21 inch single. The single tube between 2nd and 3rd funnels is a distinctive feature of this class. Complement, 75-77.

21 I Class (3 this page, 18 next page).

OAK. (LURCHER and FIREDRAKE high mainmasts.)

Special Boats.

3 *Yarrow*: **Lurcher, Firedrake, Oak** (all 1912). 765 tons. *Firedrake* 767 tons. Dimensions: 262 × 25⅝ × 9½ feet. Guns: 2—4 inch, 2—12 pdr., 1—3 pdr. AA., 1 M.G. Tubes: 2—21 inch. Designed H.P. 20,000 = 32 kts. On trials *Firedrake* made 33·1, *Lurcher* 35·34 *mean* of 8 hrs. *Oak*: 32·4. Turbines: Parsons. 2 screws. Boilers: special Yarrow oil burning; oil, *about* 170/155 tons. Built to replace three boats of this class, transferred to Royal Australian Navy, and now H.M.A.S. *Parramatta, Yarra* and *Warrego.* Complement, 70.

("I" *Class continued on next page*).

21 I Class (18 this page, 3 preceding page).

General Notes to all below.

Built under 1910-11 Programme. Armament of all: 2—4 inch, 2—12 pdr., 1—3 pdr. AA., 1 M.G., 2—21 inch tubes. Complement, 70.

To distinguish.—

JACKAL.   *Photo, Ellis, Malta.*

To Builders' Designs.

2 *Parsons*: **Badger** (1911), 799 tons, **Beaver** (1911), 810 tons. Designed H.P. 16,500 = 30 kts. Hull, etc., contracted for by Hawthorn. *Trials*: *Badger* 30.7. Parsons turbines.

1 *Thornycroft*: **Acheron** (1911) 773 tons. Designed H.P. 15,500 = 29 kts. On trial, 29.4. Parsons turbines.

1 *Yarrow*: **Archer** (1911). 775 tons. Designed H.P. 16,000 = 28 kts. Brown-Curtis turbines. *Trials*: *Archer* 30.9.

Notes.—Dimensions: *Acheron*, 252¼ × 26⅓ × 9¼ feet; others about 246 × 25¾ × 9¼ feet. 2 screws in all. Oil fuel: 182-170/158-150 tons. All Yarrow boilers.

War Losses.—*Ariel* (Minelayer), *Attack*.

Admiralty Design Boats.

1 *Beardmore*: **Goshawk** (1911). 760 tons. Parsons turbines.

3 *Clydebank*: **Hind, Hornet** 1911), **Hydra** (1912). 770.5 tons. *Trials*: *Hind* 28.1, *Hornet* 28.7, *Hydra* 28.1. Brown-Curtis turbines.

2 *Denny*: **Defender, Druid** (1911). 762-770 tons. *Trials*: *Defender* 28.3, *Druid* 28.2. Parsons turbines.

2 *Hawthorn*: **Jackal, Tigress** (1911). 745 tons. *Trials*: *Jackal* 26.9, *Tigress* 28.1. Parsons turbines.

2 *Laird*: **Lapwing, Lizard** (1911). 745 tons. *Trials*: *Lapwing* 27.2, *Lizard* 27.5. Parsons turbines.

1 *Swan Hunter*: **Sandfly** (1911). 750 tons. *Trials*: 27.7. Parsons turbines.

2 *White*: **Ferret, Forester** (1911). 750 and 760 tons. *Trials*: *Ferret* 30.2, *Forester* 29.8. Parsons turbines.

Notes.—Dimensions: 246¼ × 25¾ × 8¾-9 feet. All 3 screws, except the Clydebank boats with Brown-Curtis turbines, which have 2 screws. All Yarrow boilers, except White boats with White-Forster. Oil: *about* 180/148 tons.

War Losses: Phœnix.

17 H Class.

SHELDRAKE.

3 *Clydebank*: **Acorn, Alarm, Brisk** (1910). 760-780 tons. *Acorn* and *Alarm*, Parsons turbines; *Brisk*, Curtis turbines. *Trials*: *Acorn* 27.2, *Alarm* 27.2, *Brisk* 27.6.

1 *Denny*: **Sheldrake** (1911). 748 tons. Parsons turbines. *Trials*: *Sheldrake* 28.3.

1 *Fairfield*: **Cameleon** (1910). 747 tons. Parsons turbines. *Trials*: *Cameleon* 28.03.

3 *Hawthorn*: **Nemesis,* Nereide** (1910), **Nymphe** (1911). All 740 tons. Parsons turbines. *Trials*: *Nemesis* 27, *Nereide* 27.8, *Nymphe* 27.5.

1 *Inglis*: **Fury** (1911). 760 tons. Parsons turbines. *Trials*: 27.3.

1 *Swan Hunter*: **Hope** (1910). 745 tons. Parsons turbine. *Trials*: 27.1.

4 *Thornycroft*: **Larne, Lyra, Martin** (all 1910), **Minstrel*** (1911). All 730 tons. Parsons turbine. *Trials*: *Larne* 27.9, *Lyra* 28.7, *Martin* 28.9, *Minstrel* 28.9.

3 *White*: **Redpole, Rifleman, Ruby** (1910). All 720 tons. Parsons turbine. White-Forster boilers. *Trials*: *Redpole* 29.8, *Rifleman* 28.6, *Ruby* 29.3.

*Minstrel and *Nemesis* loaned to Japanese Navy, 1917-18, and commissioned as Japanese *Sendan* (*Minstrel*) and *Kanran* (*Nemesis*). Returned to British Navy, 1919.

Notes.—Formerly *Acorn* class. Belong to 1909-10 Programme, laid down end of 1909. Dimensions: *about* 246½ × 25¼ × 8¾ feet. Armament: 2—4 inch, 2—12 pdr., 1—3 pdr. AA.*, 1 M.G., 2—21 inch tubes. Designed H.P. 13,500 = 27 kts. 3 screws. Yarrow boilers in all, except *Redpole, Rifleman* and *Ruby*, with White-Forster. Fuel: *about* 170/140 tons oil. Complement, 72.

*In a few boats only.

To distinguish.—High bridges, thick middle funnel, no gun or tubes between 2nd and 3rd funnels. 12 pdrs. at break of fo'xle. Big ventilators between funnels.

War Losses.—*Comet, Goldfinch.*

13 G Class.

SCOURGE.

Photo, Lieut.-Com. Holberton, R.N.

3 *Clydebank* : **Beagle, Bulldog, Foxhound** (1909). 950, 952, 995 tons. Parsons turbine. H.P. 12,500.

3 *Fairfield* : **Grasshopper** (1909), **Mosquito** (1910), **Scorpion** (1910). 923, 983, 987 tons. Parsons turbines. H.P. 12,000.

1 *Hawthorn* : **Scourge** (1910). 922 tons. Parsons turbine. H.P. 12,500.

1 *Cammell Laird* : **Renard** (1909). 918 tons. Parsons turbine. H.P. 12,500.

1 *London & Glasgow* : **Rattlesnake** (1910). 946 tons. Parsons turbine. H.P. 12,000.

1 *Thames Ironworks* : **Grampus** (ex *Nautilus*), (1910). 975 tons. Parsons turbine. H.P. 12,000.

1 *Thornycroft* : **Savage** (1910). 897 tons. Parsons turbine. H.P. 12,500.

2 *White* : **Basilisk** (1910). **Harpy** (1909). 972, 976 tons. Parsons turbine. White-Forster boilers. H.P. 12,600.

General Notes.—These boats belong to the 1909-18 Programme, and were formerly known as the *Basilisk* class, or " The Mediterranean *Beagles*." Displace 897 to 995 tons. Dimensions : *average* 274½ × 28 × 10 feet. Armament : 1—4 inch, 3—12 pdr..* 1—3 pdr. AA.,† 1 M.G., 2—22 inch tubes. *Average* H.P. 12,500 = 27 kts. 3 screws. Boilers : Yarrow in all, except *Basilisk* and *Harpy*, with White-Forster. Coal : 200-241 tons. Complements for all, 96. All made 27 or a little over on *trials*, except *Grampus* 28.1, *Basilisk* 27.9, *Harpy* and *Foxhound* 27.7. Are the only coal-burning Destroyers now in British Navy, and will probably be scrapped within the next two years.

War Losses.—*Pincher, Racoon, Wolverine.*

*Scorpion 2—12 pdr.

†3 pdr. AA. not in *Basilisk, Grasshopper, Savage, Scourge.*

19 PC Boats (Converted Patrol Boats).

PC 68.

Photo, Messrs. J. S. White & Sons (Builders).

Note.—Above illustration is typical only : these vessels have varying mercantile disguises as small coasting steamers, tugs, &c. Some have only one mast forward.

2 *Barclay Curle* : **PC 55, PC 56** (both 1917). 682 tons.

2 *Caird* : **PC 42, PC 43** (both 1917). 682 tons.

1 *Connell* : **PC 63** (1917). 682 tons.

2 *Eltringham* : **PC 44.** (682 tons). **PC 65** (both 1917). 694 tons.

1 *Harland & Wolff* (Govan) : **PC 62** (1917). 682 tons.

1 *Harkness* : **PC 66** (1918). 694 tons.

1 *Tyne Iron Co.* : **PC 51** (1917). 682 tons.

6 *White* : **PC 67, PC 68** (both 1917). **PC 71—PC 74** (1918). All 694 tons.

2 *Workman Clark* : **PC 60, PC 61** (both 1917). 682 tons. **PC 69, PC 70** (both 1918). 694 tons.

Dimensions : 682 ton boats : 233 (*p.p.*), 247 (*o.a.*) × 25½ × 8-8½ feet. 694 ton boats : 233 (*p.p.*), 247 (*o.a.*) × 26¾ × 8 feet. 682 and 694 ton boats reported to have shallow bulge protection. Guns : 1—4 inch, 2—12 pdr. Torpedo tubes : removed. Carry 24-30 D.C. Machinery : Parsons or Brown-Curtis turbines. Yarrow boilers. 2 screws. Designed S.H.P. 3,500 = 20 kts. Oil : 134 tons in 682 ton boats ; 164 tons in 694 ton boats : all *max.* These two types carry extra fuel in bulges. Complement, *about* 50-55.

General Notes.—All built under Emergency War Programme. Design as P-boats, but these craft were converted or modified while building, to act as Submarine Decoy Vessels or "Q-boats." The after 4 inch gun was hidden behind various forms of dummy deck loads, *e.g.*, bales or packing cases of merchandise, trusses of hay : in a few boats it was located within a collapsible pantechnicon furniture van, or under a dummy boat built in folding sections. It was expected that, on account of shallow draught, torpedoes fired by U-boats would under-run these PC-boats, while, if hit by torpedo, bulge protection and special fillings would keep them afloat long enough to destroy the U-boat.

43 P-Boats (Patrol Boats.)

P 21.

Photo, Robertson, Gourock, N.B.

Note.—P 11, P 21, P 24, P 29, now have mainmast. P 17 has mainmast and funnel 4 feet higher. Remainder as above photo.

3 *Barclay Curle :* **P 34** (1916), **P 53, P 54** (1917).
2 *Bartram :* **P 23, P 41** (both 1916).
2 *Caird :* **P 22, P 35** (both 1916).
1 *Connell :* **P 14** (1916).
2 *Eltringham :* **P 27** (1915), **P 36** (1916).
4 *Gray :* **P 29, P 30, P 37** (all 1916), **P 45** (1917).
4 *Hamilton :* **P 75** (ex P 13, 1916), **P 38, P 57, P 58** (all 1917).
2 *Harland & Wolff (Govan) :* **P 24** (1915), **P 25** (1916).
2 *Harkess :* **P 32** (1916), **P 46** (1917).
3 *Inglis :* **P 18** (1916), **P 39, P 64** (both 1917).
1 *Napier & Miller :* **P 33** (1916).
2 *Northumberland S.B. Co. :* **P 19, P 20** (both 1916).
3 *Readhead :* **P 31** (1916), **P 47, P 48** (1917).
1 *Russell :* **P 21** (1916).
1 *Tyne Iron Co. :* **P 50** (1916).
2 *R. Thompson :* **P 28** (1916), **P 49** (1917).
4 *White (Cowes) :* **P 11** (1915), **P 40, P 52** (both 1916), **P 59** (1917).
3 *Workman Clark :* **P 15, P 16** (both 1916), **P 17** (1915).

Displacement : 613 tons. Dimensions : 230 (*p.p.*), 244½ (*o.a.*) × 23¾ × 7 feet 7 inch. Guns : Designed to mount 2—4 inch but only *P 52* has this armament ; others, 1—4 inch and (in all) 1—2 pdr. pom-pom. Tubes : 2 single 14 inch, removed from old Torpedo Boats. Two depth charge throwers and D.C. Machinery : Brown-Curtis or Parsons turbines. 2 screws. Yarrow boilers. Designed S.H.P. 3500 = 20 kts. Oil fuel : *normal* 50 tons, *max.* 93 tons. Complement, 50-54.

General Notes.—All built under Emergency War Programme. Were designed to relieve destroyers of patrol and escort work and submarine hunting. Outline scheme for these boats stipulated ; minimum size consistent with sea-keeping qualities, simplicity of construction, and adequate speed to run down submarines ; also shallow draught ; low upperworks to reduce visibility ; and economy of fuel. Built of mild steel, but with hard steel stem for ramming submarines. Large rudder area and hull strongly cut up aft to give rapid turning. Proved very useful boats and an excellent anti-submarine type in all weathers. Those converted to Decoy Ships or "Q-boats" listed as *PC* boats on the preceding page.

War Losses.—P 12, P 26.

P-boat (aircraft view).

Official R.A.F. photo.

32 Torpedo Boats.

No.	Builders.	Numbers.	Launched.	Displacement.	H.P.	Max. speed.	Tubes.	Coal or oil.	Complement.
				tons. average.		kts.		tons	
12	*Various*	36—25 ('07—8 Ests.)	1908—9	290	4000	26	3	53—41*	39
10	*Various*	23—14 ('06—7 Ests.)	1907—8	290	4000	26	3	51—40*	39
9	*Various*	8—1 ('05—6 Ests.)	1906	250	3750—3600	26	3	43—36*	35
1	White	116	1903	197	2900	25	0	44†	38

* Oil only.   † Coal.

2 *Palmer* boats : **36, 35** (1909). 313·5 tons. Dimensions : 181¾ × 17¾ × 7¼ feet. Armament : 2—12 pdr., 3—18 inch tubes. H.P. 4000 = 26 kts. Parsons turbine. Oil : 46/41 tons   *No. 24* lost during War.

4 *Hawthorn* boats : **34, 33** (1909) ; also **22, 21** (1907-8). 325·8 tons. Dimensions : 189¼ × 18½ × 7 feet. Armament : 2—12 pdr., 3—18 inch tubes. H.P. 4000 = 26 kts. 3 screws. Parsons turbine. Oil fuel : 48/41 tons.

4 *Thornycroft* boats : **32, 31** (1908), 278 tons ; also **20** (1908), 291 tons, **19** (1907), 312 tons. Dimensions : 183¼ × 18¼-18¾ × 6½ feet. Armament : 2—12 pdr., 3—18 inch tubes. H.P. 4000 = 26 kts. 3 screws. Parsons turbine. Oil : 48/41 tons.

To distinguish all above.—One tube *before* funnel, *big* ventilators between funnels. Eyes set back from stem. Funnels fairly wide apart.

(Continued on next page.)

No. 30.

Photo, Ellis, Malta.

4 *Denny* boats : **30, 29,** also **18, 17.** 272 tons. Dimensions : 183 × 18 × 6 feet. Armament : 2—12 pdr., 3—18 inch tubes. H.P. 4000 = 26 kts. Oil : 51/43 tons.

Note.—All " oily wad " T.B. *1—36* now have pole mainmast and openings under fore bridge screened in, as above illustration.

7 *White* boats : **28, 27, 26, 25** (1908), 283 tons : also **16, 15, 14** (1907), 270 tons. Dimensions : 185¼ × 18 × 6¾ feet. Armament : 2—12 pdr., 3—18 inch tubes. H.P. 4000 = 26 kts. Parsons turbine. 3 screws. Oil : 50-53/42-45 tons. No. 13 lost during War.

1 *Yarrow* boat : **23** (1907). 282 tons. Dimensions : 181 × 18 × *mean* 6¼ feet. Armament : 2—12 pdr., 3—18 inch tubes. H.P. 4000 = 26 kts. Parsons turbine. 3 screws. Oil : *normal* 49/41 tons.

To distinguish all above.—One tube *before* first funnel. Funnels fairly close together. Eyes set back from stern.

3 *Thornycroft* : **8, 7, 6** (1906). 244·7 tons. Dimensions : 171½ × 17½ × 6¾ feet. Armament : 2—12 pdr., 3—18 inch tubes. H.P. 3750 = 26 kts. Parsons turbine. 3 screws. Oil : 42/35 tons. Were originally named in order given : *Gnat, Glow-worm,* and *Gadfly.* No. 9 (ex *Grasshopper*), No. 10 (ex *Greenfly*), No. 11 (ex *Moth*), No. 12 (ex *Mayfly*), have been lost during the War.

To distinguish.—One tube *between* funnels : funnels wide apart.

5 *White* boats : **5, 4, 3, 2, 1** (1906). 261 tons. Dimensions : 178 × 17½ × 6½ feet. Armament : 2—12 pdr., 3—18 inch tubes. H.P. 3600 = 26 kts. Parsons turbine. Oil fuel : 44/37 tons. Were originally named in order given : *Spider, Sandfly, Firefly, Dragonfly, Cricket.*

To distinguish.—Tubes *before* and *abaft* first funnel. No tube before after 12 pdr. position. Funnels wide apart.

1 *White* boat : **116** (1903). 197 tons. Dimensions : 165 × 17½ × 7 feet. Armament : *Nil.* H.P. 2900 = 25 kts. 44 tons.

M. L. (Motor Launches).

M.L. 381. Some boats have mainmast right at stern for spreading W/T. aerials.

Third type : 30 originally built : **M.L. 551—580.** Built 1918. No details known, but similar to first and second types below.

Second type : 500 originally built : **M.L. 51—550.** Built 1915. 37 tons. Dimensions : 80-88 × 12¼ feet × 3′ 10″. Guns : 1—3 inch AA. or lesser calibre of AA. and other types. B.H.P. 440-450 = 19 kts. Machinery : 2 sets of Standard petrol motors. Petrol : *about* 1850 gallons. Complement, 9.

First type : 50 originally built : **M.L. 1—50.** Built 1915. 34 tons. Dimensions : 75 × 12 × 3¾ feet. Guns : 1—3 pdr. or 2 pdr. AA. and/or 1 or 2 M.G. or Lewis guns. B.H.P. 440-450 = 19 kts. Petrol : *about* 1650 gallons. Complement, 8.

General Notes.—Present boats in service can be ascertained by reference to current Navy List. Others now scrapped, being worn out. Mostly built in U.S. and Canadian Yards and shipped across the Atlantic. During War, fitted with D.C., smoke boxes, hydrophones, &c., but special gear now removed from nearly all. Petrol consumption heavy.

War Losses : Twenty-four boats, detailed in War Loss Section. *M.L. 229,* one of the eleven British M.L. on the Rhine, was almost destroyed by a petrol explosion and fire during 1919. May not be repaired.

C. M. B. (Coastal Motor Boats).

Photo wanted.

Third type : 70-ft. Some of these used as Minelayers. No details available, but are said to be capable of 40-50 kts.

C. M. B.—*(continued).*

No photo available.

55-FT. TYPE.

Second type : 55-ft. Series numbers, ***a, b, bd, c*** and ***e,*** from about ***13a*** up to ***87 b*** or above. 10 tons. Dimensions : 55 × 11 × 3 feet. Armament : Some had 2 Lewis guns on a paired mounting, others 4 Lewis guns in pairs, with 2—18 inch torpedoes in troughs at stern. Some modified to take 4 Lewis guns in pairs, with only 1—18 inch torpedo and 4 D.C. Other boats, when used for low speed work could carry 4 torpedoes in dropping gears over beams. 1 Thornycroft 375 H.P. " Y " type motor = 35 kts., but have done 41 kts. and over in service. Also Green, F.I.A.T. and Sunbeam motors. W/T. fitted in these. Complement, 3.

C. M. B. 27 = 40-FT. TYPE.   *Photo, Cribb, Southsea.*

First type : 40-ft. Original boats ***3—12,*** and later boats numbered up to ***61*** or above. Dimensions : 40 × 8½ × 3 feet. 350 H.P. Thornycroft motor = over 30 kts. 1 torpedo carried in central trough over stern. Harwich Light Cruisers used to each take a pair of these boats to sea, slung from davits, while, in the Mediterranean, light cruiser *Diamond* served as a special C.M.B. Carrier.

General Notes.—Above types designed by Messrs. Thornycrofts Ltd. Full descriptions have appeared in technical press. It need only be remarked that they discharge their torpedoes tail first from troughs over stern, then swerve on their course and allow torpedoes to run past to target. All stepped hydroplane type hulls with chine to damp down bow wave. Considering their small size, they have excellent nautical qualities. First boats were secretly built in 1916, and ran trials by night. 13 lost during War and 4 or more in Baltic operations. Boats now in commission can be ascertained from current Navy List. It is little use stating totals and numbers here, as these craft can be laid up and placed out of commission at very short notice. For full description *v.* " Engineer," April 18th, 1919, and Messrs. Thornycroft's own descriptive brochure.

D. C. B.

Are modified C.M.B. No details for publication. A few were finished about August, 1918, and good results were expected from them. The War ended before they could be put into operation.

127 Submarines (100 Completed, 27 Building).

No.	Type	First begun.	Last completed.	Displacement	H.P.	Max. speed	Fuel	Complement	T. Tubes	Max. draug't
				tons		kts.	tons			ft.
12	R 1—12.	1917	1918	$\frac{420}{500}$	$\frac{250}{1000}$	$\frac{10}{15}$	...	20	4-6	12
4	M 1—4.	1917	'20 ?	$\frac{1600}{1950}$	...	$\frac{15}{9}$	...	60	...	10
37	L 1—71.	1917	20	$\frac{890}{1070}$	$\frac{2400}{1600}$	$\frac{17\cdot3}{10\cdot5}$	76	36	4-6	$13\frac{1}{2}$
13	K 2—16, K 22.	1916	1918	$\frac{1880}{2650}$	$\frac{10000}{1400}$	$\frac{24}{9\cdot5}$	200	55	6	16
32	H 21—52.	1917	1919	$\frac{440}{500}$	$\frac{480}{320}$	$\frac{13}{10\cdot5}$	16	22	4	$11\frac{1}{4}$
7	G 3—13.	1915	1916	$\frac{700}{975}$	$\frac{1600}{840}$	$\frac{14}{10}$	44	30	5	$13\frac{1}{4}$
(3)	F 1—3.	1915	1917	$\frac{353}{525}$	$\frac{900}{400}$	$\frac{14\cdot5}{8\cdot8}$	$17\frac{1}{2}$	20	3	$10\frac{3}{4}$
22	E 21—E 55.	1915	1917	$\frac{662}{807}$	$\frac{1600}{840}$	$\frac{15}{10}$	45	30	3-5	$12\frac{1}{2}$

Notes to above Table.

Excepting *H 21-52* of "Holland" type, all above types are to Admiralty design. Above Table and description by classes on later pages, arranged alphabetically by Class Letters. Rough division by types and building dates is thus :—

61 *Ocean-going* boats : *L 1—71, M 1—4* (Monitors), *K 2—16* and *K 22, G 3—13.*
54 *Sea-going* boats : *H 21—52, E 21—55.*
12 *Coastal* boats : *R 1—12* (*F 1—3* not included).
— *Minelayers :* Various units of *L, H* and *E* types ; exact total not known.

As regards the totals given over Table for boats finished and building : These are approximate only, some of the 27 boats given as building may not be finished. Six "Later K" boats not mentioned in Table or included in total, as they seem to be stopped. Coastal *F 1—3* not included in total of completed boats, as they will be sold very soon. The *E* and *G* Classes will probably be sold off within the next eighteen months.

With reference to missing Class Letters in alphabetical order, the following brief notes may be of service. All *A. B, C* and *D* boats sold off or for sale. *J* Class presented to Australia. *N 1* (late *Nautilus*) for sale 1919, having proved more or less a failure. *S 1* (late *Swordfish*) converted into surface patrol boat. *V 1—4* for sale 1919. *W 1—4* presented to Italy during the War. No I, O, P, Q, T, U, X, Y, Z Classes.

Various surrendered German Submarines are in service under the White Ensign, but only for experiments. By agreement with all the Allies, such ex-German boats will not be added to the British Navy, but must be broken up when trials are finished.

12 R Class.

R—. *Photo, Cribb, Southsea.*

R 1—4 by Chatham D.Y., *R 5, R 6* by Pembroke D.Y., *R 7, R 8* by Vickers, *R 9, R 10* by Armstrong Whitworth, *R 11, R 12* by Cammell Laird. All launched and finished 1918.

Single hull type to Admiralty designs. Approximate dimensions : $160 \times 15\text{-}16 \times 12$ feet. Guns : 1—3 inch or 4 inch in some. Tubes : Unofficially reported to have 4 or 6—18 inch bow. Machinery : No exact details, but said to have 1 set of hot-bulb or heavy oil motors. Oil capacity small, but have an abnormal submerged endurance. Other details as Table.

Notes.—Built under Emergency War Programme. These boats (sometimes called the "Little Arthurs") were produced as a "submarine destroyer of submarines." Their outstanding feature is that—unlike nearly all other submarines in the world—they are faster below water than on the surface. They are short in length, have large rudder and hydroplane areas and small reserve of buoyancy for quick diving and rapid handling. It was intended that they should submerge and chase U-boats, and use their four bow tubes by salvo, specially big torpedo-compensating tanks with rapid flooding gear being placed in bows. Also said to have hydrophones for tracking hostile submarines.

M Class Submarine Monitors = $\left\{ \begin{array}{l} \textbf{1} \text{ Completed.} \\ \textit{3} \text{ Completing ?} \end{array} \right\}$ = 4 ?

M 1.

Photo, M. Davidson, Esq.

M 1 ex *K 18* (1918), **M 2** ex *K 19* (——), both by Vickers. **M 3** ex *K 20* (——), **M 4** ex *K 21* (——), both by Armstrong Whitworth. Launching dates of *M 2—4* not reported ; these three boats may not be finished.

Few details available.   Designed by Admiralty ; reported to be double-hulled type. Dimensions : *about* 200 × 20 × 10 feet. Guns : 1—12 inch, 35 cal., 1—3 inch AA. Machinery : Type not known, but reported to be Diesel engines. Oil fuel :   tons. Other details as Table.

Gunnery Notes.—12 inch believed to be one of those removed from old *Majestic* Class of Battleships, firing a 520 lb. projectile. No turntable, but high-angle elevation. Reported that gun is loaded and laid to high angle elevation ; then boat is dived to about 12-20 feet, leaving muzzle of 12 inch gun above water, and periscopes.   There is a bead sight on gun-muzzle, so that gun can be sighted by periscope and fired when running at shallow submersion. To re-load, it is necessary to return to surface.

General Notes.—Begun under War Emergency Programme. These "Submarine Monitors" are a unique design, but reports are not available of *M 1*'s performance during War, so that their practical worth is a matter of conjecture.

L Classes. (Totals and Description next page).

L 55.

L 20.

Photo, Cribb.

> **Photo wanted.**
>
> Classification by appearance not known.

L 18, 19, 21—27, 33—36, 52—54, 66, 69, 71.

> **Photo wanted.**

L 12, 14, 17.

(*Continued on next page.*)

Photo wanted.

L 11.

Photo wanted.

L 6.

Photc wanted.

L 5, 15 & 16.

Photo wanted.

L 4.

Photo wanted.

L 3.

Photo wanted.

L 1, 2 & 7—9.

L **Classes** $\left\{\begin{array}{l}\text{About } \textbf{23*} \text{ Completed ?} \\ \text{About } \textit{14*} \text{ Building ?}\end{array}\right\} = 37 * \text{?}$

19* *Vickers :* **L 1** ex *E 57,* **L 2** ex *E 58,* **L 3** (all 1917), **L 4. L 11. L 12. L 14. L 17—20** (all 1918), **L 21—L 23** (1919), **L 24—27. L 32** (completing 1919 ?).

2* *Swan Hunter :* **L 5** (1918), **L 33** (1919).

2* *Beardmore :* **L 6** (1918), **L 69** (1918).

2* *Cammell Laird :* **L 7. L 8** (both 1917).

2* *Denny :* **L 9** (1918), **L 54** (1919).

5* *Fairfield :* **L 15** (1917), **L 16** (1918), **L 36. L 55. L 56** (all 1919).

2* *Pembroke D.Y. :* **L 34. L 66** (1919-20 ?).

2* *Armstrong Whitworth :* **L 52. L 53** (both 1919).

1 *Scotts :* **L 71** (1919).

*All totals liable to revision. Some of the boats launched 1919 may be abandoned.

Following boats reported stopped 1918 :—

21† boats stopped : *L 28—31* (Vickers), *L 35* (Pembroke D.Y.), *L 50, 51, 63, 64, 65* (Cammell Laird), *L 67, 68* (Armstrong), *L 57—62* (Fairfield), *L 70* (Beardmore), *L 72* (Scotts), *L 73* (Denny).

14 boats never ordered : *L 13, L 37—49.*

†Liable to revision. Some may be completed.

Design and type of hull not known ; reported to be a wing-tank type designed by Admiralty. Dimensions : 222 (*p.p.*), 231 (*o. a.*)× 23½ × 13¾ feet. Guns : 1—3 inch AA. or 4 inch, but minelayers may have no guns. Torpedo tubes : in earlier boats, up to (*about*) *L 9*, 6, viz., four bow, two beam, all 21 inch ; boats above *L 9*, 6—21 inch, all in bows. Mine-laying boats numbered under *L 9* have no beam tubes—only four bow—21 inch. Machinery : 2 sets 12-cylinder solid injection Vickers type, but others may have Cammell-Laird-Fullager, Armstrong, and other types. Oil : 76 tons. Other details as Table.

Notes.—The "L Class" is in a highly complex state, owing to the variations in build, giving ten or more types by appearance. Further uncertainty is introduced by inadequate information regarding boats whose construction has been stopped. All built under Emergency War Programme, but funds for completion of some boats will fall within post-war Navy Estimates. In dimensions, H.P., speed, &c., these boats have a marked resemblance to the 1914-18 German ocean-going Submarines. Minelaying boats not known exactly, but unverified reports say *L 2, 14, 17* are equipped for sowing mines.

War Losses.— *L 10.*

13 K Class (+ 6 Building ?)

K 10.   K 12 & K 16 have gun on high fairwater *before* C.T.   *Photo, Cribb, Southsea.*

K 15 (higher funnels).   *Photo, Topical.*

K2, K5 (both by Portsmouth D.Y., 1916), **K6** (Devonport D.Y., 1916), **K3, K8, K9, K10** (all by Vickers, 1916), **K11, K12** (both by Armstrong Whitworth, 1916-17), **K14, K22,** ex *K 13* (both by Fairfield, 1916), **K15** (Scott, 1917), **K16** (Beardmore, 1917).

(*K 23—K 28 : See General Notes.*)

All double-hulled type, designed by Admiralty for service as "Fleet Submarines" with Grand Fleet. Dimensions : 334 (*p.p.*), 337 (*o.a.*) × 26½ × 16 feet. Guns : 1—4 inch, 1—3 inch AA., and (in some) 1 D.C. thrower. Torpedo tubes : 8—18 inch, viz., 4 bow, 4 beam. Machinery : see Notes below. Oil fuel : 170 tons. Other details as Table.

Engineering Notes.—These are *not* the first steam-driven boats in British Navy, having been preceded by *Swordfish* (*S 1*), now scrapped. Surface machinery consists of combined steam turbines and Diesel engine. 2 sets of single reduction turbines, one H.P. and one L.P. in each set, with double helical gearing. 2 screws. 2 Yarrow small-tube type boilers with forced draught, boilers, turbines, funnels being lagged with incombustible non-conducting materials. Small electric motors are fitted for lowering funnels and closing w.t. hatches over funnel wells. Boiler room air vents closed by hydraulic power. To assist in diving quickly, or getting away after breaking surface (while steam motors are being started up), an 800 B.H.P. 8-cylinder Diesel motor is fitted, which can also be used for surface cruising. Drive from Diesel engine is through electric motors, so that these boats have three systems of transmission, (*a*) geared turbines for steam drive, (*b*) Diesel and electric transmission, (*c*) electric battery drive when submerged. 2 high-power compressors to charge 2500 lbs. air bottles ; 2 low-power compressors to blow main ballast tanks after breaking surface. 2 electric-power bilge pumps. Hydraulic rams for raising periscopes and telescopic masts. Hydro-electric controlling gear to hydroplanes, forward hydroplanes being of housing type.

Gunnery and Torpedo Notes.—Were first completed with 2 guns before and below C.T. and 1 abaft C.T. on superstructure deck, but these were removed. For a time, these boats had only 1—3 inch, but *K 17* at time of her loss mounted 1—5.5 inch. There were also 2—18 inch tubes in superstructure, above water when in surface trim, making eight tubes in all. The original three guns and superstructure tubes were removed to D.A.M.S. and S.D. Vessels (Q-boats).

General Notes.—All built under Emergency War Programme. Were first completed with flush level bows, but showed a tendency to trim by the head and dive "on their own." To remedy this, bows were raised, as shown in above illustrations. Accommodation for officers and men is remarkably spacious for submarines. Are said to be rather hot on account of steam system of propulsion, but in the North Sea this proved rather an advantage than otherwise. Considering that these boats were of a highly experimental type, they have turned out most remarkably well. Further boats, *K 23—28* reported ordered in 1918, which were to have 6—21 inch bow tubes. Nothing further has been heard of these later boats ; they may be cancelled.

War Losses.—*K 1, 4, 17.   K 13* also foundered, but was salved and re-numbered *K 22.*

Removals.—*K 7* on Sale List, 1919.

(J Class.)

All presented in 1919 to Royal Australian Navy, *q. v* for details. *War Loss.*—*J 6.*

H Class $\left\{ \begin{array}{l} \text{about } \mathbf{20} \text{ delivered} \\ \text{about } \quad 8 \text{ } building \end{array} \right\}$ = 32.*

*Some adapted for Minelaying.

Photo wanted.

12 *Vickers* : **H 21—H 32** (launched 1917-18).

8 *Cammell Laird* : **H 33—H 40** (launched 1918-19).

6 *Armstrong Whitworth* : **H 41—H 46** (launched 1918-19).

4 *Beardmore* : **H 47—H 50** (launched 1918-19).

2 *Pembroke D.Y.* : **H 51** (1918), **H 52** (1919).

Single-hull "Holland" (Electric Boat Co.) type modified by Admiralty. Dimensions : 164½ (*p.p.*), 171 (*o.a.*) × 15¾ feet. Guns : Majority have 1—3 inch AA. Tubes : 4—21 inch bow, but minelaying boats may have only two or none. Machinery : 2 sets of Diesel engines of various types. Oil : 16 tons. Other details as Table.

Notes.—Not known how many of these boats are Minelayers. All built under War Emergency Programme. Not yet certain that all of these will be finished ; some may be cancelled. During the War, *H 1—10* type were assembled by the Canadian Vickers Co., Montreal, and crossed Atlantic under their own power. On war service, these boats proved very successful, and were about the most popular type with the British Submarine Service. *H 11—20* were assembled by the Bethlehem Steel Co. and Fore River Co., U.S.A., but were interned by the U.S. Government. On the entry of the U.S. into the War, the boats were released, but were not taken over by British Navy. Six boats (*H 13, H 16—20*) were presented to Chile, *H 14, H 15* presented to Canada, *H 11, H 12* put on Sale List, 1919. *H 21—52* were designed as an improvement on the original *H 1—10* boats, having 21 inch tubes instead of 18-inch.

War Losses.—None in above *H 21—52* Class. Of the *H 1—10* Class, *H 3, 5, 6,* lost during War.

Removals.—*H 1, 2, 4, 7, 8, 9, 10* (*H 1—10* Class), *H 11, H 12* (*H 11—20* Class), all on Sale List, 1919.

7 G Class.

Photo, Dr. J. A. Prendergast.

G3, G4, G5 (all Chatham D.Y., 1916), **G6** (Armstrongs, 1916), **G10, G13** (Vickers, 1916). Admiralty double-hull type. Dimensions : 185 (*p.p.*), 187 (*o.a.*) × 22½ × 13¼ feet. Guns : 1—3 inch AA. Torpedo tubes : 5, viz., 2—18 inch bow, 2—18 inch beam, 1—21 inch stern. Diesel engines : Vickers, Armstrong (2 sets). Oil : 44 tons. Other details as Table.

Notes.—All Emergency War Programme. Built as "Bight and North Sea Patrols," being the first genuine ocean-going boats in British Navy. Had their bows raised during War. The above boats will probably be brought home from Mediterranean during the next twelve months and placed on Sale List, except G 3 which is in home waters and may already be for sale. G 1, 2, 12, 14, on Sale List, 1914.

War Losses.—G 7, 8, 9, 11.

3 F Class.

F 2 (and F 3. F 1 slightly different).   *Photo, Messrs J. S. White & Sons.*

F 1 (Chatham D.Y., 1915), **F 2** (White, 1917), **F 3** (Thornycroft, 1916). Admiralty double-hull type. F 1, 1913-14 Programme, F 2, F 3, 1914-15 Programme. Dimensions : 150 (*p.p.*), 151 (*o.a.*) × 16 × 10¾ feet. Guns : *Nil*, but were designed to mount a 2 pdr. pom-pom. Tubes : 3—18 inch, 2 bow or beam, 1 stern. Diesel engines, 2 sets. Oil : 17½ tons. Other details as Table.

Note.—Will probably be put on Sale List at an early date.

22 E Class.—18 boats + 4 Minelayers.

Now have steel bridge screen.

E 7—20 & LATER CLASS :— 22 boats.

E 21, E 23 (Vickers, 1915), **E 25** (Beardmore, 1915), **E 27** (Yarrow, 1917), **E 31** (Scott, 1915), **E 32** (White, 1916), **E 33** (Thornycroft, 1916), **E 35** (J. Brown, 1916), **E 38** (Fairfield, 1916), **E 39, E 40** (launched by Palmers, 1916-17 and completed by Armstrongs), **E 41,* E 42** (Cammell Laird, 1915), **E 44** (Swan Hunter, 1916). **E 45,* E 46*** (Cammell Laird, 1916), **E 48** (launched by Fairfield 1916, completed by Beardmores), **E 51 *** (Scotts, 1916), **E 52** (Denny, 1916), **E53, E54** (Beardmore, 1915-16), **E 55** (Denny, 1916).

*These are Minelayers.

All Admiralty wing-tank type. Built under Emergency War Programme. First British type of submarine with internal sub-division by w.t. bulkheads and with beam tubes. Dimensions : 180 (*p.p.*), 181 (*o.a.*) × 22½ × 12½ feet. Tubes : 3 to 5—18 inch, viz., 2 bow, 0, 1, or 2 beam, 1 stern. Minelayers marked * have no beam tubes, and carry about 20 mines. Diesel engines : 2 sets of Vickers, Sulzer, Carels, M.A.N., or other types. Oil : 45 tons. Other details as Table.

Notes.—Performed splendid work during War, and proved most satisfactory. Heavy losses sustained by this class are an index to the arduous work they performed, 1915-18. E 2, 4 (of E 1—6 type), 11, 12, 29, 43, 56 (all E 7—20 and later type), put on Sale List, 1919 ; the others detailed above will be sold off as new L boats come into service.

War Losses.—E 1,* 3, 5, 6 (E 1—6 type), E 7, 8,* 9,* 10, 13, 14, 15, 16, 17, 18, 19,* 20, 22, 24, 26, 28, 30, 34, 36, 37, 47, 49, 50 (all E 7—20 and later type).

*Scuttled in Baltic.

One old and small boat, C 4, is being kept for experiments with Edison batteries, but will be sold when tests are finished.

All B, C, D boats on Sale List, 1919.

HERMES (11th September, 1919).

Displacement, 10,950 tons *normal.* Complement $\left\{\begin{array}{l}500 \text{ R.N.} \\ 130 \text{ R.A.F.}\end{array}\right\} = 680.$

Length $\left\{\begin{array}{l}p.p. \ 548 \text{ feet} \\ o.a. \ 558\frac{1}{2} \ ,,\end{array}\right\}$ Beam $\left\{\begin{array}{l}w.l. \\ \text{outside bulges, 70 feet}\end{array}\right\}$ Draught $\left\{\begin{array}{l}mean \ 18 \text{ feet.} \\ max. \ — \ ,,\end{array}\right.$

Guns (**Dir. Con.**):
  10—6 inch, 50 cal.
  4—4 inch, AA.
  4—3 pdr.
  5 M.G.
  (1 landing)
Torpedo tubes:
not known.

Armour:
  Not known—probably
    of Light Cruiser
    type.
Anti-Torp. Pro.
  Bulges.

LAUNCH OF H.M.S. "HERMES."   *Builders' Photo by courtesy of Sir W. G. Armstrong, Whitworth & Co.*

Aircraft Notes.—Reported to be similar to *Argus*, but with various improvements. Will have funnel placed right over on starboard beam. 2 hangars, each with electric-power lift and cranes at stern.

Machinery: All geared turbines, type unknown. Designed S.H.P. 40,000 = 25 kts. 2 screws. Boilers: Yarrow or Babcock. Fuel (oil only):   tons *max.*

Name	Builder	Machinery	Begun	Completed	Trials
Hermes	Armstrong Whitworth		Jan., 1918	1920 ?	

General Notes.—Begun under Emergency War Programme. Advanced to launching stage to clear slip for building a new Cunard liner. Completion suspended until further orders.

EAGLE (June, 1918), late Battleship.

Displacement, 28,000* tons.   Complement $\left\{\begin{array}{l}\text{— R.N.}\\\text{— R.A.F.}\end{array}\right\}$ = ————.

Length $\left\{\begin{array}{l}(p.p.)\ 625\ \text{feet}\\(o.a.)\ 661\quad,,\end{array}\right\}$ Beam, 92 feet.†   *Mean* draught, 29 feet.*

* As originally designed.
† May be increased by addition of bulge protection.

Guns :
6—6 inch, 50 cal.
2—3 inch, A A.
4 M.G.
(1 landing)
Torpedo Tubes :
not known.

Armour :
Designed as *Canada*
(*q.v.*) but protection
has probably been
lightened and greatly
altered.

Completing.
Will have one funnel placed on extreme starboard beam.

(No plans available.)

Aircraft Notes.—No reliable details available, but reported that various features of H.M.S. *Argus* will be used in this ship, in an improved form.

Machinery : As designed Brown-Curtis (H.P.) and Parsons (L.P.) turbines combined. S.H.P. 37'000 = 22.75 kts., but alterations in design may have raised speed to 25 kts. for same power. Boilers : 21 Yarrow. Coal (as first designed) : 1150 tons *normal*, 3300 tons *max.* + 520 tons oil fuel, but design has probably been altered to oil fuel only.

Name	Builder	Machinery	Begun	Completed	Trials
Eagle	Armstrong Whitworth	Vickers	Jan., 1913	No.	

General Notes.—Begun for Chile as *Almirante Cochrane*, a Dreadnought Battleship and sister to *Canada* (ex-Chilean *Almirante Latorre*). All work on this ship ceased in August, 1914, and she lay on her slip until 1917, when her purchase was negotiated with the Chilean Government. Her design was modified to an Aircraft Carrier or " Special Light Cruiser." Early in 1919, progress with her was slackened down and work was proceeding very slowly on her in the autumn of 1919. Her date of completion cannot be forecasted.

124

VINDICTIVE (17th Jan., 1918.)   Late Light Cruiser *Cavendish.*

Displacement, 9750 tons.   Complement $\left\{ \begin{array}{l} \text{R.N.} \\ \text{R.A.F.} \end{array} \right\}$ = -

Length 565 feet (*p.p.*). 605 feet (*o.a.*).   Beam, 65 feet.   Draught $\left\{ \begin{array}{l} \textit{Mean } 17\frac{1}{4} \text{ feet.} \\ \textit{Max. } 20\frac{1}{3} \text{ feet.} \end{array} \right.$

VINDICTIVE.

Guns :
   4—7·5 inch,   cal.
   4—12 pdr.
   4—3 inch AA.
   4 M.G.
   (1 landing).
Torpedo tubes (21 inch) :
   2 submerged.
   4 above water.

Armour :
   3″—2″ Side (amidships)..
   $2\frac{1}{2}$′—$1\frac{1}{2}$″ Side (f. & a.) ...
   1″ Upper Deck (amid.)...
   $1\frac{1}{2}$″ Lower Deck (aft) ...

Ahead :
3—7·5 in.

Astern :
3—7·5 in.

Broadside : 3—7·5 in. ; 3—21 in. tubes.

Machinery : Parsons (all geared) turbines.   4 screws.   Boilers : Yarrow.   Designed S.H.P. 60,000
=29·75 (*cf.* trials).   Fuel : 1000 tons coal and oil *normal*, 800 tons coal+1500 tons oil *maximum*.

Gunnery Notes $\left. \begin{array}{l} \\ \\ \\ \end{array} \right\}$

Armour Notes   As *Hawkins, Raleigh,* &c. on a previous page.

Engineering Notes

Name	Builder	Machinery	Begun	Completed	Trials : H.P. = kts.
Vindictive	Harland & Wolff, Belfast	Harland & Wolff, Belfast	July, 1918	Oct., 1918	63,600 = 29.12

Aircraft Notes.—No reliable details available.   Reported to carry six aeroplanes.

General Notes.—Built under Emergency War Programme.   Commenced under name of *Cavendish,* as a unit of the "Improved *Birmingham*" type of Light Cruisers.   Modified by builders before delivery as an Aircraft Carrier.

BRITISH NAVY—AIRCRAFT CARRIER.

FURIOUS (15 August, 1916). Late Cruiser.

Normal Displacement, *about* 19,100 tons, about 22,900 tons *full load.* Complement, $\left\{\begin{array}{l} \text{R.N.} \\ \text{R.A.F.} \end{array}\right\} = 737.$

Length, (*p.p.*) 750 feet, (*o.a.*) 786¼ feet. Beam, 88 feet. Draught, $\left\{\begin{array}{ll} mean & 21\frac{1}{2} \text{ feet.} \\ max. & 25 \text{ feet.} \end{array}\right.$

Guns **(Dir. Con.)**:
    10—5·5 inch, — cal.
    5—3 inch AA.
    4—3 pdr.
    5 M.G.
    (1 landing.)
Torpedo tubes (21 inch):
    16 *above water.*
    2 *submerged.*

Armour:
    3″ Belt (amidships)............
    2″ Belt (bow).
    3″-2″ Bulkheads F. & A. ....
    7″-3″ Barbettes............
    1″ Decks (H.T. at stern)..........
    3″-1½″ Decks (H.T. at stern)....
    10″ C.T.
    6″-3″ Sighting hood. ....
    3″ C.T. tube ....
    2″ C.T. base...............
Anti-Torp. Pro.
    Shallow bulge ....
    1″ H.T. vertical. ....
    ¾″ Funnel and vent screen. ...

Ahead:
6—5·5 in.

Broadside: 5—5.5 in., 9 (?)—21 inch tubes.

Astern:
2—5·5 in.

Machinery: Brown-Curtis (all geared) Turbines. 4 screws. Boilers: Yarrow. Designed S.H.P. 90,000 = 31 kts. Fuel (oil only): 750 tons *normal*, 3,393 tons *maximum.*

Armour Notes.—3″ Belt consists of 2″ plating over 1″ shell plating, as in Light Cruisers. Belt forward is set inboard, as plans. Barbettes are still in, though no large guns are mounted in them. Fo'xle, Upper Decks, 1″ H.T. Main Deck, 1¼″—1″. Lower deck at stern, 1½″—1″ flat, 2″ slopes, 3″ over rudder head—all H.T.

Internal Protection.—Bulge deeper than that of *Glorious* and *Courageous*, but *not* filled with oil fuel. There is a complete internal citadel of 1″ vertical plating from barbette to barbette, well inboard and covering magazines, shell and boiler rooms. Outside and below this citadel and on each beam, are 1″ screens, 250-300 ft. long, covering boiler and engine rooms. From within the citadel rise the ¾″ screens protecting funnel and boiler room vents.

Gunnery Notes.—Originally designed to mount 2—18 inch and 11—5.5 inch guns, provision being made to mount 4—15 inch if the 18 inch guns proved unsatisfactory. The fore 18 inch gun was never mounted, being replaced by flying-off deck and hangar. When in service in 1917-13, she fired the after 18 inch a few times, and it is said "it shook her up considerably." In 1918, the after 18 inch was also taken out, flying-on deck and after hangar added. At the same time, 1—5.5 inch was removed and other 10—5.5 inch re-distributed. The after tripod mast, with gunnery controls was also removed.

Torpedo Notes.—Submerged tubes are not satisfactory, and may be removed. There are four sets of triple 21 inch tubes on upper deck aft, and one pair of 21 inch tubes on each beam forward on upper deck. On re-construction, the 3″ (after) Torpedo Control Tower was removed and controls re-located.

Name	Builder	Machinery	Begun	Completed	Trials H.P. = kts.
Furious	Armstrong Whitworth	Wallsend Co.	June,1915	July, 1917	90,820 =

General Notes.—Built under Emergency War Programme. Designed as a modified *Courageous*, but altered to Aircraft Carrier (see Gunnery and Aircraft Notes). Since conversion, she is said to be rather light, and is good now for 32-33 kts. Including cost of alterations, this ship is said to have absorbed nearly six million pounds. Flagship, Vice-Admiral Commanding Aircraft.

Aircraft Notes and Illustrations on opposite page.

FURIOUS. (**For details, v. oppposite page.**)

Aircraft Notes.—When first completed, she carried about four Short seaplanes and six Sopwith "Pups." These were easily flown off bows, but there was difficulty in getting seaplanes shipped inboard by derricks. Experiments were made to use the forward flying-off deck for landing also, but it was found too dangerous. Later, the big after flying-on deck was added, and proved satisfactory. Forward flying-off deck is about 160 feet long, tapers to bows, has collapsible wind-breaking pallisades. There is also a power-operated lift before C. T. to hoist seaplanes from forward hangar to flying-off deck. The after flying-on deck is about 300 feet long by 100 feet wide, with stopping net just abaft funnel. There is also another lift aft for raising seaplanes from after hangar. Narrow decks on each side of the funnel connect the flying-off deck with flying-on deck, small trolleys on rails being used to move seaplanes forward or aft. No seaplanes are now carried, but only aeroplanes of "Cuckoo" (torpedo dropping) and other types.

FURIOUS. Aircraft View.   *Official R.A.F. Photo.*

ARGUS (2nd Dec., 1917). Late Liner.

Normal displacement, 15,775 tons. Complement $\left\{ \begin{array}{l} \text{R.N.} \\ \text{R.A.F.} \end{array} \right\} = 495.$

Length (*p.p.*), 535 feet (*w.l.*) 560 feet (*o.a.*) 565 feet. Beam, 68 feet. Draught, $22\frac{3}{4}$ feet, *mean.*

Guns :
2—4 inch, 50 cal.
2—4 inch AA.
Torpedo tubes :
Nil

Armour :
Nil.

ARGUS (port view).

ARGUS (starboard view.)   *Photo, C N.*

Note to Illustrations.—Two views are given, as *Argus* exemplifies dazzle-painting excellently. Note the reversed direction of diagonal striping on one beam, compared with the other.

Machinery : Parsons turbines. 4 screws. Designed S.H.P. 22,000 = 20·5 kts. Can make 20·75 kts. for short periods, but 20 kts. is usually best speed under ordinary conditions. Boilers : 12 cylindrical (6 D.E. and 6 S.E.), with Howdens forced draught. Fuel : 2000 tons oil.

Capacity, &c.—Hangar is 350 ft. long by 68 ft. wide (*over all*) and 48 ft. clear width, 20 ft. clear height. It is divided into four sections by fire-proof screens, and can accommodate 20 seaplanes.

Stores, &c.—Torpedoes are carried for Sopwith "Cuckoo" type torpedo-dropping aeroplanes ; aero-bombs, spare parts, wings, propellers, &c. Full equipment is carried for maintenance and repair of aircraft. There are large carpenters' and engineers' workshops, for executing rapid repairs.

Handling Gear.—Two electrically controlled lifts for raising aircraft from hangar to flying deck. Forward lift, 30 ft. × 36 ft. After lift, 60 ft. × 18 ft. When forward lift is at flying deck level, two roller platforms slide to the sides and uncover well opening. When lift descends, the platforms are closed together and give a 20-ft. platform for flying off. When a deck load of aeroplanes is carried, wind-breaking pallisades can be raised simultaneously to 14 ft. above flying deck. Two derricks with electric winches amidships on flying deck, and two electric cranes at stern on hangar deck level ; all to pick up aeroplanes from the water.

Flying-off.—Flying deck is 68 ft. wide and 550 ft. long. Chart-house is on hydraulic lift ; masts, jackstaff, &c., all fold down to give perfectly level flying-off space.

Landing.—Wind safety mattress (or landing net) fitted. Steam jet indicators fitted for day use and special illumination for night landings. There is a wide safety net all round flying deck.

Engineering Notes.—At the time designs were got out, a $\frac{1}{4}$-inch scale model was prepared for testing in the air tunnel at the National Physical Laboratory, Teddington, to solve various structural problems and to test eddy-making effects of hull. It was found that the emission of hot furnace gases from the usual type of funnels created such serious air disturbances, safe landings would be very difficult. Accordingly, horizontal smoke-ducts with big expelling fans were fitted, to deliver all furnace gases and smoke out over stern. Designed for 18 kts., but modifications during conversion raised speed by 2 kts.

*For all details in these notes, we are indebted to "Engineering," which published a full description of H.M.S. *Argus,* in its issue of March 28th, 1919.

Name	Builder	Machinery	Begun	Completed	Trials : H.P. = kts.
Argus	Beardmore	Beardmore	1914	Sept., 1918	

General Notes.—Begun 1914, for Italian Lloyd Sabaudo Line, as S.S. *Conte Rosso.* All work on her ceased in 1914. She was purchased in 1916 and converted to Aircraft Carrier. In appearance, she is quite unique, and she is sometimes called "The Floating Island." As a mobile hangar and floating aerodrome, she has proved very successful.

PEGASUS (ex G. E. Railway Co. s.s. *Stockholm*, built by J. Brown & Co., ——, purchased 1917). 3300 tons. Dimensions : 330 (*p.p.*), 332 (*o.a.*) × 43 × 15 (*mean*), $15\frac{2}{4}$ (*max.*) feet. Guns : 2—12 pdr. and 2—12 pdr. AA. S.H.P. 9500 = 20.25 kts. (20.8 trials). Machinery : Brown-Curtis turbines (all-geared). 2 screws. Boilers : Cylindrical. Oil fuel : 360 tons. Complement, 258 R.N. and R.A.F.

ARK ROYAL (Blyth S.B. Co., 1914, purchased 1914). 7450 tons. Dimensions : $352\frac{1}{2}$ (*p.p.*), 366 (*o.a.*) × $50\frac{5}{6}$ × 18 feet (*mean*). Guns : 4—12 pdr., 2 M.G. I.H.P. 3000 = 11 kts. Machinery : Vertical triple expansion. 1 screw. Boilers : Cylindrical. Oil : 500 tons. Complement, 180 R.N. and R.A.F.

May be re-conditioned for mercantile service.   *Photo, Topical.*

NARIANA (Denny Bros., ——, chartered 1917). 3070 tons. Dimensions : 315 (*p.p.*), 352 (*o.a*), including projection of stern gantry) × $45\frac{1}{2}$ × $13\frac{1}{6}$ feet (*mean*), $13\frac{5}{6}$ (*max.*). Guns 2—12 pdr. and 2—12 pdr. AA. S.H.P. 6700 = 19 kts. (20.32 trials). Machinery : Parsons turbines (all-geared). Boilers : Babcock & Wilcox. 2 screws. Coal : 448 tons. Complement, 278 R.N. and R.A.F.

Photo, Messrs. Lobnitz.

SLINGER (——). Experimental Aeroplane Catapult Ship, built by Messrs. Lobnitz. I.H.P. 1030 = 10 kts. No other details received.

PRINCESS MARGARET (built 1913-14, chartered and converted during War, purchased 1919). 5440 tons. Complement, 215. Dimensions: 395½ (o.a.) × 54 × 16⅚ feet (max. draught). Guns: 2—4.7 inch, 2—12 pdr., 2—6 pdr. AA., 1—2 pdr. pom-pom. S.H.P. 15,000 = 22.5 kts. (23.15 on *trials*). Oil fuel : 585 tons.

LONDON (Sept., 1899). Old Battleship of 15,000 tons, converted 1918. Complement, 481. Dimensions : 431¾ (o.a.) × 75 × 27⅔ feet (max. draught). Guns : 3—6 inch, 1—4 inch AA., 2 M.G., 1 landing. Torpedo tubes (18 inch) : 4 *submerged*. Armour : 9″, 6″ and 2″ belt, 6″ casemates, 3″ deck. Old 10″—8″ turrets also left in, though 12 inch guns, shields, etc., are removed. I.H.P. 15,000 = 18 kts. Machinery : 2 sets 3-cylinder vertical triple expansion. 2 screws. Boilers : 20 Belleville. Coal : 2000 tons *max.*

AMPHITRITE (1898). Ex-Cruiser, converted 1917. 11,000 tons. Complement, 409. Dimensions : 466 (o.a.) × 69 × 27 feet (max. draught). Guns : 4—6 inch, 1—12 pdr. Armour : 4″ deck, 6″ casemates. Machinery : 2 sets 4-cylinder vertical inverted triple expansion. Boilers : 30 Belleville. I.H.P. 18,000 = 21 kts. 2 screws. Coal : 1730 tons.

> *No photo available.*

EURYALUS (1901). Old Cruiser of 12,000 tons, partially converted to a Minelayer at Hong Kong D.Y., 1918-19, but now laid up in Reserve. Dimensions : 472 (o.a.) × 69½ × 27¾ feet max. draught. Guns : 2—9·2 inch (probably removed), 2—6 inch, 2—6 pdr. AA., 2—3 pdr. Machinery : 2 sets vertical triple expansion. 2 screws. Boilers : Belleville. I.H.P. 21,000 = 21 kts. Coal : 1600 tons *max.*

Note.

The 20th Destroyer Flotilla (Minelayers) consists of *Abdiel, Gabriel* (Leaders), *Vanoc, Vanquisher, Venturous* (Admiralty "V" type), *Tarpon, Telemachus* (Admiralty "R" Class), *Meteor* ("M" Class), used for experiments. Other "V" and "W" Destroyers were fitted as Minelayers during the War.

Submarine Minelayers are units of "L" Classes (numbers not known), *E 41, E 45, E 46, E 51,* carrying about 20 mines.

C.M.B. also used as Minelayers during War. If necessity arises, Warships of nearly all types can be quickly fitted out as Minelayers.

SIR BEVIS.

Photo, by courtesy of Messrs. Osbourne Graham.

ARD PATRICK
DONOVAN
FLYING FOX } As above view.
MINORU   } Mast *before* funnel
ROCK SAND
(*and others*)

ORMONDE

Photo by courtesy of Blyth S.B. Co.

IROQUOIS
SEFTON
SILVIO   } As above illustration.
SIR BEVIS } Mast *abaft* funnel.
(*and others*)

("24 CLASS"—24 SHIPS.)

ARD PATRICK (June, 1918), **CICERO** (July, 1918), **FLYING FOX** (March, 1918), **MINORU** (——, 1919), **ORBY** (October, 1918), **ROCK SAND** (July, 1918), **SPEARMINT** (September, 1918), **SUNSTAR** (*building?*), all eight by Swan Hunter. **BEND OR** (September, 1918), **HARVESTER** (November, 1918), **IROQUOIS** (August, 1918), **SEFTON** (July, 1918), **SILVIO** (April, 1918), **SIR BEVIS** (May, 1918), all six by Barclay, Curle. **DONOVAN** (April, 1918), **ISINGLASS** (——, 1919), **SANFOIN** (June, 1918), **SIR HUGO** (September, 1918), all by Greenock & Grangemouth Co. **GALITEE MORE** (——, 1919), **LADAS** (September, 1918), **PERSIMMON** (March, 1918), **SIR VISTO** (Dec., 1918), all by Osbourne, Graham. **ORMONDE** (June, 1918), **MERRY HAMPTON** (December, 1918), both by Blyth S.B. Co.

All 1320 tons. First delivered April, 1918, three or four not finished by September, 1919. *Sunstar* not launched and may be stopped. Dimensions : 267½ (*p.p.*). 276½ (*o.a.*) × 34⅚ × 12 feet. Guns : 2—4 inch, as designed ; those completed in 1919 may have only 3 pdr. guns or none at all. Machinery : Inverted 4-cylinder triple expansion. Boilers : Cylindrical return smoke tube. 1 screw. Designed H.P. 2500 = 17 kts. Coal : 260 tons. Complement, 82.

General Notes.—All officially rated as " Fleet Sweeping Vessels (Sloops) " and built under Emergency War Programme. Although not built as Submarine Decoy Vessels (or " Q-boats "), they have a resemblance to the Standard Cargo Ships. It is extremely difficult to distinguish bows from stern when these ships are dazzle-painted, or to separate the *Silvio* group (mast *abaft* funnel) from the *Flying Fox* group (mast *before* funnel). The *Silvio* group have rather higher bridges, mast is close to and *abaft* funnel and ventilators between bridges are rather higher. *Flying Fox* group have mast further away from and *before* funnel. *Minoru* and others completed in the summer of 1919, had after bridge cut down, the higher fore bridge indicating position of bows. Are said to be indifferent sea-boats, and roll a lot ; not so successful as the " Flowers." None lost during War. Officially classified as the " 24 Class," and not as " Racehorse Class," as this might lead to confusion with the Paddle Minesweepers named after racecourses. The whole 24 ships may not be completed finally.

"Q" Boat—Flower Type—30 Ships.

POLYANTHUS.

Photo, Messrs. Lobnitz & Co. (Builders).

COREOPSIS.

(ANCHUSA TYPE—26 SHIPS.)

CONVOLVULUS (May, 1917), **COREOPSIS** (Sept., 1917), **DIANTHUS** (Nov., 1917), **EGLANTINE** (June, 1917), **GARDENIA** (Dec., 1917), **GILIA** (Feb., 1918), **HAREBELL** May, 1918), all by Barclay, Curle. **AURICULA** (Oct., 1917), **BRYONY** (Oct., 1917), **CEANOTHUS** June, 1917), **CHRYSANTHEMUM** (Nov., 1917), all by Armstrong, Whitworth. **HIBISCUS** (Nov., 1917), **MARJORAM** (Dec., 1917), **MISTLETOE** (Nov., 1917), all by Greenock & Grangemouth Co. **LYCHNIS** (Aug., 1917), **PELARGONIUM** (March, 1918), both by Hamilton. **POLYANTHUS** (Sept., 1917), **SAXIFRAGE** (Jan., 1918), both by Lobnitz. **SILENE** (March, 1918), **SPIRAEA** (Nov., 1917), both by Simons. **SWEETBRIAR** (Oct., 1917), **TUBEROSE** (Nov., 1917), both by Swan Hunter. **SYRINGA** (Sept., 1917), **WINDFLOWER** (April, 1918), both by Workman, Clark. **IVY** (Blyth S.B. Co., Oct., 1917), **MONTBRETIA** (Irvine S.B. Co., Sept., 1917).

All 1290 tons. Completed Aug., 1917-June, 1918. Dimensions: 250 (*p.p.*), 262¼ (*o.a.*) × 35 × 11½-12 (*mean*), 12½-13¾ (*max.*) feet draught. Designed to mount 2—12 pdr., 1—7.5 howitzer or 1—200 lb. stick-bomb howitzer, 4 Depth Charge Throwers, but actually armed with 2—4 inch, 1 or 2—12 pdr. and D.C. Throwers. Machinery: 4-cylinder triple expansion. Boilers: 2 cylindrical. 1 screw. Designed H.P. 2500 = 17 kts., but some only about 16 kts. on this power; about 2800 = 17 kts. actually. Coal: 260 tons. Complement, 93. Also see *General Notes*.

(AUBRIETIA TYPE—4 SHIPS.)

AUBRIETIA (Blyth S.B. Co., June, 1916), **HEATHER** (Greenock & Grangemouth Co., June, 1916), **TAMARISK** (Lobintz, June, 1916), **VIOLA** (Ropner, July, 1916).

All 1250 tons. Completed Aug.-Oct., 1916. Dimensions: 255¼ (*p.p.*), 267¾ (*o.a.*) × 33½ × 11½ (*mean*), 12½ (*max.*) feet draught. Designed to mount 3—12 pdr., 2—3 pdr. AA., but have 2—4 inch, 1—3 pdr. AA. and D.C. throwers. Machinery, boilers, as "Anchusa Class," opposite. 1 screw. Designed H.P. 2500 = 17.5 kts., but actually can only make 15-16½ kts. with this power, and require 3000 I.H.P. for 17½ kts. Coal: 255 tons. Complement, 80.

General Notes to Anchusa and Aubrietia types.—All are Fleet Sweeping Vessels (Sloops) of the "Flower Classes," modified in external build for service as Convoy Sloops. Disguised as mercantile vessels, these ships accompanied Convoys, and acted as Submarine Decoy Vessels, or "Q-boats"—hence their popular name of the "Q-boat Flowers." Each builder was allowed to adopt a form of mercantile disguise, with the result that, by appearance, these ships are divided into 15-20 types. All were built under Emergency War Programme.

War Losses.—Owing to the nature of the service these ships were engaged on, war losses were heavy. *Anchusa, Arbutus, Bergamot, Candytuft* (all by Armstrong Whitworth), *Cowslip* (Barclay Curle), *Gaillardia* (Blyth S.B. Co.), *Rhododendron, Salvia* (both by Irvine S.B. Co.), *Tulip* (Richardson, Duck), were all lost during the War. In all, 39 vessels of *Anchusa* and *Aubrietia* types were built. Although nominally rated as "Fleet Sweeping Vessels," they have no gallows at stern, and it is doubtful if they carry sweeping gear, unless of "otter" types.

VALERIAN.

PRIMROSE.

Appearance Notes for all Types.—Majority as *Valerian*, but *Azatea, Buttercup, Campanula, Celandine, Cornflower, Godetia, Hydrangea,* completed with topmasts 40 feet higher; *Lily* completed with topmasts about 20 feet higher. Illustration for *Primrose* shows alterations to ships employed for duty on Mediterranean Convoys, Patrols, &c., mainmast, after gun and gallows, being removed to permit towing of Kite Balloons.

(ARABIS TYPE—26 SHIPS.)

BUTTERCUP (Nov., 1915), **CAMPANULA** (Dec., 1915), **CELANDINE** (Feb., 1916), **CORNFLOWER** (Mar., 1916), all four by Barclay, Curle. **GLADIOLUS** (Oct., 1915), **GODETIA** (Jan., 1916), **HYDRANGEA** (Mar., 1916), all three by Connell. **NIGELLA** (Dec., 1915), **PANSY** (Feb., 1916), both by Hamilton. **ASPHODEL** (Dec., 1915), **BERBERIS** (Feb., 1916), both by Henderson. **WALLFLOWER** (Nov., 1915), **WISTARIA** Dec., 1915), both by Irvine S.B. Co. **CROCUS** (Dec., 1915), **CYCLAMEN** (Feb., 1916), both by Lobnitz. **LOBELIA** (Mar., 1916), **LUPIN** (May, 1916), both by Simons. **MYOSOTIS** (Bow, McLachlan, April, 1916), **VERBENA** (Blyth S.B. Co., Nov., 1915), **AMARYLLIS** (Earle S.B. Co., Dec., 1915), **DELPHINIUM** (Napier & Miller, Dec., 1915), **VALERIAN** (C. Rennoldson, Feb., 1916), **ROSEMARY** (Richardson, Duck, Nov., 1915), **SNAPDRAGON** (Ropner, Dec., 1915), **POPPY** (Swan, Hunter, Nov.,1915), **PENTSTEMON** (Workman, Clark, Feb., 1916).

All 1250 tons. Completed, Dec., 1915-June, 1916. Dimensions : 255¼ (*p.p.*), 267¾ (*o.a.*) × 33½ × 11 (*mean*), 11⅓-11¾ feet (*max.* draught). *Designed* armament : 2—4.7 inch or 4 inch, 2—3 pdr. AA., but some have only 1—4.7 or 4 inch, with or without the 2—3 pdr. AA. A few are only armed with 2—3 pdr. AA. Designed I.H.P. 1400 = 17 kts., but for this speed they really have to develop about 2400 I.H.P. Machinery : 1 set 4-cylinder triple expansion. Boilers : 2 cylindrical. 1 screw. Coal : 130 tons *normal,* 260 tons *max.* = *about* 2000 miles at 15 kts. Complement, 79. Also see *General Notes.*

General Notes to "Arabis," "Azalea," and "Acacia" Types.—Single-screw Fleet Sweeping Vessels (Sloops), all built under Emergency War Programme. Popularly known as the "Flower Class," but are also referred to as the "Cabbage Class," or "Herbaceous Borders." Have triple hulls at bows to give extra protection against loss when working up mines. Very successful ships, but can only make designed speed with difficulty. Good sea-boats. Copies of this class were built in British yards for the French Navy. The last series of "Flowers" converted to Convoy Sloops (*q.v.*). Several mined during War and extensively re-built.

War Losses, Removals, &c.—*Alyssum, Aster* (both Earle S.B. Co.), *Arabis* (Henderson), *Begonia* (Barclay, Curle), *Genista* (Napier & Miller), *Mignonette* (Dunlop & Bremner), *Lavender, Nasturtium* (both McMillan), *Primula* (Swan Hunter), all lost during War. *Gentian* (Greenock & Grangemouth Co.) and *Myrtle* (Lobnitz), sunk in Baltic, 1919, during anti-Bolshevist operations. *Geranium, Marguerite, Mallow,* presented to Australian Navy. *Peony* (McMillan), sold out. *Petunia* (Workman, Clark), has also gone ; not certain if she has been lost or sold out. In all, 72 of these ships were built.

(AZALEA TYPE—9 SHIPS.)

CARNATION (Sept., 1915), **CLEMATIS** (July, 1915), both by Greenock & Grangemouth Co. **JESSAMINE** (Sept., 1915), **ZINNIA** (Aug., 1915), both by Swan Hunter. **AZALEA** (Barclay, Curle, Sept., 1915). **CAMELLIA** (Bow, McLachlan, Sept., 1915). **HELIOTROPE** (Lobnitz, Sept., 1915). **SNOWDROP** (McMillan, Oct., 1915). **NARCISSUS** (Napier & Miller, Sept., 1915).

All details as "Acacia Type" below, but these ships were designed to mount 2—4.7 inch or 4 inch and 2—3 pdr. AA. Nearly all so armed, but one or two have no 3 pdrs. Complement, 79. Also see *General Notes.*

(ACACIA TYPE—21 SHIPS.)

DAHLIA (April, 1915), **DAPHNE** (May, 1915), **FOXGLOVE** (Mar., 1915), **HOLLYHOCK** (May, 1915), **LILY** (June, 1915), all five by Barclay, Curle, **BLUEBELL** (July, 1915), **DAFFODIL** (Aug., 1915), **MAGNOLIA** (June, 1915), all three by Scotts S. B. Co. **MARIGOLD** (May, 1915), **MIMOSA** (July, 1915), both by Bow, McLachlan, **JONQUIL** (May, 1915), **LABURNUM** (June, 1915), both by Connell & Co. **HONEYSUCKLE** (April, 1915), **IRIS** (June, 1915), both by Lobnitz. **ACACIA** (April, 1915), **ANEMONE** (May, 1915), both by Swan Hunter. **VERONICA** (Dunlop, Bremner, May, 1915), **LILAC** (Greenock & Grangemouth Co., April, 1915), **SUNFLOWER** (Henderson, May, 1915), **LARKSPUR** (Napier & Miller, 1915), **PRIMROSE** (Simons, June, 1915).

All 1200 tons. Completed, May-Sept., 1915. Dimensions : 250 (*p.p.*), 262½ (*o.a.*) × 33 × 11 (*mean*), 11¼-12 feet (*max.* draught). Designed to mount 2—12 pdr. and 2—3 pdr. AA. Some still armed in this way ; others have (*a*) 2—4 inch, (*b*) 1—4 inch, (*c*) 1—4 inch and 1—12 pdr., (*d*) 2—12 pdr., with or without the 2—3 pdr. One or two armed *only* with 1 or 2—3 pdr. Designed H.P. 1400 or 1800 = 17 kts., but actually require about 2200 I.H.P. for this speed. Machinery : 1 set 4-cylinder triple expansion. Boilers : 2 cylindrical. 1 screw. Coal : 130 tons *normal,* 250 tons *max.* = *about* 2000 miles at 15 kts. Complement, 77. Also see *General Notes.*

(DANCE CLASS—12 BOATS.)

QUADRILLE.   *Photo, McClure, Macdonald.*

PADDLE MINESWEEPERS :—

A third series of these, named after birds, was projected by Admiralty, but cancelled at the end of 1918, or early in 1919. Following are only vessels known to have been contracted for and stopped :—

Fulmar
Gadwell }   Ailsa S.B. Co.
Pochard

Stormy Petrel
Tern   }   Murdoch & Murray.

Redshank
Shrike }   Contracts not placed.

MORRIS DANCE (——), **STEP DANCE** (——), builders not known, **GAVOTTE** (Mar., 1918), and **SARABANDE** (April, 1918), both by Goole Co., **TARANTELLA** (Hamilton, Oct., 1917), **PIROUETTE** (Rennie Forrest, Sept., 1917). These displace 265 tons. I.H.P. 512 = 10.4 kts., *except Gavotte* and *Tarantella*, I.H.P. 450 = 10.4 kts. **COTILLION** (——) and **MINUET** (——), both by Day, Summers, **COVERLEY** (——), and **QUADRILLE** (——), both by Ferguson Bros., **HORNPIPE** (——) and **MAZURKA** (——), both by Murdoch & Murray. All displace 290 tons. I.H.P. 450 = 9¼-10 kts. Twin screw (shallow-draught) Minesweepers with screws working in tunnels. Dimensions : 130 (*o.a.*) × 26-27 × 3½ feet. Guns : *Gavotte*, 1—12 pdr., 1—6 pdr. ; *Step Dance*, 1—6 pdr. AA. ; rest, 1—3 pdr. Machinery : Vertical compound. Boilers : Cylindrical. Fuel : 37-41½ tons oil. Complement, 22-26. Completed Nov., 1917-Sept., 1918.

Notes.—All built under Emergency War Programme. *Sword Dance* (builder unknown), sunk by Bolshevist mine in River Dvina. Further units of this Class may be completing and others cancelled, but no details are available of these extra boats.

CRAIGIE.   *Photo, Robertson, Gourock, N.B.*

(TWIN SCREW "HUNT" CLASS—LATER TYPE—87 SHIPS.)

ABERDARE (April, 1918), **ABINGDON** (June, 1918), **ALBURY** (Nov., 1918), **ALRESFORD** (Jan., 1919), **APPLEDORE** (1919), **LEAMINGTON** (ex *Aldeburgh*, Aug., 1918), all six by Ailsa S.B. Co., **BADMINTON** (Mar., 1918), **BAGSHOT** (May, 1918), **BARNSTAPLE** Mar., 1919), **SWINDON** (ex *Bantry*, 1919), all four by Ardrossan Co., **BANCHORY** (May, 1918), **BLOXHAM** (ex *Brixham*, 1919), **BRADFIELD** (May, 1919), **BURSLEM** (ex *Blakeney*, Mar., 1918), **GOOLE** (ex *Bridlington*, 1919), all five by Ayrshire Co., **BLACKBURN** (ex *Burnham*, Aug., 1918), **BOOTLE** (ex *Buckie*, June, 1919), **CAERLEON** (Dec., 1918), **CAMBERLEY** (Dec., 1918), **CARSTAIRS** (ex *Cawsand*, 1919), **CATERHAM** (Mar., 1919), all six by Bow, McLachlan, **CRAIGIE** (May, 1918), **DERBY** (ex *Dawlish*, Aug., 1918), **FAIRFIELD** (June, 1918), ***FORRES** (ex *Fowey*, Nov., 1918), **DORKING** (Sept., 1918), **DUNDALK** (Jan., 1919), **DUNOON** (Mar., 1919), all seven by Clyde S.B. Co.), **BATTLE** (1919), **FERMOY** (1919), **FORFAR** (Nov., 1918), all three by Dundee S.B. Co., **FAREHAM** (June, 1918), **FEVERSHAM** (July, 1918), **FORD** (ex *Fleetwood*, Oct., 1918), **RUGBY** (ex *Filey*, Sept., 1918), all four by Dunlop & Bremner, **BURY** (May, 1919), **CHEAM** (July, 1919), **GADDESDEN** (Nov., 1917), **GAINS-BOROUGH** (ex *Gorleston*, Feb., 1918), **GRETNA** (April, 1919), **HARROW** July, 1918), **HAVANT** Nov., 1918), **HUNTLEY** (ex *Helmsdale*, Jan., 1919), **INSTOW** (ex *Ilfracombe*, April, 1919), **NORTHOLT** (June, 1918), all ten by Jos. R. Eltringham, **IRVINE** (Dec., 1917), **KENDAL** (Feb., 1918), **KINROSS** (June, 1918), **LYDD** (ex *Lydney*, Dec., 1918), all four by Fairfield Co., **MALLAIG** (Oct., 1918), **MALVERN** (Feb., 1919), **MARAZION** (1919), **MUNLOCHY** (ex *Macduff*, June, 1918), all four by Fleming & Ferguson, **LONGFORD** (ex *Minehead*, Mar., 1919), **MARLOW** (Aug., 1918), **MISTLEY** (ex *Maryport*, Oct., 1918), **MONAGHAN** (ex *Mullion*, May, 1919), all four by W. Harkness, **NAILSEA** (ex *Newquay*, Aug., 1918), **NEWARK** (ex *Newlyn*, June, 1918), **REPTON** (ex *Wicklow*, 1919), **WEYBOURNE** (Feb., 1919), all four by A. & J. Inglis, **PANGBOURNE** (ex *Padstow*, Mar., 1918), **PETERSFIELD** (ex *Portmadoc*, Mar., 1919), **PONTYPOOL** (ex *Polperro*, June, 1918), **PRESTATYN** (ex *Porlock*, Nov., 1918), **ROSS** (ex *Ramsey*, 1919), all five by Messrs. Lobnitz, **SUTTON** (ex *Salcombe*, May, 1918), by Messrs. McMillan, **SALFORD** (ex *Shoreham*, April, 1919), **SALTASH** (July, 1918), **SALTBURN** (Oct., 1918), **SELKIRK** (Dec., 1918), all four by Messrs. Murdoch & Murray, **SHREWSBURY** (Feb., 1918), **SLIGO** (Mar., 1918), **WIDNES** (ex *Withernsea*, June, 1918), **YEOVIL** (Aug., 1918), all four by Messrs. Napier & Miller, **STAFFORD** (ex *Staithes*, Sept., 1918), **STOKE** (ex *Southwold*, July, 1918), both by Chas. Rennoldson, **CLONMEL** (ex *Stranraer*, May, 1918), **ELGIN** (ex *Troon*, Mar., 1919), **SHERBORNE** (ex *Tarbert*, June, 1918), **TIVERTON** (Sept., 1918), **TONBRIDGE** (Nov., 1918), **TRALEE** (Dec., 1918), **TRING** (ex *Teignmouth*, Aug., 1919), **TRURO** (April, 1919), **WEM** (ex *Walmer*, 1919), **WEXFORD** (1919), all ten by Messrs. Simons.

* *Forres* contracted for by Messrs. Dunlop Bremner, but contract and materials transferred to Clyde S.B. Co.

CAMBERLEY (Tender, Navigation School).   *Photo, Robertson, Gourock, N.B.*

All Emergency War Programme. First ship delivered Feb., 1918; all deliveries not completed by Oct., 1919. Displacement, 800 tons. Dimensions : 220 (*p.p.*), 231 (*o.a.*) × 28 ft. 6⅝ in. ×7½ (*mean*), — feet (*max.* draught). Guns : A few have 1—4 inch and 1—12 pdr. AA. or 2—3 pdr., but majority have only 1—6 or 3 pdr. Several not armed now. Machinery : Vertical triple expansion. 2 screws. Designed I.H.P. 2200 = 16 kts. Boilers : Yarrow. Coal : 185 tons. Complement, 74.

General Notes.—Much the same as original Ailsa Co. design of Twin-Screw Sweepers (*Belvoir, Bicester, &c.*), but slight modifications introduced in these ships by Admiralty. In 1919, several had been assigned to Special Service, *e.g., Marazion, &c.* (Tenders to Submarine Depot Ships), *Salford, Camberley, Caterham* (Tenders to Navigation School), *Petersfield* (Admiral's Yacht and for service on South American Rivers), and so on. Six have been re-named and completed as Surveying Ships (*q.v.*). But on the demobilisation of the Mine Clearance Force, the majority of these ships will be laid up. Those originally named after coastal towns, watering places, fishing ports, &c., were all re-named after inland towns and villages, to obviate misunderstanding of signals and orders.

To distinguish from original "Hunt Class."—Look rather bigger and heavier. Thicker funnel, foremast higher and stepped *through* Chart House. Searchlight on forward extension of bridge. Superstructure runs well towards mainmast and has 4 ventilators arranged in a square. Hull level, *not* broken between mainmast and gallows.

Losses (after Armistice).—*Cupar* (ex *Rosslare*, built by McMillan), *Penarth* (Lobnitz). No War Losses.

Cancelled Ships.—*Alton* (ex *Arbroath*), *Ashburton*, both by Ailsa S.B. Co.; *Bideford, Bolton* (ex *Beaumaris*), both by Ardrossan D.D. & S.B. Co.; *Atheleney, Bathgate*, both by Clyde S.B. Co.; *Beccles, Blickling*, both by Dundee S.B. Co.; *Northrepps*, by Messrs. Lobnitz; *Tain, Wembdon, Yealmpton*, all three by Messrs. Simons. Also the following ships (contractors not known):—*Clifton, Crediton* (ex *Colywn*), *Curragh, Frome, Kew, Kingussie, Knowle, Okehampton, Oundle, Radnor, Reading, Retford, Ringwood, Runcorn, Shifnal.* Also *Fairburn, Clovelly*, either cancelled or re-named; if latter, present names wanted.

BRITISH NAVY—P. W. & T. S. MINESWEEPERS.

HEXHAM.

Photo, Robertson, Gourock, N.B.

CATTISTOCK.

Photo, Robertson, Gourock, N.B.

BANBURY (Dec., 1917) and **HARPENDEN** (Feb., 1918), both by Ailsa S.B. Co. **HEXHAM** (Clyde S.B. Co., Dec., 1917). **LANARK** (Dec., 1917) and **LEWES** (Mar., 1918), both by Fleming & Ferguson. **SHINCLIFFE** (Dunlop, Bremner, Jan., 1918), **WETHERBY** (Murdoch & Murray, Mar., 1918).

BELVOIR (Mar., 1917) and **BICESTER** (June, 1917), both by Ailsa S.B. Co. **CATTISTOCK** (Clyde S.B. Co., Feb., 1917), **COTSWOLD** (Nov., 1916) and **COTTESMORE** (Feb., 1917), both by Bow, McLachlan. **CROOME** (Clyde S.B. Co., May, 1917), **DARTMOOR** (Mar., 1917) and **GARTH** (May, 1917), both by Dunlop, Bremner. **HAMBLEDON** (Mar., 1917), and **HEYTHROP** (June, 1917), both by Fleming & Ferguson. **HOLDER-NESS** (Nov., 1916) and **MEYNELL** (Feb., 1917), both by D. & W. Henderson. **MUSKERRY** (Nov., 1916) and **OAKLEY** (Jan., 1917), both by Lobnitz. **PYTCHLEY** (Mar., 1917), and **QUORN** (June, 1917), both by Napier & Miller. **SOUTHDOWN** (1917) and **TEDWORTH** (June, 1917), both by Simons. **ZETLAND** (Murdoch & Murray, 1917).

Paddle minesweepers, design by Admiralty, adapted from Ailsa Co. design for *Atherstone*, &c. (*v.* next page). Completed Jan.-June, 1918. Displacement, 820 tons. Complement, 50-52. Dimensions : 235 (*p.p.*), 249¾ (*o.a.*) × 29 ft. 0¼ in. (58 feet outside paddle boxes) × 6¾-7 feet. Guns : 1—12 pdr. (12 cwt.), 1—3 inch AA. Designed I.H.P. 1400 = 15 kts. (actually 1500 = *about* 14½ kts.). Machinery : Diagonal compound. Boilers : Cylindrical return tube. Coal : 156 tons.

Notes.—All built under Emergency War Programme. Suffer from same defects as *Atherstone*, &c. (next page). To distinguish, note that foremast is stepped *through* chart house ; two *high* ventilators abaft fore funnel ; *no* derricks abeam of second funnel. Commonly known as the "Improved Racecourse" type.

War Losses.—Nil. *Shirley* (Dunlop, Bremner) sold out for commercial service as a ferry boat, 1919.

Twin Screw Minesweepers, built to design by Ailsa Co. Completed Mar.-Oct., 1917. Displacement, 750 tons. Complement, 71. Dimensions : 220 (*p.p.*), 231 (*o.a.*) × 28 × 7 feet (*mean* draught.) Guns : 2—12 pdr., and 2—2 pdr., but some have temporary armament of 1—12 pdr. and 1—6 pdr. Designed I.H.P. 1800 = 16 kts. Machinery : 3-cylinder triple expansion. Boilers : Yarrow. Coal : 140 tons.

Notes.—All built under Emergency War Programme, and proved very successful. To distinguish from *Aberdare*, *Abingdon*, &c., note that searchlight is on tower separated from fore bridges ; foremast is stepped *abaft* chart house ; superstructure round funnel runs out to beam and does not extend far towards stern ; hull at stern breaks level between mainmast and gallows. Generally known as the "Hunt" Class.

War Losses.—*Blackmorevale* (Ardrossan D.D. Co.).

(PADDLE SWEEPERS—19 OF EARLIER GROUP.)

ERIDGE.   *Photo, Robertson, Gourock, N.B.*

ATHERSTONE (Jan., 1916) and **CHELMSFORD** (April, 1916), both by Ailsa S.B. Co., **CHELTENHAM** (Ardrossan Co., June, 1916), **CHEPSTOW** (April, 1916), **CROXTON** (April, 1916), **DONCASTER** (June, 1916) and **EGLINTON** (Sept., 1916), all by Ayrshire D.Y. Co., **EPSOM** (G. Brown, May, 1916), **ERIDGE** (Clyde S.B. Co., Feb., 1916), **GATWICK** (April, 1916) and **GOODWOOD** (June, 1916), both by Dundee S.B. Co., **HALDON** (Mar., 1916), **HURST** (May, 1916) and **SANDOWN** (July, 1916), all by Dunlop, Bremner, **LINGFIELD** (Fleming & Ferguson, April, 1916), **MELTON** (Hamilton, Mar., 1916), **NEWBURY** (A. & J. Inglis, July, 1916), **PONTEFRACT** (Murdoch & Murray, June, 1916), **TOTNES** (McMillan, May, 1916).

Paddle Mine Sweepers, built to designs by Ailsa Co. Completed, April-Oct., 1916. Displacement, 810 tons. Complement, 50. Dimensions : 235 (*p.p.*), 245¾ (*o.a.*) × 29 (58 feet over paddles) × 6¾ feet (*mean* draught). Guns : 2—12 pdr. Designed H.P. 1400 = 15 kts. Machinery : Inclined compound. Boilers : Cylindrical return tube. Coal : 156 tons.

Notes.—All built under Emergency War Programme. Fairly good sea-boats, but lose speed badly in a seaway, through paddle boxes getting choked with water. *Eridge* and *Melton* were originally fitted to carry seaplanes. To differentiate from *Banbury, Hexham,* &c., note that foremast is stepped *before* fore bridges : also these boats have derricks abeam of second funnel. Unofficially known as the " Racecourse " Class.

War Losses.—*Ascot* (Ailsa Co.), *Redcar* (Ayrshire D.Y. Co.), *Kempton* (Ferguson Bros.), *Plumpton* (McMillan). Numerous inquiries have failed to elucidate the question whether *Ludlow* (Goole Co.) has been lost or not. She is generally understood to have been mined and lost off Harwich, but *Ludlow* is included in post-war " Navy Lists," and her arrival at naval ports has been reported several times during 1919.

QUEEN VICTORIA.

* **QUEEN VICTORIA.**   Purchased 1915.   Used as Net Layer and later as Paddle Mine Sweeper.   No details known.

* **PRINCE EDWARD** (ex *Prince of Wales*).   Purchased 1915.   No details known.

* **DUCHESS OF BUCCLEUCH.**   Purchased 1916.   No details known.

* *Note.*—Although these three ships were purchased outright for H.M. Navy, it is very likely they will be re-conditioned and sold out for mercantile use in the near future.

Patrol Gunboats *Kildonan, Kilmallock, Kilmanahan, Kilmarnock, Kilmarten, Kilmead, Kilmelford,* all described on an earlier page—are fitted as Mine Sweepers.

Depot Ships.

Note—The following old warships have been allocated for service as Depot Ships, but will serve only as Accommodation Ships, Hulks for overflow purposes, &c. Since they will not be required for War Fleet and have no fighting value, details and illustrations are not given for them.

Battleships :—

Implacable	*Cæsar*	*Mars*
Venerable	*Hannibal*	*Victorious.*
Glory		

Cruisers and Light Cruisers :—

Crescent	*Imperieuse*	*Naiad*

The following vessels have been assigned to duty as Depot Ships. They will not serve in a sea-going capacity any longer, but only as Depot Ships to Local Defence Flotillas and Destroyers, Submarines, &c., in Reserve. No illustrations or details given of these ships.

For T.B.D. :—*Prince George, Essex, Europa, Dido, Apollo, Aquarius.*

For Patrol Gunboats :—*Hermione.*

For Anti-Submarine Service :—*Gibraltar.*

For Submarines :→*Rosario, Pactolus, Bonaventure, Onyx, Arrogant, Dolphin.*

Destroyer Depot Ships.

Photo wanted.

SANDHURST (ex s.s. *Manipur*, Harland & Wolff, purchased 1915 and converted by Workman, Clerk). 11,500 tons. Dimensions : 470 (*p.p.*) × 58 × 20 feet (*max.* draught). Guns : 4—4 inch, 2—6 pdr. AA. I.H.P. 4000 = 10.5 kts. Coal : 1475 tons. Complement, 269. Cyl. boilers.

Tenders : 2 Drifters.

Destroyer Depot Ships—(*Continued*).

Photo, Dr. J. A. Prendergast.

GREENWICH (Dobson & Co., completed by Swan Hunter. Purchased 1915). 8600 tons. Dimensions : 390 (*p.p.*) × 52 × 19⅜ feet (*max.* draught). Guns : 4—4 inch, 2—6 pdr. AA. I.H.P. 2500 = 11 kts. Coal : 960 tons. Complement, 261. Cyl. boilers.

Tenders : 2 Drifters.

WOOLWICH (Scotts. S. & E. Co., 1912). 3380 tons. Dimensions: 320 × 40 × 14¼ feet. Guns : 2—4 inch. H.P. 2600 = 13.5 kts. Coal : 370 tons. Complement, 263.

Tenders : 2 Drifters.

Destroyer Depot Ships—(*Continued*).

DILIGENCE (ex *Tabaristan*, 1907. Purchased 1913). 7400 tons. Dimensions : 390 (*p.p.*) × 46 × — feet. Guns : 4—4 inch. H.P. 5000 = 14.2 kts. Coal : 780 tons. Complement, 258.

Tenders : 2 Drifters.

BLENHEIM.

BLAKE (1889) & **BLENHEIM** (1890.) Both converted 1907. 9000 tons. Dimensions : 375 (*p.p.*) × 65 × 25⅔ feet (*max.* draught). Guns : 4—old 6 inch, and 2—4 inch in *Blake* ; 1—4 inch and 7—12 pdr. in *Blenheim*. Designed H.P. 20,000 = 21.1 kts. Coal : *normal*, 624 tons ; also 650 tons carried in small bags (1 cwt. each) for destroyers.

Tenders : 2 Drifters *each.*

Destroyer Depot Ships—(*Continued*).

LEANDER (1882). 4380 tons. Dimensions : 300 (*p.p.*) × 46 × 21¼ feet. (*max.* draught). Guns : 2—12 pdr., 2—6 pdr., 1 M.G. Armour : 1½″ deck amidships. H.P. 5000 = 16.5 kts. Coal : 813 tons.
Tender : 1 Drifter.

TYNE (purchased 1878). 3590 tons. Dimensions : 320 (*p.p.*) × 34 × 20 feet (*mean* draught). Guns : 1—12 pdr., 2—6 pdr. Designed H.P. 1200 = 11.7 kts. Coal : 510 tons. Complement, 172.

HECLA (purchased 1878). 5600 tons. Dimensions : 391½ (*p.p.*) × 38¾ × 21⅔ feet (*mean* draught). Guns : 4—4 inch. 1 M.G. Designed H.P. 2400 = 13.4 kts. Coal : 572 tons. Complement, 266.
Tenders : 2 Drifters.

Torpedo Sub-Depot Ships (R.F.A.)

No photo available.

* **SOBO** 4163 tons. Speed : 9 kts. Coal : 413 tons.

No photo available.

* **SOKOTO** 3870 tons. Speed : 9 kts. Coal : 380 tons.

*Purchased 1914. As it is very probable that these ships will be sold out of H.M. Navy in the near future, they are not illustrated

Submarine Depot Ships.

Note.—Light Cruiser, **FEARLESS** and Flotilla Leader **ITHURIEL,** are attached to 1st and 2nd Submarine Flotillas

Photo, Abrahams, Devonport.

AMBROSE (Clyde S.B. Co., 1915. Purchased 1915). 6480 tons. Dimensions : 387¾ (*o.a.*) × 47½ × 20½ feet. Guns : 2—12 pdr. I.H.P. 6350 = 14½ kts. Complement, 240.
Tenders : *Marazion* and 1 Drifter. (Also serve for *Pandora*.)

Photo wanted.

TITANIA (Clyde S.B. Co., 1915, purchased 1915). 5200 tons. Dimensions : 335 (*p.p.*) × 46¼ × 18¼ feet. I.H.P. 3200 = 14.5 kts. Torpedo tubes : 2. Coal : 498 tons. Complement, 245. Cyl. boilers.
Tenders : *Adamant*, 1 Drifter.

Submarine Depot Ships—*Continued.*

Photo, Dr. J. A. Prendergast.

LUCIA (Furness Withy Co., ex German Prize, *Spreewald*, converted by Clyde S.B. Co. 1916). 6005 tons. Dimensions: 366 (*o.a.*) × 45¼ × 19¾ feet. Guns: 2—3 pdr. AA. I.H.P. 2700 ×   kts. Coal: 700 tons. Cyl. boilers. Complement, 245.

Tenders : *Repton*, 1 Trawler.

Photo wanted.

PANDORA (ex *Seti*, purchased from Russia, 1914). 4350 tons. Dimensions: 330 × 43 × 16 feet. Guns: *Nil.* H.P. 2200 = 11 kts. Coal: 580 tons. Complement, 70.

Tenders : *Marazion* and 1 Drifter (also serve for *Ambrose*).

Photo, Cribb.

MAIDSTONE (Scott's S. & E. Co., 1912). 3600 tons. Dimensions: 355 × 45 × 17¾ feet. Guns: *Nil.* H.P. 2800 = 14·3 kts. Coal: 465 tons. Complement, 159.

Tenders : *Salford*, 1 Drifter.

Submarine Depot Ships—*Continued.*

ADAMANT and **ALECTO** (both Laird, 1911). 935 tons. Dimensions: 190 × 32½ × 11 feet (*mean* draught). Guns: *Adamant*, 1—4 inch. Designed H.P. 1400 = 14 kts. Coal: 180 tons. Complement, 63.

No photo available.
Similar to *St. George* below.

ROYAL ARTHUR (ex *Centaur*) (1891). 7700 tons. Dimensions: 360 (*p.p.*) × 60¾ × 26¾ feet. Guns: *Nil.* I.H.P. 12,000 = 20 kts., but 7000 = 15-16 kts. may be present *maximum.* Coal: 1230 tons. Complement, —.

Tenders to *Royal Arthur* : 2 Drifters.

ST. GEORGE (1890). Cruiser of *Edgar* type; converted 1911. 7700 tons. Dimensions: 360 (*p.p.*) × 60¾ × 23¾ feet (*mean* draught). Guns: 2—6 inch, 2—12 pdr. AA., 2—3 pdr. AA. Designed H.P. 12,000 = 19.5 kts. (present maximum H.P. 7000 for about 15-16 kts.). Coal: *normal*, 850 tons; *maximum*, 1120 tons. Complement, 301.

Tenders to *St. George* : 2 Drifters.

Submarine Depot Ships—*Continued.*

VULCAN (1889). Rebuilt 1908. 6620 tons. Dimensions: 350 × 58 × 23¼ feet (*max.* draught). Guns: 2—8.7 inch. Armour: 5″ deck (amidships), 6″ conning tower, 5″ engine hatches. Designed H.P. 12,000 = 20 kts. Can do now about 16 kts. Coal: *maximum* 1347 tons. Dürr boilers (1909). Complement, 255.

Tenders to *Vulcan* : *Alecto* and 1 Drifter.

THAMES (1885) & **FORTH** (1886). 4050 tons. Dimensions: 300 (*p.p.*) × 46 × 19¾ feet (*max.* draught). No guns. Designed H.P. 5700 = 17.2 kts. originally. Coal: 740 tons *maximum.* Fitted as Floating Workshops. Complement, 187.

Tenders to *Thames* : *Fermoy*, 1 Drifter.
Tenders to *Forth* : *Elgin*, *Forres*, 4 Trawlers.

Repair Ships—(R.F.A.).

No photo available.

SCOTSTOUN Begun, February, 1916. Launched, Completed, July, 1916. Built by Yarrows, as Repair Ship for "Insect" and "Fly" Classes of Gunboats. 300 tons. Dimensions : 132 (*p.p.*), 150 (*o.a.*) × 31 × 3¼ feet draught. I.H.P. 200 = 7.7 kts. Compound surface condensing engines. Loco. boiler. Oil : 20/36 tons.

No photo available.

BACCHUS (Hamilton & Co., 1915, purchased 1915). About 3500 tons. Dimensions : 295 × 44 × 12½ feet. Guns : Not known. I.H.P.   =   kts. Coal : 873 tons.

RELIANCE (ex *Knight-Companion*, 1910, bought 1913). 3250 tons. Dimensions : 470 × 57¾ × — feet. H.P. 3250 = 11 kts. Coal : 1700 tons.

Repair Ships—(*Continued*).

CYCLOPS (ex *Indrabarah*, 1905). 11,300 tons. Dimensions : 460 (*p.p.*) × 55 × 21 feet. Guns : 6—4 inch. Machinery : Triple expansion. Designed H.P. 3500 = 11.75 kts. Coal capacity : 1595 tons. Fitted as Floating Workshop and Distilling Ship. Complement, 294.

ASSISTANCE (1901). 9600 tons. Dimensions : 436 (*p.p.*) × 53 × 20 feet. Guns : 10—3 pdr. Machinery : Triple expansion. Boilers : Cylindrical. Fitted with Howden's forced draught. Designed H.P. (*f.d.*) 4000 = 12 kts. Coal : 2180 tons. Fitted as Floating Workshop and Distilling Ship. Complement, 283.

Salvage Vessels.

Photo wanted.

REINDEER (1884). 970 tons. Re-engined by Fairfield Co., 1918. I.H.P. 1200 =   kts.

Photo wanted.

RACER (1884, rebuilt 1916-17). 970 tons. I.H.P. 1100 = 11 kts. Re-engined with starboard machinery of old T.B. 8 submersible electric, steam centrifugal and compressed air pumps throwing 3000 tons per hour. 2—17 ton derricks.

No photo available.

MELITA (ex *Ringdove*, 1889). Ex-gunboat. 820 tons. H.P. 750 = 11 kts. Coal : 80 tons. Complement, 74.

No photo available.

MARINER (1883). Ex-Sloop and Boom Defence Vessel. 970 tons.

Also *Moonfleet, Hippopotamus* and *Rhinoceros*, built 1917. Are probably only chartered vessels which may no longer be in H.M. Navy.

Oil Tankers (R.F.A.).

Oil Tankers *Birchleaf, Appleleaf* (ex *Texol*), *Plumleaf* (ex *Trinol*), *Erivan*, &c., are understood to have been disposed of, or returned to owners. It is possible that some of the "*Ol*" Tankers detailed hereafter may have taken up commercial service.

> 1 funnel with 1 mast just before, both raking and aft of amidships.

PETROBUS, PETRELLA, PETRONEL (Dunlop, Bremner, 1918). 1024 tons. Dimensions : 164 × 28 × 11¼ feet. I.H.P. 500 = 9-10 kts. Own oil : 50 tons. Cylindrical boilers. Complement, 16.

> *Appearance unknown.*

DREDGOL (Simons, 1918). About 7000 tons. Dimensions : 326 × 54½ × 18¾ feet. I.H.P. 2400 = 11 kts. Own oil : 360 tons. Cylindrical boilers.

> 1 funnel with 1 mast before, close together, as in Standard Cargo Ships.

FRANCOL (Earle S.B. Co.), **MONTENOL** (W. Gray), **SERBOL** (Caledon S.B. Co.). All details as *Belgol* below, but of different appearance. All launched 1917.

Oil Tankers (R.F.A.)—*Continued.*

> 2 masts fore and aft : 1 funnel between. *Rapidol* a little different to other ships.

BELGOL (Irvine D.D. Co.), **CELEROL** (Short Bros.), **FORTOL** (McMillan), **PRESTOL** (Napier & Miller), **RAPIDOL** (W. Gray), **SLAVOL, VITOL** (Greenock and Grangemouth Co.). All launched 1917. 4900 tons. Dimensions : 335 × 41½ × 20½ feet. I.H.P. 3375 = 14 kts. Own oil : 300 tons. Cylindrical boilers. Complement, 39.

> 1 mast forward.
> 1 funnel aft.

BIRCHOL, BOXOL (Barclay, Curle), **EBONOL** (Clyde S.B. Co.), **ELDEROL, ELMOL** (Swan Hunter), **LARCHOL, LIMOL** (Lobnitz). All launched 1917. As *Sprucol, Teakol*, below, but these have triple expansion engines and cylindrical boilers. I.H.P. 700 = 12 kts.

> 1 mast forward.
> 1 funnel aft.

SPRUCOL, TEAKOL (Short Bros.), **OAKOL, PALMOL** (W. Gray & Co.). All launched 1917. 1925 tons. Dimensions : 220 × 34 × 12 feet. Bolinders oil engines. B.H.P. 640 = 8-10 kts. Own oil : 40 tons. Complement, 19.

Oil Tankers (R.F.A.)—*Continued.*

> 1 mast forward.
> 1 funnel aft.

CREOSOL (Short Bros.), **DISTOL, PHILOL, SCOTOL** (Tyne Iron S.B. Co.), **KIMMEROL, VISCOL** (Craig, Taylor). All launched 1916. 1920 tons. Dimensions : 220 × 34⅔ × 12½ feet. I.H.P. 700 = 9 kts. Own oil : 40 tons. Cylindrical boilers. Complement, 19.

> 2 masts, 1 funnel at stern.

MIXOL (Greenock & Grangemouth Co., 1916). **THERMOL** (Caledonian S.B. Co., 1916). 4145 tons. Dimensions : 270 × 38½ × 20¼ feet. I.H.P. 1200 = 11 kts. Oil : 150 tons.

> Photo wanted.

TREFOIL (Pembroke, 1913). 4060 tons. Dimensions : 280 × 39 × 18¼ feet. 2 sets 6-cylinder 2-cycle Diesel engines. H.P. 1500 = 12 kts. Deadweight capacity : 2000 tons. Own oil : 200 tons.

> Photos wanted.
> "*Ferol*," "*Servitor*," "*Attendant*," *Carol*"
> *one mast forward, one funnel aft.*

FEROL (Devonport, 1914). **SERVITOR** (Chatham, 1914). 2007 tons. Dimensions : 200 × 34 × 13 feet. 2 sets 4-cylinder 2-cycle Diesel engines. B.H.P. 450 = 8 kts. Deadweight capacity : 1000 tons. Own oil fuel : 29 tons.

ATTENDANT (Chatham, 1913), **CAROL** (Devonport, 1913). 1935 tons. Dimensions : 200 × 34 × 13 feet. I.H.P. 450 = 8 kts. Coal : 60 tons.

(*Continued on next page.*)

Oil Tankers (R.F.A.)—*Continued.*

BURMA (Greenock, 1911). 3945 tons. H.P. 1200 = 11 kts. Cargo capacity : 2500 tons oil fuel. Own fuel : 210 tons.

PETROLEUM (Wallsend, 1901). 9900 tons. Dimensions : 370 × $48\frac{2}{3}$ × 24 feet. H.P. 2000 = 13 kts. Oil : 426 tons.

KHARKI (1899, bought 1900). 1430 tons. H.P. 775 = 13 kts. Fuel : 90 tons.

ISLA (1903, purchased 1907). 1010 tons. Dimensions : 170 × 28 × 12 feet. H.P. 650 = 10 kts. Petrol-carrying vessel for submarines. Fuel : 75 tons.

INDUSTRY (1901). 1460 tons. H.P. 750 = 10 kts. Fuel : 180 tons.

Collier (R.F.A.)

MERCEDES (1901, purchased 1908). 9930 tons. Dimensions : 350 × $50\frac{1}{4}$ × 28 feet. H.P. 2350 = 9 kts. Coal : 750/1603 tons.

Hospital Ships.

"*Soudan* Type."—One ship assigned for duty with Atlantic Fleet, and another for duty with Mediterranean Fleet. Names not known, but one believed to be **ST. MARGARET OF SCOTLAND** of which no photographs or details are available.

Ice Breakers (R.F.A.)

> "Ermiak type."
> 2 funnels, 2 masts

SVIATOGOR (ex-Russian *Sviatogor*, Clyde, 1915-16). No details available.

> *No photo available.*

ALEXANDER (ex-Russian *Aleksandr Nevski*). Built by Armstrongs. Begun June, 1916 (for Russian Government), launched December, 1916, completed December, 1917. 3 screws (2 aft, 1 forward). Cylindrical boilers. No other details known.

Tugs.

> Photo wanted.

ST. ANNE,	ST. COLUMB,	ST. FINBARR,
ST. ARVANS,	ST. CYRUS,	ST. ISSEY,
ST. BLAZEY,	ST. FERGUS,	ST. SAMPSON.

No details available. For Target Work and General Fleet or Squadron duties.

Also many other Tugs, Tanks, &c., but as these are not attached to Fleets or Squadrons, they are not listed.

Despatch Vessels.

> Photo wanted.

WATERWITCH Begun, May 6th, 1914. Launched, October 17th, 1914. Completed, June 7th, 1915. Late Turkish *Rechid Pasha*, purchased 1915. Built by Fairfield. 400 tons. Dimensions : 165 × 26 × $6\frac{1}{2}$ feet (*mean* draught). Designed H.P. 625 = kts. *Trials :* 615 = 13.1. Triple expansion engines and cylindrical boilers. 2 screws. Coal : 34 tons. Complement, 14.

SPHINX (1882). 1130 tons. Guns : 4—4 inch, 2 M.G. H.P. 1100 = 12.5 kts. Coal : 220 tons.

Royal Yachts.

ALEXANDRA (1907). 2050 tons. Dimensions : 275 (*p.p.*) × 40 × $12\frac{1}{2}$ feet (*mean* draught). Guns : 2—7 pdr. (bronze). Parsons turbines. H.P. 4500 = 18.25 kts. (19.1 on first trials). Yarrow boilers. Coal : 270 tons. Complement, 173. *(Continued on next page.)*

Royal Yachts—*Continued.*

VICTORIA AND ALBERT (1899). 4700 tons. Dimensions : 380 (*p.p.*) × 40 × 18 feet (*mean* draught). Guns : 2—6 pdr. (bronze). H.P. 11,800 = 20 kts. Belleville boilers. Coal : *normal,* 350 tons ; *maximum,* 2000 tons. Comp. 336.

Admiralty Yacht.

ENCHANTRESS (1903). 3470 tons. Dimensions : 320 × 40 × 15 feet. Guns : 4—3 pdr. H.P. 6400 = 18 kts. Yarrow boilers. Coal : 350 tons.

Yachts.

TRIAD Yacht, S. N. O. Persian Gulf. (Caledonian S.B. Co., 1909, purchased 1915). 2354 tons. Dimensions : 264 × 35 × 15¾ feet. Guns : Not known. I.H.P. 2235 = 14 kts. Coal : 480 tons.

Yachts—*Continued.*

Photo wanted.

ALACRITY (ex Russian *Mlada*, taken over 1919). No details known. Yacht and Despatch Vessel, C.-in-C., China.

Note.—Gunboat *Hussar* is Despatch Vessel, C.-in-C., Mediterranean. Convoy Sloop *Bryony* has served as Yacht, Rear-Admiral, Ægean. Hunt Class T. S. Minesweeper *Petersfield* may also serve as Yacht on South American Station.

ROSITA (Leith, 1900). 93 tons *gross.* Dimensions : 100 × 16 ×   feet. I.H.P. 250.

DOTTER. No details known.

Admiralty Whalers.

ZEDWHALE.   *Photo, Parry & Sons.*

ARCTIC WHALE,	**CACHALOT,**	**PILOTWHALE,**
BALAENA,	**COWWHALE,**	**RIGHTWHALE,**
BELUGA,	**FINWHALE,**	**RORQUAL,**
BOWHEAD,	**HUMPBACK,**	**ZEDWHALE,**
BULLWHALE,	**ICEWHALE,**	(ex *Meg.*)

Emergency War Programme. Built 1915, by Smiths Dock Co. 336 tons. Dimensions : 139¾ × 25 × 6½ feet. Guns : 1—12 pdr., but *Zedwhale* has also 1—6 pdr. AA. and 1—3 pdr. H.P. 1000 = 12-13 kts. Coal : 60 tons. Complement, 26.

Admiralty Trawlers.

JAMES CATON.   *Builders' Photo, Messrs Lobnitz & Co.*

Nine assigned to Fleet Target Service, Atlantic and Mediterranean Fleets ; about 40 to Training and Experimental Establishments, as detailed on a later page. Disposal of rest not known.

Belong to "Castle," "Mersey," and "Strath" types. Usually as follows :—(*a*) 665 tons, 11 kts. speed, 204 tons coal ; (*b*) 547 tons, 10½ kts., 164 tons coal ; (*c*) 429 tons, 10 kts., 95 tons coal. Guns : Usually 1—12 pdr., but a few have 1—4 inch. Above illustrations typical of appearance.

Admiralty Drifters.

In addition to those detailed on next page as Tenders to Training Establishments, about 60 other Drifters are assigned as Tenders to the Atlantic, Home and Mediterranean Fleets. Displace 199 tons. Speed : 9 kts. Gun : Usually 1—6 pdr. Coal : 34-39 tons.

Surveying Service.

> **Photo wanted.**
>
> Appearance as illustration of *Craigie* on an earlier page, but these ships are painted white.

BEAUFORT (ex *Ambleside*, 1919), **COLLINSON** (ex *Amersham*, 1919), by Ailsa S.B. Co. **FITZROY** (ex *Pinner*, ex *Portreath*, 1919), **FLINDERS** (ex *Radley*, 1919), by Lobnitz & Co. **KELLET** (ex *Uppingham*, 1919), **CROZIER** (ex *Verwood*, ex *Ventnor*, 1919), by Simons & Co. Converted Twin Screw Minesweepers of "Hunt Class." 800 tons. Dimensions : 231 (o.a.) × 28½ × 7½ feet. Guns : 1—3 pdr. I.H.P. 2200 = 16 kts. Machinery : Vertical triple expansion. 2 screws. Boilers : Babcock or Yarrow. Coal : 185 tons.

ENDEAVOUR.

ENDEAVOUR (Fairfield, 1912). 1280 tons. Dimensions : 200 × 34 × 10 feet. Guns : 1—3 pdr., 2 Maxims. H.P. 1100 = 13 kts. Coal : 221 tons. Complement, 44. Specially built for survey.

Surveying Service—*Continued*.

> *No photo available.*

DAISY (Aberdeen, 1911). 510 tons. H.P. 500 = 10 kts. Coal : 107 tons.

MERLIN (1901). 1070 tons. **MUTINE** (1900). 980 tons. Guns : 2—3 pdr., 2 M.G. All about 13¼ kts. Belleville boilers. Coal : *about* 160-203 tons.

HEARTY (1885). 1300 tons. Guns : 4—3 pdr. H.P. 2100 = 14 kts.

For Sloop *Fantome*, on Surveying Service, see Australian Navy Section.

Fishery Protection Vessels.

Kilbeggan	*Kilclogher*
Kilfree	*Kilmalcolm*
Kilclief	

Above Patrol Gunboats for Fisheries Protection Service. All are described on an earlier page.

Coastguard Cruisers.

> **Photo wanted.**

SAFEGUARD (Day, Summers, 1914). 875 tons. Dimensions : 160 × 29 × 10⅔ feet. H.P. 1350 = 15 kts. Guns : 2—3 pdr. Coal : 170 tons. Complement, 39.

Builders' photo, Messrs. Hall Russell & Co.

WATCHFUL (Hall, Russell, 1912). 612 tons. Dimensions : 154 × 25 × 11¾ feet. H.P. 800 = 11.5 kts. Guns : 2—3 pdr. Coal : 150 tons. Complement, 32.

ARGON.

ARGON (ex *Argus*, 1905). 380 tons. H.P. 650 = 12.25 kts. Guns : 2—6 pdr. Coal : 55 tons.

SQUIRREL (1905). 230 tons. H.P. 300 = 10 kts. Guns : 2—3 pdr. Coal : 44 tons.

JULIA (ex *Maretanza*, 1897). 310 tons. H.P. 650. Guns : 2 old 7 pdr. M.L. Coal : 53 tons.

K

Gunnery.

Battleships ..	Collingwood St. Vincent Superb	} Turret Drill.
	Commonwealth (Sea-going Gunnery Ship).	
Monitors	Erebus Marshal Soult Terror	} Director and Fire Control.
Light Cruisers ..	Canterbury Cleopatra Cordelia	
Sloops	Lobelia Snapdragon Vestal Rinaldo (2 others ?)	} Gunnery Firing Tenders.
Destroyers ..	Sharpshooter Stork Tenacious	} Director Training.
Motor Launches	99, three others.	
Diving Tenders ..	Gannet, Raven, Sabine.	
Tug	Traveller.	
Trawlers	4.	
Drifters	1.	

Torpedoes: Whitehead Experiments and Training.

Light Cruiser .. *Champion.*

Destroyers :—

Lydiard	Satyr	Springbok
Orcadia	Seawolf	Starfish
Rocket	Skate	Strenuous
Sable	Skilful	Tormentor

Submarines .. 2 " R Class."

Trawlers .. .. 10.*

* Divided duty with Minelayers.

For Training in Torpedo Control.

8 " M " Class Destroyers or P-boats.

Submarines.

Submarines	E 23, E 41 (m),* E 54. H 27, H 31, H 33. L 21. R 2, R 3, R 7, R 8, R 12.
Depot Ships	Dolphin. Forth. Thames.
Tenders (*Hunt* Class)	Fermoy. Ross.
Drifters	2.

* (m) = Minelayer.

Anti-Submarine.

Destroyers	Christopher. Cockatrice.
Motor Launches	209, 326, 457, 478, 494, 497, 518.
Submarines	E 35, E 38, H 47, L 23, R 4.
Sloops	Auricula. Delphinium.
Depot Ships	Onyx. Pactolus.
Yachts	Dotter Rosita.
Whalers	Icewhale. Cachalot.
Trawlers	9.
Drifters	3.

For P.V. Experiments and Training.

Destroyer .. .. *Acasta.*

For P.V., Hydrophone & Minesweeping Duty.

Torpedo Boat .. .. *T.B. 6.*

Minelaying.

Destroyer	Meteor.*
Paddle Minelayers	4.†
Trawlers	10.‡

* And for Experiments.
† For Controlled Minelaying.
‡ 6 have divided duties with T.B.D. for Whitehead Experiments and Training.

Patrols and Minesweeping.

Sloops :—

Buttercup	Godetia	Pansy
Camelia	Hollyhock	Poppy
Carnation	Iris	Zinnia
Daphne	Lupin (S.N.O.)	

" Hunt " Class :—

Burslem	Gainsborough	Meynell
Cattistock	Gretna	Pangbourne
Elgin	Hambledon	Sherborne
Forres		

Patrol Gunboats :—

Kilbirnie	Kilmarnock	Kilmelford
Kilmallock	Kilmarten	Kilmersden
Kilmanahan	Kilmead	

Admiralty Drifters .. .. .. 13.

Minesweeping.

Hunt Class	Albury. Caerleon. Lydd. Stafford.
Minesweeping Trawlers	8.

Signals and W/T Experiments.

Cruiser	Antrim.
Destroyer	Truant.

Navigation.

Hunt Class	Alresford. Carstairs. Caterham.
Small Monitors	M 24, M 26.
Gunboat	Dryad (late Rattler).

Cadets.

Battleship	Temeraire.
Destroyer	Sturgeon.
Torpedo Boat	T.B. No. 23.
Sloop	Zinnia,
Motor Launches	487.

ROYAL INDIAN MARINE.

KARACHI (Indian Ocean). Graving Dock (Port Trust), $263\frac{1}{4} \times 50 \times 12\frac{3}{4}$ feet. Admiralty Chart No. 40.

Docks.

CALCUTTA.—Eleven, 535–202 feet long, 76–41 feet at entrance, 23–8 feet over sill H.W.O.S.

BOMBAY.—One dock, $1000 \times 100 \times 34$ feet ; Merewether, $525 \times 65 \times 28\frac{1}{2}$ feet ; Ritchie, $495 \times 66 + 18$ feet ; five others.

Troopships.

NORTHBROOK (Clydebank, 1907). 5820 tons. Dimensions : $360 \times 51\frac{3}{4} \times 18$ feet. H.P. $7000 = 16$ kts. Armament : 6—4 inch, 6—3 pdrs.

DUFFERIN (Vickers, 1904). 7457 tons. Dimensions : $437 \times 53 \times 19$ ft. H.P. $9800 = 19$ kts. Coal : 1200 tons. Armament : 8—4 inch, 8—3 pdrs.

RECOGNITION SILHOUETTES.

Scale : 1 inch = 160 feet.

MINTO. LAWRENCE. NORTHBROOK.

HARDINGE. DUFFERIN.

(Continued on next page.)

Troopships—(continued).

HARDINGE (Fairfield, 1900). 6520 tons. Dimensions: 407 × 51 × 19 feet. H.P. 9366 = 18 kts. Fitted with Howden's forced draught. Armament: 6—4·7 inch, 6—3 pdrs., 4 Maxims.

MINTO. *Photo, W. Ewart Williams, Esq., R.I.M.*

MINTO (Birkenhead, 1893). 930 tons gross. Dimensions: 205½ × 31½ × — feet. H.P. 2028 = 14 kts.

ELPHINSTONE (Newcastle, 1887). 950 tons. Dimensions: 205¼ × 28¼ × 14½ feet. H.P. 1670 = 14 kts.

DALHOUSIE (Greenock, 1886). 1960 tons. H.P. 1500 = 13 kts. Coal: 300 tons. Armament: 6—6 pdrs.

CANNING (Glasgow, 1882). 3300 tons. Dimensions: 285 × 36¼ × 16½ feet. H.P. 1080 = 10·5 kts. May be Kite Balloon Ship, referred to on a previous page among British Special Service Ships.

CLIVE (Glasgow, 1882). 3570 tons. Dimensions: 300 × 45½ × 16½ feet. H.P. 2300 = 12 kts.

Steamers.

No photo available.

NEARCHUS (Beardmore. Begun Oct., 1913; launched 15th Nov., 1914; completed 7th Dec., 1914.) 925 tons. Dimensions: 180 (p.p.) × 29 × 11 feet. S.H.P. 550—11 kts. (trials 650 = 11·75). Parsons geared turbines. 1 Yarrow boiler. Oil: 120 tons.

MAYO 1125 tons *gross*.

GUIDE 817 tons *gross*.

Despatch Vessel.

Photo by favour of N. O'Toole, Esq.

LAWRENCE (1886). Paddle wheel steamer. 1154 tons. Dimensions: 212 × 32¼ × 18⅓ feet. Guns: 4—6 pdr., 4 machine. H.P. 1200 = 13·5 kts. Coal: 270 tons.

Hospital Ships.

HP I—HP II. Paddle-wheel Hospital Ships. Built by Beardmore, Caird & Co., Bow, McLachlan, Lobnitz, Ailsa S.B. Co., Blyth S.B. Co., 1916-17, for Mesopotamia.

Yachts.

2 small Viceregal Yachts, *Maud* and *Lytton*.

Surveying Ships.

Photo, W. Ewart Williams, Esq., R.I.M.

INVESTIGATOR (Vickers, 1907). Gross tonnage 1015, net 515. I.H.P. 1500.

Also *Nancowry* of 70 tons gross and 7 kts. speed.

Pilot Vessel.

LADY FRASER (1908). 2062 tons. Dimensions: 270 × 38 × 13½ feet. Speed: 13·7 kts.

River Craft.

P 51, 51 (Beardmore). **P 52—57** (Caird & Co.). **P 58, 59** (——). **P 60, 61** (Lobnitz). Paddle-wheel Vessels, built 1916–17 for Tigris and Euphrates. H.P. 1200 = 15 kts. Guns: 1—3 pdr.

PALINURUS (1907). Screw River Steamer. 298 tons.

BHAMO. Composite Stern-wheel Vessel. 255 tons. Guns: 2 machine.

IRRAWADY. Paddle-wheel River Steamer. 338 tons *gross*. Guns: 2 machine.

SLADEN. Paddle-wheel River Steamer. 260 tons. Guns: 5 machine.

There are also about 24 yard craft, launches and small submarine mining vessels. Also various stern wheel and tunnel screw craft built during War by British Shipyards for service on Tigris and Euphrates.

Federated Malay States.

Bore expense of building the battleship **MALAYA**.

COMMONWEALTH OF AUSTRALIA.

ROYAL AUSTRALIAN NAVY.

Personnel :   *Minister of the Navy.*—The Rt. Hon. Sir Joseph Cook, P.C.

Navy Yards.

COCKATOO ISLAND (SYDNEY), with one completed slip, for building Light Cruisers and another large slip building. Employees about 1500–2000. May be closed down owing to labour troubles.

GARDEN ISLAND. Repairs only.

    Also a Government yard at Walsh Island, N.S.W., devoted to mercantile construction.

Private Docks, &c.

ADELAIDE (S. AUSTRALIA). Commercial harbour, 7 miles from the town.

BRISBANE (QUEENSLAND, AUSTRALIA). 25 miles up river. Navigable for ships drawing 20 feet. Coaling station. Dry dock: 431½ × 55 × 19 feet.

FREMANTLE (W. AUSTRALIA). Dry dock, originally designed as 594 feet long, but enlarged to 694 feet and may now be 910 × 100 × 34 feet (L.W.O.S.), divisible into two sections (*Dreadnought*).

HOBART (TASMANIA). Coaling station. Anchorage average, 10 fathoms.

KING GEORGE SOUND (W. AUSTRALIA). Coaling station. Fortified.

SYDNEY (N.S.W., AUSTRALIA). Fortified coaling station and base for R.A.N. Harbour excellent. Bar 27 feet at low water. Dry docks : (Sutherland) 638 × 84 × 32 feet (*Dreadnought*), (Fitzroy) 477 × 59 × 21½ feet. *Woolwich* dock (private) 675 × 83 × 28 feet (*Dreadnought*), and four smaller.

MELBOURNE. Commercial harbour. One dry dock: 470 × 80 × 27 feet, and three smaller. Port Phillip has an area of 800 square miles.

NEWCASTLE (N.S.W., AUSTRALIA). Government floating dock, 426 × 64 × 25 feet. (9500 tons).

T.B.D. & SUBMARINE SILHOUETTES (E. L. KING).

Scale : 125 feet to 1 inch.

Anzac (*Leader*).

Parramatta *class* t.b.d.

J 1—J 5 (*Submarines*).

J 7 (*Submarine*).

Scale : 1 inch = 160 feet.

GAYUNDAH *class.*

PROTECTOR.

GERANIUM.
MALLOW.
MARGUERITE.

PHILOMEL.

PIONEER.
PSYCHE.

As *Chatham* class,
British Navy.

ENCOUNTER.

BRISBANE.
MELBOURNE.
SYDNEY.

AUSTRALIA.

(INDEFATIGABLE TYPE—1 SHIP.)

AUSTRALIA (Oct. 25th, 1911).

Normal displacement, 18,800 tons (about 21,300 *full load.*) Complement, 820. (Flagship.)

Length (*waterline*),   feet. Beam, 80 feet. {*Mean* draught, 26½ feet.} Length, (*p.p.*) 555 feet, (*over all*), 590 feet.
{*Max.* draught, 30 feet.}

Guns (**Dir. Con.**) :
  8—12 inch, 50 cal.
  14—4 inch, 50 cal.
  1—4 inch anti-aircraft
  1—3 inch anti-aircraft
  (1 landing)
  4—3 pdr.
  5 machine
Torpedo tubes (18 inch) :
  2 *submerged* (broadside).

Armour (K.C.,K.N.C., Nickel) :
  6″ Belt (amidships)...
  4″ Belt (ends) ....
  2½–1″ Decks............
  7″–3″ Barbettes .....
  7″ Gunhouses ....
  10″ Conning tower......
  4″ C.T. tube............
  1″ Torp. dir. tower ...
  1½″–1″ Funnel uptakes
    (Hull+armour=10,725 tons.)

Ahead :
4 to 6—
  12 in.

Astern :
4 to 6—
  12 in.

Broadside : 8—12 in. ; 1—21 in. tube.

Machinery : Parsons turbines by builders. 4 screws. Boilers : Babcock. Designed H.P. 44,000 = 25 kts. Coal : *normal* 1000 tons, *maximum* 3170+840 tons oil fuel. Endurance : about 6,300 miles at 10 kts.

Armour Notes.—Main belt 12 feet deep, closed by 4″ bulkheads and with 1″ deck above. Lower deck 1″ amidships, 2¼″ at ends outside belt. For more detailed particulars, *v. New Zealand*, British Navy Section.

Internal Protection.

Name	Builder	Machinery	Laid down	Com-pleted	Trials (*mean*):		Boilers	Best recent speed
					30 hrs. at ¾	8 hrs. full power		
Australia	J. Brown, Clydebank	J. Brown, Clydebank	June '10	June '13	30,800 = 23·5	48,422 = 26·89	Babcock	

General Notes.—An improved *Indefatigable*, and a sister-ship to *New Zealand*, described on a previous page.

AUSTRALIA. (Topmasts and topgallant masts as Silhouette).

AUSTRALIAN LIGHT CRUISERS.

(CHATHAM CLASS—4 SHIPS.)

MELBOURNE (May, 1912), **SYDNEY** (Aug., 1912), **BRISBANE** (Sept., 1915), and **ADELAIDE** (July, 1918).

Displacement, 5400 tons. Complement, 390–392.

Length (*p.p.*), 430 feet. Beam, 49⅝ feet. $\{$ Mean draught, 15¾ feet. $\}$ Length (*over all*), 457 feet.
$\{$ Max. ,, 17¾–18½ feet. $\}$

Guns (**Dir. Con.**) :
  8—6 inch, 50 cal.
  1—3 inch anti-aircraft
  4 –3 pdr.
  4 machine
Torpedo tubes (21 inch) :
  2 broadside (*submerged*)

Armour (Hadfield :
  2″ Deck (on slopes)

Ahead :
3—6 in.

Astern :
3—6 in.

CHATHAM

Broadside : 5—6 in., 1—21 in. torpedo tube.

Machinery : Parsons turbine. 4 screws. Boilers : Yarrow. Designed H.P. (*n.d.*) 22,000, 25,000 f.d.=25 kts. Coal : *normal* 750 tons, *maximum* about 1240 tons+about 260 tons oil fuel. *Brisbane*, 1196 coal+260 oil.

Gunnery Notes.—Electric ammunition hoists.

Torpedo Notes.—7 torpedoes carried. 4 or more searchlights.

Armour Notes.—Internal protection by longitudinal and transverse bulkheads. Double bottom extends over magazine and machinery spaces. Conning Tower in *Sydney* (and others) replaced by revolving platform carrying a small aeroplane or seaplane.

Engineering Notes.—500 r.p.m.=full power. Boilers : 3 drum small tube type. Uniflux condensers.

Name	Builder	Machinery	Laid down	Com-pleted	Trials: 30 hrs. at ¾	8 hrs. full power	Boilers	Best recent speed
Melbourne	Cammell-Laird	Cammell-Laird	Apl. '11	Jan. '13		25,800=25·7	Yarrow	
Sydney	L. & Glasgow	L. & Glasgow	Feb. '11	Jun. '13	22,400=	25,572=25·7	,,	
Brisbane	Sydney	Vickers	Jan. 13	...			,,	
Adelaide	Sydney		1915	...				

General Notes.—Practically same design as British *Chatham* class. Served during War in North Sea.

MELBOURNE. Can be distinguished from *Sydney* by director tower placed over control top on foremast.

ENCOUNTER (1902, *transferred* 1912). 5880 tons. Complement, 457. Dimensions : 376 (*o.a.*)×56 ×20⅔ feet (*max draught*). Armament : 11—6 inch, 4—12 pdr., 4—3 pdr., 3 M.G., 1 landing. 2—18 inch tubes, *sub.* Designed H.P. 12,500=21 kts. 12 Dürr boilers. Coal : 1300 tons *max.*

Obsolete Light Cruisers.

Photo, Symonds & Co.

PSYCHE (1897), 2135 tons and **PIONEER** (1899), 2200 tons. Complement, 234. Armament: *Psyche*, 8—4 inch. 3 M.G. *Pioneer* has only 4—3 pdr. Tubes: 2—14 inch *above water*. Designed H.P. 7000 (*f.d.*)=20 kts. (not over 16 kts. at present). Coal: 520--540 tons.

PHILOMEL (Jan., 1890). 2575 tons. Complement, 222. Dimensions (*o.a.*): $278 \times 41 \times 16\frac{5}{6}$ (*max.*) feet. Armament: 1—3 pdr. Torpedo Tubes: 3—14 inch *above water*. Armour: $2\frac{1}{2}''$ Deck. Designed H.P. 7500=19 kts. (*f.d.*) Coal: 450 tons.

12 Destroyers.

No.	Type	Date	Dis-place-ment	H.P.	Speed	Oil	Com-ple-ment	Tubes	Max. draug't
1	*Anzac*	'16-'17	tons 1666	36,000 *t*	kts. 34	tons 416/515	116	4	12
5	*Admiralty "S"*	'17-'19	1075	27,000 *t*	36	254/301	90	4	12?
3	*Swan*	'15-'16	} 700 {	11,300 *t*	26	173·189/157	69	3	$8\frac{1}{2}$—9
3	*Parramatta*	'09-'12		10,600 *t*					

Flotilla Leader.

1 Marksman (later) Type.

1 *Denny*: **Anzac.** 1,666 tons. Dimensions: 315 ft. (*p.p.*), 325 ft. (*o.a.*) × 31 ft. 10 in. × 12 ft. $1\frac{1}{2}$in. (*max.* draught aft). Guns: 4—4 inch, 2—2 pdr. pom-poms, 1 M.G. Torpedo tubes: 4—21 inch in 2 rev. deck mountings. Machinery: Brown-Curtis turbines. 3 screws. Boilers: Yarrow small tube. Designed S.H.P. 36,000 = 34 kts. *Trials*: Oil, 416/515 tons = *about* 2500 miles at 15 kts. Complement, 116. Begun January 31st, 1916. Launched January 11th, 1917. Completed April 24th, 1917. Begun under Emergency War Programme and presented to Australia, 1919. Sister to *Parker, Seymour*, &c., of British Navy, but fo'xle of *Anzac* is $2\frac{1}{2}$ feet higher, and she has a few other small differences.

Destroyers—*Continued.*

5 "Admiralty S" type.

2 *Beardmore :* **Tasmania, Tattoo.**

1 *Doxford :* **Success.**

1 *Scott :* **Swordsman.**

1 *Swan Hunter :* **Stalwart.**

1075 tons. Dimensions : 265 (*p.p.*), 276 (*o.a.*, *Success* 277) × 26¾ × 9 feet (*mean*) draught. Armament : 3—4 inch (Mk. IV with 30° elevation), 1—2 pdr. pom-pom, 4—21 inch tubes in two twin deck mountings, 1—24 inch search-light controlled in unison with guns. May have D.C. Thrower and High Speed type of P.Vs. Machinery : Brown-Curtis all-geared turbines. 2 screws. Boilers : 3 Yarrow small tube. Designed S.H.P. 27000, = 36 kts. Fuel (oil only) : 254/301 tons = *about* 2000 miles at 15 kts. Complement, 90.

	Begun.	Launch.	Comp.		Begun.	Launch.	Comp.
Tasmania ..	18/12/17	22/11/18	29/1/19	Swordsman]	....	28/12/18	3/19
Tattoo ..	21/12/17	28/12/18	7/4/19	Stalwart ..	4/18	23/10/18	4/19
Success ..	....	29/6/18	{4/19				

Notes.—Built under Emergency War Programme and presented to Australian Navy, 1919. For any further notes, refer to description of "S Class" in British Navy Section.

Destroyers—*Continued.*

WARREGO.

Parramatta, Yarra (1910, **Warrego** (1911), **Huon** (ex *Derwent*, 1914), **Swan** (Dec., 1915), **Torrens** (Aug., (1915). Dimensions : Length (*o.a.*) 250¾ *Houn, Swan, Torrens*, 245¾ *Yarra*, 246 *Parramatta, Warrego* × 24¼ × 8 feet. Armaments : 1—4 inch, 3—12 pdrs., 3—18 inch tubes. Parsons turbines. Yarrow boilers. Radius : 2500 kts. Oil fuel. *Yarra* by Denny, Dumbarton ; *Parramatta* and *Warrego* by London & Glasgow Engineering Co., *Warrego* being re-erected at Cockatoo N.Y., Sydney. *Swan, Huon* and *Torrens* built at Cockatoo N.Y., Sydney. Are modified British "I" Class boats.

Torpedo Boat (*First Class.*)

No photo available.

Countess of Hopetoun. Tenders to *Cerberus.* No details known.

6 Submarines.

No.	Class	Begun	Comp.	Dis-place-ment Tons.	B.H.P. / E H.P.	Speed kts.	Endurance	Tubes	Comp't.
6	J 7	1916	1917	1200 / 1760	3600 / 1400	19 / 9·5	4,000 miles at 12 kts.	6	44
	J 1—5	1915	1916	1260 / 1820					

6 Ocean-going Boats.

Photo wanted.

J 7.

Photo wanted.

J 5

Photo wanted.

J 2, 3, 4.

Photo wanted.

J 1.

"J Class"—6 Boats.

6 *Admiralty* type: **J 7** (Feb., 1917), **J 5** (Sept., 1915), both by Devonport D.Y. **J 4** (Feb., 1916), **J 3** (Dec., 1915), both by Pembroke D.Y. **J 2** (Nov., 1915), **J 1** (Nov., 1915), both by Portsmouth D.Y. J 1—5, completed April-Aug., 1916; J 7, Nov., 1917. Dimensions: 270 (p.p.), 274¾ (o.a.) × 23½ × 14 feet. Armament: 1—4 inch gun and 6 —18 inch tubes (4 bow, 2 beam). Surface machinery: 3 sets of Vickers 12 cylinder solid injection, direct reversing 4 cycle 1200 B.H.P. Diesel engines (14½ i n. bore × 15 in. stroke, 380 r.p.m.). Oil: 80/91 tons. Built under Emergency Programme as "Bight Patrols." J 6 lost during War. Presented to Australia, 1918. Other details as Table.

Fleet Sweeping Vessels (Sloops).

No photo available.
See illustration of *Valerian* and *Primrose*—
British Navy Section.

Fleet Sweeping Vessel (Sloop).

No photo available,
See illustration for *Valerian*—
British Navy Section.

GERANIUM (Greenock & Grangemouth Co. Begun Aug., 1915; launched 8th Nov., 1915; completed March, 1916). **MARGUERITE** (Dunlop Bremner. Begun July, 1915; launched 23rd Nov., 1915; completed Jan., 1916). Fleet Sweeping Vessels (Sloops) of *Arabis* type. 1250 tons. Dimensions : 255¼ (*p.p.*), 267¾ (*o.a.*) × 33½ × 10½ feet (*mean*), 11¾ (*max.* draught). Guns : 1—4·7 inch, 2—3 pdr. (AA. in *Geranium*). Designed I.H.P. 2000 = 17 kts. Trials ; *Geranium*, 2312 = 17 : *Marguerite*, 2309 = 16·1. Machinery : boilers, screws, as *Mallow*, opposite. Coal : 260 tons = 2050 miles at 15 kts. Complement, 79. Built under Emergency War Programme ; presented to Australian Navy, 1919.

MALLOW (Barclay Curle. Launched 13th July, 1915; completed Sept., 1916.) Fleet Sweeping Vessel (Sloop) of *Acacia* type. 1200 tons. Dimensions : 250 (*p.p.*), 262½ (*o.a.*) × 33 × 10¼ feet (*mean*), 11¼ (*max.* load). Guns : 1—12 pdr. (12 cwt.), 2—3 pdr. AA. I.H.P. 1800 = 17 kts. Trials : 2328 = 16·3 kts. Machinery : 1 set triple expansion inverted and 2 cylindrical boilers. Coal : 250 tons = 2000 miles at 15 kts. Complement, 77. Built under Emergency War Programme ; presented to the Australian Navy, 1919.

Sloop.

Photo wanted.
1 funnel, 2 pole masts, yacht bow.

Sloop (Surveying Ship).

No photo available.

UNA (ex-German Surveying Ship *Komet*, built about 1911, captured 1914). 1438 tons. Dimensions : 210½ × 31 × 15¾ feet. Guns : 3 —4 inch, 2—12 pdr. H.P. 1300 = 16 kts. Coal ; 270 tons. Complement, 114.

FANTOME (1901, lent from Royal Navy, 1915). 1070 tons. Guns : 2—4 inch, 1—3 pdr., 2 M.G. Speed, 13½ kts. Coal : 195 tons. For Surveying Service. Complement, 135.

Obsolete Gunboats.

PROTECTOR (Elswick, 1884). 920 tons. Guns: 3—4 inch, 2—12 pdr., 4—3 pdr. H.P. 1600=14 kts. originally. Re-boilered 1910-11. Tender to Williamstown Gunnery School. (*South Australia*).

GAYUNDAH (Elswick, 1884, reported to have been re-built at Cockatoo N.Y., Sydney, 1914). 360 tons. Guns: 1—4·7, 2—12 pdr. Speed originally: 10·5 kts.

Also *Cerberus*. now Naval Depot at Williamstown, with Cruiser *Psyche* and 1st Class T.B. *Countess of Hopetoun* and *Coogee, Gannet, Gayundah, Protector* as tenders.

Submarine Depot Ship.

Photo wanted.

PLATYPUS (J. Brown, Clydebank. Begun Sept. 2nd, 1914; launched Oct. 28th, 1916; completed Mar., 1917.) 2,460 tons. Dimensions: 310 (*w.l*), 325 (*o.a*) × 44 × 15⅔ feet. (*max.* draught). Guns: *nil?* I.H.P. 3600=15½ kts. Reciprocating engines and cylindrical boilers. 2 screws. Coal: 450 tons. Complement, 357.

Fuel Ships (R.F.A.)

Photo wanted.

BILOELA. Fleet Collier, built at Cockatoo Island D.Y. Completed 1919. No details known.

Photo wanted.

KURUMBA (Swan Hunter. Begun Sept., 1915; launched Sept., 1916; completed Jan., 1917; machinery by Wallsend.) Oil Tanker. 8350 tons. Dimensions: 365 (*p p.*), 377¹¹⁄₁₂ (*o.a.*) × 45½ × 23¼ feet *max.* load draught. Guns: 3 (calibre not known). I.H.P. 2000=10 kts. Triple expansion engines and S.E. cylindrical boilers. 2 screws. Fuel: *max.*, 688 tons coal + 257 tons oil, exclusive of cargo. Complement, 65–100.

Armed Patrol Vessels.

No photo available.

COOGEE (———). 762 tons *gross*. H.P. = 16 kts. Guns: 1—4·7 inch, 2—3 pdr. Coal: 210 tons.

No photo available.

GANNET (ex *Penguin*, ———). 208 tons *gross*. H.P. 420=10 kts. Guns: 1—12 pdr. Coal: 87 tons.

No photo available.

MOORILYAN (———). 1349 tons *gross*. H.P. 2330=14·4 kts. Guns 1—4·7 inch Q.F., 2—3 pdr. Hotchkiss. Coal: 280 tons.

No photo available.

SLEUTH (ex *Ena*). 108 tons. H.P. 160= kts. Guns: 1—3 pdr.

Miscellaneous.

NUSA. 64 tons. Ex-German ship seized at Kawieng, 1914.
SUMATRA. No details known.
FRANKLIN (ex-*Adele*). 288 tons. Training Ship for Cadets. Tender to R.A.N. College, Jervis Bay.
TINGIRA. Training Ship.

DOMINION OF NEW ZEALAND.

Battle Cruiser **NEW ZEALAND** was built at the expense of the Dominion. The annual subvention of £100,000 paid by the Dominion is to be devoted to the maintenance of the Light Cruiser **CANTERBURY** and a Training Ship of 3000 tons.

Docks.

AUCKLAND. Coaling station. Excellent harbour; average 40 feet deep. Dry dock (Calliope): 521 × 66 × 33 feet. Also one smaller, able to take torpedo craft.

PORT CHALMERS (S. ISLAND). Otago dry dock, 500 × 70 × 21 feet, *and another smaller.*

Sloop.

No photo available.

FIREBRAND (ex *Torch*, 1894). Transferred from British Navy, 1917. 960 tons. Armament : 4—4 inch, 4—3 pdr., 2 M.G. Speed, 13·4 kts. Coal, 130 tons.

Gunboat.

(Training Service.)

AMOKURA (Greenock, 1889). 805 tons. Guns: 6—4 inch, 3—3 pdr. H.P. 1200 = 13 kts. Coal: 105 tons.

Miscellaneous.

A yacht, **HINEMOA,** and two small mining vessels. Also cable ship, **TUTANEKAI.**

DOMINION OF CANADA.

Minister of Marine : Hon. Col. C. C. Ballantyne.
Personnel :   *Uniforms* : As British Navy.

Stanford's Geog'l Estab.

Pacific :—

ESQUIMAULT.—Naval Dockyard. Admiralty Chart No. 576 (For Docks, see below.)

Atlantic :—

HALIFAX (NOVA SCOTIA). — Formerly Dockyard. Coaling Station. Anchorage averages 13 fathoms. Examination Base during War. (For Docks, see below.)

Private Shipyards.

CANADIAN VICKERS CO. (MONTREAL).—Affiliated to Messrs. Vickers, Ltd., Barrow-in-Furness. No details available of this establishment. "H" class Submarines built here during the War. For large Floating Dock, see Docks below.

MESSRS. YARROW, LTD. (LANG'S COVE, ESQUIMAULT).—Branch of Messrs. Yarrow, Ltd., Scotstoun, N.B. Can build ships up to 2000 tons. Slipway 315 × 30 feet (3000 tons capacity). Fitting-out Wharf 500 feet long. Repair shops; one 60-ton sheer legs; one 10-ton floating derrick. Yard covers eight acres, with Government Dock adjoining.

Docks.

COLLINGWOOD. Collingwood Dry Dock Co. 524 × 60 × 15½ feet.

ESQUIMAULT. Government Dock 450–180 × 65 × 26½ feet. Also 2400 tons patent slip.

ST. JOHNS (NEW BRUNSWICK). At Courtenay Bay, new dock *projected*, 1150 × 125 × 40 feet (*over sills*).

HALIFAX (NOVA SCOTIA). Dry dock : Halifax Graving Dock Co., 572 × 89 × 29 feet (*Dreadnought*).

KINGSTON (ONTARIO). Government dock, 290 × 55 × 18 feet.

MONTREAL. Duke of Connaught floating dock (Proprietors, Canadian Vickers Co.), 600 × 100 × 28½ feet. (*Dreadnought.*) Two other private docks, 400 × 45 × 10 feet.

PORT ARTHUR. Dry dock, 700 × 74¼ × 15½ feet.

PORT DALHOUSIE. Muir Bros'. dock, 260 × 46 × 10 feet.

OWEN SOUND. Dock, 300 × 60 × 12 feet.

QUEBEC : Canadian Government dry dock, 1150 × 120 × 30 feet, divisible into two docks, 650 and 500 feet long respectively. (*Dreadnought.*) Levis dock, 600 × 62 × 20½ feet. Three floating docks, 1600, 2200, and 2500 tons lift.

A: ROYAL CANADIAN NAVY.

RECOGNITION SILHOUETTES.

Scale : 1 inch = 160 feet.

CONSTANCE.   MALASPINA.   ACADIA.   CARTIER.

LADY GREY.   CANADA.   MONTCALM.

RAINBOW.   NIOBE.

Scale : 1 inch = 80 feet.

SUBMARINES.

H 14, H 15, CC 1, CC 2

Cruiser.

(*Depot Ship—is dismantled.*)

NIOBE (1897, transferred 1913).   11,000 tons.   Complement —.   Guns and torpedo tubes : *Is disarmed.*   Armour : Deck, 4″; Casemates, 6″.   Designed H.P. 16,500 = 20·25 kts.   Present speed : somewhere about 18 kts. or less, owing to damage received by stranding in 1914.   Coal : 2000 tons.

Light Cruiser.

(*Training Ship for Pacific Coast.*)

RAINBOW (1891, bought 1909).   3600 tons.   Complement —.   Guns and torpedo tubes : *Is disarmed.*   Deck : 2″.   Designed H.P. 9000 = 19·75 kts.   Present speed : about 12 kts.   Coal : 560 tons.

Photo wanted.

Grilse (1913). 225 tons. Dimensions: 207 × 18½ × 6 feet. Guns: 2—12 pdr. 1 torpedo tube. Designed H.P. 6000 = 30 kts. Oil: 53 tons.

Photo wanted.

Tuna (1902). 150 tons. Dimensions: 153 × 15 × 5 feet. Guns: 1—3 pdr. Torpedo tubes: 2. Designed H.P. 2000 = 24 kts. Coal: 27 tons.

4 Submarines.

Photo wanted.

2 *Holland* type: **H 14, H 15** (1918). Displacements: 364 tons *surface*, 435 tons *submerged*. Dimensions: 150¼ × 15¼ × 12¾ feet. Torpedo tubes: 4—18 inch (bow). B.H.P. 480 = 13 kts. *on surface*; H.P. 320 = 11 kts. *submerged* (for about one hour continuous running). Complement 20 – 22. Built under Emergency War Programme and presented to Canadian Navy, 1919.

Photo wanted.

1 *Holland* type: **CC 2** (Seattle Con. & D.D. Co., 1914). Displacements: 310 tons *on surface*, 373 tons *submerged*. Dimensions: 157 ft. 6½ in. × 14 ft. 11½ in. × feet. Torpedo tubes: 3—18 inch. H.P. 600 *on surface* = 13 kts.; 260 *submerged* = 10¼ kts.

1 *Holland* type: **CC 1** (Seattle Con. & D.D. Co., 1911). Displacements: 313 tons *on surface*, 373 tons *submerged*. Dimensions: 144 ft. 3½ in. × 14 ft. × 11 ft. 6 in. Torpedo tubes: 5—18 inch. H.P. 600 *on surface* = 13 kts.; 260 *submerged* = 10¼ kts.

Note. —Above two boats were begun for Chilean Navy as *Antofagasta* and *Iquique*. They were purchased by Canada just before outbreak of war.

Submarine Depot Ship.

SHEARWATER (1900). Sloop. 980 tons. Guns : 4—4 inch, 4—3 pdr., 2 machine. H.P. 1400 (f.d.)=13¼ kts. Coal : 160 tons. Lent from Royal Navy, 1914.

Sloop.

ALGERINE (1895). 1050 tons. Guns : 4—3 pdr., 3 M.G. H.P. 1400 =13½ kts. Boilers : cylindrical. Coal 160 tons. Lent from Royal Navy.

Armed Patrol Vessels.

Belongs to the Department of Naval Service.
CANADA (1904). 780 tons. Guns : 2—12 pdr., 2—3 pdr. H.P. 1600 =14 kts. Coal : 110 tons. (F.)

Armed Patrol Vessels—*Continued.*

No photo available.

FLORENCE (——). Guns : 1—3 pdr. Q.F. Speed, 12 kts.

No photo available.

HOCHELAGA (——). Guns : 1—12 pdr. Speed, 12 kts.

Belongs to Department of Customs.
MARGARET (1913). 950 tons. Guns : 2—6 pdr. Designed H.P. 2000=15½ kts, *max.* speed. Coal : 200 tons.

160

Armed Patrol Vessels—*Continued.*

No photo available

PREMIER (——). 374 tons *gross.* Guns : 1—6 pdr. Speed, 13 kts.
SEAGULL. Patrol Depot Ship. No details known.

No photo available.

STADACONA (——). Guns : 1—4 inch Q.F. Speed, 12 kts.

No photo available.

STARLING (——). Guns : 1—3 pdr. Speed, 12 kts.

Trawlers and Drifters.

Twenty-seven of these were loaned to U.S. Navy for war duties ; others served with H M. Navy during the war. No other details available.

B: CANADIAN GOVERNMENT VESSELS.

(From Official List. Arranged *alphabetically*. All speeds are *maximum*.)

Department of the Naval Service.

Note.

Vessels marked (H) were engaged in 1915 on Hydrographic Survey duty, and those marked (F) on Fishery Protection.

ACADIA.

ACADIA (1913). 1050 tons. H.P. 1200 = 12 kts. Coal : 260 tons. (H).

BAYFIELD (1889). 550 tons. Speed, 12 kts. Coal : 100 tons. (H.)

Department of the Naval Service—Continued.

CARTIER (1910). 850 tons. H.P. 830 = 12 kts. Coal : 150 tons. (H.)

CONSTANCE.

CONSTANCE (1891). 400 tons. Speed, 10 kts. Coal : 46 tons. (F.)

GULNARE (1893). 500 tons. Speed, 10 kts. Coal : 65 tons. (F.)

LILLOOET (1908). 760 tons. Speed, 11¾ kts. Coal : 140 tons. (H.)

Department of the Naval Service—Continued.

MALASPINA.

MALASPINA (1913). 850 tons. Guns : 1—6 pdr. H.P. 1350 = 14¼ kts. Coal : 200 tons. (F.)

PETREL (1902). 400 tons. Speed, 11 kts. Coal : 65 tons. (F.)

Also 4 other vessels under 500 tons, 1 iron-built, 1 composite-built, and 2 wooden-built.

Department of Marine and Fisheries.

ABERDEEN (1894). 1330 tons. H.P. 1510 = 13 kts. Coal : 125 tons.

ARANMORE (1890). 500 tons (net registered). Speed, 13 kts. Coal : 200 tons.

BELLECHASSE (1912). 576 tons. H.P. 900 = 11¼ kts. Coal : 24 tons.

CHAMPLAIN (1904). 800 tons. Speed, 11 kts. Coal : 60 tons.

DOLLARD (1913). 323 tons (net registered). Speed, . Oil fuel.

DRUID (1902). 1000 tons. Speed, 13 kts. Coal : 100 tons.

ESTEVAN (1912). 2100 tons. H.P. 1500 = 12½ kts. Coal : 350 tons.

GRENVILLE (1914). tons. H.P. 900 = kts. Coal : 100 tons.

J. D. HAZEN (1916). Ice breaker. 4900 tons. Dimensions : 275 × 57½ × 19 feet (*max* draught). Designed H.P. 8000 = kts. Coal : 1300 tons. Was transferred to Russia, 1915 or 1916, but is reported to have returned to Canada from the White Sea in 1918.

(*Continued on next page.*)

B: CANADIAN GOVERNMENT VESSELS.

Department of Marine and Fisheries (continued):—

EARL GREY (ex-Russian *Kanada*, ex-Canadian *Earl Grey*). (Vickers, 1909). 3400 tons. 250 × 47½ × 17¾ feet. H.P. 6000 = 17 kts. (did 18 on trial). Boilers: cylindrical Is specially built for ice-breaking.

LADY GREY.

LADY GREY (1906). 1080 tons. H.P. 2300 = 14 kts. Coal: 200 tons.

LADY LAURIER (1902). 1970 tons. H.P. 1800 = 13 kts. Coal: 175 tons.

LAMBTON (1906). 510 tons. Speed, 11 kts. Coal: 92 tons.

Photo, Lieut. Com. Saal, R.C.N.

MINTO (1899). 2070 tons. H.P. 2900 = 15½ kts. Coal: 290 tons.

Department of Marine and Fisheries (continued):—

MONTCALM.

MONTCALM (1904). 3270 tons. H.P. 3225 = 14 kts. Coal: 425 tons.

NEWINGTON (1889). 475 tons. Speed, 10 kts. Coal: 85 tons.

PRINCESS (1896). 850 tons. Speed, 11 kts. Coal: 124 tons.

QUADRA (1801). 1260 tons. Speed, 11 kts. Coal: 200 tons.

SIMCOE (1909). 1630 tons. Speed, 12½ kts. Coal: 100 tons.

STANLEY (1888). 1890 tons. Speed, 15½ kts. Coal: 250 tons.

Photo, "Syren and Shipping."

VIGILANT (Polson I.W., 1918). No details available.

Also 4 other ships, 1 steel-built and 3 wooden-built. *Wilfrid* (ex S.S. Wilfrid C., 1897), 90 tons *gross*, purchased 1918.

Department of Militia and Defence:—

Three small vessels *Alfreda* (1904), 270 tons: *Armstrong* (1903), 230 tons; and *Beryl* (1903), 45 tons. All 9½—8 kts. speed.

Department of Public Works.

TYRIAN (1869). 1300 tons. Speed, 10 kts. Coal: 340 tons.

Also *Speedy* (1896). 420 tons. 12 kts. speed.

Department of Railways and Canals:—

DURLEY CHINE (1913). 5173 tons. Speed, 10½ kts. Coal: 457 tons.

MULGRAVE (1892). 925 tons. Speed, 14 kts. Coal: 40 tons.

SCOTIA (1901). 2550 tons. Speed, 12 kts. Coal: 120 tons.

SHEEBA (1912). 5668 tons. Speed, 10½ kts. Coal: 340 tons.

(Also 13 other smaller vessels.)

Department of the Post Office:—

LADY EVELYN (1901). 680 tons. Speed, 14 kts.

Department of Agriculture:—

ALICE (1907). 550 tons. Speed, 11½ kts.

And 4 smaller vessels.

NEWFOUNDLAND.

PETREL. Armed Patrol Vessel. Speed about 10 kts. Guns: 1—3 pdr. Q.F.

Also old *Briton* (ex-*Calypso*) as Training Ship.

EGYPT.

ENSIGN & JACK.	SULTAN'S STANDARD.	Red ▥
		White ☐

River Gunboats.

MELIK, SHEIK, SULTAN (1897). 140 tons. Speed, 11 kts. 2 screws in tunnels. Guns: 1—12 pdr. + 1—24 pdr. howitzer, 3 machine.

FATEH, NASIR, ZAFIR (1896). 128 tons. Stern-wheel Steamers. Speed, 12 kts. Guns: 1—12 pdr. +1—24 pdr. howitzer, 4 machine.

ABU KLEA, HAFIR, METEMMEH, TAMAI. Stern-wheel Steamers. Guns: 1—22 pdr. in first; 1—9 pdr. in others.

Also 24 other River Steamers, built 1908-1885.

Transport, &c.

GHARBIEH. 3700 tons. Also another steamer, **MUKBIR,** of 420 tons.

There are also 5 Paddle-wheel Steamers and about 15 Tugs.

Yacht.

MAHROUSSA (1865, rebuilt 1906). 3417 tons. Parsons turbine. H.P. 5500 = 17·5 kts.

Also 2 other small Yachts, and 3 Despatch Vessels.

Customs Cruisers.

ABDUL MONEIM (Clydebank, 1902). 598 tons. Guns: 1—3 pdr. H.P. 1000 = 13 kts.

NOUR-EL-BAHR (1884). 450 tons. Guns: 1—3 pdr. H.P. 870 = 13·5 kts.

RESHID. About 650 tons. Guns: 2—6 pdr.

Ports and Lights Administration.

AIDA. 723 tons. 1 gun. H.P. 130 =   ?

Also about 25 launches and miscellaneous craft.

NYASALAND.

Gunboat.

GWENDOLEN (1897). 350 tons. Guns: 4—6 pdr., 4 machine. Speed 11½ kts.

Adventure, Pioneer. (1892). 30 tons. Speed, 12 kts.

Dove, Paddle Gunboat of 20 tons. Speed, 8 kts. Armed with 1 M.G.

NORTHERN RHODESIA.

Two Thornycroft motor patrol boats, **Mimi & Tou-tou,** originally intended to act as tenders to Greek seaplanes. They were requisitioned and shipped out to Lake Tanganyika in 1915, where they sank the German gunboat *Hedwig von Wissmann* and captured the *Kingani,* now British **Fi-fi.**

BRITISH EAST AFRICA.

Rose (1901). Speed, 8 kts.

M'Vita, Patrol Boat.

NATAL.

Before the war, only possessed a Tug, **Sir John** (1897), and a Surveying Ship, **Churchill.**

NIGERIA.

Empire, Kapelli, Kampala, Sarota, Valiant. Stern-wheel Gunboats, built about 1902. Speed, 10 kts.

Sultan (1907), **Etobe, Egori.** (1909). Stern-wheel Steamers. Speed, 8-10 kts.

Raven (1904). Stern-wheel Steamer. 260 tons. Speed, about 9 kts.

Corona (——). 320 tons. Speed, 9 kts. Governor's Yacht.

Ivy (1896). Yacht.

Also a Stern-wheel Tug of 428 tons. There are also about 18 other small launches and miscellaneous craft.

UNITED STATES FLEET.

Revised from 1918-19 Edition of official handbook, "Ships' Data, U.S. Naval Vessels."

FLAGS.

Red | Blue | White | Yellow

ENSIGN & MERCANTILE

JACK

ADMIRAL

VICE ADMIRAL

REAR ADMIRAL SENIOR

REAR ADMIRAL

PRESIDENT'S FLAG

REVENUE

NAVAL MILITIA

SECRETARY OF THE NAVY

Senior officer when of or below rank of captain flies a blue triangular flag. Assistant-Secretary of Navy has a flag same as Secretary's with colours reversed, i.e., white ground and blue anchor and stars.

NEW YORK.

to	miles
Bermuda	680
Boston (Mass.)	315
Brest	2954
Cherbourg	3066
Colon	1985
Galveston	1910
Gibraltar	3670
Havana	1320
Havre	3125
Jamaica	1495
Key West	1180
La Guayra	1840
Liverpool	3062
New Orleans	1710
Norfolk Navy Yard	300
Pernambuco	3690
Philadelphia (Pa.)	240
Portsmouth Navy Yard	330
Portsmouth (England)	3060
Wilhelmshaven	3570

NEW YORK
(via Panama Canal)

to	miles
Callao	3328
Colon	1981
Hong Kong	11,684

	miles
Iquique	3837
Manila	11,585
Puget Sound	6074
San Francisco	5299
Shanghai	10,885
Sydney	9811
Valparaiso	4630
Yokohama	9835

PORT ROYAL

to	miles
Bermuda	810
Key West	450
New York	650
Pensacola	785

KEY WEST

to	miles
Bermuda	1100
Boston (Mass.)	1387
Galveston	730
Jamaica (Port Royal Harbour)	850
New York	1180
Pensacola	235
Philadelphia	1020
Port Royal Naval Station	450
Portsmouth Navy Yard	1400

MARE ISLAND

to	miles
Auckland (N. Zealand)	5965
Esquimault	750
Honolulu	2095
Kiao-chau	5600
Manila	7500
Panama	3424
Puget Sound	800
Yokosuka	4500

KAVITE

to	miles
Amoy	700
Hong Kong	650
Kiao-chau	1325
Nagasaki	1300
Saigon	875
Singapore	1320
Vladivostock	2080
Yokosuka	1720

Secretary of the Navy: Hon. J. Daniels.   *Chief Constructor*: Rear-Admiral D. W. Taylor.

Uniforms.

Admiral of the Navy. | Rear-Admiral. | Captain. | Commander. | Lieut-Commander. | Lieutenant. | Ensign.

Note.—Lieutenants, junior grade, have 1½ stripes. Chief Warrant Officers one stripe broken with blue. Line Warrant Officers star without any stripe. Staff Warrant Officers under Chiefs have no sleeve mark: Engineers same as Line Officers (interchangeable). Other branches than executive wear no sleeve star, but have distinctive colours between the sleeve stripes.

Colour of significance (between the sleeve stripes): *Medical*, dark maroon; *Pay*, white; *Constructors*, purple; *Civil Engineers*, light blue: *Professors of Mathematics*, olive green. In 1919 the undress uniform of U.S. Naval officers was altered to a pattern resembling that of the British Navy.

Personnel.—War, 450,000. Post-war establishment not known yet.

Mercantile Marine.—Lloyds Return, 1919, gives 9,773,000 tons sea-going and 2,160,000 on the Great Lakes.

Coinage.—Dollar (100 cents) = approximately 4s. 2d. British at pre-war rate of exchange.

Overseas Possessions.—Panama Canal Zone, Porto Rico, Virgin Islands, Alaska and Aleutian Islands, Guam, Tutuila, Wake and Johnston Islands, Philippine Islands.

NEW CONSTRUCTION.—Bureau of Construction and Repairs Return to August 31st, 1919 : 148 Destroyers, 60 Submarines, 7 Mine Sweepers, 34 Tugs, 12 Oil Tankers and 31 Ford Eagles are in various stages of completion.   6 Destroyers, 2 Submarines, 3 Tugs, and 6 Ford Eagles completed during August, 1919.

COLORADO, begun 29th May, 1919. *WASHINGTON*, 30th June, 1919.

Removal of 5 inch guns from Dreadnoughts.—First pair of bow guns removed from all ; also 5 inch gun, dead over stern.

HUNTINGTON (1919).   *Photo, U.S. Navy Publicity Bureau.*

CHESTER (1919).   *Photo, U.S. Navy Publicity Bureau.*

BIRMINGHAM (1919).   *Photo, U.S. Navy Publicity Bureau.*

CINCINNATI, RALEIGH, rated as non-effective.

ANNISTON, PRINCETON, DON JUAN DE AUSTRIA, ISLA DE LUZON, ESSEX, YANTIC, GOPHER, DUBUQUE, MARIETTA, ANNAPOLIS, PETREL, ELCANO, VILLALOBOS, QUIROS, PAMPANGA, SAMAR, for sale.

Monitor **AMPHITRITE** for sale.   **OZARK, MONTEREY, MONADNOCK** rated as non-effective.

Destroyers : All boats of the *Drayton* and *Flusser* ("Flivver") types are withdrawn to reserve and rated as non-effective. All *Flusser* class for sale.
Coast Torpedo Vessels : All rated as non-effective and for sale.
Old Torpedo Boats : To be offered for sale at the first opportunity. C.T.B. No. 10 is rated as non-effective.
Submarines : A considerable number rated as non-effective ; no details known.
Submarine Chasers : About 150 to be offered for sale.
Submarine Depot Ship : Alert non-effective. *Transport* **Hancock** for sale.
Converted Yachts : **Eagle** for sale. Practically all others now rated as non-effective.   Anticipated that all these ships will be done away with.
Yachts Armed during War : All in process of return to owners.

Note.—Reported that in all, 160 ships of all classes are to be sold out. *Maine* class of Battleships, *Frederick, Montana, North Carolina, South Dakota, Charleston, St. Louis* (Cruisers), *Cheyenne, Tallahassee, Tonopah* (Monitors), and various Submarines placed in Reserve with nucleus crews. *Alabama* class and *Kearsarge* class Battleships put out of commission with all ships noted as non-effective and for sale above.

Naval Militia.—Merged into Naval Reserve during War. Future status uncertain. The various State Authorities may maintain Naval Militia, but the Navy Department will not recognise such Establishments, inasmuch as they complicate the Reserve question. The State of Oregon has accepted the gift of the old Battleship *Oregon* as a relic.

PERKINS.   *Photo, U.S. Bureau of Navigation.*

General Note to all Navy Yards on Atlantic and Pacific Coasts.

In 1919 U.S. Government placed orders for two 20,000 ton floating docks and eight 10,000 ton floating docks. When delivered, these will be assigned to the most suitable ports.

Navy Yards.

NEW YORK (& **BROOKLYN**).—3rd Naval District. Depôt and shipbuilding yard. Two slips before war. Two new slips suitable for building largest types of Dreadnoughts and Battle-Cruisers begun 1917, when new plant was also installed, workshops re-arranged and renovated, new offices and general stores built, and magazine stores greatly enlarged.

Dry docks :
- (1) granite, 330 × 66 × 25 feet.
- (2) concrete, 440 × 90 × 26 feet.
- (3) wood 613 × 105¾ × 29½ feet.
- (4) granite and concrete, 700 × 120 × 35 feet.

Naval hospital here. Admiralty Chart No. 3204, 2491. Rise of Spring Tide, 4¾ feet. On Long Island : Naval Diving School, Bay Shore and Rockaway Aviation Stations.

Note.—Private docks. The Erie Co. at Brooklyn has two timber docks : (1) 485 × 100 × 20 feet ; (2) 620 × 85 × 25 feet.

Private Floating Docks and Patent Slips.

Situation	Docks		Slips.	
	No.	Capacity—tons.	No.	Capacity—tons.
BROOKLYN ...	12	1100—15000*	4	1000—2000
NEW YORK ...	4	2000— 3500†		...
HOBOKEN ...	5	1000—10000‡		...
STATEN I. ...	4	1800— 4200	2	1000—4500
JERSEY CITY...	3	1800— 4200		...
PERTH AMBOY .	3	1500— 2500	1	1000
WEEHAWKEN .	1	1800		...
NEWBURGH ...		...	1	1000

* 15,000-ton Floating Dock, property of Morse Iron Works, 478 × 110 × 28 feet.

† In 1919 there were 15 docks up to 350 ft. long in the New York district.

‡ 10,000-ton Floating Dock, property of Tietjen and Lang D.D. Co., 468 × 98 × 22 feet.

(Norfolk chart on left joins here.)

(Hampton Roads as above Map.)

NORFOLK, Va.—5th Naval District. To be the dockyard section of the Hampton Roads Navy Operating Base. Depôt and shipbuilding yard. Naval hospital here. One or more slips for building Dreadnoughts or Battle-Cruisers begun 1917. (1) Wood dock, $460 \times 85 \times 25\frac{1}{2}$ feet ; (2) granite, $303 \times 60 \times 25\frac{1}{4}$ feet ; (3) granite dock, $550 \times 112 \times 34$ feet. New 1917-18 dock, over 1000 ft. long $\times 110 \times 43\frac{1}{2}$ feet, divisible into 2 sections, about 650 and 350 feet long ; to have electric towing gear, 50-ton electric crane, and hydraulic lifts for rapid handling of repair materials, &c. Capable of being emptied in 30 mins. ; floating pontoon crane 150 tons, and auxiliary 25 tons on hoist. In 1917 new foundry, workshops, and plant for making mines begun, new plant installed and old renovated. Three patent slips here each 1500 tons. Admiralty Chart No. 2818, 2843a.

HAMPTON ROADS NAVY OPERATING BASE (continuation to N. and N.W. of Norfolk Chart).—5th Naval District. Site on ground of Jamestown Exposition was purchased here in 1917, where it is intended that in conjunction with the Norfolk N.Y., a great Naval Base shall be established which will be developed into the principal warship port on the Atlantic coast. Plans as laid down during 1917 by the Navy Department, contemplated the following works : Submarine and Aviation Bases ; Training Station for 10,000 men ; Fuel Station (for coal and oil) ; Depots for fleet stores, mines, torpedoes and anti-submarine nets, &c.

Admiralty Chart No. 1227,2482.   Rise of Spring Tide, 5 feet (Charlestown Naval Yard).

Navy Yards (ATLANTIC COAST).

BOSTON, MASS.—1st Naval District. Depôt. One granite dock, $389 \times 46 \times 26$ feet; one granite and concrete dock, $729 \times 101\frac{1}{2} \times 30\frac{1}{2}$ feet. Naval hospital here. Also two wooden private docks and four patent slips 1000–2300 tons.

LEAGUE ISLAND, PHILADELPHIA PA.— 4th Naval District. Depôt. Two new slips to build Dreadnoughts or Battle-Cruisers. New workshops, foundry and Marine Barracks, 1917-18. One wooden dock, $420 \times 89 \times 25\frac{1}{2}$ feet; second dock, granite and concrete, $707 \times 104 \times 30$ feet. New dock, $1022 \times 144 \times 43\frac{1}{2}$ feet, divisible into two sections, viz., 684 feet outer section and 338 feet inner section. Pier 1000 feet long, with 350-ton crane. Aircraft base and flying ground; also Government seaplane factory. Naval hospital here.

WASHINGTON.   No docks.   Yard devoted to ordnance construction. Naval hospital here.

PORTSMOUTH, N.H.—1st Naval District. One granite and concrete, $720 \times 101\frac{1}{2} \times 30\frac{2}{3}$ feet. Naval hospital here.

CHARLESTON, S.C.--6th Naval District. 2nd class Navy yard. Dry dock, $503 \times 113 \times 34\frac{1}{4}$ feet.

Naval Stations.

NARRAGANSET BAY, R.I.

NEWPORT, R.I.—2nd Naval District. Chief torpedo station. Manufactory of torpedoes, etc. Naval war college and apprentice-training station. Naval hospital and coal depôt.

CAPE MAY, N.J.—4th Naval District. Base for Submarines and Navy Airships. 349 acres bought 1919 for developing this Station.

NEW LONDON, CONN.—2nd Naval District. Submarine Training Station.

Note.—Charleston, Norfolk, and Bradford, R.I., are stations for petrol and oil fuel. A large number of Naval Stations and Training Camps, Aviation Schools, &c., created during the war have been abolished. 9th, 10th and 11th Naval Districts are on the Great Lakes. Doubtful if any stations are maintained there now.

PRIVATE DOCKS, &c.

(exclusive of those in New York and Brooklyn districts, previously listed).

NEW LONDON (CONN.), three patent slips, 1000–2000 tons. PHILADELPHIA, one floating dock (3500 tons) and two patent slips (1000 and 2300 tons). CAMDEN (N.J.), three patent slips, 1200–1500 tons. BALTIMORE (MD.), Wm. Skinner & Sons dry dock, $600 \times 80 \times 22\frac{1}{2}$ feet. Columbian Iron-works Dock (wood), $437 \times 80 \times 21$ feet. Maryland Steel Co., Sparrow Point, wood and steel floating dock, 20,000 tons. Also one 3000 ton floating dock and two patent slips (2000 and 1500 tons). At Portland (Me.), Savannah (Ga.), Jacksonville (Fla.), small patent slips of 1200 tons (Jacksonville, one 4500 ton floating dock).

Mercantile Ports (ATLANTIC COAST *.

(In order of importance, with approximate tons of shipping cleared per year in brackets).

New York, N.Y. ($13\frac{1}{4}$ million ?); Boston, Mass. ($1\frac{3}{4}$ million); Philadelphia, Pa. ($2\frac{1}{4}$ million); Baltimore, Md. ($1\frac{1}{4}$ million); Hampton Roads, Va. ($\frac{3}{4}$ million); Portland, Me. ($\frac{1}{3}$ million).

* Figures compiled 1913-14.   Post-war statistics not available yet.

LEAGUE ISLAND.
Admiralty Chart No. 2564.

PORTSMOUTH N.H.
Admiralty Chart No. 2482,2487.
Rise of Spring Tide, $8\frac{1}{2}$ feet.

U. S. PRIVATE SHIPYARDS.—ATLANTIC.

(Warship builders *only*. Revised from details furnished by firms named, 1919.)

Bath I.W.

BATH IRONWORKS (BATH, ME.). Build battleships, scout cruisers, destroyers and torpedo vessels, mercantile vessels of fast passenger types and large steam yachts of very fast design. Slips: one 600 ft., one 500 ft., three 350 ft. Cranes: one 100-ton stiff leg derrick (electric), one 35-ton floating sheer-legs (steam), three 15-ton electric locomotive cranes for steel runways. Yard covers 13 acres. Water-front 1000 feet. Plant up-to-date. Yard builds boilers, engines, equipment for ships, &c. Employees: 1300 (peace), 2000 (war).

Bethlehem Fore River.

FORE RIVER PLANT, BETHLEHEM SHIPBUILDING CORPORATION (QUINCY, MASS.). 21 launching slips, 41 building slips, 20 building slips for submarines and four for 300 ft. destroyers. One 20-ton lift hammer-head crane, one 75-ton lift gantry crane, 16 overhead cranes over slips, capacity 5 and 10 tons and one 50-ton lift overhead crane. Yard covers 85 acres and water-front 1¼ miles. Yard builds boilers, machinery and equipment. Plant thoroughly modern. Employees, 14,356.

Bethlehem Squantum.

NAVAL DESTROYER PLANT, BETHLEHEM SHIPBUILDING CORPORATION (SQUANTUM, MASS.). 10 building slips with electric bridge cranes and three wet slips. Maximum length of slips 310 ft. (*n.p.*). One 20-ton stiff leg derrick; one 10-ton guy derrick; wet slips have one 25-ton and two 10-ton bridge cranes. Yard covers 60 acres approximately. Water-front about 3600 feet. Boilers, engines, &c., supplied by other Bethlehem Plants. Employees, about 9000.

Cramps.

MESSRS. THE WM. CRAMP & SONS SHIP & ENGINE-BUILDING CO. (PHILADELPHIA, PA.). Build dreadnoughts, battle cruisers, scout cruisers, destroyers and mercantile vessels of all types. 8 slips. Longest ship which can be built, 850 feet. One 100-ton floating derrick with 25-tons auxiliary lift; one 70-ton lift revolving hammer-head crane; numerous other cranes to lift 5—25 tons. Graving dock 433 ft. *over all*; width at entrance 69 ft. (top), 48 ft. (bottom); depth of water 20½ ft. H.W.O.S. and 15½ ft. L.W.O.S. Patent slips: one 3000-ton and one 1000-ton railways. Area of yard 175 acres. Water-front 6300 ft. Yard builds boilers, machinery and naval equipment. Plant is up-to-date. Employees, 7000 (peace), 11,500 (war).

Fore River.

FORE RIVER CO. (QUINCY, MASS.). Nine big slips. Area, 40 acres. Yard railway of 4 miles. Depth of water in channel, 33 feet. Employees, about 12,000 now. New Yard, 1917-18.

Note.—This firm has made no return of its shipyard, plant, &c., for several years past. Above details may not be correct now.

Harlan, Wilmington.

(LATE HARLAN & HOLLINGSWORTH Co.)

HARLAN SHIPBUILDING PLANT (WILMINGTON, DELAWARE). 35 acres. Water frontage, 1800 feet. Depth at low tide, 22 feet. 5 slips, able to build up to 15,000 tons. Dry dock, 330 × 90 × 13½ feet. Equipment thoroughly up-to-date. Employees, 1000.

Note.—Above details are not up-to-date.

Hollands.

ELECTRIC BOAT CO. (GROTON, CONN.) Submarines of the "Holland" type, which are chiefly built at the Fore River Co.'s Yard.

Lake Co.

LAKE TORPEDO BOAT CO. (BRIDGEPORT, CON.). Submarines of the "Lake" type.

Newport News.

NEWPORT NEWS SHIPBUILDING & DRY DOCK COMPANY (NEWPORT, VA.). 125 acres. Deep water alongside. Water-front, ¾ mile. One 140-ton revolving derrick, one 100-ton sheer-leg, one 50-ton floating derrick, one 10-ton ditto. Very large modern shops. Total employees 11,500. Eight big slips. Dry docks: (2) 804 × 80 × 30 feet; (3) 537½ × 79 × 24½ feet; (1) 593 × 50 × 24½ feet.

New York S.B. Co.

NEW YORK SHIPBUILDING CO. (CAMDEN, N.J.). Can build dreadnoughts, cruisers, destroyers, mine-layers and sweepers, naval tenders and all classes of mercantile vessels, with boilers, machinery, and all equipment. 9 big slips, 4 smaller and 10 for destroyers. Yard can build ships up to 1000 ft. long, and covers 190.6 acres. Water-front about ⅘ths of a mile. Plant up-to-date. All machine tools and cranes electrically driven. Hydraulic and compressed air plant. Employees about 7000 (peace), 19,000 (war).

Todd, Brooklyn.

TODD SHIPYARDS CORPORATION (TEBO YACHT BASIN YARD, BROOKLYN, N.Y.). Three slips, 250 ft. long. Two 30-ton floating cranes. Two floating docks: (1) 105 × 23 ft. to lift 600 tons *d.w.* (2) 150 × 64 ft. to lift 1100 tons *d.w.* Yard covers 25 acres. Plant is modern. Employees, 1000. Associated firms:—Robin D.D. & Repair Co., Brooklyn, N.Y.; Tietjen & Lang D.D. Co., Hoboken (10,000-ton floating dock); Clinton Plant, Brooklyn; Quintard Iron Works, N.Y. (build engines, &c., for ships built by Todd Co.); White Fuel Oil Engineering Co., N.Y. Also see Pacific Coast for Tacoma Yard.

Also a very large number of other shipyards solely engaged on mercantile construction.

SAN JUAN, PUERTO RICO.
Admiralty Chart No. 478,3408.   Rise of Spring Tide, 1 foot.

NEW ORLEANS, LA.—8th Naval District. Floating dock, 525×100×28¼ feet.

PENSACOLA, FLA.—8th Naval District. 2nd class yard. 8th Naval District. Big new Aviation Station for seaplanes, dirigibles, kite-balloons, &c. Floating dock, 450×82×27 feet (12000 tons).

KEY WEST.—7th Naval District. No docks. Submarine and Aircraft Station.

Small Naval Stations may also exist at San Juan (Porto Rico) and St. Thomas (Virgin Islands).

Private Docks.

NEW ORLEANS : Government dock, 525×100×28 feet, and two floating docks, 2000 and 2500 tons.
MOBILE (ALA.) : Pinto Dry Dock, 232×86×17 feet, and two floating docks, 1000 and 1400 tons.

Private Shipyards.

Various New Yards established 1917-18. Do not undertake Naval construction, all being devoted to mercantile contracts.

Mercantile Ports.*

(In order of importance and approximate tons of shipping cleared annually).

New Orleans (2¼ million) ; Galveston, Texas (½ million) ; Mobile, Ala. (¾ million) ; Pensacola, Fla. (½ million) ; Savannah, Ga. (⅓ million) ; Key West (½ million).

* 1911 figures : post-war statistics not available.

GUANTANAMO BAY (CUBA). Fleet Anchorage and Exercising Grounds. Small repairs undertaken here. Fuel Depôt. Admiralty Chart No. 904.

Canal about 50 miles long.   Channel 300–1000 feet wide at bottom; depth 41–85 feet.   Time of passage about 10 hours.

PACIFIC ENTRANCE TO PANAMA CANAL. Heavily fortified.   Graving Dock, No. 1, Balboa. 1110 × 110 × 41½ feet.   Also fuel depot for 300,000 to 350,000 tons of coal at Balboa. 2—250 ton floating cranes.

ATLANTIC ENTRANCE TO PANAMA CANAL.   Heavily fortified.   Dock and Coal Depot at Cristobal same size as Balboa (see opposite).   In the Canal, Gatun and Miraflores Locks (over 1000 × 110 × 41½ feet) can be used as docks.

U. S. NAVY YARDS AND STATIONS—PACIFIC.

Divided into 2000 yard squares. Uniform scale. Soundings in fathoms. Heights in feet.

Sketch map of district.

BREMERTON, PUGET SOUND.—13th Naval District. Naval Station. Slips for building Scout Cruisers or Auxiliaries begun here during 1917.

Dry docks :
(1) Wood ... ... $618 \times 73 \times 27\frac{1}{4}$ feet.
(2) Granite and concrete ... $801\frac{2}{3} \times 113 \times 35\frac{1}{4}$ feet.

Divided into 2000 yard squares.   Uniform scale.   Soundings in fathoms.   Heights in feet.

SAN FRANCISCO HARBOUR.   **MARE ISLAND.**—12th Naval District.   Depôt and Navy Yard (22 miles N. of San Francisco), of which small Map is given on next page.   Slip to build Dreadnoughts of 600 feet length, or above, begun at Mare Island in 1916 or 1917.   Destroyers also built.   Dry Docks: (1)   Granite   ... $418 \times 88 \times 27\frac{1}{2}$ feet.
(2)   Concrete   ... $883 \times 102 \times 31\frac{1}{2}$ „

Principal Private Yards.—Pacific Coast.

Note :　No Pacific Coast Shipyards have made returns for several years past.

BETHLEHEM SHIPBUILDING CORPORATION (San Francisco).　Large new yard and engine shops at Alameda, new yard projected at Risdon.　Builds Destroyers.

CALIFORNIA SHIPBUILDING CO. (Long Beach, Cal.),　Submarine builders.

MORAN & CO. (Seattle, Puget Sound).　One big slip.　Floating dock 468 × 85 × 27½ feet (12,000 tons) and another *smaller.*

SEATTLE DRY DOCK AND CONSTRUCTION CO. (Seattle, Washington).　Now controlled by Skinner & Eddy, Seattle.　Floating dock, 325 × 100 (extreme) × 25 feet, for 6000 tons ; one floating dock for 2500 tons ; one patent slip, 3000 tons.

TODD DRY DOCKS & CONSTRUCTION CO. (Tacoma, Washington).　No details available.　Is building Cruisers.　12,000 ton floating dock completing at end of 1918.

✿ UNION IRON WORKS CO. (San Francisco).　(Affiliated to the Bethlehem Shipbuilding Co.) 38 acres.　Three dry docks (Hunters Point) : (1) 750 × 103 × 30 feet (28,000 tons), (2) 485 × 97 × 24 feet (10,000 tons), (3) 1110 × 110 × 41½ feet.　Three small floating docks of 2500 and 1800 tons and a third of unknown capacity.　Six slips of 600 feet long, fully equipped with electric cranes, etc., and 4 smaller.　Five wharves 585 × 50 feet, berthing for 15 average sized vessels. .　One sheer leg 100 tons, one 40 tons.　2 marine railways.　All plant dates from 1910 or later.　*Employees :* Average 2300.　Enlarged 1917.

* Details not revised since 1911.　Title may have been altered to BETHLEHEM UNION PLANT.

Also 30–40 new shipyards on Pacific coast, but these are engaged in mercantile construction only.

MARE ISLAND.　Admiralty Chart No. 2887.

(For Docks, see previous page.)

CAVITE P.I. (Asiatic Station).　Admiralty Chart No. 975,976

ENTRANCE TO MANILA BAY.　(Asiatic Station).

(Continued on next page.)

U. S. HARBOURS, Etc.—PACIFIC & ASIATIC.

Divided into 2000 yard squares.   Uniform scale.   Soundings in fathoms.   Heights in feet.

Naval Hospital.

LAS ANIMAS, CAL.

Naval Stations.—2ND CLASS, PACIFIC.

PEARL HARBOUR (1) Honolulu. (2) Pearl Harbour, on S. side of Island of Oahu, about 10–15 miles west of Honolulu. Large dock here, $1001 \times 114 \times 34\frac{2}{3}$ feet.

TUTUILA (SAMOA).

Asiatic Naval Stations.

CAVITE (P.I.) Small dry dock at Manila. Maps on preceding page.

OLONGAPO (P.I.) Dewey Floating dock, 18,500 tons, 501′ $0\frac{3}{4}$″ × 100′ × 37′ 0″ ?

Chief Mercantile Ports.—PACIFIC COAST.*

Seattle ($2\frac{1}{4}$ million) ; San Francisco ($1\frac{1}{4}$ million).

* These figures were compiled before 1914, and can no longer be regarded as really trustworthy.

OLONGAPO & PORT SUBIC.

TUTUILA (SAMOA).
Admiralty Chart No. 1730.

U. S. NAVAL ORDNANCE, TORPEDOES, &c.

Principal Guns in the U. S. Fleet.

(Corrected from the official figures, 1913.)

Built at Washington Gun Factory, proved at Indian Head, Ind., and Potomac Range.

Notation.	Nominal Calibre.	Mark or Model.	Length in Calibres.	Weight of Gun.	Weight of A.P. Shot.	Service Initial Velocity.	Maximum penetration firing *capped* A.P. direct impact against K.C. armour.			Approximate Danger Space average ship, at			Muzzle Energy
							9000	6000	3000	10,000	5000	3000	
	inch.			tons.	lbs.	ft. secs.	in.	in.	in.	yards.	yards.	yards.	
A⁸	16	...	45-50	128 ?	2100 ?	...	...	...	...	...	...	...	...
A⁷	14	...	45	63½	1400	2600	18	...	...	...	...	...	...
A³	13	I. & II	35	61½	1130	2000	8	9¾	12	110	310	550	31,333
A⁶	12	VII	50	56·1	870	2950	11·0	13·9	17·5	...	...	...	52,483
A⁶	12	VI	45	53·6	870	2850	10·6	13·3	16·6	...	...	...	48,984
A⁵	12	V	45	52·9	870	2700	9·8	12·3	15·5	..	...	...	43,964
A⁴	12	III & IV	40	52·1	870	2600	9·3	11·7	14·8	...	...	...	40,768
A³	12	III & IV	40	52·1	870	2400	8·3	10·5	13·3	...	126	264	34,738
A²	12	I & II	35	45·3	870	2100	7·2	8·8	11·2	100	390	580	26,596
A²	10	III	40	34·6	510	2700	6·9	9·0	11·9	140	460	700	25,772
	10	I & II	30	25·1	510	2000	5·0	6·1	8·0	...	...	...	14,141
A	8	VI	45	18·7	260	2750	4·4	6·1	8·6	45†	...	...	13,630
B	8	V	40	18·1	260	2500	4·0	5·3	7·5	45	...	...	11,264
C	8	III & IV	35	13·1	260	2100	3·6	4·2	6·0	...	...	...	7,948
C	6	...	52	...	...	...	...	...	...	...	...	...	...
C	6	VIII	50	8·6	105	2800	2·3	3·2	5·2	...	...	...	5,707
D	6	VI	50	8·3	105	2600	2·2	2·9	4·7	75	250	470	4,920
D*	6	IX	45	7·0	105	2250	2·1	2·5	3·8	...	..	..	3,685
E*	6	IV, VII	40	6·0	105	2150	2·1	2·4	3·6	35	150	355	3,365
E*	5	VII	51	5·0	50	3150	1·4	1·8	3·4	...	...	...	3,439
	5	VI	50	4·6	50	3000	1·4	1·7	3·2	...	...	...	3,122
	5	V & VI	50	4·6	60	2700	1·6	2·0	3·5	...	...	...	3,032
F*	5	II, III, IV	40	3·1	50	2300	1·4	1·7	2·6	...	...	...	1,834
F*	4	VIII	50	2·9	33	2800	1·2	1·5	2·6	...	...	...	1,794
F*	4	VII	50	2·6	33	2500	1·2	1·4	2·2	...	...	...	1,430
F*	4	III,IV,V,VI	40	1·5	33	2000	...	1·2	1·7	...	...	..	915
F	3	V, VI, S-A	50	1·0	13	2700	...	0·8	1·2	...	...	...	658
F*	3	II, III	50	0·9	13	2700	...	0·8	1·2	...	...	...	658

* = Brass cartridge case.   † = Calculated for a 20 ft. target.

Guns of 1899 and later have Vickers breech, etc.   All guns use nitro-cellulose.

Anti-aircraft guns are 3 inch (13 pdr.) and 1 pdr.

16 inch, 50 cal. in *Massachusetts* class (6) and *Constellation* class (6).

16 inch, 45 cal. in *Colorado* class.

14 inch, 50 cal. mounted in *California* (2), and *New Mexico* (3) classes.

14 inch, 45 cal. mounted in *Texas* (2), *Nevada* (2) and *Pennsylvania* (2) classes.

12 inch, 50 cal. mounted in *Arkansas* (2) and *Utah* (2) classes.

12 inch, 45 cal. mounted in *Delaware* (2), *Idaho* (2), *Louisiana* (2), *Kansas* (4), and *S. Carolina* (2) classes.

12 inch, 40 cal. mounted in *Maine* (3), *New Jersey* (5), and *Ozark* (4) classes.

" Director " fire-controls have been installed in all the Dreadnoughts and Battleships back to the *New Jersey* type. Dreadnoughts have enlarged elevation to main guns, and directors for 5 inch guns. *Star shell* for 3, 4 and 5 inch guns. Range : 3-6 land miles. Time fuze ignites lamp and expels parachute and burner through base of shell. Shell usually detonates at 1000 feet, and 800,000 candle-power burner burns for 30 seconds, lighting up sea over ½ mile radius. *Non-ricochet shell* (flat-nosed) for 3, 4, 5 and 6 inch guns. Fired at elevation over 2° and delay action fuze begins on impact with water. *Y-gun* has two barrels set at 90° with powder chamber common to both barrels. Range : *about* 30 yards. *Davis non-recoil gun* (9 pdr.) consists of 2 guns placed breech to breech. Recoil absorbed by expulsion of powder charge case from after gun ; aimed by tracer bullets from Lewis gun fixed on barrel. 8 inch Trench Mortar Howitzer under test.

Aircraft Bombs.—20 lb. Cooper, 112, 163, 230, 270, 520 lbs. Mark VI is 10 inch diameter and 6 feet long.

Paravanes.

Generally as British Navy types, with minor modifications in inhaul gear.

Depth Charges.

18 inch diameter, 28 inches long. 300 lb. T.N.T. or Amatol charge. Detonation controlled by hydrostatic valve, with safety device to 20 feet depth. Effective up to 100 feet.

Torpedoes.

Built at the Torpedo Station, Newport (Rhode Island), and the Naval Gun Factory, Washington, D.C. No exact details are available. Ranges of torpedoes were improved by experiments in 1914, and a new type of net-cutter, which gave excellent results on trials, has been adopted. A new torpedo model is said to have been adopted recently of a simplified pattern, possessing few Bliss-Leavitt features. New 24 inch non-gyro model said to be under test. Nearly all ships are now equipped with submarine signalling and receiving sets.

NEW U. S. FLEET ORGANISATION, ~ 1919.

(Exclusive of Ships on Asiatic Station and in European Waters.)

ATLANTIC FLEET.

Fleet Flagship : *Pennsylvania.*

BATTLESHIP FORCE :—

2nd Battleship Squadron.

3rd Division :—
Connecticut (Flag)
Louisiana
New Hampshire
Kansas

4th Division :—
Minnesota (Flag)
South Carolina
Michigan

3rd Battleship Squadron.

5th Division :—
Utah (Flag)
Florida
Delaware
North Dakota

7th Division :—
Pennsylvania
(Force Flag)
Oklahoma
Nevada
Arizona

CRUISER FORCE :—

1st Cruiser Squadron, 1st Division : *Huntington* (Flag), *Wheeling, Topeka, Castine.*

DESTROYER FORCE :—

3rd DESTROYER SQUADRON (ACTIVE).

Flagship (D) : *Rochester.*

First Flotilla. Tender : *Dixie.* 5th, 6th, 7th Divisions, each composed of six " flush-deck " type T.B.D.

Second Flotilla. Tender : *Bridgeport.* 8th, 9th and 28th Divisions, each composed of six " flush-deck " type T.B.D.

Third Flotilla. Tender : *Panther.* 19th, 20th and 22nd Divisions, each composed of six " flush-deck " type T.B.D.

1st DESTROYER SQUADRON (RESERVE).

Flagship (D) : *Chester.*

Seventh Flotilla. Tender : Not yet selected. 1st Division composed of 7 *Aylwin* class T.B.D. ; 2nd Division composed of 6 *Cushing* class T.B.D. ; 3rd Division composed of 5 *Conyngham* Class T.B.D. and *Cummings.*

Eighth Flotilla. Tender : Not yet selected. 4th and 26th Divisions, each composed of six " flush-deck " type T.B.D., and 26th Division composed of five " flush-deck " type T.B.D.

Ninth Flotilla. Tender : Not yet selected. 24th, 27th and 36th Divisions, each composed of six " flush-deck " type T.B.D.

SUBMARINE FORCE :—

7th Division. Tender : *Camden.* Eight " S " type submarines.
12th Division. Tender : *Rainbow.* Five " S " type submarines.
15th Division. Tender : *Bushnell.* Three " AA " type submarines.

MINE FORCE :—

First Squadron (Planters) : *San Francisco* (Flag), *Shawmut.*
Second Squadron (Sweepers) : 1st and 2nd Divisions, each composed of six " Bird " class Sweepers.

TRAIN FORCE :—

Flagship (Train) : *Columbia.*

Repair Ship : *Prometheus.* Hospital Ships : *Solace* (to be placed on reserve shortly). *Mercy.* Supply Ships : *Bridge, Culgoa.* Fuel Ships : *Nereus, Mars, Nero, Cæsar, Proteus, Arethusa, Maumee, Pecos.* Target Repair Ship : *Lebanon.* Tugs : Thirteen in number.

IN RESERVE AND/OR OUT OF COMMISSION :—

8 Battleships, 6 Cruisers, *about* 40 Destroyers, Coast Torpedo Vessels, &c. Total of Submarines not known. Also various Monitors, Gunboats, Auxiliaries, &c.

PACIFIC FLEET.

Fleet Flagship : *New Mexico.*

BATTLESHIP FORCE :—

1st Battleship Squadron.

1st Division :—
Virginia (Flag)
New Jersey
Rhode Island

2nd Division :—
Georgia (Flag)
Nebraska
Vermont

4th Battleship Squadron.

6th Division :—
Wyoming (Flag)
Arkansas
New York
Texas

8th Division :—
New Mexico
(Force Flag)
Tennessee
Idaho
Mississippi

CRUISER FORCE :—

2nd Cruiser Squadron. 2nd Division : *Seattle* (Flag), *Cleveland, Denver, Tacoma, Marblehead, Machias, Vicksburg.*

DESTROYER FORCE :—

4th DESTROYER SQUADRON (ACTIVE).

Flagship (D) : *Birmingham.*

Fourth Flotilla. Tender : *Melville.* 10th, 11th and 12th Divisions, each composed of six " flush-deck " type T.B.D.

Fifth Flotilla. Tender : *Prairie.* 13th, 14th and 15th Divisions, each composed of six " flush-deck " type T.B.D.

Sixth Flotilla. Tender : *Buffalo.* 16th, 17th and 18th Divisions, each composed of six " flush-deck " type T.B.D.

2nd DESTROYER SQUADRON (RESERVE).

Flagship (D) : *Salem.*

Tenth Flotilla. Tender : *Black Hawk.* 29th and 31st Divisions, each composed of six " flush-deck " type T.B.D.; and 30th Division, five " flush-deck " type T.B.D.

Eleventh Flotilla. Tender : Not yet selected. 22nd, 23rd and 35th Divisions, each consisting of six " flush-deck " type T.B.D.

Twelfth Flotilla. Tender : Not yet selected. 32nd, 33rd and 34th Divisions, each comprising six " flush-deck " type T.B.D.

SUBMARINE FORCE :—

11th Division. Tender : *Savannah.* Eight " S " type Submarines.
16th Division. Tender : *Beaver.* Six " S " type Submarines.

MINE FORCE :—

Third Squadron (Planters) : *Baltimore* (Flag), *Aroostook.*
Fourth Squadron (Sweepers) : 3rd and 4th Divisions, each composed of six " Bird " class Sweepers.

TRAIN FORCE :—

Flagship (Train) : *Minneapolis.*

Repair Ship : *Vestal.* Hospital Ship : *Mercy.* Supply Ships : *Rappahannock, Glacier, Celtic.* Fuel Ships : *Orion, Vulcan, Neptune, Brutus, Jupiter, Jason, Neches, Kanawha, Cuyama, Brazos.* Target Repair Ship : *Nanshan.* Radio Repair Ship : *Saturn.* Tugs : Eleven in number.

Also various craft attached to the 12th Naval District (Mare Island), 13th Naval District (Bremerton), 14th Naval District (Hawaii); and Canal Zone.

ONE FUNNEL.

MONTEREY.   MONADNOCK.   AMPHITRITE   HELENA class (2 ships).   OZARK class (4 ships)

AILEEN.   HAWK.   EAGLE.   GLOUCESTER.   VESUVIUS
(Experimental Torpedo Ship).

SYLVIA.   SYLPH.   VIXEN.   YANKTON.   SCORPION.

WASP.   DOROTHEA.   GOPHER.   VICKSBURG PRINCETON.   YANTIC.   ALERT.

MAYFLOWER
(Presidential Yacht).   GLACIER
(Supply Ship).   BUSHNELL
(Submarine Depot Ship).   (Continued on next page.)

M

ONE FUNNEL—*continued.*

DOLPHIN.

YORKTOWN.

D. JUAN D'AUSTRIA.
("*Petrel*" *similar.*)

CASTINE *class.*

MARIETTA *class.*

PATAPSCO *class.*

SONOMA & ONTARIO.
(*Have gun forward now as*
"*Patapsco.*")

BIRD *class.*
(*Mine Sweepers.*)

FULTON.
(*Submarine Depot Ship.*)

LEBANON.

SACRAMENTO.

PANTHER.
(*Destroyer Depot Ship.*)

CELTIC.
(*Supply Ship.*)

PROMETHEUS & VESTAL.
(*Repair Ships.*)

LEONIDAS.

BRIDGE.
(*Supply Ship.*)

BLACK HAWK.
(*T. B. D. Depot Ship.*)

MELVILLE.
(*T. B. D. Depot Ship.*)

SUPPLY.
(*Supply Ship.*)

BUFFALO, DIXIE & PRAIRIE.
(*T. B. D. Depot Ships.*)

CULGOA.
(*Supply Ship.*)

ANNAPOLIS.

(*Continued on next page.*)

ONE FUNNEL—*continued.*

HANCOCK.

MARS & VULCAN.
(Colliers.)

KANAWHA & MAUMEE.
(Oil Tankers,)

NEPTUNE.
(Collier).

JUPITER
(Collier).
Note.—Twin funnels, masts and derricks abreast.

ALABAMA *class* (3 ships).
Note.—Two funnels abreast, closely paired.

NEVADA & PENNSYLVANIA *classes* (4 ships).

NEW MEXICO *class* (3 ships).

TWO FUNNELS.

CINCINNATI.

ISLA DE LUZON.

ANNISTON.
MARBLEHEAD.

RALEIGH.

SAN FRANCISCO.
(*Mine Layer.*)

NEW ORLEANS *class* (6).

BALTIMORE
(*Mine Layer*).

OLYMPIA.

CHICAGO.

AROOSTOOK
SHAWMUT
(*Mine Layers*).

MINNEAPOLIS.

NASHVILLE.

DENVER *class* (6 ships).

MONOCACY
PALOS
(*River Gunboats*).

PADUCAH *class* (2 ships).

(*Continued on next page.*)

TWO FUNNELS—*Continued.*

KEARSARGE *class* (2 ships).

S. CAROLINA *class* (2 ships).
Half-cased funnels. Appearance distinctive.

DELAWARE *class* (2 ships).
Distinguish from " Utah " class by both cage masts being before funnels.

UTAH *class* (2 ships).

ARKANSAS *class* (2 ships).

TEXAS *class* (2 ships).

Can be distinguished by number and arrangement of after turrets ; also by spacing of funnels and cage masts.

THREE FUNNELS.

MAINE *class* (3 ships).
Low freeboard aft ; " Ohio " shorter funnels.

NEW JERSEY *class* (5 ships).
*Note.—Some ships have mainmast close to third funnel.
Identify by two-tier turrets.*

KANSAS *class* and LOUISIANA *class* (6 ships).
Note,—" New Hampshire " has half-cased funnels.

(Continued on next page.)

THREE FUNNELS—*Continued*.

FOUR FUNNELS.

BROOKLYN.

ROCHESTER.
Flagship (**D**).

COLUMBIA.

CHESTER *class* (3 ships).
All Flagships (**D**.) *"Birmingham" and "Salem" half-cased funnels.*

SEATTLE
(*as Seaplane Carrier*).

MONTANA
NORTH CAROLINA
(*Half cased funnels*).

PITTSBURGH *class* (5 ships).
(*To distinguish, note ventilators between funnels, number of tops on mainmast, position of cranes, space between 1st funnel and foremast, &c*).

CHARLESTON
ST. LOUIS
(*Differ a little from one another*).

TORPEDO CRAFT :   Those marked * have no torpedo tubes as shown by silhouette.   c.t.v. = coast torpedo vessel.

EAGLE boats (56).*   t.b. No. 9.*   t.b. No. 6.*   t.b. No. 4.*   t.b. Nos. 1,* 2.*   t.b. Nos. 10,* 11,* 12.*   t.b. Nos. 5* & 7.

WINCHESTER.*
(For testing PVs.)   t.b. Nos. 13,* 14,* 15,* 16,* 17.*   t.b. No. 3*   "Three funnel FLIVVERS."
(12 t.b.d. of DRAYTON class.)   t.b.d. CONNER, STOCKTON.   t.b. No. 8.

WHIPPLE, c.t.v.   TRUXTON & WORDEN, c.t.v.   HULL class, c.t.v. (2).   LAWRENCE class, c.t.v. (2).   BAINBRIDGE class, c.t.v. (8).

FLUSSER & REID t.b.d.   SMITH & LAMSON.   PRESTON (9), DRAYTON class (4),
AYLWIN class (8), all t.b.d.   ALLEN, CONYNGHAM, and
CUSHING classes t.b.d. (17).   "Flush Deckers."
(223 t.b.d.)

SUBMARINES.   Special Scale : 1 inch = 80 feet.

A class (6).   C class (5).   D, E, F classes (7).   G 1.   G 4.

H & K classes (17).   O class (16).   L class (11).   M 1.

(MASSACHUSETTS CLASS—6 SHIPS.)

INDIANA, MASSACHUSETTS, MONTANA, NORTH CAROLINA, IOWA, SOUTH DAKOTA.

Normal displacement, 43,200 tons, (*full load,*   tons). Complement, 1191—1351.

Length (*w.l.*), 660 feet. Beam, 104¾ feet. { *Mean* draught, 33 feet. } Length (*o.a.*), 684 feet.
{ *Max.*   „   „   }

Guns (**Dir. Con.**):
12—16 inch, 50 cal. (A⁹)
16—6 inch, 53 cal.
4—3 inch anti-aircraft.
4—6 pdr. (saluting)
Torpedo tubes (21 inch):
2 *submerged*

Armour :
(*No details known.*)
Anti-torpedo pro. :—
Special.

Official sketch not available.

Appearance : 2 cage masts, 1 "quadruple funnel."

No Plans available.

Reported to mount their 12—16 inch guns in two double-tier (sextuple ?) turrets.

Machinery :   Turbines, with electric reduction gear. (2 main generators, 4 propelling motors)
4 screws. Boilers :

Designed H.P. 60,000 = 23 kts. Fuel (oil only) : *normal,*   tons ; *maximum,*   tons.

Name	Builder	Machinery	Laid down	Com-pleted	Last refit	Trials	Boilers	Best recent speed
Indiana	New York N.Y.	...						
Massachusetts	Fore River	Fore River						
Montana	Mare Isl. N.Y.	..						
N. Carolina	Norfolk, N.Y.	...						
Iowa	Newport News	Newport News						
S. Dakota	New York N.Y.	...						

General Notes.—Authorized 1917 : *No. 49* (*S. Dakota*), *50* (*Indiana*), *51* (*Montana*). Authorized 1918 : *No. 52* (*N. Carolina*), *53* (*Iowa*), *54* (*Massachusetts*). None laid down by June 1st, 1919. Estimated cost per ship, without guns or armour, 15½ million dollars, *before* war ; revised estimate on same basis *after* war, 21 million dollars for each ship.

(MARYLAND CLASS—2 SHIPS.)
COLORADO, MARYLAND, WASHINGTON and *WEST VIRGINIA.*
Normal displacement, 32,600 tons.   *Full load*, 33,590 tons.   Complement, 1119 (War, 1626).

Length (*w.l.*), 600 feet.   Beam, 97 feet 3½ inches.   { *Mean* draught, 30½ feet }   Length (*o.a.*), 624 feet.
{ *Max.*   „   31 ft. 3½ in. }

Official Sketch.

Guns (**Dir. Con.**) :
  8—16 inch, 45 cal. (A⁹)
  14—5 inch, 51 cal.
  4—3 inch (anti-aircraft)
  4—6 pdr. (saluting)
Torpedo tubes (21 inch):
  2 *submerged.*

Armour :
  16″—14″ Belt...............
  8″ Belt (aft) ....
  3″ Deck (ends)............
  16″—9″ Funnel bases ...
  18″—9″ Turrets ....
  16″ Conning tower and
     tube....................

Plans.

As for *California* and *Tennessee* on next page, but 2—16 inch guns in each of
the four barbettes.   Note regarding reduction of 5 inch guns in *California*
class also applies to these ships.

Ahead :
4—16 in.
—5 in.

Astern :
4—16 in.
—5 in.

Broadside : 8—16 inch, 7—5 inch, 1—21 inch torpedo tube.

Machinery : In *Colorado* and *Washington*, Westinghouse turbines and electric reduction gear ;
in *Maryland* and *W. Virginia*, G.E. turbines with electrical reduction gear.   Designed S.H.P. 28,900
= 21 kts.   4 screws.   Boilers : 8 Babcock & Wilcox.   Fuel (oil only) : *normal*   tons ; *maximum*   tons.
Gunnery Notes.—16 inch are a new model, successfully proved at Indian Head, 1917.
Armour Notes. } Generally as those describing *California* class on next page, and *New Mexico, Pennsylvania* and
Engineering Notes. }   *Nevada* classes on subsequent pages.

Name	Builder and Machinery	Laid down	Completed	Trials	Boilers	Best recent speed
Colorado	New York S.B. Co.	1919	Jan., '22†		Babcock	
Maryland	Newport News	Apl.,'17	June, '21*		Babcock	
Washington	New York S.B. Co.	Jun ,'19	July, '22*		Babcock	
W. Virginia	Newport News	1919	...		Babcock	

General Notes.—Authorised 1916 as *No. 46 (Colorado), No. 47 (Maryland), No. 48 (Washington)*, and *No. 49 (W. Virginia).*
Maryland and *W. Virginia* to be fitted with Division Flag Officers' Quarters.   Except for change in primary
armament, and slight increase in displacement, they are identical in nearly all respects with *California* class,
described on next page.
        * Estimated completion dates, liable to change.
        † Contract dates : *Colorado* will probably not be ready till 1921.

CALIFORNIA *class* (2 ships).

*CALIFORNIA** and **TENNESSEE** (April, 1919).

Normal displacement 32,300 tons. *Full load*, 33,190 tons. Complement, 1119 (War 1630).

Length (*w.l.*), 600 feet. Beam, 97 feet 3½ inches. { *Mean* draught, 30 feet } Length *over all*, 624 feet.
{ *Max* „ 31 feet }

* Provisional launching date, Sept., 1919.

CALIFORNIA *class.* *Official sketch.*   *From a copyright photo by E. Muller, Junr.*

Guns (**Dir. Con.**) :
12—14 inch, 50 cal. (A⁷)
14—5 inch, 51 cal.
4—3 inch, (anti-aircraft)
4—6 pdr. (saluting)
2—1 pdr.
2 M.G.
2 landing.
Torpedo tubes (21 inch):
2 *submerged.*

Armour :
14″ Belt ……………….. ▮
8″ Belt (aft) …………… ▨
3″ Deck (ends) ………. ▨
15″—9″ Funnel bases … ▮
18″—9″ Turrets………… ▮
16″ Conning tower and
tube …… …………… ▮

Ahead :
6—14 in.
—5 in.

Astern :
6—14 in.
—5 in.

Broadside : 12—14 in., 7—5 in. ; 1—21 in. torpedo tube.

Note to Plans. —22—5 inch shown only 14—5 inch may be mounted. Alterations in 5 inch gun positions not yet known.

Machinery : *California*, G. E. turbines with electric reduction gear. *Tennessee*, Westinghouse turbines with electric reduction gear, 4 screws in both ships. Boilers : 8 Express Bureau type in *California*, 8 Babcock in *Tennessee*. Designed H.P. 28,500 = 21 kts. Fuel (oil only) : *normal* 2200, *maximum* 3328 tons.

⁕*Gunnery Notes.*—The 14 inch mountings are specially designed for large degree of elevation, up to 30°.
⁕*Armour Notes.*—Generally as *New Mexico*, *Pennsylvania* and *Nevada* classes on subsequent pages.
Engineering Notes.—Generally as those relating to *New Mexico* on next page. Four alternating current motors, one to each propeller shaft, supplied by current at 3400 volts, from 2 turbo-generators. Motors are wound for 36 and 24-pole connections, operating on former as squirrel-cage machines, and on latter as wound-rotor machines. Oil for trials : 1467 tons and 187 tons feed water. Estimated weight of machinery : *California*, 1805 tons ; *Tennessee*, 1983 tons. Heating surface : 50984 sq. ft. for Express Bureau type boilers in *California* ; 41,768 sq. ft. + 4168 sq. ft. (superheated) for Babcock boilers in *Tennessee*.

Name	Builder	Machinery	Laid down	Completed	Refit	Trials	Boilers	Best recent speed
California	Mare Island Y.		Oct. 16,				Express	
Tennessee	New York Yard		May,'17	Feb. '20†			Babcock	

General Notes.—Authorised 1915 as No. 43 (*Tennessee*) and 44 (*California*). The above design is practically identical with *New Mexico* class on next page. The anti-torpedo protection in these ships has been most carefully studied, and is believed to be excellent.   * Unofficial Notes.   † Estimated date of completion.

NEW MEXICO *class* (3 ships).

NEW MEXICO (April, 1917), **IDAHO** (June, 1917) and **MISSISSIPPI** (January, 1917).

Normal displacement, 32,000 tons. *Full load*, 33,000 tons. Complement, 1117.*

Length (*waterline*), 600 feet. Beam, 97½ feet 4½ in. { *Mean* draught, 30 feet. } Length *over all*, 624 feet.
{ Max. „ 31 „ }

Guns (**Dir. Con.**):
12—14 inch, 50 cal. (A⁷).
14—5 inch, 51 cal.
4—3 inch (anti-aircraft)
4—6 pdr. (saluting)
2—1 pdr.
2 machine
1 landing
Torpedo tubes (21 inch):
2 submerged.

*War; N.M. 1560, I. & M. 1600.

Armour :
14″ Belt (amidships) ......
8″ Belt (aft) ....
„ Deck ends ....
15″–9″ Funnel base ......
18″–9″ Turrets
16″ Conning tower & tube

Ahead :
6—14 in.
—5 in.

NEW MEXICO

Astern :
6—14 in.
—5 in.

Broadside : 12—14 in., 7—5 in., 1—21 in. torpedo tube.

Machinery : *New Mexico :* G.E. turbines with electric reduction gear (see *Notes*). *Idaho :* Parsons 4-shaft (geared cruising) turbines. *Mississippi :* Curtis 4-shaft (geared cruising) turbines. 4 screws in all three ships. Boilers : 9 Babcock & Wilcox. Designed H.P., *New Mexico* 27,500, others 32,000 = 21 knots. Fuel : Oil only, *normal* 2200 tons, *maximum* 3271 tons.

Armour and Gunnery Notes.—Generally as *Pennsylvania* and *Nevada* classes, but have still greater degree of internal protection. It is unofficially reported that they have *triple* bottoms and double longitudinal bulkheads, the space between outer bulkhead and inner skin being filled up with shock-absorbing materials. As designed, it was intended they should mount 45 calibre 14 inch guns, but while building, the more powerful 50 calibre model of the 14 inch gun was adopted.

Engineering Notes.—*New Mexico* has 2 turbine-driven generating units and 4 propelling motors. Generators are bipolar alternators. For economical cruising speeds of 15—18 knots and under, one generator is used on 36-pole connection. For higher speeds, 24-pole connection will be employed. One generator can drive ship at 19 kts. in emergency. 175 propeller r.p.m. = full speed. Estimated weight of machinery, *New Mexico* 2351 tons, *Idaho* 2408 tons, *Mississippi* 2298 tons. Estimated heating surface, 55,458 sq. feet (+ 4476 feet superheaters in *New Mexico*). 250 lbs. pressure at steam chest. Electric installation, 6—300 k.w., 120—240 volt turbo-generators in *New Mexico*, 4 in other ships. Oil on trials 1467 tons and 209 feed water.

Name.	Built at.	Machinery.	Laid down.	Completed	Trials. (4 hrs.)	Boilers.	Best recent speed.
New Mexico	New York Yard	New York Yard	Oct., '15	May, '18	31,000 = 21·3	Babcock	
Idaho	N. York S.B. Co.	N. York S.B.Co.	Jan., '15	Mar., '19		Babcock	
Mississippi	Newport News	Newport News	Apl., '15	Dec., '17		Babcock	

General Notes.—Authorised 1914, as No. 40 (*New Mexico*), 41 (*Mississippi*) and 42 (*Idaho*). *New Mexico* fitted with Division Flag Officer's quarters. Originally, only two ships were to have been built, but the sale of the old *Idaho* and *Mississippi* to Greece contributed two-thirds of the cost for a third unit. *New Mexico* was first named *California*. The type is derived from the *Nevada* design through the *Pennsylvania* class, upon which all the above are improvements. The electrical transmission of *New Mexico* was adopted through the excellent results given by the Melville-Macalpine electric-drive system in the Fleet Collier *Jupiter*. She is expected to be very economical in fuel and steam consumption.

*Unofficial Notes.

IDAHO.

Photo, New York Shipbuilding Co.

MISSISSIPPI.

Copyright photo, O. W. Waterman.

Note to Plans.—These are not uniform in scale with other plans in this book. Delete (*a*) the 4—5 inch guns before and abeam of first barbette ; (*b*) the 4—5 inch guns abaft fourth barbette : thus reducing the 22—5 inch shown on plans to the present armament of 14—5 inch.

(PENNSYLVANIA CLASS—2 SHIPS).

PENNSYLVANIA (March, 1915) & ARIZONA (June, 1915).

Normal displacement, 31,400 tons. *Full load*, 32,567 tons. Complement, 1117.*

Length (*waterline*), 600 feet. Beam, 97 feet. { Mean draught, $28\frac{5}{6}$ feet. } Length *over all*, 608 feet (p p. 596 ft.).
{ Max. ,, $29\frac{5}{6}$,, }

Guns (**Dir. Con.**) :
12—14 inch, 45 cal. (A^7)
14—5 inch, 51 cal.
4—3 in (anti-aircraft)
4—3 pdr. (saluting)
2—1 pdr.
2 M.G.
2 landing
Torpedo tubes (21 inch) :
2 *submerged*

* War :—
Penn. 1574. Ariz. 1620.

Armour :
14″ Belt (amidships) ....
8″ Belt (aft) ....
3″ Deck (ends) ....
15″—9″ Funnel base ....
18″—9″ Turrets
16″ Conning tower & tube ...
(Total, 8072 tons.)

Ahead :
6—14 in.
—5 in

PENNSYLVANIA

Astern :
6—14 in.
—5 in.

Broadside : 12—14 in., 7— 5 in., 1—21 in. torpedo tube.

Machinery : *Pennsylvania*, Curtis (geared cruising) turbines. 4 screws. *Arizona* Parsons, (geared cruising) turbines. 4 screws. Boilers : 12 Babcock. Designed H.P. (*Pennsylvania*), 31,500 (*Arizona*) 34,000 = 21 kts. Fuel : oil only, *normal* 2,322 tons (694.830 gallons).

* *Armour Notes.*— Generally as for *Nevada* class on next page. Increase of armour weight due to increased internal protection against submarine explosions and greater length of belt. Armour for each triple barbette, $226\frac{1}{2}$ tons. *Arizona* has cement backing to belt, instead of teak, and armoured fire-control tops.

* *Gunnery and Fire Control Notes.*—14 inch guns mounted in single sleeve, and can be fired as one piece. Maximum elevation enlarged to 30° in 1917. Triple positions weigh about 650 tons each (guns, mountings and armour). Hoists deliver 1 round per 40 secs., which may be improved to 2 rounds per minute, but three rounds fired per turret per minute probably represents actual rate of fire in service. Breech blocks worked by hand power. Interior of the shields to 14 inch guns very roomy and well arranged.
Each barbette has a built-in R.F. to rear of shield, ends projecting beyond sides and protected by armoured hoods. Large R.F. in central control station in upper storey of conning tower, where the director is also located probably. Small-base R.F. on roof of super-firing barbette shields and in fire-control tops.

Engineering Notes.—Oil fuel carried for trials, 1548 tons and 209 tons feed water. Heating surface, 53,322 sq. feet. Weight of Machinery : *Pennsylvania*, 2396 tons. ; *Arizona*, not yet ascertained (2250 tons estimated). 4—300 k.w. 125-volt turbo-generators in *Pennsylvania* ; *Arizona* same, but 120-240 volts. In *Pennsylvania*, 240 r.p.m. = full power ; in *Arizona*, 220 r.p.m. = full power.

Name	Builder	Machinery	Laid down	Completed	Trials Full Power : 12 hrs.	Boilers	Best recent speed
Pennsylvania	Newport News	Newport News	Oct.'13	June,'16	29,366 = 21·05	Babcock	
Arizona	New York Yard	New York Yard	Mar.'14	Oct. '16		Babcock	

General Notes.—Pennsylvania authorized 1912, as *No. 38*, *Arizona* 1913, as *No. 39*. Both ships are enlarged and improved *Nevadas*. They have proved excellent sea boats, very steady gun platforms, and have proved to be very economical ships. Their general design is marked by great simplicity and a very high standard of excellence. Living quarters are very roomy and well ventilated. Taken all round, these two ships represent one of the most successful, if not the most successful, of all Dreadnought designs up to the present time.
* Unofficial Notes.

PENNSYLVANIA.

Copyright Photo, O. W. Waterman.

Note to Plans.—8—5 inch guns removed during War, but from which positions not known, beyond the fact that they were taken from main and upper decks. These guns may now be remounted in new positions.

OKLAHOMA (March, 1914) & NEVADA (July, 1914).

Normal displacement, 27,500 tons. *Full load,* 28,400 tons. Complement, 1049.*

Length (*waterline*), 575 feet.   Beam, 95¼ feet.   { Mean draught 28½ feet. } Length *over all,* 583 feet.
{ Max.   ,,   29⅔ ,, }

Guns (Dir. Con.):
- 10—14 inch, 45 cal. (A⁷)
- 12—5 inch, 51 cal.
- 4—3 inch (anti-aircraft)
- 4—3 pdr. (saluting)
- 2—1 pdr.
- 2 machine.
- 1 landing.

Torpedo tubes (21 inch):
- 2 submerged

*War : Nevada, 1598, Oklahoma, 1628.

Armour:
- 13½" Belt (amidships) ....
- 8" Belt (aft)..........................
- 13½" Bulkheads ....
- 13½" Funnel base ....
- 3" Deck ... ...
- 18"—9" Triple Turrets.. \
- 16"—9" Double turrets .. /
- 16" Conning tower and tube .....

(Total weight, 7664 tons.)

OKLAHOMA.   *Copyright Photo. O. W. Waterman.*

Ahead :
5—14 in.
—5 in.

Broadside : 10—14 in., 6—5 in., 1—21 in. torpedo tube.

Astern :
5—14 in.
—5 in.

Machinery: *Oklahoma,* Triple expansion; *Nevada,* Curtis (geared cruising) turbines. 2 screws in both. Boilers: O, 12 Babcock; N, 12 Yarrow. Designed H.P. 24,800 = 20·5 kts. Coal: none. Oil, 598,400 gallons (2000 tons), *maximum capacity.* Radius of action: 4000 miles at full speed, 10,000 miles at 10 kts.

Armour Notes.—Main belt is 400 feet long by 17½ feet wide; 8½ feet of it being below *l.w.l.* Lower edge is 8". The ends are unarmoured, the battery also. Plates are applied in vertical strakes. Two protective decks, upper 3" flat, lower 1½" flat, 2" on slopes. Barbette bases are 13½" thick, but turrets are only 4½" where below protective deck and behind belt. Barbette shields: 18" port plate for triple positions, 16" port plate for twin positions, 10" sides, 9" back 5" roof. Sighting slits in conning tower closed by splinter-proof shutters. There is a signalling station protected by 16" armour behind conning tower. These ships mark a new era in naval construction, being the first to embody the "everything or nothing" idea in the matter of protection.

Gunnery Notes.—Guns in the triple turrets in one sleeve, can be fired as one piece. Maximum elevation of 14-inch guns enlarged to 30° in 1917.

Engineering Notes.—*Nevada* has 2 H.P. and 2 L.P. Curtis turbines. Cylinders of *Oklahoma* are H.P. 35", I.P. 59", L.P. (2) 78". Stroke, 48". Total heating surface, 48,000 sq. feet. Weight of machinery, *Nevada,* 1880 tons; *Oklahoma,* 1998 tons. Electric installation in both is 4 generating sets of 300 k.w., 125 volts, 2400 amp. each. Boilers are in 6 compartments and occupy less than 70 feet of length. Boilers are large tube "Express" type, those specially designed by Messrs. Babcock & Wilcox for *Oklahoma* proving most satisfactory. No superheaters. Electric-driven f.d. blowers proved too unreliable, and were replaced by steam turbine-driven blowers. All oil fuel carried in double bottom; no wing tanks.

NEVADA.   *Photo, U.S. Navy Recruiting Bureau.*

Note to Plans—9—5 inch guns removed from upper and main decks during War and ports plated up. Plans cannot be revised at present, because positions so dealt with have not been described. The 5 inch gun over stern has been suppressed. These 9—5 inch may now be re-mounted in new positions

Name	Builder	Machinery	Laid down	Completed	Trials (Full Power—12 hrs.)	Boilers	Best recent speed
Oklahoma	N. York Shipb'g	N.Y. Shipb'ld'g	Oct. '12	May,'16	21,703 = 20·58	Babcock	22
Nevada	Fore River Co.	Fore River	Nov.'12	Mar. '16	23,312 = 20·53	Yarrow	

General Notes.—Authorized 1911 as No. 36 (Nevada), 37 (Oklahoma).
* Unofficial Notes.

189

TEXAS CLASS—2 SHIPS.

NEW YORK (Oct., 1912) & **TEXAS** (May, 1912).

Normal Displacement, 27,000 tons. *Full load*, 28,367 tons. Complement, 1026.※

Length (*waterline*), 565 feet. Beam 95¼ feet. $\left\{\begin{array}{l}\text{Mean draught, } 28\frac{1}{2} \text{ feet.}\\ \text{Max. ,, ,, } 29\frac{2}{3} \text{ ,, ,,}\end{array}\right\}$ Length *over all*, 573 feet.

Guns (Dir. Con.):
10—14 inch, 45 cal. (A⁷)
16—5 inch, 51 cal.
2—3 inch anti-aircraft
4—3 pdr. (saluting)
2—1 pdr.
2 M.G.
2 landing.
Torpedo tubes (21 inch):
4 submerged

" War : N.Y., 1554 (Flag-C-in-C., 1538);
Texas, 1612.

Armour (Midvale) :
12" Belt (amidships)......
" Belt (bow) ....
" Belt (aft) ....
" Deck...................
" Upper Belt ...
14"—8" Turrets...
" Barbettes.............
" Battery ....

Ahead :
4—14 in.
—5 in.

TEXAS.

Astern :
4—14 in.
—5 in.

Broadside: 10—14 in., 8—5 in. ; 2—21 in. torpedo tubes.

Machinery : Vertical triple expansion, 4 cylinder. 2 screws. Boilers : 14 Babcock (8 with super-heaters). Designed H.P. 28,100 = 21 kts. Coal : *normal* tons ; *maximum*, 2918 tons in *New York* ; 2960 tons in *Texas*. Oil : 400 tons.

Engineering Notes.—Builders of turbine engines in the U.S. refused to adopt the standards laid down by the Navy Department. Accordingly, in these ships, reciprocating engines were reverted to, to show the turbine builders that the Navy Department was determined to have turbines built to official specification, or else the older type of engines would be taken up again. Cylinders: H.P. 39", I.P. 63", L.P. (2) 83". Stroke: 48". Grate area : 1554 sq. feet. Heating surface: 52,213+3267 sq. feet (superheaters). Weight of machinery : 2375 tons. Electrical installation : 4 sets each of 300 k.w., 125 volts. 2400-amps., by General Electric Co.

Name	Builder	Machinery	Laid down	Completed	Trials :* Full Power.	Boilers	Best recent speed
Texas	Newport News	Newport News	Apl. '11	Mar. '14	28,373 = 21·05	Babcock	22
New York	New York Yard	New York Yard	Sept. '11	Apl. '14	29,687 = 21·47	Babcock	...

* Both ships were light on trials -about 750 tons under normal displacement.

General Notes.—Authorised 1910 as No. 34 (N.Y.) and 35 (Texas). Both ships fitted as flagships. First design for these ships is said to have included 15 –12-inch guns in five triple turrets. Are very economical ships.

Note to Plans.—Delete (a) the foremost pair of 5 inch guns, (b) the fifth 5 inch gun from bows on each beam, (c) the 5 inch gun over stern, thus reducing 21—5 inch on plans to present armament of 16—5 inch. But the 5—5 inch removed during War may be re-mounted in new positions.

TEXAS.

Photo, U.S. Navy Recruiting Bureau.

Note that all U.S. Dreadnoughts are now as above photo, viz., (a) aeroplanes and flying-off platforms on barbette crowns ; (b) deflection scales painted on gun-houses ; (c) large charthouse at foot of fore cage mast ; (d) range clocks on cage masts—all these being features adopted from British Navy.

NEW YORK.

Copyright photo, O. W. Waterman.

Note.—These ships are distinguishable from the *Arkansas* class owing to the funnels being smaller and fore funnel nearer foremast.

(ARKANSAS CLASS—2 SHIPS.)

ARKANSAS (Jan., 1911), & WYOMING (May, 1911).

Normal displacement, 26,000 tons. *Full load,* 27,243 tons. Complements, 1056 and 1041.*

Length (*waterline*), 554 feet. Beam, 93¼ feet. { Mean draught, 28½ feet. Max. „ 29⅔ feet. } Length *over all,* 562 feet.

*War: 1594 (flag 1663).

Guns (**Dir. Con.**) :
- 12—12 inch, 50 cal.
- 16—5 inch, 51 cal.
- 2—3 inch (anti-aircraft)
- 4—3 pdr. (saluting)
- 2—1 pdr.
- 2 machine
- 2 landing

Torpedo tubes (21 inch) :
- 2 submerged

Armour (Midvale) :
- 11″ Belt amidships ......
- 5″ Belt (ends) ....
- 12″–9″ Turrets ...
- 11″ Turret bases ......
- 6½″ Casemates (*see Notes*)
- 12″ Conning tower........

ARKANSAS.

Ahead :
4—12 in.
—5 in.

Astern :
4—12 in.
—5 in.

Broadside : 12—12 in., 8—5 in., 1—21 in. torpedo tube.

Machinery : Parsons turbine. 4 screws. Boilers : 12 Babcock. Designed H.P. 28,000=20·5 kts.
Coal : *normal* 1669 tons ; *maximum,* 2754 tons in *Arkansas ;* 2704 tons in *Wyoming.* Oil, 400 tons.
Radius of action, about 8000 miles at 10 kts.

Gunnery Notes.—Height of guns above water: No. 1 turret, 28¼ feet; No. 2, 36¼ feet; No. 3, 33 feet; No. 4, 25 feet;
No. 5, 31¼ feet; No. 6, 23¼ feet.
Arcs of training: (1) 300°, (2) 270°, (3) 280°, (4) 260°, (5) 330°, (6) 300°.

Armour Notes.—Main belt 400 feet long, 9″ on bottom edge, 11″ on upper edge. Upper belt is same, but is 11″ on bottom
edge and 9″ on upper. Internal protection is by 1¾″ high-tensile longitudinal bulkheads. Two protective decks
over all machinery and magazine spaces, one deck at ends. 6½″ armour and 1½″ splinter bulkheads to funnel uptakes,
up to main deck.

Engineering Notes.—Approximately 148 r.p m.=10·5 kts., 215=15 kts., 300=20 kts., 320=22 kts. Grate area: 1428 sq. feet.
Heating surface: 64,234 sq. feet. Weight of machinery: 2178 tons in *Arkansas,* 2095 tons in *Wyoming.* Electrical
installation : 4 sets each 300 k.w., 125 volts, 2400 amps., by General Electric Co. Searchlights: 16. It was first
intended that these ships should have combined turbines and reciprocating engines, but the plan was dropped in
favour of complete turbine propulsion.

Name	Builder	Machinery	Laid down	Completed	Trials (mean) 24 hrs. at 19	4 hrs. f.p.	Boilers	Best recent speed
Arkansas	N.Y.Shipbld. Co Cramp	N.Y.Shipbld.·Co. Cramp	Jan.,'10 Feb.,'10	Sept.,'12 Sept.,'12	= 20,784=19·21	28,533=21·05 31,437=21·22	Babcock Babcock	21·15 22·45
Wyoming								

General Notes.—Authorised 1909, as No. 32 (*Wyoming*). 33 (*Arkansas*). Contracts awarded Sept. & Oct., 1909. Both fitted
as flagships, and when so serving, complements are 1116 for *Arkansas,* and 1117 for *Wyoming.* Freeboard: Forward,
25′: amidships, 19′ 2″; at No. 6 turret, 18′; at stern, 16′ 3″.

Unofficial Notes.

ARKANSAS.

Copyright photo, O. W. Waterman.

WYOMING.

Official photo, U.S. Naval Air Service.

Note to Plans. 5—5 inch removed from upper and main decks during War and ports plated up. Positions so dealt
with not known, except that stern 5 inch shown on plans is removed. These guns may be re-mounted in new
positions.

(UTAH CLASS—2 SHIPS.)

UTAH (Dec. 1909) & **FLORIDA** (May, 1910).

Normal displacement 21,825 tons. *Full load*, 23,033 tons. Complement, 944 (as flagship, 980).*

Length (*waterline*), 510 feet. Beam, 88¼ feet. {*Mean* draught, 28½ feet. / *Max.* „ 30 „ } Length *over all*, 521½ feet

*War: 1384 (flag 1422).

Guns (Dir. Con.) :
10—12 inch, 45 cal. (A⁵)
12—5 inch, 51 cal.
2—3 inch anti-aircraft
4—6 pdr. (saluting)
4 machine
2 landing
Torpedo tubes (21 inch) :
  2 *submerged*

Armour (Midvale) :
11″ Belt (amidships) ....
3″ Belt (ends) ....
 ″ Deck (slopes) ....
10″ Upper belt (amidships)
12″—8″ Turrets (N.C.)
 ″ Turret bases ....
6½″ Battery amidships ......
6½″ Casemates ....
 ″ Conning tower ....

Ahead :
4— 12 in.
—5 in.

Astern :
4—12 in.
—5 in.

Broadside : 10—12 in., 6—5 in., 1—21 in. torpedo tube.

Machinery : Parsons turbine. 4 screws. Boilers : 12 Babcock. Designed H.P. 28,000 = 20·75 kts. Coal : *normal* 1667 tons ; *maximum* 2581 tons in *Utah* ; 2560 tons in *Florida*. Oil, 400 tons. *Nominal* radius, 6720 miles at 10 kts., about 4600 at 19 kts. and 3000 at full speed.

°*Armour Notes.*—Main belt 8¼ feet wide ; upper belt 8 feet wide. 2″ splinter bulkheads between all 5 inch battery guns. ¼″ wall in rear. Special sub-division and powerful pumping system against damage by mines or torpedoes.

°*Gunnery Notes.*—Height of guns above water : in fore fore-turret, 33 feet ; after fore-turret, 40 feet ; amidship turret, 32 feet ; in after pair of turrets, 25 feet.

Engineering Notes.—Although turbines are adapted for superheated steam, no superheaters are installed. Have new type feed heaters. Grate area : 1428 sq. feet. Heating surface : 64,234 sq. feet. Weight of Machinery : *Florida*, 2152 tons ; *Utah*, 2064 tons. Electrical installation : 4 sets, each 300 k.w., 125 volts, 2400 amps., by General Electric Co. *Florida* on trials developed 41,810 shaft h.p. inclusive of main engines and all auxiliaries. In *Utah* 192 r.p.m. = 21 kts. ; 313 = 21 kts. Searchlights : 16.

Name	Builders	Machinery	Laid down	Com-pleted	Trials Full Power.	Turbines	Boilers	Best recent speed
Florida	New York Y.	New York Yard	Mar.,'09	Sep.,'11	40511 = 22·08	Parsons	Babcock	
Utah	N.Y.Shipbld.Co	N.Y.Shipbld. Co.	Mar.,'09	Aug.,'11	27026 = 21·04	Parsons	Babcock	

General Notes.—Authorised 1908, as No. 30 (*Florida*), 31 (*Utah*). *Florida* fitted as flagship.

°*Unofficial Notes.*

FLORIDA.

Copyright photo, O. W. Waterman.

UTAH.

Copyright photo, O. W. Waterman.

Note to Plans.—Delete foremost pair of 5 inch guns on *upper* deck ; also the foremost pair of 5 inch on *main* deck ; thus reducing 16—5 inch shown to present armament of 12—5 inch. The 4—5 inch removed during War may be re-mounted in new positions.

(DELAWARE CLASS—2 SHIPS).

DELAWARE (February, 1909), & **NORTH DAKOTA** (November, 1908).

Normal displacement, 20,000 tons.   Full load, 22,060 tons.   Complement, 946.*

Length (*waterline*), 510 feet.   Beam, 85¼ feet. $\left\{\begin{array}{l}\textit{Mean draught, 27 feet.}\\ \textit{Max. ,, 28}\tfrac{5}{6}\textit{ ,,}\end{array}\right\}$ Length *over all*, 518¾ feet.

* War : *Delaware*, 1384 ; *N. Dakota*, 1284.

Guns (Dir. Con.) :
10—12 inch, 45 cal. (A⁵).
14—5 inch, 51 cal.
2—3 inch (anti-aircraft)
4—3 pdr. (saluting).
2 machine.
2 landing.
Torpedo tubes (21 inch).
  2 submerged.

Armour (Krupp and Midvale) :
11″ Belt (amidships) .....
3″ Belt (ends) ....
 ″ Deck (slopes) ....
10″ Upper belt (amidships)
12″-8″ Turrets (N.C.) ......
Turret bases (N.C.) ......
5″ Battery (amidships) (N.C.)

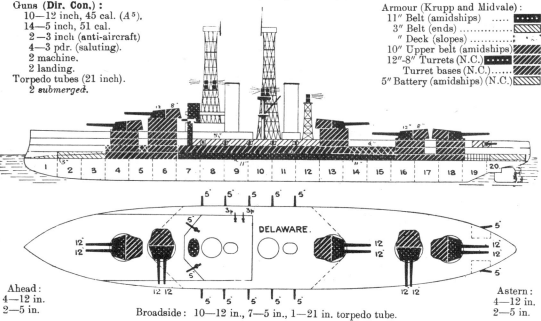

DELAWARE

Ahead :
4—12 in.
2—5 in.

Astern :
4—12 in.
2—5 in.

Broadside : 10—12 in., 7—5 in., 1—21 in. torpedo tube.

DELAWARE.

Photo, U.S. Navy Recruiting Bureau.

Machinery : *Delaware*, 2 sets triple expansion. 2 screws. *N. Dakota*, originally Curtis turbines but re-engined 1916-17 with Parsons turbines and reduction gear. 2 screws. Boilers : 14 Babcock. Designed H.P. 25,000 = 21 kts. Coal : *normal*, 1016 tons ; *maximum*, 2732 tons in *Delaware*, 2740 tons in *N. Dakota*. Also 380 tons oil.

Gunnery Notes.—*Delaware* fitted 1917 with new ammunition hoists and latest type of fire-controls.

Armour Notes.—Main belt 8 feet wide, 6¾ feet of it below waterline at full load displacement, 11″ thick amidships, upper belt, 7⅔ feet wide. Splinter-proof armour on uptakes and ventilators within citadel and in battery and upper deck.

Engineering Notes.—Cylinders of *Delaware* are 38½″ (H.P.) 57″ (I.P.) 2-76″ (L.P.) × 48″ stroke. Full speed, *Delaware* = 128 revs. *N. Dakota*, 263 r.p.m. for 21 kts., 229 for 19 kts., 142½ for 12 kts.* Trial consumption : 1·83 lbs. per H.P. all purposes. At 12 kts. *Delaware* burned 100 tons per 24 hours, *N. Dakota* 140 tons.* Grate area : 1439 sq. feet. Heating surface : 61,943 sq. feet. Weight of machinery : *D.* 2036 tons, *N.D.* 2047 tons.* 4—300 k.w. 125-volt turbo-generators. *Delaware* was the first U.S. ship to have forced lubrication which proved so successful, it was afterwards fitted to all the older battleships with reciprocating engines.

Nominal Radii : About 6500 at 12 kts., 4600 at 18 kts., 3000 at 21·5 kts. for *N. Dakota*.* Somewhat more for *Delaware*.

Name.	Builder.	Laid down	Completed	Trials : Full power.		Boilers	Best recent speed
Delaware	Newport News	Nov., 1907	Feb., '10	=19·74	24,578=21·56*	Babcock	21·98
North Dakota	Fore River Co.	Dec., 1907	Apl., '10	=	31,300=21·01	Babcock	22·25

Delaware, after steaming 19,000 miles, did 21·86 *max.* and averaged 21·32 for 24 hours.

NORTH DAKOTA (1919).

Photo, U.S. Navy Recruiting Bureau.

New R.F. station, Director Tower of fore cage mast, "coffee-box" S.L. tower to after funnel.

These ships have especially large boilers. The grates are 7ft. long by 14¾ft. wide=about 100 sq. ft. per boiler.

General Notes.—*N. Dakota* has a torpedo defence control platform under s.l. platform, abaft after funnel. Authorised 1906, as No. 28 (D) and 29 (N.D.) Cost, without armament, £789,200. *N. Dakota*, large refit, 1916.

* These particulars relate to first trials of *North Dakota*, when originally engined with Curtis turbines. No details available of any trials run with new Parsons turbines and reduction gear.

(S. Carolina Class—2 Ships).

SOUTH CAROLINA (1908) & MICHIGAN (May, 1908).

Normal displacement, 16,000 tons. *Full load* displacement, 17,617 tons. Complement, 813.*

Length (*waterline*), 450 feet. Beam, 80¼ feet. { Mean draught, 24½ feet. } Length *over all*, 452¾ feet.
{ Max ,, 27 feet. }

Guns (Dir. Con.):
8—12 inch, 45 cal. (A⁵).
14—3 inch, 13 pdr.
2—3 inch anti-aircraft
(a) 2—3 pdr. } S.C.
2—1 pdr. }
(b) 4—3 pdr. Mich.
2 M.G. } both
2 landing }
Torpedo tubes (21 inch):
2 submerged.
(Total about 1150 tons).

* War Complements: *Michigan* 1154;
S. Carolina 1354, flagship 1368.

Armour (S.C. Krupp; M. Midvale):
11"—9" Belt (amidships)......
1½" Belt (ends) ....
3" Armour deck (slopes) (*see notes*)
10" Bulkheads ....
12"—8" Turrets (N.C.)......
10"—8" Turret bases (N.C.)
10"—8" Lower deck, redoubt
12" Conning tower (N.C.)
9" Tube ....
(About 4000 tons).

Ahead:
4—12 in.

Astern:
4—12 in.

Broadside: 8—12 in., 7—3 in.; 1—21 in. torpedo tube.

Machinery: 2 sets vertical 4 cylinder triple expansion. 2 screws (outward turning). Boilers: 12 Babcock (1906 model) in 3 compartments. Designed H.P. 16,500=18·5 kts. Coal: *normal* 900 tons; *maximum* 2437 tons in *Michigan*, 2433 tons in *S. Carolina*.

Armour Notes.—Main belt, 8 feet wide; 6¾ feet of it below waterline; top and bottom, 9"; waterline, 11"—10¼". Redoubt belt 8" at upper edge, 10" lower. Low turrets with small bases. Fronts of turrets, 12"; sides, 8". Redoubt, 300 ft. long. Armour deck forward and amidships is 1½" on slopes, aft it is 3".

Gunnery Notes.—Hoists, electric. Big guns manœuvred electrically. Arcs of fire, 270° each turret. Fore turret guns 24 ft. above water, "after fore turret" guns 32 feet. Barbette of this rises 12 feet above the deck. Twelve hoists for 3 inch guns. *South Carolina* fitted with new ammunition hoists and latest type of fire-control system, 1917.

Engineering Notes.—Cylinders are 32" (H.P.), 52" (I.P.), 2—72" (L.P.)×48" stroke. Pressure, 265 lbs. Revolutions full power=121. Machinery, etc., weighs 1555 tons in *Michigan* and 1533 tons in *S. Carolina*. Grate area, 1050 sq. feet. Heating surface, 47,220 sq. feet. 4 sets 200 k.w. 125-volt turbo-generators. The first large U.S. ships to be fitted for burning oil fuel, though they do not appear to carry oil. Electric-driven f.d. blowers.

Name	Builder	Laid down	Completed	Trials (mean)		Boilers	Best recent speed
S. Carolina	Cramp	Dec., '06	Mar., '10		17,607=18·86	Babcock	19·68
Michigan	N.Y. Ship Bldg. Co.	Dec., '06	Jan., '10	13,253=17·95	16,016=18·79	Babcock	20·01

General Notes.—Authorised 1905 as *Nos. 26* (*Michigan*) and *27* (*S. Carolina*). These ships, though laid down after, were projected *before* the British *Dreadnought* and so may be considered as the first "Dreadnoughts" (*i.e.*, all big gun ships). They are good sea-boats, but roll heavily. In January, 1918, *Michigan's* lattice foremast fell during a gale. She has been re-equipped with a new lattice foremast of the latest type. * Unofficial Notes.

SOUTH CAROLINA.

Photo, O. W. Waterman.

Note to Plan.—8—3 inch, 14 pdr., either temporarily or permanently dismounted during War. Positions from which these guns were removed are not known, and guns cannot be deleted from plans. They were probably taken from the upper deck battery.

CONSTELLATION, CONSTITUTION, LEXINGTON, RANGER, SARATOGA,
and *NUMBER (6).*

Normal displacement, 35,300 tons. *Full load,* tons. Complement,

Length *(w.l.).* 850 feet. Beam, 90 feet. $\left\{\begin{array}{l}Mean\ \text{draught, }31'\ 3\frac{1}{2}''\\Max.\quad,, \quad\quad —\end{array}\right\}$ Length *(o.a.),* 874 feet.

Guns (Dir. Con.):
  8—16 inch, 50 cal. *(A⁷)*
  16—6 inch, 53 cal.
  4—3 inch, (anti-aircraft)
  4—6 pdr., (saluting)
Torpedo tubes (21 inch):
  2 *submerged.*
  8 *above water.*

Armour (*See Notes*) :

  (No details available.)

Anti-Torpedo protection :
  Bulge or triple bottom
  and wing B H.

Machinery : Turbines (see Table) and electric reduction gear. Boilers : 20 White Forster.
Designed H.P 180,000 = 35 kts. Fuel : oil only, *normal* tons, *maximum* tons.

Gunnery Notes.—Originally designed with 10—14 and 18—5 inch guns.

Engineering Notes.—Electric drive is said to consist of four 35,000 or 45,000 Kw. turbo-generators (each 50' 7" × 22' 0" wide × 15' 0" deep) installed on two decks, occupying a space of 55×55×35 feet. Boilers also installed on *two* decks, half being *above* the waterline. Total heating surface, 198,000 sq. ft.+18,000 sq. ft. superheaters. Estimated weight of machinery, 6172 tons. 4 main generators and 8 propeller motors in electric drive.

Armour Notes.—Armour contracted for by Bethlehem, Carnegie and Midvale Steel Companies. No official figures are available, but it has been unofficially reported there will be an incomplete waterline belt 600 feet long by 17½ feet deep, 8 feet of the depth being below the waterline at normal draught.

Aircraft Notes.—It was originally intended that all these ships should be equipped with launching catapults, stowage spaces, special derricks and operating gear for seaplanes.

Name.	Builder.	Machinery.	Laid down.	Completed.	Trials.	Turbines.	Best recent speed.
Constellation	Newport News	Newport News				W'stinghouse	
Constitution	Philadelphia, N.Y.	...				G.E.	
Lexington	Fore River	Fore River				G.E.	
Ranger	Newport News	Newport News				W'stinghouse	
Saratoga	New York S.B. Co.	N. York S.B. Co.				G.E.	
Number (6)	Philadelphia, N.Y.	...				G.E.	

General Notes.—*Constellation* and *Lexington* fitted with Division Flag Officers' Quarters. Estimated cost before war, £5,560,000 each. The design has been adversely criticised in the States, firstly, on account of the use of electric drive in the place of geared turbines, and secondly, on account of half the boilers being above the waterline, where, it is alleged, they are entirely unprotected. To these strictures, the Bureau of Construction and Repairs (Navy Department) replied that after careful and thorough examination, geared turbines were found to offer no appreciable advantage of the electric-drive system. As for the unprotected condition of the boilers above the waterline, it was officially stated that a certain measure of protection was given to these generators, but the form of defence could not be publicly explained. Before the war, it was anticipated that the enormous cost and novelty of these ships would result in very slow construction. If war had not intervened, they could not have been completed before 1920 or 1921. Estimated cost : (without guns or armour) 16¼ million dollars each; (with guns and armour) 30 million dollars each.

Note.

Construction of " Constellation," " Constitution," " Lexington " and " Saratoga " was authorised under the 1916 Section of the Three Years' Programme. " Ranger " belongs to the 1917 Section, and " Number (6) " to the 1918 Section.

No ships of this class begun by June 1st, 1919. Design again modified for the third time, during July—September, 1919. Final design may be different to that given opposite.

VERMONT. (Note to photo: Main deck battery now removed.)   *Photo, U.S. Naval Air Service.*

KANSAS (Sept., 1905), **VERMONT** (Aug., 1905), **MINNESOTA** (April, 1905), **NEW HAMPSHIRE** (—1906). *Normal* displacement, 16,000 tons. *Full load* displacement, 17,650 tons (*N. H.* 17,784 tons). Complement, 963. Length (*waterline*), 450 feet. Beam, 76⅚ feet. *Max.* draught, 26⅔ feet. Length *over all*, 456¼ feet. Guns (**Dir. Con.**): 4—12 inch, 45 cal., 8—8 inch, 45 cal., 12—3 inch, 13 pdr., 2—3 inch anti-aircraft. Torpedo tubes (21 inch): 4 *submerged*. Armour (Krupp): 9″ Belt (amidships), 4″ Belt (ends), 3″ Deck (slopes), 7″ Lower deck side, 10″ Barbettes, 12-8″ Turrets to these, 7″ Battery, 2″ Casemates (for 14 pdrs.), 6½″—6″ Small turrets 9″ Conning tower, 5″ Director station (near C.T.). Machinery: 2 sets vertical 4 cylinder triple expansion. 2 screws (outward turning). Boilers: 12 Babcock. Designed H.P. 16,500 = 18 kts. Coal: *normal* 900 tons; *maximum*, 2455 tons in *Kansas*, 2486 in *Vermont*, 2420 in *Minnesota*, 2592 in *N. Hampshire*. Built 1904-8.

LOUISIANA (Aug., 1904) & **CONNECTICUT** (Sept., 1904). As *Kansas*, &c., above, but differ as follows:—Displacement: *Full load*, 17,666 tons. Complement, (as flagship, 998). Armour (Krupp): 11″—9″ Belt (amidships), 3″ Deck (flat on belt), 12″—8″ Turrets (N.S.), 10″—7½″ Turret bases (N.C.), 7″ Lower deck redoubt, 7″ Battery, 2″ Casemates (14 pdr.), 6″ Secondary turrets (N.C.). Designed H.P. 20,525 = 18 kts. Coal: *maximum* 2446 tons, *Louisiana*; 2510 tons, *Connecticut*. Built 1903-6. Appearance similar to *Vermont* above.

NEW JERSEY. (Main deck battery now removed.)   *Photo, O. W. Waterman.*

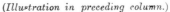

(Illustration in preceding column.)

VIRGINIA (April, 1904), **NEW JERSEY** (Nov., 1904), **GEORGIA** (Oct., 1904), **NEBRASKA** (Oct., 1904), **RHODE ISLAND** (May, 1904). *Normal* displacement, 14,948 tons. *Full load* displacement, 16,094 tons. Complements (nucleus.) Length (*waterline*), 435 feet. Beam, 76¼ feet. *Max.* draught, 525⅚ feet. Length *over all*, 441¼ feet. Guns (Model, '99): 4—12 inch, 40 cal. (A⁴), 8—8 inch, 45 cal., 8—3 inch, 13 pdr., 2—3 inch AA. Torpedo tubes (21 inch): 4 *submerged*. Armour (Krupp and H.N.): 11″—8″ Belt (amidships), 4″ Belt (ends), 3″ Deck (flat on belt amidships), 10″—7½″ Barbettes (H.N.), 12″—8″ Turrets (H.N.), 6″ Secondary turrets, 6″ Lower deck side (H.N.), 6″ Battery (H.N.), 9″ Conning tower (K.N.C.) Machinery: 2 sets 4 cylinder vertical inverted triple expansion. 2 screws. Boilers: 12 Babcock. Designed H.P. 25,463 = 19 kts. Coal: *normal* 900 tons; *maximum* 1961 to 2031 tons (average 1995). Built 1901-7.

MISSOURI.   *Photo: U. S. Navy Recruiting Bureau.*

OHIO (May, 1901), **MAINE** (July, 1901), **MISSOURI** (Dec., 1901). *Normal* displacement, 12,500 tons. *Full load* displacement, 13,500 tons. Complement (nucleus.) Length (*waterline*), 388 feet. Beam, 72¼ feet. *Max.* draught, 25⅓ feet. Length *over all*, 393⅚ feet. Guns (M. '99): 4—12 in., 40 cal. (A⁴) (Mk. III, mod. 3), 8—6 inch, 50 cal., 2—3 inch AA. Torpedo tubes (18 inch): 2 *submerged*. Armour (Krupp): 11″—7½″ Belt (amidships), 4″ Belt (bow), 10″ Bulkhead (aft), 2½″ Deck (on slopes), 4″ Deck (aft), 12″ Turrets (H.N.), 12″—8″ Turret bases, 6″ Lower deck side, 6″ Battery, 6″ Casemates (forward), 10″ Conning tower. Machinery: 2 sets vertical inverted triple expansion 4 cylinder, except *Missouri*, which is 3 cylinder. 2 screws. Boilers: 12 Thornycroft, except *Maine*, 12 Babcock. Designed H.P. 16,000 = 18 kts. Coal: *normal* 1000 tons; *maximum* 2331 tons, *Ohio*; 1904 tons, *Maine*; 1933 tons, *Missouri*. Built 1900-1904.

196

WISCONSIN.   *Photo, O. W. Waterman.*

ALABAMA (May, 1898), **ILLINOIS** (October, 1898), **WISCONSIN** (November, 1898). *Normal* displacement, 11,552 tons. Complement (nucleus). Guns : 4—13 inch, 35 cal. (A^3), 8—6 inch, 40 cal., 2—3 inch AA. No torpedo tubes. Armour (Harvey-nickel) : 16½—9½″ Belt, 4″ Belt (bow), 4″ Deck (aft), 12″ Bulkheads, 14″ Turrets, 15″—10″ Turret bases, 5¼″ Upper belt and battery, 6″ Casemates, 10″ Conning tower. Machinery : 2 sets vertical triple expansion. 3 cylinders. 2 screws. Boilers : 8 single-ended cylindrical, except *Illinois*, 8 Mosher. Designed H.P. *forced* 11,207 = 16 kts. Coal : *normal* 850 tons; *maximum,* 1481 tons *Alabama ;* 1522 tons *Illinois ;* 1447 tons *Wisconsin.* Built 1896-1901.

KEARSARGE.   *Photo, U. S. Navy Recruiting Bureau.*

KEARSARGE & **KENTUCKY** (*both* March, 1898). *Normal* displacement, 11,520 tons. Complement (nucleus). Guns : 4—13 inch, 35 cal. (A^3), 4—8 inch, IV, 35 cal., 8—5 inch, 40 cal., 2—3 inch AA. Torpedo tubes : none. Armour (Harvey-nickel) : 16½″—9½″ Belt, 4″ Belt (bow), 5″ Deck (aft), 2¾″ Deck (flat on belt) 4″ aft, 10″ Fore bulkhead, 12″ After bulkhead, 17″-9″ Turrets (for 13in.), 9″ Turrets (for 8 inch), 15¼″—12½″ Barbettes, 5¼″ Lower deck side, 5½″ Battery, 7″ & 6″ Battery (bulkheads), 10″ Conning tower. Machinery : 2 sets vertical triple expansion 3 cylinder. 2 screws. Boilers : 8 Mosher (fitted 1910-11). Designed H.P. 10,500 = 16 kts. Coal : *normal* 410 tons ; *maximum* 1679 tons in *Kearsarge,* 1658 tons in *Kentucky.*

TONOPAH.   *Photo, O. W. Waterman.*

TONOPAH (1901).
CHEYENNE (1900).
OZARK (1901).
TALLAHASSEE (1901).

3235 tons. Complements, 237. Dimensions : 252 × 50 × 12½ feet (*mean* draught). Guns : 2—12 inch (40 cal.) 4—4 inch, 1—3 inch AA., 2—6 or 3 pdr., 2—1 pdr. Armour : Krupp, 11″ belt and turret H.P. 2400 = 12 kts. Coal : *maximum, Ozark* 304 tons, *Tallahassee* 344 tons, *Tonopah* 346 tons, *Cheyenne* 132 tons coal + 60,816 gallons of oil fuel.

MONTEREY (1891). 4084 tons. Guns : 2—12 inch, 35 cal., in fore turret ; 2—10 inch, 30 cal., in after turret ; 6—6 pdr., 1—1 pdr. Armour (Harvey) : 13″—5″ belt, 8″ turrets. Base of fore turret 13″, of after turret 11½″. Designed H.P. 5000 = 14 kts. Babcock boilers. Coal, 211 tons. Complement, 228.

AMPHITRITE (1883). 3990 tons. Guns : 4—10 inch, 30 cal., 2—4 inch, 40 cal., 2—3 pdr., 2—1 pdr. Armour : Iron belt 9″, steel turrets 11½″—7½″. H.P. 1600 = 10·5 kts. Coal : 271 tons.

Note.
MONADNOCK listed as a Submarine Depot Ship, but will probably be withdrawn from this duty in the near future and placed out of commission.

SEATTLE (as Seaplane Carrier—main deck battery now removed).   *Photo, O. W. Waterman.*

NORTH CAROLINA⁕ (October, 1906), **MONTANA**⁕ (December, 1906), **SEATTLE** (March, 1905). *Normal* displacement, 14,500 tons. *Full load*, 15,981 tons. *Seattle*, 15,712 tons. Complement (nucleus). Length (*waterline*), 502 feet. Beam, $72\frac{5}{6}$ feet. *Maximum* draught, 27 feet. Length *over all*, $504\frac{1}{2}$ feet. Guns (M. '99): 4—10 inch, 40 cal., 4—6 inch, 50 cal., 12—3 inch, 14 pdr., 2—3 inch anti-aircraft, 4—6 or 3 pdr. (saluting). Torpedo tubes (21 inch): 4 *submerged*. Armour (Krupp; but part Midvale in *N.C.* and *M.*): 5″—3″ Belt, 3″ Deck (ends), 5″ Lower deck side, 6″ Lower deck bulkheads, 8″—4″ Barbettes (N.C.), 9″—5″ Turrets, 5″ Battery, 2″ Battery for 14 pdrs., 9″ Conning tower (fore), 5″ Tube (N.C.), 5″ After C. T. (N.C.). Machinery: 2 sets 4 cylinder triple expansion. 2 screws, outward turning. Boilers: 16 Babcock. Designed H.P. 23,000 = 22 kts. Coal: *normal* 900 tons; *maximum*, *N. Carolina* and *Montana*, 2164 tons; *Seattle*, 2062 tons. Built 1903-8. Fitted with Seaplane Catapults. *Memphis* of this class wrecked 1916.

PITTSBURGH.

(Illustration in preceding column.)

HUNTINGTON (April, 1903), **PUEBLO** (April, 1903), **PITTSBURGH** (Aug., 1903), **FREDERICK** (Sept., 1903) & **SOUTH DAKOTA**⁕ (July, 1904). Displacement, *normal*, 13,680 tons, *full load*, 15,138. Complement (nucleus). Length (*waterline*), 502 feet. Beam, $69\frac{1}{2}$ feet. *Maximum* draught, 26 feet at *full load* displacement. Length (*over all*), 504 feet. Guns (model 1899): 4—8 inch, 45 cal. (A), 4—6 inch, 50 cal., 10—3 inch, 14 pdr., 50 cal., 2—3 inch anti-aircraft. Torpedo tubes (18 in.): 2 *submerged*. Armour (Krupp): 6″ Belt, $3\frac{1}{2}$″ Belt (ends), 4″ Deck (on slopes), 5″ Upper belt, 4″ Bulkheads, 6″ Turrets (N.C.), 5″ Battery, 6″ Casemates (N.C.), 9″ Conning tower (N.C.). Machinery: 2 sets 4 cylinder vertical triple expansion. 2 screws. Boilers: 16 or 20 Babcock & Wilcox. Designed H.P. 23,000 = 22 kts. Coal: *normal* 900 tons; *maximum*, S. *Dakota* 2233 tons; *Frederick* and *Huntington*, 2098 tons; *Pittsburgh*, 1992 tons; and *Pueblo*, 1976 tons. Built 1901-8.

⁕*South Dakota* to be re-named.

ST. LOUIS.   *Photo, O. W. Waterman.*

(Officially rated as First Class Cruisers.)

CHARLESTON (Jan., 1904), **ST. LOUIS** (May, 1905). Displacement, *normal*, 9700 tons, *full load*, 10,839 tons. Complement (nucleus). Length (*waterline*), 424 feet. Beam, 66 feet. *Maximum* draught, $24\frac{5}{6}$ feet. Length *over all*, $426\frac{1}{2}$ feet. Guns: 12—6 inch, 50 cal., 4—3 inch, 14 pdr., 2—3 inch AA., and in *Charleston* only, 4—3 pdr. (saluting). Torpedo tubes: *nil*. Armour (Krupp): 4″ Belt, 3″ Deck, 4″ Lower deck redoubt, 4″ Battery, 5″ Conning tower. Machinery: 2 sets vertical 4 cylinder triple expansion. 2 screws. Boilers: 16 Babcock. Designed H.P. 21,000 = 21·5 kts. Coal: *normal* 650 tons; *maximum* 1818 and 1793 tons. Begun 1902, completed 1905-6. *Milwaukee* of this class wrecked 1917.

New photo wanted.

Photo, Rau.

BROOKLYN (1895). *Normal* displacement, 9215 tons; *full load*, 10,068 tons. Complement, 729. Length (*waterline*), 400½ feet. Beam, 64⅔ feet. *Maximum* draught, 26½ feet. Guns: 8—8 inch, 35 cal. (*E*), 8—5 inch, 40 cal., 2—3 inch (anti-aircraft), 4—6 pdr. (saluting). Torpedo tubes: *Nil*. Armour (Harvey): 3″ Belt, 6″ Deck (amidships), 3″ Deck (ends), 8″ Barbettes, 5½″ Hoods to barbettes, 6″ Hoists, 4″ Shields (fixed), 5″ guns, 7½″ Conning tower. Machinery: 4 sets vertical triple expansion. 2 screws. Boilers: 7 cylindrical (5 double-ended and 2 single-ended). Designed H.P. *forced* 18,000 = 21 kts. Coal: *normal* 900 tons; *maximum* 1449 tons. Laid down 1893. Completed 1896. Reconstructed 1909.

Photo, Lieut. H. Reuterdahl, U.S.N. R.F.

(*Flagship, Destroyer Force, Atlantic Fleet.*)

ROCHESTER (ex *Saratoga*, ex *New York*). (December, 1891.) (Reconstructed 1907-08.) *Normal* displacement, 8150 tons; *full load*, 8900 tons. Complement, 630. Length (*waterline*), 380½ feet. Beam, 64⅗ feet. *Maximum* draught, 24⅖ feet. Guns: 4—8 inch, 45 cal. (*A*), 8—5 inch, 50 cal., 8—3 inch AA. Torpedo tubes: *Nil*. Armour (Harvey nickel): 4″ Belt, 6″ Deck (amidships); (Krupp) 6″—4″ Barbettes, 6½″ Turrets; 5″ Hoists, 7″ Conning tower. Machinery: 4 sets vertical triple expansion. 2 screws. Boilers (1907): 12 Babcock. Designed H.P. *forced* 16,500 = 21 kts. Coal: *normal* 750 tons; *maximum* 1100 tons. Laid down at Philadelphia, Sept., 1890. Completed 1893. Re-named *Saratoga*, 1911, and again re-named *Rochester*, 1917. Large refit in 1917.

Building.

To have 4 funnels, 2 pole masts.

NUMBER (4), NUMBER (5), NUMBER (6), NUMBER (7), NUMBER (8), NUMBER (9), NUMBER (10), NUMBER (11), NUMBER (12), and *NUMBER (13).*

Normal displacement, 7100 tons; *full load*, 7610 tons. Complement, 364.

Length (*waterline*), 550 feet. Beam, 55 feet. { *Mean* draught, 13′ 6″ } Length *over all*, 555½ feet.
{ *Max.* „ 14′ 4½″ }

Armour:

Guns:

8—6 inch, 52 cal.
2—3 inch anti-aircraft
2—3 pdr.

(Not known.)

Torpedo tubes (21 inch):

2 in twin deck mounting *above water*

Machinery: Turbines (see Table for types), with reduction gears. Designed S.H.P. 90,000 = 35 kts. 4 screws. Boilers: see Table. Fuel: oil only; capacity unknown.

Name.	Built and Engined by	Laid down	Com-pleted	Trials	Turbines.	Boilers	Best recent speed
Number (4)	Todd Co., Tacoma	Dec.'18	Aug. '21 †		Westinghouse	12 Yarrow	
Number (5)	„ „	Dec.'18	Dec. '21 †		„	12 Yarrow	
Number (6)	„ „	1919	July, '22 †		„	12 Yarrow	
Number (7)	Union Ironworks		...		„	...	
Number (8)	„ „				„	...	
Number (9)	Wm. Cramp & Sons		Jan. '21 †		„	12 White-F	
Number (10)	„ „ „		Sept. '21 †		„	12 White-F	
Number (11)	„ „ „		Nov. '21 †		...	...	
Number (12)	„ „ „		Dec. '21 †		...	...	
Number (13)	„ „ „		Feb. '22 †		...	...	

* Nos. 7—10 not begun up to June 1st, 1919. † Contract dates for completion.

General Notes.—Each equipped with catapults, derricks, &c., for launching and handling four seaplanes. Estimated cost (without guns) in 1916, five to six million dollars each; revised estimate 1919, 7¼ million dollars each.

New photo wanted, as re-armed 1917-18.

OLYMPIA (November, 1892). *Normal* displacement, 5865 tons (*full load* 6588 tons). Complement, 439. Length (*waterline*), 340 feet. Beam 53 feet. *Maximum* draught, 25 feet. Guns: 10—5 inch (51 cal.), 2—1 pdr. Armour: $4\frac{3}{4}''$ deck on slopes, 2″ flat.

Machinery: 2 sets vertical inverted triple expansion. 2 screws. Boilers: 4 double-ended and 2 single-ended. Designed H.P. *forced* 17,000 = 21·69 kts. Coal: *normal* 500 tons; *maximum* 1169 tons.

General Notes.—Laid down at San Francisco, June, 1891. Completed 1895. Cost, *complete*, about £550,000. Flagship of the late Admiral Dewey, at battle of Manila. Reconstructed partially 1901-03, re-armed 1917-18.

COLUMBIA (see next column for details).   *Photo, O. W. Waterman.*

(*Flagship, Train, Atlantic Fleet.*)

MINNEAPOLIS.   *Photo, Geiser.*

(*Flagship, Train, Pacific Fleet.*)

COLUMBIA (July, 1892), & **MINNEAPOLIS** (August, 1893). Displacement, 7,350 tons. Complement, 480 and 489. Length (*waterline*), $411\frac{1}{2}$ feet. Beam, $58\frac{1}{4}$ feet. *Maximum* draught, $24\frac{1}{2}$ feet. Guns: 3—6 inch, 45 cal., 4—4 inch, 40 cal., 2—3 inch AA. (and 2—1 pdr. in *Minneapolis*).

Machinery: 3 sets vertical inverted triple expansion. 3 screws. Boilers: 8 double-ended, 2 single-ended cylindrical. Designed H.P. *forced* 18,500 = 22·80 kts. Coal: *normal* 750 tons; *maximum* 1561 tons in *Columbia*, 1433 tons in *Minneapolis*.

CHICAGO (1885). Displacement, 4500 tons. Complement, 333. Armament: 4—5 inch, 51 cal., 1—3 pdr., 2—1 pdr., 2 M.G. Designed H.P. 9000 = 18 kts. Boilers: 6 Babcock + 4 S.E. Coal: 870 tons.

BIRMINGHAM.

Photo, O. W Waterman.

(CHESTER CLASS—3 SHIPS.)

SALEM (July, 1907), **BIRMINGHAM** (May, 1907), **CHESTER** (June, 1907).

Normal Displacement, 3750 tons ; *full load*, 4687 tons. Complement, 392 (*B'ham* 410, flag 451).

Length (*waterline*), 420 feet. Beam, 47 feet. { Maximum draught, $18\frac{3}{4}$ feet. } Length *over all*, 423 feet.
{ Mean ,, $16\frac{3}{4}$ }

Guns : (**Dir. Con.**)
  4—5 inch, 51 cal.
  2—3 inch, 50 cal.
  1—3 inch A A.
Torpedo tubes (21 inch):
  2 *above water*.

Armour :
  2″ Nickel on w.l..........
  2″—1″ Steering gear
    protection...........
  2″—1″ Protection to
    engines.............
  No conning tower.

Note.

Re-armed 1917-18. No plans available of new gun positions.

Machinery : *Salem*, G. E. turbines with reduction gear (new 1916-17). *Chester*, Parsons' turbine. 4 screws. *Birmingham*, 2 sets 4 cylinder triple expansion. 2 screws. Boilers : various (*see Notes*). Designed H.P. *Salem* (with new turbines) 20,000, *Birmingham* and *Chester*, 16,000 = 24 kts.

Coal : *normal* 475 tons ; *maximum*, *Salem* and *Birmingham* 1433 tons ; *Chester*, 1408 tons.

Name.	Builder.	Laid down.	Completed.	Refit.	Trials :— 4 hours full p.	Boilers.	Best recent speed.
Salem (t)	Fore River Co.	Aug., '05	July, '08	1916-17	15,273 = 25·95*	12 Fore River	
Birmingham	Fore River Co.	Aug., '05	Apl., '08		15,476 = 24·32	12 Fore River	
Chester (t)	Bath Ironworks	Sept., '05	Apl., '08		25,400 = 26·52†	12 Normand	

* With original Curtis turbines.　† Light on trials, 3673 tons.

General Notes :—Authorised 1904, re-armed 1917-18. Average cost, *exclusive of armament*, £325,000 each. These ships are good sea boats, but roll heavily. All now serve as Flagships to Destroyer Forces, Atlantic and Pacific Fleet. Are very lightly built, and cannot maintain full power for any length of time.

CLEVELAND. (Foremost pair of 5 inch guns on main deck now removed.)　*Photo, O. W Waterman.*

(DENVER CLASS—6 SHIPS.)

CHATTANOOGA (March, 1903), **CLEVELAND** (September, 1901), **DENVER** (June, 1902), **DES MOINES** (September, 1902), **GALVESTON** (July, 1903), & **TACOMA** (June, 1903).
(Wood sheathed and coppered). *Normal* displacement, 3,200 tons. Complement, 299 to 338. Length (*waterline*), 292 feet. Beam, 44 feet. *Maximum* draught, 17 feet. Guns (model 1899) : 8—5 inch, 50 cal., 6—6 pdr., 2 landing. No torpedo tubes. Armour (Harvey-nickel) : $2\frac{1}{2}$″ Deck (on slopes), $\frac{1}{4}$″ (flat) Machinery : 2 sets 4 cylinder triple expansion. 2 screws. Boilers : 6 Babcock & Wilcox. Designed H.P. 5,398 = 16·5 kts. Coal : *normal* 467 tons ; *maximum* 705 to 741 tons = 7,000 miles at 10 kts. *nominal*.

Notes.—15 " Long arm " doors to the first four. Length *over all* varies from 308′-6″ to 309′-10″. Are remarkably good sea boats.

Name.	Builder	Machinery	Laid down	Completed	Refit	Trials full p.	Boilers	Present best speed
Chattanooga	Crescent Co. P.		1900	1904		5227 = 16·65		
Cleveland	Bath Ironw'rks		1900	1903		4586 = 16·45		...
Denver	Neafie & Levy		1900	1904		6073 = 16·75		
Des Moines	Fore River Co		1900	1904		5059 = 16·65	Babcock in all.	
Galveston	W. R. Trigg		1901	1905		4984 = 16·41		15·7
Tacoma	Union Ironw'k.		1900	1904		5233 = 16·58		16

(NEW ORLEANS CLASS—2 SHIPS.)

(RALEIGH CLASS—2 SHIPS.)

RALEIGH.

Photo, U. S. Recruiting Bureau.

ALBANY.

Photo, O. W. Waterman.

CINCINNATI.

Photo, U. S. Navy Recruiting Bureau.

NEW ORLEANS (Dec., 1896) & **ALBANY** (Jan., 1899). *Normal* displacement, 3430 tons (*full load*, 3954). Complement, 326. Length (*w.l.*), 326 feet. Beam, $43\frac{3}{4}$ feet. *Maximum* draught, 19 feet. Length *over all*, $354\frac{5}{8}$ feet. Guns (U.S. models) : 8—5 inch, 50 cal., 2—3 or 1 pdr. No torpedo tubes. Armour (Harvey-nickel) : $3\frac{1}{2}''$ Deck (slopes) and Cofferdam amidships, no gun shields, $1\frac{1}{4}''$ Deck (flat). Machinery : 2 sets 3 cylinder triple expansion. 2 screws. Boilers : 4 double-ended. Designed H.P. *forced* 7500 = 20 kts. Coal : *normal* 450 tons ; *maximum* 782 tons in *Albany*, 693 tons in *New Orleans*.

General Notes.—Laid down at Elswick (for Brazil) as the *Amazonas* (*New Orleans*) and *Abreu* (*Albany*). Purchased by U. S. (1898) just before war with Spain. *Albany* completed 1900, *New Orleans* 1898. Re-armed with U. S. guns, 1907.

RALEIGH (Norfolk N.Y., March, 1892) & **CINCINNATI** (New York N.Y., Nov., 1892). *Normal* displacement, 3183 tons (*full load* 3339 tons). Complement : 282 and 317. Length (*w.l.*), 300 feet. Beam, 42 feet. *Maximum* draught, $19\frac{1}{2}$ feet. Length *over all*, 306 feet. Guns (M. '99) : 9—5 inch, 40 cal., 4—6 pdr. S.A. No torpedo tubes. Armour (steel) : $2\frac{1}{2}''$ Armour deck, 2″ Conning tower. Machinery : 2 sets 4 cylinder vertical triple expansion (new 1900-2). 2 screws. Boilers : 8 Babcock and Wilcox. Designed H.P. 8,000 = 18 kts. Coal : *normal* 396 tons ; *maximum* 720 tons. Laid down 1892, completed 1894, re-built and re-armed 1901-3.

(*Continued on next page.*)

U. S. THIRD CLASS CRUISERS & GUNBOATS.

Old Third Class Cruisers—*continued.*

ANNISTON.

MARBLEHEAD.   *U.S. Navy photo.*

ANNISTON (ex *Montgomery*, 1891), **MARBLEHEAD** (1892). 2072 tons. Complement, 260—263. Dimensions: 257 *w.l.* × 37 × 14½ feet, *mean* draught. Guns: 8—4 inch. Designed H.P. 5400 = 17 kts. Machinery: 2 sets inverted triple expansion. Boilers: *Anniston* 6 Almy; *Marblehead* 3 D.E. and 2 S.E. Coal: 346 tons.

Gunboats.

Building & Completing.

NUMBER (22). To be built by Charleston, N.Y., begun June, 1919. **ASHEVILLE** (Charleston N.Y.) (July, 1918). *Normal* displacement, 1575 tons. Complement,   Length (*waterline*), 225 feet. Beam, 41¼ feet. *Mean* draught, 11⅓ feet. Guns: 3—4 inch, 50 cal. Machinery: Parsons turbine with reduction gear. 1 screw. Boilers: 3 Bureau (modified Thornycroft). Designed H.P. 800 = 12 kts. Fuel,   tons.

SACRAMENTO (Feb., 1914). *Normal* displacement, 1425 tons. Complement, 163. Length (*waterline*), 210 feet. Beam, 50⅚ feet. *Mean* draught, 11½ feet. Guns: 3—4 inch, 50 cal.; 2—3 pdr.; 2—1 pdr. Machinery: 1 set triple expansion. Boilers: 2 Babcock. H.P. (on trials), 1022 = 12·78 kts. Coal: *maximum*, 428 tons. Built by Cramps. Completed, 1914.

Photo wanted.

SAMOA (ex German s.s. *Staatssekretaer Solf*) (1913, seized 1917). 550 tons. Complement, 32. Dimension: 131 (*waterline*) × 25½ ×   feet. Guns: 4—3 pdr., 2 M.G. Machinery: 1 set vert. compound. H.P., Speed and Fuel not known.

WILMETTE (ex s s. *Eastland*, 1903, taken over 1918). 2,600 tons. Complement, 181. Length (*waterline*), 265 feet. Beam, 38½ feet. Draught,   feet. Guns: 4—4 inch, 2—3 inch AA., 2—1 pdr. Machinery; 2 sets triple expansion. 2 screws. Boilers: Designed I.H.P. 4000 = 16·5 kts. Fuel,   tons.

Gunboats—*continued.*

DUBUQUE.   *Photo, Navy Dept.*

DUBUQUE (1904), **PADUCAH** (1904). *Normal* displacement, 1085 tons. Complement, 190 and 176. Length (*waterline*), 174 feet. Beam, 35 feet. *Mean* draught, 12¼ feet. Guns: *Dubuque*, 2—4 inch, *Paducah*, 4—4 inch, and in both, 4—6 pdr., 2—1 pdr. Machinery: 2 sets triple expansion. 2 screws. Boilers: 2 Babcock. Designed H.P. 1000 = 12·9 kts. Coal: *maximum* 252 tons.

WHEELING.   *Photo, Fons.*

MARIETTA & WHEELING (1897). *Normal* displacement, 990 tons. Complements, 182 and 163. Length (*waterline*), 174 feet. Beam, 34 feet. *Mean* draught, 12 feet. Guns: 4—4 inch, 40 cal.; 2—3 pdr.; 2—1 pdr. (+1-Y in *Wheeling*). Machinery: 2 sets vertical triple expansion. 2 screws. Boilers: *Marietta*, 2 Babcock; *Wheeling*, 2 single-ended. Designed H.P. 1250 = 13 kts. Coal: *maximum*, 234 and 256 tons. *Nominal* radius: 4000 at 10 kts.

(Mainmast of *Princeton* removed).   *Photo, Abraham & Sons.*

ANNAPOLIS (1896). **NEWPORT** (1896). **PRINCETON.**
Normal displacement, 1010 tons. Complement, 165—147. Length (*waterline*), 168 feet. Beam, 36 feet. *Mean* draught, 12 feet. Guns: *Annapolis*, 6—4 inch, 4—6 pdr., 1 Y-gun. *Newport*, 1—4 inch, 2—3 inch, 2—6 pdr. *Princeton*, none. Machinery: 1 set vertical triple expansion. 1 screw. Boilers: 2 Babcock. Designed H.P. 800 = 12 kts. Coal: 235 tons.

Notes.—Vicksburg now Fisheries Protection Gunboat, Alaska.

HELENA (1896) & **WILMINGTON** (1895). Displacement, 1392 tons. Complement, 207 *average*. Length (*waterline*), 250¾ feet. Beam, 39⅔ feet. *Mean* draught, 9 feet. Guns: 8—4 inch, 40 cal.; 4—3 pdr. Machinery: 2 sets vertical triple expansion. Designed H.P. 1988 = 13 kts. Coal: *maximum*, 258 tons in *Wilmington*; 307 tons in *Helena*. *Nominal* radius: 2200 miles at 10 kts.

Photo, copyright, Rau.

NASHVILLE (1895). 1371 tons. Guns: 8—4 inch, 4—6 pdr., 2—1 pdr., 2 machine. 2¼″ sponsons to 4 inch guns. H.P. 2500 = 16 kts. Coal: 381 tons. Complement 188.

Machias.   *Photo, U.S. Navy.*

CASTINE (1892), **MACHIAS** (1891). 1177 tons. Complement, 182—177. Guns: *Castine*, 2—4 inch, 6—6 pdr., 2—1 pdr., 1 Y-gun; *Machias*, 4—4 inch, 2—3 pdr., 2—1 pdr. Speed, 15½ to 16 kts. Coal: *Castine*, 246 tons; *Machias*, 267 tons.

No photo available.

YORKTOWN (1888). 1710 tons. Complement, 219. Guns: 6—5 inch, (40 cal.), 4—6 pdr., 2—1 pdr. Original speed, 17 kts. Coal: 336 tons.

Mainmast now removed.

PETREL (1888). Displacement, 890 tons. Complement, 135. Guns: 4—4 inch, (40 cal.), 2—3 pdr., 2—1 pdr. Designed H.P. 1000 = 11·5 kts. Coal: 198 tons.

DON JUAN DE AUSTRIA (1887). 1130 tons. Guns: 4—4 inch, 2—1 pdr. H.P. 941 = 12·2 kts. Coal: 201 tons.

No photo available.

ISLA DE LUZON (1887). 1030 tons. Guns: 4—3 pdr. Speed: *about* 11 kts. Coal: 159 tons.

(Used as Yacht by the Secretary of the Navy.)

DOLPHIN (1884). 1486 tons. Complement, 156. Guns : 2—3 inch, 4—6 pdr. Speed, 15·5 kts. Coal : 255 tons.

No photo available.

NANTUCKET (ex *Rockport*, ex *Ranger*, 1876). 1261 tons. Guns : 1—4 inch, 2—3 inch. I.H.P. 500=10 kts. Coal, 182 tons.

Mainmast now removed.

ALERT (1875). 1100 tons. Complement : 137. Dimensions : 177⅓ × 32×13 feet (*mean* draught). Guns : 1—6 pdr. H.P. 500=10 kts. 2 Babcock boilers. Coal : 202 tons.

ESSEX (1874). 1375 tons. Guns : 6—3 pdr. H.P. 800=10 kts. Coal : 155 tons.

GOPHER (1871). 840 tons. 5—3 pdr., 4—1 pdr. Speed, 9 kts. Coal : 80 tons.

WOLVERINE (1842). 685 tons. H.P. 365=10·5 kts. Paddle wheel. Coal : 115 tons. Guns : 6—3 pdr.

YANTIC (1864). 900 tons. 4—3 pdr., 2—1 pdr. H.P. 310=8·3 kts. Coal : 130 tons.

Small Gunboats for Service in the Philippines.

MONOCACY.   *Photo, Leslie's Weekly.*

MONOCACY (1914), **PALOS** (1914). 190 tons. Complement, 47. Guns : 2—6 pdr., 6 machine. Machinery : 2 sets vertical compound. Boilers : 2 Babcock. Designed H.P. 800=13¼ kts. Coal : 34 tons. Built at Mare Island Navy Yard and re-erected by Shanghai Dock and Engineering Co.

Photo wanted.

QUIROS (1895), **VILLALOBOS** (1896). 360 tons. Complement, 56. Guns : 4—3 pdr. Designed H.P. 550=11 kts. Coal : 70 tons.

No photo available.

CALLAO (1888), **PAMPANGA** (1888), **SAMAR** (1888). 243 tons. Guns : *Callao* none ; others 4—3 pdr. Speed, 10 to 10½ kts. Coal : 33 tons. Old gunboats captured in Spanish War.

No photo available.

ECLANO (1885). 620 tons. Complement, 99. Guns : 4—4 inch, 4—3 pdr. Speed, 11 kts. Coal : 98 tons. Old gunboat captured in Spanish War.

Note.

Romblon, Bobol, Cebu, Jolo, Marie Duque, (Uraga Dock Co , 1902-3), are small gunboats belonging to the War Department, Philippines. 350 tons. Guns : 3 small Q. F. Designed H.P. 450=10 kts.

258 + *166** + *12†* = *436* U. S. DESTROYERS.—Tabulated Details.

*Building, completing, or under contract. July 1st, 1919. Expected that about 81 boats will be finished between July-December, 1919, and the remainder in 1920. Monthly deliveries of new T.B.D. : about 12-15 boats.

†Not under contract or construction, July 1st, 1919.

No.	Class.	First begun.	Last completed	Displacement.	Length (w.l.) × Beam × Mean draught.			Designed H.P. } = kts. speed.	Max. Fuel.	Guns. AA = Anti-Aircraft.	Torpedo tubes.	Complement. Peace/War
				tons.					tons.			
68	Various Yards...	1918	1920	1215						Brooks 4—5 inch (51 cal.) 1—3 inch AA.	12—21 inch	..
100	Various Yards...	1918	1920	1215	310	31	9⅓	{ 27,000t— 25,000t } =35	..			
11	Newport News ..	1917	1919	1213								
10	N. Y/S. B. Co.	1917	1919	1211						4—4 inch (50 cal.) 2 or 1—3 inch AA. or 2—1 pdr. AA.	12—21 inch	114/139
52	Fore River Union I.W.	1917	1919	1185								
21	Cramp	1917	1919	1165	310	31	9	{ 27,000t— 24,200t } =35	..			
17	Bath I. W. Navy Yards	1917	1919	1154								
6	Caldwell	1916	1917	1125	310	30⅔	8	{ 18,500t = 30 20,000t = 32 }	260 oil	5 or 4—4 in. (50 cal.) 2—1 pdr. AA.	12—21 inch	103/139
6	Allen	1915	1917	1110	310	29⅚	9⅓	17,000t = 29.5	290 oil	4—4 inch (50 cal.) 2—1 pdr. AA.	12—21 inch	103/136
5	Conyngham	1914	1916	1050	310	29⅚	9¾	17,000t = 29.5	290 oil	4—4 inch (50 cal.)	8—21 inch	101/132
6	Cushing	1913	1915	1050	300	30⅓	9½	16,000tr =29	287—327 oil	4—4 inch (50 cal.)	8—21 inch	101/133
8	Aylwin	1912	1915	1040								
21	Drayton	1909	1912	742	289	26⅙	8⅓	12,000t = 29½	186—269 oil	5—3 inch (50 cal.)	6—18 inch	91/107
5	Flusser	1908	1910	700	289	26	8	10,000t = 28	250—324 coal	5—3 inch (50 cal.)	6—18 inch	88/113

In above Table, displacements and dimensions are generally the average for each class. Dates refer to time first boat of class was begun and the last boat commissioned for service. Launching dates are given in description by classes on subsequent pages. In H.P. column, t = turbines, tr = turbines combined with reciprocating engines. Majority of boats carry Y-guns and depth charges now, but these are not officially listed.

68 Boats by various Yards. (Flush Deckers.)

Photos wanted.

Bethlehem, San Francisco.		Begun.	Launch.	Comp.
	Chase ..	Yes	....	....
	Farquhar ..	13/8/18	18/1/19	....
	Farragut ..	4/7/18	21/11/18	....
	Fuller ..	4/7/18	5/12/18	....
	J. F. Burns ..	4/7/18	10/11/18	....
	Kennedy ..	25/9/18	15/2/19	....
	Kidder ..	5/3/19	....	....
	La Valette ..	Yes	....	....
	Marcus ..	....	22/8/19	....
	Mervine ..	....	11/8/19	....
	Mullany ..	....	....	....
	Nicholas ..	11/1/19	....	....
	P. Hamilton ..	25/9/18	21/2/19	....
	Percival ..	4/7/18	5/12/18	....
	Reno ..	4/7/18	22/1/19	....
	R. Smith ..	Yes	....	....
	Selfridge ..	Yes	....	....
	Shirk ..	13/2/19	....	....
	Sloat ..	18/1/19	....	....
	S. P. Lee ..	31/12/18	22/3/19	....
	Somers ..	4/7/18	28/12/18	....
	Stoddert ..	4/7/18	8/1/19	....
	Thompson ..	14/8/18	15/1/19	....
	Wm. Jones ..	2/10/18	....	....
	Wood ..	23/1/19	....	....
	Woodbury ..	3/10/18	8/2/19	....
	Yarborough ..	27/2/19	....	....
	Young ..	20/1/19	....	....
	Zeilin ..	20/1/19	....	....

Navy Yards.		Begun.	Launch.	Comp.
	Hulbert ..	18/11/18	....	....
	Litchfield ..	15/1/19	5/7/19	....
	Noa ..	18/11/18	....	....
	Trever ..	Yes	....	....
	Wasmuth ..	Yes	....	....
	W. B. Preston ..	18/11/18	....	....
	Zane ..	15/1/19	5/7/19	....

N.Y.S.B. Co.		Begun.	Launch.	Comp.
	Brooks ..	11/6/18	24/4/19	....
	Fox ..	25/6/18	12/6/19	....
	Gilmer ..	25/6/18	24/5/19	....
	Humphreys ..	31/7/18	18/7/19	....
	Kane ..	3/7/18	....	....

12 boats (not contracted for): *Nos. 348—359.* Construction of these boats may not be proceeded with.

3 *Bath I. W.*: *Nos. 345, 346, 347.* Designed S.H.P. 26,000 = 35 kts. Parsons turbines and reduction gears. 2 screws. 4 Normand boilers—27,000 sq. ft. heating surface. Other details as " General Notes."

39 *Bethlehem S. B. Co. (San Francisco)*: **Chase, Farquhar, Farragut, Fuller, John Francis Burns, Kennedy, Kidder, La Valette, Marcus, Mervine, Mullany, Nicholas, Paul Hamilton, Percival, Reno, Robert Smith, Selfridge, Shirk, Sloat, S. P. Lee, Somers, Stoddert, Thompson, William Jones, Wood, Woodbury, Yarborough, Young, Zeilin,** *Nos. 326—335.* Designed H.P. 27,000 = 35 kts. Machinery : in *Farragut, Fuller, J. F. Burns* and *Percival*, Curtis turbines with reduction gear ; in others, G. E. turbines and reduction gear. 2 screws. 4 Yarrow boilers—27,540 sq. ft. heating surface. Other details as " General Notes."

6 *Mare Island N. Y.*: **Lichfield, Trever, Wasmuth, Lane,** *Nos. 340—341.* S.H.P., speed, turbines, boilers, as Bath I. W. boats above. Other details as· " General Notes."

3 *Norfolk N. Y.*: **Hulbert, Noa, William B. Preston.** S.H.P., speed, turbines, boilers, as Bath I. W. boats above. Other details as " General Notes."

5 *New York S. B. Co.*: **Brooks, Fox, Gilmer, Humphreys, Kane.** Designed S.H.P. 27,000 = 35 kts. Westinghouse turbines with reduction gear. 4 White-Forster boilers—27,500 sq. ft. heating surface. Other details as " General Notes."

General Notes.—Normal displacement, 1215 tons (1308 *full load*). Dimensions : 310 (*w.l.*) × 30′ 11½″ × 9¼ feet *mean* draught (9′ 9¾″ *full load*). Armament : 4—5 inch, 51 cal., 1—3 inch, 23 cal. AA., 12—21 inch tubes in 4 triple deck mountings. (S.H.P., speed, machinery and boilers are separately noted under builders.) Oil fuel :   tons. Complement,   Are same as boats described immediately hereafter, but are more powerfully armed.

100 boats, by various yards, (Flush Deckers).

Photos wanted.

Bethlehem (Quincy).

	Begun.	Launch.	Comp.
Aulick	3/12/18	11/4/19	......
Bancroft	4/11/18	21/3/19	......
Belknap	3/10/18	14/1/19	28/4/19
Gillis ..	27/12/18	......	......
Ingram	15/10/18	28/2/19	30/4/19
McCalla	25/9/18	18/2/19	30/4/19
McCook	10/9/18	31/2/19	19/5/19
Rodgers	5/10/18	26/4/19	......
Turner	21/12/18	17/5/19	......
Welles..	18/11/18	8/5/19	......

Bethlehem (Squantum).

	Begun.	Launch.	Comp.
Bailey ..	3/6/18	5/2/19	Yes
Ballard	3/6/18	7/12/18	5/6/19
Breck ..	24/5/19	......	......
Delphy	20/4/18	18/7/18	30/11/18
Doyen	24/3/19	26/7/19	......
Edwards	20/4/18	10/10/18	24/4/19
Greene	3/6/18	2/11/18	9/5/19
Henshaw	31/12/18	28/6/19	......
Laub ..	20/4/18	25/8/18	17/3/19
McCawley	4/11/18	14/6/19	......
McDermut	20/4/18	6/8/18	27/3/19
Mc Lanahan ..	20/4/18	22/9/18	5/4/19
Meade	24/9/18	24/5/19	......
Meyer ..	6/2/19	......	......
Moody	10/12/18	28/6/19	......
Morris	20/7/18	12/4/19	Yes
Sharkey	14/4/19	......	......
Shubrick	3/6/18	31/12/19	3/7/19
Sinclair	10/10/18	2/6/19	......
Swasey	27/8/18	7/5/19	Yes
Thornton	3/6/18	22/3/19	Yes
Tingey	8/8/18	24/4/19	Yes
Toucey	26/4/19	......	......
(283) ..	8/5/19		
(285) ..	3/6/19		
(286) ..	16/6/19	Not launched.	
(287) ..	30/6/19	Not completed.	
(288) ..	30/6/19		

Cramp.

	Begun.	Launch.	Comp.
Alden ..	24/10/18	7/6/19	......
Barker	30/4/19	......	......
Borie ..	30/4/19	......	......
Broome	8/10/18	14/5/19	......
Chandler	19/8/18	19/3/19	......
Hovey	7/9/18	26/4/19	......
Long ..	23/9/18	26/4/19	......
S. Thompson	24/3/19	......	......
Southard	18/8/18	31/3/19	......
Tracy ..	3/4/19	......	......
(216) ..	21/5/19	......	......
(217) ..	12/6/19	......	......

Newport News.

	Begun.	Launch.	Comp.
A. P. Upshur	20/8/18	......	......
Clemson	11/5/18	5/9/18	Yes
Dahlgren	8/6/18	20/11/18	Yes
Dallas..	25/11/18	......	......
G. E. Badger	24/9/18	......	......
Goldsboro'	8/6/18	20/11/18	......
Graham	7/9/18	......	......
Herndon	25/11/18	......	......
Hunt ..	20/8/18	......	......
Mason	10/7/18	......	......
Satterlee	10/7/18	21/12/18	......
Semmes	10/7/18	21/12/18	......
W. C. Wood	24/9/18	......	......

N.Y./S.B. Co.

	Begun.	Launch.	Comp.
Childs	19/3/19	......	......
Hatfield	10/6/18	17/3/19	......
J. L. Paulding	31/7/18	......	......
King ..	28/4/19	......	......
McFarland	31/7/18	......	......
Overton	30/10/18	......	......
Sands	22/3/19	......	......
Sturtevant	23/11/18	......	......
(244) ..	27/3/19		
(245) ..	2/4/19		
(246) ..	27/5/19		
(247) ..	16/6/19		
(248) ..	26/7/19		
(249) ..	30/7/19		
(250) ..	Yes		

U.I.W.

	Begun.	Launch.	Comp.
Chauncey	17/6/18	29/8/18	......

10 *Bethlehem S. B. Co.* (Quincy): **Aulick, Bancroft, Belknap, Gillis, Ingram, McCalla, McCook, Rodgers,** (ex *Kalk*), **Turner, Welles.** Designed S.H.P. 27,000 = 35 kts. Curtis turbines and reduction gear. 2 screws. 4 Yarrow boilers—27,540 sq. ft. heating surface. Other details as " General Notes."

35 *Bethlehem Destroyer Plant* (Squantum): **Bailey, Ballard, Breck, Delphy, Doyen, Edwards, Greene, Henshaw, Laub, McCawley, McDermut, McLanahan, Meade, Meyer, Moody, Morris, Sharkey, Shubrick, Sinclair, Swasey, Thornton, Tingey, Toucey,** *Nos.* 284—288 (begun), *Nos.* 289—295 (contracted for). Designed S.H.P. 2700 = 25 kts. Curtis turbines with reduction gear. 4 Yarrow boilers—27,540 sq. ft. heating surface. Other details as " General Notes."

25 *Cramp* (Philadelphia): **Alden, Barker, Borie, Broome, Chandler, Hovey, Long, Smith Thompson, Southard, Tracy,** *Nos.* 216, 217 (begun), *Nos.* 218—230 (contracted for). Designed S.H.P. 27,500 = 35 kts. Parsons turbines with reduction gear, 2 screws. 4 White-Forster boilers—27,500 sq. ft. heating surface in *Chandler, Hovey* and *Southard,* 27,000 in remainder. Other details as " General Notes."

14 *Newport News :* **Abel P. Upshur, Branch, Clemson, Dahlgren, Dallas, George E. Badger, Goldsborough, Graham, Herndon, Hunt, Mason, Satterlee, Semmes, Welborn C. Wood.** (Contract for *Nos.* 200—205 has been cancelled). Designed S.H.P. 27,000 = 35 kts. Westinghouse turbines with reduction gear. 2 screws. 4 White-Forster boilers—27,500 sq. ft. heating surface. Other details as " General Notes."

15 *New York S. B. Co.:* **Childs, Hatfield, James L. Paulding, King, McFarland, Overton, Sturtevant,** *Nos.* 244—250. Designed S.H.P. 27,000 = 35 kts. Machinery: *Hatfield* has Parsons turbines and reduction gear; remainder Westinghouse turbines and reduction gear. 2 screws in all; also 4 White-Forster boilers—27,500 sq. ft. heating surface. Other details as " General Notes."

1 *Union I. W.:* **Chauncey,** Designed S.H.P. 27,500 = 35 kts. Curtis turbines with reduction gear. 2 screws. 4 White-Forster boilers—27,500 sq. ft. heating surface.

General Notes.—*Normal* displacement, 1215 tons (1308 *full load*). Dimensions : 310 (*w.l.*) × 30′ 11½″ × 9⅓ feet *mean* draught (9′ 9¾″ *full load*). Armament : 4—4 inch, 50 cal., 1—3 inch, 23 cal. AA., 12—21 inch tubes in 4 triple deck mountings. (S.H.P., speed, machinery, boilers, as separately noted to each class). Oil fuel: —— tons. Complement, 139 (War).

11 Newport News boats. (Flush Deckers.)

LAMBERTON.

Photo by courtesy of Navy Dept. (Bureau C. & R.).

11 *Newport News* : **Abbott, Bagley, Breese, Gamble, Haraden, Hopewell, Lamberton, Montgomery, Radford, Ramsay, Thomas.**

General Notes.—*Normal* displacement 1213 tons, 1306 *full load*). Dimensions : 310 (*w.l.*) × 30' 11¼" × 9' 3⅝" *mean* draught (9' 9¾" *full load*). Armament : 4—4 inch, 50 cal., 2—3 inch, 23 cal. AA. Designed S.H.P. 25,000 = 35 kts. 2 screws. Machinery : Parsons (geared cruising) turbines. Boilers : 4 Thornycroft—28,000 sq. ft. heating surface. Oil : —— tons. Complement, 139 (War).

		Begun.	Launch.	Comp.
Abbot	..	5/4/18	4/7/18	Yes
Bagley		11/5/18	19/10/18	Yes
Breese		10/11/17	11/5/18	23/10/18
Gamble		12/11/17	11/5/18	29/11/18
Haraden		30/3/18	4/7/18	6/6/19
Hopewell		19/1/18	8/6/18	Yes

		Begun.	Launch.	Comp.
Lamberton	..	1/10/17	30/3/18	22/8/18
Montgomery	..	2/10/17	23/3/18	26/7/18
Radford	..	2/10/17	5/4/18	30/9/18
Ramsey	..	21/12/17	8/6/18	Yes
Thomas	..	23/3/18	4/7/18	Yes

10 New York S. B. boats. (Flush Deckers.)

Photo wanted.

10 *New York S. B. Co.* : **Babbitt, Badger, De Long, Dickerson, Herbert, Jacob Jones, Leary, Schenck, Tattnall, Twiggs.**

General Notes.—Displacements, 1211 tons *normal* (1304 or 1306 *full load*). Dimensions : 310 (*w.l.*) × 30' 11¼" × 9¼ feet *mean* draught (9' 9¼" *full load*). Armament : 4—4 inch, 50 cal., 2—3 inch, 23 cal. AA. Torpedo tubes : 12—21 inch, in 4 triple deck mountings. Designed S.H.P. 36,000 = 35 kts. 2 screws. Machinery : Parsons turbines with reduction gear. 4 Thornycroft boilers—27,048 sq. ft. heating surface. Oil only : —— tons. Complement, 139 (War).

		Begun.	Launch.	Comp.
Babbitt	..	19/2/18	30/9/18	....
Badger	..	9/1/18	24/8/18	29/5/19
De Long	..	21/2/18	29/10/18	....
Dickerson	..	25/5/18	12/3/19	....
Herbert	..	9/4/18	18/5/19	....

		Begun.	Launch.	Comp.
Jacob Jones	..	21/2/18	20/11/18	....
Leary	..	6/3/18	21/12/18	....
Schenck	..	26/3/18	23/4/19	....
Tattnall	..	1/12/17	5/9/18	26/6/19
Twiggs	..	23/1/18	28/9/18	28/7/19

52 Fore River & Union I. W. boats. (Flush Deckers.)

LUCE (& Fore River boats).

RINGGOLD (& Union I. W boats).   *Photo, Lieut. H. Reuterdahl, U.S.N./R.F.*

26 Fore River : *Bell, Bush, Colhoun, Cowell, Foote, Crosby, Dyer, Gregory, Israel, Kalk (ex Rodgers), Kimberley, Lansdale, Little, Luce, Maddox, Mahan, Maury, Meredith, Murray, Palmer, Sigourney, Stevens, Stribling, Stringham, Thatcher, Walker.*

Trials : Bell, 34·76. Colhoun, 34·65. Dyer, 34·75. Gregory, 34·75. Israel, 34·34. Kimberley, 34·8. Luce, 34·81. Maury, 34·59. Murray, 34·84. Sigourney, 34·7. Stevens, 34·53. Stringham, 34·8.

26 Union I. W. : *Anthony, Burns, Champlin, Chew, Crane, Gridley, Harding, Hart, Hazlewood, Hogan, Howard, Ingraham, Ludlow, Mackenzie, McKean, McKee, Mugford, O'Bannon, Renshaw, Ringgold, Rizal, Robinson, Schley, Sproston, Stansbury, Williams.*

Trials : Robinson, 34·2. Schley, 35.2.

Displacement, 1185 tons *normal* (1278 tons *full load*). Dimensions : 310 (*w.l.*) × 30' 11¼" × 9' 1¾" (*mean*) draught (9⅝ feet *full load*). Armament : 4—4 inch, 50 cal. and (*a*) 2—3 inch, 23 cal. AA., or (*b*) 2—1 pdr. AA. Tubes : 12—21 inch in 4 triple deck mountings. Designed S.H.P. 27,000 = 35 kts. Machinery : *Gridley, Harding, McKee, McKean, Ringgold, Robinson*, G. E. turbines with reduction gear ; all other boats, Curtis with reduction gear. 2 screws (*Gridley* only, 3). 4 Yarrow boilers—27,540 sq. ft. heating surface. Oil fuel: tons. Complement, 139 (*Ludlow* and *Mackenzie*, 114). *Rizal* built at expense of Philippines Government, and to be manned by Filipino crew.

FORE RIVER BOATS :—

		Begun.	Launch.	Comp.				Begun.	Launch.	Comp.
Bell	..	15/11/17	20/4/18	1/8/18		Luce	..	9/2/18	29/6/18	11/9/18
Bush	..	4/7/18	27/10/18	19/2/19		Maddox	..	27/7/18	27/10/18	10/3/19
Colhoun	..	19/9/17	21/2/18	12/6/18		Mahan	..	4/5/18	4/8/18	24/10/18
Cowell	..	15/7/18	23/11/18	17/3/19		Maury	..	25/2/18	4/7/18	23/9/18
Crosby	..	23/6/18	28/9/18	24/1/19		Meredith	..	29/6/18	22/9/18	29/1/19
Dyer	..	26/9/17	13/4/18	2/7/18		Murray	..	22/12/17	3/6/18	20/8/18
Foote	..	7/8/18	14/12/18	21/3/19		Palmer	..	29/5/18	18/8/18	22/11/18
Gregory	..	25/8/17	25/1/18	31/5/18		Sigourney	..	25/7/18	16/12/17	14/5/18
Israel	..	26/1/18	22/6/18	20/8/18		Stevens	..	20/10/17	13/1/18	24/5/18
Kalk	..	19/8/18	21/12/18	29/3/19		Stribling	..	14/12/17	29/5/18	23/8/18
Kimberley	..	21/6/17	4/12/17	27/4/18		Stringham	..	19/10/17	30/3/18	2/7/18
Lansdale	..	20/4/18	21/7/18	26/10/18		Thatcher	..	8/6/18	31/8/18	14/1/19
Little	..	18/6/17	11/11/17	5/4/18		Walker	..	18/6/18	14/9/18	31/1/19

UNION I. W. BOATS :—

		Begun.	Launch.	Comp.				Begun.	Launch.	Comp.
Anthony	..	18/4/18	10/8/18	Yes		Mackenzie	..	4/7/18	29/7/18	
Burns	..	15/4/18	4/7/18	Yes		McKean	..	12/2/18	4/7/18	Yes
Champlin	..	31/10/17	7/4/18	11/11/18		McKee	..	29/10/17	3/3/18	7/9/18
Chew	..	2/1/18	26/5/18	12/12/18		Mugford	..	20/7/18	......	......
Crane	..	7/1/18	4/7/18	Yes		O'Bannon	..	......	......	......
Gridley	..	1/4/18	4/7/18	Yes		Renshaw	..	8/5/18	21/9/18	......
Harding	..	12/2/18	4/7/18	24/1/19		Ringgold	..	20/10/17	14/4/18	11/11/18
Hart	..	8/1/18	7/7/18	Yes		Rizal	..	26/6/18	21/9/18	
Hazlewood	..	24/12/17	22/6/18	Yes		Robinson	..	31/10/17	28/3/18	19/10/18
Hogan	..	......	......	......		Schley	..	29/10/17	28/3/18	16/8/18
Howard	..	......	......	......		Sproston	..	20/4/18	18/8/18	Yes
Ingraham	..	12/1/18	7/7/18	Yes		Stansbury	..			
Ludlow	..	7/1/18	9/6/18	23/12/18		Williams	..	25/3/18	4/7/18	Yes

(*Continued on next page.*)

21 Cramp boats (Flush Deckers).

DENT.

Photo by courtesy of Navy Dept. (Bureau C. & R.)

17 Bath I.W. & Navy Yard boats (Flush Deckers).

EVANS.

U.S. Navy photo.

21 *Cramp*: **Barney, Bernadou, Biddle, Blakely, Breckinridge, Cole, Dent, Dorsey, Du Pont, Elliott, Ellis, Greer, J. Fred Talbott, Lea, Rathburne, Roper, Talbot, Tarbell, Upshur, Waters, Yarnall.**

Displacements : 1165 tons *normal* (1247 tons *full load*). Dimensions : 310 (*w.l.*) × 30′ 11¼″ × 9 feet *mean* draught. *Full load* draught, 9½ feet. Armament : 4—4 inch, 50 cal., 2—3 inch, 23 cal. AA., 12—21 inch tubes in 4 triple deck mountings. Designed S.H.P. 26,000 = 35 kts. Machinery : Parsons turbines with reduction gear. Boilers : 4 White-Forster—27,500 sq. ft. heating surface. Oil : tons. Complement, 103/139 (War). Trials : Cole 41·1 (unofficial), *Dent* 35·11, *Dorsey* 35·16, *Talbot* 35·3, *Upshur* 35·2.

4 *Bath I. W.* : **Aaron Ward, Buchanan, Crowninshield, Hale.** These boats have 2—3 inch, 23 cal. AA. guns. Designed S.H.P. 24,200 = 35 kts. Otherwise as " General Notes " below.

4 *Bath I. W.* : **Evans, Philip, Wickes, Woolsey.** These boats have 2—1 pdr. auto. AA. Designed S.H.P. 24,610 = 35 kts. Trials : *Philip* 35.53, *Wickes* 35.34. *Woolsey* 24,575 S.H.P. = — kts. Otherwise as " General Notes " below.

6 *Mare Island N. Y.* : **Boggs, Claxton, Hamilton, Kennison, Kilty, Ward.** These boats have 2—3 inch, 23 cal. AA. guns. Designed S.H.P. 26,000 = 35 kts. Otherwise as " General Notes " below.

2 *Mare Island N. Y.* : **Fairfax, Taylor.** These boats have 2—1 pdr. AA. guns. Designed S.H.P. 24,200 = 35 kts. Otherwise as " General Notes " below.

1 *Charleston N. Y.* : **Tillman.** As *Boggs, Claxton, &c.*, above.

General Notes.—Displacements : 1154 tons *normal* (1247 *full load*). Dimensions : 310 (*w.l.*) × 30′ 11¼″ × 9 feet *normal* draught (*full load* draught, 9½ feet). Armament : 4—4 inch, 50 cal. (AA. guns are separately noted), 12—21 inch tubes in 4 triple deck mountings. Designed S.H.P. and speed as separately noted. Machinery : Parsons turbines with reduction gear. 2 screws. 4 Normand boilers—27,000 sq. ft. heating surface. Oil fuel only : — tons. Complement, 139 (War).

	Begun.	Launch.	Comp.
Barney	26/3/18	5/9/18	14/3/19
Bernadou	4/6/18	7/11/18	19/5/19
Biddle	22/4/18	3/10/18	22/4/19
Blakely	26/3/18	19/9/18	8/3/19
Breckinridge	11/3/18	17/8/18	27/2/19
Cole	25/6/18	11/1/19	19/6/19
Dent	30/8/17	23/3/18	9/9/18
Dorsey	18/9/17	9/4/18	16/9/18
Du Pont	2/5/18	22/10/18	30/4/19
Elliott	24/2/18	4/7/18	25/1/19
Ellis	8/7/18	30/11/18	7/6/19

	Begun.	Launch.	Comp.
Greer	24/2/18	1/8/18	31/12/18
J. F. Talbott ..	8/7/18	14/12/18	30/6/19
Lea	18/9/17	29/4/18	21/10/18
Rathburne ..	12/7/17	27/12/17	24/6/18
Roper	31/2/18	17/8/18	15/2/19
Talbot	12/7/17	20/2/18	20/7/18
Tarbell	31/12/17	28/5/18	27/11/18
Upshur	19/2/18	4/7/18	20/12/18
Waters	26/7/17	9/3/18	8/8/18
Yarnall	12/2/18	19/6/18	29/11/18

	Begun.	Launch.	Comp.
A. Ward ..	1/8/18	....	....
Buchanan ..	29/6/18	2/1/19	....
Crowninshield ..	5/11/18	Yes	24/7/19
Hale ..	7/10/18	Yes	12/6/19
Evans ..	28/12/17	30/10/18	11/11/18
Philip ..	1/9/17	25/7/18	24/8/18
Wickes ..	26/6/17	25/6/18	31/7/18
Woolsey ..	1/11/17	17/9/18	30/9/18

	Begun.	Launch.	Comp.
Boggs	15/11/17	25/4/18	23/9/18
Claxton	25/4/18	15/1/19	......
Hamilton ..	8/6/18	15/1/19	......
Kennison ..	14/2/18	8/6/18	......
Kilty	15/12/17	25/4/18	Yes
Ward* ..	15/5/18	1/6/18	24/7/18
Fairfax ..	10/7/17	15/12/17	6/4/18
Taylor	15/10/17	14/2/18	Yes
Tillman	29/7/18	......	......

*Note rate of building.

6 Caldwell class.

	Begun.	Launch.	Comp.			Begun.	Launch.	Comp.
Conner ..	16/10/16	21/8/17	10/2/18	Caldwell ..	..	9/12/16	10/7/17	1/12/17
Stockton ..	13/10/16	17/7/17	26/11/17	Gwin ..	..	21/6/17	22/12/17	19/10/18
Craven ..	20/11/17	29/6/18	19/10/18	Manley ..	..	22/8/16	23/8/17	15/10/17

STOCKTON (& CONNER).

Photo, Lieut. H. Reuterdahl, U.S.N/R.F.

2 *Cramp :* **Conner, Stockton.** *Conner,* 1225 tons *full load* ; *Stockton,* 1238 tons *full load*. Designed H.P. 20,000· = 30 kts. Parsons (geared cruising) turbines. 3 screws. Boilers : 4 White-Forster—22,520 sq. ft. heating surface. *Trials :* Conner 30·17, Stockton 30.12.

Note.—These two boats have 5—4 inch, 2—4 inch being paired on the fo'xle mounting. Otherwise as " General Notes " below.

> *" Manley," flush deck type ; appearance of " Craven,"*
>
> *" Caldwell, " Gwin," not known,*

1 *Norfolk N. Y. :* **Craven.** 1187 tons *full load*. Designed H.P. 20 000 = kts. Parsons turbines, with reduction gear. 2 screws. Boilers : 4 Thornycroft—21,500 sq. ft. heating surface.

1 *Mare Island N. Y. :* **Caldwell.** As *Craven,* above, but engined with G. E. Curtis turbines and reduction gear. *Trials :* 31.7.

1 *Seattle Con. & D. D. Co. :* **Gwin.** 1228 tons *full load*. Designed H.P. 18,750 = 30 kts. Parsons turbines with reduction gear. 2 screws. Boilers : 4 Yarrow—22,252 sq. ft. heating surface.

1 *Bath I. W. :* **Manley** (1917). As *Craven,* above, but boilers 4 Normand—21,500 sq. ft. heating surface. *Trials :* 32·23.

General Notes.—*Normal* displacement : 1125 tons, *full load* as separately noted. Dimensions : 310 (*w.l.*) × 30¾ × 8 feet (*mean draught*). *Full load* draught : 9 feet 5¼ inches. Armament : *Conner* and *Stockton* 5—4 inch (50 cal.), others 4—4 inch (50 cal.), (and in all) 2—1 pdr. auto. anti-aircraft, 12—21 inch tubes in 4 triple deck mountings. 260 tons oil fuel. Complement 103/139 War *Conner* and *Stockton* 134.

6 Allen class.

SAMPSON. *Davis* has after S.L. *before* mainmast on high lattice tower.

Photo, O. W. Waterman.

2 *Bath I.W. :* **Allen** (1916), **Davis** (1916). 1071 tons (1185 *full load*). Designed H.P. 17,500 = 30 kts. Parsons (geared cruising) turbines. Machinery weighs 350 tons. Boilers : 4 Normand—22,500 sq. ft. heating surface. *Trials :* Allen, 30·29 ; *Davis,* 30·36 kts.

2 *Fore River :* **Rowan** (1916), **Sampson** (1916). 1110 tons (1125 *full load*.) Designed H.P. 17,000 = 29·5 kts. Curtis (geared cruising) turbines. Machinery averages 385 tons. Boilers : 4 Yarrow—21,500 sq. ft. heating surface. *Trials :* Rowan, 29·57 kts. ; *Sampson,* 29·52 kts.

1 *Mare Island Navy Yard :* **Shaw** (1916). Displacement, H.P. and speed as *Rowan.* Parsons (geared cruising) turbines. Boilers : 4 Thornycroft.

1 *Cramp :* **Wilkes** (1916). 1110 tons (1124 *full load*). Designed H.P. 17,000 = 29·5 kts. Parsons (geared cruising) turbines. Machinery weighs 367 tons. Boilers : 4 White-Forster. Trials : 29·58 kts.

General Notes.—Dimensions : 310 (*w.l.*) × 29⅝ × 9¼ to 9½ feet *mean draught. Full load* draught of first two : 9 ft. 9½ in. Others, 10 ft. 8¼ in. Armament : 4—4 inch (50 cal.), 2—1 pdr. auto. anti-aircraft, 12—21 inch deck tubes in 4 triple deck mountings. Designed H.P. 17,000=29·5 kts. Oil fuel : 290 tons (estimated). Complement : 103/136 war,

(Continued on next page.)

5 Conyngham Class.

CONYNGHAM.   *Photo, U.S. Navy Recruiting Bureau.*

2 *Cramp:* **Conyngham** (1915). **Porter** (1915). 1090 tons (1205 *full load.*) Designed H.P. 18,000=29½ kts. Parsons (geared cruising) turbines. Machinery weighs 375 tons. Boilers : 2 White-Forster—24,000 sq. ft. heating surface. Trials : *Conyngham,* 29·63 kts. ; *Porter,* 29·58 kts.

1 *New York S.B. Co.:* **Wainwright** (1915). 1050 tons (1265 *full load*). Designed H.P. 17,000=29½ kts. Parsons (geared cruising) turbines. Machinery averages 369 tons. Boilers : 4 Normand—21,500 sq. ft. heating surface. Trials : 29·67 kts. (*Jacob Jones* of this type lost during war.)

1 *Fore River :* **Tucker** (1915). Displacements as *Conyngham.* Designed H.P. 17,000=29½ kts. Curtis (geared cruising) turbines. Machinery weighs 369 tons. Boilers : 4 Yarrow—21,500 sq. ft. heating surface. Trials : 29·56 kts.

1 *Bath I.W.:* **Wadsworth** (1915). 1060 tons (1174 *full load*). Designed H.P. 17,000=29½ kts. Parsons turbines with reduction gear. Machinery weighs 323 tons. Boilers : 4 Normand—21,500 sq. ft. heating surface. Trials : 30·67 kts.

General Notes.—Dimensions : 310 (*w.l.*) × 29⅚ × 9⅜ to 9⅚ feet (*mean* draught). *Full load* draught 10 feet 1¼ inches to 10 feet 8¼ inches. Armament : 4—4 inch (50 cal.). 8—21 inch tubes in 4 twin-deck mountings. Designed H.P. 17,000=29·5 kts. 290 tons oil fuel. Complement : 101, (132 war)

TUCKER (of *Conyngham* class).   *Copyright Photo, O. W. Waterman.*

6 Cushing Class.

NICHOLSON.   *Copyright Photo, O. W. Waterman.*

1 *Fore River :* **Cushing** (1912). 1050 tons (1071 *full load*). Parsons (geared cruising) turbines. Machinery weighs 360 tons. Boilers : 4 Yarrow—21,500 sq. feet heating surface. Trials : 29·18 kts.

1 *New York S.B. Co. :* **Ericsson*** (1914). 1090 tons (1211 *full load*). 3 sets Parsons turbines with reciprocating machinery weighs 364 tons. Boilers : 4 Thornycroft—26,936 sq. ft. heating surface. Trials : 29·29 kts.

1 *Bath I.W. :* **McDougal** (1914). 1025 tons (1139 *full load*). Two sets Parsons turbines and two reciprocating. Machinery weighs 325 tons. Boilers : 4 Normand—21,509 sq. feet heating surface. Trials : 30·7 kts

3 *Cramp :* **Nicholson** (1914), **O'Brien*** (1914), **Winslow** (1915). 1050 tons (1171 *full load*). 2 Cramp-Zoelly turbines with 2 reciprocating. Machinery weighs 351 tons. Boilers : 4 White-Forster—21,600 sq. feet heating surface. Trials : *Nicholson* 29·08 kts., *O'Brien* 29·17 kts., *Winslow* 29·05 kts.

General Notes.—Dimensions are about 300 (*w.l.*) × 30¼ × 9 feet 4 inches to 9 feet 9 inches (*mean*). *Full load* draught : 9 feet 8 inches to 10 feet 9 inches. Armament : 4—4 inch (50 cal.), 8—21 inch tubes in 4 twin-deck mountings. Designed H.P. 16,000=29 kts. Oil fuel : 309 tons, but *McDougal* carries 327 tons. Complement : 101, (war 132.) Built to guaranteed radius at 15 kts.

* Have very low mainmasts.   (*Continued on next page.*)

8 Aylwin Class.

(Unofficially known as " Thousand Tonners."

DUNCAN.   *Copyright photo, O. W. Waterman.*

4 *Cramp:* **Aylwin, Balch, Benham, Parker** (1913). 1036 tons (1156 *full load*). Cramp-Zoelly turbines. Machinery : 347 tons. Boilers : 4 White Forster—21,600 sq. feet heating surface. Oil fuel : *Aylwin,* 287 tons ; *Balch,* 306 tons ; *Benham,* 295 tons ; *Parker,* 317 tons. Trials : *Aylwin* 29·6, *Balch* 29·62, *Benham* 29·59, *Parker* 29·55 kts.

2 *Bath I.W.:* **Cassin, Cummings** (1913). 1020 tons (1139 *full load*). Parsons turbines and reciprocating engines. Machinery : 329 tons. Boilers : 4 Normand—21,509 sq. feet heating surface. Oil fuel : 312 tons. Trials : *Cassin* 30·14, *Cummings* 30·57 kts.

1 *New York S. B. Co.:* **Downes** (1913). 1072 tons (1190 *full load*). Turbines and reciprocating engines. Machinery : 386 tons. Boilers : 4 Thornycroft—26,456 sq. feet heating surface. Oil fuel : 306 tons. Trials : 29·07 kts.

1 *Fore River :* **Duncan** (1913). 1014 tons (1133 *full load*). Turbines and reciprocating engines. Weight : 348 tons. Boilers : 4 Yarrow—21,500 sq. feet heating surface. Oil fuel : 290 tons. Trials : 29·14 kts.

Note.— Dimensions *about* 300 (*w.l.*)×30½×9¼ to 9¾ (*mean*). Full load draught 10¼ to 10¾ feet. *Designed* H.P.: 16,000=29 kts. Armament : 4—4 in. (50 cal.). 8—21 in. tubes in four twin-mountings. Complement 101, war 134. Built to specified radius at 15 kts. Reciprocating engines not used over 15 kts. Very economical steamers. *Benham* reported to have had 4″ guns in twin mountings, installed during 1917 for experimental purposes.

21 Drayton Class.

(Unofficially known as " Flivver Type.")

All 742 tons (883 *full load*). Dimensions : 289 (*w.l.*)×26¼×8½ (*mean*). Armament : 5—3 inch, 50 cal., 6—18 inch tubes (in pairs). Designed H.P. 12,000=29½ kts. Oil capacity varies from 186 to 269 tons. *Full load* draught from 9¼ to 11 feet. Complement 91, war 107.

TRIPPE.   *Photo, U.S. Navy Recruiting Bureau.*

5 *Bath I.W.:* **Drayton** (1910), **Jenkins** (1912), **Jouett** (1912), **Trippe** (1910), **Paulding** (1910). Machinery : Parsons turbines. Weight of machinery : 263 tons in first three. 270 tons in *Trippe,* 269 tons in *Paulding.* Boilers : 4 Normand. Oil fuel : *Drayton,* 191 tons ; *Jenkins,* 222 tons ; *Jouett,* 225 tons ; *Trippe,* 233 tons ; *Paulding,* 269 tons. Trials : *Drayton,* 30·83 ; *Jouett.* 32·27 ; *Jenkins,* 31·27 ; *Paulding,* 32·80 ; *Trippe,* 30·89.

No photo available.

4 *New York S. B. Co.* **Ammen** (1910), **Burrows** (1910), **Jarvis** (1912), **McCall** (1910). Parsons turbine. 3 screws. Machinery : 269 tons in *Jarvis,* 288 tons in others. Boilers : 4 Thornycroft. Oil fuel : 188 tons in *McCall* ; 223 in *Jarvis* ; 227 in *Ammen* and *Burrows.* Trials : *Ammen,* 30·48 ; *Burrows,* 30·67 ; *Jarvis,* 30·01 ; *McCall,* 30·66 kts.

(Continued on next page.)

21 **Drayton class**—*Continued*.

(General details given on preceding page.)

BEALE.   *Copyright photo, O. W. Waterman.*

4 *Cramp*: **Beale** (1912), **Mayrant** (1910), **Patterson** (1911), **Warrington** (1910). *Mayrant* re-engined **1916-17** with Westinghouse turbines and mechanical reduction gear (284 tons). *Warrington* has Cramp-Zoelly turbines. 2 screws. Weight of machinery, 284 tons. Oil, 200 tons. Boilers: 4 White-Forster. *Beale* and *Patterson* have Parsons turbines. 3 screws. Machinery: 273 tons. Oil fuel: 227 tons. Boilers: 4 White-Forster. Trials: *Beale*, 29·65; *Mayrant*, 30·22; *Patterson*, 29·69; *Warrington*, 30·12 kts.

For photo, see U.S. Addenda page.

---

4 *Fore River*: **Henley** (1912), **Perkins** (1910), **Sterett** (1910), **Walke** (1911). *Henley* re-engined **1916-17** with Westinghouse turbines and mechanical reduction gear (305 tons). Other three Curtis turbines only (300 tons). 2 screws. Boilers: 4 Yarrow. Oil fuel: *Perkins* and *Sterett*, 193 tons; *Walke*, 201 tons; *Henley*, 230 tons. Trials: *Henley*, 30·32; *Perkins*, 29·76; *Sterett*, 30·37; *Walke*, 29·78 kts.

ROE.   *Photo, Lieut. H. Reuterdahl, U.S.N./R.F.*

4 *Newport News*: **Fanning** (1912), **Monaghan** (1911), **Roe** (1909), **Terry** (1909). Parsons turbines. 3 screws. Machinery: 276 tons. Boilers: 4 Thornycroft. Oil fuel: 225 in *Fanning*, 186 to 190 in other three. Trials: *Fanning*, 29·99; *Monaghan*, 30·45; *Roe*, 29·60; *Terry*, 30·24 kts.

5 **Flusser class.** "Flivver" type.

All 700 tons (*full load*, 902 tons). Dimensions: 289 (*w.l.*) × 26 × 8 feet (*mean*). Armament: 5—3 inch, 50 cal., 6—18 inch tubes, in 3 twin deck mountings. Designed H.P. 10,000 = 28 kts. Complement: 88 (113, War).

REID.   *Copyright photo, O. W. Waterman.*

2 *Bath I.W.*: **Flusser** (1909), **Reid** (1909). *Full load* draught 10 feet. Parsons turbines. 3 screws. Machinery, 228 tons. Boilers: 4 Normand. Coal: 324 tons. Trials: *Flusser*, 30·41; *Reid*, 31·82 kts.

2 *Cramp*: **Lamson** (1909), **Smith** (1909). *Full load* draught, 10 feet 7 inches. Parsons turbine. 3 screws. Machinery: 250 tons. Boilers: 4 Mosher. Coal: *Lamson*, 291 tons; *Smith*, 305. Trials: *Lamson*, 28·61; *Smith*, 28·35 kts.

1 *New York Shipbuilding*: **Preston** (1909). *Full load* draught, 11 feet. Parsons turbines. 3 screws. Machinery: 255 tons. Boilers: 4 Thornycroft. Coal: 290 tons. Trials: 29·18 kts.

U. S. COAST TORPEDO VESSELS.

15 Coast Torpedo Vessels.

(Are Old Destroyers not serviceable for duty with Fleet. Are unofficially known as "Tinclads.")

No.	Class	Date	Displacement	H.P.	Max. speed	Coal	Complement	T. tubes	Max. draug't
			tons		kts.	tons			feet.
8	Bainbridge†	'00-'02	420	8000	28	184-209	76/91	2	6½
3	Truxtun†	'00-'02	433	8300	28*	177-187	76/91	2—4	6
2	Hull†	'00-'02	414	8000	28*	158	76/91	2	6
2	Lawrence†	'99-'01	400	8400	28*	108-119	76/91	2	6¼

* Only just reached this speed on first trials. Present *max.* speed 25 kts. *or less.*
† May be re-numbered as *CTB 1—16.*

8 Bainbridge class.

1 *Gas Engine Co.* **Stewart*** (1902). Machinery, 205 tons. Boilers: 4 Seabury. Coal, 194 tons. Trial speed: 29·69 kts.

2 *Neafie and Levy.* **Bainbridge*** (1901), **Barry*** (1902). Machinery, 209 tons. Boilers: 4 Thornycroft. Coal: 183 tons. Trials: *Bainbridge,* 28·45; *Barry,* 28·13. *Chauncey,* of this class, lost during the War.

2 *Trigg.* **Dale*** (1900), **Decatur*** (1900). Machinery, 204 tons. Boilers: 4 Thornycroft. Coal: 186 tons. Trials: *Dale,* 28; *Decatur,* 28·10 kts.

3 *Union Iron Works.* **Paul Jones*** (1902), **Perry*** (1900), **Preble*** (1901). Machinery, 206 tons. Boilers: 4 Thornycroft. Coal: 184 tons. Trials: *Paul Jones,* 28·91; *Perry,* 28·32; *Preble,* 28·03 kts.

General Notes.—All 420 tons (*full load 592 tons*). Dimensions: *about* 245 (*w.l.*)×23×6¼ feet (*mean*). Designed H.P. 8000 = 28 kts., but none of them can get anywhere near this now. Armament: 2—3 inch, 4—6 pdr., 2—18 inch tubes. (1 twin mounting in *Paul Jones, Perry* and *Preble,* 2 single in other ships.) Complement, 76. (91 war).

Note.—May be re-numbered thus:—*CTB 1* (Bainbridge), *CTB 2* (Barry), *CTB 3* (Dale), *CTB 4* (Decatur), *CTB 10* (Paul Jones), *CTB 11* (Perry), *CTB 12* (Preble), *CTB 13* (Stewart). and names transferred to new T.B.D. building.

7 Other Boats.

("*Whipple*" *differs in appearance : see Silhouettes*).

3 *Truxtun class:*—**Truxtun*** (1901), **Whipple*** (1902), **Worden*** (1902). 433 tons. H.P. 8300 = 28 kts. Armament: 2—3 inch (fore and aft). 4—6 pdr. Tubes: in *Truxtun* and *Worden,* 4—18 inch in 2 twin mountings: in *Whipple,* 2—18 inch in 1 twin mounting. Coal: 177, 179 and 188 tons. Complement 76. (91 war).

Note.—May be re-numbered *CTB 14, CTB 15, CTB 16* respectively, and names transferred to new T.B.D. building.

(*4 funnels—like Truxton's, but higher*).

2 *Hull class:*—**Hopkins*** (1902), 420 tons, and **Hull*** (1902), 408 tons. H.P. 8000 = 28 kts. Armament: 2—3 inch, 6—6 pdrs. 4—18 inch tubes (in twin mountings). Coal: 158 tons. Complement 76. (91 war).

Note.—May be re-numbered *CTB 6* and *CTB 7* respectively, and names transferred to new T.B.D. building.

2 *Lawrence class:*—**Lawrence*** (1900), **Macdonough*** (1900). 400 tons. H.P. 8400 = 28 to 29 kts. Armament 7—6 pdr. 2—18 inch tubes. Coal: 108 and 119 tons. Complement 76. (91 war).

Note.—May be re-numbered as *CTB 8* and *CTB 9* respectively, and names transferred to new T.B.D. building.

17 Old Torpedo Boats.

No	Type.	Date.	Dis-place-ment.	H.P.	Max. speed.	Coal.	Com-ple-ment.	T. Tubes.	Mean draug't
			tons		kts	tons			feet
3	Nos. 10—12	'00-'01	175	3920	28.5	44	42-36	0	5
5	Nos. 13—17	'99-'02	196	3000	26	74/87	43-24	0	6—4¾
1	No. 8	'98-'99	280	5600	30	101	75	2	7
1	No. 7	'98-'99	255	5850	27·4	91	65	2	6¾
1	No. 4	'97-'98	146	4200	22·5	33	42	0	4½
1	No. 5	'97-'99	279	5600	30	97	65	0	6
1	No. 6	'97-'98	105	1750	22·5	max. 27	31	0	4
1	No. 3	'96-'97	105	3800	30	42	78	0	4¾
2	Nos. 2, 1	'95-'98	142	2200	24·5	45	37	0	5
1	No. 9	'95	150	1900	17·5	38	34	0	6

5 *ex Shubrick* class :— **No. 15** (ex *Shubrick*, 1899) and **No. 16** (ex *Thornton*, 1900), 200 tons. **No. 14** (ex *De Long*, 1900) and **No. 13** (ex *Blakely*, 1900), 196 tons. **No. 17** (ex *Tingey*, 1901), 165 tons. H.P. 3000 = 26 kts. (*Shubrick* did 28 on trial). Thornycroft or Normand boilers. Armament: *No. 13* has 3—3 pdr., 1 M.G.; *Nos. 14, 15* and *17*, 2—1 pdr., 1—Y gun. *No. 16* disarmed. No tubes in any of these boats. Coal: *max.* 74 to 87 tons. Complement, 43-24.

No. 8 (ex *Bailey*, 1899) (Built by Gas Engine Co. and Seabury). 280 tons. H.P. 5600 = 30 kts. Normand boilers. Armament: 4—6 pdr. S.A, 1 Y-gun. 2—18 inch tubes. Coal: 101 tons. Complement, 75.

No photo available.

3 *ex-Barney* class :—**No. 11** (ex *Barney*, 1900), **No. 12** (ex *Biddle*, 1901), **No. 10** (ex *Bagley*, 1900). 175 tons. Designed H.P. 3920 = 28·5 kts. Normand boilers. Armament: *No. 11* has 3—1 pdr., *No. 12* has 3—1 pdr, 1 Y-gun, *No. 10* has 2—1 pdr, 1 Y gun. No tubes in any of these boats. Coal: 44 tons. Complement 42-36.

1 *Wolff & Zwicken*: **No. 7** (ex *Goldsborough*, 1899). 255 tons. Guns: 4—3 pdr. Torpedo tubes: 2—18 inch. I.H.P. 5850 = 27·4 kts. on first trials. 3 Thornycroft boilers. Coal: 91 tons. Complement, 65.

(Continued on next page.)

1 *Bath I. W.:* **No. 4** (ex-*Dahlgren*, 1899). 146 tons. Designed H.P. 4200 = 22.5 kts. Normand boilers. Armament: 2—1 pdr. auto. anti-aircraft, 1 Y-gun, no tubes. Coal: 33 tons. Complement, 42.

No photo available.

1 *Union I. W.:* **No. 5** (ex-*Farragut*, 1898). 279 tons. Guns: 4—3 pdr., 1 Y. No tubes. Designed H.P. 5600 = 30 kts. 3 Thornycroft boilers. Coal: 97 tons. Complement, 65.

1 *Herreshoff Co.:* **No. 6** (ex-*Morris*, 1898). 105 tons. Designed H.P. 1750 = 22.5 kts. Boilers: 2 Normand. Armament: 3—1 pdr. No tubes. Coal: *max.* 27 tons. Complement, 31.

No photo available.

1 *Herreshoff Co. :* **No. 3** (ex-*Dupont*, 1897). 105 tons. Guns: 3—3 pdr., 1 M. G. and 1 Y. No tubes. Designed H.P 3800 = 30 kts. 3 Normand (modified) boilers. Coal: 42 tons. Complement, 78.

2 *Columbian I. W.:* **No. 2** (ex-*Rodgers*, 1896), **No. 1** (ex-*Foote*, 1896). 142 tons. Guns: *No.* 2, 3—3 pdr., 1—1 pdr., *No. 1*, 3—1 pdr. No tubes. Designed H.P. 2000—2400 = 24.5 kts. 2 Mosher boilers. Coal: 45 tons. Complements 37 and 36.

1 *Schichau* type : **No. 9** (ex-*Somers*, Elbing, Germany, 1895). 150 tons. Guns: 3—1 pdr., 1 M. G., 1 Y. No tubes. Designed H.P. 1900 = 17.5 kts. 1 Loco. boiler. Coal: *max.* 38 tons. Complement, 34.

U. S. SUBMARINES.

Summary to July 1st, 1919, of all Types.

(Exclusive of surrendered German boats.)

101 Completed.

65 *Building* and *completing.*

10 Authorized, but not yet under contract or construction

Note.

The only official information published with regard to U.S. Submarines merely mentions contractors, place of construction and building dates.

Details in Table opposite and on subsequent pages, giving displacements, dimensions, H.P., speed, armament, endurance and complement, are entirely from unofficial sources, and must be regarded as only approximate.

No.	Type	Date	Displacement	H.P.	Max. speed	Fuel or Battery Endurance.	Complement	T. Tubes	Max. draug't
	Ocean-going :		tons		kts.				feet
9	"Fleet 1—9"	Proj.	...	...	...	...	...	...	...
3	AA 2, AA 3 (H) / AA 1 (H)	'17-'20 / '15-'19	1100 / 1490	4000 / 1350	20 / 10-12	For 7000 miles.	37	4	15
11	S 3—S 13 (BD)								
9	S 2, 14—S 17 (L) / S 48—S 51 (L)	'17-'20	800-850 / 910-1090	1200	16-14 / 12-11	...	...	4	13-15
31	S 1, S 18—S 47 (H)								
	Coastal:								
7 / 20	R 21—R 27 (L) / R 1—R 20 (H)	'17-'20	500-570	...	...	...	...	...	...
6	H 4—H 9 (H)	1918	...	...	...	...	...	...	...
6 / 10	O 11—O 16 (L) / O 1—O 10 (H)	'16-'18	485-500 / 570-630	1200 / 750	14 / 10-11	For 5500 miles at 11½ kts	...	4	...
4 / 3	N 4—N 7 (L) / N 1—N 3 (H)	'15-'17	340 / 400	900 / 620	13 / 10-11	For 2500 miles at 11 kts. / 100-120 at 5 kts.	18	4	12
1	M 1 (H)	'13-'16	490 / 680	1800	14 / 10-11	For 3000 miles at 14 kts. / For 140 miles.	...	4	14
4 / 7	L 5—L 8 (L) / L 1—L 4 / L 9—L 11 (H)	'13-'16	450-490 / 570-720	1300 / 750	14 / 10·5	For 4500 miles at 11 kts. / For 150 miles at 5 kts.	...	4	...
8	K 1—K 8 (H)	'11-'14	380-390 / 520-530	1000 / 680	14 / 10·5	For 4500 miles at 10 kts. / For 120 miles at 5 kts.	18	4	12½
3	H 1—H 3 (H)	'10-'13	350 / 470	9·0 / 620	1.1 / 10·5	For 2300 miles at 11 kts. / For 100 miles at 5 kts.	18	4	12
1	G 4 (Li)	'09-'14	358 / 458	1000 / 410	14 / 9·5	For 1680 miles at 8 kts. / For 40 miles at 5 kts.	...	4	11
2	G 1, G 3 (L)	'09-'16	400 / 490	1200 / 520	14 / 9·5	For 2500 miles at 8 kts. / For 70 miles at 5 kts.	...	2-4	...
2	F 2, F 3 (H)	'09-'12	330 / 400	480 / 350	12 / 10·5	For 2300 miles at 11 kts. / For 100 miles at 5 kts.	18	4	12
2	E 1, E 2 (H)	'09-'12	290 / 340	360 / 250	12 / 11	For 2100 miles at 11 kts. / For 100 miles at 5 kts.	15	4	...
3	D 1—D 3 (H)	'07-'10	228 / 340	600 / 330	12 / 9·5	For 1240 miles at 9-10 kts.	15	2	...
5	C 1—C 5 (H)	'05-'09	238 / 273	500 / 230	10 / 9	For 800 miles at 8 kts. / For 80 miles at 5 kts.	15	2	...
3	B 1—B 3 (H)	'05-'07	150 / 170	250 / 150	8 / 7	For 540 miles at 9 kts. / For 12 miles at 4 kts.	10	2	...
6	A 2—A 7 (H)	'00-'03	80 / 122	160 / 70	7 / 5	For 300 miles at 8·5 kts. / For 12 miles at 4 kts.	9	1	...

(BD) = "Bureau Design," i e., by Bureau of Construction, Navy Dept.   (H) = Boats built by Electric Boat Co. ("Hollands") or to their designs.   (L) = Boats built by Lake Co., or to their designs.   (Li) = Fiat-Laurenti boat built by Cramps.

Ex-German Submarines.

The following surrendered German Submarines have been transferred to U.S. Navy :—

4 *Ocean-going* type : *U 117*, *U 111*, *UB 148*, *UB 88*.

1 *Mine-Laying* boat : *UC 97*.

1 other boat, type unknown.

These six boats are not to be incorporated in the regular Navy. They are to be used for experiments only, and then broken up.

54* + 9 *projected* "Fleet Submarines."

*Uncertain how many finished.

Note.—Contracts with Electric Boat Co. for 9 Submarines (*Nos. 159—167*), and with Lake T. B. Co. for 4 Submarines (*Nos. 173—176*), cancelled December, 1918.

Projected.

9 *type unknown :* "*Fleet 1—Fleet 9*," authorized, but not yet contracted for or begun. No details known. **Will be** numbered in *AA* or *BB* series.

Completing or building.

3 *Holland type :* **AA 1** (ex-*Schley*, Fore River Co., 1918, **AA 2, AA 3** (1919, by Fore River Co.). Dimensions : about 264 (*w.l.*), 270 (*o.a.*) × 23 × 14 feet. Machinery : 4 sets of 1000 H.P. Nlseco Diesel engines *on surface*, arranged in tandem pairs to 2 screws. Armament : 2—3 inch AA. guns and 4 tubes.

"Fleet Submarines"—*Continued.*

Photo wanted.

11 "*Bureau design*" boats : **S 3**—*S 13 ;* all by Portsmouth N. Y. *S 3* launched 1918 and completed 1919, *S 4*, *S 5*, begun December, 1917, *S 6*, *S 7*, begun January, 1918, *S 8*, begun November, 1918, *S 9* begun January, 1919, *S 10*—*S 13* not yet begun. No details known.

Building or Completing.

9 *Lake* type : **S 2** (1919), **S 14**—**S 17** (1919-20), and *S 48*—*S 51* (*building*). All by Lake T. B. Co. Believed to be similar to *S 1*, *S 18*—*S 47* given below.

Photo wanted.

31 *Holland* type : **S 1** (1918), **S 18—47** (1919-20), viz., *S 1*, *S 18*—*S 29* by Fore River S. B. Co., *S 30**—*S 41* by Union I. W., *S 42*—*S 47* (contracts not assigned). Dimensions : about 230 × 20 × 12-15 feet. Machinery : 2 sets of 600-750 H.P. Nlseco Diesel engines. Will have large radius of action *on surface.* Armament : 1 or 2 guns and 4 tubes.

Note.—*S 30* built at expense of Philippines Government and will be manned by a Filipino crew.

Continued on next page.

Note.—" *Number* 108 " a small experimental boat, will not be built.

Photo wanted.

7 *Lake* type : **R 21 —R 27** (1918-19), all built by Lake T. B. Co. No details known ; believed to resemble *O 11—O 16*. R 21, 22, 24, 25 and 27 are completed.

Photo wanted.

20 *Holland* type : **R 1—R 20** (1918-19), viz., *R 1—R 14* by Fore River S. B. Co., *R 15—R 20* by Union I. W., San Francisco. No details known, but believed to resemble *O 1—O 10*. R 1, 2, 3, 4, 7, 8, 9, 10, 18, 19 and 20 are completed.

Photo wanted.

6 *Holland* type : **H 4—H 9** (1918), built by Bremerton D. Y., Puget Sound. No details known, but probably of same type as British *H Class* Submarines.

Photo wanted.

6 *Lake* type : **O 11—O 16** (1917-18), viz., *O 11—O 13* by Lake T. B. Co., *O 14—O 16* by California S. B. Co. Dimensions : about 172 × 18 × — feet. 1—3 inch AA. gun. 4 torpedo tubes. Machinery : 2 sets Sulzer Diesel engines. Radius of action as *O 1—O 10* below. Completed 1918.

O3.

Photo, N. G. Moser.

10 *Holland* type : **O 1—O 10** (1917-18), viz., *O 1* by Portsmouth N. Y., *O 2* by Bremerton, Pugent Sound, N. Y., *O 3*—*O 10* by Electric Boat Co. and Fore River Co. Dimensions : about 175 × 17 × — feet. 1—3 inch AA. gun. 4 torpedo tubes. Machinery : 2 sets of 4-cycle Nlesco Diesel engines. Electric batteries weigh 65 tons. Radius of action : 5000-6000 miles, at 11-12 kts. *on surface*. Completed 1918.

Photo wanted.

4 *Lake* type : **N 4, N 5, N 6, N 7,** (launched 1916-17) by Lake T. B. Co. Dimensions : about 155 × 14½ × — feet. 1—3 inch AA. gun. 4 torpedo tubes. Machinery : 2 sets Sulzer Diesel engines. Radius of action : about 2500 miles at cruising speed *on surface* ; 100-120 miles at 5 kts. *submerged*. Completed 1918.

(*Continued on next page.*)

Photo wanted.

---

3 *Holland* type : **N1—N3** (1916-17) viz., N 1—N 3 by Electric Boat Co., and Seattle Con. and D. D. Co. Dimensions : about 147 × 16 × 12 feet. 1—3 inch AA. gun. 4 torpedo tubes. Machinery : 2 sets 450 H.P. Nlseco Diesel engines. Radius of action : 2500 miles at cruising speed *on surface*, and 100-120 miles at 5 kts. *submerged*.

Photo, copyright by E. Muller, Junr.

1 *Holland* type : **M 1.** (Electric Boat Co., 1915.) Dimensions : 165 × 16 × 13½ feet. Armament : 1—3 inch, 50 cal. gun (high angle anti-aircraft model) and 4 torpedo tubes. Machinery : 2 sets of 8 cylinder 900 H.P. Nlseco Diesel engines. Radius of action : 3000 miles at 14 kts. *on surface*. Has three periscopes.

Photo wanted.

---

4 *Lake* type : **L5** (Lake T. B. Co., 1915), **L6, L7** (Craig S. B. Co., Long Beach, Cal., 1916), **L8** (Portsmouth N. Y., 1917). Dimensions : about 165 × 14¾ × feet. 1—3 inch AA. gun. 4 torpedo tubes. Machinery : 2 sets of 600 B.H.P. Busch Sulzer Diesel engines. Radius of action : about 4500 miles *on surface* at cruising speed, 150 miles at 5 kts. *submerged*.

L 3.

Photo, U. S. Navy Recruiting Bureau.

7 *Holland* type : **L1—4, L9—11** (1914-15), viz., Electric Boat Co. Dimensions : about 169 × 17½ × feet. 1—3 inch AA. gun. 4 torpedo tubes. Machinery : 2 sets of 650 H.P. Nlseco Diesel engines in *L* 1—4 and 9—11. Radius of action : about 4500 miles *on surface* at cruising speed, and 150 miles at 5 kts. *submerged*. Cost £650,000 each.

Note.—L 6 and L 7 contracted for by Lake Co., but were built by the California S. B. Co., Long Beach, Cal.

K 5.

Photo, U. S. Navy Recruiting Bureau.

8 *Holland* type : **K1** (ex-*Haddock*), **K2** (ex-*Cachalot*), **K3** (ex-*Orca*), **K4** (ex *Walrus*), and **K5—K8.** (1913-14.) K 1, 2, 5, 6, by Fore River, K 3, 7, 8, by Union I. W., K 4 by Moran Co. Dimensions : about 153 × 16¾ × 12 feet. 4 bow torpedo tubes. 8 torpedoes carried. Machinery : 2 sets 6-cylinder 500 B.H.P. Nlseco Diesel engines. Radii of action : 4500 miles at 10 kts. *on surface*, 120 miles at 5 kts. *submerged*.

H 1, H 2.

Photo, Navy Dept. (Bureau C. & R.)

3 *Holland* type : **H1** (ex-*Seawolf*), **H2** (ex-*Nautilus*), and **H3** (ex-*Garfish*). (1913.) H 1, H 2 by Union I. W., H 3 by Moran Co. Dimensions : about 150 × 16 × feet. 4 torpedo tubes. Radii of action : about 2300 miles at 11 kts. *on surface*, 100 miles at 5 kts. *submerged*.

(*Continued on next page.*)

Photo (copyright) by E. Muller, Junr.

1 *Laurenti-Cramp* type : **G 4** (ex-*Thrasher*) (1912). Fiat-Laurenti type built by Cramp. Dimensions : 157½×17¼×9¼ feet.
   4 torpedo tubes. Radius of action : *about* 1700 miles at 8 kts. *on surface*, 40 miles at 5 kts. *submerged.*

G 1.   Photo wanted of *G* 3.   *Photo (copyright), by E. Muller, Jr.*

2 *Lake* type : **G 1** (ex-*Seal*); and **G 3** (ex-*Turbot*) (1912-13). *G 1* built by Newport News, *G 2*, *G 3*, by Lake T. B. Co.
   Dimensions : *about* 161×13× feet. 2 or 4 torpedo tubes. Radii of action : 3500 at 8 kts. *on surface* ; 70 miles at 5
   kts. *submerged.* *G 2* foundered 1919.

No photo available.

2 *Holland* type : **F 2** (ex-*Barracuda*), and **F 3** (ex-*Pickerel*), (1911). *F 2* by Union Ironworks, *F 3* by Moran Co.,
   Seattle. Dimensions *about* 140×15× feet. 4 torpedo tubes. Radii 2300 at 11 kts. *surface*, 100 at 5 kts. *submerged.*
   Reported to have been re-engined during 1915-16 with Nlesco & Craig Diesel engines. *F 4* (ex-*Skate*) foundered
   before the war, was salved and stricken from the Navy Register. *F 1* (ex-*Carp*) lost during the war.

Photo, H. Reuterdahl, Esq.

2 *Holland* type : **E 1** (ex-*Skipjack*), and **E 2** (ex-*Sturgeon*), (1911). Built by Fore River Co. 4 torpedo tubes. Radii
   2100 at 11 kts. *surface*, 100 at 5 kts. *submerged.* *E 2* experimentally equipped with Edison nickel batteries.

Photo, Boston News Co.

3 *Holland* type : **D 1** (ex-*Narwhal*), **D 2** (ex-*Grayling*), and **D 3** (ex-*Salmon*). (1909-10). Built by Fore River Co.
   Dimensions : 134½×11× feet. 4 torpedo tubes. Radius of action *on surface*, 1240 miles at cruising speed of
   9-10 kts.

(Canal Zone).   *Photo, Copyright, E. Muller, Jr.*

5 *Holland* type : **C 1** (ex-*Octopus*), **C 2** (ex-*Stingray*), **C 3** (ex-*Tarpon*), **C 4** (ex-*Bonita*), **C 5** (ex-*Snapper*). (1903-9).
   Built by Fore River Co. Dimensions, *about* 105½×15× feet. 2 torpedo tubes. Nominal radius, 800 at 8 kts.
   surface, 80 at 5 kts. *submerged.*

(*Continued on next page.*)

8 or 9 Old Holland Boats.

Will probably be stricken from the Navy Register within next twelve months, Are on Asiatic Station.

No photo available.

3 *Holland* type : **B1** (ex-*Cuttlefish*), **B2** (ex-*Viper*). **B3** (ex-*Tarantula*). (1906-7). Built by Fore River Co., Quincy, Mass. Dimensions: *about* $82\frac{1}{4} \times 12\frac{3}{4} \times$ feet. 2 torpedo tubes in bows. Radii of action: 540 miles at 9 kts. *on surface;* 12 miles at 4 kts. *submerged.* Possess very little practical worth now.

5 or 6 *Holland* type : **A2** (ex-*Plunger*). **A3** (ex-*Adder*). **A4** (ex-*Grampus*), **A5** (ex-*Mocassin*), **A6** (ex-*Pike*) or **A7** (ex-*Porpoise*). (1901-3). A2, 4, 6, 7, by Crescent Shipyard, Elizabeth Port, N.J., A3, A5, by Union Ironworks, San Francisco. Dimensions: $64 \times 11\frac{1}{2} \times 12$ feet 1 torpedo tube in bows. Single benzine motors. Radii. 300 at 8·5 kts. *surface;* 12 at 4 kts. *submerged.* Practically non-effective now. A7 was badly damaged at Cavite, P.I., during July, 1917, through a fuel explosion. Considering her age, she is hardly worth repairing and has probably been scrapped.

Mine Laying Boats.

No Submarines of this type reported building or in service, but it is not impossible that some of the R and S types may be adapted for this duty.

Fabricated Patrol Vessels.

EAGLE 17.   *Photo by courtesy of the Ford Motor Co , Detroit.*

53 "EAGLE BOATS" :—

Eagle 1—4	**Eagle 27—34**	**Eagle 46—54**
Eagle 6—14	**Eagle 36—44**	**Eagle 56—60**
Eagle 16—24		

Missing Numbers :—Twelve boats were allotted to Italian Government, viz., 5, 15, 25, 35, 45, 55, 65, 75, 85, 95, 105, 112. In December, 1918, contracts for 61—112 (inclusive of both numbers) were cancelled, but boats over 61 for Italian Navy are reported as proceeding to completion.

Down to *Eagle* 12, launched 1918, remainder 1919.

45 boats building and completing July 1st, 1919.

Displacement, *normal* 500 tons, *full load* 615 tons.

Dimensions : Length, 200 feet (*p.p.* and *o.a.*). Beam, $25\frac{1}{2}$ feet. *Mean* draught, $7\frac{1}{4}$ feet ; *full load,* $8\frac{1}{2}$ feet.

Armament : 2—4 inch (50 cal.), 2—3 inch AA., 2 M.G., 1 Y-gun (depth charge projector). Carry depth charges.

Machinery : Ljungstrom turbine with planetary reduction gear. 2 Sterling w.t. boilers. 1 screw. Designed H.P. 2500 = 18 kts. Fuel : 105 tons coal + 45 tons oil. Endurance : 3500 miles at 10 kts. Machinery weighs 77.73 tons. Heating surface, 3000 sq. feet.

Complement, 72.

Notes.—Complement, 73. Assembled by Ford Eagle Boat Plant, River Rouge ; machinery and fittings by Ford Plant, Highland Park, Detroit. Estimated cost, £275,000 per vessel, but this has been largely exceeded. Are the American equivalent of the British "P-boats." The first British P-boat was commissioned on January 1st, 1916 ; the first Eagle Boat on October 28th, 1918. A very large sum of money was spent on erecting the fabricating plant for the Eagle Boats. British shipbuilders, without any extraordinary preparations, additional plant or slips, produced the larger British P-boats in about the same time as the Ford Eagle Boats are built.

SC 200.

Photo, **Navy** *Dept. (Bureau C. & R.)*

331 110-FOOT BOATS :—

SC 1—4	**SC 143—145**	**SC 275—301**
SC 6	**SC 147—159**	**SC 303—310**
SC 17—27	**SC 164—169**	**SC 320—346**
SC 34—59	**SC 178—186**	**SC 349**
SC 61—64	**SC 188—208**	**SC 351—356**
SC 68—74	**SC 210—218**	**SC 405**
SC 77—116	**SC 220—242**	**SC 407—409**
SC 118—131	**SC 244 —248**	**SC 411—441**
SC 133—138	**SC 250—273**	**SC 443**
		SC 444.

Missing Numbers :—Transferred to French Government—*SC 5, SC 7—16, SC 28—33, SC 65—67, SC 75—76, SC 140—142, SC 146, SC 160—163, SC 170—177, SC 243, SC 249, SC 313—319, SC 347—348, SC 350* (all of first contract), *SC 357—404, SC 406* (all second contract). Transferred to Cuba : *SC 274, 302, 311, 312* (all first contract). Never built : *SC 159.* Contracts cancelled : *SC 410, 442, 445—448* (third contract). War losses : *SC 60, 117, 132, 187, 209, 219* (all first contract).

Built 1917-19. *Designed* displacement, 54 tons ; *actual* displacement, owing to heavier guns and other alterations, 77 tons *normal,* 85 tons *full load.* Wooden hulls. Length, 105 feet (*p.p.*), 110 feet (*o.a.*). Beam, 14 feet 8¼ ins. *Mean* hull draught, 5 feet 5½ ins., *full load* aft, 5 feet 8½ ins. Machinery : three sets of 220 B.H.P. Standard petrol motors = 18 kts. *designed* speed. Owing to added weights, 16·85 kts. is reported to be actual full speed. 2400 gallons petrol = 900 miles at 10 kts. Complement, 27. Have small radius W/T.

Armaments : Designed for 1—6 pdr. and 2 M.G., but these were only mounted in a few boats. Majority have 1—3 inch (23 cal.), 2 Colt M.G. and 1 Y-gun. Some boats have an extra 6 pdr. Carry depth charges.

Hydrophone Gear : Boats fitted out in this way have either (*a*) K-tube fish hydrophones of 30 miles acoustic radius, or (*b*) SC and MB hydrophone tubes built into (and insulated from) hull of 3 miles acoustic radius. All boats with hydrophones carry extra load of depth charges.

Notes.—Quick rollers with period of about 5 secs. A very full description of these craft was given in the " Journal of the U.S. Naval Institute " in an article contributed by Comm. J. A. Furer, Construction Corps, U.S.N. To this article we are indebted for the majority of foregoing details and following Table.

TABLE OF BUILDERS :—

(Boats transferred to France and Cuba and War Losses not deleted.)

Builders.		Boats and numbers.		
Name.	Address.	First contract.	Second contract (for French government)	Third contract.
New Orleans Naval Station	New Orleans, La.	1—4 114—115	....	443—444 ....
New York Navy Yard	Brooklyn, N. Y.	5—64	....	....
Mathis Yacht Bldg. Co.	Camden, N. J.	65—74 209—213	(381—385)	426—430
Hiltebrant D. D. Co.	Kingston, N. Y.	75—89	(371—375)	421—425
Elco Co.	Bayonne, N. J.	90—105	(361—364)	....
Charleston Navy Yard	Charleston, S. C.	106—113	....	....
Norfolk Navy Yard	Norfolk, Va.	116—136	....	....
Hodgdon Bros.	E. Boothbay, Me.	137—138	....	....
Hartman-Greiling Co.	Green Bay, Wis.	140—141	....	....
Rocky River D. D. Co.	Rocky River, Ohio	142—143	(403—406)	437—438
Vinyard S. B. Co.	Milford, Del.	144—146	....	....
L. E. Fry & Co. (E. J. Wright)	Clayton, N.Y.	147—148 337—338	....	....
Dubuque Boat & Boiler Wks.	Dubuque, Iowa	149—150	....	....
Gibbs Gas Engine Co.	Jacksonville, Fla.	151—155 204—208	(365—370)	....
F. M. Blount	Pensacola, Fla.	156—159	....	....
Howard E. Wheeler	Brooklyn, N. Y.	160—168	....	339—441
Matthews Boat Co.	Port Clinton, Ohio	169—178	(386—392)	431—433
International S. B. & Marine Eng. Co.	Upper Nyack, N. Y.	179—188	....	....
General S. B. & Aero Co.	Washington, D. C.	189—203	....	....
Alexander McDonald	Mariner's Harbor, L. I., N. Y.	214—217	....	434—436
Newcomb Life Boat Co.	Hampton, Va.	218—222	....	....
N. Y. Yacht, Launch & Engine Co.	Morris Heights, N. Y.	223—242	(393—242)	....
Eastern Shipyard Co.	Greenport, N. Y.	243—247	....	....
Camden Anchor-Rockland Machine Co.	Camden, Me.	251—252	....	407—408
Geo. Lawley & Son	Neponset, Mass.	253—272	....	....
Mare Island Navy Yard	Mare Island, Cal.	273—287	....	....
Puget Sound Navy Yard	Bremerton, Wash.	288—312	....	....
Robert Jacob	City Island, N. Y.	313—317	....	....
Luders Marine Const. Co.	Stamford, Conn.	318—322	....	....
Kyle & Purdy	City Island, N. Y.	323—327	(376—380)	....
Great Lakes B. B. Corp.	Milwaukee, Wis.	328—329	....	419—420
Burger Boat Co.	Manitowoc, Wis.	330	....	....
Smith & Williams Co.	Salisbury, Md.	331—232	....	....
Barrett S. B. Co.	Mobile, Ala.	333—336	....	....
American Car & Found. Co.	Wilmington, Del.	339—346	....	....
College Point Boat Corp.	College Point, N. Y.	347—356	(357—360)	413—418
Clayton S. & B. Bldg. Co.	Clayton, N. Y.	....	....	411—412
Chance Marine Const. Co.	Annapolis, Md.	248—250	409	....

Motor Patrol Boats.

464 of these craft were purchased, chartered or loaned by private owners, for War Duty. The multiplicity of their types renders any description impossible. The majority have gone back to their owners, and it is doubtful if any will be retained by the Regular Navy.

Tenders to Torpedo Craft.

Third class cruiser, **BIRMINGHAM,** is fitted for and serves as flagship to T.B.D. in full commission, Pacific Fleet. She is described on a previous page.

Third class cruiser, **SALEM,** serves as flagship to T.B.D. in reserve, Pacific Fleet. Is described on a previous page.

First class cruiser, **ROCHESTER,** is flagship to T.B.D. in full commission, Atlantic Fleet. Third class cruiser, **CHESTER,** is flagship to T.B.D. in Reserve, Atlantic. Both ships described on preceding pages.

Two Tenders to Torpedo Craft, Pacific Fleet, and three Tenders to Torpedo Craft, Atlantic Fleet, not selected at the time these pages were prepared ; accordingly, they cannot be listed.

Projected.

WHITNEY, DOBBIN. Both ships authorized but not yet under contract or construction. 10,600 tons. Dimensions : 460 (*w.l.*) 483⅚ (*o.a.*) × 61 × 21 feet (*mean* draught). Guns : 8—5 inch, 4—3 inch AA. Torpedo tubes : 2—21 inch. Geared turbines. 1 screw. Designed S.H.P. 7000 = 16 kts. Coal : 1107 tons. Complement, —. Generally sister ships to *Holland,* Tender to Submarines.

Tenders to Torpedo Craft—*Continued.*

Photo, C. E. Waterman.

(*Pacific Fleet.*)

MELVILLE (1915). 7150 tons. Complement, 397. Dimensions : 400 × 54½ × 20 feet (*mean* draught). Guns : 8—5 inch (51 cal.), 1—3 inch AA., 2—3 pdr. Torpedo tubes : 1—18 inch. Machinery : Parsons turbines and Westinghouse reduction gear. 2 Babcock and Wilcox boilers. H.P. (*on trials*) 4006 = 15.09 kts. Fuel : 900 tons *oil.*

Copyright photo (see Note).

(*Pacific Fleet Reserve Flotillas.*)

BLACK HAWK (Cramp, 1913, ex-Grace Steamship Co. S.S. *Santa Catalina,* taken over 1917). 13,500 tons. Dimensions : 404½ × 53¾ × 28½ feet. Guns : 4—5 inch, 2 M.G. I.H.P. 3400 = 13 kts. Oil : 2108 tons. Complement, 442. Served 1917-18 as Repair Ship to Mine Force.

Note.—Above illustration from " The Northern Barrage," prepared by U.S. Mine Force, and published by U.S. Naval Institute, Annapolis.

Tenders to Torpedo Craft—*Continued.*

Photo wanted.

(*Atlantic Fleet.*)

BRIDGEPORT (Vegesack, Germany, 1901, ex-North German Lloyd S.S. *Breslau,* seized 1917). 8600 tons. Dimensions : 429½ × 54¼ × 28¼ feet. Guns : 8—5 inch, 2 M.G. I.H.P., 3600 = 12.5 kts. Coal : 1060 tons. Complement, 386.

(*Atlantic Fleet.*)

DIXIE (ex *El Sud*), (1893). 6114 tons. Complement, 448. Dimensions : 391 × 48¼ × 20 feet (*mean* draught). Armament : 10—3 inch, 2—6 pdr., 2—1 pdr., 2 M.G. H.P. 3800 = 14.5 kts. Coal : 1100 tons.

(*Continued on next page.*)

Tenders to Torpedo Craft.

(Pacific Fleet.)

BUFFALO (*ex El Cid*), (1892). 6000 tons. Complement: 424. Dimensions: $391 \times 48\frac{1}{4} \times 19\frac{1}{2}$ feet. Armament: 6—4 inch, 4—3 pdr., 2—1 pdr., 2 M.G. H.P. 3600 = 14·5 kts. Coal: 1408 tons.

PRAIRIE.   *Official Photo, U.S. Naval Air Service.*
(Pacific Fleet).

PRAIRIE (*ex El Sol*), (1890). 6620 tons. Complement: 350. Dimensions: $404\frac{3}{4} \times 48\frac{1}{4} \times 20\frac{3}{4}$ feet (*mean* draught). Armament: 10—3 inch, 2—1 pdr., 2 M.G. H.P. 3800 = 14·5 kts. Coal: 1331 tons.

(Atlantic Fleet).

PANTHER (1889). 3380 tons. Complement: 242. Dimensions: $304\frac{3}{4} \times 40\frac{3}{4} \times 15\frac{3}{4}$ feet (*mean* draught). Guns: 4—3 inch. H.P. 3200 = 13·5 kts. Coal, 691 tons.

Tenders to Torpedo Craft—*Continued.*

(Asiatic Fleet.)

POMPEY (1888). Ex-Collier, 3085 tons. Complement: 121. Dimensions: $234 \times 33\frac{1}{2} \times 15\frac{5}{6}$ feet (*mean* draught). Guns: 4—6 pdr. Speed: 10·5 kts. Coal: 205 tons.

Tenders to Submarine.

> *Projected.*

HOLLAND. Authorized; not yet under contract or construction. 10,600 tons. Dimensions: 460 (*w.l.*), $483\frac{5}{6}$ (*o a.*) × 61 (*extreme*) × 21 feet (*mean* draught). Guns: 4—5 inch, 2—3 inch AA. Geared turbines. 1 screw. Designed S H P. 7000 = 16 kts. Oil : 1107 tons. Complement, . Generally sister ship to *Whitney* and *Dobbin*, Tenders to Torpedo Craft.

BUSHNELL.   *U.S. Navy Photo.*
(Atlantic Fleet).

BUSHNELL (1915). 3580 tons. Complement: 194. Dimensions: $300 \times 45\frac{2}{3} \times 15$ feet (*mean* draught). Guns: 4—5 inch (51 cal.), 2—3 pdr. (saluting). Machinery: Turbines with reducing gear. H.P. (*on trials*) 2617 = 14·15 kts. Fuel: 660 tons oil.

Tenders to Submarines—*Continued.*

Photo, Copyright, E. Muller. Jr.

FULTON (ex-*Niagara*) (1914). 1408 tons. Complement: 173. Dimensions: $216 \times 35 \times 13$ feet (*mean* draught). Guns: 2—3 inch (50 cal.), 1—1 pdr. auto. anti-aircraft. Torpedo tubes: None officially listed, but from published plans and photos 4 tubes appear to be mounted on foc's'le in two twin deck-mountings. Machinery: 1100 B.H.P. 6-cyl. 2-cycle Nlseco Diesel engine. 1 screw. Designed speed: 12·25 kts.; 12·34 *on trials*. Fuel: 234 tons *oil*.

> **Photo wanted.**

(Pacific Fleet.)

BEAVER (Newport News, 1910, purchased 1918). 5970 tons. Dimensions: 380 (*o.a.*) × 47 × 21 feet (*max.* draught), Guns: 4—5 inch, 2—3 inch AA., 2—1 pdr., 2 M.G. 1 screw. I.H.P. 4500 = 16·5 kts. Fuel: 2350 barrels oil fuel. Complement, 373.

> **Photo wanted.**

(Atlantic Fleet).

CAMDEN (Flensburg, Germany, 1900, ex-German-Australian ss. *Kiel*, seized 1917). 9000 tons (estimated). Dimensions: $403\frac{3}{4}$ (*o.a.*) × 48 × feet. Guns: 4—4 inch, 2—3 inch AA., 2—1 pdr , 4 M.G. I.H.P. 2550 = 12 kts. Coal: 975 tons. Complement, 345.

(Continued on next page.)

Tenders to Submarines—*continued*.

Photo wanted.

(Pacific Fleet.)

SAVANNAH (Flensburg, Germany, 1899, ex-Hamburg-American S.S. *Saxonia*, seized 1917). 10,800 tons. Dimensions : 414 × 46 × 26½ feet.   Guns : 1—5 inch, 2 M.G. I.H.P. 2000 = 10·5 kts.   Coal : 743 tons + 531 tons additional stowage = 1274 tons.   Complement, 412.

No photo available.

(Atlantic Fleet.)

RAINBOW (1890, purchased 1898).   4300 tons.   Dimensions : 351¾ × 41 × 17¼ feet.   Guns : 4—5 inch, 2 M.G.   I.H.P. 1800 = 12 kts.   Coal : 1166 tons.   Complement, 274.

MONADNOCK (1883).   3990 tons.   Guns : 4—10 inch, 2—4 inch, 4—6 pdr., 2—1 pdr.   Armour : Iron belt 9″, steel turrets 11½″—7½″.   H.P. (*on trials*) 2163 = 11·63 kts.   Coal : 395 tons.   Complement, 228.

Note.—Above Old Monitor Submarine Depot Ship, Asiatic Fleet, with *Mohican* as Tender.   She is to be withdrawn from service and placed out of commission.

A:—Aircraft Carriers.
B:—Tenders to Seaplanes.
C:—Kite Balloon Ships.

U.S. Dreadnoughts now carry and fly off small aeroplanes from barbette crowns, in the same way as British Ships.

Armoured Cruisers, **NORTH CAROLINA** and **SEATTLE** were specially equipped to serve as Seaplane Carriers and Depot Ships.   See illustration of *Seattle* on an earlier page.   Doubtful if these Armoured Cruisers are still on this duty.

Mine Layers, **AROOSTOOK** and **SHAWMUT**, acted as Tenders to the *NC* Flying Boats on Cross-Atlantic Flight.

Kite Balloons worked by nearly all classes of warships.

Up to the present, no special Aircraft Carriers, like British *Argus, Furious, Nairana*, etc., have been added to U.S. Navy.

Tenders to Submarine Chasers.

Cruisers, **SALEM** and **CHICAGO**, Auxiliary **PRAIRIE**, Coastguard Cruiser **SNOHOMISH**, Armed Yacht *Yacona* and various Tugs have been used for convoying Submarine Chasers across the Atlantic.   They will be released from this duty when all *SC*-boats have been withdrawn from European waters.

Gunboat, **VICKSBURG**, listed as Fisheries Protection Vessel, Alaska, also serves as Parent Ship to four Submarine Chasers.

Photo, Lieut. H. Reuterdahl, U.S.N./R.F.

LEONIDAS (1898).   Ex-Fuel Ship.   4023 tons.   Dimensions : 274 × 39¼ × 17⅔ feet.   Complement, 167.   Guns : 1—6 inch, 2—3 inch, 2 M.G.   H.P. 1100 = 8½ kts.   Coal : 205 tons.

Similar to "Leonidas" above.

HANNIBAL (1898).   Ex-Fuel Ship.   4000 tons.   Dimensions : 274 × 39¼ × 17⅔ feet.   Complement, 295.   Guns : 1—6 inch, 2—3 inch, 2 M.G.   H.P. 1100 = 9 kts.   Coal : 491 tons.

Ammunition Ships.
Building.

NITRO, PYRO (both building by Puget Sound, N.Y.). 10,600 tons. Dimensions : 460 × 61 × 21 feet.   Guns : 4—5 inch, 4—3 inch AA. Designed S.H.P. 5300.   Speed, 16 kts.   Parsons (geared) turbines. 2 screws.   Fitted with plant for powder testing and cooling, also large cold storage capacity for meat, in addition to ammunition-carrying spaces.

Mine Planters.

Note.—The Mine Planting Force during the War consisted of the ex-Cruisers *San Francisco* and *Baltimore*, and Converted Liners *Aroostook, Canandaigua, Canonicus Housatonic, Quinnebaug, Roanoke, Shawmut,* with *Blackhawk* as Tender. *Aroostook* and *Shawmut* are retained, and *Black Hawk* assigned to new duties ; the other vessels have been reconditioned for Mercantile Service. These ships laid the Northern Barrage from Scotland to Norway.

Same as " Shawmut " below.

(*Pacific Fleet.*)

AROOSTOOK (Cramps, 1907. Ex-S.S. *Bunker Hill,* of Eastern Steamship Co., purchased 1917 and converted into Mine Planter). All details as *Shawmut,* below. Served as Tender to *NC* Flying Boats during Cross Atlantic Flight.

SHAWMUT (AROOSTOOK same).   *Photo, O. W. Waterman.*

(*Atlantic Fleet.*)

SHAWMUT (Cramps, 1907. Ex-S.S. *Massachusetts,* of Eastern Steamship Co., purchased 1917 and converted into Mine Planter). 3800 tons. Complement, 314. Dimensions : 395 (*o.a.*) × 52¼ × 16 feet (*mean*). Guns : 1—5 inch, 2—3 inch AA., 2 M.G. Reciprocating engines and 8 S. E. boilers. 2 screws. H.P. 7000 = 20 kts. Fuel : 400 tons coal + 160 tons oil. Served as Tender to *NC* Flying Boats during Cross-Atlantic Flight.

Mine Planters—*continued.*

(*Atlantic Fleet.*)   *Photo, U. S. Navy.*

SAN FRANCISCO (1889). Displacement, 4083 tons. Complement, 315. Dimensions : 410 (*w.l.*) × 49¼ × 18¾ (*mean*) feet. Armament : 4—5 inch, 2—1 pdr., 2 M.G. Carries 300 Mark II mines. 4 searchlights. Designed H.P. 8500 = 19 kts. 8 Babcock boilers. Coal : 663 tons.

(*Pacific Fleet.*)   *Photo, U. S. Navy*

BALTIMORE (1888). Displacement, 4413 tons. Complement, 345. Dimensions : 327½ (*w.l.*) × 48⅔ × 19½ (*mean*) feet. Guns : 4—5 inch, 51 cal., 2—3 inch AA., 2 M.G. Armour : 4″ deck. Designed H.P. 8500 = 20 kts. Boilers : 8 Babcock. Coal : *maximum* 1092 tons.

Mine-Sweepers.

In addition to the vessels described below, about 100 other ships (such as Trawlers, Tugs, etc.) were chartered or purchased for War Duty. It is not definitely known yet how many of these vessels will be retained in the Post-War Fleet Organisation, and so no attempt is made to describe them this year. For Tugs, fitted as Mine Sweepers, see a subsequent page.

Photo wanted.

2 masts. 1 funnel.

(" BIRD " CLASS—54 BOATS.)

LAPWING, OWL, ROBIN, SWALLOW, SANDERLING, AUK, CHEWINK, CORMORANT, GANNET (all built by Todd S. B. Co., Tebo Yacht Basin, Brooklyn, N. Y.).

TANAGER. CARDINAL, ORIOLE, CURLEW, GREBE, MALLARD, ORTOLAN, PEACOCK (all built by Staten Id. S. B. Co., N. Y.).

AVOCET, BOBOLINK, LARK, REDWING, RAVEN, SHRIKE (all built by Baltimore D. D. & S. B. Co.).

PELICAN, FALCON, OSPREY, SEAGULL, TERN (all built by Gas Engine & Power Co., Morris Heights, N. Y.).

TURKEY, WOODCOCK, QUAIL PARTRIDGE (all built by Chester S. B. Co.)

SANDPIPER, WARBLER, VIREO, WILLET (all built by Philadelphia Navy Yard).

SWAN, WHIPPOORWILL, BITTERN (all built by Alabama S. B. & D. D. Co., Mobile).

WIDGEON, TEAL, BRANT (all built by Sun S. B. Co., Chester).

KINGFISHER, RAIL (both built by Puget Sound Navy Yard).

EIDER, THRUSH (both built by Pusey & Jones, Wilmington).

FINCH, HERON (both built by Standard S. B. Co., N. Y.).

FLAMINGO, PENGUIN (both built by New Jersey D. D. & T. Co., Elizabeth Port).

PIGEON. Builder not known. Built 1918-19. 950 tons normal, 1009 *full load* at 10¼ feet aft. Dimensions : 187¾ (*o.a.*) × 35½ × 9¾ feet (*mean* draught). Guns : 2—3 inch AA., 2 M.G. Machinery : 1 set triple expansion and 2 B. & W. boilers. Designed I.H.P. 1400 = 14 kts. Oil fuel only

Note.—*Condor, Plover, Goshawk* and *Nos. 55, 56, 57* stopped. Nine boats still unfinished on July 1st, 1919. These craft may also serve as Mine Layers, Tugs, Coastguard Cutters and Salvage Ships.

Fuel Ships.
(Oil Carriers.)

TWELVE OIL TANKERS are listed in the monthly returns of U.S. naval construction, but are not included in the official Handbook, "Ships' Data." They are believed to be vessels, ordered by the Government from the Emergency Fleet Corporation and transferred to Navy. No details known.

Photo wanted.

("Pecos" Atlantic Fleet, "Neches" & "Brazos" Pacific Fleet).

BRAZOS (1919), *NECHES, PECOS*: all three building by Boston N.Y. 14,800 tons. Dimensions: $475\frac{2}{3}$ (o a.) $\times 56 \times 26\frac{2}{3}$ feet *mean*. Recipro. engines and 4 B. & W. boilers. Designed I.H.P. 5200 = 14 kts. Deadweight capacity 9600 tons. Guns: 4—5 inch.

KANAWHA (& CUYAMA).   Photo, O. W. Waterman.

Photo wanted.

("Kanawha," "Cuyama" Pacific Fleet. "Maumee" Atlantic Fleet).

CUYAMA (1916) **MAUMEE** (1915), **KANAWHA** (1914). Oil Tankers. 14,500 tons. Dimensions: $475\frac{1}{2} \times 56 \times 26\frac{1}{4}$ (*mean*). *Cuyama* and *Kanawha* reciprocating engines, 5200 H.P. *Maumee* 2-cycle Diesel motors 5000 H.P. Speed: 14 kts. Fuel capacity: 7500 tons cargo oil, 1575 tons own bunker oil. Guns: *Cuyama* 4—5 inch; *Maumee* 4—4 inch; *Kanawha* 4—4 inch, 2 M.G.

Fuel Ships.—Continued.
(Colliers and Oil Carriers.)

(Pacific Fleet).

JASON (1912), **ORION** (1912). 19,250 tons. Dimensions: $536 \times 65 \times 27\frac{2}{3}$ (*mean*). Speed: 14 kts. Fuel capacity (deadweight to designed draft): 10,500 tons cargo fuel + 2000 tons own bunker fuel. *Maximum* cargo capacity (close stowage): 11,500 tons coal + 2575 tons oil. Guns: 4—4 inch.

No photo available.

(Atlantic Fleet).

NEREUS (1913), **PROTEUS** (1912). 19,080 tons. Dimensions: $522 \times 62 \times 27\frac{2}{3}$ (*mean*). Speed: 13 kts. Fuel capacity (deadweight to designed draft): 10,500 tons cargo fuel + 2000 own bunker fuel. *Maximum* cargo capacity (close stowage): 11,800 tons coal + 1125 tons oil or 10,100 tons coal + 3050 tons oil. Guns: 4—4 inch.

(Pacific Fleet).   Photo, O. W. Waterman.

NEPTUNE (1911). 19,480 tons. Dimensions: $542 \times 65 \times 27\frac{2}{3}$ (*mean*). Speed: 13 kts. Fuel capacity (deadweight to designed draft): 10,500 tons cargo fuel + 2000 tons own bunker fuel. *Maximum* cargo capacity (close stowage): 10,200 tons coal + 2925 tons oil or 11,700 tons coal + 1250 tons oil. Guns: 4—4 inch.

Fuel Ships—Continued.
(Colliers and Oil Carriers.)

(Pacific Fleet).   Photo, O. W. Waterman.

JUPITER (1912). 19,360 tons. Dimensions: $542 \times 65 \times 27$ (*mean*). Speed: 14 kts. Fuel capacity (deadweight to designed draft); 10,500 tons cargo fuel + 2000 tons own bunker fuel. *Max.* cargo capacity (close stowage); 11,600 tons coal + 127 tons oil or 10,100 tons coal + 3075 tons oil. Guns: 4—4 inch.

(Colliers—"Mars" Atlantic Fleet. "Vulcan" Pacific Fleet).

MARS (1909), **VULCAN** (1909). 11,250 tons. Dimensions: $403 \times 53 \times 24\frac{3}{4}$ (*mean*). Speeds about 12 knots. Fuel capacity (deadweight to designed draft), 7200 tons cargo fuel + 300 tons own bunker fuel. *Max.* capacity (close stowage); 7600 tons cargo fuel + 825 tons own bunker fuel. Guns: 4—4 inch.

(Colliers bought during Spanish-American War. (As) = Asiatic Fleet. (A) = Atlantic Fleet. (P) = Pacific Fleet).

(As) **ABARENDA** (1892). Ex-Collier, 6680 tons. Dimensions: $325\frac{1}{2} \times 42 \times 22\frac{5}{8}$ (*Plimsoll mark*). Guns: 4—6 pdr. H.P. 1050 = 9 kts. *Max.* fuel capacity: 3500 tons cargo + 825 own bunkers.

(As) **AJAX.** 9250 tons *approx.* Dimensions: $387\frac{1}{2} \times 46\frac{1}{2} \times$ H.P. 3000 = 10 kts. *Max.* fuel capacity; 4800 tons cargo + 500 own bunkers. Guns: 4—6 pdr.

(A) **ARETHUSA.** 6160 tons. Dimensions: $343\frac{1}{2} \times 42\frac{1}{4} \times 22\frac{3}{4}$. (*Plimsoll mark*). H.P. 1700 = 10 kts. *Max.* fuel capacity, 4450 tons *oil*. Guns: 4—3 inch, 2 M.G.

(P) **BRUTUS.** 6550 tons. $332\frac{1}{2} \times 41\frac{1}{2} \times 23$. (*Plimsoll mark*). H.P. 1200 = 10 kts. *Max.* fuel capacity; 4850 tons cargo + 450 tons own bunkers. Guns: 4—6 pdr.

(A) **CÆSAR.** 5940 tons. Dimensions: $322 \times 44 \times 19\frac{2}{3}$. (*Plimsoll mark*). H.P., 1500 = 10 kts. *Max.* fuel capacity: 3250 tons cargo + 800 tons own bunkers. Guns: 4—6 pdr.

(A) **NERO.** 6100 tons. Dimensions: $323\frac{1}{2} \times 41 \times 21\frac{1}{2}$. (*Plimsoll mark*). H.P., 1000 = 9 kts. *Max.* fuel capacity: 4300 tons cargo + 300 tons own bunkers. Guns: 1—3 inch, 4—6 pdr.

STERLING. (Out of commission). 5660 tons *approx.* Dimensions: $284 \times 37 \times$ H.P.: 1000 = 11 kts. *Max.* full capacity: 2750 tons cargo + 475 tons own bunkers. Guns: 4—6 pdr.

Supply Ships.

(*Atlantic Fleet.*)   *Photo, U.S. Navy.*

BRIDGE (1916). 8500 tons. Complement, 238. Dimensions: 423 × 55¼ × 20⅔ feet (*mean* draught.) Guns: 4—5 inch, 50 cal., 1 M.G. H.P. 4000 = 14 kts. Reciprocating engines. 2 screws. Fuel: 1000 tons *oil*.

Photo wanted.

(*Pacific Fleet.*)

RAPPAHANNOCK (Vegesack, Germany, 1913, ex-North German Lloyd s.s. *Pommern*, seized 1917). 17,000 tons. Complement, Dimensions: 471¼ × 59¼ × 26¾ feet. Guns: 1—5 inch, 1—3 inch. I.H.P. 4850 = 11·5 kts. Coal: 3060 tons.

(*Refrigerator and Supply Ship, Pacific. Fleet.*)

GLACIER (1891). 8325 tons. Complement, 149. Dimensions: 355⅔ × 46 × 25⅓ feet (*mean* draught). Guns: 1—5 inch, 2—3 inch. H.P. (*on trials*) 2127 = 12·3 kts. Coal: 939 tons.

Supply Ships—*Continued.*

(*Refrigerator and Supply Ship, Pacific Fleet.*)

CELTIC (1891). 6750 tons. Complement, 152. Dimensions: 383 × 44¼ × 21 feet (*mean* draught). Guns: 4—3 inch, 50 cal., 1—3 inch AA. H.P. 2200 = 10·5 kts. Coal: 757 tons.

(*Supply Ship, Atlantic Fleet.*)

CULGOA (1889). 6000 tons. Complement, 142. Dimensions: 346⅓ × 43 × 21¾ feet (*mean* draught). Guns: 4—3 inch, 50 cal., 1—3 inch AA. H.P. 2350 = 13·25 kts. Coal: 980 tons.

(*Atlantic Fleet.*)

SUPPLY (1873). 4325 tons. Complement, 128. Dimensions: 355⅔ × 43⅓ × 19½ feet (*mean* draught) Armament: 4—6 pdr., 2—1 pdr. H.P. (*on trials*) 1009 = 9·66 kts. Coal: 1053 tons.

Repair Ships.
Projected.

MEDUSA (authorized; not yet begun). 10,000 tons. 460 × 70 × 19 feet. Guns: 4—5 inch, 4—3 inch AA. Geared turbines. Designed S.H.P. 7000 = 16 kts.

U.S. Navy Photo.

("*Prometheus*," *Atlantic Fleet*; "*Vestal*," *Pacific Fleet*.)

PROMETHEUS (1908). **VESTAL** (1908). 12,585 tons. Guns: 4—5 inch, 50 cal. (+ 1—3 inch AA. in *Vestal* only). H.P. 7500 = 16 kts. Coal, *Prometheus*: 1614 tons; *Vestal*: 1422 tons. Babcock boilers.

(*For Target Repairs: Pacific Fleet.*)

NANSHAN. 5140 tons. Dimensions: 295⅔ × 39 × feet. H.P., 1400 = 10½ kts. *Max.* fuel capacity; 425 tons. Guns: 4—6 pdr.

Photo, U.S. Navy.

(*For Target Repairs: Atlantic Fleet.*)

LEBANON (1897). 3285 tons. Dimensions: 249 (*o.a.*) × 37⅓ × 17¼ feet. Guns: 1—6 inch, 2—3 inch. 2 M.G. H.P. 1000 = 10 kts. Coal: 192 tons. Complement, 61.

(*For Radio Repairs: Pacific Fleet.*)

SATURN. 4840 tons. Dimensions: 297 × 40½ × feet. H.P., 1500 = 11 kts. *Max.* fuel capacity: 400 tons. Guns: 1—6 inch, 2—3 inch.

Salvage Department.

Following ships in European waters: **CHESAPEAKE** (1900), 2000 tons; 1—3 inch gun; speed 11 kts. **FAVORITE** (1907), 950 tons; guns: 2—3 inch, 1—3 inch AA., 2 M.G.,; speed 14 kts. **MANNA HATA. UTOWONA:** No details known. This unit may be demobolised in the near future.

Navy Transports.

Projected.

HEYWOOD. (*Authorized; not yet begun*). 10,000 tons. Complement 258. Dimensions: 460×64×19 feet. Guns: 4—5 inch, 2—3 inch AA., 2—6 pdr., 2—1 pdr. Turbines and B. and W. boilers. Designed S.H.P. 5400 = 10 kts. Fuel, 1200 tons. Assigned to Philadelphia N.Y. for building.

Photo wanted.

HENDERSON (1916). 10,000 tons. Complement: 214. Dimensions: $482\frac{3}{4}×61×20$ feet (*mean* draught). Guns: 8—5 inch, 50 cal., 2—3 inch, 2—1 pdr. H.P. 4000 = 14 kts. Reciprocating engines. 2 screws. Fuel: 1200 tons *oil*. Has Sperry gyro. stabilisers. To take 2000 men and 32 horses.

Photo, Capt. F. C. Bowen, R.M.L.I.

HANCOCK (1879). 8500 tons. Complement: 227. Dimensions: $465\frac{1}{2}×45\frac{1}{3}×24\frac{1}{4}$ feet. (*mean* draught). Guns: 4—3 inch, 2—3 inch AA., 2—3 pdr., 6—1 pdr., 2 M.G. H.P. 3100 = 13 kts. Coal: 1423 tons.

Hospital Ships.

Building.

RELIEF (*building* at Philadelphia, N.Y.) 9800 tons. Dimensions: 460 (*o.a.*)×61×$19\frac{1}{2}$ feet. Designed H.P. 5250 = 16 kts. Parsons (geared) turbines. 2 screws. Babcock and Wilcox boilers. Oil: 2032 tons.

Photo wanted.

(Pacific Fleet).

COMFORT (ex-Ward Liner *Havana*, built by Cramp, 1906), 10,102 tons, and **MERCY** (ex-Ward Liner *Saratoga*, built by Cramp, 1907), 10,112 tons. Complement 322. Dimensions: $430×50\frac{1}{6}×$ 24 to 26 feet. I.H.P. 8500 = 18 kts. Coal: 1010/1060 tons. Purchased 1918.

Photo, U.S. Navy.

(Atlantic Fleet).

SOLACE (1896). 5700 tons. Complement: 153, out of which 59 only are U. S. naval ratings. Dimensions: 377×44×22 feet (*mean* draught). H.P. 3200 = 15 kts. Armament: *Nil*.

Tugs.

Note: For **BRANT, CARDINAL, SANDPIPER** (Tugs, Pacific Fleet) and **PEACOCK, WARBLER, WILLETT** (Tugs, Atlantic Fleet), see "Bird Class Mine-Sweepers" on a preceding page.

NUMBER 21—39, building and completing. **ALLEGHENY**❊ (1917), **SAGAMORE**❊ (1917). Ocean-going Tugs of 1000 tons. $149\frac{1}{4}$ $×30×14\frac{3}{4}$ feet. Guns: 2—3 inch AA., 2 M.G. I.H.P. 1800 = 13 to 14 kts. Oil, 279 tons.

❊ Both Atlantic Fleet.

NUMBER 48—85. Building. Tugs of 215 tons. $82\frac{1}{4}×20×8\frac{3}{4}$ feet. Guns: 2—1 pdr., 1 M.G. H.P. 300 = 10 kts. Oil fuel only.

(Pacific Fleet).

DREADNAUGHT (1917), **UNDAUNTED** (1917). 450 tons. Guns: 1—3 pdr., 2 M.G. I.H.P. 1000 = 11·5 kts. Oil fuel only.

(Atlantic Fleet).

CHEMUNG (ex-*Pocahontas*, 1916), **WANDO** (1916). 575 tons. Dimensions: $123\frac{1}{2}×26\frac{2}{3}×11\frac{1}{2}$ feet. 2—3 pdr., 1 M.G. H.P. 800 = 11 kts. Oil fuel only.

("Arapho" Atlantic Fleet. "Mohave" Pacific Fleet).

ARAPHO (1914), **MOHAVE** (1914). 575 tons. 2—3 pdr. H.P. 800 = 10 to 11 kts. Oil: 149 tons.

(Atlantic Fleet).

LYKENS (1913). 625 tons *gross*. Dimensions: 157×29×15 feet. Guns: 1—3 inch, 2 M.G. H.P. 1000 = kts.

ONTARIO. *Photo, U.S. Navy.*

(Pacific Fleet.)

SONOMA (1912) and **ONTARIO** (1912). 1120 tons. Dimensions: 175 (*p.p.*) × 34 × $12\frac{1}{2}$ feet (*mean*). Guns: 1—3 inch AA., 2 M.G. Speed: 13 kts. Coal: 440 tons (*average*). These two tugs are ocean-going, and available as repair ships.

(Continued on next page).

Tugs—*Continued.*

(Atlantic Fleet.)

PATAPSCO (1908), **PATUXENT** (1908). 755 tons. Dimensions: 148 × 29 × 12¼ feet. Guns: 1—3 inch AA., 2 M.G. H.P. 1160 = 13 kts. Coal: 324 tons.

(Pacific Fleet.)

SEA ROVER (1902). tons. Guns: 1—3 inch, 2 M.G. I.H.P. 700 = 10 kts. Fuel: 1200 barrels oil fuel.

(Atlantic Fleet.)

POTOMAC (1897). 785 tons. Guns: 2—3 pdr. H.P. 2000 = 16 kts. Coal: 200 tons.

(Asiatic Fleet.)

PISCATAQUA (1897). 854 tons. Guns: 2—3 pdr., 2 M.G. H.P. 2000 = 16 kts. Coal: 236 tons.

(Asiatic Fleet.)

WOMPATUCK (1896). 462 tons. Guns: 2—1 pdr., 1 M.G. H.P. 650 = 13 kts. Coal: 130 tons.

(Pacific Fleet.)

IROQUOIS (1892). 702 tons. Guns: 2—3 pdr. H.P. 1000 = 13¼ kts. Oil fuel.

(Pacific Fleet.)

ASPINET (ex-*Apache*, 1889). 650 tons. Guns: 2—1 pdr., 2 M.G. I.H.P. 550 = 10 kts. Coal: 123 tons.

Also many other Tugs not assigned to fleet duties.

Converted Yachts.

(See next page for Table of Yachts purchased during War.)

WASP (1898). 630 tons. Guns: 2—3 pdr., 2—1 pdr. H.P. 1800 = 16½ kts. Coal: 79 tons.

SYLPH (1898). 152 tons. Armament: 2 M.G. H.P. 550 = 15 kts. Coal: 48 tons. Complement, 31.

DOROTHEA (1897). 594 tons. Guns: 3—3 inch, 2 M.G., 1 Y-gun. H.P. 1560 = 14 kts. Coal: 80 tons. Boilers: Yarrow.

Converted Yachts—*Continued.*

Photo, Lieut F. S. Dowell, U S.N.

(Presidential Yacht.)

MAYFLOWER (1896). 2690 tons. Armament: 2—3 inch, 1—3 inch AA., 4—6 pdr. H.P. 2400 = 14½ kts. Coal: 537 tons. Complement, 180.

SCORPION (1896). 775 tons. Armament: 4—6 pdr. H.P. 2800 = 17·8 kts. Coal: 136 tons. Complement, 87. Station Ship at Constantinople; interned during War. Reported relieved by *Galveston*, 1919.

VIXEN (1896). 806 tons. Guns: 4—3 pdr., 2—1 pdr. H.P. 1250 = 16 kts. Coal: 190 tons.

Photo, H. Reuterdahl, Esq.

HAWK (1891). 375 tons. Guns: 1—3 pdr., 2—1 pdr. H.P. 900 = 14¼ kts. Coal: 70 tons.

EAGLE (1890) 434 tons. Armament: 2—6 pdr. H.P. 850 = 12·5 kts. Coal: 68 tons. Complement, 69.

Photo, H. Reuterdahl, Esq.

AILEEN (1896). 192 tons. Guns: 1—3 pdr., 2—1 pdr. H.P. 500 = 14 kts. Coal: 46 tons.

YANKTON (1893). 975 tons. Armament: 2—3 inch, 2—3 pdr., 2 M.G. H.P. 750 = 14 kts. Coal: 174 tons. Complement, 86. 1″ deck amidships.

SYLVIA (1882). 302 tons. Guns: 3—1 pdr. 2 M.G. H.P. 165 = 9 kts. Coal: 60 tons.

The following Table gives the names and brief details of Yachts purchased and armed for War Service. Material (S) = Steel; (I) = Iron; (C) = Composite; (W) = Wood. Where two building dates are given, second date is of reconstruction. Tonnages are *gross* unless otherwise stated.

Present disposal of these vessels not known. Large Yachts, like *Aphrodite, Corsair, Kwasind* may be retained by the Navy and the other craft sold out. *Isabel* rated as a Destroyer during the War.

A very large number of other Yachts acquired for the war by Charter and free lease omitted, as all these vessels have been (or will be) returned to their owners,

Winchester listed on next page with experimental vessels.

Photo : favour of Commodore R. P. Forekew, N.Y.N.M.

GLOUCESTER (1891). 786 tons. Guns: 5—3 pdr., 2—1 pdr. H.P. 2000 = 17 kts. Coal: 120 tons. Boilers: Babcock.

Name (Material).	Built.	Tons. Gross.	Kts.	Guns.
Actus (S)	1907	99	16	2—3 inch
Adelante (I)	1883	141	12	*Nil*
Aphrodite	1899	1500*	15	4—3 inch / 2 M.G.
Arcady (W)	1898	167	13	1—3 pdr. / 2 M.G.
Arcturus (S)	1912	456	12	2—3 inch / 2 M.G.
Chilhowee (W)	1898	95	14	2—1 pdr. / 2 M.G.
Christabel (I)	1893	248	11½	2—3 inch / 2 M.G.
Cigarette (S)	1905	99	22	1—1 pdr. / 1 M.G.
Corona (S)	1905	304	..	2—3 inch / 2 M.G.
Corsair (S)	1899	1600*	19	4—3 inch / 2 M.G.
Despotch (S)	1913	287	16.3	*Nil*
Druid (S)	1902	539	17	2—3 inch / 2 M.G.
Emeline (S)	1898	407	11½	2—3 pdr. / 2 M.G.
Felicia (S)	1898	213	14	3—3 pdr. / 2 M.G. / 1 Y
Florence (C)	1903	104	12	1—6 pdr. / 2—3 pdr.
Galatea (S)	1914	367	14	3—3 inch / 2 M.G.
Hauoli (S)	1902	304	13.8	2—3 inch / 2 M.G.
Helenita (S)	1902	304	13.8	2—3 inch / 2 M.G.
Isabel	1917	797	28.8	4—4 inch / 2—1 pdr. A.A. / 4—18 inch tubes
Kwasind (S)	1914	400*	16	2—3 inch / 2 M.G.
Legonia II (S)	1909	244	13	4—6 pdr. / 2 M.G.
Lydonia (S)	1912	497	12	4—3 inch / 2 M.G.
Margaret (S)	1899 1913	283	..	2—3 inch / 2 M.G.
May (S)	1891	1100*	13	1—4 inch / 2—3 inch / 2 M.G.
Narada (S)	1889	505	12	..
Naushon (S)	1895 1900	135	13	2—6 pdr. / 2 M.G.

*Displacement.   (*Continued on next page.*)

Converted Yachts.—*continued.*

Name (*Material*).	Built.	Tons. Gross.	Kts.	Guns.
Niagra (S)	1898	703	13	4—4 inch 2— M. G. 1 Y
Nokomis (S)	1917	872	16	4—3 inch 2 M. G.
Onward (S)	1906	157	13.8	2—6 pdr. 2 M. G.
Parthenia (W)	1903	144	12½	1—3 pdr. 1 M. G.
Phalarope (W)	1881	55	12	1—1 pdr. 1 M. G.
Piqua (S)	1899	575*	20	4—3 inch 1—6 pdr. 2 M. G.
Remlik (S)	1903	600*	14	2—3 inch 2 M. G.
Reposo II (W)	1882 1892	157	·14	1—3 pdr. 2 M. G. 1 Y
Sachsen (S)	1902	217	13	1—6 pdr. 2—3 pdr. 2 M. G.
Sati'la (W)	1902	106	10.4	1—3 pdr. 1 M. G.
Sialia (S)	1914	558	14½	2—3 inch (Davis) 2 M. G.
SP 237 (S)	1910	219	13	4—6 pdr.
SP 427 (W)	1888	157	18	2—6 pdr.
SP 507 (S)	1909	195	14	3—3 pdr. 2 M. G. 1 Y
SP 524 (S)	1913	161	14	1—3 pdr.
SP 582 (S)	1907	161	15	2—2 pdr. 2 M. G.
SP 852 (C)	1899	74	10	1—3 pdr. 2 M. G.
Stinger (—)	1917	47	14¾	1—1 pdr. 1 M. G.
Thetis (W)	1917	98*	12	2—3 inch 2 M. G.
Vega (S)	1907	276	15	1—3 inch 1—6 pdr. 2 M. G.
Wacondah (S)	1901	190	18	2—6 pdr. 2 M. G.
Wanderer (S)	1897	362	12	2—3 inch 2 M. G.
Wenonah (S)	1915	200	12	2—3 inch 2 M. G.
Yacona (S)	1898	527	12	2—3 inch 2 M. G.
Zara (S)	1891	184	10	2—6 pdr. 2 M. G.
Zoraya (W)	1901	129	12	2—3 pdr.

*Displacement.

Surveying Service.

Vessels withdrawn from this Service during War. Present allocation of ships not known.

Non-Naval Vessels belonging to Coast and Geodetic Survey and Lighthouse Service served with Regular Navy during War on Patrol and Distant Service, but have now returned to their normal duties.

For Fisheries Duties (Alaska.).

Has no mainmast now.

(Gunboat.)

VICKSBURG (1896). 1010 tons. Guns : 6—4 inch, 4—3 pdr., 2—1 pdr. H.P. 800 = 12 kts. Boilers : 2 single-ended. Coal : 243 tons.

(Tenders, four *SC* boats : *SC* 309, *SC* 310, *SC*——, *SC* ——.)

Ship reserved for Experimental Services.

Photo wanted.

Resembles T.B.D. Raised fo'xle with Chart House, 2 thick funnels, 2 masts.

(Yacht converted for Testing PVs.)

WINCHESTER (Bath I. W., 1916). 437 tons. Dimensions : 225 × 21 × 7½ feet. Guns : 1—3 inch, 1—6 pdr., 2 M.G., 1 Y-gun. Parsons turbines and Normand boilers. S.H.P. 7000. Trial speed : 31.65 kts. Fuel : Oil only. 35,000 gallons = 1632 miles at 17.3 kts. Purchased for $300,000, 1917.

(Experimental Torpedo Ship.)

VESUVIUS (1888). Ex-"Dynamite Cruiser." 930 tons. Armament : 1—3 pdr. signalling. Original speed : about 21½ kts., much less now. Torpedo tubes : 1—21 inch *sub.*, 1—18 inch *sub.*, 2—18 inch *above water.*

U. S. NAVAL MILITIA (in 1916).

California.

Columbia (District of)

Connecticut.

Florida.

Illinois.

Indiana.

Louisiana.

Maine.

Massachusetts.

Maryland.

Michigan.

Minnesota.

Missouri.

New Jersey.

New York.

North Carolina.

Oregon.

Ohio.

Pennsylvania.

Rhode Island.

Washington.

Revised 1919 from "Ships' Data," U.S. Naval Vessels. **Armaments** listed those mounted during War, when ships served on Patrol and Distant Service with the Regular Navy. Proposed 1919, that the Coastguard Service should be merged into the Regular Navy.

5 CUTTERS building and completing by Norway Con. Co., Everett, Wash. 1600 tons. 240 × 39 × 14 feet. S.H.P. 2600 = 16 kts. (These details unofficial.)

ACUSHNET. Steel, 1 screw. 800 tons. Dimensions: 152 × 29 × 13¾ feet Speed, 12·5 kts. Guns: 2—1 pdr., 1 Y-gun.

ALGONQUIN (1898). Steel, 1 screw. 1181 tons. Dimensions: 205 × 32 × 13½ feet. Speed, 16 kts. Guns: 4—3 inch, 2 M.G.

ANDROSCOGGIN (1908). Wood, 1 screw. 1605 tons. Dimensions: 210 × 35 × 17½ feet. Speed, 13·2 kts. Guns: 3—3 inch, 1—6 pdr., 2 M.G., 1 Y-gun. Usually on Grand Banks for Fisheries Duty.

APACHE (1891). Iron, 1 screw. 708 tons. Dimensions: 175 × 29 × 9¼ feet. Speed, 12 kts. Guns: 3—3 inch, 2 M.G., 1 Y-gun.

BEAR (1874). Wood, 1 screw. 1700 tons. Dimensions: 198 × 28½ × 18¼ feet. Speed not known. Guns: 3—6 pdr.

No photo available.

(Depot Ship.)

COLFAX (1871). Iron, 610 tons. Dimensions: 179½ × 25 × 9 feet. No other details known.

Photo wanted.

COMANCHE (1896). Steel, 2 screw. 670 tons. Dimensions: 169 × 27 × 9 feet. Guns: 1—3 inch, 2—6 pdr.

GRESHAM (1897). Steel, 1 screw. 1090 tons. Dimensions: 205 × 32 × 11 feet. Speed, 13 kts. Guns: 4—3 inch, 2 M.G.

Photo, Seward, Weymouth.

ITASCA (*ex Bancroft*, 1893). Steel, 2 screws. 980 tons. Dimensions: 189 × 32 × 13 feet. Speed, 14·37 kts. Guns: 2—3 inch, 2—6 pdr., 1 Y-gun.

MANNING (1897). Composite, 1 screw. 1155 tons. Dimensions: 205 × 32 × 13 ft. Speed, 14 kts. Guns: 4—4 inch, 2 M.G.

Cruising Cutters—*Continued.*

MORRILL (1889). Iron, 1 screw. 420 tons. Dimensions : 145 × 24 × 9 ft. Speed : 13·2 kts. Guns : 1—3 inch, 2—6 pdr., 2 M.G.

ONONDAGA (1898). Steel, 1 screw. 1192 tons. Dimensions : 205 × 32 × 13 feet. Speed : 14·5 kts. Guns : 4—6 pdr.

Photo wanted.

OSSIPEE (1915). Steel, 1 screw. 908 tons. Dimensions : 165¾ × 32 × 11¾ feet. Speed : 12·6 kts. Oil fuel only. Guns : 2—3 inch, 2 M.G.

PAMLICO (1907). Steel, twin screw. 451 tons. Dimensions : 158 × 30 × 5 ft. Speed : 11·2 kts. Guns : 2—6 pdr.

SEMINOLE (1900). Steel, 1 screw. 860 tons. Dimensions : 188 × 29 × 11 feet. Speed : 14·7 kts. Guns : 4—3 inch, 2 M.G., 1 Y-gun.

SENECA (1908). Steel, 1 screw. 1445 tons. Dimensions : 204 × 34 × 17 feet. Speed : 13·2 kts. Guns : 4—4 inch, 2 M.G., 1 Y gun.

Cruising Cutters—*Continued.*

Photo wanted.

SNOHOMISH. Steel, 1 screw. 879 tons. Dimensions : 152 × 29 × 15 feet. Speed : 12·5 kts. Guns : 1—3 inch, 2—6 pdr., 2 M.G.

Photo wanted.

TALLAPOOSA (1915). Steel, 1 screw. 912 tons. Dimensions : 165¾ × 32 × 11¾ feet. Speed : 12·7 kts. Oil fuel only. Guns : 1—4 inch, 2—6 pdr., 2 M.G., 1 Y-gun. Derelict Destroyer for Gulf of Mexico.

TUSCARORA (1902). Steel, 1 screw. 739 tons. Speed : 14·2 kts Dimensions : 178 × 30 × 11 feet. Guns : 1—3 inch, 2—6 pdr., 1 Y-gun.

Cruising Cutters.—*Continued.*

Photo, U.S. Navy Publicity Bureau.

UNALGA (1912). Steel, 1 screw. 1180 tons. Dimensions: 190 × 32 × 13 feet. Speed 13 kts. 3—6 pdr.

WINDOM (1896). Steel, twin screw. 670 tons. Dimensions: 170 × 27 × 9 ft. Speed 12 kts.

YAMACRAW (1909). Steel, 1 screw. 1082 tons. Dimensions: 191 × 32 × 14 feet. Speed, 13 kts. 2—4 inch, 2—3 inch, 2 M.G.

Harbour Cutters.

ARCATA (1903). Wood, 1 screw. 130 tons. Dimensions: 85 × 17 × 10ft.

ARUNDEL (ex *Manhattan*) (1873). Iron, 1 screw. 174 tons. Dimensions: 102 × 20 × 8 feet.

CALUMET (1894). Iron, 1 screw. 169 tons. Dimensions: 94 × 20 × 8 feet. 2—6 pdr., 2 M.G.

Harbour Cutters—*continued.*

DAVEY (1908). Steel, 1 screw. 153 tons. Dimensions : 92 × 19 × 10ft. 1—1 pdr.

Photo wanted.

EMMA KATE ROSS (1882). Iron, 1 screw. 350 tons. Dimensions : 104 × 20 × 10 feet.

GOLDEN GATE (1896). Steel, 1 screw. 220 tons. Dimensions: 110 × 20 × 9 feet.

Harbour Cutters—*continued.*

GUTHRIE (1895).   Iron, 1 screw.   126 tons.   Dimensions : 88×17×
9 feet.

No photo available.

HARTLEY (1875).   Wood, 1 screw.   48 tons.   Dimensions : 64×
11×6 feet.

HUDSON (1893).   Iron, 1 screw.   174 tons. Dimensions : 96×
20×9 feet.   Guns : 1—1 pdr.

Harbour Cutters—*continued.*

MACKINAC (1903).   Steel, 1 screw. 220 tons.   Dimensions :
110×20×10 feet. *Sig.*: GVHB. Guns : 1—6 pdr., 1 M.G.

Photo, " Syren & Shipping."

MANHATTAN (1918).   Steel, 1 screw.   Ice Breaker, Salvage
Vessel, Tug and Fire Float. **379** tons. 120¼×24×10¾ feet. 12 kts.

No photo available.

VERGANA (——).   128 tons.   No other details.

Harbour Cutters—*continued.*

WINNISIMMET (1903).   Steel, 1 screw.   174 tons.   Dimensions :
96×20×9 feet. Guns : 2—1 pdr.

WISSAHICKON (1904).   Steel, 1 screw.   174 tons.   Dimensions :
96×20×8 feet. Guns : 1—1 pdr.

WOODBURY (1864).   Wood, 1 screw.   500 tons.   Dimensions :
146×28×11 feet.   1 gun.
Note.—Above probably re-named or scrapped as there is a new T.B.D.
Woodbury.

11 Launches.

ACTIVE (——) — tons. ADVANCE (1917), 11 tons. ALERT
(1907), 17 tons. GUARD (1913), 52 tons. GUIDE (1907), 32
tons. MAGOTHY (1895), 83 tons. PATROL (1899), 15 tons.
PENROSE (1883), 30 tons. SCOUT (1896), 30 tons. SEARCH
(1907), — tons. TYBEE (1895), 40 tons.

(IMPERIAL) JAPANESE NAVY.

ADDENDA AND CORRECTIONS.

PRIVATE SHIPBUILDING YARDS.—The Koshiura Dockyard, near Kine, has been bought by the Kawasaki Dockyard Co., and will be devoted to the construction of Submarines. The Bingo Dockyard, in the Inland Sea, has been acquired by the Osaka Ironworks Co. The Osaka Ironworks Yard at Sakurajima may be closed down.

NEW CONSTRUCTION.—An official project has been discussed for raising the Fleet Establishment to the "8—8—8" Standard, *viz.*, one squadron of Battleships (under eight years old), one squadron of Battle-Cruisers (under eight years old), one squadron of Battleships (over eight years old). This project cannot be realised till the output of yards has been increased very considerably.

KONGO class.—Following are additional notes and corrections : Armour : Main belt is 12′ 5″ deep, 8″ thick, and extends between Barbettes Nos. 1 and 4. Upper belt between Barbettes Nos. 1 and 3, 6″ thick, and carried up to forecastle deck. Bulkheads : Main belt is closed by diagonal bulkheads of 8″—6″ aft and by a 6″—5″ bulkhead forward. Upper belt closed by 6″ B.H. aft and 9″—6″ B.H. forward. Tubes are located in sections 5, 10, 19, 23, on profile plan, and, except in the case of the tubes in wake of No. 3 Barbette, Starboard Tube is before Port Tube. 3 inch guns are probably 14 pdrs.

FUJI.—As noted below, a new Destroyer has been named *Fuji*. Not known if Battleship of this name is removed from the Imperial Navy or re-named.

TWO NEW LIGHT CRUISERS projected under 1919-20 section of the 1918-24 Naval Programme.

AKASHI.

A new Naval Aviation Station is to be established at Himomura, Kama Province, near Kure D.Y.

ITSUKUSHIMA removed from List of Effective Warships, but available for subsidiary naval purposes.

Destroyers.

Following 10 boats to be built under 1919-20 Section of the 1918-24 Naval Programme:
First Class : *Akikaze, Hokaze, Shiokaze, Tachikaze, Yukaze.*
Second Class : *Ao-i, Fuji, Hagi, Kiku, Susuki.*
Minekaze launched Feb., 1919. **Sawakaze** launched Jan., 1919. **Yakaze** launched April, 1919. **Murakumo** and **Yugiri** removed from List of Effective Warships, but available for subsidiary purposes.

Torpedo Boats.

Hayabusa, Kasasagi, Manadzuru, removed from List of Effective Warships, but available for subsidiary naval purposes.

Submarines.

Seven further boats, **Nos. 44-50,** are projected under 1919-20 section of the 1918-24 Naval Programme. Ex-German Submarines have been renumbered thus :—**O1** (ex-*U125*), **O2** (ex-*U46*), **O3** (ex-*U85*), **O4** (ex-*UC90*), **O5** (ex-*UB99*). **O6** (ex-*UB125*), **O7** (ex-*UB143*).

Depot Ships, Fleet Auxiliaries, &c.

Reported that electric drive is to be installed in some Special Service Ships of 200 to 300 tons, for experimental purposes.

YENTO (Maru) and **YENOSHIMA (Maru)** may also be named correctly as **ENTO (Maru)** and **ENOSHIMA (Maru)**.

In addition to the Mine Layers given, the following old ships are used as Mining Vessels :

DAI SHICHI SHINTEN (1901), **DAI NI KWAITEN (Maru)** (1900), **DAI NI OMINATO (Maru)** (1900), **DAI ICHI TENKYO** (1899), **TAKESHIKI (Maru)** (1899), **NASAMI (Maru)** (1899), **DAI GO SHINTEN** (1898), **DAI SAN SHINTEN** (1888), **KEIKWAN (Maru)** (——).

TWO NEW OIL TANKERS to be built under 1918-24 Naval Programme (1919-20 Section). The "Jiji Shimpo," of August 17th, reports that Oil Tanker **SHIJIKI** was sunk in a typhoon, off Tanegashima, on August 15th. **MATSUE** removed from List of Effective Warships, but available for subsidiary duties. **YURAGAWA (Maru)** reported to have been disposed of, either by sale or breaking up ; no longer exists.

IMPERIAL JAPANESE NAVY.

Revised, 1919, by the Navy Department, Tokyo, by courtesy of H. E. The Minister of Marine.

(The Acting-Editor has also to acknowledge the use of many useful notes and sketches, kindly furnished to "Fighting Ships" by Mr. K. Shimada in 1918.)

MINISTER OF THE NAVY

Errata.

On Map :—
For **KOREA** read **CHOSEN**.
For **YEZO** read **HOKKAIDO**.
For **MASANPHO** read **CHINKAI**.

ENSIGN — JACK & MERCANTILE ENSIGN — IMPERIAL STANDARD — TRANSPORT

Red — White — Gold — Blue

ADMIRAL — VICE ADMIRAL — REAR ADMIRAL — COMMODORE — SENIOR OFFICER — OFFICER COMMANDING TORPEDO DIVISION

YOKOSUKA

	to			knots.
Hakodate	...	...	...	450
Hong Kong	...	...	...	1580
Honolulu	...	...	...	3400
Kobe	...	...	...	300
Kure	...	...	...	400
Manila	...	...	...	1720
Nagasaki	...	...	...	760
Ryojun (Port Arthur)	...			1350
Saigon	...	...	...	2400
Shanghai	...	...	...	1050

NAGASAKI

	to			knots.
Chemulpo	...	...	...	446
Foo-chau	...	...	...	650
Hong Kong	...	...	...	1067
Keilung (Formosa)	...			630
Kiao-chau	...	...	...	450
Kure	...	...	...	240
Kobe	...	...	...	340
Maidzuru	...	...	...	400
Manila	...	...	...	1300
Chinkai	...	...	...	170
Matsumai	...	...	...	750
Pescadores	...	...	...	820
Ryojun (Port Arthur)	...			585
Takeshiki	...	...	...	120
Saigon	...	...	...	1990
Shanghai	...	...	...	330
Vladivostock	...	...	...	620
Wei-hai-wei	...	...	...	480

TAKESHIKI

	to			knots.
Kiao-chau	...	...	...	420
Maidzuru	...	...	...	340
Chinkai	...	...	...	70
Matsumai	...	...	...	600
Nagasaki	...	...	...	120
Ryojun (Port Arthur)	...			500
Vladivostock	...	...	...	520
Wei-hai-wei	...	...	...	430

MAIDZURU

	to			knots.
Matsumai	...	...	...	440
Nagasaki	...	...	...	400
Ominato	...	...	...	465
Takeshiki	...	...	...	340
Vladivostock	...	...	...	620

(RYOJUN) PORT ARTHUR

	to			knots.
Hong Kong	...	...	...	1275
Kiao-chau	...	...	...	280
Nagasaki	...	...	...	585
Vladivostock	...	...	...	1170
Wei-hai-wei	...	...	...	100

MATSUMAI

	to			knots.
Maidzuru	...	...	...	440
Nagasaki	...	...	...	750
Ryojun (Port Arthur)	...			1150
Takeshiki	...	...	...	600
Vladivostock	...	...	...	380
Yokosuka	...	...	...	560
Nearest Russian coast (150 English miles N.E. by E. of Vladivostock)	...	...		250

RUSSIA
GULF OF TARTARY
La Perouse Straits
VLADIVOSTOCK
YEZO
MATSMAI HAKODATE
Straits of Tsugaru OMINATO
Port Lazareff
KOREA
NIPPON
Masanpho Fusan
Takeshiki
TOKIO YOROHAMA
Simonoseki Straits MAIDZURU YOKOSUKA
KURE KOBE
INLAND SEA
SASEBO
NAGASAKI

0 50 100 200
KNOTS

JAPANESE DOCKYARDS.

Divided into 2000 yard squares.   Uniform scale.   Soundings in fathoms.   Heights in feet.

YOKOSUKA

KURE.

MAIDZURU.

RYOJUN (PORT ARTHUR).

Imperial Dockyards.   Principal Naval Harbours (Ching-ju-fu).

YOKOSUKA (in Sagami).   Fleet Base, Dockyard, T.B.D., Submarine and Aircraft Stations. Fortified. Six slips, one for battle-cruisers, two for Dreadnoughts, three smaller. Docks No. 5, $747 \times 115 \times 41$ feet, able to take any ship, and No. 4, $538 \times 98\frac{1}{2} \times 32$. Also one dock (No. 2) $447 \times 94\frac{1}{2} \times 29$ feet; two others: No. 1, $298 \times 82 \times 21$ feet; No. 3, $265 \times 45 \times 18$ feet. Employees (in 1914) 8000. Naval Engineering Academy here. Naval Aviation Station at Oihama.   Admiralty Chart No. 997.

KURE (in Aki).   Fleet Base, Dockyard, T.B.D., and Aircraft Base.   Three slips.   Docks No. 1, $413 \times 58\frac{1}{2} \times 28$ feet; No. 2, $485\frac{1}{2} \times 81 \times 35\frac{1}{2}$ feet.   No. 3, $666 \times 100 \times 34$ feet. Perhaps a fourth big dock.   Ordnance and Armour Plate built here. Cadets Academy at Etajima.   Admiralty Chart No. 3469.

*SASEBO (in Hizen).   Fleet Base, Dockyard, T.B.D. and Aircraft Base.   One slip.   There are four docks here: (1) $435 \times 94 \times 29$; (2) $475 \times 85 \times 32$; (3) $538 \times 93\frac{1}{2} \times 33$ feet. (4) $777 \times 111 \times 38$ feet. Perhaps a fifth big dock. There is also a floating dock for torpedo craft here (1500 tons). Admiralty Chart No. 359.

MAIDZURU (or MAIZURU) (in Tango).   Admiralty Chart No. 2174. One dock 450 feet long, one small for t.b. (completed 1908), a third dock 540 feet long completed 1913.   Perhaps a fourth dock.

RYOJUN (PORT ARTHUR).   Dry docks: No. 1, $370 \times 72 \times 30$ feet; No. 2, $500 \times 92\frac{1}{2} \times 32$ feet.   Admiralty Chart No. 1236-1798.

DAIREN (Dalny).   Naval dock, $381 \times 43 \times 19\frac{3}{4}$ feet.

CHINKAI (Korea), previously known as Masampo.

* See next page for Map.

242

Divided into 2000 yard squares.　　Uniform scale.　　Soundings in fathoms.　　Heights in feet.

SASEBO.

Lesser Naval Harbours (*Yoko*).

OMINATO. Torpedo base.) Repair Stations for T.B.D., &c. Small 1500 ton Floating
BAKO (Pescadores).) Dock at each.

Mercantile Marine.

June, 1919, 2,325,000 tons *gross*. A considerable amount of new mercantile tonnage is being built.

Coinage.

Yen (100 **sen**) = 2s. 0¼d. British, $0.50 U.S.A., *about*.

Principal Mercantile Ports.

Yokohama, Hakodate, Nagasaki, Moji, Kobé, Dairen (Dalny).

Overseas Possessions.

Formosa. Karafuto (Saghalien), Pescadores. Protectorate in Chosen (Korea). Kiaochau Peninsula and Tsingtao leased from China.

KIAO-CHAU and TSINGTAO (China). German naval base in the Far East, occupied by the Anglo-Japanese Expeditionary Army, 1914. There used to be a floating dock here, 410 × 100 × 30 feet (12,000 tons), but it was probably destroyed by the Germans before surrender. Tsingtao is only being used as a commercial harbour, but the naval base facilities, created during German occupation, are at the disposal of Japanese warships in any emergency.

Private Docks.

Details of Private Docks will be found on a later page (after the Silhouettes), with a full description of the Private Japanese Shipbuilding Yards.

Principal Naval Guns. * = Q.F. with brass cartridge case.

Notation.	Calibre.	Length in calibres.	Model.	Weight of Gun.	Weight of A.P. shot.	Maximum Initial Velocity.	Maximum penetration firing A.P. capped at K.C.		Danger space against average ship, at			Service rate of Fire Rounds per minute.
							5000 yards.	3000 yards.	10,000 yards.	5000 yards.	3000 yards.	
	inches.			tons.	lbs.	F. S.	inches.	inches.				
A⁸	14	45	V	82	1400	...	...	...	...	...	...	...
A³	12·6	40	C	66	990	2306	12	15	...	...	...	0·2
A⁵	12	45	('04)	58½	850	2800	16	20	185	500	780	...
A³	12	40	E	49	850	2423	12	15½	120	450	720	1
A³	10	45	E	32½	500	2710	10¼	13½	150	480	720	3
A³	10	45	O	32	490	2500	9¾	12½	130	450	700	...
B	9	35	O	19¼	268	2400	5½	7¼	...	...	...	...
A*	8	45	O	15½	188	2800	7½	10¼	105	430	625	1
A	8	45	E	17⅓	250	2740	7	10	110	425	600	1·2
B*	8	40	E	15½	250	2580	5½	7½	100	400	580	1·2
C	6	45	('04)	8½	100	3000	4½	6½	75	250	475	...
C	6	50	V	8	100	3000	4½	6½	75	250	475	6
E*	6	40	E	6½	100	2500	3	4½	65	210	435	7
F*	6	40	E	6	100	2220	2½	4	35	150	360	8
E*	5·5	...	...	...	...	...	...	...	...	...	...	...
F*	4·7	45	...	...	...	...	...	...	...	...	...	...
F*	4·7	40	E	2	45	2150	...	2½	...	...	...	8
F*	4·7	32	E	1⅔	36	1938	...	...	...	...	...	8-6
F*	3	...	...	...	14	...	...	...	...	...	...	...
F*	3	40	...	2	12	2200	...	...	...	...	...	...

In the Model column C = Schneider-Canet; E, Elswick; O, Obukhoff (Russian); V, Vickers.

16 inch in *Kaga, Tosa, Nagato* and *Mutsu* ?

14 inch, 45 cal. in *Ise* class (2), *Fuso* class (2), *Kongo* class (4).

12 inch, 50 cal. in *Settsu*.

12 inch, 45 cal. in *Settsu, Satsuma, Aki, Kurama, Ibuki, Ikoma, Katori, Kashima, Iwami, Mikasa.*

12 inch, 40 cal. in *Asahi, Shikishima, Fuji.*

10 inch, 45 cal. in *Satsuma, Aki, Kashima, Katori, Suwo, Okino-shima,* * *Mishima.* *

8 inch, 40-45 cal. in 1st Class Cruisers, *Kurama, Ibuki.*

6 inch, 50 cal. in *Fuso* class (2), *Kongo* class (4), *Settsu.*

6 inch, 40-45 cal. in *Aki* and older Battleships, 1st and 2nd Class Cruisers, &c.

5·5 inch in *Ise* class (2), *Tatsuta* class (2).

* May have been removed from these ships.

Note.

Kure Naval Arsenal has concluded experiments with anti-aircraft guns. Large numbers of these guns are now being manufactured for all classes of warships and defences of naval harbours.

(All details tabulated above are unofficial.)

Ordnance Factories.

Guns manufactured at Kure, N.Y. Also by Muroran Steel Works, Hokkaido, owned by Hokkaido Colliery & S.S. Co., Messrs. Vickers Ltd. and Sir W. G. Armstrong-Whitworth & Co., and licensed to build Armstrong and Vickers' types of guns. There are also Japanese "Yamanouchi" types of small types of guns.

Shells manufactured by Muroran Steel Works, Kobe Iron & Steel Works, Kawasaki Zosen Kaisha, Mitsubshi Zosen Kaisha, Nippon Heiki Kaisha, and other firms.

Armour Plates.

From Imperial Iron Works, Yawata, Kyushu and Kure D.Y.

Torpedoes.

Size	Name or Mark	Air Pressure lbs.	Charge lbs.	Max. Range at kts.		Type of Heater
21″	...	...	...	...	...	...
18″	...	...	...	...	...	...
15″	...	...	...	...	...	...
14″	...	...	...	...	...	...

Torpedoes built by Mitsubishi Zosen Kaisha, Kobé Steel Works (output, 250 torpedoes p.a.), and by Navy Yards which also construct tubes.

Mines.—No details known.

Searchlights.—No details known.

JAPANESE NAVY.

Official Classification of Ships.

The official classification, instituted in 1912, is as follows:—

Battleships.	Battle-Cruisers.	1st class Cruisers (over 7000 tons).	2nd class Cruisers (under 7000 tons).	1st class Coast Defence Ships (over 7000 tons).	2nd class Coast Defence Ships (under 7000 tons).	1st Class Gunboats (over 800 tons).	2nd Class Gunboats (under 800 tons).
Kaga	*Akagi*	Nisshin	*Oh-i*	Iwami	Okinoshima	Mogami	Saga
Tosa	*Amagi*	Kasuga	*Kitakami*	Fuji	Mishima	Yodo	Uji
Mutsu	Kirishima	Aso	*Kiso*	Suwo	Chiyoda	Chihaya	Fushimi
Nagato	Haruna	Idzumo	*Kuma*		Akitsushima		Toba
Hiuga	Hi-yei	Iwate	*Tama*		Manshu		Sumida
Ise	Kongo	Yakumo	Tatsuta		Matsue		
Yamashiro	Kurama	Adzuma	Tenriu		Hashidate		
Fu-so	Ibuki	Asama	Hirado		Karasaki		
Settsu	Ikoma	Tokiwa	Chikuma		Komahasni		
Aki			Yahagi		Wakamiya		
Satsuma			Tone		Musashi		
Kashima			Niitaka		Yamato		
Katori			Tsushima				
Mikasa			Tsugaru				
Asahi			Chitose				
Shikishima			Suma				
Hizen			Akashi				

Destroyers:—1st class, over 1000 tons; 2nd class, 1000-600 tons; 3rd class, under 600 tons.
Torpedo boats:—1st class, over 120 tons; 2nd class, under 120 tons.

Present System of Nomenclature : Battleships named after Provinces; Light Cruisers after Rivers; 1st Class Destroyers after Winds; 2nd Class Destroyers after Trees.

Personnel and Uniforms.

Minister of Marine : Admiral Tomasaburo Kato, G.C.M.G.

Personnel : Active, in 1916, 63,225 all ranks—more than this now. Yearly entries about 5,000—6,000 conscripts and 5,000—6,000 volunteers. Serve 4 years on active list and 7 years in reserve.

Reserves :—35,000 or more.

INSIGNIA OF RANK—EXECUTIVE OFFICERS—SLEEVES. (Changed to this; 1908).

Sho-i Ko-hoshei.
Midshipman.

	Tai-sho.	Chu-sho.	Sho-sho.	Tai-sa.	Chu-sa.	Sho-sa.	Tai-i.	Chu-i.	Sho-i	
Executive Branch:										
Corresponding British or U.S.:	*Admiral*	*Vice-Ad.*	*Rear-Ad.*	*Captain.*	*Commander.*	*Lieut. Com.*	*Lieutenant.*	*Sub-Lieut.*	*Acting Sub-Lieut.*	Has a stripe half the width of a Sho-i.

BAND between stripes. (BRANCHES, with but after Executive).

Violet	Kikwan (*Engineer*) (with executive rank and curl. Titles as above with the prefix Kikan).
Red	Gun-i (*Doctor*).
White	Shukei (*Paymaster*).
Brown	Zosen (*Constructor*).
,,	Zoki (*Engineer-Constructor*).
Purple	Zohei (*Gun Constructor*).
Blue	Suiro (*Hydrographer*).

without curl.

CAP.

The cap is the same as the British (but without gold embroidery in the senior ranks).

CAP BADGE.

Small anchor, surrounded by cherry leaves.

The senior officer of any branch on board the ship always carries the affix "*cho.*" Thus: Ho-jitsu-cho (*Gunnery*), Sui-rai-cho (*Torpedo*), Ko-kai-cho (*Navigator*), Guni-i-cho (*Senior Doctor*), Shukei-cho (*Senior Paymaster*).

Undress is a military tunic (dark blue) with the sleeve insignia of rank in black braid only, with curl for executives and engineers. Other branches cannot be distinguished from each other in this tunic.

ONE FUNNEL.

SUMIDA
(*River Gunboat*).

SAGA
(*Gunboat*).

KUROKAMI *class* (3?)
(*Mine Layers*).

KOMAHASHI
(*Submarine Depot Ship*).

HASHIDATE
(*Training Ship*).

YURAGAWA Maru
(*Training Ship*).

MANSHU
(*Naval Transport*).

WAKAMIYA
(*Seaplane Carrier*).

KARASAKI
(*Submarine Depot Ships*).

CHIYODA

MUSASHI *class* (2)
(*Surveying Ships*).

Note.

Appearance of following Special Service Ships not known. Information regarding their appearance would assist in preparation of their Recognition Silhouettes.

T.B.D. Depot Ships :—ISUSAN, KENKAI, REKISAN, (Marus), SHIROGANE.

Mine Layers :—NINOSHIMA, YENOSHIMA, KUROSHIMA, TOSHIMA, NATSUSHIMA, ASHIZAKI, KATOKU, SOKUTEN (all Marus), KATSURIKI.

Oilers and Tankers :—ERIMO, NOTORO, SHIRETOKO, SUNOSAKI (Maru), TSURUGIZAKI, SHIJIKI.

Fleet Collier :—MUROTO.

Supply Ship :—NOSHIMA.

Transport :—TAKASAKI (*and Auxiliaries*) KOSHU, ROZAN, SEITO.

Repair Ship :—KWANTO (Maru).

Salvage Ships :—KURIHASHI, YODOHASHI, SARUHASHI, ITAHASHI.

TWO FUNNELS.

FUSHIMI & TOBA
(*River Gunboats*).

YODO.

AKASHI.

SUMA.

KASUGA *class* (2 ships).
("*Nisshin*" *attached to T.B.D.*)

FU-SO *class* (2 ships).

ISE *class* (2 ships).

CHIHAYA.

CHITOSE.

AKITSUSHIMA.

(Two Funnel types continued on next page.)

TWO   FUNNELS—*continued.*

OKINOSHIMA *class* (2 ships).
(*Barbettes may have been removed.*)

FUJI.

ASAHI.
(*Training Ship.*)

ASAMA *class* (2 ships).
("*Tokiwa*" *Training Ship.*)

MIKASA.

KATORI.

KASHIMA.

IWAMI.

SATSUMA.

IKOMA.

THREE   FUNNELS.

MOGAMI

TATSUTA *class* (2 ships).
(*Silhouette is approximate only.*)

(Three Funnel Types continued on next page.)

JAPANESE WARSHIPS RECOGNITION SILHOUETTES (*Re-arranged, 1919.*)

THREE FUNNELS—*continued.*

NAGAURA Maru.
(Submarine Depot Ship.)

NIITAKA *class* (2 ships).

TONE.

YAKUMO.
(Training Ship.)

SUWO.
(Training Ship.)

SHIKISHIMA.

IDZUMO *class* (2 ships).
"*Idzumo*" *attached to T.B.D. Flotillas.*

TSUGARU.
(Training Ship.)

HIZEN.

KURAMA
(*Ibuki* same without tripods).

SETTSU.

ADZUMA.
(Training Ship.)

AKI.

KONGO *class* (4 ships).
("*Kongo*" *has fore-funnel further forward.*)

FOUR FUNNELS.

Aso.
(*Tender to Submarines.*)

Hirado *class* (3 ships).

TORPEDO CRAFT.   Scale : 1 inch = 160 feet.

Shiritaka t b.

Nos. 68—75 t.b.
(8 Schichau *type*.)

(1)   (2)
Hayabusa *class* t.b. (11)

Kagero *class* t.b d. (3).

Urakaze t.b.d.

Momo *class* t.b.d (10).

Sakura *class* t.b.d. (2).
(May now have raised fore funnels.)

Kaba *class* t.b.d. (10).

Amatsukaze *class* t.b.d. (4).

Akebona *class* t.b.d. (2).
Asashiho *class* t.b.d. (2).

Later Arare *class* t.b.d. (33).
Earlier Arare *class* t.b.d. (2).
(*Vary a little in details.*)

Yamakaze *class* t.b.d. (2).

SUBMARINES.   Scale : 1 inch = 80 feet.

(These Silhouettes are only approximate.)

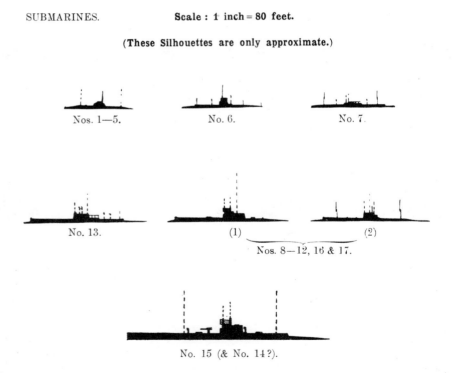

Nos. 1—5.   No. 6.   No. 7.

No. 13.   (1)   (2)
Nos. 8—12, 16 & 17.

No. 15 (& No. 14 ?).

PRINCIPAL PRIVATE ESTABLISHMENTS (including Private Docks).

Firms marked * are Warship Builders.   Zosen Kaisha = Shipbuilding Co.

ASANO ZOSEN KAISHA, Ushioda, Tsurumi. Large new Yard, covering 250 acres, completed 1918. Extensions over another 250 acres *projected*. Already has six concrete slips, 600 feet long. Four concrete slips of 800 feet length and two of 500 feet length *projected*. One 80-ton floating crane and many small travelling cranes for yard and fitting-out basin. Is to undertake warship construction.

FUJINAGATA COMPANY, Osaka.

HARADA DOCKYARD COMPANY. Osaka.

HARIMA COMPANY, Aioi.

*ISHIKAWAJIMA COMPANY, Tokyo and Uraga. Extended 1917. At Tokyo: graving dock, $270 \times 41\frac{3}{4} \times 12$ feet. At Uraga: graving dock No. 1, $482\frac{1}{4} \times 70 \times 35\frac{1}{2}$ feet; No. 2, $448\frac{1}{4} \times 65\frac{1}{2} \times 25\frac{1}{4}$ feet.

*KAWASAKI DOCKYARD COMPANY, Hyogo Works, Kobé (and at Darien or Dalny, North China). Build, engine, and equip warships and mercantile vessels of all classes. Six building slips, *i.e.*, one of 720 feet, one of 550 feet, one of 530 feet, one of 475 feet, one of 420 feet, and one of 410 feet. One graving dock $407 \times 64 \times 24$ feet. Also several patent slips. Floating cranes: one 200-ton, and several smaller. Yard covers 133 acres, and has a water-front of 1000 metres. Total number of persons employed 12,000. Licensees for the Curtis Marine Steam Turbine, Ansaldo-Laurenti types of submarines, and the Ansaldo-Fiat Diesel engines.

KUHARA ZOSEN KAISHA, Tokuyama, Shimonoseki. New large Yard, *completing*.

*MITSU BISHI ZOSEN KAISHA :—
(a) Kobé Yard.—Build, engine, and equip destroyers and mercantile vessels. Three building slips : two of 510 feet and another (length not known). Floating docks : one 12,000-ton and one 7000-ton. Large cranes : one 100-ton sheer-leg and one 40-ton floating crane. Yard covers 46 acres, with a water-front of 1700 metres. Number of persons employed 7500.
(b) Nagasaki Yard.—Warships and mercantile vessels of all types built here ; also engines, boilers, equipment, &c. Seven building slips : one of 767 feet, one of 605 feet, one of 602 feet, one of 540 feet, one of 510 feet, one of 451 feet, and one of 418 feet. Three graving docks, *viz.* : No. 3, $728 \times 96\frac{1}{2} \times 34\frac{1}{2}$ feet (*Dreadnought*); No. 1 (Tategami), $523 \times 89 \times 26\frac{1}{4}$ feet (*Dreadnought*); and No. 2 (Mukaijima), $371 \times 66 \times 23\frac{1}{2}$ feet. Large cranes : one 150-ton hammer crane ; one 60-ton ; and one 34-ton floating cranes. Yard covers 127 acres, and has a water-front of 2750 metres. Number of persons employed 15,500. Licensees for the Parsons' Marine Steam Turbine.
(c) Hikoshima (Moji).—Docks here, dimensions not known.

ONO ZOSEN KAISHA, Osaka.

*OSAKA IRONWORKS, Sakurajima, Osaka and Innoshima. At Osaka : graving dock, $259 \times 33 \times 12\frac{1}{3}$ feet.

SUZUKI COMPANY, Harima. Took over the Toba Shipbuilding Co. and Bingo Dockyard Co. during 1917. Licensees for Sulzer Diesel Engines.

*URAGA DOCK COMPANY, Uraga. Build destroyers, torpedo craft, and mercantile vessels ; also build boilers and engines, &c. Five building slips, *viz.* : two of 500 feet and three of 400 feet. Dry docks : one of $469 \times 68 \times 29$ feet, and the other of $452 \times (60-69) \times 32$ feet. Yard covers 37 acres, and has a water-front of 970 metres. Total number of persons employed 5000.

YOKOHAMA DOCK COMPANY, Yokohama. Up till recent times only undertook repair work, but is now extended and equipped for shipbuilding. Graving docks : No. 1, $483\frac{1}{2} \times 93\frac{1}{2} \times 27\frac{3}{4}$ feet ; No. 2, $375 \times 60\frac{2}{3} \times 26\frac{1}{4}$ feet ; No. 3, 481 (*o.a.*) $\times 66\frac{3}{4} \times 21\frac{1}{3}$ feet.

Other Private Docks are :—Hakodate, dry dock $480\frac{1}{4} \times 81\frac{3}{4} \times 30\frac{1}{4}$ feet ; also another larger dry dock, of which details are not available. At Nagasaki : Matsu Ironworks dry dock, $310 \times 48 \times 17$ feet ; and Messrs. Y. Iwasaki's patent slip (1200 tons). At Osaka : Temposan No. 3, $256\frac{1}{2} \times 44 \times 13\frac{3}{4}$ feet ; No. 1, $245 \times 38 \times 12\frac{1}{2}$ feet ; also two old wooden docks. In all there are twelve small docks at Osaka, and in the island of Innoshima, close by, five more, of which the largest is $425 \times 59 \times 27$ feet. At Toba, the Toba Ironworks has a small dock, $245 \times 42 \times 13\frac{1}{2}$ feet (may now belong to the Suzuki Co., of Harima).

Notes.

The Kawasaki and Mitsu Bishi Companies are, of course, the two great private warship-building establishments.

Attention must be called to the fact that during the War Japan's capacity for building warships and mercantile vessels has expanded enormously. Owing to low labour charges Japanese construction is probably now the cheapest in the world. A very large quantity of mercantile tonnage is now on order, or building, in Japanese yards to Allied or neutral orders for Japanese shipping companies. All yards of any importance have been expanded and are working to their full capacity, and many new shipbuilding firms have been established. New Japanese destroyers are constructed very quickly. In addition to carrying out construction for the Allied Governments and mercantile orders, Japanese private yards have built new warships for the Allied Governments.

NEW CONSTRUCTION.

According to accounts published in the British and Foreign Press, the Navy Department contemplates a Six Years' Programme for the period 1918-24. The financial outlay is estimated at £30,004,000 for the construction of the following new ships :—

> 4 BATTLE-CRUISERS,
> 3 LIGHT CRUISERS,
> 21 DESTROYERS (1st and 2nd Class).
> 48 SUBMARINES,
> 6 SPECIAL SERVICE SHIPS.

At the end of 1923 it is intended that the Battle Fleet should be composed of the following ships :—

8 DREADNOUGHTS : *Ise, Hiuga, Fuso, Yamashiro, Nagato, Mutsu, Kaga* and *Tosa*.

6 BATTLE-CRUISERS : *Haruna, Kirishima, Akagi, Amagi*, and two others. The last four have still to be built.

The 1918-24 Naval Programme is only to be regarded as an interim measure. If financial conditions permit, it is the intention of the Navy Department (according to report) to introduce a new Programme in 1921, with a view to expanding the Fleet to the "Eight-eight Standard," *i.e.*, to form one squadron of Dreadnoughts and one squadron of battle-cruisers, each squadron being composed of eight units.

AMAGI, AKAGI, "C" & "D" (all projected ; not yet begun).

Displacement, *about* 40,000 tons.   Complement,

Length,   feet.   Beam,   feet.   Draught,   feet.

Guns : *not known.*

Armour : *not known.*

Note.

No details known of these ships. The Navy Department has advised "Fighting Ships" that up to May, 1919, the design of these battle cruisers had not been decided upon.

Machinery : Geared turbines.   screws. Boilers : Miyabara or Kansei. Designed H.P.   =
kts. Fuel : *normal*   tons ; *maximum*   tons.

Name	Builder.	Machinery.	Laid down.	Com-pleted.	Trials.	Boilers.	Best recent speed.
Amagi*	...	...	...	...	...	...	...
Akagi*	...	...	...	...	...	...	...
" C "	...	...	...	...	...	...	...
" D "	...	...	...	...	...	...	...

General Notes.—Projected under 1918-24 Programme. *To be begun at Kure and Yokosuka Dockyards under 1919-20 Section of 1918-24 Programme.

KAGA (building), TOSA (building), NAGATO (building), and MUTSU (building).

Normal displacement, 32,000 tons.   Complement,

Length,   feet. Beam,   feet. Draught,   feet.

Guns (*unofficial*) :
  8—16 inch.
  —5·5 inch.
  (Some anti-aircraft.)
  4 M.G.
  4 Landing.
Torpedo tubes (21 inch) :
  (*Not known.*)

Armour :
  " Belt ....
  " Ends ....
  " Deck ....
  " Turrets ....
  " Battery ....
  " Conning tower ...

(Special anti-torpedo protection.)

Note.

No plans available ; not certain that these four battleships are of uniform design.

Nagato is to be floated out during November, 1919.

Mutsu's provisional launching date is October, 1919, but she may not get afloat till 1920.

Machinery : Geared turbines.   screws. Boilers : Miyabara or Kansei. Designed H.P.   =24 kts.
Fuel : *normal*   tons, *maximum*   tons.

Name	Builder	Machinery	Laid down	Com-pleted	Trials	Boilers	Best recent speed
Kaga	Kure D.Y.	...	To be	...	=	...	...
Tosa	Kawasaki Co., Kobe.	Kawasaki	Sept., 1919	...	=	...	...
Nagato	Kure D Y.	...	Aug., 1917	1920	=	...	...
Mutsu	Yokosuka D.Y.	...	1918		=	...	...

General Notes.—*Nagato* provided for by 1916 Programme, and laid down in dry dock at Kure D.Y. during the summer of 1917. *Mutsu* provided for by 1917 Programme. *Kaga* and *Tosa* by 1918 Programme.

せ い ） **ISE** (Nov., 1916),   か ３ ひ **HIUGA** (Jan., 1917).

Normal Displacement, 31,260 tons.   Complement, 1,360.   Length (*p.p*). 640 feet.

Beam, 94 feet.   *Max*. draught, $28\frac{1}{3}$ feet.   Length (*o.a*.), 683 feet.

Guns (Japanese) :
  12—14 inch, 45 cal. (A^8)
  20—5·5 inch, — cal.
  16—12 pdr.
  4—12 pdr. (anti-aircraft).
Torpedo tubes (21 inch) :
  6 *submerged.*

Armour (Japanese) :
  12″—9″ Belt ....
  4″ Belt (Ends)... ......
  2—1$\frac{1}{4}$″ Decks ....
  12″ Turrets..............
  6″ Battery..............
  12″ C.T. ... .

HIUGA.*   *Photo by courtesy of the Navy Department, Tokyo.*

Ahead :
4—14 in.
6 to 8—5·5 in.

Astern :
4—14 in.
6—5·5 in.

Broadside: 12—14 in., 10—5·5 in.

ISE.*   *Photo by courtesy of the Navy Department, Tokyo.*

Machinery: Brown-Curtis turbines in *Ise*; Parsons turbines in *Hiuga*. 4 screws. Boilers: 24 Kansei.   Designed H.P. 45,000＝23 kts.   Fuel: *normal* 1000 tons; *maximum* 4000 tons coal ＋1000 tons oil.

Armour Notes.—As *Fuso* class (next page).

Note.—In above illustrations of *Ise* and *Hiuga* running trials, chart-house and bridges are not fully built, and searchlights are not in position. The large tanks at base of after-tripod mast, in view of *Ise*, are temporarily shipped for trial purposes.

General Notes.—Built under the 1914 Naval Programme. These ships are an improved and slightly faster *Fuso* type. It is unofficially reported that they are strongly protected against aerial attack by three specially thick protective decks over vital parts of the hull. They may not have the 16—12 pdr. listed. Special attention is reported to have been paid to the rapid replenishment of fuel, stores, ammunition, &c. Usual internal protection against mine and torpedo explosions by minute sub-divisions, wing bulkheads over machinery magazine spaces, &c.

Name	Built by	Machinery	Laid down	Completed	Trials. H.P. = kts.	Boilers	Turbines
Ise	Kawasaki Co.	Kawasaki Co.	May '15	Dec. '17	＝ 23·3.	Kansei.	Curtis-
Hiuga	Mitsu Bishi Co.	Mitsu Bishi Co.	May '15	Mar. '18		Kansei.	Parsons

ぶさふ **FU-SO** (March, 1914), ろしまや **YAMASHIRO** (Nov. 1915),

Normal Displacement 30,600 tons.   Complement, 1243 and 1272.
Length (*p p*): 630 feet.   Beam, 94 feet.   *Max.* draught, 28½ feet.   Length *over all*, 673 feet.

Guns (Japanese):
12—14 inch, 45 cal. (A⁸)
16—6 inch, 50 cal.
12—12 pdr.
4—12 pdr. *(anti-aircraft).*
4 machine.
4 landing.
Torpedo tubes (21 inch):
6 *submerged*

Armour:
12"—9" Belt (amidships)
4" Belt (ends) .....
2" and 1¼" Decks...
12" Turrets..........
6" Battery..........
12" Conning tower...

YAMASHIRO   *Photo by courtesy of the Navy Department, Tokyo.*

FU-SO.

Ahead:
4—14 in.
4—6 in.

Broadside : 12—14 in., 8—6 in.

Astern:
4—14 in.,
4—6 in.

Armour Notes: (unofficial). 12 inch belt over amidships barbettes, boiler and engine rooms; 9 inch belt between end pairs of superfiring barbettes. 6 inch battery closed by bulkheads at first and fifth barbettes.

Gunnery Notes: (unofficial). R.F. in roof of each gun-house, over C.T. and Torpedo control tower (aft) and in fire-control top.

Torpedo Notes: 10 searchlights. Net defence right up to stern.

Machinery: Brown-Curtis turbines. 4 screws. Boilers: 24 Miyabara ; *Yamashiro* may have Kansei. Designed H.P. 40,000=22·5 kts. in *Yamashiro*, 22 kts. in *Fuso*. Fuel: *normal*, 1000 tons *maximum* 4000 tons coal + 1000 tons oil fuel.

Name.	Builder.	Machinery.	Laid down	Com-pleted.	Trials. H.P. = kts.	Turbine	Boilers	Best recent speed
Fu-So	Kure	Kawasaki	Mar.'12	Nov.'15	46,500= 23.	Curtis	Miyabara	
Yamashiro	Yokosuka	Kawasaki	Dec. '13	Apl.,'17	....	Curtis	Miyabara	

General Notes.—*Fu-so* 1911 Naval Programme, *Yamashiro* 1913 Programme. *Fu-so* built in dry dock and floated out March, 1914.

FU-SO.   *Photo by courtesy of the Imperial Japanese Embassy.*

つつせ **SETTSU** (March, 1911).

Normal displacement, 21,420 tons.   Complement, 1000.

Length (*p.p.*), 500 feet.   Beam, 84⅙ feet. $\begin{cases} Maximum \text{ draught, } 28\frac{1}{4} \text{ feet.} \\ Mean \quad\quad ,, \quad\quad 27\frac{1}{2} ,, \end{cases}$ Length *over all*, 533 ft.

Guns (M. '04) (*See Notes*):
  12—12 inch, 45 and 50
    cal. (A^5)
  10—6 inch, 50 cal.
  8—4·7 inch, 50 cal.
  12—12 pdr.
  4 Machine.
  4 Landing.
Torpedo tubes (18 inch):
  4 *submerged* (broadside).
  1   ,,   (stern).
    (4458 tons.)

Armour (Krupp):
  12″ Belt (amidships) ...... ▪▪▪▪▪
  4″ Belt (ends) (N.C.) ...... ▨▨▨
  3″ and 1⅛″ Armour decks
  7″-4″ Lower deck side ⎫
  11″ Turrets .... ⎬ ▪▪▪▪▪
  11″ Turret bases ...... ⎭
  6″ Battery ....
  10″ Conning tower........ ▨▨▨
    (4960 tons.)

Ahead:
6—12 in.

KAWACHI.

Astern:
6—12 in.

Broadside : 8—12 in.

SETTSU.   *Photo by courtesy of the Navy Department, Tokyo.*

Machinery: Curtis turbine; 2 screws.   Boilers: 16 Miyabara.   Designed H.P. 25,000 = 20.5 kts.
Coal: *normal*, 1100 tons; *maximum*, 2300 tons + 400 tons oil fuel.

Gunnery Notes.—The 12 inch guns in end barbettes are 50 calibres long; those in the four beam barbettes are only 45 calibres long. With the exception of 12 pdrs. (make unknown), all calibres are Elswick models.

Engineering Notes.—Weight of machinery, 2146 tons.

Name.	Built at	Machinery.	Laid down.	Com-pleted.	H.P.	Trials. kts.	Turbines	Boilers.	Best recent speed.
Settsu	Kure D.y.	Kure D.y.	Jan., '09	1912	15 000 =	18.3 =	Curtis	Miyabara	

Notes.—*Kawachi*, a sister ship to *Settsu*, destroyed by explosion in Tokuyama Bay, July, 1918

うかんこ **KONGO** (May, 1912), **HI-YEI** (Nov., 1912),

なるは **HARUNA** (Dec., 1913), ましりき **KIRISHIMA** (Dec., 1913).

Normal displacement, *Kongo, Hi-yei,* 27,500 tons; *Haruna, Kirishima,* 27,613 tons. Complement, 980.

Length (*o.a*)., 704 feet. { *Haruna, Kirishima* : Beam, 92½ feet. *Max.* draught, 27 feet.
{ *Kongo, Hi-yei* : „ 92 „ „ „ 27½ „

Guns (*see Notes*) :
  8—14 inch, 45 cal. (A⁸)
  16—6 inch, 50 cal.
  8—12 pdr. (semi-automatic)
  (Some anti-aircraft ?)
  4 Machine.
  4 landing
Torpedo tubes (21 inch) :
  8 *submerged* (4 twin)

Armour (Krupp) :
  8″ Belt (amidships) ......
  4″—3″ Belt (ends) ......
  2¾″ Deck ....
  9″ Turrets.................
  6″ Battery.................
  10″ Conning tower ... .
  6″ T. Control tower ...

HIYEI. *Photo by courtesy of The Imperial Japanese Embassy.*

KONGO class

Ahead :
4—14 in.
2 to 4—6 in.

Broadside : 8—14 in., 8—6 in.

Astern :
4—14 in.
4—6 in.

Machinery : Parsons 4-shaft (in *Haruna* only Curtis 4-shaft) turbines.   Designed H.P. 64,000 = 27·5 kts.
Boilers : See Notes.   Fuel : *normal,* 1,200 tons ; *maximum,* 4,000 tons + 1,000 tons oil.

Name	Builder	Machinery	Laid down	Completed	Trials	F.P.	Turbine	Boilers	Re-fit
Kongo	Vickers	Vickers	Jan.'11	Aug. '13	44,800 = 25	78,000 = 27·3	Parsons	Yarrow	1916
Hi-yei	Yokosuka	Mitsu Bishi	Nov.'11	Mar.'14			Parsons	Kansei	
Haruna	Kawasaki	Kawasaki	Mar.'12	Mar. '15		82,000 = 27·77	Curtis	Yarrow	
Kirishima	Mitsu Bishi	Mitsu Bishi	Mar.'12	Apr. '15		80,000 = 27·54	Parsons	Yarrow	

General Notes.— *Kongo* 1910-11 Programme, others 1911-12 Programme.

These Notes are not from any official data.

Appearance Notes.—All four ships now have raised fore-funnels, as *Hiyei* above, but *Kongo* has her fore funnel further forward and well away from the second funnel.

Gunnery Notes.—In *Kongo* guns are Vickers models ; but in other three ships all calibres are of Japanese manufacture.   *Kongo* has combined Vickers (hydraulic) and Janney-Williams (electric) manœuvring systems for her barbettes ; there is also a small auxiliary hydraulic installation, generally used for cleaning purposes, which can be used in emergency for working the 14-inch guns.   In the three Japanese-built ships no 12 pdrs. are mounted on the barbette crowns.   *Kongo's* 12 pdr. as plans.   *Kongo* is reported to be armed with a special 14, pdr. Vickers model, instead of 12 pdrs. but this is very questionable.

Armour Notes.—Plans not correct : Belt stops about 40 feet from bows and 33 feet from stern.   The 6″ Battery and lower deck side extend to fore barbette.

Anti-Torpedo Protection Notes.—Internal sub-division by longitudinal and cross bulkheads.   Extra protection given by armour to all magazine spaces.   Port and starboard engine rooms are divided by an unpierced longitudinal bulkhead along keel-line.   It is said contract for *Kongo* stipulated she should float with 50 feet of her side blown away, should not heel more than 11°, and *automatically* regain the vertical in a specified length of time, though at an increased draught.

Aircraft Notes.—Experiments with launching of seaplanes from *Kongo's* decks took place during September, 1917.   Anti-aircraft guns mounted now in these ships.

Torpedo Notes.—Tubes are twin submerged type, at varying levels, some being only 6 feet below waterline.   *Kongo* has combined hydraulic and electrically-operated tubes.   In *Haruna*, tubes are Elswick 21-inch side-loading, hydraulically operated.

Engineering Notes.—In *Kongo, Hiyei* and *Kirishima* Parsons turbines have H.P. rotors on outboard shafts and L.P. on inner shafts, with astern turbines aft and in same casing.   *Kongo's* 36 Yarrow boilers are in five compartments.   Pressure : 205 lbs. per sq. inch.

1905 JAPANESE SEMI-DREADNOUGHT. (First-class Battleship.) (20 knot.)

AKI (April, 1907).

Displacement, 19,800 tons.   Complement, 937.

Length (o.a.), 492 feet; (p.p.), 460 feet.   Beam, 83⅔ feet.   *Maximum* draught, 28 feet.

Guns (Elswick M. '04):
  4—12 inch, 45 cal. (A^5).
  12—10 inch, 45 cal. (A^3).
  8—6 inch, 45 cal.
  8—12 pdr.
  4 Machine.
  4 Landing.
Torpedo tubes (18 inch):
  4 *submerged* (broadside).
  1 *submerged* (stern).
        (4040 tons.)

Armour (Krupp):
  9″ Belt (amidships) ...
  6″ Belt (bow) (N.C.) ...
  4″ Belt (aft) ....
  2″ Deck ....
  7″ Upper belt...........
  8″ Turrets ....
  9¾″ Turret bases ......
  7″ Bases to 10 in. turrets
  7″ Battery for Q.F.(N.C.)
        (4842 tons.)

Ahead:
2—12 in.
4—10 in.
2—6 in.

Broadside: 4—12 in., 6—10 in., 4—6 in.

Astern:
2—12 in.
4—10 in.
2—6 in.

Machinery: Curtis turbine. 2 screws. Boilers: 15 Miyabara. Designed H.P. 24,000 = 20 kts. Coal: *normal*, 900 tons; *max.*, 2000 tons, + 170 tons oil fuel.

*Gunnery Notes.—Turrets worked both electrically and hydraulically.

*Torpedo Notes.—Bullivant net defence; main deck shelf.

*Engineering Notes.—Weight of machinery, 2146 tons. R.P.M. 100 = 8½ kts., 160 = 14 kts., 210 = 18½ kts., 250 = 20¼ kts.

Name.	Builder.	Machinery.	Laid down.	Completed.	Trials. Full power.		Turbines.	Boilers.
Aki	Kure	Fore River Co., U.S.A.	Mar. '05	1910	16,115 = 18·6	28,740 = 20·25	Curtis	Miyabara

General Notes.—Hull and fittings, 6764 tons. Equipment 754 tons. Refitted, 1915.

* These notes are unofficial.

R

SATSUMA まつま (November, 1906).

Normal displacement, 19,350 tons.   Complement, 937.

Length (*waterline*), 479 ft.   Beam, 83½ ft.   *Maximum* draught, 28 ft.   Length *over all*, 482 ft.; *p.p.*, 450 ft.

Guns (Elswick M. '04) :
  4—12 inch, 45 cal. (A^5).
  12—10 inch, 45 cal. (A^3).
  12—4·7 inch, 45 cal.
  4 Machine.
  4 Landing.
Torpedo tubes (18 inch) :
  4 *submerged* (broadside).
  1 *submerged* (stern).

Armour (Krupp) :
  9″ Belt (amidships) ...
  6″ Belt (bow) (N.C.) ...
  4″ Belt (aft) ....
  2″ Deck ....
  7″ Upper belt............
  7″—9″ Turrets ....
  9″ Turret bases ....
  5″ Battery for Q.F.(N.C.)

Ahead :
2—12in.
4—10in.

Broadside : 4—12 in., 6—10 in.

Astern :
2—12 in.
4—10 in.

Machinery : 2 sets vertical triple expansion.   2 screws.   Boilers : 20 Miyabara.   Designed H.P. 17,500 = 18·25 kts.   Coal : *normal* 750 tons ; *maximum* 2000 tons, + 300 tons oil fuel.
※*Gunnery Notes*—Turrets worked both electrically and hydraulically.
※*Torpedo Notes.*—Net defence ; main deck shelf.
※*Engineering Notes.*—

Name.	Builder.	Machinery.	Laid down.	Com-pleted.	Refit.	Trials. H.P.	kts.	Boilers.	Best recent speed.
Satsuma	Yokosuka	Yokosuka	May, '05	Apl. '10	1916	18,507 =	18.95	Miyabara	

* These notes are unofficial.

FORE TOP.

FORE TURRET.

まらく **KURAMA** (Oct., 1907) & **IBUKI** (Nov., 1907). きふい

Normal displacement, 14,600 tons.   Complement, 845.

Length (*p.p.*), 450 feet.   Beam, $75\frac{1}{2}$ feet.   *Max.* draught, $26\frac{2}{3}$ feet.   Length *over all*, 485 feet.

Guns (Japanese):
  4—12 inch, 45 cal. (A⁵)
  8—8 inch, 45 cal. (A)
  14—4·7 inch, 50 cal.
  4 Machine
  4 landing.
Torpedo tubes (18 inch):
  3 *submerged*
        (4458 tons.)

Armour (Krupp):
  7″ Belt (amidships) .... ▨▨▨
  4″ Belt (ends) (N.C.) .... ⊞⊞⊞
  2″ Armour deck...............
  5″ Lower deck redoubt...... ▨▨▨
  7″ Turrets (N.C.) .... ▥▥▥
  7″ Turret bases (N.C.) ▨▨▨▥▥▥
  5″ Battery .... ▨▨▨
  6″ Secondary turrets (N.C.) ▨▨▨
  8″ Conning tower (fore) ... ▥▥▥
  6″   „   „   (aft) ...... ▨▨▨
        (4960 tons.)

Broadside: 4—12 in., 4—8 in.

Ahead:
2—12
4—8

Astern:
2—12
4—8

Machinery: *Kurama*, 2 sets reciprocating. 2 screws. *Ibuki*, Curtis turbine. Boilers: Miyabara. Designed H.P., *Kurama*, 22,500 = 21·25 kts.; *Ibuki*, 27,000 = 22 kts. Coal: *normal*, 600 tons; *maximum*, 2000 tons + about 250 tons oil.

Armour Notes—Main belt is $7\frac{1}{2}$ feet wide, thinning at ends.

Gunnery Notes—Loading positions, big guns: all round. Hoists: electric. Big guns: hydraulic and electric gears; secondary turrets, electric gear. Arcs of fire: 12 inch, 270°; secondary turrets, about 130°.

Torpedo Notes—Bullivant net defence to both ships.

Engineering Notes—Weight of machinery, 2078 tons.

Name.	Builder	Machinery	Laid down	Completed	Trials.		Boilers.	Best recent speed
					at 4/5.	*6 hrs. f.p.*		
Kurama	Yokosuka	Yokosuka	Aug,'05	Oct.,'09			Miyabara in both.	
Ibuki	Kure	Fore River Co., U.S.A.	May,'06	1910	20,978 = 21.	27,353 = 20·87		

General Notes.—Weights: hull and fittings, 6105 tons; equipment 731 tons. *Ibuki* launched six months after laying down.
*These notes are unofficial

KURAMA.   *Photo, Symonds.*

IBUKI.

Differences.—*Kurama* has tripod masts, and slightly taller funnels. Yard on foremast is high up with searchlight top *under*. In *Ibuki*, yard is lower down, with searchlight top *above* yard.

(New photo of this ship wanted.)   *Photo, Symonds.*

IKOMA (April, 1906).   まこい、

(*Training Ship*: *Gunnery and Torpedoes.*)

Displacement, *normal* 13750 tons ; *full load* 15,150 tons. Complement, 817.
Length (*p.p.*), 440 feet; (*o.a.*), 475 feet. Beam, 75 feet. *Mean* draught, 26 feet.

Guns (*see Notes*)
4—12 inch, 45 cal. (A⁵)
10—6 inch, 45 cal.
8—4·7 inch.
6—12 pdr.
Torpedo tubes (18 inch) :
2 *submerged.*
1 *above water* (stern).
(1719 tons.)

Armour (Krupp C. & N.C.) :
7″ Belt (amidships) ....
4″ Belt (ends) ....
2″ Armour deck
5″ Lower deck redoubt ....
9-7″ Turrets ....
7″ Turret bases ....
5″ Lower deck side ....
5″ Casemates (N.C.) ....
8″ Conning tower (fore) ....
6″   ,,   ,,   (aft) ....
(3547 tons.)

Ahead :
2—12 in.
2—6 in.

Astern :
2—12 in.
2—6 in.

Broadside : 4—12 in., 6—6 in.

Machinery : 2 sets reciprocating. 2 screws. Boilers : Miyabara. Designed H.P. 19,000 = 20·5 kts.
Coal : *normal*, 600 tons ; *maximum*, 2000 tons + 150 tons oil fuel. Weight of machinery, 2132 tons. Built
and engined by Kure D.Y. 1905-7. On first trials made 21·9 kts. with 22,670 I.H.P. Refitted 1918-19.
Tsukuba, of this class, destroyed by explosion, Jan., 1917.

1919 Corrections to Plans.—Main deck 6 inch battery removed and ports plated up. 4—4·7 inch over old two-tier sponsons
removed. 6—6 inch now mounted on shelter deck, viz : 4 over old two-tier sponsons (in old 4·7 inch positions) and 2
abeam of second funnel.

(Is second unit of the "KATORI" CLASS.)

ま | か   **KASHIMA** (March, 1905). Displacement, 16,400 tons. Complement, 946. Length (*o.a.*),
470 feet. Beam, 78 ft. 1¼ in. *Max.* draught, 26 ft. 7½ in. Guns : 4—12 inch, 45 cal. (A⁵), 4—10 inch,
45 cal. (A³). 12—6 inch, 45 cal., 10—12 pdr., 3—3 pdr., 4 M.G., 2 field. Torpedo tubes (18 inch) :
5 *submerged.* Armour (Krupp) : 9″ Belt (amidships), 6½″ Belt (ends), 3″ Deck on slopes, 9″ Turrets
(K.C.), 9″—5″ Turret bases, 8″—6″ Secondary turrets (K.C.), 6″ Lower deck (side), 6″ Battery, 9″
Conning tower, 4″ Upper deck battery. Machinery : 2 sets 4 cylinder vertical quadruple expansion.
2 screws. Boilers : 20 Kansei. Designed H.P. 16,000 = 18·5 kts. Coal : *normal*, 750 tons ;
maximum, 2,150 tons. Built at Elswick 1904-6. Refitted 1916.

りとか

りとか :   **KATORI** (July, 1905). Displacement, 15,950 tons. Complement, 946. Length
(*o.a.*), 455¾ feet. Beam, 78 feet. *Max.* draught, 27 feet. All other details as
Kashima above, except *max.* coal, 1860 tons. Built by Vickers 1904-6. Refitted 1916. *To
distinguish* : Funnels closer together than *Kashima* ; fore topmast is *before* mast.

MIKASA さかみ (November, 1900). (Reconstructed 1907-08.) Displacement, 15,362 tons. Complement, 830. Length (*waterline*), 415 feet. Beam, 76¼ feet. *Maximum* draught, 26 feet. Length *over all*, 432 feet. Guns: 4—12 inch, (45) cal. (A⁵), 14—6 inch, 45 cal., 20—12 pdr., 2—3 pdr., 2—2½ pdr., 2 Maxims. Torpedo tubes (18 inch): 4 *submerged*. Armour (Krupp): 9″ Belt (amidships), 4″ Belt (ends), 12″ Bulkheads, 3″ Deck (slopes), 14″—10″ Barbettes, 10″—8″ Turrets to these, 6″ Lower deck redoubt, 6″ Battery (K.C.), 6″ Casemates (N.C.). Machinery: 2 sets 3 cylinder vertical triple expansion. 2 screws. Boilers: 25 Belleville. Designed H.P. 15,000 = 18 kts. Coal: *normal* 700 tons; *maximum* 1500 tons. Built by Vickers, Barrow., 1899-1901. Sunk 1905. Salved and rebuilt 1906.

From "The Navy," Tokyo.

HIZEN (ex-Russian *Retvizan*) (October, 1900). (Reconstructed 1907-08.) Displacement, 12,700 tons. Complement, 791. Length (*waterline*), 376 feet. Beam 72¼ feet. *Maximum* draught, 26 feet. Guns: 4—12 inch, 40 cal. (A⁴) (Obukhoff), 12—6 inch, 45 cal. (Japanese), 14—12 pdr., 4—2½ pdr., 2 M.G. Torpedo tubes (18 inch): 2 *submerged* (25° abaft). Armour (Krupp): 9″—6″ Belt (amidships), 4″ Belt (bow), 9″ Bulkhead, 3″ Deck (slopes), 6″ Lower deck redoubt, 10″ Turrets (N.C.), 9″ Turret bases (N.C.), 5″ Battery (N.C.), 10″ Conning tower (N.C.). Machinery: 2 sets, 3 cylinder triple expansion. 2 screws. Boilers: 24 Niclausse. Designed H.P. 16,000 = 18 kts. Coal: *normal* 1016 tons; *maximum* 2000 tons. Built by Cramp, Philadelphia. Scuttled at Port Arthur, 1904, and captured on fall of fortress. Salved and repaired, 1905-6

Asahi is something like *Mikasa*, but easily distinguished from her because her fore funnel is much nearer fore mas[t] than *Mikasa's*. *(Gunnery Training Ship.)*

ひさあ **ASAHI** (March, 1899). *Normal* displacement, 14,765 tons. Complement, 836. Length *over all*, 425¼ feet. Beam, 75¼ feet. *Maximum* draught, 27¼ feet. Guns: 4—12 inch, 40 cal. (A⁴), 14—6 inch, 40 cal., 20—12 pdr., 2—3 pdr., 2—2½ pdr. Torpedo tubes (18 inch): 4 *submerged*. Armour (Harvey Nickel): 9″ Belt (amidships), 4″ Belt (ends), 14″ Bulkheads, 3″ Deck (amidships slopes), 14″—10″ Barbettes, 10″—8″ Turrets to these, 6″ Lower deck redoubt, 6″ Casemates (14). 14″ Conning tower, 4″ After tower. Machinery: 2 sets vertical triple expansion. 2 screws. Boilers: 25 Belleville. Designed H.P. 16,000 = 18 kts. Coal: *normal* 700 tons; *maximum* 1690 tons. Built by Thomson, Clydebank, 1897-1900.

ましき志 **SHIKISHIMA** (November, 1898). 14,580 tons. Complement, 836. Length (o.a.), 438 feet. Beam. 75½ feet. *Max.* draught, 27¼ feet. Guns: As *Asahi* above. Torpedo tubes: As *Asahi* above, but has an additional 18 inch tube *above water*. Armour, machinery, screws and boilers also as *Asahi*. Designed H.P. 14,500 = 18 kts. Coal (*max.*): 1590 tons. Built by Thames Ironworks, 1897-1900.

IWAMI みはい (July, 1902). (ex-Russian *Orel* reconstructed, 1907). *Normal* displacement, 13,516 tons. Complement, 806. Length (*p.p.*), 376½ feet. Beam, 76 feet. *Mean* draught, 26 feet. Length *over all*, 397 feet. Guns (Japanese): 4—12 inch, 45 cal. (A⁴), 6—8 inch, 45 cal., 16—12 pdr., 4—2½ pdr., 4 M.G. Torpedo tubes (15 inch): 2 *submerged* (broadside), 1 above water (*bow*). Armour (Krupp): 7½″–6″ Belt (amidships), 4″ Belt (ends), 3″ Armour deck (slopes), 10″ Turrets (N.C.), 10″ Turret bases (N.C.), 6″—4″ Upper belt, 10″ Conning tower. Machinery: 2 sets vertical 4 cylinder triple expansion. 2 screws. Boilers: 20 Belleville. Designed H.P. 16000 = 18 kts. Coal: *normal* 750 tons; *maximum* 1520 tons. Laid down at Galernii Island, June, 1900, and completed for sea in September, 1904. Captured in Battle of Tsushima, 1905.

(*Cadets' Training Ship*).

うはす **SUWO** (ex-Russian *Pobieda*. May, 1900). *Normal* displacement (after reconstruction), 13,500 tons. Complement, 787. Length (*waterline*), 424 feet. Beam, 71½ feet. *Maximum* draught, 25¼ feet. Length *over all*, 435 feet. Guns (Obukhoff): 4—10 inch, 45 cal. (A⁵), 10—6 inch, 45 cal., 16—12 pdrs., 4 machine, 2 field. Torpedo tubes (15 inch): 2 *submerged* (at 20° abaft). Armour (*See Notes*): 9″—6″ Belt; 2¾″ Deck (on slopes); 10″ Turrets; 8″ Turret bases; 5″ Lower deck side; 5″ Casements (10); 10″ Conning tower (K.N.C.) Machinery: 3 sets vertical 3 cylinder triple expansion. 3 screws. Boilers: 30 Bellevilles, placed fore and aft. Designed H.P. 14,500 = 18 kts. Coal: *normal* 1063 tons; *maximum* 2100 tons. Also 250 tons liquid fuel. Scuttled at Port Arthur, 1904, and captured on fall of fortress. Salved and re-fitted 1905-6.

(*Seamanship Training Ship*).

ふ **FUJI** (March, 1896). 12,649 tons. Complement, 741. Length (*waterline*), 390 feet. Beam, 73 feet. *Maximum* draught, 27 feet. Guns: 4—12 inch, 40 cal., 10—6 inch, 40 cal., 16—12 pdr. 4—3 pdr. 4—2½ pdr. Torpedo tubes (18 inch): 4 *submerged*, 1 above water (bow). Armour (Harvey): 18″ Belt (amidships). 14″ Bulkheads. 2½″ Deck (flat on belt), 4″ Lower deck redoubt. 14″ Barbettes. 6″ Casemates. 14″ Conning tower. Machinery: 2 sets 4 cylinder vertical triple expansion. 2 screws. Boilers: 10 Miyabara. Designed H.P. *forced* 13,500 = 18 kts. Coal: *normal* 700 tons; *maximum* 1200 tons.

*****OKINOSHIMA** (ex-Russian *General Admiral Graf Apraxin*, 1896) 4126 tons, & ましみ **MISHIMA** (ex-Russian *Admiral Senyavin*. 1894). 4460 tons. 3—10 inch, 45 cal. (*AAA*). (*Mishima* has 4—10 inch) with, in both 4—4·7 inch, 10—3 pdrs., 2—2½ pdr. Armour: 10″—8″ belt amidships. 8″ turrets. Designed H.P. 5000 = 16 kts. Boilers: 8 Belleville. Coal: *maximum* 450 tons. Both captured in Battle of Tsushima, 1905.

*****Note*.—Reported-1919 that 10-inch guns had been removed and that both ships were serving as Ice Breakers. Previously these ships were Barracks for Boys.

NISSHIN. (KASUGA also has plain funnels now).   *Photo, Seward. Weymouth.*

"Nisshin" attached to T.B.D. Flotillas.

NISSHIN (Feb., 1903) & **KASUGA** (Oct., 1902).   かすか

Displacement 7,750 tons. Complement 610 and 595.

Length (*waterline*), 357 feet. Beam, 61 feet 11 ins. *Maximum* draught, 25¼ feet.

Guns (Elswick):
- 4—8 inch, 45 cal. (*A*).
- 14—6 inch, 45 cal.
- 10—12 pdr.
- 4—2½ pdrs.
- 2 Maxims.
- 2 Field guns.

Torpedo tubes (18 inch):
- 4 *above water* (in casemates).

Armour (Terni):
- 6″ Belt (amidships) ...... ⊠
- 4½″ Belt (ends) .... ▨
- 1½″ Deck (on slopes) ......
- 5½″ Turrets ....⊠
- 5½″ Turret bases (N.C.)... ⊠
- 6″ Lower deck side ...... ⊠
- 4½″ Lower deck bulkheads
- 6″ Battery (N.C.) .... ⊠
- 4½″ Battery (bulkheads)... ▨
- 4¾″ Conning tower ...... ▨

Ahead:
2—8 in.
4—6 in.

Astern:
2—8 in.
4—6 in.

Broadside : 4—8 in., 7—6 in.

Machinery : 2 sets 3 cylinder vertical triple expansion. 2 screws. Boilers : 12 Kansei. Designed H.P. 13,500 = 20 kts. Coal : *normal*, 650 tons ; *maximum*, 1,200 tons. *General Notes.*—Laid down for Argentina by Ansaldo, Genoa, in 1902, as the *Moreno* and *Rivadavia*. Purchased end of 1903 by Japan for £760,000, just before outbreak of Russo-Japanese War. Both had large refits 1914. *Kasuga* stranded at N.W. entrance to Banka Straits, Dutch East Indies, during January, 1918, and was not refloated till May. She has undergone extensive repairs in a Japanese dockyard.

(*Tender to Submarines*).   *Photo, His Honour Mr. Justice Ballon.*

そあ   **ASO** (ex-Russian *Bayan*). (La Seyne, 1900). Displacement, 7800 tons. Complement, 791. Length (*waterline*), 443 feet. Beam 57½ feet. *Max.* draught, 22 feet. Length *over all*, 450 feet. Guns : 2—8 inch, 45 cal. (*A*), 8—6 inch, 45 cal., .16—12 pdr., 4—2½ pdr. Torpedo tubes (at 20° abaft): 2 *submerged*. Tubes are 15 inch. Armour (Krupp): 8″ Belt (amidships), 4″ Belt (forward), 8″ Bulkhead (aft), 3¼″—2½″ Upper belt, 7″ Big gun turrets, Hoists, &c., 3¼″ Battery redoubts, 6½″ Conning tower. (Total about 1500 tons. Machinery : 2 sets vertical triple expansion. 2 screws. Boilers : 24 Belleville. Designed H.P. 16,500 = 21 kts. Coal : *normal* 550 tons ; *maximum* 1100 tons. Scuttled at Port Arthur, 1905, and captured on fall of fortress. Re-floated and re-fitted in Japan, 1905-6.

IDZUMO.   *"Idzumo" attached to T.B.D. Flotillas.*   *Photo, Seward, Weymouth.*

むつい   **IDZUMO** (Elswick, 1899) &   てはい   **IWATE** (Elswick, 1900).

Displacement, 9750 tons. Complement, 658.   Length (*p.p.*), 400 feet. Beam, 68½ feet. *Maximum* draught, 24¼ feet. Length *over all*, 434 feet Guns (Elswick): 4—8 inch, 40 cal. (*B*), 14—6 inch, 40 cal., 12—12 pdr., 4—2½ pdr., 2 M.G. Torpedo tubes : 4 *submerged*. Armour (Krupp) : 7″ Belt (amidship), 3½″ Belt (ends), 2½″ Deck (slopes), 5″ Lower deck (redoubt), 6″ Turrets and bases, 2½″ Casemates, 14″ Conning tower. (Total 2100 tons.) Machinery by Humphry and Tennant : 2 sets 4 cylinder triple expansion. 2 screws. Boilers : Belleville. Designed H.P. 16,000 = 20·75 kts. Coal : *normal* 550 tons ; *maximum* 1400 tons. Begun at Elswick 1898-99, and completed 1901. *Idzumo* made 22·04 kts. on acceptance trials and *Iwate* 21·74.

(Cadets' Training Ship)   *Photo by favour of G. Blackaby, Esq.*

まつあ **ADZUMA** (St. Nazaire, 1899). Displacement, 9426 tons. Complement, 644. Length *(waterline)*, 430 feet. Beam, 59½ feet. *Maximum* draught, 25 feet. Length *over all*, 452½ feet. Guns (Elswick): 4—8 inch, 40 cal. (B), 12—6 inch, 40 cal..16—12 pdr., 4—2½ pdr. Torpedo tubes: 4 *submerged*. Armour (Krupp mostly): 7″ Belt (amidships), 3½″ Belt (ends), 2½″ Deck (on slopes), 6″ Turrets and bases (H.N.), 6″ Casemates (H.N.), 5″ Side above belt. (Total weight, 2000 tons). Machinery: 2 sets vertical triple expansion. 2 screws. Boilers: 24 Belleville. Designed H.P. 17,000 = 21 kts. Coal: *normal* 600 tons; *maximum* 1200 tons.

(Cadets' Training Ship.)

もくや **YAKUMO** (Vulcan Co., 1899). Displacement, 9,735 tons. Complement, 698. Length *(p.p.)*, 390 feet. Beam, 64¼ feet. *Mean* draught, 23¾ feet. Length *over all*, 434 feet. Guns: 4—8 inch, 40 cal. (B)., 12—6 inch, 40 cal., 16—12 pdr., 4—2½ pdr. Torpedo tubes (18 inch): 4 *submerged*. Armour (Krupp): 7″ Belt (amidships), 3½″ Belt (ends), 2½″ Deck (slopes), 6″ Turrets (N.C.), 6″ Turret bases (N.C.), 5″ Lower deck side, 6″ Casemates (8), 10″ Conning tower. (Total weight, 2040 tons.) Machinery: 2 sets vertical triple expansion. 2 screws. Boilers: 24 Belleville. Designed H.P. 15,500 = 20½ kts. Coal: *normal* 550 tons; *maximum* 1200 tons. *Armour Notes*: Belt is 7 feet wide.

Токіwa *(Cadet Training Ship).*   *Photo by favour of G. Blackaby, Esq.*

まさあ **ASAMA** (March, 1898). はきと **TOKIWA** (July, 1898). Displacement 9700 tons. Complement 648. Length *(o.a.)*, 442 feet. Beam, 67¼ feet. *Maximum* draught, 24¼ feet. Guns (Elswick): 4—8 inch, 40 cal. (B), 14—6 inch, 40 cal., 12—12 pdr., 4—2½ pdr. Torpedo tubes (18 inch): 4 *submerged*. Armour (Harvey-nickel): 7″ Belt (amidships), 3½″ Belt (ends), 2″ Deck (slopes), 5″ Upper belt (amidships), 3½″ Bulkheads to it, 6″ Turrets and bases, 6″ Casemates (10), 14″ Conning tower. (Total, 2100 tons.) Machinery: 2 sets 4 cylinder triple expansion. 2 screws. Boilers: 12 Miyabara. Designed H.P. *forced* 18,000 = 21½ kts. Coal: *normal* 550 tons; *maximum* 1400 tons. Both built at Elswick. Very 'handy' ships. *Asama* was badly damaged by grounding on Pacific Coast of Central America, in December of 1914. Was salved and has been repaired and re-fitted.

1889   SECOND CLASS COAST DEFENCE SHIP.

たよち **CHIYODA** (June, 1890). Displacement 2439 tons. Complement 324. Length, 308 feet. Beam, 41⅔ feet. *Maximum* draught, 15½ feet. Guns (Elswick): 10—4·7 inch, 40 cal. 15—3 pdr. Torpedo tubes: 2 *above water*. Armour (chrome steel): 4½″ Belt, 1″ Deck at ends [Deck flat on belt.] Machinery: 2 sets triple expansion. 2 screws. Boilers (1898): 12 Belleville without economisers. Designed H.P. 7000 = 19 kts. Coal: *normal* 330 tons; *maximum* 420 tons.

Building —
Details unofficial.

KUMA (July, 1919), *TAMA (building)*, *OH-I (building)*, *KITAKAMI (building)*, *KISO (building)*.
Normal displacement: 5500 tons.   Complement,
Length (*o.a.*), 500 feet.   Beam, 49·6 feet.   *Mean* draught , 15·6 feet.

Guns :   Armour :
  7—5.5 inch, — cal.   (*Not known.*)
  — Anti-aircraft.
  — M.G.
  Torpedo tubes : 4.

No plans available.

Machinery :   Turbines. Boilers :   screws. Designed H.P.   =
33 kts. Fuel : *normal,*   tons ; *maximum,*   tons.

Name.	Builder.	Machinery	Laid down.	Completed.	Refit.	First Trials.	Boilers.	Best recent speed.
Oh-i Kitakami Kiso	Kawasaki Sasebo D.Y. Mitsubishi Nagasaki	Kawasaki ... Mitsubishi	1919					
Kuma Tama	Sasebo D.Y. Nagasaki D.Y		Aug. '18 Aug. '18					

General Notes.—*Kuma* and *Tama* begun under the 1917 Naval Programme ; *Oh-i, Kitakami, Kiso* under 1918 Programme.

Photo wanted.
(For approximate appearance, see Silhouettes).

TATSUTA (29th May, 1918) & **TENRIU** (11th March, 1918).
Normal displacement, 3500 tons.   Complement, 332.
Length (*o.a.*): 440 feet.   Beam : 40¾ feet.   *Mean* draught : 13 feet.

Guns :   Armour :
  4—5 5 inch, —cal.   (*Not known.*)
  2 M.G.
  Torpedo tubes :
  6 *above water.*

No plans available.

Ahead :   *4—5·5 inch guns mounted on centre line in positions*   Astern :
1—5·5 in.   *shown by Silhouette.*   1—5·5 in.

Broadside : 4—5·5 in.

Machinery : Parsons or Curtis turbines. 3 screws. Boilers : 10 Kansei. Designed H.P. (unknown)
= 28 kts. Fuel : *normal,*   tons ; *maximum,*   tons.

Name	Builder	Machinery	Laid down	Completed	Trials	Boilers	Best recent speed.
Tatsuta Tenriu	Sasebo D.Y. Yokosuka D.Y.		July, '17 May, '17	1919	33 kts. (unofficial)	Kansei Kansei	

General Notes.—Begun under the 1916 Naval Programme.

CHIKUMA.   *Photo by courtesy of the Imperial Japanese Embassy.*

とらひ **HIRADO** (June, 1911). きはや **YAHAGI** (Oct., 1911).
まくち **CHIKUMA** (April, 1911).

Normal displacement 4950 tons. Complement 403.
Length (*p.p.*), 440 feet; *o.a.*, 475 feet. Beam, 46½ feet. *Max.* draught, 16½ feet.

Guns :
  8—6 inch, 50 cal.
  4—12 pdr.
  2 M.G.
Torpedo tubes (18 inch)
  3 *above water.*
   (363 tons.)

Armour :
  3″ Deck (amidships)
  2″ Deck (ends) ......
  4″ Conning tower...
   (439 tons.)

HIRATO. class.

Machinery : Curtis turbines ; (2 screws), except *Yahagi*, Parsons turbines. (4 screws). Boilers :
16 Kansei. Designed H.P. 22,500 = 26 kts. Coal : *normal* 500 tons ; *maximum* 900 tons + 300 oil.

Name	Builder	Machinery	Laid down	Completed	Trials H.P. = kts.	Boilers	Best recent speed
Hirado	Kawasaki Co.	Kawasaki Co.	Aug.,'10	Oct., '12	....	Kansei in all.	
Yahagi	Mitsu Bishi	Mitsu Bishi	June,'10	July,'12	27,408 = 26.8		
Chikuma	Sasebo Yard	Kawasaki Co.	May, '10	May,'12	24,974 = 26.8		

Weight of hull, etc., 2278 tons. *Hirado* returned to Japan early in 1918 after having steamed 26,000 miles in nine months on active service.

ね と **TONE** (Oct., 1907).
Normal displacement 4105 tons. Complement 401.
Length (*p.p.*), 360 feet; *o.a.*, 406 feet. Beam, 47¼ feet. *Mean* draught, 16¾ feet.

Guns :
  2—6 inch, 50 cal.
  10—4·7 inch, 50 cal.
  2—12 pdr.
  2 M.G.
Torpedo tubes (18 in.) :
  3 *above water.*
   (261 tons.)

Armour :
  3″ Deck (amidships)
  2″ Deck (ends) ....
  4″ Conning tower ......
   (458 tons.)

Ahead :
  1—6 in.
  2—4·7 in.

Astern :
  1—6 in.
  2—4·7 in.

TONE.

Broadside : 2—6 in., 6—4·7 in.

Machinery : 2 sets triple expansion. 2 screws. Boilers : 16 Miyabara. Designed H.P. 15,000 =
23 kts. Coal : *normal* 300 tons ; *maximum* 890 tons + 125 tons oil.

Name.	Builder	Machinery	Laid down	Completed	Refit	Trials	Boilers	Best recent speed
Tone	Sasebo	Mitsu Bishi Co.	1906	1909			Miyabara	

Correction to plans : Two 4·7 inch guns removed, positions unknown.

NIITAKA has foremast aft of fore bridges; TSUSHIMA has foremast stepped through charthouse.

いかたいに NIITAKA. ましつ TSUSHIMA.

NIITAKA (1902) & TSUSHIMA (Dec., 1902).

Displacement, 3420 tons. Complement, 307.

Length, 334½ feet. Beam, 44 feet. *Maximum* draught, 16 feet.

Guns (Elswick):
6—6 inch, 40 cal.
10—12 pdr.
4—2½ pdr.
Torpedo tubes:
None.

Armour (steel):
2½″ Deck .... ⊞⊞⊞
[Cellulose belt.]
4″ Conning tower
(K.N.C.) .... ⊞⊞⊞

Ahead:
3—6 in.

Astern:
3—6 in.

Broadside: 4—6 in.

Machinery: 2 sets triple expansion. 2 screws. Boilers: 16 Niclausse. Designed H.P. 9400 = 20 kts. Coal: *normal* tons; *maximum* 600 tons. Laid down 1900 at Yokosuka and Kure. A similar ship, *Otowa*, wrecked 1917. *Niitaka*, on patrol service during war, has steamed 50,000 miles in two years.

る か ー **TSUGARU** (ex Russian *Pallada*). (Aug., 1899.) Displacement 6630 tons. Complement 532. Length (*waterline*), 410 feet. Beam, 55 feet. *Maximum* draught, 21¼ feet. Length *over all*, 415⅜ feet. Guns (Russian): 10—6 inch, 45 cal., 12—12 pdr., 4—M.G. Torpedo tubes (18 inch): 2 *above water*. Armour: 2½″ Deck, 4″ Hoists, 6″ C. T. (Harvey), 4½″ Engine hatches. Machinery: 3 sets horizontal 3 cylinder triple expansion. 3 screws. Boilers: 24 Belleville. Designed H.P. 11,600 = 20 kts. Coal: *normal* 900 tons; *maximum* 1430 tons. Sunk at Port Arthur, October, 1904. Salved August, 1905. Used as a Training Ship.

せとち **CHITOSE** (January, 1898). Displacement 4992 tons. Complement 434. Length (*waterline*), 396 feet. Beam, 49¼ feet. *Maximum* draught, 18 feet. Guns: 2—8 inch, 40 cal. (*B*)., 10—4·7 inch, 12—12 pdr., 2—2½ pdr. Torpedo tubes (18 inch): 4 *above water*. Armour: 4½″ Deck (amidships). Machinery: 2 sets vertical triple expansion. 2 screws. Boilers: 12 Miyabara. Designed H.P.: *forced* 15,500 = 22·5 kts. Coal: *normal* 350 tons; *maximum capacity* 1000 tons. Built and engined by Union Ironworks, San Francisco. Laid down 1896, completed 1899. Made 22·87 kts. on first trials with 12,500 H.P. A sister ship, *Kasagi*, wrecked in Tsugaru Straits, 1916.

Now has fire-control top on foremast and a very small mainmast.

いかあ **AKASHI** (1897). Displacement 2800 tons. Complement, 310. Length, 295¼ feet. Beam, 41¾ feet. *Maximum* draught, 16⅓ feet. Guns (Elswick): 2—6 inch, 40 cal., 6 —4·7 inch, 40 cal., 12—3 pdr. Torpedo tubes (14 inch): 2 *above water.* Armour: 2″ Deck, 4½″ Shields to 6 inch guns. Machinery: 2 sets vertical triple expansion. 2 screws. Boilers: 8 cylindrical (probably replaced now by Kansei or Miyabara). Designed H.P. 7600=19·5 kts. Coal: *normal* 200 tons; *maximum* 600 tons.

Note.—Was intended to be a sister ship to *Suma* (given below), but as *Suma* proved a poor sea boat, *Akashi* was built up amidships.

まきつきあ **AKITSUSHIMA** (1892). 3172 tons. Comp. 314. Dimensions :—302×43×(*Max.*) 18½ feet. Armament: 4—6 inch, 6—4·7, 10—3 pdr. 2—14 inch tubes. 3″ Deck. Machinery: 2 sets vertical triple expansion. 2 screws. Boilers: 8 Miyabara. Designed H.P. *natural* 8500=19 kts. Coal: 550 tons.

ます **SUMA** (1895). 2700 tons. Comp. 310. Dimensions: 305½×39¼×(*max.*) 16½ feet. Armament (Elswick): 2—6 inch, 40 cal., 6—4·7 inch, 40 cal., 12—3 pdr. 2 tubes. 2″ Deck. 4½″ Shields to 6 inch guns. Machinery: 2 sets vertical triple expansion. 2 screws. Boilers: 4 Miyabara. Designed H.P. *forced* draught 8500=20 kts. Coal: *normal* 200 tons; *maximum* 600 tons. (See *Note* to *Akashi* above).

(*Conscripts' Training Ship.*)

てたしは **HASHIDATE** (1891). 4277 tons. Comp. 360. Dimensions: 295×51×(*max.*) 21¼ feet. Armament: 1—12·6 inch Canet, 11—4·7 inch, 6—12 pdr., 2—3 pdr., 2 M., 2—14 in. tubes. Armour (steel): 12″ Barbette with 4″ shield, 1½″ deck. Machinery: 2 sets triple expansion. 2 screws. Boilers: 8 Miyabara (1903). Designed H.P. 5400=16 kts. Coal: 680 tons.

(*Above ship still in service as Training Cruiser*).

JAPANESE GUNBOATS.

1st Class Gunboats (*Itto Hokan*).
(Over 800 tons).

みかも **MOGAMI** (Nagasaki, 1907). 1350 tons. Comp. 178. 316×31½×11½ feet. Guns: 2—4·7 inch (50 cal.), 4—12 pdr. Armour: 2½″ deck. Torpedo tubes: 2—18 inch. Machinery: Parsons turbine. 3 screws. No cruising turbines. Designed H.P. 8000=23 kts. Boilers: 6 Miyabara. Coal: *normal*, tons; *maximum*, 350 tons + 70 tons oil. First turbine-engined ship of Japanese Navy.

とめよ **YODO** (Kobe, 1907). 1250 tons. Comp. 193. 305½×32×11 feet. Guns: 2—4·7 inch, 50 cal., 4—12 pdr. Armour: 2½″ deck. Torpedo tubes: 2—18 inch. Machinery: 2 sets 4 cyl. triple expansion. Designed H.P. 6500=22 kts. Boilers: 4 Miyabara. Ccal: *normal*, tons; *maximum* 340 tons+80 tons oil.

やはち **CHIHAYA** (1901). 1263 tons. Comp. 167. Guns: 2—4·7 inch, 4—12 pdr. 2—18 inch tubes. Designed H.P. 6000= 21 kts. Boilers: Thornycroft. Coal: *normal* 200 tons; *maximum* 450 tons.

2nd Class Gunboats (*Nito Hokan*).
(Under 800 tons).

Photo by courtesy of the Navy Department.

SAGA (Sasebo, 1912). 785 tons. Complement 98. 210×29½×9¼ feet. Guns: 1—4·7 inch, 2—12 pdr., 1 machine. Machinery: Triple expansion. 3 screws. Boilers: 2 Kansèi. Designed H.P. 1600=15 kts. Coal: *maximum* 400 tons.

2nd Class Gunboats—*Continued*.

UJI (1903). 620 tons. Complement 86. 180½×27¼×7 feet. Armament: 4—12 pdr, 3 M.G. H.P. 1000=13 kts. Belleville boilers. Coal: 150 tons.

River Gunboats.

FUSHIMI (1906). 180 tons. Complement 45. 160×24½×2¼ feet. Guns: 2—6 pdr., 4 M. 800 H.P.=14 kts. Yarrow boilers. Coal: 25 tons.
Also **TOBA** (1911). 250 tons. Complement 59. 180×27¼×2½ feet. Guns: 2—12 pdr., 6 M. 1400 H.P.=15 kts. Coal: 80 tons.

SUMIDA (1903). 126 tons. Complement 40. 145×24×2 feet. Guns: 2—6 pdr., 4 M. 550 H.P. = 13 kts. Thornycroft boilers. Coal: 40 tons.

73 + 15 Destroyers.

Boats over 1000 tons are officially rated first class ; 1000—600, second class ; and under 600 tons, third class.

Totals.	Class.	Date.	Displacement.	H.P.	Max. Speed.	Fuel.	Complement.	Tubes.	Max. Draught.
			tons.		kts.	tons.			feet.
	First Class :—					...	...	...	...
4	*Okikaze*	'18—'20	1345	...t	...t				
2	*Minekaze*	'17—'19				...	...	...	...
2	*Tanikaze*	'16—'18	1300	28,000 t	34	...	128	6	10½
4	*Amatsukaze*	'15—'17	1227	27,000 t	34	145+195	145	6	10½
2	*Umikaze*	'08—'11	1150	19,500 t	31·5	250+180	139	3—4	9¼
	Second Class :—								
8	*Momi*	'18—'19	850	...t	...	...	...	...	...
6	*Tsubaki*	'17—'18	835	16,000 t	31·5	90+210	109	6	7¾
4	*Momo*	'15—'16							
10	*Kaba*	'14—'15	665	9,500	30	90+125	92	4	8½
1	*Urakaze*	'13—'15	955	22,000 t	28	248	117	4	10½
2	*Sakura*	'11—'13	605	9,500 t	30	125+30	92	4	7¼
	Third Class :—								
33	*Arare*	'05—'08	375—381	6,000	29	{ 100 or 95+15 }	61	2	8¼—9
2	*Asagiri*	'02—'04							
2	*Asashiho* (T)	'01—'04	333	7,000	31	96	60	2	8½
2	*Akebono* (Y)	'97—'00	306	6,000	31	90-95	55	2	8
3	*Kagero* (T)	'97—'00	326	5,400	30	81	61	2	7¼

(T)=Thornycroft. (Y)=Yarrow type. *t*=Turbine.

8+7 1st Class Destroyers (over 1000 tons).
7 Minekaze class. (2 Minekaze + 5 Okikaze.)

Building or Completing.

(Photo wanted of *Minekaze* or
Sawakaze, if completed).

7 *Minekaze* class :— **Minekaze, Okikaze, Nadakaze, Shimakaze.** All building or completing by Maidzuru D.Y. ; **Sawakaze, Hakaze,** and **Yakaze** all building or completing by Mitsubishi Co. at or Kobé. 1345 tons. Dimensions : × × feet. Armament : 4—4.7 inch, 2 M.G. and 6 torpedo tubes. Designed S.H.P. = kts. Machinery : turbines and Kansei boilers. Fuel : tons. Complement, . *Minekaze* and *Sawakaze* belong to the 1917 Programme ; *Okikaze, Nadakaze, Shimakaze, Hakaze* and *Yakaze* to the 1918 Programme. Launching dates not known.

8 + 7 1st Class Destroyers (continued.)
2 Tanikaze class.

Photo wanted.

2 *Tanikaze* class : **Tanikaze** (Maidzuru D.Y., 1918) and **Kawakaze** (Yokosuka D.Y., 1917). 1300 tons. Dimensions : 320 × 29¼ × 9½ feet. Armament : 3—4.7 inch, 6 tubes in three twin deck mountings. Two searchlights. Designed H.P. 28,000 = 34 kts. Machinery : Parsons turbines. Boilers : Kansei. Complement, 128. *Kawakaze* belongs to the 1917 Programme, *Tanikaze* to the 1916 Programme.

4 Amatsukaze class.

AMATSUKAZE.   *Photo by courtesy of the Navy Department, Tokyo.*

4 *Amatsukaze* class : **Amatsukaze** and **Isokaze** (both launched at Kure, Oct., 1916). **Hamakaze** (Nagasaki, Oct., 1916), and **Tokitsukaze** (Kobe, Dec., 1916).* 1227 tons. Dimensions : 310 (*p.p.*), 326½ (*o.a.*) × 2 × 9½ feet. Armament : 4—4.7 inch (40 cal.), 2 M.G., and 6—18 inch tubes in 3 twin deck mountings. 1 searchlight. Machinery : 3 sets Parsons turbines and Kansei boilers. Designed H.P. 27,000 = 34 kts. Fuel : 145 tons coal + 195 tons oil. Complement, 145. Built under the 1915 Naval Programme.

**Note.—*Tokitsukaze* wrecked ; salved in three sections, March, 1918, and practically rebuilt at Kure D.Y.

(*Continued on next page.*)

8 + *7* 1st class Destroyers—*continued.*

2 Umikaze class.

Fore-funnel now raised.

2 *Umikaze* class: **Umikaze** (Maidzuru, 1910) and **Yamakaze** (Nagasaki, 1911). 1150 tons. Dimensions : 310 (*p.p.*) 323¾ (*o.a.*) × 27¾ × 9 feet (*mean* draught) Armament : 2—4·7 inch (40 cal.), 5—12 pdr. Torpedo tubes : in *Umikaze*, 4—18 inch into two twin deck mountings ; ir *Yamakaze*, 3—18 inch in single deck mountings. One searchlight. Machinery : 3 sets Parsons turbine and Kansei boilers. Designed H.P. 19,500=31·5 kts. Fuel : 250 tons coal + 180 tons oil = 2700 miles at 15 kts. Complement, 139. Trials : *Umikaze* 33·46 kts.

23 + *8* 2nd class Destroyers.

(1000 to 600 tons).

Note.—During 1918, the British Destroyers *Minstrel* and *Nemesis* were loaned to the Japanese Navy and commissioned under the Japanese Flag as H.I.M. Ships *Kenran* and *Sendan.* Both boats have been returned to the British Navy.

8 Momi class.

Photo wanted.

8 *Momi* class : **Momi** and **Kaya** (Yokosuka D.Y.), **Kuri** and **Nire** (Kure D.Y.), **Nashi** and **Taka** (Kawasaki Co., Kobe), **Kaki** (Uraga Co.), and **Tsuga** (Ishikawajima Co.). 850 tons. Dimensions : × × feet. Armament : Guns unknown, 4 torpedo tubes. Designed S.H.P. = kts. Machinery : turbines + Kansei boilers. Fuel : tons. Complement, . Built under 1918-19 Programme. Launching dates not known, some may be unlaunched, others completing. Probably much the same as *Momo* class in next column.

23 + *8* 2nd class Destroyers—*continued.*

10 Momo class (4 Momo + 6 Tsubaki).

Photo, Seward, Weymouth.

10 *Momo* class : **Maki** and **Keyaki** (Sasebo D.Y., 1918), **Kuwa** and **Tsubaki** (Kure D.Y., 1918), **Enoki** (Maidzuru D.Y., 1918), and **Nara** (Yokosuka D.Y., 1918). **Yanagi** (1917) and **Momo** (1916), both built at Sasebo ; **Kashi** (1916) and **Hinoki** (1916), both built at Maidzuru. 835 tons. Dimensions : 275 (*o.a.*) × 25 × 7¾ feet. Armament : 3—4·7 inch, 2 M.G., and 6—18 inch tubes in two twin and two single deck mountings. One searchlight. Machinery : 3 sets Curtis turbines and 4 Kansei boilers. Designed H.P. 16,000=31·5 kts. Fuel : 90 tons coal + 210 tons oil. Complement, 109. The first six provided for by Special 1917 Programme. The last four built under the 1915 Naval Programme.

10 Kaba class.

10 *Kaba* class :—**Kaba** (Yokosuka), **Kaede** (Maidzuru), **Kashiwa** and **Matsu** (Nagasaki), **Katsura** (Kure), **Kiri** (Uraga), **Kusunoki** and **Ume** (Kobe), **Sakaki** (Sasebo), and **Sugi** (Osaka). All launched February-March, 1915. 665 tons. Dimensions : 260 (*p.p.*) 274 (*o.a.*) × 24 × 7·9 feet. Armament : 1—4·7 inch, 4—12 pdr. (2 anti-aircraft model) and 4—18 inch tubes. Machinery : 3 sets, 4-cylinder triple expansion and 4 Kansei boilers. Designed H.P. 9,500=30 kts. Fuel : 90 tons coal + 135 tons oil. Complement, 92. These boats are said to have been built in seven months. Built under 1914 Naval Programme, and served in Mediterranean during war. 12 Replicas built in Japanese Yards for French Navy—see French *Tribal* class, *Algerien, Arabe,* &c.

(*Continued on next page.*)

JAPANESE DESTROYERS

23 + 8 2nd Class Destroyers—*Continued.*

1 Special Boat.

1 *Yarrow* type: **Urakaze** (Yarrow, Scotstoun, 1915). 955 tons. Dimensions: 275 (*p.p.*) 283 (*o.a.*) × 27·5 × 9·5 feet. Armament: 1—4·7 in., 4—12 pdr., 4—21 inch tubes in two twin deck mountings. Machinery: 22,000 H.P. turbines = 28 kts. Yarrow large tube boilers. Fuel: 248 tons oil only. Endurance about 1800 miles at 15 kts. Complement, 117.

Note.—It was intended that this boat should have a Diesel engine for cruising speed, combined by Föttinger hydraulic transmission to the turbines. Owing to the War, the Föttinger gear and Diesel engine were never delivered. They were replaced by a big oil tank. *Kawakaze* (sister-boat) ceded to Italy, and now Italian *Audace.*

2 Sakura Class.

Fore funnel may now be raised.

2 *Sakura* class:—**Sakura** (1911), **Tachibana** (1912). Both built at Maidzuru. 605 tons. Fuel: 125 tons coal + 30 tons oil; otherwise as 10 *Kaba* class, on preceding page.

42 3rd Class Destroyers (under 600 tons).

33 Later *Arare* type, viz.:—5 built at Maidzuru: **Ayanami** (1909), **Isonami** (1908), **Uranami** (1907), **Oite** and **Yunagi** (1906); 2 built at Uraga: **Kikudzuki** (1907), and **Nagatsuki** (1906); 4 built at Nagasaki: **Matsukaze, Minadzuki, Shirayuki** and **Shiratsuya** (all 1906); 1 built at Osaka: **Hayate** (1906); 5 built at Kobe: **Hatsuharu, Shigure, Udzuki** (all 1906), **Asakaze** and **Harukaze** (both 1905); 4 built at Sasebo: **Mikadzuki, Nowaki, Yudachi** (all 1906), and **Yugure** (1905); 12 built at Yokosuka: **Hatsuyuki, Hibiki** (both 1906), **Arare, Fubuki, Hatsushimo, Kamikaze, Kisaragi, Nenohi, Ushiho, Wakaba, Yayoi** (all 1905), and **Ariyake** (1904). 375—381 tons. Dimensions: 227 to 234⅓ (*o.a.*) × 21⅓ × 6 feet. Armament: 6—12 pdr., and 2—18 inch tubes. 1 searchlight. Designed H.P. 6,000 = 29 kts. Coal: 100 tons, but *Ayanami, Isonami,* and *Uranami* have 95 tons coal + 15 oil. Endurance about 1,200 miles at 15 kts. Complement 61.

Also

2 Earlier *Arare* type: **Asagiri** (1903), **Murasame** (both built at Yokosuka, 1902). Generally the same as the above 33 boats, but have 2—12 pdr., and 4—6 pdr. guns.

Note to "Arare" type Plans.—2—12 pdr., not shown, are mounted abeam of 2nd and 3rd funnels.

(6 pdr. on forebridge now replaced by a 12 pdr.)

2 *Thornycroft* type:—**Asashiho** (1902), **Shirakumo** (1901), 333 tons. Guns: 2—12 pdr., 4—6 pdr. Torpedo tubes: 2—18 inch. H.P. 7000 = 30 to 31 kts. Boilers: Thornycroft. Coal: 96 tons. Complement, 60.

42 3rd Class Destroyers—*Continued.*

Note.

All T.B.D. listed below now used only as Tenders to Torpedo Schools. Will probably be removed from the Navy in the near future.

Note to Plans.—The 6 pdr. on forebridge has been replaced by a 12 pdr.

2 *Yarrow* type:—**Akebono, Oboro** (both 1899). 306 tons. Dimensions: 220 × 20½ × 5 feet. Guns: 2—12 pdr., 4—6 pdr. Torpedo tubes: 2—18 inch. H.P. 6000 = 31 kts. Coal: 90—95 tons. Complement, 51.

Note to Plans.—The 6 pdr. on forebridge has been replaced by a 12 pdr.

3 *Thornycroft* type:—**Kagero** (1899), **Shiranui** (1899), **Usugumo** (1900). 326 tons. Dimensions: 210 × 19½ × 6 feet (*mean* draught). Guns: 2—12 pdr., 4—6 pdr. Torpedo tubes: 2—18 inch. H.P. 5400 = 30 kts. Coal: 81 tons. Complement, 61.

20 Torpedo Boats.

No.	Type.	Date.	Displacement.	H.P.	Maximum Speed.	Coal.	Complement.	Tubes.
			Tons.		kts.	tons.		
	First class :—							
11	*Hayabusa* (N)	'00-'04	150-152	4200	28½-29	24·26	30	3
1	*Shirataka* (S)	1900	115	2600	25	24	30	3
	Second class :—							
8	(67—68) (70—75) (S)	1903	87-89	1200	23½-24	26·5	23	3

(S) = Schichau type. (N) = Normand type.

1st Class Torpedo Boats

(*Itto Suiratei*).

(A) *Hayabusa* class (*Normand* type). Note position of mast and bridge, and compare with (B) on next page, where details of this class are given.

s

1st Class Torpedo Boats—*Continued*.

(B) *Hayabusa* class: Compare with (A) on preceding page.
11 *Hayabusa* class (*Normand* type), viz.:—9 *Kure D.Y.*: **Aotaka, Hato, Hibari, Kari, Kiji, Sagi, Tsubame**
(all 1903), **Kamome** and **Uzura** (1904,; 2 *Kawasaki Co., Kobe*; **Hashitaka** (1903), and **Otori** (1904).
150 to 152 tons. Dimensions : 147 × 16 × 4½ feet. Armament : 1—6 pdr., 2—3 pdr., 3—14 inch tubes.
Machinery : 2 sets triple expansion. Designed H.P. 4200=28·5 to 29 kts. Coal : 26 tons.

No photo available.

(See Silhouettes for appearance.)

---

1 *Schichau* type: **Shirataka** (1898) 127 tons. Dimensions : 132×15·3× 4.3 feet. Armament : 3—3 pdr., 3—14 inch
tubes. 1 Searchlight : Designed H.P. 2600=28 kts. originally, 25 kts. now. Coal : 24 tons.

2nd Class Torpedo Boats.

(*2tô Suiratei*)

Are only used now for Harbour Duty.

No photo available.

(See Silhouettes for appearance.)

---

8 *Schichau* type: **Nos. 70—75, 67—68** (built at Yokosuka, Sasebo and Kure, 1902-3). 87 to 89 tons. Dimensions :
128 × 16½ × 3½ feet. Armament : 2 —6 pdr., (Yamanouchi) and 3—14 inch tubes. Designed H.P. 1200=23¼ to 24 kts.
Coal : 26¼ tons.

---

20 + *23?* Submarines (*Sensuikan*).

No.	Type	Date	Displacement	H.P.	Max. speed	Fuel.	Complement	T. Tubes	Max. draug't
	Ocean-going:—		tons		kts.	tons.			
17	*Nos. 27 —43*	Bldg.	...	...	...	...	...	...	...
5/6	*No. 14 ? &* *Nos. 22—26* } (ND)	'17—'20	700-900 1000—1200	...	...	...	...	...	...
4	*Nos. 18—21* (AL?)	'15—'18	700 1070	...	...	...	...	...	...
1	Sea-going:— *No. 15* (SL)	'12—'16	450 670	2000	17 10	...	...	6	10
2	Coastal:— *Nos. 16, 17* (VJ)	'15—'16	300 320	...	...	...	...	...	...
1	*No. 13* (VJ)	'10—'12	278 322	...	11	} About 15	16	2	12
3	*Nos. 10—12* (VJ)	'10—'11	280 314	600	13 8				
2	*Nos. 8, 9* (V)	'07—'08	290 320	600 180	13 8				
2	*Nos. 6, 7*	'05—'06	79 86	...	10·5 8·6	...	...	1	...
5	*Nos. 1—5* (H)	'05—'06	106 125	160 70	9 7	...	9-10	1	9

(ND)=Navy Department design. (AL)=Ansaldo-Laurenti design. (SL)=Schneider-Laubeuf design.
(V)=Vickers type. (VJ)=Vickers type, modified by Japanese Navy Department. (H)=Holland type.

Ex-German Submarines.

The following ex-German Submarines were taken over at British Naval Ports in 1919, and have proceeded to Japan :—
6 *Ocean-going* boats : *U 43, U 46, U 55, U 125, UB 125, UB 143.*
2 *Mine-Laying* boats : *UC 90, UC 99.*

These boats are only allowed to be used for experiments, and must be broken up. They are not to be incorporated in
the Imperial Navy, and accordingly, they are not included in above Table, or described in the following pages.

9 *or* 10 (+ *17 ?*) Ocean-going boats.

Building and Completing.

17 boats ; *types unknown* : **Nos. 27—43.** Building or completing by Navy Yards and private shipyards, under 1918-19 Naval Programme. No details known.

Building and Completing ?

5 or 6 *Navy* type : **No. 14 ?** and **Nos. 22—26.** Builders not known. Built about 1917-20. Displace 700-900 tons *on surface*, 1000-1200 tons *submerged*. No other details available.

Note.—*Nos. 22—26* built under 1917-18 Programme. Not certain that *No. 14* belongs to this class. The original *No. 14* was ceded to French Navy and a new *No. 14* was ordered to replace her. This second *No. 14* may really be a sister-boat to *No. 15* (see next column).

Photo wanted.

4 (type uncertain) : **No. 18** and **Nos. 19—21,** built about 1915-18 by Kure D.Y. and Kawasaki Co., Kobé. Believed to be Ansaldo-Laurenti boats, displacing 700 tons *on surface* and 1070 tons *submerged*. *No. 18* belongs to the 1915-16 Programme ; *Nos. 19—21* to the 1916-17 Programme.

1 (+ *1 ?*) Sea-going boat.

Photo wanted.

1 *Schneider-Laubeuf* type : **No. 15** (Chalon-sur-Saône, France, 1914). Displaces 450 tons *on surface*, 670 tons *submerged*. Dimensions : *about* 182 × 19 × 10 feet. Machinery : 2 sets of 1000 B.H.P. Schneider-Carels Diesel motors = 17 kts. *on surface*. *Submerged* speed : *about* 9½-10 kts. Armament : 1 small Q.F. gun, 2 bow torpedo tubes and 4 tubes in w.t.c. under superstructure.

Note.—A similar boat, *No. 14*, ceded to French Navy in 1914, and now French *Armide*. Not certain if a replica of *No. 15* is being built in Japan as a second *No. 14*.

15 Coastal boats.

Note.—Some of the 17 new boats, *Nos. 27—43*, listed in preceding column, may be of Coastal types.

Photo wanted.

(See Silhouette for appearance.)

2 *Modified Japanese-Vickers* type : **Nos. 16** and **17,** built at Kure D.Y., 1916, under 1915-16 Programme. Displace 300 tons *on surface*, 320 tons *submerged*. Otherwise much the same as *Nos. 8, 9, 10—12*, given on next page.

Photo wanted.

(See Silhouette for appearance).

1 *Modified Japanese-Vickers* type : **No. 13** (Kawasaki Co., Kobé, 1911). Displaces 278 tons *on surface*, 322 tons *submerged*. Otherwise much the same as *Nos. 8, 9, 10—12* on next page.

(*Continued on next page*.)

15 Coastal Boats.

Photos wanted.

(See Silhouettes.)

5 *Vickers-Japanese* type: **No. 12—10** (Kure D.Y. and Kawasaki Co., Kobe, 1910-11), **Nos. 9** & **8** (Vickers, Barrow, 1908). Displacements vary a little, but are generally similar to British "C" class submarines. Dimensions about 135 × 13½ × 12 feet. 2 bow tubes. Radius of action about 1000 miles *on surface* at 10 kts.

No photo available.

(See Silhouettes.)

1 *type unknown*: **No. 7** (Kawasaki Co., 1906-7). Displacement: 79 tons *on surface*, 86 tons *submerged*. Dimensions: 85 × 8 × feet. 1 bow torpedo tube. 1 set petrol motors. Nothing else known about this boat. Considering her size and age, she may be almost worthless now.

15 Coastal Boats—*continued*.

No photo available.

(See Silhouettes.)

1 *type unknown*: **No. 6** (Kawasaki Co., Kobe, 1906-7). Details as for No. 7 but is of different appearance. Doubtfully reported that this boat was rebuilt 1918-19 as an experimental Minelayer.

No photo available.

(See Silhouettes.)

5 early *Holland* type: **Nos. 5—1** (1905-6, imported from U.S.A. about time of Russo-Japanese War). Dimensions: 66 × 11¾ × feet. 1 bow torpedo tube. Petrol engine of 160 H.P. for surface running. 1 screw. Probably of little effective value now.

JAPANESE DEPOT SHIPS.

Destroyer Depot Ships.

1st Class Cruisers, **NISSHIN** and **IDZUMO,** attached to T.B.D. Flotillas.

Photo wanted.

ISUSAN (Maru). (——) 217 tons. No other details known.

Photo wanted.

KENKAI (Maru). (——) 315 tons. No other details known.

Destroyer Depot Ships—*continued*.

Photo wanted.

REKISAN (Maru). (——). 450 tons. 129½ × 22¼ × 8¾ feet. Guns : Not known. I.H.P. 202 = 8.7 kts. No other details known.

Photo wanted.

SHIROGANE. (——). 413 tons. No other details known.

Submarine Depot Ships.

1st Class Cruiser **ASO** is Tender to Submarines.

Photo by courtesy of the Navy Department, Tokyo.

KOMAHASHI. (Sasebo, 1913). 1230 tons. 227 × 35 × 17¾ feet. Guns : 3—12 pdr. H.P. 1824 = 13.9 kts. Was originally built as a Naval Transport.

(*Continued on next page.*)

Submarine Depot Ships—*continued.*

KARASAKI (ex *Ekaterinoslav*, 1896, captured 1904). 6,710 tons. Dimensions : 440 × 49½ × 15¾ feet (*max.* draught). Armament : 1—12 pdr. H.P. 3200 = 13 kts.

NAGAURA (Maru) (ex-Gunboat *Tatsuta*, Elswick, 1894). 850 tons. 240 × 27½ × 9½ feet. Guns : Not known. I.H.P. 5000 = 21 kts. Coal : 155 tons.

Seaplane Depot Ship.

Photo by courtesy of the Navy Department.

WAKAMIYA (1901). 7600 tons. Dimensions : 365 × 48¼ × 19 feet. Armament : 2—12 pdr. H.P. 1600 = 9½ kts. Carries 4 seaplanes. Was originally built as a Naval Transport.

Note.—Now has hangars at foot of each mast, **as shown by Silhouette.**

Mine Layers.

Building or Completing.

NINOSHIMA (Maru). Building or completing at Kure D.Y. No details known. 1918-19 Programme.

Photo wanted.

YENOSHIMA (Maru). Built under 1917 Special Programme, at Maidzuru D.Y. No details known.

KUROKAMI.   *Photo, Navy Dept., Tokyo.*

YENTO (Maru,) Mar., 1917 ; **KATASHIMA (Maru)** Feb., 1917), both built at Maidzuru D.Y., and **KUROKAMI (Maru)** Kure D.Y., Feb., 1917. 800 tons. Built under 1916-17 Programme. No other details known.

Mine Layers—*continued.*

Photo wanted.

KUROSHIMA (Maru) and **TOSHIMA (Maru).** Both built at Sasebo D.Y. about 1915-17. 433 tons. 150 × 25 × 7½ feet. Guns : Not known. H.P. 600 = 12 kts.

Note.—May be sister ships to *Ashizaki Maru* and *Katoku Maru,* given below.

Photo wanted.

KATSURIKI. (Kure D.Y., Oct., 1916). 2000 tons. Built under 1915-16 Programme. No other details known.

Photo wanted.

ASHIZAKI (Maru) 433 tons, and **KATOKU (Maru).** 300 tons. Both launched at Maidzuru D.Y., Oct., 1915. Guns : Not known. H.P. 700 = 12 kts. Built under 1915-16 Programme.

Photo wanted.

NATSUSHIMA (Maru). (Yokosuka D.Y., March, 1911). 421 tons. 200 × 22½ × 5½ feet. Guns : Not known. H.P. 500 = 12 kts.

(*Continued on next page.*)

Mine Layers—*Continued.*

> Photo wanted.

SOKUTEN (Maru). No details known.

Mine-Sweepers.

Some of the Mine Layers, detailed above, probably equipped also as Sweepers. No exact details known.

Oilers & Tank Vessels.

> *Building or Completing.*

ERIMO (——), **NOTORO** (——) and **SHIRETOKO.** All building or completing by Kawasaki Co., Kobé. 8,000 tons. Belong to 1918-19 Programme. No other details known.

> Photo wanted.

SUNOSAKI (Maru) (Yokosuka D.Y., June, 1918). 9800 tons. Guns : Some small Q.F. H.P. 6000 = 14 kts. Carries 5000 tons oil. Built under 1916-17 Programme.

Oilers & Tank Vessels—*Continued.*

> Photo wanted.

TSURUGIZAKI (Kure D.Y., June, 1917). 1970 tons. $220\frac{1}{2} \times$ 31 × 14 feet. H.P. 900 = 9 kts. Cargo : 1,100 tons oil. Built under 1916-17 Programme.

> Photo wanted.

SHIJIKI (Kure D.Y., March, 1916). 5300 tons. 300 × 42 × $20\frac{1}{4}$ feet. H.P. 2500 = 12 kts. Own fuel : 540 tons oil., Cargo : 3000 tons oil. Built under 1915-16 Programme.

Also 10 (or more) other small Tank Vessels ; names and details not known.

Fleet Colliers.

> *Building or Completing ?*

MUROTO (1918). 8750 tons. Other details as Noshima below.

> *Completing.*

NOSHIMA (Mitsubishi Co., Kobé, Feb., 1919). 6000 tons. I.H.P. 2640 = 12.5 kts. Coal : 877 tons. Built under Special 1918-19 Programme.

Naval Auxiliaries and Transports.

KOMAHASHI (Submarine Depot Ship) and **WAKAMIYA** (Seaplane Carrier), both listed on preceding page. Were both originally built as Naval Transports, and can be so used if necessary.

> *No photo available.*

ROZAN (ex-German S.S. *Ellen Rickmers*, built at Geestemünde 1906, and captured 1914). 4117 tons *gross.* Dimensions : 367.7 × 47.7 × 27.4 feet (*depth of hold*). H.P. 1600 = 11 kts.

> Photo wanted.

SEITO (ex-German S.S. *Durendart*, built at Flensburg, 1906, and captured 1914). 3844 tons *gross.* Dimensions : 340.5 × 49.2 × feet. H.P. 1525 = 10 kts.

> Photo wanted.

KOSHU (ex-German S.S. *Michael Jebsen*, built by Howaldt, Kiel, 1904, and captured 1914). 1521 tons *gross.* Dimensions : 251.1 × 36.1 × 18.9 feet (*depth of hold*). H.P. 800 = 9.5 kts.
Now has fore topmast.

MANSHU (ex-*Manchuria*, 1901). 3916 tons. Complement, 193. Guns : 2—12 pdr., 2—3 pdr. I.H.P. 5000 × 17.6 kts. Coal : 400 tons.

(*continued on next page.*)

Naval Auxiliaries & Transports—*continued.*

No photo available.

MATSUÉ (ex-*Sungari*, 1898). 2550 tons. Complement, 126. Guns: 2—12 pdr., 2—3 pdr. I.H.P. 1500 = 13 kts. Coal: 130 tons and some oil fuel.

Photo wanted.

TAKASAKI (——). 4746 tons. No other details known.

Despatch Vessels, Yachts, &c.
None ?

Repair Ship.

Photo wanted.

KWANTO (Maru) (1898). 10,000 tons. 410 × 49½ × feet. I.H.P. 2500 = 10 kts. speed.

Salvage Ships.

Photo wanted.

KURIHASHI (Maru) (——). 1040 tons. 182 × 80¼ × 11¾ feet. I.H.P. 1200 = kts.

Photo wanted.

YODOHASHI (Maru) (——). 870 tons. 159 × 27¾ × 12½ feet. I.H.P. 718 = kts.

Photo wanted.

SARUHASHI (Maru) (——). 600 tons. 140 × 26½ × 10½ feet. I.H.P. 885 = kts.

Photo wanted.

ITAHASHI (Maru) (——). 333 tons. No other details known.

Surveying Ships.

Photo by courtesy of the Ministry of Marine.

MUSASHI (Yokosuka, 1886, **YAMATO** (Kobe, 1885). Composite built. 1502 tons. Guns: 4—12 pdr., 4—3 pdr. H.P. 1622. Original speed was 13½ kts. Coal: 145 tons.

Training Ships.
(All described on preceding pages :)—

For Gunnery :
ASAHI. Battleship.
For Torpedoes (at Yokosuka) :
TSUGARU. 2nd Class Cruiser.
For Gunnery and Torpedoes :—
IKOMA. 1st Class Cruiser.
For Seamanship :
FUJI. Battleship.
For Engineer Branch : ?

YURAGAWA (Maru). No details known. Doubtful if this ship is still in service.
For Cadets :
SUWO. Coast Defence Battleship.
ADZUMA. ⎫
TOKIWA. ⎬ 1st Class Cruisers.
YAKUMO. ⎭
For Conscripts :
HASHIDATE. 2nd Class Coast Defence Ship.
For Boys :
Old 2nd Class Coast Defence Ships, **OKINOSHIMA** and **MISHIMA**, are reported to be used for this service as Barracks, but may now be serving as Ice Breakers.

FRENCH FLEET.

(Officially Revised, 1919, by order of H.E. The Minister of Marine.

CHERBOURG

to			knots.
Bermuda	...	...	2933
Brest	...	...	210
Copenhagen	...	...	834
Devonport	...	...	111
Dunkirk	...	...	180
Lorient	...	...	300
Kronstadt	...	...	1500
Portsmouth	...	...	72
Rochefort	...	...	410
Stockholm	...	...	1258
Toulon	...	...	1817
Wilhelmshaven	...	...	476

TOULON

to			knots.
Aden	...	...	2882
Ajaccio	...	...	160
Algiers	...	...	405
Bizerta	...	...	450
Brest	...	...	1659
Constantinople	...	...	1356
Genoa	...	...	164
Gibraltar	...	...	713
Kronstadt	...	...	3289
Lorient	...	...	1656
Port Mahon	...	...	207
Malta	...	...	612
Naples	...	...	407
Oran	...	...	542
Port Said	...	...	1485
Portsmouth	...	...	1864
Saigon	...	...	7150
Sevastopol	...	...	1654
Spezia	...	...	195
Tangiers	...	...	738
Taranto	...	...	766

BREST

to			knots.
Algiers	...	...	1360
Bermuda	...	...	2811
Cherbourg	...	...	210
Devonport	...	...	139
Gibraltar	...	...	953
Liverpool	...	...	407
Malta	...	...	1934
Kronstadt	...	...	1672
New York	...	...	2954
Oran	...	...	1876
Portsmouth	...	...	226
Rio de Janeiro	...	...	4837
Rochefort	...	...	260
Toulon	...	...	1659
Wilhelmshaven	...	...	686

ORAN (Torpedo Station)

to		knots.
Algiers	...	400
Bizerta	...	650
Gibraltar	...	225
Toulon	...	542

BIZERTA

to			knots.
Algiers	...	...	400
Gibraltar	...	...	875
Malta	...	...	240
Oran	...	...	650
Spezia	...	...	430
Toulon	...	...	450

SAIGON

to		knots.
Hong Kong	...	930
Manila	...	875
Port Arthur	...	2065
Singapore	...	640

MERCANTILE MARINE : 1051 steamers of 1,842,108 tons *gross.*
998 sailing ships of 466,348 tons *gross.*

COINAGE : 1 franc (100 centimes) = 9½d. British, 19 cents American.

TRADE PORTS (in order of importance): Marseilles, Havre, Dunkirk, Bordeaux, Boulogne, Calais, Dieppe, Rouen.

OVERSEA POSSESSIONS : Corsica, Algeria, Tunis, Senegal, etc. Madagascar, Guiana, Martinique, S. Pierre, New Caledonia, Pondicherry, Annam, Cochin China, Tonquin.

FRENCH FLEET.

ADDENDA AND CORRECTIONS:—1.

Flags (1919).

Drawings prepared from information furnished by courtesy of the Ministry of Marine, Paris.

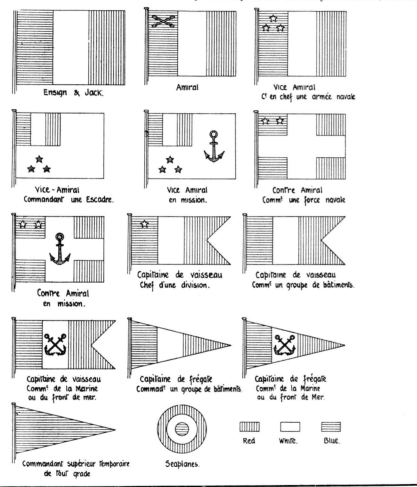

Ensign & Jack.

Amiral

Vice Amiral
Cᵗ en chef une armée navale

Vice - Amiral
Commandant une Escadre.

Vice Amiral
en mission.

Contre Amiral
Commᵗ une force navale

Contre Amiral
en mission.

Capitaine de vaisseau
Chef d'une division.

Capitaine de vaisseau
Commᵗ un groupe de bâtiments.

Capitaine de vaisseau
Commᵗ de la Marine
ou du front de mer.

Capitaine de frégate
Commadᵗ un groupe de bâtiments.

Capitaine de frégate
Commᵗ de la Marine
ou du front de Mer.

Commandant supérieur temporaire
de tout grade

Seaplanes.

Red.   White.   Blue.

Scale : 1 inch = 160 feet.

SILHOUETTES.

ARA ("*Aviso.*")

OPINIÂTRE *t.b.d.*

NORMANDIE class Dreadnoughts.—Reported that, if these ships are completed, their equipment will be brought up-to-date by the installation of director fire controls, " quadripod " masts, flying-off platforms, and aeroplanes on barbette crowns, &c. Unofficial statements have been published, saying that schemes have been considered for completing *BÉARN* as a Battle-Cruiser, armed with 6—17 inch guns. It must be added that, owing to the high costs of material and labour, it is doubtful if all or any of the *Normandie* class will be finished. *Béarn* may be launched to clear her slip and be left uncompleted.

The main turrets of **PATRIE, REPUBLIQUE,** and **POTHUAU** have been removed to Gunnery Schools ashore, but the below-deck portions of the turrets are left in these ships. They now have deck houses on fox'le and quarter decks. **PATRIE** has one *above water* tube over stern.

SIX NEW LIGHT CRUISERS, of a "*Modified Lamotte-Picquet*" type, projected under the 1919 Naval Programme. 4750 tons. Guns : 8—5·5 inch. Armour : 2″ Side amidships, 1″ Deck. Speed, 30 kts.

Regarding deletion of *Lamotte-Picquet* from this Edition of "Fighting Ships" : this ship was actually begun, but never got beyond a very elementary stage of construction. Building may be resumed to above design, and this ship may be built under 1919 Programme.

BRUIX may be removed from the Effective List soon, with all Protected Cruisers.

Add the following to Lists of

Gunboats.

Photo wanted.

DUBOURDIEU, DU CHAUFFAULT, DUPERRÉ, DUMONT-D'URVILLE, DE CONEDIC, DÉCRES. These are Diesel-engined Gunboats of a modified *Vaillante* type, launched by Lorient and Rochefort Dockyards, 1918. *Dubourdieu* completed about June, 1919. Further Gunboats of this and other new types reported to be cancelled.

River Gunboat **STYX** (not listed), removed from Effective List.

SIX NEW DESTROYERS, of 2000 tons displacement, projected under the 1919 Naval Programme. Guns : 3—5·5 inch. Speed, 35 kts.

Opiniâtre (of *Temeraire* class) has been re-boilered and given four funnels, as Silhouette opposite.

Following Torpedo Boats reported removed from Effective List :
Chasseur, Arc, Flamberge, Epée.

Torpedo Boats : Nos. *195, 208—229* to be sold out.

ADDENDA AND CORRECTIONS :—2.

Sloop or Despatch Vessel (*Aviso*).

ARA.   *Builders, Photo.*

ARA (launched by Camper & Nicholson, Southampton, 1917, purchased during War for French Navy). 1296 tons. Dimensions : 213.5 (*o.a.*) × 31.12 × 14.25 feet (*mean draught*). Machinery : 2 sets Diesel motors. B.H.P. 2135 = 14 kts. 2 screws. Fuel : 120 tons crude oil. Guns : 2—5.5 inch, 2—9 pdr., 2 M.G. on AA. mountings, 2 D.C. throwers.

Also armed Yachts **ATMAH, DIANA, LUCIOLE, PHOENIX RIVOLI,** of which no details have come to hand.

Training Ships and Establishments.

Flagship, R.A. :— **PATRIE.**

FOR GUNNERY.

Battleships	*Verité* / *Republique*
Cruiser	*Pothuau**
Gunboats	*La Hire* / (Another)†
Torpedo Boats	*No. 281* / (Another)†

*Sea-going Gunnery Ship.   †Not yet selected.

FOR TORPEDOES.

Battleship	*Patrie*
T.B.D.	*Sarbacane*
T.B.	*No. 360* / (Another)*
Submarine Chaser	(One)*

*Not yet selected.

FOR TORPEDO EXPERIMENTS AND RESEARCH.

Trawlers	*Caille* / *Printemps*
Submarine Chaser	*No. 31*

FOR HYDROPHONES.

Tug	*Vigoreux**
T.B.	*Orage*
Trawler	*Henriette No. 1**
Submarines	(Two)†

*May also mean : one ship of *Henriette* type.
†To be selected.

FOR ENGINEERS.

T.B.D.	*Cavalier*
T.B.	*No. 222* (*Rouable*)
M.L.	(Three)*
Trawlers or Patrol Boats	(Two, of *Perce-Niege* type)*

*To be selected.

FOR CADETS.

Cruiser	*Jeanne d'Arc*
T.B.D.	*Aventurier*
T.B.	*Typhon*
Gunboat	*Sans Souci*
Harbour Vessel	*Bougainville*

FRENCH FLEET.

ADDENDA AND CORRECTIONS:—3.

Naval Ordnance (converted from official 1919 Table furnished by courtesy of the Ministry of Marine).

	13.4		12					10.6		9.4			7.6			6.5				5.5		3.9
Calibre (ins.)	13.4		12					10.6		9.4			7.6			6.5				5.5		3.9
Do. (c/m)	34		30					27		24			19			16				14		10
Mark	1912		1906-10	1906	'93-96'M	1893-96	1893	1893-6	1893	1902-6	1893-6	1893	1902	1893-6	1893	'93-'96M	1893-6	1893	'91 (II)	1910	1893	'91 &'93
Length (calibres)	45		45	45	40	40	40	40	45	49.5	40	40	50	40	40	45	45	45	45	55	45	45
Weight of Gun (English tons)	65.33		54.7	54.7	47.3	47.3	43.4	34.5	34.9	29.1	23.6	20.4	14.9	12.5	10.2	7.96	7.96	6.52	6.94	5.17	4.01	1.67
Weight of Shell (capped) in lbs.	A.P. 1190.5	Ogival 1256.6	922.3	960.4	770.3	770.3	770.3	579.1	579.1	487.2	374.8	374.8	199	199	199	121	121	121	121	80.5	84	35.5
Weight of Charge (lbs.)	330.7	337.3	267.4	282.2	284.4	244.7	217.2	197.4	148.8	148.1	147.4	127.9	84	74.5	49.2	45.6	43.7	28.9	28.9	22.7	16	8.16
Max. Pressure (lbs.)	59,525	57,320	57,320	57,320	61,729	63,934	51,808	62,831	47,619	57,320	63,934	52,910	59,083	61,739	47,400	47,400	61,739	44,092	44,092	55,155	53,706	52,911
Muzzle-Velocity (ft.-secs.)	2624.7	2605	2559	2559	2839	2674	2559	2674	2559	2625	2723	2625	3117	2756	2526	2953	2838	2527	2527	2723	2395	2329
Remaining Velocity at 21,872 yds. / 20,000 m.	..	1309	..	..	..	..	..	..	..	..	..	..	..	..	..	..	..	..	..	..	..	..
Remaining Velocity at 16,404 yds. / 15,000 m.	1178	1462	..	..	..	..	..	..	..	1102	..	..	..	..	..	..	..	..	..	..	..	..
Remaining Velocity at 10,936 yds. / 10,000 m.	1473	1762	1529	1529	1411	1325	1260	1203	1188	1348	1135	1112	1106	1010	992	928	918	922	922	860	905	856
Remaining Velocity at 5468 yds. / 5000 m.	1640	2162	1992	1992	2028	1893	1801	1798	1739	1896	1755	1654	1860	1571	1447	1417	1351	1257	1257	1230	1168	1033
Angle of descent at 20,000 m.	..	25° 10″	..	..	..	..	..	..	..	..	..	..	..	..	..	..	..	..	..	..	..	..
Angle of descent at 15,000 m.	21° 10″	14° 50″	..	..	..	..	..	..	..	25° 50″	..	..	..	..	..	..	..	..	..	..	..	..
Angle of descent at 10,000 m.	9° 30″	7° 35″	9° 25″	9° 25″	9° 50″	11° 20″	12° 40″	13° 10″	13° 50″	11° 10″	14° 40″	16° 10″	14° 10″	18° 10″	20° 50″	23° 20″	24° 30″	26° 30″	26° 30″	27° 30″	28° 40″	34° 10″
Angle of descent at 5000 m.	3° 10″	2° 53″	3° 14″	3° 14″	3° 0″	3° 20″	3° 40″	3° 30″	13° 50″	3° 20″	3° 40″	4° 0″	3° 10″	4° 10″	5°	4° 20″	5° 10″	6° 20″	6° 20″	6° 10″	7° 20″	9° 20″

(Charts to uniform scale : Soundings in fathoms. Heights in feet.

DUNKIRK.   **For details see next page.**

For Flags, 1919,

see Addenda Page.

CALAIS.   **For details see next page.**

<table>
<tr><td>Vice-Amiral.</td><td>Contre-Amiral.</td><td>Capitaine de vaisseau.</td><td>Capitaine de fregate.</td><td>Lieutenant de vaisseau.</td><td>Enseigne.</td><td>Enseigne 2e classe and Aspirant</td></tr>
<tr><td></td><td>Rear-Ad.</td><td>Captain.</td><td>Commander.</td><td>Lieut.</td><td>Lieut. (junior).</td><td>Sub-Lieut. and Midshipman. (U.S. Ensign.)</td></tr>
</table>

Corresponding British or U.S. Navies.

Note.—New rank of Capitane de corvette, introduced June, 1917, with four gold stripes on sleeve, and intermediate between ranks of Capitane de fregate and Lieutenant de vaisseau. Equivalent to British or U.S.A. rank of Lieut.-Commander.

Only one of the Capitaine de fregate's upper stripes is gold : the other is white.

Epaulettes with parade uniform are of the usual sort, *except* that—

A Vice-Admiral's epaulettes have the usual anchor and 3 stars.

A Rear-Admiral's „ „ „ „ 2 „

Caps are the usual shape, but have gold bands round. The cocked hat carries the tri-colour.

Before the war, personnel was about 65,000 including reserves.

Minister of Marine—Mons. Georges Leygues.

FRENCH NAVAL BASES.

(To Uniform Scale : Soundings in fathoms. Heights in feet).

CHANNEL.

For Charts, **see preceding page.**

DUNKIRK. Fine harbour. Breakwater. Torpedo, Submarine and Aircraft base. There are five docks here—one $622 \times 69 \times 26\frac{1}{4}$, two $357\frac{1}{4} \times 46 \times 26$ or 21 feet, and one smaller.

CALAIS. Torpedo and submarine base. Dock, $426\frac{1}{4} \times 69 \times 28\frac{1}{2}$.

Private Docks.

BOULOGNE. Floating Dock, $236\frac{1}{4} \times 62\frac{1}{4}$ feet (1000 tons).

DIEPPE. Dry Dock, $361 \times 59 \times 27$ feet.

HAVRE. (No. 4). $674\frac{1}{4} \times 98\frac{2}{3} \times 28\frac{1}{2}$ feet ; also 2 large and 3 small docks.

GRANVILLE. Dry Dock, $225 \times 46\frac{1}{2} \times 23$ feet.

PAIMPOL. Dry Dock, $229\frac{1}{2} \times 36 \times$ feet.

CHERBOURG. Admiralty Chart No. 2602. Rise of Spring Tide, $17\frac{3}{4}$ feet.

CHERBOURG. Protected by a breakwater about two miles long. **Heavily fortified.**

Dry Docks.

No. 1	$360 \times 62\frac{1}{3} \times 32\frac{1}{2}$ feet.	No. 5	$656 \times 93\frac{1}{4} \times 39\frac{1}{2}$ feet
„ 2	$393 \times 62\frac{1}{3} \times 32\frac{1}{2}$ „	„ 6	$606 \times 69\frac{1}{2} \times 29\frac{1}{4}$ „
„ 3	$390\frac{1}{2} \times 62\frac{1}{3} \times 32\frac{1}{2}$ „	„ 7	$265 \times 59 \times 20\frac{1}{2}$ „
„ 4	$360 \times 62\frac{1}{3} \times 32\frac{1}{2}$ „	„ 8	$257 \times 59\frac{1}{2} \times 20\frac{1}{2}$ „

Floating Submarine Salvage Dock, about 200×28 feet.

T.B.D., T.B., and S/M. built here.

ATLANTIC COAST.

BREST. Admiralty Chart No. 3427. Rise of Spring Tide, $19\frac{1}{2}$ feet.

BREST. There is only one dock able to take big modern warships. There are eight smaller docks unable to take any modern warship of importance. Forts, very numerous and powerful. Very big dock in town, $737 \times 114 \times 34$. Particulars of naval docks :

Nos. 1 & 3	$574\frac{1}{4} \times 70\frac{1}{4} \times 35\frac{1}{2}$	No. 7	$410 \times 87\frac{3}{4} \times 35\frac{1}{2}$ ⎫ Can be used
„ 2 & 4	$518\frac{1}{4} \times 91\frac{3}{4} \times 35\frac{1}{2}$	„ 8	$354 \times 66\frac{1}{4} \times 35\frac{1}{2}$ ⎭ as one dock.
No. 5	$377\frac{1}{4} \times 66\frac{1}{4} \times 35\frac{1}{2}$	„ 9	$387 \times 66\frac{1}{4} \times 35\frac{1}{2}$
„ 6	$223 \times 47\frac{3}{4} \times 16$		

Docks Nos. 7 and 8 are being united with a view to being used as a building yard.

Two Naval docks, 656×144 feet are under construction.

LORIENT. Dockyard and Base for Torpedo Craft and Submarines. No. 1, $380\frac{1}{2} \times 56\frac{1}{3} \times 20\frac{1}{2}$ feet ; No. 2, $620 \times 86\frac{1}{2} \times 29\frac{1}{3}$ feet ; No. 3, *proj.* $620 \times 92 \times 32$ feet.

ROCHEFORT. The three docks here cannot accommodate modern big ships. The largest is $489 \times 67\frac{1}{2} \times 25\frac{1}{4}$.

There is a Government dock at LA PALLICE (ROCHELLE), $553 \times 72 \times 30\frac{1}{2}$ feet, and another smaller.

Note.—During the war, various minor naval and aircraft stations were established along Atlantic Coast, principally for anti-submarine duties.

Big Private Docks.

BREST. (Town) $737 \times 114 \times 34$ feet.		BORDEAUX. $594 \times 108\frac{1}{4} \times 33$ feet ; $505 \times 72 \times 23$ feet.
ST. NAZAIRE. (C.G.T.) $731\frac{1}{4} \times 98\frac{1}{4} \times 29$ feet (enlarged).		LA ROCHELLE. $590 \times 72 \times 30$ feet.

FRENCH NAVAL BASES—MEDITERRANEAN.

(To uniform scale.   Divided into 2000 yard squares.   Soundings in fathoms.   Heights in feet.)   **Dockyards named in heavy type.**

TOULON.   Admiralty Chart No. 151-2608.

AJACCIO.   Admiralty Chart No. 429.

Large Private Docks (*Mediterranean*).

MARSEILLES.—(No. 1) $595\frac{1}{2} \times 61 \times 22\frac{1}{2}$ feet, and No. 7, $669\frac{1}{4} \times 82 \times 29\frac{1}{2}$ feet.

TOULON.   Very strongly fortified.   Aircraft and Submarine base.   Destroyers, T.B. and Submarines built here in Dockyard.

Dry Docks.

			CASTIGNEAU.			
MISSIESSY.	No. 1	$427 \times 93\frac{1}{4} \times 30\frac{1}{2}$	CASTIGNEAU.	No. 1	$325 \times 70\frac{1}{2} \times 25\frac{1}{2}$	
,,	,, 2	$427 \times 93\frac{1}{4} \times 30\frac{1}{2}$	,,	,, 2	$385\frac{1}{2} \times 70\frac{1}{2} \times 27\frac{1}{2}$	
,,	,, 3	$585 \times 93\frac{1}{4} \times 30\frac{1}{2}$	.,	,, 3	$535 \times 75\frac{1}{2} \times 27\frac{1}{2}$	
,,	,, 4	$600 \times 92 \times 32\frac{1}{2}$				

Floating dock for torpedo craft.   Submarine Floating Salvage Dock, "Atlas" $300 \times 42\frac{2}{3}$ feet, 1000 tons lift.   Also 3 small docks in the Arsenal Principal.

Naval Aviation Centres.

Very large establishment at Fréjus, St. Raphael, near Toulon.   Also Training School at Berre, near Marseilles.

Naval Bases.—(*Continued*).

AJACCIO.   } Fortified harbours used by the French fleet.   No docks.
BONIFACIO. }

ALGIERS.   Coaling Station.   Two dry docks (No. 1) $455 \times 74 \times 28$ feet; (No. 2) $268 \times 54 \times 19$ feet.   Average depth of harbour, 8 fathoms.

ORAN.   Torpedo base.   Excellent harbour, with an average depth of five fathoms.   Two breakwaters.   Fortified.   Floating Submarine Salvage Dock 210×64 feet.

BIZERTA.   Submarine and Aircraft base.   Lies inside a narrow channel.   One large dock suitable for any warship, one small one.   Floating dock for torpedo craft.   (No. 1) $656 \times 90\frac{1}{2} \times 33\frac{1}{2}$;   (No. 3) $295 \times 46\frac{1}{2} \times 17\frac{1}{4}$;   (No. 4) $656\frac{1}{4} \times 90\frac{1}{2} \times 33\frac{1}{2}$.   Submarine Salvage Ship *Vulcain* stationed here.

Note.—Temporary Naval Base established at Beyrout.   During the War the French Fleet was first based at Malta, but was transferred to Corfu.   Milo, Mudros, Salonika, Salamina, Gulf of Patras, were netted for use as anchorages for French Warships.

ORAN.   Admiralty Chart No. 812.

BIZERTA.   Admiralty Chart No. 1569.

DAKAR (Senegal).   Admiralty Chart No. 1001.

FRENCH **COLONIAL** NAVAL BASES.

African W. Coast.

DAKAR (Senegal).   Naval dry dock here, $629\frac{3}{4} \times 92\frac{2}{3} \times 30\frac{1}{2}$ feet.

African E. Coast.

Also one or two small Naval Stations in Madagascar;   location not known.

In the Far East.

SAIGON.   Situated 42 miles up the Donnoi River.   Anchorage average, 9 fathoms.   One large dry dock $518 \times 72 \times 30$ feet, and two small ones.   Floating Dock 400×66 feet, 10,000 tons lift.   Slip for building ships up to 300 feet long.

Modern Naval Guns. (All details unofficial.)

Notation.	Calibre.		Length.	Model.	Weight of gun.	Weight of A.P. shot.	Initial velocity.	Penetration against K.C.			Approximate Danger Space for average ship at		
	m/m.	inches.	cals.		tons.	lbs.	f.s.	9000 in.	6000 in.	3000 in.	10,000 yards.	5000 yards.	3000 yards.
A^8	340	13·4	...	1911	67	1433	2657	12	16	20	...	...	...
A^6	305	12	50	1906	57	970	3005	11	14	18	200	640	
A^5	305	12	45	1902	50	731	3000	8	13	17	160	610	
A^4	305	12	45	1896	46½	644	2870	7	12	15	150	570	1080
AA	305	12	40 & 45	'93, '91	46½	644	2700	4½	9	12	150	510	1050
AAA	274	10·8	45	1896	35½	476	2870	5	10	13½	150	540	1020
AA	274	10·8	45 & 40	1893	35	476	2625	3	7	11¼			
A^2	240	9·4	50	'02-'06	24	375	2969	4	9	14			
A	240	9·4	40	1893	22¾	317½	2625	3	6	9	144	540	1080
A	194	7·6	45 & 50	1902	15	185	3117	...	6	9	144	...	...
B	194	7·6	40	1896	12½	185	2870	...	5	8¼	120	525	1080
C	194	7·6	40 & 45	'93 & '91	10½	165	2625	...	3½	6	96	435	1020
C	164	6·5	45	1902	9¼	114½	3002		4¼	7		330	750
D	164	6·5	45	1896	9	114½	2870		4	6		285	630
E	164	6·5	45	1891	7	99¼	2625		...	4½		240	585
F	164	6·5	45	1887	6½	99¼	2297		...	3	...	150	360
F	138	5·5	55	1910	...	81	...	...	...	...	...	...	...
F	138	5·5	45	'93-'87	6½	{81½ / 77}	2395	...	...	3	...	120	300
F	100	3·9	55	'92 & '93	2¼	31	2494	...	...	2½	...	...	...
F	100	3·9	45	1891	1½	31	2428	...	...	2	...	...	...

NOTES ON GUNS.

In addition to the above guns, there are various models of 65 m/m (9 pdr.) and 47 m/m (3 pdr.) guns, some types being semi-automatic; also usual anti-aircraft models, 1 pdr. and machine guns.

Projectiles.—Capped A.P. for all calibres. Melinite shell for all guns.

Funnel Marking System, etc.

Big Ships:—1st squadron, 1 white band; 2nd squadron, 2 white bands. Ships in division distinguished by funnel on which bands are painted: i.e. flagship on foremast funnel, 2nd on 2nd, etc. Ships different to others, no marks.

Destroyers:—Coloured bands. 1st flotilla blue, 2nd white, 3rd red, 4th green, 5th black. Also initials of names on bows, and flotilla colour on name scroll on stern.

Torpedoes. (Details unofficial.)

Whitehead pattern, made at Toulon Torpedo Factory; also Schneider pattern at Schneider & Cie's works.

French Designation.	Diameter.	Length.	Charge.	Pressure in chamber.	Maximum range.
	inches.	feet.	lbs.	lbs. per sq. in.	
1904 model	18	19½	198	2150	6000
45 c/m long	18	16½	198	1270	2000
45 c/m short	18	13¾	185	1000	1500
38 c/m long	15	18¾	100	1000	1000
38 c/m short	15	16½	85		1000

Notes.—All fitted with gyros. Mines are Sautter-Harlé type.

General Notes.

Colour of Ships.

Big ships.—Grey all over, but some have grey-green or greenish-brown turrets, or black barbette shields.

Destroyers, etc.—Light grey; have identity letters, taken from their names, painted on bows—e.g., CL = Claymore, FF = Fanfare, EH = Enseigne Henry.

Submarines.—Sea green or light grey; have identity letters painted on bows or "air rudders" on the same system as destroyers. Camouflage schemes also used.

Guns.

13·4 inch, M. '11, in Bretagne class (3).

12 inch, M. '02-'06, 45 cal., in Danton class (5), 50 cal., in J. Bart class (4).
M. '02, 45 cal., in Verité class (3).
M. '96, 45 cal., in Republique and Patrie.
M. '93, 40 cal., in St. Louis.

10·8 inch, M. '96, 45 cal., in Henry IV.

9·4 inch, M. '06, 50 cal., in Danton class (5).

9·4 inch, M. '93, 40 cal., in D'Entrecasteaux.

7·6 inch, 50 cal., in Verité class (3), W. Rousseau class (2), E. Renan, Jules Michelet.

7·6 inch, 45 cal., in V. Hugo class (2), and 40 cal. in older armoured cruisers.

6·4 inch, 50 cal., in Patrie class (2), and 45 cal., in cruisers.

5·5 inch, 55 cal., in J. Bart class (4), Bretagne class (3), and Normandie class (5).

FRENCH PRIVATE YARDS.

Principal Private Yards (arranged alphabetically).

CHANTIERS DE BRETAGNE (formerly De la Brosse & Fouché), Nantes. Destroyers, t. b., etc,

CHANTIERS DE LA GIRONDE, Bordeaux. All kinds of warships. Water front: 623 yards. Area of works: about 48 acres. Four slips: (1) 597 feet, (2) 515 feet, (3) 436 feet, (4) 590½ feet. Titan cranes to first two. One dock, which can be used for building: 594 × 121½ × 32¼ feet, with 140 ton electric crane. Special submarine workshop: 141 × 49 feet. Firm allied to Schneider et Cie.

CHANTIERS DE LA LOIRE. Works at St. Nazaire (all kinds of warships) and Nantes. Machinery works at Saint Denis.

CHANTIERS DE PROVENCE. Yard at Port de Bouc.

CHANTIERS DE ST. NAZAIRE (Penhoet). Principal yard St. Nazaire. Works also at Rouen. All kinds of warships.

CHANTIERS NAVALS FRANÇAIS, Caen. 10 slips, 400-500 feet; 4 slips, 300 feet. Covers 1250 acres.

DYLE & BACALAN, Bordeaux. Destroyers, t.b., etc. Five slips, longest of which is 394 feet. Served with two 40 ton cranes. Machinery: 7000 h.p.

FORGES ET CHANTIERS DE LA MEDITERRANÉE. Principal yard La Seyne, near Toulon. Other yards at Havre, Granville and Marseilles. 3 slips, (a) 492 feet, (b) 590 feet, (c) 656 feet. All kinds of warships built at La Seyne, smaller craft at other yards. Total employés circa 6500.

AUGUSTIN NORMAND & Cie. Destroyer, torpedo boat and submarine works at Havre. Build ships up to 4000 tons. Yard covers 4 hectares. Large water front. Employees: 1500. Build submarine mine-layers, Diesel engines, Normand and Normand-Sigaudy boilers, etc.

SCHNEIDER & Cie. (formerly Schneider-Canet). Le Creusot Works: Ordnance, Munitions, Armour Plate. Havre, Honfleur and Hoc Works: Aviation and Diesel engines, proving range. Chalon-sur-Saône Yard: Destroyers, torpedo boats and submarines. Champagne-sur-Seine Works: Electric equipment for submarines. La Londes-les-Maures Works (7ar): Torpedoes. Station de Creux St. Georges (near Toulon): For testing submarines.

SOCIETÉ PROVENCALE DE CONSTRUCTIONS NAVALES, Marseilles.*

SOCIETÉ NORMANDE DE CONSTRUCTIONS NAVALES, Havre and Cherbourg.*

*Firms allied to Schneider & Cie.

Scale : 1 inch = 160 feet.

FRENCH WARSHIPS RECOGNITION SILHOUETTES.

NO FUNNELS.

ONE FUNNEL.

FRIPONNE type (7).
(Gunboats.)

Nos. 1, 2.   Nos. 3, 4.   Nos. 5, 6.   Argus class (2 ships).

(River Gunboats.)

Vulcain.
(Submarine Salvage Ship.)
Two funnels abeam, very wide apart.

Nancy type (31 ?)
(Convoy Despatch Vessels.)
Silhouette approximate only

NOTE.—One Funnel Types continued on next page.

ONE FUNNEL—(continued from preceding page).

CERBERE & PLUTON.
(Mine Layers.)

SEINE.
(Naval Transport.)

VILLE D'YS.
(Convoy Sloop.)

ESCAUT & AILETTE.
(Convoy Despatch Vessels.)

CAMPINAS.
(Aircraft Carrier.)

VAILLANTE class (2).
(Gunboats)

OISE type (2 ?)
(Despatch Vessels.)

YSER type (2).
(Despatch Vessels.)

SUIPPE.
(Convoy Despatch Vessel.)

SCARPE.
Convoy Despatch Vessel.)

(1) BIEN-HOA.
VINH LONG.

(2) TOURVILLE.
(Depôt Ship for Submarines.)
DUGUAY-TROUIN.

RHÔNE.
(Oil Tanker.)

GARONNE.
Ex-MEUSE.
(Oil Tankers.)

MANCHE & VAUCLUSE.
(Surveying Ships.)

TWO FUNNELS—(continued on next page).

ARDENT type (27)
(Gunboats.—Vary a little in details.)

MARNE type (2 ?)
(Despatch Vessels.)

ALTAIR type (5).

CASSIOPÉE, REGULUS.

"Star Class" (7).
(Sloops.)

TWO FUNNELS—(*continued*).

D'IBERVILLE.

LAVOISIER.

DUNOIS *class* (2 ships).

COSMAO.

D'ESTREES.

SURCOUF.

BRUIX.

DESCARTES.

REQUIN.

HENRI IV.

ST. LOUIS.

BRETAGNE (*approximate*).
(*Reported modified 1919 as above Silhouette.*)

LORRAINE.
PROVENCE.

Present existence doubtful:—

KERSAINT.

THREE FUNNELS.

DEMOCRATIE.

FRANCE.
PARIS.

JEAN BART.*
COURBET.†
†*Has derricks as " France" and " Paris."*
**Has cranes as above Silhouette.*

VERITÉ *   REPUBLIQUE.
JUSTICE.   PATRIE.
Stump topmast to mainmast.
(Some have small derricks instead of cranes abeam
of 2nd funnel.)

D'ENTRECASTEAUX.

POTHUAU.
(May have no mainmast now.)

DU CHAYLA.
CASSARD.
FRIANT *(Repair Ship).*

FOUDRE.
(Aircraft Carrier).

FRENCH WARSHIPS (four to six funnels), RECOGNITION SILHOUETTES.

FOUR FUNNELS.

GUICHEN.

JURIEN DE LA GRAVIERE.

DESAIX *class* (2 ships).

JULES MICHELET.

VICTOR HUGO.
JULES FERRY.*
* Has cranes between 1st and 2nd funnels instead of derricks.

AUBE AND MONTCALM *classes* (6 ships).
(*Impossible to differentiate these classes except quite close*).

FIVE FUNNELS.

CONDORCET.

VERNIGAUD.

DIDEROT.
VOLTAIRE.

SIX FUNNELS.

ERNEST RENAN.

WALDECK ROUSSEAU *class* (2 ships).

JEANNE D'ARC.

T

Note.—Some T.B.D. now have raised forefunnels.

No. 193 t.b.

Nos. 208—369 t.b.

Mistral *class* t.b. (11).

Old "Sea-going" t.b. Forban, Grondeur much the same as these types.

Mousquet, Flamberge and Durandal *classes* t b.d. (25).

Claymore *class*, t.b.d. (21).

(Vary a little in details.)

Janissaire t b.d.
(Eleventh boat of *Huzzard* class.)

Casque t.b.d.

"Tribal" *class* (12).

Temeraire *class* t.b.d. (4).

Pique *class* t b.d. (2).

Spahi (6)
&
t.b.d. = Huzzard *class* (10).
(Some have foremast abeam of forefunnel.)

Chasseur (4)

Cimiterre,*
Magon,
Mangini.
Protet, *and others.*

Bisson,
Dehorter,
and others.

Bouclier,*
C. Bory,
F. Garnier, *and others.*

C. Lucas.
(Twelfth boat of *Bory* class.)

E. Roux.
M-P. Lestin.

Bory *class* t.b.d. (11).
Bouclier and *Cimiterre* nominally units of "*Casque* type," and not included in total for "*Bory* class."

TURQUOISE.

EMERAUDE.
OPALE.
RUBIS.
TOPAZE.

ROLAND MORILLOT.

COULOMB.
(Modified Pluviôse class.)

AMAZONE.
ANTIGONE.
ARMIDE.

CURIE.
(Modified Pluviôse class.)

ARCHIMÈDE.

Modified Pluviôse class :—
ARAGO.   FRIMAIRE.
BRUMAIRE.   MONTGOLFIER.
EULER.   NEWTON.
FARADAY.   NIVÔSE.
FRANKLIN.

VOLTA.

LE VERRIER.

(Modified Pluviôse class.)

CLORINDE.
CORNELIE.

AMARANTE.   ARTÉMIS.
AMPHITRITE.   ASTRÉE.
ANDROMAQUE.   ATALANTE.
ARÉTHUSE.
(2 Mine Laying boats of this class
have no guns.)

BELLONE.
GORGONE.
HERMIONE.

DAPHNÉ.

FULTON,
JOESSEL.

DUPUY DE LOME.
SANÉ.

GUSTAVE ZÉDÉ.
NEREÏDE.*
(*Has no telescopic funnel.)

LAPLACE.   REGNAULT.
LAGRANGE.   ROMAZOTTI.

(Normandie Class—5 Ships.)

NORMANDIE (Oct., 1914), **GASCOGNE** (Sept., 1914), **LANGUEDOC** (May, 1915),
FLANDRE (Oct., 1914), and *BEARN* (*building*).

Displacement, 25,230 tons. Complement,

Length (*waterline*), 576 feet. Beam, feet. *Maximum* draught, feet

Guns (Mod. '11):
12—13·4 inch, 45 cal. (A⁷).
18—5·5 inch, 55 cal. (M. '10).
(Some anti-aircraft.)
4—3 pdr.
Torpedo tubes : 6.

Armour:
″ Belt (amidships) ......
″ Belt (bow) ....
″ Belt (aft) ....
″ Deck ....
″ Side above belt }

″ Big gun turrets ......
″ Barbettes ....
″ Battery.. ....
″ Conning tower ......
(Special anti-torpedo
protection.)

No Plans available.

Note.

All work on these ships was stopped soon after the outbreak of war. In 1918-19 their design was considerably altered. Full details of the changes effected are not yet available, but the Ministry of Marine has communicated these points :—

(*a*) Main battery of 12—13·4 inch guns retained ;

(*b*) Number of 5·5 inch guns reduced to 18 from 24 ;

(*c*) Six torpedo tubes to be retained ;

(*d*) Speed raised from 21·5 to 25 knots ;

(*e*) Special anti-torpedo protection (*soufflage contre-torpilles*) given to hull.

Machinery : Turbines.   screws. Boilers : various types. Designed H.P.   =25 kts. Fuel   tons *normal*,   tons *full load.* Endurance :   miles at   kts.

Name	Builder	Machinery	Laid down	Completed	Trials	Turbines	Boilers	Best max. speed
Normandie	S. Nazaire (Lre)	S. N. (Loire)	July, '13					
Gascogne	Lorient	A. & C. de Bretagne	Oct., '13	?				
Languedoc	Gironde	Gironde	July, '13					
Flandre	Brest	...	Oct., '13					
Bearn	La Seyne	La Seyne	Jan., '14					

General Notes.—Designed by Chief Constructor Doyère. Fitted very wide bilge keels. Freeboard forward, 23 feet; aft, 16½ feet. Belong to 1913 programme.

(BRETAGNE CLASS—3 SHIPS.)

BRETAGNE (April, 1913), **LORRAINE** (September, 1913), **PROVENCE** (April, 1913).

Normal displacement, 23,230 tons.   Complement, 1109.

Length (*waterline*), 541⅓ feet.   Beam, 88½ feet.   *Maximum* draught, 29 feet.   Length *over all*, 544½ feet

Guns (M. '11):
- 10—13·4 inch, 45 cal. (A⁷)
- 22—5·5 inch, 55 cal. (M. '10)
- 4—3 pdr.
- 2—1 pdr.
- 2 landing.

Torpedo tubes (18 inch) M. '12:
- 4 *submerged*

Armour:
- 10¾″ Belt (amidships) ..
- 7″ Belt (ends) ....
- Deck (*see Notes*) ....
- 10″—6″ Lower deck side
- 17″—10″ Turrets........
- 11″ Turret bases (N.C.)
- 7″ Secondary battery ...
- 12½″ Conning tower ......

PROVENCE (1).

Copyright Photo, M. Bar, Toulon.

Note.

Bretagne reported re-built 1918-1919 with fore tripod mast (with big fire control top), raised fore funnel and mainmast, cut down to stump. No photo available but approximate change in appearance shown by Silhouette.

LORRAINE

Ahead :
4—13·4 in.
4—5·5 in.

Astern :
4—13·4 in.
4—5·5 in.

Broadside : 10—13·4 in., 11—5·5 in.

Machinery : Parsons turbine.   4 screws.   Boilers : see *Notes*.   Designed H.P. 29,000=20 kts.
Coal : *normal* 900 tons ; *maximum* 2680 tons.   Also 300 tons oil.

Gunnery Notes.—Carry 100 rounds per gun for 13·4 inch and 275 per gun for the 5·5 inch. Janney electro-hydraulic mountings to big guns. Special cooling for magazines—temperature 77° Fahr. Magazines can be completely flooded inside ten minutes. Height of guns above l.w.l.: 1st turret, 30½ feet ; 2nd, 37½ feet ; 3rd, 33½ feet ; 4th, 28¼ feet ; 5th, 21½ feet. Arcs of training : Nos. 1 and 5, 270° ; Nos. 2 & 4 280° ; No. 3, 120° either beam. Arcs of secondary guns : 120°.

Torpedo Notes.—Bullivant net defence. 8—36″ and 2—30″ searchlights. 4—200 k.w. dynamos. Torpedoes : 1912 Schneider, 6000 yards range. 24 carried. Also 30 blockade mines.

Armour Notes.—Turrets of maximum thickness at ports, instead of uniform thickness as in *J. Barts.* (See Addenda Notes.) The double bottom is carried to the under side of protective deck. Main belt is 13½ feet wide, 5⁷⁄₁₂ feet below and 7⅞ above l.w.l. Battery 197 feet long with 7 in. bulkheads. Protective decks : lower 2″ slopes, 1¾″ flat. Upper, 1¾″ flat on top of belt.

Engineering Notes.—Boilers : *Bretagne*, 24 Niclausse ; *Lorraine*, 24 Belleville ; *Provence*, 18 Guyot du Temple. Grate area : *Bretagne*, 2,090 sq. feet ; *Lorraine*, 2,030 sq. feet ; *Provence*, 1,492 sq. feet. Heating surface : *Bretagne*, 64,660 sq. feet ; *Lorraine*, 63,700 sq. feet ; *Provence*, 62,585 sq. feet. Pressure, 256 lbs. per sq.in. 300 turbine r.p.m. 2,700 tons coal in 13 bunkers, 250 tons oil in 4 tanks. Endurance : 4,700 miles at 10 kts. 2,800 at 18¾ kts.

Name	Builder	Machinery	Laid down	Completed	Trials	Turbines	Boilers	Best recent speed
Bretagne	Brest	La Seyne	July '12	Sept. '15		Parsons	Niclausse	
Lorraine	S.Nazaire (Pen.)	S.Nazaire (Pen.)	Nov. '12	1916		Parsons	Belleville	
Provence	Lorient	La Seyne	June '12	June '15		Parsons	D.T.Guyot	

General Notes.—B., L. and P. belong to the 1912 programme, one of them being a replace ship for the *Liberté*, blown up September, 1911. Estimated cost, £2,908,000 per ship=£126 per ton. Bilge keels : 213×2¾ feet. Bulkheads are longitudinal and transverse ; latter solid amidships.

*Unofficial.

PROVENCE (2).

Addenda Notes.—According to the 1917 Edition of "Flottes de Combat," the barbette shields are not of uniform design. Those for the end barbettes are 13·1″ thick, for the super-firing barbettes 9¾″ thick and for the central barbette 15¾″ thick.

COURBET (Sept., 1911), **JEAN BART** (Sept., 1911), **PARIS** (Sept., 1912) & **FRANCE** (Nov., 1912).
Normal displacement, 23,120 tons.   *Full load,* 25,850 tons.   Complement, 1108.
Length (p.p.), 541⅓ feet.   Beam, 88½ feet.   *Maximum* draught, 29 feet.   Length *over all,* 544½ feet.

Guns (M. '06) :
12—12 inch, 50 cal. (A⁶).
22—5·5 inch, 55 cal. (M. '10).
4—3 pdr.
2—1 pdr.
2—landing.
Torpedo tubes (18 inch) :
4 *submerged.*

Armour :
11¾″ Belt (amidships)......
7″ Belt (bow) (N.C.) ...
7″ Belt (aft) (N.C.) ......
2¾″ Deck ....
10″—6″ Lower deck side
12½″ Turrets (N.C.) ......
11″ Turret bases (N.C.)...
7″ Secondary battery ...
11¾″ Conning tower (N.C.)

Ahead :
8—12 in.
6—5·5 in.

Astern :
8—12 in.
10—5·5 in.

Broadside : 10—12 in., 11—5·5 in.

Machinery : Parsons turbine. 4 screws. Boilers : 24 Belleville or Niclausse. Designed H.P. 28,000 = 20 kts.
Coal : *normal* 906 tons ; *maximum* 2452 tons. ; also 250 tons oil. Endurance at 10 kts., 2700 at 18¾ kts.
Armour Notes.—Belt, 13¼ feet wide ; 7¾ feet of it above water, 5½ feet of it below. For about 325 feet it is 10¾″.
Upper belt 7″ thick forms redoubt for secondary battery. The 4—5·5 inch aft. are in casemates. Prot. decks :
2¾″ curved from lower edge of belt to l.w.l. level. Above that a flat 1¼″ deck from end to end on top of main
belt. Above again is a 1⅕″ splinter deck against aerial attack. Conning tower is in three stories. 10¾″
communication tube. Two armoured fire control stations on top.
Gunnery Notes.—Amidship 12 inch 180°, the centre line turrets 270° each. The 5·5 inch 120°.
Height of guns above water : Turrets (1) 30½ feet, (2) 37¾ (amidships) 25 feet, (5) 28½ feet, (6) 21⅓ feet ;
upper deck battery, 5·5 inch, 21½ feet ; main deck, 5·5 inch aft, 11¾ feet. Ammunition carried : 100 for each
12 in., 275 for each 5·5 inch, 300 for each 3 pdr. Westinghouse refrigerators in magazines. 77°F.
Torpedo Notes.—8 searchlights (36 inch), also 2—30 inch. Carries 12 torpedoes and 30 blockade mines.
Engineering Notes.—Pressure : 256 lbs. outer shafts : H.P. turbines ; inner, L.P. Condensers (2) : 32,076 sq. feet cooling surface
Turbines : 300 r.p.m. Belleville oil fuel system.

Name	Builder	Machinery	Laid down	Completed	Trials Full power	Boilers	Best recent speed
J. Bart	Brest		Nov., '10	June '13	= 22·04	Belleville	22·6
Courbet	Lorient		Sept., '10	Sept. '13	= 20·74	Niclausse	
Paris	La Seyne		Nov., '11	Aug. '14	35,610 = 21·6	Belleville	
France	St. Nazaire		Nov., '11	July '14	...	Belleville	

General Notes.—Designed by M. Lyasse. Construction very fine and highly finished in details. Average cost about £2,475,000.
The heavy weight of deep 7″ belt at ends makes them pitch in a head sea. On the other hand, J. Bart was twice torpedoed in the
bows by an Austrian submarine and her heavy bow belt contributed largely to her survival.
* Unofficial.

COURBET.   *Photo, M. Bar, Toulon.*

Note :—Rig reported altered 1918-1919 as shown by Silhouettes, viz : *J. Bart* and *Courbet,* topgallant
masts added to mainmast ; mainmast of *Paris* and *France* cut down to stump.

JEAN BART. This ship only has " goose-neck " cranes in place of derricks.   *Photo, Geiser, Algiers.*

(DANTON CLASS—4 SHIPS).

DIDEROT (April, 1909), **CONDORCET** (April, 1909), **VERGNIAUD** (April, 1910), and
VOLTAIRE (Jan., 1909).

Normal displacement, 18,890 tons.   Complement, 923.
Length (*waterline*), 475¾ feet.   Beam, 84⅔ feet.   { Mean draught, 27 feet. }   Length *over all*, 481 feet.
{ Max.   „   28⅔ „ }

Guns (M '02–'06) :
   4—12 inch, 45 cal. (A⁵).
   12—9·4 inch, 50 cal. (A³).
   16 or 14—3 in. (14 pdr.),
             65 cal.
   (2 —3 pdr., S.A.)
   4—3 pdr. (AA.)
   2—3 pdr. (landing).
   2—1 pdr.
Torpedo tubes (M'04, 18 inch) :
   2 submerged (broadside).

Armour :
  10½″ Belt (amidships) ......
  6″ Belt (ends) ....
  3″ Deck (flat on upper belt)
  3″ Deck (below belt)   ...
  9″-6″ Lower deck side
  2½″ Upper belt (bow) ......
  12½″ Turrets (big guns) (N.C)
  11″ Turret bases (N.C.)......
  8¾″ Secondary turrets (6)
          (N.C.)
  12″ Conning tower (N.C.)...
     Total weight about 4800 tons.

Ahead :
2—12 in.
4—9·4 in.

Astern :
2—12 in.
4—9·4 in.

Broadside : 4—12 in., 6—9·4 in.

Machinery : Parsons turbine. 4 screws. Boilers : 26 Belleville or Niciausse. Designed H.P. 22,500 =
19·25 kts. Coal : *normal* 965 tons ; *maximum* 2100 tons. Endurance : 3750 miles at 10 kts., 2300 at 18½ kts.

Armour Notes.—Main belt is about 6½ feet wide, about 2½ feet of it below waterline. Lower edge is 3″
thick. There is a deck on top of the main belt as well as below it. Fore bulkhead 7″, aft ditto, 8″–7″.

Gunnery Notes (unofficial).—Arcs of fire : Big guns, 260°. Secondary guns about 140° or more. Rounds
carried : 12 in., 74 per gun ; 9·4 in., 100 per gun ; 12 pdrs., 500 per gun. The 14 pdr. guns are a
Schneider Canet model. Some 14 pdr. and 3 pdr. removed during the War ; may not be remounted.
14 pdr. positions on plans not correct.

Engineering Notes.—Bellevilles of these ships have 332 elements and 8852 tubes. Niclausse 339 elements
and 8814 tubes. Both types equipped for burning oil fuel.

Name.	Builder.	Machinery.	Laid down	Com-pleted.	24 hrs.	Trials. 10 hrs.	3 hrs	Boilers	Best recent speed
Diderot	St. Nazaire	St. Nazaire	Oct. '07	Sept.,'11	=18·4	=19·48	=19·9	Niclausse	
Condorcet	St. Nazaire	St. Nazaire	Aug. '07	June '11	=18·02	=19·31	=19·7	Niclausse	
Vergniaud	Bordeaux	F. & Ch., Medit.	Nov. '07	Dec. '11	=17·74	=19·20	=19·63	Niclausse	19·25
Voltaire	La Seyne	F. & Ch., Medit	July, '07	Aug.'11	=18·60	=19·78	=20·66	Belleville	

General Notes.—Average cost, £2,190,000 each. They are not very successful ships, and consume quantities of coal
at cruising speed. Some of these have lateral anti-torpedo "caissons" along hull below waterline ; others
have not. *Danton* of this class lost during War. *Voltaire* twice torpedoed by U-boat 1918 and repaired.

CONDORCET.

Notes.

Vergniaud has had her mainmast cut down to height of funnels ; no photo
    available of this ship.

Mirabeau of this class stranded on Crimean Coast, Feb., 1919. Salved April, 1919,
    after removal of forward 12 inch barbette and side armour. Will be used
    as a Target Ship.

DIDEROT (AND VOLTAIRE).

Notes (unofficial).

All ships listed on this page will probably be relegated to reserve or used as Training Ships. *Verité* and *Republique* will probably become Gunnery Training Ships; their after 12 inch turrets may be removed and replaced by smaller guns for instructional purposes. *Patrie* may be modified for service as a Torpedo Training Ship.

During the war, some of the lighter guns in *Dèmocratié, Justice,* and *Verité* were removed and may not be remounted.

DÉMORCRATIE.   *Photo by courtesy of E. L. King, Esq.*

JUSTICE (VERITÉ stump topmast to mainmast).   *Photo, Geiser, Algiers.*

. REPUBLIQUE.   *Photo, Geiser, Algiers.*

REPUBLIQUE (Sept., 1902) & **PATRIE** (Dec., 1903). Displacement: 14,865 tons. Complement: 789. Length (*waterline*), 439 feet. Beam, 79½ feet. *Maximum* draught, 27½ feet. Length *over all*, 443¾ feet. Guns—(M '93-'96): 4—12 inch, 45 cal. (A⁴), 18—6·4 inch, 50 cal., 25—3 pdr., 2—1 pdr. Torpedo tubes (18 in.): 2 *submerged*. Armour: 11¾" Belt (amidships), 7" Belt (ends), 3" Deck (flat below belt), 10"—5" Upper belt, 3" Upper Belt (forward), 12½" Turrets, 11" Turret (bases), 5½" Casemates, 5½" Small turrets, 4" Bases to these, 13" Conning tower. Machinery: 3 sets vertical inverted triple expansion. 3 screws. Boilers: 24 Niclausse. Designed H.P. 18,000 = 18 kts. Coal: *normal* 905 tons; *maximum* 1825 tons. *Nominal* radius 6,000 at 10 kts.

Notes.—Republique built at Brest, 1901-6, machinery by Indret; *Patrie* built at La Seyne, 1902-6, machinery by F. & C. de la Med. Both made 19 kts. on trials

DÉMOCRATIE (April, 1904), **JUSTICE** (September, 1904), **VERITÉ** (May, 1907). *Normal* displacement, 14,868 tons. Complement, 762. Length (*waterline*), 439 feet. Beam, 79½ feet. *Maximum* draught 28 feet. Length *over all*, 443¾ feet. **Guns:** 4—12 inch, 45 cal. (A⁵)., 10—7·6 inch, 50 cal. (A)., 12 or 13—9 pdr., 4—3 pdr., 4—3 pdr (AA.), 2—3 pdr. (landing), 2—1 pdr. Torpedo tubes (1904 pattern): 2 *submerged*. Armour: 11¾" Belt (amidships), 9" Belt (forward), 7" Belt (aft), 2¾" Deck, 10" Upper belt (amidships), 5½" Upper belt (ends), 3" Top of belt (forward) (N.C.), 12½" Main turrets (N.C.), 11" Turret bases (N.C.), 5½" Casemates (4) (N.C.), 5½" Secondary turrets (6) (N.C.), 11" Conning tower (N.C.) Machinery: 3 sets vertical inverted triple expansion, 4-cylinder. 3 screws. Boilers: 22 Belleville or 24 Niclausse. Designed H.P. 18,000 = 18 kts. Coal: *normal* 900 tons; *maximum* 1285 tons. *Nominal* radius: 6000 at 10 kts.

Notes.—Justice built at La Seyne 1903-7, *Democratie* at Brest, 1903-7, both engined by F. & C. de La Med. *Verité* built at Bordeaux, 1903-8, and engined by Indret. Made 19¼-19½ kts. on trials and all still steam well.

Coast Defence Ships *(rated as Cuirassé garde-côtes).*

Photo, Geiser.

Notes.

All ships listed on this page may be condemned within the next few months. *St. Louis* reported to be a Hulk now and virtually non-effective.

Charlemagne (sister to *St. Louis*), *Carnot* and *Charles Martel* have been removed from effective list; all are Hulks. *Jauréguiberry* has been disarmed; is only an Accommodation Ship now.

Some of these vessels may be used as Target Ships and for experiments.

HENRI QUATRE (Aug., 1899). Displacement, 8807 tons. Complement, 457. Length (*waterline*), $354\frac{1}{2}$ feet. Beam, $72\frac{3}{4}$ feet. *Maximum* draught, 23 feet. Guns—(M. '93– '96): 2—10·8 inch, 40 cal. (A[3]), 7—5·5 inch, 45 cal., 12—3 pdr., 2—1 pdr. Torpedo tubes (18 inch): 2 *submerged* (20° before beam). Armour (Harvey-nickel): $11\frac{3}{4}''$ Belt (amidships), 8″ Belt (ends), 5″—3″ Armour deck, flat, 10″ Turrets, $11\frac{1}{2}''$ Turret bases, $4\frac{1}{2}''$ Lower deck side. $4\frac{1}{2}''$ Battery (redoubt), $4\frac{1}{2}''$ Small turret (aft), 8″ Conning tower. Machinery: 3 sets vertical triple expansion. 3 screws. Boilers: 12 Niclausse. Designed H.P. 11,500 = 17·2 knots. Coal: *normal* 735 tons; *maximum* 1100 tons. Built at Cherbourg D.Y. 1897-1902.

1895 Old Battleships.

Photo, Geiser, Algiers.

ST. LOUIS (Sept., 1896). Displacement, 11,100 tons. Complement, 648. Length (*waterline*), $380\frac{3}{4}$ feet. Beam, $66\frac{1}{2}$ feet. *Maximum* draught, $27\frac{1}{2}$ feet. Length *over all*, $385\frac{1}{2}$ feet. Guns (M. '91-'93): 4—12 in., 40 cal. (A[3]), 10—5·5 in. 45 cal., 8—3·9 in., 4—3 pdr., 2 landing. 4 M.G. Torpedo tubes (18 inch): 2 *submerged*. Armour (Harvey): 16″ Belt (amidships), 10″ Belt (ends) (chrome), $2\frac{3}{4}''$ Armour deck (flat on belt), $1\frac{1}{2}''$ Deck (flat below belt), 9″ Fore turret, 11″ After turret, 8″ Turret hoists, 3″ Battery, 5″ Battery bulkheads, 12″ Conning tower. Machinery: 3 sets 4 cylinder triple expansion. 2 screws. Boilers: 20 Belleville. Designed H.P. 15,000 = 18 kts. Coal: *normal* 680 tons; *maximum* 1100 tons. Built at Lorient D.Y. 1895-1900.

REQUIN (1885, re-constructed 1901-3). 7214 tons. Complement, 332. Length, (*w.l.*) 324·4 feet. Beam, 73 feet. *Mean* draught, 23 feet. Guns: 2—10·8 inch (40 cal.), 8—3·9 inch, 12 smaller. Armour (compound): $19\frac{1}{2}''$ belt (amidships), $12\frac{1}{2}''$ belt (ends), 3—4″ deck, flat on belt, turrets (Harvey Nickel) $9\frac{1}{4}''$ with $8\frac{1}{4}''$ bases, $11\frac{3}{4}''$ conning tower. Machinery: 2 sets compound. Niclausse boilers. Designed H.P. 11,200 = 15·5 kts. Coal: *normal* 400 tons, *maximum* 800 tons.

WALDECK-ROUSSEAU. (WALDECK ROUSSEAU CLASS— 2 SHIPS). *Photo, Geiser, Algiers.*

EDGAR QUINET (Sept., 1907), **WALDECK ROUSSEAU** (March, 1908).

Normal displacement, 14,100 tons. Complement, 892.

Length (*waterline*), 515 feet. Beam, 70⅔ feet. *Max.* draught, 27½ feet. Length *over all*, 521⅓ feet.

Guns—(M. '02):
14—7·6 inch, 50 cal. (A).
(20)—9 pdr.*
(2)—9 pdr.*
2—1 pdr. or M.G.
Torpedo tubes (18 inch):
2 submerged.
* See Notes.

Armour:
6¾″ Belt (amidship)
3″ Belt (ends) ....
6″ Bulkhead (aft) ...
2½″ Deck (slopes) ...
6″ Turrets (N.C.) ...
5″ Turret bases ...
6″ Casemates (4) ...
10″ Conning tower ...
(Total weight 3400 tons).

Ahead:
{ —7·6

Astern:
6—7·6

Broadside: 9—7·6 in.

Machinery : 3 sets vertical triple expansion. 3 screws. Boilers : *See Notes.* Designed H.P. 36,000 = 23 kts. Coal : *normal* 1,242 tons ; *maximum* 2,300 tons. *Nominal endurance :* 6560 miles at 10 kts.

Gunnery Notes.—9 pdr. positions on plans not correct. Reported in 1919 that W. Rousseau had only 12—9 pdr., 2—9 pdr. AA., and perhaps, 4—3 pdr. AA.

Name	Builder	Machinery	Laid down	Com-pleted	30 boilers 10 hours	Full power 3 hours	Boilers	Best recent speed
E. Quinet	Brest Yard		Nov.,'05	1911	36,828 = 23·8	40,291 = 23·9	40 Belleville	
W. Rousseau	Lorient Yard		June,'06	1911		35,286 = 23·1	42 Niclausse	

ERNEST RENAN (March, 1906),

Normal displacement 13,640 tons. Complement 824.

Length (*waterline*), 515 feet (o.a. 521⅔ feet). Beam, 70 feet. *Max.* draught, 27½ feet.

Guns :
4—7·6 inch, 50 cal. (A)
12—6·5 inch, 45 cal.
16—9 pdr.
2—9 pdr.
8—3 pdr.
2—1 pdr.
Torpedo tubes (18 inch) :
2 submerged.
(1904 Model torpedoes)

Armour:
6¾″ Belt (amidships)
3½″ Belt (ends) ......
6″ Bulkhead (aft) ...
2½″ Deck (slopes) ...
6″ Main turrets (N.C.)
4″—5″ Turret bases {
4″ Casemates (4)(N.C)
4″ Secondary turrets (8)
5″ Bases to these ...
8″ Conning tower (N.C)
(Total weight about 3400 tons).

Machinery : 3 sets vertical triple expansion. 3 screws. Boilers : 42 Niclausse. Designed H.P. 36,000 = 23 kts.
Coal : *normal* 1354 tons ; *maximum* 2300 tons. *Nominal endurance :* 6700 miles at 10 kts.
Armour Notes.—Belt is 12¼ feet wide, 4¾ feet of it below waterline. Upper edge 5″ thick ; bottom 3½″.
Gunnery Notes.—Loading positions, big guns : all round. Hoists : electric to all guns. All guns manœuvred electrically and hand. Arcs of fire : Big turrets 240° ; secondary turrets 150° ; casemates, 110°. Height of guns above water : Bow and secondary turrets, 29½ feet ; after turret, 22 feet. Forward casemates, 20 feet ; after casemates, 12 feet.
General Notes.—Laid down at St. Nazaire, Aug., 1904 ; completed, 1909. Made 24·24 kts. on first trials with 37,685 H.P. Mainmast removed 1918.

* Gunnery Notes unofficial.

JULES MICHELET (Aug., 1905).   Displacement 13,370 tons.   Complement 770.   Length (*waterline*), 489 feet.   Beam, 70¼ feet.   *Max.* draught, 27⅔ feet.   Guns: 4—7·6 inch, 50 cal. (*A*), 12—6·5 inch, 45 cal., 2—9 pdr., 24—3 pdr., 2 M.G.   Torpedo tubes (18 inch): 2 *submerged.*   Armour: 6¾" Belt (amidship), 3" Belt (ends), 6" Bulkhead (aft), 2½" Deck (slopes), 6" Turrets, 5" Turret bases, 4" Casemates (4), 4" Small turrets (8), 5" Bases to these, 8" Conning tower.   Machinery: 3 sets vertical triple expansion.   3 screws.   Boilers: 28 Du Temple-Guyot.   Designed H.P. 29,000 = 22 kts. (Trials, 30,438 = 22·9.)   Coal: *normal* 1330 tons; *maximum* 2100 tons.   Begun at Lorient D.Y. 1904, completed 1908.

Photo, Geiser.

JULES FERRY.   *Photo, Geiser, Algiers.*

JULES FERRY (August, 1903), & VICTOR HUGO (March, 1904).   *Average* displacement 12,518 tons.   Complements, 737—731.   Length (*o.a.*), J.F. 486⅔ feet., V.H. 489 feet.   Beam, 70¼ feet.   *Mean* draught, 26½ feet.   Guns (M. '96): 4—7·6 inch, 45 cal., 16—6·5 inch, 45 cal., 24—3 pdr., 2—9 pdr., 2 M.G.   Torpedo tubes (18 in.): 2 *submerged.*   Armour: 6¾" Belt (amidships), 3" Belt (ends), 5" Bulkhead (aft), 2¼" Deck (slopes), 8" Turrets, 8" Turret bases, 5½" Casemates (4), 5½" Small turrets, 8" Conning tower.   Machinery: 3 sets vertical 4 cylinder triple expansion.   3 screws.   Boilers: 28 Guyot in *J. Ferry*; 28 Belleville in *V. Hugo.*   Designed H.P. 27,500 = 22 kts.   Coal: *normal* 1330 tons; *maximum* 2100 tons.   Endurance at 10 kts., 6630; at 20 kts., 2600 miles.
Notes.—*J. Ferry* built at Cherbourg, 1901-5; *V. Hugo* at Lorient, 1903-7.   Both engined by Indret, and made about 23 kts. on trials.   *Leon Gambetta* of this class lost during the war.

GLOIRE.   *Photo, Geiser, Algiers.*

GLOIRE (June, 1900), MARSEILLAISE (July, 1900), CONDE (March, 1902), and AMIRAL AUBE (May, 1902).   *Average* displacement 10,376 tons.   Complement, 630.   Length (*waterline*), 452⅔ feet.   Beam, 66¼ feet.   *Maximum* draught, 25½ feet.   Length *over all*, 458⅜ feet.   Guns (M. '96): 2—7·6 inch, 45 cal. (*A*), 8—6·5 inch, 45 cal., 6—3·9 inch, 2—9 pdr., 18—3 pdr.   Torpedo tubes (18 in.) 2 *submerged*).   Armour: 6¾"—4" Belt, 2½" Deck (slopes), 8" Turrets (N.C.), 4" Hoists, 5" Lower deck side, 2¼" Bow, 4¾" Casemates (4), 4¾" Small turrets (4), 3¾" Bases to these, 8" Conning tower.   Machinery: 3 sets vertical triple expansion.   3 screws.   Boilers: 28 Belleville or Niclausse.   Designed H.P. 20,500 = 21 knots.   Coal: *normal* 970 tons; *maximum* 1700 tons.
Notes.—*Gloire* and *Condé* built at Lorient, 1899-1901; *Marseillaise* at Brest, 1900-03; *A. Aube* at St. Nazaire, 1900-04.   Made 21·5, 21·3, 21·6, and 22·8 kts. on trials respectively.

DUPLEIX (April, 1900), & DESAIX (March, 1901).   Displacement 7552 tons.   Complement 520.   Length (*waterline*), 433 feet.   Beam, 58½ feet.   *Mean* draught, 24¼ feet.   Guns—(M. '96): 8—6·4 inch, 45 cal., 4—3·9 inch, 2—9 pdr., 10—3 pdr., 4 M.G.   Torpedo tubes (18 in.): 2 *submerged.*   Armour: 4" Belt (amidships), 3½" Belt (bow), 2⅜" Armour deck, 4" Turrets, 4" Turret bases, 6" Conning tower.   Machinery: 3 sets 3 cylinder vertical triple expansion.   3 screws.   Boilers: 24 Belleville.   Designed H.P. 17,100 = 21 kts.   Coal: *normal* 880 tons; *maximum* 1200 tons.   Begun at Rochefort and St. Nazaire, 1897-8, and completed 1903-4.   *Kleber* of this class lost during the war.

GUEYDON (September, 1899), **MONTCALM** (March, 1900). Displacement 9102 tons. Complement, 600. Length (*waterline*), 452¾ feet. Beam, 63¾ feet. *Max.* draught, 25 feet. Length *over all*, 459 feet. Guns (M. '93 & '96) : 2—7·6 inch, M. '93, 8—6·5 inch, M. '93-'96, 2—9 pdr., 20—3 pdr. Torpedo tubes (18 inch) : 2 *submerged*. Armour (Harvey Nickel) : 6¾" Belt (amidships), 4" Belt (ends), 3" Forecastle, 2" Deck (on slopes), 3"-2¼" Lower deck side, 8" Turrets, 5" Turret bases, 4" Casemates (8), 6" Conning tower. Machinery : 3 sets vertical triple expansion. 3 screws. Boilers : 20 Niclausse or Normand. Designed H.P. 19,600 = 21 kts. Coal : *normal* 1030 tons ; *maximum* 1,650 tons. Begun at Lorient and La Seyne, 1898 : completed, 1902.

BRUIX. (L. TREVILLE same, but no topmast to mainmast.)

BRUIX (Rochefort, 1894). 4810 tons. Complement, 375. Guns (M '87) : 2—7·6 inch (45 cal.), 6—5·5 inch, 4—9 pdr., 1—3 pdr. 4—18 inch tubes *above water* (*probably removed*). Armour : 3⅝" Belt and 4" Turrets (steel). Designed H.P. 8700 (*f.d.*) = 18·5 kts. Boilers : 16 Belleville. Coal : 540 tons.

LATOUCHE-TREVILLE (Havre, 1892). 4760 tons. Complement 368. Designed H.P. 8000 (*f.d.*). Coal : 530 tons. Appearance and other details as *Bruix* above. Both these old cruisers have rendered excellent service during the war, *Latouche-Treville* specially distinguishing herself on numerous occasions.

(*Cadets' Training Ship.*)

JEANNE D'ARC (June, 1899). Displacement 11,300 tons. Complement 657. Length (*waterline*) 475¾ feet. Beam, 63¾ feet. *Maximum* draught, 26½ feet. Guns—(M. '93) : 2—7·6 inch, 40 cal. (*B*), 14—5·5 inch, 45 cal., 16—3 pdr., 8—1 pdr. Torpedo tubes (18 inch) : 2 *submerged*. Armour (Harvey) : 6" Belt (amidships), 4" Belt (bow), 3" Belt (aft), 2¼" Deck (on slopes), 7¾" Turrets, 4" Turret bases, 3" Lower deck, 5" Casemates (8), 6" Conning tower. Machinery : 3 sets vertical inverted triple expansion. 3 screws. Boilers : 48 Du Temple (small tube). Designed H.P. 33,000 = 23 kts. (Best actual : 29,690 I.H.P. = 21·7). Coal : *normal* 1400 tons ; *maximum* 1900 tons. Laid down at Toulon, October, 1896. Completed 1902,

Mainmast reported removed.   (*Gunnery School Ship.*)   *Photo, Geiser.*

POTHUAU (1895). Displacement 5,460 tons. Complement 424. Length (*waterline*), 371 feet. Beam, 50½ feet. *Maximum* draught, 22½ feet. Guns—(M '93) : 2—7·6 inch, 40 cal., 10—5·5 inch, 45 cal., 12—3 pdr., 8 M.G. Torpedo tubes : 4 *above water*. Armour : 3¼" Belt (amidships), 1¼" Belt (ends), 3⅜" Deck (reinforcing belt), 7" Turrets, 3" Hoists to these, 2" Casemates, 2" Hoists to these, 9½" Conning tower. Machinery : 2 sets horizontal triple expansion. 2 screws. Boilers : 18 Belleville. H.P. 10,400 = 19 kts. Coal : *normal* 538 tons ; *maximum* 790 tons.

Copyright photo, M. Bar, Toulon.

JURIEN DE LA GRAVIÈRE (July, 1899). Displacement, 5690 tons (sheathed and coppered). Complement 469. Length (*waterline*). 449½ feet. Beam, 49¼ feet. *Mean* draught, 23 feet. Guns: 8—6·5 inch, 2—9 pdr., 45 cal., 10—3 pdr., 6 M.G. Torpedo tubes (18 inch): 2 *submerged.* Armour (Harvey Nickel): 3″ Deck (cellulose belt), 6½″ Conning tower, 2″ Chrome shields, 1¾″ Casemates. Machinery: 2 sets vertical triple expansion. 3 screws. Boilers: 24 Guyot. H.P. *full power*, 18,400 = 22·9 kts. Present speed is poor. Coal: *normal* 560 tons; *maximum* 1100 tons. Laid down at Lorient. Nov. 1897. Completed 1903.

Copyright photo, M. Bar, Toulon.

D'ESTRÉES (Rochefort, Oct., 1899). Displacement 2460 tons (sheathed and coppered). Complement 250. Length (*waterline*), 311⅔ feet. Beam, 39⅓ feet. *Mean* draught, 17½ feet. Guns—(M'93 & '91): 2—5·5 in., 45 cal., 5—3·9 in., 45 cal., 1—9 pdr., 8—3 pdr. Torpedo tubes: (*removed*). Armour (hard steel): 1½″ Deck (cellulose belt). Machinery: 2 sets triple expansion. 2 screws. Boilers: 8 Normand. Designed H.P. 8500 = 20 to 21 kts. Coal: *normal* 350 tons; *maximum* 550 tons. Begun, 1897; completed 1899.

GUICHEN (May, 1897). Displacement, 8,280 tons (sheathed). Complement. 560. Length (*waterline*), 436⅓ feet. Beam, 54¾ feet. *Maximum* draught, 24½ feet. Guns—(M. '91): 2—6·5 inch, 45 cal., 6—5·5 inch, 45 cal., 12—3 pdr., 5—1 pdr. Torpedo tubes · (*removed*). Armour (Harveyed): 2½″ Deck (cellulose belt), 1½″ Casemates, 2″ Gun shields, 6¼″ Conning tower (fore). Machinery: 3 sets 4 cylinder triple expansion. 3 screws. Boilers: 28 Lagrafel d'Allest. Designed H.P. 24,000 (*f.d.*) = 23 kts. Coal: *normal* 1,460 tons; *maximum* 2,030 tons. Laid down at St. Nazaire, 1895; completed, 1899.

D'ENTRECASTEAUX (June, 1896). Displacement, 8,123 tons (sheathed and coppered). Complement 521. Length (*waterline*), 393½ feet. Beam, 58½ feet. *Maximum* draught, 26 feet. Guns—(M. '93): 2—9·4 inch, 40 cal. (*may have been removed*), 12—5·5 inch, 45 cal., 12—3 pdr., 4 Maxims. Torpedo tubes (18 inch): 2 *submerged.* Armour (Harvey): 3¼″ Armour deck, 9″ Turrets, 4″ Turret bases, 2⅜″ Casemates (8, all chrome steel), 10″ Conning tower. Machinery: 2 sets triple expansion. 2 screws. Boilers: Cylindrical (5 double-ended). Designed H.P. 14,500 = 19·5 kts. (*never made*); present speed 18 kts. or *less.* Coal: *normal*, 650 tons; *maximum*, 950 tons. Laid down at La Seyne, 1894, completed 1899.

This Old Cruiser is rated as an "Aviso" or Sloop.

Now has short mainmast.

LAVOISIER (1897). 2,320 tons. Complement 248. Armament (M. '91): 4—5·5 inch, 45 cal., 2—3·9 inch, 10—3 pdr. 2—18 inch tubes *above water*. Armour: 1½″ Deck, 2″ Main deck sponsons. H.P. *about* 7,000 = 21·5 kts. Coal: *maximum* 380 tons. Boilers: 16 Belleville.

DESCARTES (1894). Displacement, *about* 4030 tons. Complement, 378. Guns: 4—6·5 inch, 45 cal., 10—3·9 inch, 8—3 pdr., 4—1 pdr. Torpedo tubes: 2—18 inch, *above water*. Armour: 2″ Deck, 2″ Casemates to 6·5 guns on main deck. Designed H.P. 8500 = 19 kts. Coal: *maximum* 680 tons. Boilers: 16 Bellevilles (*without* economisers).

Cosmao.

Surcouf.

CASSARD (1896), **DU CHAYLA** (1895). Old Cruisers of about 3,950 tons. Complement, 374. Length (*waterline*), 324¾ feet. Beam, 45 feet. *Maximum* draught, 22 feet. Guns—(M. '87): 6— 6·5 inch, 45 cal., 4—3·9 inch, 8—3 pdr., 2—14 inch tubes *above water*. Armour: 3″ Deck, 2″ Sponsons to the four main deck 6·4 inch guns. H.P. 10,000 = 19·8 kts. Coal: *maximum*, 624 tons. Boilers: Lagrafel d'Allest. *Friant* of this class now Repair Ship.

COSMAO (1889), **SURCOUF** (1889). Old Cruisers of about 2000 tons. Armament: 4—old 5·5 inch, 7 or 5—3 pdr., 4 machine. Designed H.P. 6000 = 20 kts. Coal: 260 to 300 tons.

FRENCH "AVISOS."– SLOOPS OR DESPATCH VESSELS.

Building or Completing.

AMIENS (La Seyne).	**LIEVIN** (La Seyne).
ARRAS.	**LUNEVILLE.**
BAPAUME (Lorient D Y.)	**NANCY** (Cherbourg D.Y., 1919).
BAR-LE-DUC.	**PERONNE.**
BELFORT.	**REIMS.**
CALAIS (La Seyne).	**REMIREMONT.**
CHALONS.	**REVIGNY.**
CHATEAU-THIERRY.	**ROYE.**
COMPIEGNE.	**SENLIS.**
COUCY.	**TAHURE** (La Seyne).
CRAONNE (La Seyne).	**TOUL.**
DUNKERQUE.	**VAUQUOIS** (St. Nazaire).
EPERNAY.	**VERDUN** (Brest D.Y., 1918).
EPINAL.	**VIMY** (St. Nazaire).
LASSIGNY.	**VITRY-LE-FRANCOIS** (St. Nazaire).
LES EPARGES.	

Despatch and Anti-Submarine Vessels of 700 tons. Dimensions : 246 ft. 0 in. × 24 ft. 7 in. × 9 ft. 2 in. Guns : 2—5·5 inch, 1—14 pdr. AA., 4 M.G. Carry 20 depth charges. Fitted with four searchlights ; also have hydrophones, depth charge throwers and other anti-submarine gear. Designed S.H.P. 5000 = 20 kts. Machinery : 2 sets turbines. 2 screws. Boilers : 2 Normand oil-burning. Fuel :   tons oil. Endurance :   miles at   kts. Complement :

Note.—Not known how many of these have been launched. The construction of *Noyon, Soissons, Pont Betheny* (?) and about thirty other ships of this class has been stopped. Appearance is given approximately by silhouette. Reported to have a special rating as "Avisos Contre-Torpilleurs." Design is a modification of *Ailette, Ancre, Escaut,* &c., given in next page. Built under 1917 or 1918 War Programme.

SCARPE. (*Suippe* same, but with straight stem.)

Note that the two 3·9 inch guns, fore and aft, are disguised as derrick booms, while the 9 pdr. guns amidships, on each beam, are hidden behind lowering bulwarks.

ESCAUT & AILETTE.

Photo wanted.

ANCRE.

AILETTE (Brest D.Y., 1918).   **SCARPE** (——— 1918).
ANCRE (Lorient DY., 1918).   **SUIPPE** (Lorient D.Y., 1918).
ESCAUT (Brest D.Y., 1918).

Despatch Vessels of 650 tons. Dimensions : 256 feet 2 inches × 26 feet 5 inches × 8 feet 10 inches. Guns : 4—3·9 inch, 2—9 pdr. A.A., one or two M.G. Designed H.P. 5000 = 21 kts. Machinery : reciprocating. Boilers : two (type unknown). 2 screws. Oil fuel : 135 tons = 4000 miles at 10 kts. Complement, 65.

Note.—Modifications of *Aisne, Marne, Meuse,* &c., described on a later page. Externally they are disguised by varying appearances as mercantile vessels, like convoy sloop *Ville D' Ys* below. Built under 1917 War Programme.

Photo wanted.

(See Silhouette for appearance.)

VILLE D' YS (ex-*Andromède*, Swan Hunter, Wigham Richardson & Co., Wallsend-on-Tyne, June, 1917. Convoy sloop of 1490 tons. Dimensions · 255 feet 3 inches (*p.p.*) 276 feet (*o a.*) × 35 feet × 12 feet 3 inches. Guns : 2 —5·5 inch, 3 —14 or 9 pdr. Designed I.H.P. 2500 = 17 kts. Machinery : 1 set 4-cyl. triple-exp. Boilers : 2-cyl. 1 Screw. Coal : 270 tons = 2400 miles at 12 kts. Complement, 108 (war, probably inclusive of " panic " parties), about 90 (peace).

Note.—Generally same build as British convoy sloops. Built under 1916 War Programme. Reported to have been begun for British Navy as *Andromeda* and turned over to French Navy.

(*Continued on next page.*)

ALDEBARAN.

ALTAIR.

(Builders' Photo, by courtesy of Messrs. Wm. Hamilton & Co).

305

("ETOILE" or "STAR" Class—7 Ships.)

(Plans by courtesy of Ministry of Marine).

ALDEBARAN } (Barclay, Curle, Whiteinch,
ALGOL } N.B., 1916).
ALTAIR } (Wm. Hamilton, Port
ANTARES } Glasgow, N.B., 1916).

BELLATRIX (Henderson, Glasgow, 1916).
CASSIOPÉE } (Barclay, Curle, Whiteinch, N.B,
REGULUS } 1917).

Sloops, displacing 1250, 1420 and 1470 tons. Dimensions : $225\frac{1}{4} \times 33\frac{1}{2} \times 11\text{-}12\frac{1}{4}$ feet. Guns : 2—5.5 inch, 2—6 pdr. A.A. Are fitted as Fleet Sweeping Vessels. Designed I.H.P. 2500 = 17 kts. (All made 17.2-17.6 kts. on trials.) Machinery : 1 set, 4 cyl. triple expansion. Boilers : Not known. 1 screw. Coal : 260 tons = 2400 miles at 12 kts. Complement, 92.

Notes.—These sloops are practically replicas of the British " Flower Class " Sloops, being built in pairs by British shipyards. *Rigel,* the companion boat to *Bellatrix* by Messrs. Henderson, lost during the War. All built under 1916 War Programme.

(Continued on next page.)

OISE (& SOMME ?).

MARNE (& AISNE ?).

YSER (& MEUSE ?).

Note.

Though the design of these Despatch Vessels is uniform, the latitude allowed to the building yards has resulted in differing appearances. Classification by appearance has not been positively established, but it is believed that the vessels built by same yard have the same appearance.

AISNE (Lorient D.Y., 1916).　　**SOMME** (Brest D.Y., 1917).

MARNE (Lorient D.Y., 1916).　　**OISE** (Brest D.Y., 1917).

MEUSE (Rochefort D.Y. 1918).,　　**YSER** (Rochefort D.Y., 1917).

Despatch Vessels displacing 650-680 tons. Dimensions : $256\frac{1}{6} \times 26\frac{5}{12} \times 8\frac{5}{8}$ feet. Armament : 4—3·9 inch, 3—9 pdr. AA., 2—6 pdr. Designed I.H.P. 4000 = 20·5-21 kts. Machinery : Reciprocating. Boilers : 2 (types unknown). 2 screws. Oil fuel : 135-145 tons = 4000 miles at 10 kts. Complement, 97. All built under 1916 War Programme.

(Continued on next page.)

"Avisos"—Despatch Vessels or Sloops (*Continued*).

No Photo available.
Clipper bow, 1 funnel, 2 pole masts.

CHAMOIS (Port de Bouc, 1905). Despatch Vessel of 431 tons. Dimensions : $168\frac{2}{3} \times 25\frac{1}{3} \times 9\frac{1}{2}$ feet. Guns (*not known*). H.P. 600 = 12 kts. Boilers : du-T. Guyot. Coal : 70 tons. Was Training Ship for Navigation before the War.

Despatch Vessel **FLAMANT,** built 1915-18, has been assigned to Fisheries Protection Duty, and is listed with Miscellaneous French Ships on a later page.

Sloop—Present existence doubtful.

KERSAINT (1897). 1296 tons (sheathed). Dimensions : $225\frac{1}{4} \times 34\frac{1}{2} \times 15$ feet. Guns : 1—5·5 inch, 5—3·9 inch, 7 small. No torpedoes. Designed H.P. 2400 = 15 kts. 1 screw. Coal : 200 tons = 2000 miles at 12 kts.

KERSAINT.

Note.

This Sloop reported to have been stranded on a coral reef near Tahiti (Pacific), during March, 1919, but her total loss has not yet been officially announced. Considering her age, it is not likely that salvage will be attempted.

Gunboats (*Cannonères*).

CONQUERANTE.

VAILLANTE type :—2 Diesel-engined boats.

CONQUERANTE (1917), **VAILLANTE** (1917). Builders unknown. 457 tons. Dimensions : *about* $211 \times 22\frac{7}{12} \times 8\frac{1}{6}$ feet. Guns : 2—3·9 inch. Carry D.C. B.H.P. 1800 = 17 kts. Machinery : 2 sets of 900 B.H.P. Sulzer-Diesel engines. Oil fuel : 30 tons. Complement, 65.

Notes.—Are a modified *Friponne* design, for which see below. Both built under 1917 War Programme.

IMPATIENTE.

FRIPONNE type :—7 Diesel-engined boats.

BOUFONNE (Lorient D.Y., 1916).	**IMPATIENTE** (Brest D.Y., 1916).
CHIFFONNE (——, 1917).	**MIGNONNE** (Brest D.Y., 1917).
DILIGENTE (Brest D.Y., 1916).	**SURVEILLANTE** (Brest D.Y., 1916).
FRIPONNE (Lorient D.Y., 1916).	

Displacement : 355 tons. Dimensions : $199\frac{2}{3} \times 22\frac{7}{12} \times 8\frac{1}{6}$ feet. Guns : 2—3.9 inch. Carry D.C. and may also be equipped as Mine Sweepers. B.H.P. 900 = 15 kts. Machinery : 2 sets 450 B.H.P. Sulzer-Diesel engines. Oil : 30 tons = 3000 miles at 10 kts., 1600 miles at 15 kts. Complement, 50.

Notes.—Generally the same design as the 27 *Ardent* type (steam-driven) Gunboats on next page, but above seven Gunboats have Diesel engines and no funnels. *Mignonne,* 1917 War Programme, others all 1916 War Programme.

(*Continued on next page.*)

ARDENT.

BOUDEUSE.

Copyright Photo, M. Bar, Toulon.

(ARDENT type—27 Steam-engined boats.)

DEDAIGNEUSE.

Copyright Photo, M. Bar, Toulon.

AGILE (Brest D.Y., 1916).
ALERTE (Rochefort D.Y., 1916).
ARDENT (Brest D.Y., 1916).
AUDACIEUSE (Port de Bouc, 1917).
BATAILLEUSE (Port de Bouc, 1917).
BELLIQUEUSE (Bordeaux, 1917).
BOUDEUSE (La Seyne, 1916).
CAPRICIEUSE (Nantes, 1916).
COURAGEUSE (Rochefort D.Y., 1916).
CURIEUSE (Lorient D.Y., 1916).
DEDAIGNEUSE (Bordeaux, 1916).
EMPORTÉ (———, 1916).
ENGAGEANTE (Brest D.Y., 1917).
ESPIÈGLE (Rochefort D.Y., 1916).

ETOURDI (Lorient D.Y., 1916).
EVEILLE (La Seyne, 1917).
GRACIEUSE (Lorient D.Y., 1916).
IMPETUEUSE (———, 1917).
INCONSTANT (Brest D.Y., 1916).
LURONNE (———, 1917).
MALICIEUSE (Chantiers de Provence, Port de Bouc, 1916).
MOQUEUSE (Lorient D.Y., 1916).
RAILLEUSE (Chantiers de Provence, Port de Bouc, 1917).
SANS SOUCI (Lorient D.Y., 1916).
TAPAGEUSE (Port de Bouc, 1916).

Displacement : 350 tons. Dimensions : $197\frac{1}{2} \times 22\frac{7}{12} \times 8\frac{1}{6}$ feet. Guns : 2—3.9 inch. Carry D.C. Designed I.H.P. 1800-1200 = 17-15 kts. Machinery : Reciprocating. Boilers : Various water-tube types. Fuel : 85 tons coal = 3000 miles at 10 kts., 1600 miles at full speed. Complement, 55.

Notes.—Built as Anti-Submarine Gunboats or "Cannonieres Contre-Sousmarins." At the end of the War, many of these boats were reported to have been converted for Mine Sweeping Service. Some have been engined with machinery stripped from old Coastal Torpedo Boats ("Torpilleurs de Defence Mobile"). They vary a little in build, but the illustrations given are believed to be typical of these boats. Note that masts are stepped well to starboard of the centre-line. *Audacieuse, Batailleuse, Impetueuse* and *Luronne*, 1917 War Programme ; all others, 1916 War Programme.

Old Torpedo Gunboats (*Contre-Torpilleurs*).

Now has small pole mainmast.

D'IBERVILLE (1893). Displacement, 967 tons. Complement, 140. Length, 262½ feet. Beam, 26⅝ feet. *Maximum* draught, 13 feet. Guns: 1—3·9 inch (bow), 3—9 pdr., 6—3 pdr. Designed H.P. 5000 = 21·5 kts. Coal: *maximum* 145 tons. Cylindrical boilers.

Copyright photo, G.E.G.

DUNOIS (1897) & **LA HIRE** (1898). Torpedo Gunboats. Displacement, 900 tons. Complement, 148. Length, 254½ feet. Beam, 27⅝ feet. *Maximum* draught, 12¾ feet. Guns: in *Dunois* 6—9 pdr., in *La Hire* 12—3 pdr. No tubes. Designed H.P. 6400 = 23 kts. (never made), now 19-20 kts. Coal: 160 tons. Boilers: Normand.

River Gunboats (*Cannonières Fluviales*).

E and F.

C and D.

A and B.

A—L. (Brest and Lorient N.Y., 1915). —— tons. 91·8 × 16·4 × 5 feet. Are variously armed as follows :—(*a*) 1—5·5 inch, 2 or 1—6 pdr. AA., 2 M.G., (*b*) 2—3·9 inch, 1—14 pdr. AA., 2 M.G. Speed: 10 kts. These boats were built during the War for service on the rivers Marne, Meuse and Yser. The French Rhine Flotilla consists of 4 of the above gunboats, 3 Submarine Chasers and 20 M.L.

River Gunboats (*Continued*).

Note : All boats in this column built for service abroad,

> **Photo wanted.**
>
> Has 1 mast forward with 1 fighting top, 2 funnels and a small pole mast aft.)

BALNY (1914). Built by Chantiers de Bretagne, Nantes. 213 tons. Dimensions : 171½ × 22 × 3¾ feet. H.P., 800 = 14 kts. Guns: 6—1 pdr., 2 machine. Fouché w.t. boilers. Coal : 27 tons.

> **Photo wanted.**

DOUDART DE LA GRÉE (1909). 230 tons 167¼ × 22 × 3¼ feet. Guns: 6—1 pdr. H.P. 920 = 14 kts. Coal : 50 tons. Complement, 57 Built by Chantiers de Bretagne, Nantes.

> *No photo available.*

PEI-HO (1901). 123 tons. Speed, 10 kts. Guns: 3—1 pdr.

ARGUS and **VIGILANTE** (1900). Both built by Thornycroft. 130 tons. Speed, 13 kts. Guns: 2—3·5 inch, 4—1 pdr. (In China.)

90 + 1 Destroyers.*

Totals.	Class.	First Begun.	Last Completed.	*Normal* Displacement.	I.H.P.	*Max.* Speed.	*Max.* Coal or Oil	Complement.	*Max.* Draught.	Tubes.
2	*Tribal* class	1917	1917	tons. 690	10000	kts. 29	tons. 100+120	87	feet. $9\frac{5}{8}$	4
4	*Temeraire* class	1910	1914	950	18000	32 *t*	240+92	102	$10\frac{1}{4}$	4
1	*E. Gabolde* class	1913	†	905	20000	31 *t*	200	...	10	6
12	*Bory* class	1910	1915	880-780	17000-13500	31-30 *t*	200-140	83	10	4
3	*Casque* class	1908	1912	820-790	14400-13000	31 *t*	140	83	10	4
11	*Huzzard* class	1906	1912	514-407	8600-7200	28 *t & tr*	100-110	77-69	10	3
21	*Claymore* class	1903	1911	415-340	6400	$30\frac{1}{2}$-28	80	71	$11\frac{1}{2}$	2
18	*Mousquet* class	1900	1904	370-310	7300-6000	$30\frac{3}{4}$-28	75	71	$10\frac{1}{2}$	2
4	*Flamberge* class	1900	1902	310	5600-4800	27-26	70	71	$10\frac{1}{2}$	2
3	*Durandal* class	1899	1901	305					$8\frac{1}{2}$	2
2	*Pique* class	1900	1902	310	5700	26	70	71	$8\frac{3}{4}$	2

t=turbines.　　*tr*=turbines and reciprocating.

* Ex-Russian boats not included in this total.

† *E. Gabolde* not yet finished.

3 Russian T.B.D.*

The following Russian Destroyers have been taken over temporarily by the French navy. At present, they are under the French flag and manned by French crews.

1 *boat* : **Quentin Roosevelt** (Russian *Boiki*). For details see Russian (Baltic) Section.

2 *boats* : **R1** and **R2** (Russian *Bespokoini* and *Kapitan Saken*). For details see Russian (Black Sea) Section.

* These boats are not included in Table in preceding column.

12 Tribal Boats. (1917 War Programme.)

KABYLE

Copyright Photo. M. Bar, Toulon.

12 built by Japanese Yards : **Algerien, Annamite, Arabe, Bambara, Hova, Kabyle, Marocain, Sakalave, Sénégalais, Somali, Tonkinois, Touareg.** Built by Kawasaki Co., Mitsu Bishi Co., and other Japanese Yards. All begun March, 1917, launched May and July, 1917, and completed July and September, 1917. Average time of construction 5 months. 690 tons. Dimensions : 260 (*p.p.*), $271\frac{1}{4}$ (*o.a.*) × $27\frac{1}{4}$ × $7\frac{3}{4}$ feet. *Normal* draught, $9\frac{5}{6}$ feet ; *load* draught,　　Armament : 1—4·7 inch, 4—12 pdr. (one 12 pdr. is AA.) and 4—18 inch torpedo tubes in two twin deck mountings. Designed H.P. 10,000=29 kts. ; made about 30 on trials. turbines and　　boilers. Fuel : 100 tons coal + 120 tons oil=3000 miles at 15 kts. and 950 miles at full speed. Complement, 87.

Note.—These boats are practically replicas of the Japanese *Kaba* class T.B.D.

4 Temeraire type:—Purchased Boats.

TEMERAIRE.

4 *Chantiers de Bretagne* (*Nantes*) : **Aventurier** (ex-*Salta*), **Intrepide** (ex-*Rioja*), **Opiniâtre** (ex-*San Juan*), and **Temeraire** (ex-*Mendoza*) (all 1911). *Normal* displacement : 950 tons; *full load*, 1180 tons. Dimensions : 284½ × 28¼ × 8⅚ feet *normal* draught. *Full load* draught, 10¼ feet. Armament (Bethlehem) : 4—4 inch, 4—18 inch tubes. Designed H.P. 18,000 = 32 kts. Machinery : Curtis turbines + 5 White-Forster boilers. Fuel capacity : 240 tons coal + 92 oil. Radii of action : 3,000 miles at 15 kts.

Note.—Built for Argentina and purchased by France immediately before outbreak of war.

1 Special Boat. (1913 Programme).

(Building or Completing).

Plans by courtesy of French Ministry of Marine.

1 *Normand, Havre* : **Enseigne Gabolde** (——). 905 tons. Dimensions : 269 × 26·9 × 10 feet. Armament : 3—3·9 inch, 2—9 pdr., 6—18 inch torpedo tubes in two triple deck mountings. Designed H.P. 20,000 = 31 knots. Parsons geared turbines. Normand boilers. Fuel : 200 tons.

Note.—On plans 100 = 3·9 inch and 65 = 9 pdr. guns. Work on this T.B.D. was suspended during the War. Began in Dec., 1913 ; launch not yet reported.

12 Bory Type.

General Note.—All these boats are armed with 2—3·9 inch, 4—9 pdr., 4—18 inch tubes in pairs. All adapted for mine sweeping and carry D.C. Endurance : about 1,500 miles at 15 kts. and 400—500 at full speed. Complement, 83. They differ according to builders in appearance, dimensions, H.P., turbines, &c. Tubes are in echelon, and not on centre line as shown in plan.

War Losses : *Boutefeu, Faulx, Fourche, Renaudin.*

(1913 Programme).

M. LESTIN (reversed fore tripod mast).

2 *Rochefort Dockyard* : **Enseigne Roux** (1915), **Mecanicien-Principal Lestin** (1915). 880 tons. Dimensions : 271 × 29·9 × 10 feet. Designed H.P. 17,000 = 30 kts. Fuel : 200 tons oil. Endurance for these two boats := about 2,000 miles at 15 kts. and 550 miles at full speed.

(1911 Programme).

1 *Toulon Dockyard* : **Commandant Lucas** (1914). 800 tons. Dimensions : 272·4 × 26 × 10 feet. Laval Turbines. 2 du Temple-Guyot boilers. Designed S.H.P. 15,000 = 31 kts. Fuel : 140 tons oil. Practically sister-boat to *Protet* and *Bisson* on next page.

311

(Continued on next page.)

(1910 Programme Boats).

All armed with 2—3.9 inch, 4—9 pdr., and 4—18 inch tub^es in pairs.   Endurance: *about* 1500 miles at 15 kts., and 400-500 miles at full speed.   All equipped for Mine Sw^eeping, and carry D.C.
(With *C. Lucas* on preceding page, three b^oats below built under 1911 Programme.)

1 *Rochefort Dockyard :* **Protet** (1913).   800 tons.   Dimensions : 272.4 × 26 × 10 feet.   Laval turbines.   2 du Temple Guyot boilers.   Designed H.P. 15,000 = 31 kts.   Fuel : 140 tons oil.   Practically sister-boat to *C. Lucas* and *Bisson.*

1 *Ch. de Bretagne (Nantes) :* **Magon** (1913).   851 tons.   Dimensions : 272.4 × 25.6 × 10 feet.   Laval turbines.   Du Temple Guyot boilers.   Designed S.H.P. 15,000 = 30 kts. (32.2 on trials).   Fuel : 150 tons oil.

1 *Schneider & Cie (Creusot) :* **Mangini** (1913).   800 tons.   Dimensions : 253½ × 25.7 × 10 feet.   Designed H.P. 16,000 = 30 kts.   Zoelly turbines.   Du Temple Guyot boilers.   Fuel : 160 tons oil.

No Photo available.

1 *Normand (Havre) :* **Francis Garnier** (1912).   780 tons.   Dimensions : 244¾ × 25 × 10½ feet.   Designed H.P. 13,500 = 31 kts.   Turbines : Parsons.   Boilers : Normand.   Fuel : 148 tons oil.

1 *Toulon D. Y. :* **Bisson** (1912).   800 tons.   Dimensions : 272.4 × 26 × 10 feet.   Laval turbines.   2 du Temple-Guyot boilers.   Designed S.H.P. 15,000 = 31 kts.   Fuel : 140 tons oil.   Practically sister-boat to *C. Lucas* and *Protet.*

Copyright Photo, M. Bar, Toulon.

DEHORTER.
1 *Ch. de Normandie (Rouen) :* **Dehorter** (1912).   870 tons.   Dimensions : 248¾ × 25¼ × 10 feet.   Designed H.P. 14,000 = 31 kts.   Turbines : Parsons.   Boilers : Normand.   Fuel : 140 tons oil.

(Continued on next page.)

FRENCH DESTROYERS.

12 Bory Type—*Continued.*

(1910 Programme Boats.)

All boats given on this page are armed with 2—3·9 inch, and 4—9 pdr. guns, 4—18 inch torpedo tubes, in pairs. All adapted for mine-sweeping and carry D.C. For other details see general notes on preceding page.

No photo available.

1 *Soc. de la Loire (St. Nazaire):* **Capitane Mehl** (1912). 800 tons. Dimensions: 256¾×25¼×10 feet. Turbines: Parsons. Boilers: Normand. Designed S.H.P. 15,000=31 kts. Fuel: 140 tons oil.

No photo available.

1 *Soc de la Gironde (Bordeaux).* **Commandant Riviere** (1912). 800 tons. Dimensions: 256¾×25¾×10 feet. Breguet turbines, Du Temple-Guyot boilers. Designed S.H.P. 14,500=31 kts. Trials: 15,760=32·3 kts. Fuel: 140 tons oil.

1 *Dyle & Bacalan (Bordeaux).* **Commandant Bory** (1912). 780 tons. Dimensions: 253½×25¼×10 feet. Schneider-Zoelly turbines, Du Temple-Guyot boilers. Designed S.H.P. 14,115=31 kts. Fuel: 110 tons oil.

3 Casque Type (1908 Programme).

Generally identical with preceding *Commandant Bory* type. All armed with 2—3·9 inch and 4—9 pdr. guns, with 4—18 inch torpedo tubes in pairs. All three boats equipped for mine sweeping. Complement, 81. In all, fuel 140 tons oil only. Endurance ; about 1500 miles at 15 kts., 400 miles at full speed.

BOUCLIER. *Copyright photo, M. Bar, Toulon.*

1 *Normand (Havre).* **Bouclier** (1911). 780 tons. Dimensions: 237×24·9×9·4 feet. Designed H.P. 14,000=31 kts. (35·3 on trials), Turbines: Parsons. Boilers: Normand. Fuel: 140 tons oil.

1 *Ch. de la Gironde (Bordeaux).* **Cimeterre** (1911). 894 tons. Dimensions: 213·3×26×10 feet. Designed H.P. 13,500=31 kts. Breguet turbines. Du Temple Guyot boilers. Trials: 31·2.

313

(Continued on next page.)

Armed with 2—3·9 inch, 4—9 pdr., and 4—18 inch tubes in pairs; also adapted for mine-sweeping and carry D.C. For other details see Note on page preceding this.

1 *Forges et Ch. de la Mediterranée (Havre):* **Casque** (1910). 820 tons. Dimensions: 246·5 × 24·8 × 10 feet. Designed H.P. **14,400** = 31 kts. (34·9 on trials). Parsons turbines. Normand boilers. Has been employed during the war as a Flotilla Leader.

11 Hussard type.

Differ in design according to builders, but all armed with 6 —9 pdr. guns and 3—18 in. tubes (2 deck and 1 bow). Designed H.P. ranges from 8600 S.H.P. down to 7200 I.H.P. for speed of 28 kts., but *Voltigeur, Cavalier, Chasseur* and *Mameluk* made over 30 kts on trials. Radius of action, about 1000 miles at 15 kts., but *Cavalier* and *Janissaire* (oil fuel in both) about 1300 miles at 15 kts. Complements, 77 to 79. *Maximum* fuel in all, about 100 tons. Plans opposite for all five boats on this page; remaining seven on next page as plans for *Hussard*.

For description by classes, see next column on this page and first column on next page.

CAVALIER. (Other boats may also have raised fore funnels.)

1 *Ch. de la Bretagne (Nantes):* **Voltigeur** (1909), 445 tons.   Dimensions: 215 × 22½ × 9¾ feet.   2 *Normand (Havre):* **Cavalier** (1910), 527 tons, and **Chasseur** (1909), 492 tons.   Dimensions: 222 × 22 × 10 feet.   Turbines: *Voltigeur,* Rateau with reciprocating; *Chasseur, Cavalier.* Parsons.   Boilers: Normand; oil-burning in *Cavalier.*   Fuel: *Voltigeur* and *Chasseur,* 100 tons coal. *Cavalier,* 110 tons oil only.   Trials: *Voltigeur,* 31·3; *Chasseur,* 30·4; *Cavalier,* 31·1.

1 *Ch. de la Gironde (Bordeaux):* **Tirailleur** (1908). 479 tons. Dimensions: 207 × 22·8 × 9¾ feet. Breguet turbines and reciprocating engines. Du Temple-Guyot boilers. Coal: 100 tons. Trials: 28·82.

1 *Ch. de Normandie (Rouen):* **Janissaire** (1910). 514 tons. Dimensions: 223 × 21·9 × 10·3 feet. Parsons turbines. White-Forster boilers. Oil 100 tons. On trial made 28·5 kts.

11 Hussard type—*(continued)*.

All armed with 6—9 pdr. and 3—18 inch tubes.   For other details, see Note on page preceding this.

2 *Rochefort Dockyard:* **Enseigne Henry** and **Aspirant Herbert** (1911) 475 tons. Dimensions: 221×21·6×10·3 feet. Designed H.P. 7500 = 28·5 kts. Coal: 100 tons. Trials: E. Henry 28·3 kts., A. Herbert 28·5 kts.

Note.—These boats have *four* funnels in pairs, the foremost funnel being close up against the chart house, and mast abeam of funnel.

MAMELUK (and other boats).   *Copyright photo, M. Bar, Toulon.*

2 *Ch. de la Loire* (Nantes): **Hussard** (1908), 409 tons, and **Mameluk** (1909) 407 tons. Dimensions: 216½×22½×9¾ feet.
1 *Dyle & Bacalan* (Bordeaux): **Lansquenet** (1909), 542 tons. Dimensions: 221×20·8×10 feet.
1 *F. & C. de la Med.* (Havre): **Spahi** (1908), 455 tons. Dimensions: 224×21¼×9½ feet.
Machinery of all, reciprocating. Boilers: *Spahi*, Normand; others, Du Temple-Guyot. Coal: 100 tons in all. Trials: *Hussard*, 30·4; *Mameluk*, 30·6; *Spahi*, 28·7; *Carabinier* lost during the War.

48 Boats of Older Types (built 1898-1911).

All are armed with 1—9 pdr., 6—3 pdr. and 2 tubes, and complement, 71. Boats on this page: 18 inch tubes; on next page, 15 inch.   Plans for all types as shown on this page.

FANFARE * †   Some boats have mast very close to or almost abeam of fore funnel, as above.   *Photo, Bissonier.*

Radius of action of all boats on this page 950 miles at 15 kts.

CLAYMORE.   Some boats have mast before funnel, as above.   *Photo, Cribb, Southsea.*

21 *Claymore* class: **Carquois,** **Coutelas, Fleuret, Glaive, Mortier, Obusier, Pierrier, Poignard, Stylet, Trident** and **Tromblon** (Rochefort D.Y., 1905-8); **Cognee, Hache*** and **Massue*** (Toulon D.Y., 1907-8); **Claymore** and **Fanfare†** (Normand, Le Havre, 1905-08); **Oriflamme** and **Sabretache** (Ch. de la Bretagne, Nantes, 1908); **Fanion** (Dyle and Bacalan, Bordeaux, 1908); **Gabion** and **Sape** (Soc. de St. Nazaire, Penhoët, 1907). 340 to 415 tons. Dimensions: 196·8×21·7×11·5 feet. Designed H.P. 6400; all made 28 to 30·4 kts. on trials. Boilers: Du Temple-Guyot or Normand. Coal: 80 tons.

* Converted to mine-layers.   † Has ¾″ armour amidships.

Older Types—*(Continued)*: Armament: 1—9 pdr., 6—3 pdr. Boats on this page only, 2—15 inch tubes. Radius of action, 950 to 920 miles at 15 kts.

MOUSQUETON (and *Arbalète* class.)

Copyright Photo, M. Bar, Toulon.

(25 boats, viz., 18 *Mousquet* class + 4 *Flamberge* class + 3 *Durandal* class).

18 *Mousquet* class:—**Arbalète, Arquebuse, Épieu, Fronde, Harpon,** and **Sagaie** (Normand, Le Havre, 1902-3), **Francisque, Carabine, Sabre,** and **Sarbacane,*** (Rochefort D.Y.), 1902-3,) **Bélier, Javeline,** and **Pistolet** (Ch. de la Bretagne, Nantes, 1902-3), **Arc** and **Mousqueton** (Cherbourg D.Y., 1904), **Bombe** (F. & C. de la Med. Havre, 1903), **Baliste** and **Dard** (Soc. de St. Nazaire, Rouen, 1903). 310-370 tons. Dimensions : 185·4 × 20·6 × 10·5 feet. H.P. 6000—7300 = 29 to 30·8 kts. on trials. (*Arbalète* 31·5 kts.) Coal : 75 tons.

**Converted into mine-layers.*

Also

4 **Escopette, Flamberge, Pertuisane,** and **Rapière**, (Rochefort D.Y. 1900-01). H.P. 4800-5200 = 26-27 kts. on trials, otherwise as *Arbalète* class above.

Also

3 **Durandal, Fauconneau** and **Hallebarde** (Normand, Le Havre, 1899-1900). 310 tons. Dimensions : 180·4 × 20·6 × 7·8 feet. H.P. 5600 = 27 kts. Coal : 67 tons.

2 boats : **Épée, Pique,** (F. & C. de la Mediterranee, Granville, 1900). 310 tons. Dimensions : 185¾ × 20·6 × 9⅞ feet. H.P. 5600 = 26 kts. Normand boilers. Coal : 67 tons. These 2 boats have *four* funnels in pairs, the foremost two being higher than the aft pair.

(Torpilleurs de haute mer.)

2 screws. 15 inch torpedoes. Boilers : Normand, Thornycroft, and Du Temple Guyot.

Totals.	Type.	Date.	Displacement.	I.H.P.	Max. Speed.	Coal.	Complement.	Tubes.	Max. Draught.
					kts.	tons			feet
11	*Mistral*	1901	150—186	4018	28·2	25	32	3	8
1	*Forban*	1895	150	3200	31·2	15	30	2	7¼
1	*Grondeur*	1892	130	1750	23·8	10	28	2	5

All are Normand type. The *Forban* and *Mistral* class considerably exceeded 30 knots on *trial*.

Copyright photo, G. E. G.

11 *Normand* type : **Bourrasque, Cyclone, Mistral,* Rafale, Siroco*** (Normand, Havre) ; **Simoun,* Typhon*** (F. & C. de la Med., Granville) ; **Audacieux,* Trombe*** (F. & C. de la Bretagne, Nantes) ; **Borée, Tramontane** (Dyle & Bacalan, Bordeaux). All launched 1900-01. 2—3 pdr. guns and 3 tubes. Radius of action ; 2500 miles at 10 kts. * These boats have ¾" armour amidships.

2 *Normand* type : **Forban** (1895). 2—3 pdr., 2 tubes. Radius of action : 2000 miles at 12 kts.

(Continued on next page.)

Sea-going Torpedo Boats—*(continued)*.

1 *F. & C. de la Méditerranée, Granville*: **Grondeur** (1892). 2—1 pdr. 2 torpedo tubes.

---

103 *(or less)* Torpilleurs de Defence Mobile.

Totals.	Numbers.	First Begun	Last Completed	Displacement	I.H.P.	Max. Speed	Coal	Complement	Tubes	Max. Draught
				tons		kts.	tons			
63	369—295	'03	'07	96-101	2000	26	11	23	3—1	$8\frac{3}{4}$
39	292—208	1899	1904	86-94	1500-2000	25	11	22	2	9
1	193	1894	1899	80	1100	21	10	16	2	$8\frac{1}{2}$

Notes on Torpilleurs de Defence Mobile.

Uncertain how many of these boats are now in service. Reported during 1919 that majority were being surveyed, with a view to breaking-up ; only those numbered above 300 may be kept for further service.

Following boats have double numbers or number and name :—*292 (21S), 291 (20S), 286 (19S), 285 (18S), 284 (17S), 255 (16S), 242 (6S), 222 (Rouable), 215 (Foyer), 208 (Marteau), 193 (Moulouya)*.

All boats are *Normand types.* Several exceeded 27 kts. on original trials, but few can exceed 25 kts. now.

All originally armed with 2—1 pdr. guns and 2 or 3—15 inch tubes, but these have been removed from some boats—see *Notes* below.

63 *(or less)* *Normand* type Nos. **369—295,** of 96 to 101 tons. *Nominal* full speed radius 200 miles. At 10 kts., 1800 mile.

Notes.—A large number of these Torpedo Boats were modified during the War for service as Coastal Patrol Boats, Guardships over Net Barrages, Boom Defences, &c., and for short-distance convoy work. The two amidships 15 inch torpedo tubes were removed and replaced by either a 14 pdr. gun (75 mm. field gun on naval mounting) or by a 9 pdr. gun or 2—3 pdr. guns. The stem 15 inch tube was retained, although it was of little use at full speed or in any seaway.

39 *(or less)* *Normand* type : **292—208** and **193,** of 86-94 and 80 tons. From *No.* 202 and upwards, two funnels—appearance more or less as 369-295 above.

Notes.—Many of these old boats have been disarmed and dismantled, to provide engines for new gunboats.

317

Submarine Chasers (*Chasseurs de Sousmarins*).

> **Photo wanted.**
>
> *Same appearance as U.S. SC-boats.*

97—*100 foot type*: **C1, C4—C51** and **C52—100.** Built by U.S. Navy Yards and smaller ship-building firms, 1917–18. *Designed* displacement, 54 tons; *actual* displacement, 77 tons. Dimensions: 105 ft. (*p.p.*), 110 ft. (*o.a.*) × 14 ft. 8¾ in. × 5 ft. 5½ in. (*mean* hull draught). Machinery: 3 sets of 220 B.H.P. Standard petrol motors, totalling 660 B.H.P = 17 kts. Petrol: 2400 gallons = 900 miles at 10 kts. Armament: *C 1—C 50* were sent across the Atlantic with 2—6 pdrs. only and may still retain these guns; *G 51—C 100* have 1—3 inch (23 cal.) gun. M.G. may have been added by French Navy. Carry depth charges. Complement, 26.

Notes.—Begun for U.S. Navy as follows: *SC 5, SC 7—16, SC 28—33, SC 65—67, SC 75—76, SC 140—142, SC 146, SC 160—163, SC 170—176, SC 243, SC 249, SC 313—319, SC 347—348, SC 350* (all boats of first U.S. contract), *SC 357—404, SC 406* (second U.S.) contract for French Government). The U.S. *SC 177*, being in European waters, was transferred to the French Navy in place of *SC 405* under second contract. Were renumbered as *C 1—49* and *C 50—99* of French Navy, out of which *C 2, C 3* and another boat (*C 100 ?*) have been lost.

* For builders under SC-numbers see Submarine Chaser Section of U.S. Navy. Details taken from article by Com. J. A. Furer, Construction Corps. U.S.N., published in "Journal, U.S. Naval Institute."

M. L. (*Vedettes*).

French Official War Photo.

70—*85 foot type*: **VI—20, V 22, V 24—26, V 28—61** (built in England 1917) and **V 62—73** (built in Canada 1917-18). About 30–35 tons. Complement, 8–10. Length, 80–85 feet. Beam, 12–13 feet. Draught, 4-5 feet. Armament: 1—75 mm. field gun converted to naval mounting, 2 D.C. Machinery: 2 sets petrol motors = 20–22 kts. *nominal*, 19 kts. about best *maximum* at sea for any length of time. Radius of action: about 500 miles at full speed and 1000 miles at 12–15 kts. *or less*. Fuel: about 2000 galls. petrol. *V 21, V 23* and *V 27* lost during the War.

43 + 7 Submarines (*Sousmarins*).

No. in Class.	Type and Design.	Date.	Displacement. Surface / Submerged (tons)	H.P. Surface / Submerged	Speed Surface / Submerged (kts)	Endurance. Surface / Submerged	Tubes or Gear.	Complement.
	Ocean-going:							
2	*Joessel* class (S)	'14—'20	900 / 1250	2700 / 1650	16·5 / 11	4200 miles at 10 kts. / 115 miles at 5 kts.	8-10 S	40
4	*Lagrange* class (H)	'14—'20	840 / 1130	2600 / 1650	16·5 / 11	1200 miles at 10 kts. / 115 miles at 5 kts.	10 S	40
2	*Dupuy de Lôme* class (H)	'15—'16	833 / 1100	4000 / 1700	18 / 11—12	1350 miles at 14 kts. / 150 miles at 5 kts.	8 S	40
2 {	*Néréide* (S)	'13—'16	787 / 1000	4800 / 1700	20 / 10	3500 miles at 12 kts. / 110 miles at 5 kts.	8 S	40
	Gustav Zédé (S)	'12—'14		4000 / 1700	19 / 10	2300 miles at 10 kts. / 110 miles at 5 kts.		
	Sea-going:							
3	*Lieut. O'Byrne* class (L)	'17—'20	350 / 500	1000 / 460	14 / 8·5	...	4	24
3	*Armide* class (L)	'14—'16	460 / 665	2200 / 850	17·5 / 11	2600 miles at 11 kts. / 150 miles at 5 kts.	6	27
1	*Daphne* (H)	'14—'16	640 / 945	1600 / 1400	15 / 10	2300 miles at 14 kts. / 100 miles at 5 kts.	10	35
3	*Bellone* class (H)	'14—'16	520 / 780	2100 / 1400	17 / 11	2300 miles at 10 kts. / 115 miles at 5 kts.	8	29
5	*Amarante* class (H)	'13—'15	410 / 550	1200 / 700	14 / 8	1500 miles at 10 kts. / 80 miles at 5 kts.	8	27
2	*Clorinde* class (R)	'13—'15	410 / 570	1300 / 810				
1	*Archiméde* (H)	'07—'11	577 / 810	1700 / 1000	15·2 / 10·9	2500 miles at 10 kts. / 100 miles at 5 kts.	7	30
13	Modified *Pluviôse* class (L)	'07—'14	400 / 505	840 / 600	13 / 9	1450 miles at 10 kts. / 80 miles at 4·5 kts.	7	26
	Mine Layers:							
2	*Paul Chailly* class (—)	'17—'20	...	...	...	...	...	...
2	Of *Amarante* class (H)	'13—'15	410 / 550	1200 / 700	14 / 8	1500 miles at 10 kts. / 80 miles at 5 kts.	...	...
	Coastal:							
1	*Roland Morillot*	'16—'17	263 / 324	280 / 240	8¼ / 6	4500 miles at 5 kts. / 70 miles at 3 kts.	2	21
4	*Emeraude* class (M)	'03—'08	390 / 447	600 /	11-12 / 9	1000 miles at 8 kts. /	4	25

(H)=Hutter. (L)=Laubeuf. (M)=Maugas. (R)=Radiguet. (S)=Simonet.

Note to Illustrations of Submarine Types on following pages :—

With the exception of *Atalante*, photographs are not up-to-date, but later views than those published cannot be secured at present. During 1918—19, steel bridge screens, W/T. masts, guns, and jumping wires were added to French submarines. Their present appearance is given by Silhouettes.

FRENCH SUBMARINES—OCEAN-GOING BOATS.

Surrendered German Submarines.

The following German Submarines were assigned to the French Navy during 1919. No attempt is made to describe these boats, because, after being examined, they are to be dismantled and broken up.* These boats are not to be incorporated in the French Navy. Those who desire particulars are referred to the German Submarine Section of 1918 " Fighting Ships."

1 Cruiser : *U139* boat.

3 Converted Mercantiles : *U151, U153, U157.*

16 Ocean-going boats : *U166, U160, U119, U113, U108, U105, U94, U91, U81, U57, U35, UB142, UB126, UB94 UBS4, UB73.*

8 Mine-Laying boats : *U79, UC104, UC103, UC100, UC74, UC58, UC27, UC23.*

5 Coastal boats : *UB24. UB14, UB8, UB6, UB4.*

Several of the above boats foundered or were wrecked when being navigated from British to French ports.

* The French Submarine *Roland Morillot,* ex-German *UB26,* is a prize of war and outside the terms of this agreement between the Allied Navies.

2 Joessel Class (Ocean-going—*Diesel.*)

> **Photo wanted.**

2 *Simonet* type : **Fulton** (1919) and **Joessel** (1917). Both built at Cherbourg D.Y. Displacements : 900 tons *on surface,* 1250 tons *submerged.* Dimensions : × × feet. Machinery : *on surface,* 2 sets Schneider Diesel engines, 2700 B.H.P. = 16½ kts. *Submerged* speed : 11 kts. Endurance : *on surface* and *submerged* about the same as *Lagrange* class in next column. Armament : 1 or 2—14 pdr. guns and 8 or 10 tubes, and/or torpedoes carried in external cradle gears. Complement, 40.

4 Lagrange Class (Ocean-going—*Diesel*).

> **Photo wanted.**

4 *Hutter* type : **Lagrange** (1917), **Laplace** (——),* **Regnault** (1919),† and **Romazotti** (1917). All launched at Toulon D.Y., 1917. Displacements : 840 tons *on surface,* 1130 tons *submerged.* Dimensions : 246⅔ × 21 × 13 feet. Machinery : *on surface,* 2 sets 1300 B.H.P. Sulzer-Diesel engines, totalling 2600 B.H.P. for 16½ kts. *Submerged* speed : 11 kts. Endurance : *on surface,* 2500 miles at 14 kts., 4200 miles at 10 kts. When *submerged,* 115 miles at 5 kts. Armament : either (*a*) 1—3·9 inch and 1—14 pdr. gun, or (*b*) 2—14 pdr. guns. 10—18 inch tubes or torpedoes carried in external cradle gears. Complement, 40.

*Laplace also reported as built at Rochefort D.Y.

†*Regnault* not yet finished : is being modified to obviate defects developed by *Lagrange* on trials.

2 Dupuy de Lome Class (Ocean-going—*Steam*).

SANÉ. *Copyright photo, M. Bar, Toulon.*

2 *Hutter* type : **Dupuy de Lòme** (1915) and **Sané** (1916). Both built at Toulon D.Y. Displacements : 833 tons *on surface,* 1100 tons *submerged.* Dimensions : 246⅔ × 21 × 13 feet. Machinery : *on surface,* 2 sets of turbines and oil-fired boilers : I.H.P. 4000 = 18 kts. *Submerged* speed : 11 to 12 kts. Endurance : 1350 miles at 14 kts. *on surface,* 150 miles at 5 kts. *submerged.* Armament : 2—14 pdr. guns and 8—18 inch torpedo tubes and/or external cradle gears. Complement, 40.

(*Ocean-going Types continued on next page.*)

2 Gustave Zédé Class.

(Ocean-going ; one boat *Diesel*, one boat *steam*.)

Note.—These two Submarines are usually rated together as a class. They have the same dimensions, displacement, and armament, but for comparative purposes, they were built with different systems of surface propulsion.

Photograph wanted.

1 *Simonet* type : **Néréide** (Cherbourg D.Y., 1914). Displacements, dimensions, armament and complement, as *Gustave Zédé* below. Machinery : 2 sets 2 cycle 8 cyl. 1200 B.H.P. Schneider-Carels Diesel engines, 2400 H.P.=20 kts. *on surface*. Electric motors + batteries 1700 H.P. = 10 kts. *submerged*. Radius of action : *about* 3500 miles at 12 kts. *on surface*.

1 *Simonet* type : **Gustave Zédé** (Cherbourg D.Y., 1913). Displacements : 787 tons *on surface*, 1000 tons *submerged*. Dimensions : 243 × 19½ × 12¾ feet. Machinery : 2 sets geared turbines + 4 Normand-Du Temple oil-burning boilers, 4000 H.P. = 19 kts. *on surface*. Electric motors + batteries, 1700 H.P. = 10 kts. *submerged*. Radii of action : 2300 miles at 10 kts. and 1800 miles at 14 kts. *on surface*. Armament : 1—14 pdr. and 1—3 pdr. Q.F. guns. Torpedo tubes : 2—18 inch tubes + 6—18 inch torpedoes carried in external dropping gears. Complement, 40.

3 Lieut. O'Byrne Class (Sea-going—*Diesel*).

Building or completing.

3 *Laubeuf* type : **Lieutenant O'Byrne. Dupetit-Thouars,** and **Henri Fournier,** building or completing by Schneider, Chalon-sur-Saône. Displacements : 350 tons *on surface*, 500 tons *submerged*. Dimensions : *about* 173.9 × 15.4 × feet. Machinery : 2 sets Schneider-Carels Diesel engines, 1000 B.H.P. = 14 kts. *on surface*. *Submerged* speed : 8½ kts. Armament : 1 small Q.F. gun and 4 torpedo tubes. Complement, 24.

3 Armide Class (Sea-going—*Diesel*).

Photo wanted.

3 *Laubeuf* type " Dc " : **Amazone,** (1916), **Antigone** (1916), and **Armide** (ex-Japanese *No.* 14, 1915). Built by Schneider et Cie, Chalon-sur-Saône. Displacements : 460 tons *on surface*, 665 tons *submerged*. Dimensions : 184⅜ × 17 × 10½ feet. Machinery : 2 sets, Schneider-Carels Diesel engines, 2200 H.P. = 17½ kts. *on surface*. *Submerged* speed : 11 kts. Armament : 1—1 pdr. Q.F. gun. Torpedo tubes : 2 internal + 4 torpedoes carried in external dropping gears.

Note.—*Amazone* and *Antigone* begun for Greek Navy ; *Armide* for Japanese Navy. All three taken over for French Navy during War. Reported that *Amazone* and *Antigone* have been converted to Mine-Layers.

1 Daphné Class (Sea-going—*Diesel*).

Photo wanted.

1 *Hutter* type : **Daphné** (Toulon D.Y., 1915). Displacements : 640 tons *on surface*, 945 tons *submerged*. Dimensions : 223 × 18½ × 12½ feet. Machinery : 2 sets 800 B.H.P. Sulzer Diesel engines, 1600 H.P. == 15 kts. *on surface*. *Submerged* speed : 11 kts. Endurance : *on surface* (a) 2300 miles at 14 kts., (b) 4000 miles at 11-12 kts., 100 miles at 5 kts. when *submerged*. Armament : 1—14 pdr. gun, 10—18 inch torpedo tubes or torpedoes carried in external dropping gears. Complement, 35. Is an enlarged *Archimede* design. *Diane* of this type lost during the War.

(*Continued on next page.*)

3 **Bellone class** (Sea-going—*Diesel*).

[Photo wanted.]

3 *Hutter* type : ***Bellone*** and ***Hermione*** (Rochefort D. Y., 1914 and 1913), ***Gorgone*** (Toulon D. Y., 1915). Displacements, 520 tons *on surface*; 780 tons *submerged*. Dimensions : 196·8 × 17·7 × 12 feet. Machinery : 2 sets Sulzer or Sabathé-Diesel engines, 2100 H.P. = 17 kts. *on surface*. *Submerged* speed, 9 kts. Endurance *on surface*, 2300 miles at 10 kts., 115 miles at 5 kts. *submerged*. Armament : 1—3 pdr. Q.F. gun. 8—18 inch torpedo tubes or torpedoes carried in external dropping gears. Complement, 29. Similar to *Archimede*, but somewhat smaller.

5 **Amarante class** (Sea-going—*Diesel*).

ATALANTE.

Copyright Photo, M. Bar, Toulon.

*5 *Hutter* type: ***Amarante, Arethuse, Artemis*** and ***Atalante*** (Toulon D. Y., 1913), ***Andromaque*** (Cherbourg D. Y., 1913), ***Amphitrite*** and ***Astrée*** (Rochefort D. Y., 1914). Displacements : 410 tons *on surface*; 550 tons *submerged*. Dimensions : 174 × 16¾ × 10—11 feet. Machinery : 2 sets Sabathé-Diesel engines, 1200 H.P.=14 kts. *on surface*. *Submerged* speed, 8 kts. Radii of action, 1950 miles at 10 kts. *on surface*. 80 miles at 5 kts. *submerged*. Armament: 1—3 pdr. Q.F. gun, 8—18 inch torpedo tubes or torpedoes carried in external dropping gears. Complement 30. Are an improved and faster type derived from Laubeuf's " modified *Pluviose* " boats at foot of next column. *Ariadne* of this class lost during the war
*7 boats are named but two of these (names unknown) have been converted to Mine Layers.

2 **Clorinde class** (Sea-going *Diesel*).

[Photo wanted.]

2 *Radiguet* type: ***Clorinde*** (Rochefort D. Y., 1913), ***Cornelie*** (Rochefort, 1913). Displacements : 410 tons *on surface*; 570 tons *submerged*. Electric motors + batteries of 410 H.P. All other details as the *Amarante* class above.

1 **Special boat** (Sea-going—*Steam*).

1 *Hutter* type: ***Archimede*** (Cherbourg D. Y., 1909). $\frac{577}{810}$ tons. Dimensions : 199¾ × 18¼ × 13¼ feet. Machinery 2 sets triple expansion steam engines, 1700 H.P.=15 kts. *on surface*. *Submerged* speed, 10—11 kts. Endurance 2500 miles at 10 kts. *on surface*; *submerged*, 100 miles at 5 kts. Armament : 1—3 pdr. gun; 6—18 inch (M'04) torpedoes carried in external dropping gears + 1 bow tube. Complement, 31. Has proved very successful i service.

13 **"Modified Pluviôse" class** (Sea-going—*Diesel*).

(Also known as " Brumaire class").

COULOMB.

Copyright photo, M. Bar, Toulon.

13 *Laubeuf* type viz:—

5 *Cherbourg Dockyard :* ***Brumaire*** and ***Frimaire*** (1911) ***Euler*** and ***Nivôse*** (1912), ***Franklin*** (1913).
4 *Rochefort Dockyard :* ***Faraday*** and ***Volta*** (1911), ***Montgolfier*** and ***Newton*** (1912).
4 *Toulon Dockyard :* ***Arago, Coulomb. Curie**** and ***Leverrier*** (1912).

Displacements : About 400 tons *on surface*, 505 tons *submerged*. Dimensions : Length 166¼ to 172 feet. Beam : 16 to 17¾ feet. Draught : 10¼ feet. Armament : 1—3 pdr. gun, and 7—18 torpedoes carried in external cradle gears.
Machinery of these boats : 2 sets Diesel engines. H.P. 840 = 13 kts. *on surface*. Electric motors and batteries, 600 H.P =9 kts. *submerged*. Endurance : 1450 miles at 9-10 kts. *on surface*. 80 miles *submerged* at 4½ kts. Complement, 26

**Curie* captured by Austro-Hungarian Navy Dec. 1914, and during 1915-18 was the Austro-Hungarian Submarine *XIV*. Recovered by French Navy in 1918.

2 Paul Chailly class (Mine Laying).

Building or Completing.

2 boats, *type unknown*: **Paul Chailley,** begun at Havre, 1917, **Pierre Callot,** begun at Bordeaux, 1917. No details known, beyond the fact that both are large Mine-Layers. Will probably be completed during 1920.

Reported that *Amazone* and *Antigone*, of *Armide* class, have been converted to Mine-Layers, but this report has not been verified. Also see *Pluviôse* class on next page.

2 of Amarante class (Mine Laying—*Diesel*).

Photo wanted.

2 *Laubeuf* type : *Names unknown*, but are units of *Amarante* class (*v.* preceding page), built or converted for mine-laying duties. All details as *Amarante* class, except that torpedo tubes are replaced by an unknown number of mines.

1 Captured German boat (Coastal—*Diesel*).

Photo by courtesy of Senor Pascual Rey, Corunna.

Above view of German *UB 23* is generally correct for appearance of Roland Morillot (ex-*UB 26*).

1 *ex-German* boat : **Roland Morillot** (ex-German *UB 26*, launched by Weser Co., Bremen, 1916, captured during 1916). Displacements : 263 tons *on surface*, 324 tons *submerged*. Dimensions : 118½ × 14¼ × 12 feet. Machinery : 2 sets, 140 H.P. 6-cylinder oil motors = 8½ kts. *on surface*; *submerged* speed, 5¾ to 6 kts. Endurance : 4500 miles at 5 kts. *on surface*; 70 miles at 3 kts. *submerged*. Armament : 1—3 pdr., 1 M.G., 2 (bow) 18 inch torpedo tubes. Carries 4 torpedoes. Oil : 22/28 tons. Complement, 21.

4 Emeraude class (Coastal—*Diesel*).

4 *Maugas* type : **Emeraude** (1906), **Opale** (1906), **Rubis** (1907), and **Topaze** (1908). Dimensions : *about* 149 × 12.8 × 12.3 feet. *Surface* displacement, about 390 tons; *submerged*, 447 tons. Speeds : 11-12 kts. *on surface*; 8 kts. *submerged*. 1—9 pdr. gun and 4—18 inch torpedo tubes. Complement, 25. *Saphir* of this class lost during the War.

Note.—A fifth boat, *Turquoise*, captured by Turks during the War. Was repaired and commissioned for service in the Turkish Navy as the *Mustedieh Ombashi*. Has been recovered by the French Navy, but it is doubtful if she will be assigned to any active form of service.

FRENCH SUBMARINES.

11 Pluviôse Class (Sea-going—Steam).

Present disposal uncertain. Not included in Summary Table on preceding page.

6 *Cherbourg Dockyard* : **Germinal, Pluviôse** and **Ventôse** (1907); **Messidor** (1908); **Fructidor** and **Thermidor** (1909).

3 *Rochefort Dockyard:* **Berthelot, Watt** (1909); **Giffard** (1910).

2 *Toulon Dockyard:* **Ampère** (1908), **Gay-Lussac** (1910).

Displacements: About 400 tons *on surface;* 505 tons *submerged.* Dimensions: $166\frac{1}{4}$ to $167\frac{1}{2}$ × $16\frac{1}{2}$ to $17\frac{1}{2}$ × $10\frac{1}{2}$ to $10\frac{3}{4}$ feet. Armament: 1—3 pdr. gun and 6—18 inch torpedoes in cradle gears outside hull. These **may** be removed—see Notes.

Machinery of all above : 2 sets triple expansion steam engines. Du Temple oil-burning boiler. H.P. 700 = $12\frac{1}{4}$ kts. *on surface.* Electric motors and batteries, 460 H.P = 8 kts. *submerged.* Radius of action: 1400 miles *on surface* at 8 kts; 60 miles *submerged* at $4\frac{1}{2}$ kts. Complement, 26.

Notes.

Reports on future disposal of above boats are very contradictory. *Papin* and *Cugnot* of this class have been condemned, and will be broken up; both are deleted. *Messidor* and others reported to be dismantled. Not certain if they are being broken up or if they are being converted to Minelayers. One or two boats may also be kept for Training Duties.

Destroyer Depot Ships.

(Soutiens de Torpilleurs.)

(None.)

Submarine Depot Ships.

(Soutiens de Sous-Marins).

An old armoured ship, **TOURVILLE** (ex *Gironde*, 1878), is used as a Harbour Depot Ship, also Sloop *Satellite*. Destroyers are also employed as Tenders to Submarines.

T.B. **No. 273** and Repair Ship **Friant** (next page) attached to Submarine Flotillas.

Submarine Chaser Depot Ships.

Soutiens de Vedettes Contre-Sousmarins.)

(Not known.)

Aircraft Carriers.

(Portes-Avions.)

Photo, M. Bar, Toulon.

CAMPINAS (ex-liner of Chargeurs Reunis, built ———, and taken over during war). 3319 tons. Dimensions: 357·6 × 42·7 × 23·2 feet. Guns : not known. I.H.P. 1460 = 11·8 kts. on trials ; present best speed, 10 kts. 1 set triple-exp. engines. 2 Boilers. Coal : 988 tons. Two hangars for 6-10 machines and K.B. gear.

(Also Aviation School Ship.)

FOUDRE (October, 1895). Displacement 6100 tons. Complement 328. Length, 380½ feet. Beam, 51¼ feet. *Maximum* draught, 23½ feet. Guns: 8--3·9 in., 4--9 pdr., 2--3 pdr. Armour: Deck 3½″, 4″ casemates. Designed H.P. 11,500 = 19 kts. *Trials* (1897): I.H.P. 11,930 = 19·57 kts.

Note.—Russian (Black Sea) seaplane carrier **ALMAZ** is temporarily in French navy. Carries 4 seaplanes.

Mine Layers *(Mouilleurs de Mines.)*

PLUTON. *Photo by courtesy of Messrs. A. Normand.*

PLUTON (1913), 660 tons, & **CERBERE** (1912). Both built by Messrs. Augustin Normand, Havre. 566 tons. Dimensions: 193½ × 27¼ × 10¾ feet. Guns : 2—3·9 inch and 1—3 pdr AA. Designed H.P. 6000 = 20 kts. Coal : 150 tons. Carry 120 mines.

Destroyers *(used for Mine-Laying).*

Carquois (1907), *Hache* (1906), *Massue* (1906), of *Coutelas* class ; *Sarbacane* of *Arbalete* class—all described on preceding pages.

Submarine Mine Layers.

Paul Chailly and *Pierre Callot* listed on an earlier page. Two submarines of *Amarante* class have been adapted for mine laying ; names and number of mines carried not known.

Mine Sweepers *(Drageurs de Mines).*

Note.—All destroyers of the *Bouclier* class, and nearly all gunboats of the *Diligente*, *Friponne* and *Vaillante* types are fitted as mine sweepers, also various Torpedo Boats and Submarine Chasers.

Photo wanted.

CHARRUE (1914), **HERSE** (1914), **PIOCHE** (1914), **RATEAU** (1914). 255 tons. Guns : 2—3 pdr. Designed H.P. 600 = 12 kts. Coal : 35 tons.

(Continued on next page.)

Mine Sweepers—(continued).

> No Photo available.

ORIENT (1908), 380 tons. **IROISE** (1907), 240 tons. **LORIENTAIS** (1901), 430 tons. **DAMIER** (1897), 155 tons. **ALCYON I** (——), 300 tons. Speeds: 8-10 kts. Above ships are Trawlers purchased into Navy 1910-12. Further Mine-Sweeping Trawlers, which may not be permanently retained for naval service, are listed on next page.

Oil Tankers (Petroliers.)

> Same appearance as "Rhône" below.

—————— (ex-Meuse, 1915, present name not known). 7500 tons. Speed, 13 kts. Carries 6400 tons of oil as cargo.

> See Silhouettes for appearance.

GARONNE (1911). Oil Tanker. 10,800 tons. H.P. 2600 = 13 kts. Carries 7000 tons oil as cargo.

Photo, M. Bar, Toulon.

RHÔNE (1910). Oil Tanker. 7830 tons. H.P. 2100 = 11 kts. Carries 4500 tons oil as cargo.

Salvage Ship.

> For appearance, see Silhouettes.

VULCAIN (1909). 330 tons. Speed: 13 kts.

Repair Ship. (Navire-Atelier.)

> No Photo available.

FRIANT (1893). Old Cruiser of 3944 tons, converted for service as Repair Ship. Present H.P., speed and armament, not known.

Transports.

> No Photos available.
> For "Seine," see Silhouette.

SEINE (1913). 3160 tons. Designed H.P. 1950 = 13 kts. Guns: 2—3·9 inch, 1—9 pdr. Coal: 295 tons.
LOIRET (ex-S.S. Paris, purchased 1900). 2200 tons. Guns: 1—9 pdr. H.P. 1060 = 11 kts.
Also Ancturus, Evangéline, Gâvres, Marguerite VI and Prado.

Hospital Ships. (Navires-hôpital.)

VINH-LONG (1881), **BIEN HOA** (1880). 5500 tons. Speed: nominal 13 kts. Draughts: about 22 feet.
DUGUAY-TROUIN (ex-Tonquin, 1878). 5445 tons. Designed H.P. 2700 = 14 kts.

Surveying Ships.

Photo, N. D.

MANCHE (1890), **VAUCLUSE** (1891). About 1600 tons. Armament: Manche has 1—9 pdr. and 2—3 pdr.; Vaucluse has 2—3 pdr. Speed about 10-11 kts.
UTILE (1894). 400 tons. Speed: 13 kts. Guns: 1—3 pdr. Also Sonde (1911) of 51 tons. 10 kts. speed.

Yacht.

> No Photo available.

JEANNE BLANCHE (1894, rebuilt 1913). 420 tons. Guns: 4—1 pdr. H.P. 820 = 12 kts. Complement, 37.

Fishery Protection.

> Photo wanted.

FLAMANT (Dec., 1916). Despatch Vessel of 610 tons. 154 × 28 × 13 feet. Guns: 1—14 pdr., 1—1 pdr. I.H.P. 1100 = 15 kts. Coal: 100 tons.
T.B.D. **Rafale** (described on an earlier page).
Trawlers Sentinelle and Sajou.

Navy Trawlers.

Following Trawlers built during the War to the order of the Ministry of Marine, for service as Patrol Boats, Mine Sweepers, &c. Some may be sold out to private owners now.

"Bird" Class :—

Canard, Colombe, Coq, Faisan, Gelinotte, Héron, Paon, Perdreau, Pigeon, Pingouin, Pintade, Pluvier, Ramier, Tourterelle, Vanneau, all 677 tons.

Alouette, Becfigu, Bergeronnette, Caille, Canari, Chardonneret, Colibri, Corneille, Engoulevant, Etourneau, Fauvette, Grive, Linotte, Loriot, Martinet, Martin-Pêcheur, Mauviette, Merle, Moineau, Ortolan, Passereau, Perruche, Pie, Pierrot, Pinson, Pivert, Roitelet, Rossignol, Rouge-Gorge, Sansonnet, all of 460 tons.

"Fish" Class :—

Equille, Gardon, Goujon, Lamproie, Murène, all 669 tons ; *Ablette, Anguille, Barbeau, Brême, Brochet, Carpe,* all 460 tons ; *Perche, Tanche, Truite,* 410 tons.

"Insect" Class :—

Cigale, Coccinelle, Criquet, Libeluelle, all 430 tons.

"Flower" Class :—

Campanule, Clematite, Jacynthe, Jonquille, Lavande, Marjolaine, Paquerette, Perce-Niege, Renoncle, Sauge, Tulipe, Violette. Have Diesel engines and no funnels.

"Tree" Class :—

Cedre, Chêne, Erable, Frêne, Hêtre, Orme, Platane, Peuplier, all 360 tons.

"Rock" Class :—

Albâtre, Basalte, Gypse, Meulière, Pyrite, Silex, Quartz, all 380 tons.

Miscellaneous :—

Autruche, Caribou, Eole, Onagre, all 471 tons ; *Mathurin* and *Troupier,* with Sulzer Diesel engines, *Coetlogon, Nemerica, Thuga, Victoire, Yucea, &c., &c.*

Tugs. *(Remorqueurs.)*

Two large sea-going boats, **CENTAUR** (1915) & **TRAVAILLEUR.**
Following Tugs of 360 tons built during the War :—
Clameur, Fracas, Tapage, Tintamare, Tumulte, Vacarme.
Crabe, Calmar, Homard, Tourteau.
Also many other smaller tugs and tanks.

Training Ships. *(Navires-Ecole.)*

At the time these pages were prepared, the allocation of French Warships for Training Duties had not been definitely decided on. It is proposed that the majority of French Armoured Cruisers shall be employed on Training Duties.

For Gunnery :—

Battleships **VERITÉ, REPUBLIQUE,** Coast Defence Ship **REQUIN,** Old Cruisers **POTHUAU** and **LATOUCHE-TREVILLE**—all described on preceding pages.

HAVRE. Gunboat. No details known, but reported to be an old Cross-Channel Steamer purchased into the Navy during War.

For Torpedoes :—

Battleship **PATRIE** and Armoured Cruiser **VICTOR HUGO,** both described on preceding pages. Also 6 Torpedo Craft, names unknown.

For W/T. Experiments :—

For Experiments with Aircraft and K. B. :—

For Mining Experiments :—

For Hydrophone Experiments :—

5 Submarines and Torpedo Boats. Names not known.

For Training Personnel for Submarines :—

Some old Submarines may be retained for this service. Names not yet known.

For Engineers :—

For Cadets :—

Cruiser **JEANNE D'ARC** used for this Duty up to 1914. She has reverted to same service now. Is described on an earlier page.

MOROCCO.

(French Protectorate.)

SIDI-EL-TURKI.

SIDI-EL-TURKI (1898). 450 tons. 154 × 23 × 13 feet. Guns : 2—12 pdr. *Maximum* speed : 12.5 kts.

1 funnel, 3 masts.

EL HASSANEH (1882). 1164 tons. 240¾ × 34 × feet. Guns : 1 old 6 inch, 4 machine. *Nominal* speed : 10 kts. Coal : 100 tons.

NOOR-EL-BAHR (1898) and two Coastguard Ships, built in Germany about 1906, also reported to exist.

ITALIAN NAVY.

ADDENDA AND CORRECTIONS.

MERCANTILE MARINE.—Lloyds' Return, 1919, states total of Sea-going Steamships as 1,238,000 tons gross.

PRIVATE SHIPBUILDING YARDS.—A new Yard has been established by Messrs. Gio Ansaldo & C., at Cotrona, Calabria.

Austrian Dreadnought, **TEGETTHOF,** reported to be refitting for service in the Italian Navy.

Dreadnought, **LEONARDO DA VINCI,** re-floated 18th August, 1919.

Old Battleship, **SARDEGNA,** is now only a Floating Workshop.

Old Cruiser, **FRANCESCO FERRUCCIO,** is now Cadets' Training Ship.

Light Cruisers, **SAIDA** and **ADMIRAL SPAUN,** of late Austrian Navy, reported to be refitting for service in the Italian Navy.

Colonial Cruiser, **BASILICATA,** sunk by explosion, in Red Sea or Suez Canal, 1919.

Destroyers, *Csepel* and *Tatra,* of the late Austrian Navy, may be taken over for the Italian Navy.

Following German Submarines taken over by Italy, subject to the provision that the boats are only used for experiments and broken up. They are not to be added to the Italian Navy :—

4 Ocean Going : *U 163, U 120, U 114, U 54.*
3 Smaller Ocean Going : *UB 102, UB 95, UB 80.*
3 Mine-Layers : *UC 98, UC 94, UC 93.*
Austrian Submarines interned at Venice are : *XL, XXVIII, XXI, V.* Details given in Austrian Navy Section. Not certain if these boats will be added to Italian Navy or not.

"MOBILE BATTERIES."

Three further ships completed are : **MONTE SANTO, PASUBIO, SABOTINO.** Not certain if these are the three "Mobile Batteries" listed on a later page as building or completing, or if they are extra vessels.

The 12 "Convoy Gunboats" listed as building are Ford "Eagle Boats" building in the United States. For numbers and full details, *v.* United States Navy Section.

Motor Ship, **ALULA,** is Depôt Ship in the Red Sea. No details known of this ship.

Another Ocean-going Tug is **TREMITI.** No details of this ship received.

(ROYAL) ITALIAN NAVY.

Revised 1919, from Official List, "Regia Marina Italiana, Maggio 1919," and other information furnished by courtesy of H.E. The Minister of Marine.

Correction to above Map: *delete* AUSTRIA.

Principal Mercantile Ports.

Genoa (*Genova*), Naples (*Napoli*), Leghorn (*Livorno*), Palermo, Venice (*Venezia*), Catania (Sicily).

Private Docks.

GENOA : Three graving docks, Bacino di Darsena, $267\frac{1}{4} \times 78\frac{3}{4} \times 22$ feet ; No. 1, $571 \times 81\frac{3}{4} \times 30\frac{1}{2}$ feet ; No. 2, $702 \times 60\frac{1}{3} \times 28$ feet. Floating dock, $257 \times 46 \times 17$ feet, 2900 tons lift.
LEGHORN ; Orlando Bros., $451 \times 71\frac{3}{4} \times 23$ feet. 2 patent slips for 1500 tons.
NAPLES : Municipal No 1, $659\frac{1}{2} \times 95 \times 33\frac{1}{2}$; No. 2, $348\frac{2}{3} \times 60 \times 23$ feet.
PALERMO (Sicily) : Dock, $565 \times 85\frac{3}{4} \times 27\frac{3}{4}$ feet. Patent slip, 1500 tons.

Colonies : Eritrea, Italian Somaliland, Tripoli and Cyrenaica (Libia Italiana).
Minister of Marine : Contr' Ammiraglio Sachi (June, 1919).
Personnel : About 40,000 *active* personnel *before war.*

Mercantile Marine (*1916*).

684 steamers of 1,035,815 tons *net.*
517 sea-going sailing ships of 210,814 tons *net.*

Coinage.

Lira (100 centesimi) = 10*d.* British, about 20 cents. U.S.A. Value varies.

327

TARANTO.

SPEZIA.

TARANTO.

NAPLES.

TABLE OF DISTANCES.

MADDALENA		
to		knots.
Ajaccio	...	60
Bonafacio	...	20
Naples	...	210

SPEZIA		
to		knots.
Ajaccio	...	160
Bizerta	...	430
Genoa	...	50
Leghorn	...	40
Maddalena	...	175
Malta	...	580
Naples	...	290
Taranto	...	630
Toulon	...	195
Venice	...	1000

NAPLES		
to		knots.
Ajaccio	...	265
Bizerta	...	315
Bonafacio	...	225
Maddalena	...	210

TARANTO			VENICE		
to		knots.	to		knots.
Bizerta	...	550	Pola	...	75
Malta	...	310	*Taranto*	...	575
Messina	...	220	Toulon	...	1197
Naples	...	380			
Venice	...	575			

TRIESTE to

		MILES.			MILES.
Brindisi	... ...	372	*Pola*	... ...	61
Cattaro	... ...	337	Smyrna*	...	902
Constantinople*	...	1050	„ †	...	1000
„ †	...	1152	Salonika*	...	950
Corfu	... ...	480	„ †	...	1049
Fiume	... ...	110	Toulon	...	1169
Gibraltar	...	1648	Wilhelmshaven§	...	3207
Malta	... ...	730	„ ‡	...	3744
Piraeus*	...	708	Zeebrugge§	...	3050
„ †	...	839	„ ‡	...	3756

* By Canal of Corinth.
†By Cape Matapan.
§ By English Channel.
‡ By North of Scotland and West of Ireland.

Royal Dockyards.

SPEZIA.   Docks : No. 5, $702 \times 105\frac{1}{2} \times 33$ feet ; No. 6, $508 \times 90 \times 33$ feet ; No. 4, $354\frac{1}{4} \times 71\frac{1}{2} \times 29$ feet ; Nos. 3 and 2, $430 \times 77 \times 30$ feet ; No. 1, $358 \times 71 \times 30$ feet. Two large slips. (At Muggiano, there is a special testing dock for submarines belonging to Fiat-San-Giorgio Co.)   Total employees about 5300. Admiralty Chart No. 155.

NAPLES (NAPOLI).   One small Government dock, $247 \times 62 \times 19\frac{1}{2}$ feet.   New large dock, *projected*, 1918.   One small slip.   Total employees 3029.   Good anchorage.   Commercial harbour and various new harbour works *projected*.   There are two municipal docks (*v.* preceding page).   Admiralty Chart No. 1728.

CASTELLAMARE.   No docks.   Building yard.   Two large slips, two small.   Total employees 1920.

TARANTO.   One dock, "Principe do Napoli," $709 \times 108 \times 32\frac{1}{2}$ feet (2 sections).   Floating dock, $365 \times 61 \times 25$ feet (4800 tons), and another smaller (2900 tons).   One large slip.   Total employees 1561.   Admiralty Chart No. 1643.   Two 130 ton old Krupps are mounted in a turret on San Pietro.

MADDALENA (Sardinia).   No docks.   Total employees 113.   **MESSINA** (Sicily) : Government Dock $343 \times 71\frac{1}{3} \times 26$ feet.

Torpedo Craft, Submarine and Naval Aircraft Stations : Spezia, Naples, Taranto.   Also minor Naval Stations at Genoa, Maddalena, Gaeta, Messina.

Arsenals.

Royal Dockyards.

VENICE (VENEZIA). One dock, No. 4, $656 \times 106 \times 38\frac{1}{2}$ feet; one dock for long cruisers, No. 1, $525 \times 78 \times 25\frac{1}{2}$ feet; one small dock No. 2, for third-class cruisers, $295 \times 59 \times 19\frac{1}{2}$ feet. Two large slips, one small slip. Submarines built in this yard. Employees 2797. Depth of Port Lido, 29 feet. Malamocco, 28 feet at low water. Commercial harbours at both. Admiralty Chart No. 1483.

TRIESTE. No Government docks. One slip. Two Private docks here, $456 \times 73 \times 19$ feet and $360 \times 54 \times 18\frac{3}{4}$ feet; there is a dock at San Rocco, across the bay, $414 \times 66 \times 21$ feet. Two floating of 2,000 and 1,500 tons. Admiralty Chart No. 1434. Rise of Spring Tide, 2 feet.

POLA (Late Austro-Hungarian Naval Base). Heavily fortified. Slips: One 690 feet long and two smaller. Two dry docks: (a) $467 \times 85 \times 27\frac{3}{4}$ feet and (b) $397 \times 86 \times 31\frac{1}{2}$ feet. Floating docks: (c) $585 \times 111 \times 37$ feet (22,500 tons); (d) $459\frac{1}{2} \times 90 \times 32\frac{1}{4}$ feet (15,000 tons); (e) $300 \times 82\frac{1}{2} \times 20$ feet; (f) small, only used for torpedo craft, 1,000 tons lift, completed June, 1914. Employés 4500. 3 slips. Naval hospital. Admiralty Chart No. 202. Rise of Spring Tide, $3\frac{1}{2}$ feet.

Torpedo Craft, Submarine & Naval Aircraft Stations: Venice, Brindisi. Also minor Naval Station at Ancona.

(For BRINDISI, see next page).

BRINDISI. No docks known to exist Admiralty Chart No. 1492.

VALONA. Fleet Anchorage used by Italian Navy. Admiralty Chart No. 1589.

Charts to Uniform Scale, divided into 2,000-yard squares.   Soundings in fathoms.   Heights in feet.

VALONA.

Uniforms.

(*Note.*—A five pointed silver star is worn on lapel of coat.)

INSIGNIA OF RANK ON SLEEVES.   *NOTE.*—STAFF OFFICERS HAVE NO CURL.

Ammiraglio	Vice-Ammiraglio.	Contr'-Ammiraglio.	*Capitano di Vascello.	Capitano di Fregata.	Capitano di Corvetta.	Tenente di Vascello.	Sottotentete di Vascello.	Guardia-marina.
Admiral.	*V.-Admiral.*	*R.-Admiral.*	*Captain (senior).*	*Captain (junior).*	*Commander.*	*Lieut.*	*Sub-Lieut.*	*Midshipman.*

(*) Sotto-Ammiraglio: New rank reported introduced, equivalent to British Commodore, and intermediate between Contr' Ammiraglio and Capitano di Vascello.

Lesser rank Allievo di marina (*Naval Cadet*).

Note.—Primo tenento has a gold band on shoulder strap for 12 years seniority. All lieutenants have stars on their shoulder straps corresponding to their stripes.

Other branches: Ingegnere (*Constructor*), Macchinista (*Engineer*), Medico (*Doctor*), Commissario (*Paymaster*)—with relative rank with the executives, without curl.

Colours: *Constructors,* dark purple; *Engineers,* black; *Doctors,* blue; *Paymasters,* red.

Note.—All officers under arms on duty wear a blue sash over right shoulder, ending in a blue knot at left hip; worn with belt. Officers on staff duty wear it on opposite shoulder, and without belt. Undress tunic has insignia of rank on shoulder straps, with stars as stripes. Senior lieutenants wear a piece of gold under the stars of shoulder strap.

OFFICIAL TABLE OF NAVAL ORDNANCE.

Official Designation:— Calibre mm/length cal.	381/40	305/46	305/40	254/45	254/45	254/40	203/45	190/45	152/50	152/45	152/40	120/50	120/45	102/45	102/35	76/50	76/45	76/17
Mark A = Armstrong, V = Vickers S =	A. V. e S.	A. e V.	A.	A.	V.	A.	A.	A. e V.	A.	S.	A.	A. e V.	A.	S.–A.	S.	A. e V.	S.	S.
Date of introduction.	1914	1909	1900-04	1907	1906	1899-93	1897	1908-1906	1918-1913	1911	1899-1916	1909	1913-18	1917	1914-15	1909	1911	1912
Designation by Calibre, c/m.	38.1	30.479	30.479	25.4	25.4	25.4	20.32	19.05	15.24	15.24	15.24	12	12	10.2	10.2	7.62	7.62	7.62
Calibre, in inches	15	12	12	10	10	10	8	7.5	6	6	6	4.75	4.75	4	4	3	3	3
Lengths — Total, in feet	51.67	47.77	41.707	39.07	38.715	34.699	31.126	29.22	25.94	23.42	20.77	20.38	18.38	15.715	12.247	13.271	11.722	4.593
Lengths — Rifled Bore, in inches	511.7	477.9	383.42	358.4	370.5	341.1	308.9	281.7	256.6	21.92	199.8	204.64	174.64	150.74	114.29	126	107.2	44.88
Lengths — Powder Chamber, in inches	81.5	97.7	92.12	74.91	74.91	55.19	47.4	51.65	44.6	44.6	37.7	28.64	35.03	27.16	23.50	22	25.4	—
Lengths — Bore, in calibres	34.11	37.3	31.95	35.84	37.05	34.11	38.61	37.5	42.77	36.54	33.31	43.31	36.96	37.53	28.46	42	35.73	14.96
No. of Grooves	120	72	48	60	70	42	32	44	36	56	28	36	36	40	32	28	2⅝	24
Twist of Rifling, in calibres	44.927	30	00–600 600–30	30	00–30	30	00–30	00–30	33	36	30	30	30	—	—	30	35.9	22
Total Weight, in tons	83.56	62.99	51.77	34.49	35.339	30.511	19.586	14.478	8.100	7.025	6.503	3.662	4—035	2.327	1.200	1.122	0.698	0.104
Firing Charge — Armour-piercing projectile, lb	—	346	194	185	185	90.38	51.807	70.987	—	—	18.077	—	—	—	—	—	—	—
Firing Charge — Common Shell H.E., lb.	326.27	279.9	194	185	185	90.38	51.807	70.987	32.79	30.64	18.077	14.66	9.589	9.479	6.50	3.02	3.571	0.529
Weight — Armour-piercing projectile, lb.	—	997.2	942.7	494	494	494	269	200.39	—	— —	107.07	—	—	—	—	—	—	—
Weight — Shell H.E., lb.	1929	884.4	881.74	489.8	489.8	189.8	256.23	498.5	110.22	103.61	102.38	48.74	48.74	30.31	30.31	14.05	14.05	11.68
Weight — Shrapnel, lb.												55.33	55.33	33.28	33.28	15.08	15.08	11.68
Bursting Charge — Armour-piercing projectile, lb.	—	16.63	9.79	4.37	4.37	4.37	2.003	2.332			1.014							
Bursting Charge — Shell H.E., lb.	84.85	53.13	53.13	29.86	29.86	29.86	14.704	11.706	5.996	7.528	6.90	2.711	2.711	2.866	2.866	1.102	1.102	0.782
Bursting Charge — Shrapnel, lbs.												0.65	0.65	0.474	0.474	0.236	0.236	0.165
Muzzle Velocity, in ft. secs.	2296.6	2755.9	2346.8	2788.77	2788.77	2411.46	2.559	2788.77	2854	2723	2280	2788	2460	2788	2460	2460	2460	1230
Muzzle Energy —Total tons per sq. inch	20	18.63	15.75	17.71	17.71	15.09	16	17.98	18.37	16.86	13.73	18.37	15.75	18.37	18.37	18.37	15.75	12.47

15″ 40 cal. in *Caracciolo* and *Faa' di Bruno*.
12″ 46 „ *Duilio* class (2 ships), *G. Cesare* class (2 ships), and *D. Alighieri*.
12″ 40 „ *V. Emanuele class* (4 ships).
10″ 45 „ *S. Marco* class (2 ships) and *Pisa*.
10″ 40 „ *A. di St. Bon* class (2).
8″ 45 „ *V. Emanuele* class (4 ships).
7.5″ 45 „ *San Marco* class (2), and *Pisa*.
6″ 50 „ *Caracciolo*, *Duilio* class (2 ships).
4.7″ 50 „ *Dante Alighieri*, *Marsala* class (2), *Quarto*, and *Libia*.

Note.—Above list of guns mounted in various classes is unofficial. 12 inch and 7.5 inch guns of unknown types reported to be mounted in " Mobile Batteries."

Torpedoes, Mines, D.C., Air Bombs, &c.

No reliable details available. Torpedoes manufactured by State Arsenals and Whitehead & C., Societa Italiana, Naples.

Colour of Ships.

Battleships, Cruisers, Light Cruisers, Destroyers, are all very light grey. Destroyers have identity letters, taken from their names, painted on bows, *e.g.*, AC = *G. Acerbi*, AU = *Audace*, BR = *P. Bronzetti*, IV = *Impavido*, PL = *R. Pilo*, OR = *V. Orsini*, MT = *A. Mosto*, etc.

Official Classification of Ships. (C)=for Colonial Service.

" Navi di Battaglio."

1st Class.
(*Caracciolo*
| A. Doria
| C. Duilio
| C. di Cavour
| G. Cesare
(Dante Alighieri

2nd Class.
| V. Emanuele
| R. Elena
| Roma
| Napoli
| San Giorgio
| San Marco
(Pisa

3rd Class.
| A. di St. Bon
| E. Filiberto
(Dandolo

Esploratori .—

N. Bixio
Marsala
Quarto
Leone
Tigre
Pantera
Lince
Aquila
Nibbio
Falco
Sparviero
C. Mirabello
C. A. Racchia
A. Riboty
A. Poerio
G. Pepe
Agordat
Coatit

" Navi Sussidiarie."

1st Class.
(Sardegna
| Sicilia
| Re Umberto
| Zenson
| Cortellazzo
| Bronte
| Trinacria
| Eritrea
(Europa

2nd Class.
(Campania (C)
| Basilicata (C)
| Libia
| Etruria (C)
| Lombardia (C)
| Piemonte (C)
| Etna
| Vulcano
| G. Bausan
| Bengasi
| F. Gioia
(A. Vespucci

3rd Class.
(Faa' di Bruno
| A. Magnaghi
| Acheronte
| Flegetonte
| Cocito
| Lete
| Stige
| Eridano
(Anteo

4th Class.
S. Caboto (C)
E. Carlotto (C)
Goito
Tripoli
Minerva
Iride
Montebello
Archimede
Guiliana
Cunfida
Misurata
Tobruk
C. Verri
Ciclope
Atalante
Ercole]
Tevere
Gariglíano
Verde
Pagano
Miseno
Palinuro

Note.—Destroyers, " Sea-Going Torpedo Boats," Coastal T.B. and Submarines are as listed on subsequent Ship Pages. Above Table merely shows how Official Classification departs from order of Classification adopted for " Fighting Ships." On Ship Pages, tonnages and fuel capacities are stated in *metric* tons.

ITALIAN DOCKYARDS.

Private Yards.

(All undertake Naval Construction).

GIO. ANSALDO & C. (GENOA & SESTRI PONENTE, also at CORNIGLIANO & SAMPIERDARENA, &c., consists of 28 establishments in various parts of Italy.) Build, engine, and completely equip warships and mercantile vessels of all types. Slips: 3 large and 8 smaller at Sestri Ponente, also three slips at Genoa Harbour, also other slips at Cantiere Savoia, Corrigliano. Area of works: hectares. Number of Employees, 60,000. (Also see ANSALDO-SAN GIORGIO Co.)

FRATELLI ORLANDO & C. (LEGHORN). Build and engine warships and mercantile vessels of all types. Are affiliated to Acciaierie di Terni (Armour Plate and Shell Foundry) and Vickers-Terni (Ordnance Works). No. of slips: Docks, one, 451 feet (o.a.) × 71¾ feet × 23 feet. Area of works: hectares. Number of employees: .

ODERO & C. (SESTRI PONENTE, near Genoa). Build and engine warships of all classes. No. of slips: Area of works: . Number of employees: . (Build battleships at Foce, near Genoa). (Above are the three greatest Italian warship-building firms).

ANSALDO-SAN GIORGIO, LTD. (MUGGIANO, SPEZIA). Build warships and mercantile vessels. Specialise in construction of Laurenti type submersibles and Diesel engines.

C. & T. T. PATTISON (NAPLES). Build destroyers, torpedo boats, mine sweepers, &c., also boilers, turbines, &c.

CANTIERE NAVALE FRANCO TOSI (LEGHORN & TARANTO). Build destroyers, torpedo boats, submarines and mine layers or sweepers. Also boilers, turbines ("Tosi" type), and Diesel engines.

CANTIERE NAVALE RIUNITI (SPEZIA & PALERMO). Build torpedo craft and submarines.

OFFICINE MECCANICHE (MILAN & NAPLES). Build Belluzo turbines and other machinery.

OFFICINE INSUBRI (MILAN). Construct large Diesel engines for naval purposes.

S. A. V. I. N. E. M. (Società Anonima Veneziana Industrie Navale e Meccaniche), GIUDECA, Venice. Build boilers, machinery, &c.

Scale : 1 inch = 160 feet.   ITALIAN WARSHIPS : RECOGNITION SILHOUETTES.

ONE FUNNEL.

FAA' DI BRUNO. *(Monitor.)*

ANTEO. *(Salvage Ship.)*

ACHERONTE *class* (5).

TEVERE.

CICLOPE.

ATLANTE.

BASILICATA *class* (2).

VULCANO. *(Repair Ship).*

BRONTE.

MISENO and PALINURO. *(Training Ships).*

CALABRIA.

GARIGLIANO.

A. VESPUCCI and F. GIOIA. *(Training Ships).*

TWO FUNNELS.

AGORDAT *class* (2 ships).
(*May be Mine Layers.*)

EUROPA.
(*Aircraft Carriers & S/M Depot. Wind screens forming
sides to hangers may be furled back.*)

ZENSON.

RE UMBERTO.
(*Two funnels abreast, forward.*)

ST. BON, E. FILIBERTO.*
*Has no lower top on mast.

VARESE *class* (2 ships).

SARDEGNA *class* (3 ships).
Note.—*Two funnels forward closely paired. (Funnels half cased)*

CORTELLAZZO.

PIEMONTE.

LIGURIA.
(**Mine Layer.** *May have screens
rigged along quarter deck*).

ELBA.

TRIPOLI.

GOITO.

MINERVA & IRIDE.

ETNA.
(*Training Ship*).

LOMBARDIA,* ETRURIA & PUGLIA.†
*Has heavy circular top half way up masts,
† Mine Layer.

GIOVANNI BAUSAN.
(*Distilling Ship.*)

Torpedo Gunboats, now Mine Layers.

TWO FUNNELS.—*(Continued.)*

Dandolo (*Harbour Service*).

TRINACRIA (*Royal Yacht*).

BENGASI (*Transport*).

A. DORIA.
C. DUILIO.

C. DI CAVOUR.
G. CESARE.
(*No longer have searchlights before and abaft funnels.*)

THREE FUNNELS.

MONTEBELLO.
(*Training Ship.*)

QUARTO.

LIBIA.

PISA.

NAPOLI.
ROMA.

V. EMANUELE.
R. ELENA.

FOUR FUNNELS.

MARSALA.
N. BIXIO.

SAN GIORGIO.
SAN MARCO.

D. ALIGHIERI.

TORPEDO CRAFT.   Scale : 1 inch = 160 feet.

O.L.T. 74, 75, (t.b.)

SAFFO class t.b. (4)

68S—134S t.b. (7)

PN, OS, AS, RM, OL, t.b. (42)

ANIMOSO t.b.d.

AUDACE t.b.d.

PALESTRO class t.b.d. (8)

POERIO class t.b.d. (2)

C. MIRABELLO class t.b.d. (3)
("C. A. Racchia" has short mainmast.)

F. RISMONDO t.b.

"Later C" t.b. (2)

"Earlier C" t.b. (6)

"A" class t.b. (6)

"O" class t.b. (4)

"P" class t.b. (3)

GABBIANO t.b.

CONDORE and
PELLICANO t.b.

LAMPO class t.b.d. (5)

(1)

(2)

CARABINIERE class t.b.d. (5)
ARTIGLIERE class t.b.d. (5)
ZEFFIRO class t.b.d. (3)

FULMINE t.b.d.

INDOMITO class t.b.d. (4)
ARDENTE class t.b.d. (2)

G. C. ABBA class t.b.d. (8)

SIRTORI class t.b.d. (11)

AQUILA class t.b.d. (4)

Scale : 1 inch = 80 feet.

DELFINO.

NAUTILUS.

H 1—8 (7).

SQUALO class (5)*

VELELLA class (6)*

G. FERRARIS,*
G. PULLINO.*

X 2, X 3.
(Mine Layers.)

ARGONAUTA.*

F 1—21 class (21).

FOCA.*

N 5, N 6.

ATROPO.*

X 1.

W 3.*

W 1.*

W 2.*

N 1—4 class (4).

A. BARBARIGO class (4).

G. PACINOTTI.

P. MICCA class (6).

* These boats may be
    (a) Out of commission or for training duties ;
    (b) Awaiting disposal ;
    (c) Under survey for sale ;
    (d) Condemned for sale.

(DUILIO CLASS— 2 SHIPS).

CAIO DUILIO (April, 1913) and **ANDREA DORIA** (March, 1913).

Normal displacement, 24,500 tons.   Complement, 1074.

Length (*p.p.*) 554·3 feet.   Beam, 91·8 feet.   *Mean* draught, 30·7 feet.   Length *over all*, 575 feet, 9ins.

Guns (Armstrong or Vickers) :
13—12 in., 46 cal. (A⁵).
16—6 inch (50 cal.)
13—14 pdr.*
6—14 pdr. (A.A.)
2 M.G.
4 landing.
Torpedo tubes (18 inch) :
2 broadside (*submerged*).
1 stern (*submerged*).
*3—14 pdr. temporarily removed during war.

Armour (Terni) :
9¾″-8″ Belt (amidships) {
5″ Belt (ends)..............
1¾″ and 1⅔″ Decks
6¾″ Lower deck side ......
9½″ Barbettes ....}
11 Turrets to these ...}
6¾″ Battery.................
11″ Conning tower (fore) .
6¾″ Conning tower (aft) .

Ahead :
5—12 in.
4—6 in.

Astern :
5—12 in.
4—6 in.

Broadside : 13—12 in., 8—6 in.

Machinery : Parsons turbine.   4 screws.   Boilers : 20 Yarrow.   Designed S.   H.P. 24,000 = 22 kts., but actually need 33,000–35,000 S.H.P. for this speed.   Coal : *normal* 1000 tons ; *maximum* 1200 tons and 800 tons oil fuel = about 4000 miles at 10 kts. and 2600 miles at 19 kts.

†*Gunnery Notes* :   ⎰ As *C. di Cavour* class on next page.   Range-finders mounted to the rear of roof of each barbette
†*Torpedo Notes* :   ⎱ shield in armoured hoods and over each C.T.   3 inch (14 pdrs.) are 50 cal. Armstrong or 60 cal. Vickers.   8 searchlights.   †All details unofficial.

Name	Builder	Machinery	Laid down	Completed	Trials H.P.=kts.	Boilers	Best recent speed
Caio Duilio	Castellamare D.Y.	Ansaldo	Apr.'12	1915	35,000 = 22.	Yarrow	
Andrea Doria	Spezia	Ansaldo	Mar.'12	May '15	32,000 = 21.5.	Yarrow	

General Notes.—Are improved type of *C. di Cavour* design, 16—6 inch being substituted for 18—4·7 inch.   Otherwise—and excepting altered appearance—there is very little difference between the classes.   Designed by Engineer—Gen. Masdea.   These ships exceed their designed displacement of 22.500 tons in the same manner as *Cavour* and *Cesare* and require to develop 10,000 S.H.P. in excess of designed S.H.P., to reach their designed speed.

337

ANDREA DORIA.

Note.

To distinguish from *C. di Cavour* class, note that *both* tripod masts are before funnels.   Funnels are also *equal* in height.   Amidships triple barbette is on same level as *quarter-deck* triple—compare *Cavour* class where it is on level with forecastle triple.   General appearance much lighter than *Cavours*.

CAIO DUILIO.   Has had a circular F.C. or R.F. top added to fore tripod mast.   In summer of 1918 had no fore topmast.

Y

(G. Cesare Class—2 Ships).

CONTE DI CAVOUR (Aug., 1911), **GIULIO CESARE** (Oct., 1911).

Normal displacement, 24,500 tons). Complement, 1074.

Length (p.p.) 554·3 feet. Beam, 91·8 feet. *Mean* draught, 30·7 feet. Length *over all*, 557 feet 9 inches.

Guns (Elswick) :
13—12 in.,46 cal.
18—4·7 inch, 50 cal.
12—14 pdr., 50 cal.*
6—14 pdr. AA.
2 machine.
4 landing.
Torpedo tubes (18 inch) :
2 broadside (*submerged*)
1 stern (*submerged*)

* 3—14 pdr. temporarily removed during war.

Armour (see *Notes*) :
9¾″–8″ Belt (amidships)
5″ Belt (ends)...............
1¾″ & 1⅔″ Decks ....
6¾″ Lower deck redoubt
9½″ Barbettes ....
11″ Turrets to these......
5″ Battery ....
11″ Conning tower (fore)...
6¾″ Conning tower (aft) ...

Ahead :
5—12 in.
8—4·7 in.

Astern :
5—12 in.
6—4·7in.

Broadside : 13—12in., 9—4·7 in.

Machinery : Parsons turbine. 4 screws. Boilers : various, see *Notes*. Designed S.H.P. 24,000 = 22 knots, but actually require 32,000 to 32,500 S.H.P. for this speed. Coal : *normal* 1000 tons ; *maximum*, in *C. di Cavour* 1300 tons coal + 930 tons *oil* ; in *G. Cesare* 1450 tons coal + 850 tons *oil*. Endurance : about 4540 miles at 10 kts., and 2900 miles at 19 kts. :

Gunnery Notes.—Arcs of fire : End triples 300°, super-firing twin barbettes 310°, amidships triple 130° each beam. 14 pdr. can be transferred to different mountings in various positions in these ships. These notes are unofficial.

Armour Notes.—*C. di C.*, Terni ; *G.C.*, Bethlehem.

Torpedo Notes.—Bullivant net defence to both.

Name	Builder	Machinery	Laid down	Completed	Trials Full Power.		Boilers	Best recent speed
					H.P.	kts.		
C. di Cavour	Spezia D.Y.	Orlando	Aug.,'10	Jan. '15	32,500 =	22	20 Yarrow	
G. Cesare	Ansaldo	Ansaldo	Jun. '10	Mar. '14	30,740 =	21·7	24 Babcock	

General Notes.—Designed by Engineer Gen. Masdea. Were designed to displace 22,500 tons at 27¾ feet *mean* draught. Alterations during construction added 2000 tons to displacement and 3 feet to *mean* draught. They can only reach their designed speed with difficulty.

CONTE DI CAVOUR.   Note double " starfish " on each mast ; 2 bridges on legs of fore and main tripod masts. Funnels almost equal in height.

GIULIO CESARE   Note figurehead, square bridge round fore C. T., small box top on foremast. Fore funnel noticeably higher than after funnel.

Note.

A third ship of this class, **LEONARDO DA VINCI,** was sunk by explosion at Taranto in August, 1916. Contradictory reports say (*a*) she was refloated August, 1919 ; (*b*) salvage work has been abandoned.

DANTE ALIGHIERI (August, 1910).*

Normal displacement, 20,500 tons.   Complement, 991.

Length (*p.p.*) 519·7 feet.   Beam, 87·4 feet.   *Mean* draught, 30·1 feet.   Length *over all*, 549·5 feet.

* Official Italian List gives 20 Oct., 1910, as launching date.

Guns (Elswick) :
12—12 in., 46 cal. (A⁵)
20—4·7 inch, 50 cal.
12—14 pdr., 50 cal.*
6—14 pdr.. AA.
2 M.G.
4 landing.
Torpedo tubes (18 inch.) :
 2 broadside (*submerged*).
 1 stern (*submerged*).
* 3—14 pdr. temporarily removed
   during war.

Armour (Terni) :
9⅞″ Belt (amidships) ▪▪▪▪▪
6″ Belt (forward) ......
4¾″ Belt (aft) ......
1¾″ & 1⅝″ Decks ......
8¾″ Lower deck redoubt
9″ Barbettes ....
11″ Turrets to these = ▪▪▪▪▪
4″ Secondary Turrets
      (4)
4″ Batteries ....
11″ Conning tower...... ▪▪▪▪▪
8″ C.T. (aft) ....

Ahead :
3—12 in.
4—4·7 in.

DANTE ALIGHERI.

Astern :
3—12 in.
4—4·7 in.

Broadside : 12—12 in.
10—4·7 in.

Machinery : Parsons turbine. 4 screws. Boilers : 23 Blechynden. Designed S.H.P. 24,000＝23 kts,
but actually requires about 31,000 H.P. for this speed.   Coal: *normal* 1000 tons ; *maximum* 2200 tons,
+ 300 tons oil fuel＝4520 miles at 10 kts. and about 3000 miles at 19 kts.

°*Gunnery Notes.*—Triple turrets are to Armstrong design, hydraulic power with special Ansaldo electric gear as reserve,
4·7 inch reported to have been fitted with improved breech mechanism in 1913-14 to give faster rate of fire.

* Not from any official source.

Name	Builder	Machinery	Laid down	Completed	Trials H.P = kts.	Boilers.	Best recent speed
D. Alighieri	Castellamare	Ansaldo	June 09	Sep. '12	31,980＝23·8	Blechynden	

General Notes.—Designed by Engineer-Gen. Masdea. Was originally designed for 19,500 tons displacement, with a
draught of 28½ feet *mean*, but alterations made during construction resulted in an addition of 1000 tons to displacement and about 2¼ feet to draught. Consequently, she only attains her designed speed with difficulty. Triple
steering gear, steam, special Ansaldo electric gear and manual power.

Detail view of amidships triple barbette.

Photo by courtesy of " Daily Mirror"

1914 ITALIAN BATTLE CRUISER (27 knots).

CARACCIOLO (building).

Normal displacement, 30,900 tons. Complement,

Length (*p.p.*), 661·4 feet.   Beam, 97·1   *Mean* draught, 30·4 feet.   Length *over all*, 691 feet.

Guns :
   8—15 inch, 40 cal.
  14—6 inch, 50 cal.
   8—4 inch, 45 cal.
  16—2 pdr. (AA.)
Torpedo tubes :
   (not known).

Armour :
  11·8″ Belt (amidships)
      Belt (ends) ....
    $4\frac{1}{3}$″ Deck ....
      Side above belt ......
  15·7″ Barbettes ....
      Turrets ....
      Battery.................
      Conning Tower ......
      Funnel bases ....
  (May have bulge protection).

Building.

No plans available.

15 inch guns arranged as in British " Queen Elizabeth " class, viz., four barbettes on centre line, the inner positions super-firing over extreme positions.

Machinery : 4—shaft Parsons turbine. 2 or 4 screws. Boilers : 20 Yarrow (⎯ —tube mixed coal and oil burning). Designed S.H.P. 105,000=27 kts. Coal : *normal*   tons ; *maximum* 2000 tons+2000 tons *oil.*

Notes.

Under the 1914 Naval Programme, four Super-Dreadnoughts were projected. These were *Caracciolo, Cristoforo Colombo, Marcantonio Colonna and Francisco Morosini.* They were begun as follows :—

Name.	Builder.	Begun.
Caracciolo,	(see Table opposite).	
C. Colombo,	Ansaldo, Genoa.	14 March, 1915.
M. Colonna,	Odero, Genoa.	3 March, 1915.
F. Morosini,	Orlando, Leghorn.	27 June, 1915.

Work on all four ships ceased during the War. During summer of 1918, hull of *C. Colombo* was dismantled ; *M. Calonna* and *F. Morosini* were cancelled at the end of 1918 and have been dismantled too. *Caracciolo* is proceeding slowly and will be finished as a battle-cruiser. During the War, design was revised, and among other alterations, the following changes were made : (*a*) 6 inch guns reduced by two, 8—4 inch and 16—2 pdr. AA. substituted for 20 —14 pdr., (*b*) belt reduced to 11·8″ and protective deck increased to $4\frac{1}{3}$″. (*c*) H.P. raised from 70,000 to 105,000 and speed increased from 25 to 27 kts. Designed by Engineer-Gen. Ferrati. All figures given are official.

Name	Builder	Mchinery	Laid down	Com-pleted	Trials	Boilers	Best recent speed
A. *Caracciolo.*	Castellamare D.Y.		Oct. '14				

(V. EMANUELE CLASS—4 SHIPS.)

VITTORIO EMANUELE (Oct., 1904), **REGINA ELENA** (June, 1904), **NAPOLI** (Sept., 1905), **ROMA** (April, 1907).

Displacement, 12660 tons.   Complement, 743.

Length (*p.p.*), 435 feet.   Beam, 73⅓ feet. $\begin{cases} Maximum \text{ draught, } 27\frac{2}{3} \text{ feet.} \\ Mean \quad\quad ,, \quad 25\frac{3}{4} \text{ ,,} \end{cases}$ Length *over all*, 475 feet 5″.

Guns :
  2—12 inch, 40 cal.
  12—8 inch, 45 cal.
  16—14 pdr., 40 cal.
  4—14 pdr., A.A.
  2—3 pdr.
  2 Maxims.
  2 landing.
Torpedo tubes (18 in.) :
  2 *submerged* (broadside).

Armour (Terni) :
  9·8″ Belt........................ ■■■■■
  4″ Belt (ends) .... ▭▭▭▭
  2·4″ Deck (reinforcing) ......
  8″ Bulkheads ....
  8″ Barbettes (N.C.) .... ▨▨▨
  8″ Turrets ....
  8″ Lower deck (side) ...... ▨▨▨
  2″ Lower deck (bow) ...... ▨▨▨
  6″ Secondary turrets (6)... ▧▧▧
  3¼″ Tertiary battery .... ▨▨▨
  10″ Conning tower (N.C.) ■■■■■

Ahead :
1—12 in.
8—8 in.

Astern :
1—12 in.
8—8 in.

Broadside : 2—12 in., 6—8 in.

Machinery : 2 sets 4 cylinder vertical inverted triple expansion.   Designed H.P. 19,000 = 21·5 kts. 2 screws.   Boilers : *V. Emanuele* and *R. Elena*, 28 Belleville ; *Napoli*, 22 Babcock & Wilcox, and *Roma*, 18 Babcock & Wilcox.   Coal : *normal* 1000 tons ; *maximum* 2000 tons

Aircraft and Gunnery Notes.—14 pdr. A.A. are mounted singly on crowns of 12-inch turrets and central 8-inch turrets, but *Roma* has no A.A. guns or crown of fore 12-inch turret.   R.F. positions over fore C.T. and behind each central 8-inch turret, 2—14 pdr. on each 8 in. turret, the 14 pdr. battery ports being plated up now.   4 large S.L. in 2 tops on each mast and small S.L. at after end of boat deck.

Name	Builder	Machinery	Laid down	Completed	Last Refit	First Trials: 24 hours	6 hours	Boilers	Best recent speed
V. Emanuele	Castellamare	Orlando	Sept.'01	Sept.'07		16,000=21	19.424=21·5	Belleville	21·9
R. Elena	Spezia	Odero	Sept.'01	May,'07		15,473=20·33	19,298=22·7	Belleville	
Napoli	Castellamare	Hawthorn Gup.	Oct.'03	Nov.'08		15,400=20·3	20,400=22·1	Babcock	
Roma	Spezia	Ansaldo	Sept.'03	Dec.'08		16,000=20·5	21,900=22	Babcock	22

General Notes.—Designed by the late General Cuniberti.   Average cost per ship, £1,000,000. The *Napoli* and *Roma* have less superstructure and are somewhat lighter, but have the same horse power (not fitted as flagships).

V. EMANUELE.   Note crows' nests high on each mast.

Note.

R. ELENA as V. EMANUELE, but differs thus : (*a*) No crows' nests high up on masts. (*b*) Forward. S.L. platforms rather higher up foremast. (*c*) Flying bridge over C.T. as shown on Silhouettes for *V. Emanuele* and *R. Elena*.

ROMA (*Napoli* same appearance).   Note different shape of funnels.   Foremast is *against* fore funnel, and has F.C. top.   "Starfish" low on mainmast.

AMMIRAGLIO DI ST. BON (April, 1897), & **EMANUELE FILIBERTO** (Sept., 1897).
Displacement, 9800 tons. Complement, 541. $344\frac{1}{2}$ (p.p.) $\times 69\frac{1}{4} \times 24\frac{3}{4}$ feet (*max.* draught.) Guns:
4—10 inch, 40 cal., 8—6 inch, 40 cal. (removed temporarily), 8—4·7 inch (removed temporarily)
in *A. di St. Bon*, 4—14 pdr. AA., 8—6 pdr., 2—1 pdr.; in *E.F.* 6—14 pdr., 4—14 pdr., AA.,
2—1 pdr. In both, 1 M.G., 1 landing, and 4—18 inch tubes *above water.* Armour (Harvey
nickel) : $9\frac{3}{4}''$ Belt (amidships), 4″ Belt (ends), 3″ Deck, 6″ Bulkheads, 6″ Lower deck side, 7″
Barbettes, 6″ Hoods to these (fronts), 6″ Battery, 6″ Conning tower. 2 screws. Boilers : 12 cylindrical.
Designed H.P. 13,500 = 18 kts. Coal : 1000 tons.

Re Umberto *after* 1916-17 reconstruction.   (*Photo by courtesy of the Ministry of Marine*).
SICILIA (1891). 13,298 tons. **SARDEGNA** (1890). 13,822 tons. **RE UMBERTO** (1887,
rebuilt 1916-17). 13,251 tons. Complement about 730. Guns (Armstrong): 4—old 13·5 inch (40
cal.), *4—14 pdr. AA. Torpedo tubes : 5 *above water.* Armour (steel) : 4″ Belt with $4\frac{1}{4}''$-2″ Deck
$+ 2\frac{3}{4}''$ Bulkheads, $14\frac{1}{4}''$ Barbettes, $11\frac{3}{4}''$ Conning tower. I.H.P. 15,000 = 20 kts. Boilers : 16-18
cylindrical. Coal : about 1400 tons.   * Removed from *Re Umberto.*   342

SARDEGNA   SICILIA
(Funnels of the *Re Umberto*, as photo.)

Re Umberto before 1916-17 reconstruction.   No photo available of *Sardegna* and *Sicilia* ; they are as
above photo but have half-cased funnels as sketched. For description *v.* preceding column.

DANDOLO (1878) (reconstructed 1897). 12,262 tons. Complement, 281. Guns: 4—10 in., 40 cal.,
7—6 in. (3 of these temporarily removed), 5—4·7 in. (all these temporarily removed), 11—14 pdr.
AA., 16—6 pdr., 2—1pdr. Tubes : 4—18 inch *above water.* Armour (steel) : Belt amidships,
$21\frac{1}{4}''$, Turrets (Harvey), 10″. H.P. 7400 = 15·5 kts. 4 return flame boilers. 2 screws. 720
tons coal.

(San Giorgio Class—2 Ships.)

SAN GIORGIO (July, 1908), SAN MARCO (December, 1908).

Displacement $\begin{cases} San\ Giorgio,\ 10,200\ tons \\ San\ Marco,\ 11,000\ tons \end{cases}$ Complement $\begin{cases} S.G.\ 689 \\ S.M.\ 691 \end{cases}$

Length (p.p.), 429 feet 11 in.   Beam, 69 feet. $\begin{cases} S.G.\ mean\ draught:\ 24\ feet,\ max.\ 26\frac{1}{4}\ feet. \\ S.M.\ mean\ ,,\ 25\frac{1}{2}\ feet,\ max.\ 27\ feet. \end{cases}$
Length over all, $462\frac{1}{4}$ feet.

Guns :
4—10 inch, 45 cal.
8—7·5 inch, 45 cal.
10—14 pdr.
6—14 pdr. AA.
2—3 pdr.
2 machine.
2 landing.
Torpedo tubes (18 inch) :
2 submerged (broadside).
1 submerged (stern).

Note to Plans.

Now rigged with *two* masts.

Armour (S.M., Midvale ; S.G., Terni) :
8″ Belt (amidships) ...
$2\frac{1}{4}$″ Belt (ends)
$1\frac{3}{4}$″ & $1\frac{1}{2}$″ Decks.........
7″ Lower deck redoubt
8″ Main barbettes ...
$5\frac{1}{4}$″ Turrets to these...
7″ Citadel...............
$6\frac{1}{4}$″ Secondary turrets
$9\frac{3}{4}$″ Conning towers (4)

SAN GIORGIO.

Ahead :
3—10 in.
4—7·5 in.

Astern :
2—10 in.
4—7·5 in.

Broadside : 4—10 in., 4—7·5 in.

Machinery : S. Marco, Parsons turbine ; 4 screws. S. Giorgio, 2 sets 4 cylinder inverted triple expansion ; 2 screws. Boilers : various. See *Notes.* Designed H.P., S. Giorgio, 18,000 I.H.P. = 22·5 kts. ; S. Marco, 20,000 S.H.P. = 23 kts. Coal : *normal* 700 tons ; *maximum* 1570 tons. Endurance : at 10 kts., 6270 miles for San Giorgio, 4800 miles for San Marco ; 2640 miles at 20 kts. for San Giorgio, about 2500 miles at $21\frac{1}{4}$ kts. for San Marco.

Gunnery Notes.—All guns electrically controlled. Central pivot mountings. Fore 10 inch, 31 feet above waterline ; after 10 inch, 22 feet ; 8 inch guns 22 feet above water. Armoured fire-control towers between 7·5 inch barbettes. (These details are *not* official).

SAN MARCO.

SAN GIORGIO.

To distinguish between these two ships note the following differences :

SAN GIORGIO.	SAN MARCO.
Side built up under fore bridges into superstructure.	Side not built up under fore bridges.
FOREMAST: has small top with wide yard under same. Topmast is *abaft.* Both yards wide and far apart. This mast is rather shorter than main mast.	FOREMAST: has no top. Two narrow yards close together and high up on topmast. Topmast is *before* mast. Mast is equal in height to mainmast.
Searchlights on bridge between foremast and 1st funnel.	1ST FUNNEL : Searchlights built off fore side.
1ST FUNNEL : has no searchlight platforms.	2ND FUNNEL : searchlights *high* on *fore* side.
2ND FUNNEL : searchlights *low* on *after* side.	MAINMAST: has no top.
MAINMAST: has box top.	3RD FUNNEL : no bridge.
3RD FUNNEL : bridge across fore side.	4TH FUNNEL : searchlights *high* (on after side).
4TH FUNNEL : searchlights *low* (on after side).	ALL FUNNELS : *plain* with low berthings.
ALL FUNNELS : *half-cased* for about quarter of height.	

Name.	Builder.	Machinery	Laid down.	Completed	Trials full power		Boilers	Best recent speed
					H.P.	Kts.		
S. Giorgio	Castellamare D.Y.	Ansaldo	May,'05	June'10	19.595	= 23	14 Blechynden	
S. Marco	Castellamare D.Y.	Ansaldo	Jan.,'07	July'10	23,030	= 23·75	14 Babcock	

General Notes.—Designed by Engineer Lieut-Gen. Masdea. In 1913, S. Giorgio grounded badly off C. Posillipo (Bay of Naples), but was salved and repaired. She was again badly damaged by stranding in Straits of Messina early in 1914.

PISA (Sept., 1907).

Displacement, 10,600 tons. Complement, 685.

Length (*p.p.*), 426½ feet. Beam, 68 feet 11 ins. *Mean* draught 24⅓ feet. *Maximum* draught, 25⅙ feet.
Length *over all*, 460 feet 11 ins.

Corrections to Plans.

Now has foremast with R.F. top and searchlight bridge across fore side of first funnel.

Guns (Vickers):
    4—10 inch, 45 cal.
    8—7·5 inch, 45 cal.
    14—14 pdr., 50 cal.
    6—14 pdr. (AA)
    2—3 pdr.
    2 M.G.
    2 landing.
Torpedo tubes (18 inch):
    2 *submerged* (broadside)
    1 *submerged* (stern)

Armour (Vickers):
    8″ Belt (amidships) ......
    3¼″ Belt (ends) ...
    1¾″ & 1½″ Decks ....
    7″ Lower deck redoubt
    6½″ Main barbettes ...
    8″ Turrets to these......
    7″ Citadel ....
    7″ Secondary turrets ...
    7″ Conning tower ......

Ahead:
2—10 in.
4—7·5 in.

PISA.

Astern:
2—10 in.
4—7·5 in.

Broadside: 4—10 in., 4—7·5 in.

Machinery: 2 sets 4 cylinder inverted triple expansion. 2 screws. Boilers: 22 Belleville
Designed H.P. 20,000 = 23 kts. Coal: *normal* 680 tons; *maximum* 1570 tons. Endurance: 6,270 mile
at 10 kts., 2,300 miles at 21¼ kts.

Gunnery Notes.—All guns electrically controlled. Central pivot mountings. Guns 22 feet above water.

Name	Builder	Machinery	Laid down	Completed	Trials	Boilers	Best recent speed
Pisa	Orlando, Leghorn	Orlando	July,'05	Dec.,'01	24 hrs. = 21·4 kts. 6 hrs. 20,528 = 23·3 ,,	Belleville	

General Notes.—Designed by Engineer-General Orlando. The *San Giorgio* class (v. preceding page) is a slightly enlarged **Pisa**. A sister-ship, *Amalfi*, lost in the war.

Note.

The addition of a foremast to this Armoured Cruiser, during the War, has considerably changed her appearance. It is possible for her to be mistaken now for one of the two Battleships, *Victor Emanuele* and *Regina Elena*. *Pisa* can easily be picked out by these features: (*a*) flush-decked hull from end to end; (*b*) hull not recessed for end-on fire of beam turrets; (*c*) main barbettes close to central superstructure; (*d*) only two small turrets slightly sponsoned, on each beam; (*e*) foremast well away from fore funnel; (*f*) searchlight bridge across fore funnel; (*g*) funnels thicker and not so high as those in *V. Emanuele* class; (*h*) small space between mainmast and third funnel; (*i*) superstructure abaft mainmast very long; (*j*) sloping stern with sternwalk.

2 Old Armoured Cruisers.

F. FERRUCCIO.

Photo, Civicchioni.

VARESE (Aug., 1899), **FRANCESCO FERRUCCIO** (April, 1902). Displacement, 7350 tons. Complement 552. Length (*p.p.*), 344 feet. Beam, 59¾ feet. *Maximum* draught, *about* 24 feet. Guns : 1—10 inch, 45 cal., 2—8 inch, 45 cal., 14—6 inch, 40 cal. (12 temporarily removed during war), 6—14 pdr., 5—14 pdr. AA., 1 machine, 2—3 pdr., 1 lar.ding. Torpedo tubes (18 inch): 4 *above water*, in 6 inch casemates. Armour (Terni): 6″ Belt (amidships), 3″ Belt ends, 1½″ Deck, 6″ Lower deck (redoubt), 6″ Barbettes (N.C.), 6″ Hoods to these (N.C.), 6″ Battery (N.C.), 5″ Battery bulkheads, 6″ Conning tower (N.C.). Machinery : 2 sets triple expansion. 2 screws. Boilers (24): *Varese*, 24 Belleville; *F. Ferruccio*, 24 Niclausse. Designed H.P. 13,500 = 20 kts. Coal: *normal* 650 tons; *maximum* 1215 tons.

General Notes:—*Varese* built by Orlando, 1898—1901. *F. Ferruccio* at Venice, 1899—1904. Made about 20 kts. on trials, but present speed about 17 kts. *G. Garibaldi* of this class lost during the war.

Old Cruiser (Non-effective).

No mainmast now.)

VETTOR PISANI (1895). Old Cruiser of 7250 tons. Complement, 400. Guns : Removed. Armour (Harvey) : 6″-4½″ Belt, 1½″ Deck, 6″ Lower deck side and Battery, 6″ Conning tower; vertical plating may have been stripped from hull. H.P. 13,000 = 18·6 kts. now. 8 cylindrical boilers. Fuel : Oil only.

Note.—Sister ship *Zenson* (ex-*Carlo Alberto*) now Transport; as also is another old Cruiser, *Cortellazzo* (ex-*Marco Polo*), of a different type. Both these converted Cruisers are listed as Miscellaneous Ships on later pages,

---

ITALIAN NAVY.

1913 Italian (Colonial) Cruisers.

BASILICATA.

Photo by courtesy of the Minister of Marine.

BASILICATA (July, 1914) and **CAMPANIA** (July, 1914).
Displacement, 2480 tons (sheathed and coppered). Complement, 240.
Length (*p.p.*) 249·4 feet. Beam, 41¾ feet. *Max.* draught, 16⅔ feet. Length *over all*, 272·3 feet.

Guns :
6—6 inch, 45 cal.*
2—14 pdr.*
3—14 pdr. AA.
Torpedo tubes :
2 *above water*.
* *These guns temporarily removed during war. May not yet be remounted.*

Armour :
1″ Deck ...
2″ Conning tower......

Ahead :
3—6 in.

Astern :
3—6 in.

Broadside : 4—6 in.

Machinery : 2 sets vertical triple expansion. 2 screws. 4 cylindrical boilers. Designed H.P. 5000 = 16·5 kts. (*not attained on trials*). Coal: *normal* 200 tons, *full load* 500 tons = 4300 miles at 10 kts. and about 2000 miles at 15 kts.

Name	Builder	Machinery	Laid down	Completed	Trials	Boilers	Best recent speed
Basilicata	Castellamare D.Y.		Aug. '13	Aug. '17	About 5000 H.P. = 15·7 kts.	Cyl.	
Campania	Castellamare D.Y.		Aug. '13	Sept. '16		Cyl.	

General Notes.—Were built for Colonial Service. Both were built in tandem on one slip, and successively launched on the same day. Are an improved *Calabria* type.

Note.—These two Ships and "Quarto" (v. next page) are officially rated as "Esploratori" (Scouts) with the Destroyers (or Flotilla Leaders) of over 1000 tons.

(Nino Bixio Class—2 Ships).

MARSALA (March, 1912), NINO BIXIO (Dec., 1911).

Displacement, 3,500 tons.   Complement, 298.

Length (p.p.), 429·8 feet.   Beam, 42·8 feet.   *Mean* draught, 13·4 feet.   Length *over all*, 460 feet

MARSALA.   To distinguish, note (a) only *one* top on foremast; (b) only *one* yard, high up on fore topmast; (c) main topmast removed, leaving old top standing as truck of mainmast *over* yard; (d) Searchlights to port and starboard of *fourth* funnel.

Guns :
6—4·7 inch (50 cal.)
6—3 inch (14 pdr.)
2—2 pdr. AA.
Torpedo tubes (18 inch) :
2 *above water.*
(Also mine-laying gear.)

Armour :
1⅝" Deck (amidships) [:::::]
¾" Deck (ends) ...... [:::::]

Machinery : Curtis turbine. 3 screws. Boilers : 14 Blechynden (12 oil-burning, 2 coal-burning).
Designed S.H.P. 22,500 = 28 kts.   Fuel capacity : 130 tons coal + 520 tons oil = 3000 miles at 10 kts.

Name	Builder	Machinery	Laid down	Completed	Trials kts.	Boilers	Best recent speed
Marsala	Castellamare D.Y.	Off. Mecc, Naples	Feb. '11	Sept. '14	= 27·3	Blechynden	
Nino Bixio	Castellamare D.Y.		Feb. '11	May '14	=	Blechynden	

General Notes.—Carry 200 blockade mines. Designed by Engineer-General Rota.

NINO BIXIO.   To distinguish note the following : (a) *three* tops on foremast (lowest with searchlights) and yard under upper top; (b) pole mainmast shorter than that in *Marsala* with short yard and top under yard; (d) searchlights to port and starboard of *third* funnel.

1909 ITALIAN SCOUT CRUISER (Mine Layer).

QUARTO (Aug., 1911).

Displacement, 3,280 tons. Complement, 253.

Length (*p.p.*), 413.4 feet. Beam, 42.1 feet. *Mean* draught, 13 feet. Length *over all*, 431¾ feet.

Guns :
6—4.7 inch (50 cal.)
6—3 inch (14 pdr.)
2—2 pdr. AA.
Torpedo tubes (18 inch) :
2 *above water.*
(Also mine-laying gear.)

Armour :
1⅝″ Deck (amidships) ▨
¾″ Deck (ends) ...... ▨

Machinery : Parsons turbine. 4 screws. Boilers : 10 Blechynden (8 oil-burning, 2 coal-burning).
Designed S.H.P. 25,000 = 28 kts. Fuel capacity : *maximum,* 50 tons coal + 490 tons oil = 3270 miles at 10
kts., or 1220 miles at 25.7 kts.

Name	Builder	Machinery	Laid down	Completed	Trials H.P.	kts.	Boilers	Best recent speed
Quarto	Venice Y.	Odero	Oct.'09	Sep.'12	28,400 =	28.6	Blechynden	29.5

General Notes.—Carries 200 blockade mines. Designed by Engineer-Col. Truccone.

1907 ITALIAN CRUISER.

LIBIA (ex Turkish *Drama*, Nov., 1912). 4500 tons. Complement, 317. Dimensions : 340
(*o.a.*) × 47¼ × 16 feet. Armament : 2—6 inch, 45 cal., 8—4.7 inch, 50 cal., 2—14 pdr. AA., 6—1 pdr.
2—18 inch tubes (*above water*). Deck, 4″. Designed H.P. 12,500 = 22 kts. 16 Niclausse boilers.
Coal : *normal* 275 tons, *maximum* 640 tons. Endurance : 4500 miles at 10 kts. Built and engined
by Ansaldo. Was begun by Ansaldo for Turkish Navy in 1911 and appropriated by Italy on
outbreak of Turko-Italian War. Not completed until 1913.

OLD ITALIAN COLONIAL CRUISER.

CALABRIA (1894). 2492 tons. Sheathed and zinced. Complement, 208. Dimensions : 265¾ (*o.a.*) ×
41⅔ × 17¼ feet (*max.*) Armament : 4—6 inch, 6—6 pdr., 2—1 pdr., 2 Machine, 2—18
inch tubes (*above water*). 2″ Deck. Designed H.P. 4000 = 16 kts. Boilers : 4 Cylindrical. Coal :
maximum 500 tons. Built at Spezia.

ELBA. (Flagship, C-in-C.)

PUGLIA LOMBARDIA similar, but has only one big circular fighting top round each mast, just above ensign gaffs. Present appearance of ETRURIA not known.

LIGURIA

	PUGLIA	ELBA	LIGURIA	LOMBARDIA	ETRURIA
Launched ..	1898	1893	1893	1893 (rebuilt '07)	1889
Displ. (tons) ..	3100	2730	2460	2280	2280
Length (ft. *o.a.*)	$289\frac{1}{3}$	$289\frac{1}{3}$	$289\frac{1}{3}$	$278\frac{1}{4}$	$278\frac{1}{4}$
Beam (ft.) ..	$40\frac{1}{2}$	$41\frac{3}{4}$	$40\frac{2}{3}$	$39\frac{1}{4}$	$39\frac{1}{4}$
*Max.*draught(ft.)	$19\frac{1}{4}$	$17\frac{1}{2}$	$19\frac{1}{4}$	$16\frac{2}{3}$	$16\frac{2}{3}$
Guns	7—14 pdr. A.A.	6—4.7 inch*	4—14 pdr. A.A.	4—4.7 inch*	6—4.7 inch*
Torpedo Tubes (*above water*)	2—18 inch	2—18 inch*	———	2—18 inch*	2—18 inch*
Designed I.H.P.†	7500	7500	7500	7500	7500
Speed (knots) ..	19.5	19.5	19.5	19.5	19.5
Coal (tons) ..	480	500	500	430	430
Complement ..	164	204	154	191	152

* Reported to be disarmed ; guns and tubes removed.   † All have four cylindrical boilers.

Note.

PUGLIA
LIGURIA } Both Mine Layers. Each carries and lays 60 mines.

LOMBARDIA served during War as Submarine Depot Ship ; may be so employed still.

ETRURIA sunk August, 1918. Has been raised and is being repaired.

PIEMONTE (Elswick, 1888).   2640 tons.   Complement, 264.   Dimensions (*p.p.*), 305 × 38 × 16⅔ feet (*maximum*).   Armament : 10—4·7 inch, 1—14 pdr. AA., 6—6 pdr., **2**—1 pdr., 1 Maxim. 2—18 inch tubes (*above water*).   Deck, 3″.   Conning tower, 3″.   H.P. 12,197 = 22·3 kts. *on trials*.   4 Cylindrical boilers.   Coal : *normal* 200 tons, *maximum* 560 tons.

(*Training Ship for Cadets.*)   *Photo, Abrahams, Devonport.*

ETNA (1885).   3740 tons.   Complement, 239.   Dimensions : 283½ × 43½ × 20 feet (*maximum*).   Armament : 2—6 inch*, 1—14 pdr.*, 2—6 pdr.*   Deck, 2″.   Designed H.P. 6400 = 17 kts.   4 cyl. boilers.   Coal : 630 tons.

* Disarmed during later stages of the War and served as a Harbour Flagship.   May have resumed old duty as Cadets' Training Ship.   Guns given as officially listed by Ministry of Marine.

ITALIAN DESTROYERS (*Cacciatorpediniere*).

Summary Table.

9 + (*over 4*) **Flotilla Leaders** } **63** *completed.*
54 Destroyers. } = (*over 4*) *building.*

Total	Type.	Date	Displ'ce-ment. metric	S/I.H.P.	Max. Speed.	Fuel⁰	Comple-ment	Tubes	Max. Dra'ght
			tons		kts.	tons.			feet
	Flotilla Leaders :—								
?	" *Improved Àquila* " (PN)	*Bldg.*	1890	48,000 *t*	*35*	..	..	6	..
4	*Leone* (AS)	*Bldg.*	2200	42,000 *t*	*34*	*400*	..	6	..
4	*Aquila* (PN)	'13-'19	1600	44,000 *t*	*34*	*260*	139	4	..
3	*Mirabello* (AS)	'14-'16	1540	35,000 *t*	35	*350*	140	4	..
2	*Poerio* (AS)	'13-'15	1030	20,000 *t*	32	*275*	99	4	..
	Destroyers :—								
8	*Palestro* (OL)	'17-'19	880–950	24,000 *t*	32	*170*	..	4	..
11	*Sirtori* (OS)	'16-'18	810	18,000 *t*	33	*170*	100	4	8¾
1	*Audace* (Y)	'13-'16	955	21,500 *t*	30	*245*	119	4	9½
8	*Abba* { (PN) } { (OS) }	'13-'16	770	18,000 *t*	30	*150*	71	4	..
4	*Indomito* (PN)	'12-'14	690	15,000 *t*	30	*120*	71	4—2	..
1	*Animoso* (OS)	'11-'13	700	14,000 *t*	30	*130*	75	4	..
2	*Ardente* (OL)	'11-'13	686	15,000 *t*	30	*120*	71	2	..
10	*Ascaro* (AS)	'12-'13	398			*50+33*	53	3	..
	Carabiniere (AS)	'09-'10	420	6000	28.5	90	50	3	..
	Artigliere (AS)	'06-'07	390			80			
3	*Zeffiro* (PN)	'02-'04	380	5200	30	80 / 60	58	4	7½
5	*Lampo* (Sc)	'99-'01	360	5200	30	80 (coal)	58	2	8½
1	*Fulmine* (AS)	'97-'00	340	4800	26	60 (coal)	46	2	8¾

(AS)=Ansaldo, Sestri-Ponente. (OL)=Orlando, Leghorn. (OS)=Odero, Sestri-Ponente. (PN)=Pattison, Naples. (Sc)=Schichau. (*t*)=Turbines.

* In Fuel column, figures in italics denote oil fuel. *Ascaro* has 50 tons coal + 33 tons oil. *Zeffiro* class have 80 tons coal *or* 30 tons oil.

Flotilla Leaders.*

**Note.*—There is no official Italian rating corresponding to this. All the large T.B.D. on this page, *Aquila* class and *Poerio* class on next page, are officially rated as *Esploratori* (Scouts) with Light Cruisers of *Bixio* and *Quarto* types.

(?) "Improved Aquila" Class.

Building.

*(*Total number unknown*) : Are units of " Improved *Aquila* " class, building by Pattison, Naples. Names not yet known. 1890 tons. Dimensions : 327·2 (*p.p.*) × 32·8 × 11 feet (*mean*). Guns : 8—4·7 inch (45 cal.), 2—14 pdr. **AA.**, 2—2 pdr. AA. Tubes : 6 in two triple deck mountings. Designed S.H.P., 48,000 = 35 kts. 2 Tosi turbines. 4 Thornycroft oil-burning boilers. 2 screws.

*Will probably carry 50–100 mines.

---

4 Leone Class.

Building or completing.

4* *Ansaldo* type : *Leone,*† *Lince,*† *Pantera,*† *Tigre.*† *Building* or completing. 2200 tons. Dimensions : 359·6 (*p.p.*) × 34 × 11·5 feet (*mean*). Guns : 8—4·7 inch (45 cal.), 2—14 pdr. (40 cal.) AA., 2—2 pdr. AA. Tubes : 6 in two triple deck mountings. Designed S.H.P., 42,000 = 34 kts. 2 Parsons turbines. 4 Yarrow oil-burning boilers, 2 screws.

*A fifth boat, *Leopardo*, projected ; not certain if she has been begun or proceeded with.

†All will probably carry 100 mines.

4 Aquila class.

(All three alike.)   *Photo by courtesy of the Ministry of Marine.*

4 *Pattison* type: **Falco*** (1919), **Nibbio*** (1918), **Sparviero*** (1917), **Aquila*** (1916). 1600 tons. Dimensions: 308·5 (*p.p.*) × 31 × 10·7 feet (*mean*). Guns: (a) *Falco,* 6—4·7 inch, 40 cal., 2—14 pdr., 40 cal., 2—2 pdr. AA.; (b) *Nibbio, Sparviero, Aquila,* 3—6 inch, 40 cal., 4—14 pdr., 40 cal., AA., 2—2 pdr. AA. Tubes: 4—18 inch, in two twin deck mountings. Designed S.H.P., 44,000 = 34 kts. 2 Tosi turbines. 4 Thornycroft oil-burning boilers. 2 screws. Endurance: 1700 miles (15 kts.), 380 miles (full speed).

Note.—These four destroyers were to have been built for the Rumanian Navy. Were originally named *Vifor, Viscol, Vartez* and *Vijelie.* Appropriated for Italian Navy on outbreak of war with Austria-Hungary.

*All four are Mine Layers, carrying 50 mines each.

3 Mirabello class.

C. A. RACCHIA.   *Short* mainmast, no bridge athwartship abaft of first funnel. Funnel caps are slightly conical.
(For description, see next column.)

3 Mirabello class (continued).

C. MIRABELLO.   *High* mainmast. Bridge abaft of fore-funnel. Funnel caps strongly conical in shape.

3 *Ansaldo* type: **Carlo Mirabello*** (1914), **Carlo Alberto Racchia** (1916), **Augusto Riboty*** (1915). 1540 tons. Dimensions: 331·4 (*p.p.*) × 32 × 10·6 feet (*mean*). Guns: in *C. A. Racchia,* 6—4 inch, 35 cal., 2—2 pdr. AA. Tubes: 6—... inch in three twin deck mountings; *C. Mirabello* and *A. Riboty,* 8—4 inch, 1 or 2—2 pdr. AA. and 4 tubes in two twin deck mountings. Made 33·75 kts. on trials. 4 Yarrow oil-burning boilers. 2 Parsons turbines. 2 screws. Endurance: 2840 miles (15 kts.), 500 miles (full speed).

*These two boats are Mine Layers, each carrying 100 mines.

2 Poerio class.

G. PEPE.

2 *Ansaldo* type: **Alessandro Poerio** (1914), **Guglielmo Pepe** (1914). 1030 tons. Dimensions: 272·6 (*p p.*) × 26·3 × 9·3 feet. Armament: 4 inch, 5 in *Poerio,* 6 in *Pepe,* 2—2 pdr. AA. 4—18 inch torpedo tubes in two twin-deck mountings. H.P. 20,000=30 kts. 3 Yarrow oil-burning boilers. 2-shaft Parsons turbines. Endurance: 2930 miles (15 kts.), 745 miles (full speed).

Note.

The Russian Destroyer " Zorki " has been taken over by the Italian Navy. For details, see Russian (Black Sea) Section.

11 Sirtori class.

V. ORSINI.

11 *Odero* type : **Agostino Bertani,* Giacomo Medici,* Giuseppe la Farina,*** and **Nicola Fabrizi*** (all 1917) ; **Angelo Bassini,* Francesco Stocco, Giacinto Carini,* Giovanni Acerbi, Giuseppe la Masa,* Giuseppe Sirtori,** and **Vicenzo Orsini** (all 1916). 810 tons. Dimensions : 238 (*p.p.*) × 24 × 9.2 feet (*mean*). Guns : (*a*) *A. Bertani, G. Medici, G. la Farina,* 6-- 4 inch, 2—14 pdr. : *N. Fabrizi, A. Bassini, G. Carini, G. la Masa,* 4—4 inch, 2—12 pdr. (*c*) *F. Stocco, G. Acerbi, V. Orsini,* 6—4 inch, 2—2 pdr. A.A. Tubes (in all) : 4—18 inch, in two twin-deck mountings. Made about 34·1 kts. on trials. 2 Tosi turbines. 4 Thornycroft oil-burning boilers. 2 screws. Endurance : 1700 miles (15 kts.), 470 miles (full speed). *Benedetto Cairoli,* of this class, lost during War.

* These 7 boats are Mine Layers, each carrying 10 mines.

8 Palestro class.

PALESTRO. *Photo by courtesy of Flli. Orlando.*

8 *Orlando* type : **Calatafimi, Castelfidardo, Confienza, Curtatone. Monzambano, Palestro, San Martino, Solferino.** Launched 1918-19. 880 tons.* Dimensions : 256.6 (*p.p.*)* × 24.9 × 8.7 feet (*mean*). Guns : 4—4 inch, 45 cal., 2—14 pdr., 30 cal. A.A., 2—2 pdr. A.A. Tubes : 4 in two twin-deck mountings. Designed S.H.P. 24,000 = 32 kts. 2 Zoelly turbines. 4 Thornycroft oil-burning boilers. 2 screws.

*In *Calatafimi, Castelfidardo, Curtatone* and *Monzambano,* length *p.p.* is about 262.5 feet, and displacement is about 950 tons.

1 Special Boat.

1 *Yarrow* type : **Audace** (ex-Japanese *Kawakaze,* Scotstoun, N.B., 1915). 955 tons. Dimensions : 275 (*p.p*) × 27½ × 9½ feet (*max.*). Guns : 7—4 inch, 2—2 pdr. A.A. Tubes : 4—18 inch, in two twin mountings. Made 34.5 kts. on trials. 2-shaft Parsons turbines and 3 Yarrow large-tube, oil-burning boilers. Endurance : 2180 miles (15 kts.), 560 miles (full speed).

Note.—This boat must not be confused with *Audace* built in 1912-13 by Orlando, as a sister boat to *Animoso* (v. next page). The Orlando *Audace* was sunk during the War, and the Japanese *Kawakaze* (closely resembling the lost *Audace*) was purchased by Italy and re-named *Audace.*

(*Continued on next page*).

8 Abba class.

G. C. ABBA.

2 *Pattison* boats : **Francesco Nullo, Antonio Mosto,** (both 1914).
6 *Odero* boats : **Rosolino Pilo, Giuseppe Carlo Abba, Ippolito Nievo, Simone Schiaffino, Pilado Bronzetti** (all 1914), **Giuseppe Missori** (1915). 770 tons. Dimensions : 236.2 (*p.p.*) × 24 × 8.8 feet (*mean*). Guns : 5—4 inch, 2—2 pdr. A.A. Tubes : 4 single 18 inch. Made about 31.8 kts. on trials. 2 Tosi turbines and 4 Thornycroft oil-burning boilers. 2 screws. Endurance : 1700 miles (15 kts.), 440 miles (full speed).

1 Special boat.

1 *Orlando* type : **Animoso** (1913). 700 tons. Dimensions : 245.4 (*p.p.*) × 24.6 × 8.4 feet (*mean*). Guns : 5—4 inch, 2—2 pdr. A.A. Tubes : 4 single 18 inch. On trials made 36.1 kts. with (about) 18,000 S.H.P. 2-shaft Zoelly turbines and 4 White-Forster oil-burning boilers. 2 screws. Endurance : 1650 miles (15 kts.), 410 miles (full speed). Her sister boat, *Audace*, was lost during the War.

4 Indomnito class.

INDOMITO.

4 *Pattison* type (Thornycroft design) : **Indomito** (1912), **Impavido, Insidioso, Irrequieto** (1913). 690 tons. Dimensions : 238 (*p.p.*) × 24 × 8.4 feet. Guns : 5—4 inch, 2—2 pdr. A.A. Tubes : 2—18 inch, but *Indomito* only has 4 single 18 inch. On trials 18,200 S.H.P. = 35.8 kts. 2 Tosi turbines and 4 oil-burning Thornycroft boilers. 2 screws. Endurance : 1520 miles (15 kts.), 360 miles (full speed). *Impetuoso* and *Intrepido* of this class lost in the War.

2 Ardente class.

ARDITO.

2 *Orlando* type : **Ardito** (1912), **Ardente** (1912). 686 tons. Dimensions : 238 (*p.p.*) × 24 × 8.4 feet (*mean*). Guns : 5—4 inch, 2—2 pdr. A.A. Tubes : 2 single 18 inch. On trials, 15,150 S.H.P. = 33.4 kts. 2-shaft Parsons turbines and 4 oil-burning Thornycroft boilers. 2 screws. Endurance : 1520 miles (15 kts.), 360 miles (full speed).

10 Carabiniere/Artigliere class.

ASCARO. Some boats rigged like this.

GARIBALDINO. Has been lost, but some of the boats detailed below are rigged like this, with very short pole mast right at stern.

10 *Ansaldo* (Improved *Nembo*) type :—

5 *Carabiniere* class : **Ascaro** (1912), **Pontiere** (1910, reconstructed 1913), **Alpino, Carabiniere, Fuciliere** (1909). *Ascaro* 398 tons, others 420 tons. Dimensions, H.P., speed as *Artigliere* class below. Guns as *Artigliere* class below, except *Ascaro*, with 2—14 pdr. and 4—6 pdr. Carry 90 tons oil fuel, except *Ascaro*, with 50 tons coal+33 tons oil. Endurance : 915 miles for *Ascaro*, 1250 miles for others, all at 15 kts. *Garilbadino* lost during War.

5 *Artigliere* class : **Corazziere** (1909), **Lanciere, Artigliere** (1906), **Bersagliere, Granatiere** (1906). 390 tons. Dimensions : 211½ (*p.p.*) × 20 × 6⅔ to 7 feet (*mean*). Guns : 4—14 pdr. Tubes : 3 single 18 inch. On trials, 6500 I.H.P. = 29·1 kts. 3 Thornycroft boilers and 2 screws. 80 tons coal. Endurance : 1000 miles at 15 kts.

5 Lampo class.

5 *Schichau* type : **Dardo, Euro, Lampo, Strale, Ostro** (1899-1901). 320 tons. Dimensions : 196¾ × 21¼ × 8½ feet. Armament : 4—14 pdr., 2—18 inch tubes. All have Schulz boilers. 31·2 kts. on trials. Endurance : 1100 miles at 15 kts.

3 Zeffiro class.

ZEFFIRO.

Espero, Zeffiro 3 funnels as above. *Aquilone* 2 funnels as silhouettes, *q.v.*

3 *Nembo* class (Thornycroft pattern) : **Aquilone** (1902), **Espero, Zeffiro** (both 1904). Built by Pattison, Naples. 380 tons. Dimensions : 208 (*p.p.*) × 19½ × 7½ feet. Armament : 4—14 pdr., 4—18 inch tubes. Boilers : 3 Thornycroft, oil-burning in *Aquilone* and *Espero* (80 tons coal), coal-burning in *Zeffiro* (60 tons oil). On trials, 5350 I.H.P. = 30·3 kts. Turbine and *Nembo* and *Borea* of this class have been lost during the War. Endurance : 1000 miles at 15 kts.

1 Old Boat.

1 *Odero* type : **Fulmine** (1898). 340 tons. Dimensions : 200 × 21 × 8¾ feet. Armament : 4—6 pdr., 2—18 inch tubes. 4 Blechynden boilers. Designed for 28 kts. but never exceeded 26 kts. Endurance : 820 miles at 15 kts.

(Also see next page for other T.B.)

28 Sea-going Boats *(Torpediniere di alto mare).*

No.	Class.	Date.	Dis-place-ment.	H.P.	Max. Speed.	Fuel.	Com-ple-ment.	Tubes.	Max. Draught
			tons.		kts.	tons.			feet.
2	" Later C " (PN)	1908–9	216	3000	25	30 tons oil	33	3	7⅓
6	" Earlier C " (PN)*	1906–7	216	3000	25	40 tons coal	35	3	7½
6	" A " (OS)*	1906–7	216	3000	25	{ 40 tons coal / 30 tons oil	35 / 33 }	3	7½
1	Gabbiano (SY)	1907	162	2000	25	18 tons oil	27	2 or 3	7½
4	" O " (OS)*	1905–7	210	3000	25	40 tons coal	35	3	7¼
3	" P " (PN)*	1905–6	210	3000	25	30 tons coal	32	3	7¼
4	" S " (S)	1905–6	210	3000	25	40 tons coal	35	2	..
1	Pellicano (OS)	1899	154	2700	26	38 tons coal	28	2	7¾
1	Condore (AS)	1898	169	2300	26	26 tons oil	26	2	7

(PN) = Pattison, Naples. (OS) = Odero, Sestri-Ponente. (S) = Schichau. (SY) = Spezia D.Y.

Note.—All belong to a common design and are armed with 2—14 pdr., 3—18 inch tubes, arranged as *Pegaso* plan. The 3—3 pdr. guns, shown on plans, were replaced during war by 2—14 pdr. guns.

PEGASO

Photo wanted.

(For appearance, see Silhouettes.)

---

2 *Later C* class: **Calipso, Climene** (Pattison, Naples, 1908). 216 tons. Dimensions : 164·3 × 17·4 × 5·7 feet (*mean*). Guns : 1—14 pdr., 1—14 pdr. AA. Tubes : 3 single 18 inch. On trials, 3183 I.H.P. = 26 kts. 2 oil-burning Thornycroft boilers and 2 screws.

Photo wanted.

(For appearance, see Silhouettes.)

---

6 " Earlier C " class: **Canopo, Centauro** (both 1907), **Cassiopea, Calliope, Cigno, Clio** (all 1906). Built by Pattison, Naples. 216 tons. Dimensions : 164·3 × 17·4 × 5·7 feet (*mean*). Guns : 2—14 pdr. AA. Tubes : 3 single 18 inch. On trials, 3260 I.H.P. = 27·2 kts. 2 coal-burning Thornycroft boilers and 2 screws.

Mainmast removed from some boats.

6 " A " class : **Airone, Ardea, Albatros, Astore, Arpia** (all 1907), **Alcione** (1906). Built by Odero, Sestri-Ponente. 216 tons. Dimensions : 164·3 × 17·4 × 5·7 feet (*mean*). Guns : 2—14 pdr. AA. Torpedo tubes : 3 single 18 inch. On trials, 3260 I.H.P. = 25·8 kts. 2 Thornycroft coal-burning boilers, except *Airone* with 2 Thornycroft oil-burning boilers and 30 tons oil instead of 40 tons coal. 2 screws in all.

Now rigged with 2 pole masts.

1 *Navy* type : **Gabbiano** (Spezia D.Y., 1907). 162 tons. Dimensions : 159 × 17·5 × 5·5 feet. Guns : 2—3 pdr. Tubes : 2 or 3 single. On trials 2200 I.H.P. = 26 kts. 2 coal-burning Normand boilers and 2 screws.

4 " O " class : **Orfeo** (1907), **Olimpia, Orsa** (both 1906), **Orione** (1905). Built by Odero, Sestri-Ponente. 210 tons. Dimensions : 167·3 × 19·7 × 5 feet (*mean*). Guns : 1—14 pdr., 1—14 pdr. AA. Tubes : 3 single 18 inch. On trials, 3300 I.H.P. = 25·4 kts. 2 coal-burning Blechynden boilers and 2 screws.

(Continued on next page.)

ITALIAN TORPEDO BOATS.

Sea-going Torpedo Boats (continued.)

3 "P" class: **Pegaso, Procione, Pallade** (all 1905). Built by Pattison, Naples. 210 tons. Dimensions: 164.3 × 17.4 × 5.7 feet. Guns: 2—14 pdr. AA. Tubes: 3 single 18 inch. On trials, 3160 I.H.P. = 26.6 kts. 2 Thornycroft coal-burning boilers and 2 screws.

Photo. Cicicchioni.

4 "S" class: **Saffo, Sagittario, Sirio, Spica** (Schichau, 1905). 210 tons. Dimensions: 164 × 19.7 × 5.2 feet (mean). Guns: 2—14 pdr. AA. 2 single 18 inch tubes. On trials, I.H.P. 3120 = 26 kts. 2 Schulz-Thornycroft coal-burning boilers and 2 screws.

PELLICANO. (*Condore* has funnels more apart.)
1 *Odero* boat: **Pellicano** (1899). 154 tons. Guns: 2—3 pdr. Tubes: 2—14 inch. Speed: 23 kts. 2 Blechynden boilers.
1 *Ansaldo* boat: **Condore** (1898). 170 tons. Guns: 1—14 pdr., 2--3 pdr. Tubes: 2—14 inch. Speed: about 20 kts. (25.7 trials). 2 Normand boilers.

80 Coastal Torpedo Boats. (*Torpediniere Costiere.*)

No.	Class.	Date.	Displacement. tons.	H.P.	Max. Speed. kts.	Fuel. tons.	Complement.	Tubes.	Max. Draught. feet.
2	{ 74 O.L.T. } { 75 O.L.T. }	1917-'18	200	4500 t	29	20 oil			
4	70 C.P.—73 C.P.	1917-'18	169	3500	28—31	.. oil			
6	58 O.L.—63 O.L.	1915-'16	160	3700	28.1	.. oil		2	
24	{ 52 A.S.—57 A.S. } { 46 O.S.—51 S.O. } { 40 P.N.—69 P.N }	1915-'18	160—165	3500	28—29	13 oil			
36	{ 1 P.N.—38 P.N. } { 13 O.S.— 24 O.S. } { 25 A.S.—32 A.S. } { 39 R.M. }	1910-'14	125	2700—3200*	27.5—31.5	15 tons oil	23	2	5
1	*F. Rismondo*†	1910	110	2400	26	28 tons oil	20	2	..
7	134 S.—68 S. (S.)	'87-'93	79	700—1000	19	19 tons oil or 17 tons coal	17	2	6¾

t = turbines.   * 33 boats recipro. engines, 2 turbines, 1 turbine and recipro. combined.   † Captured Austrian T.B.

Note:—

The letters, following numbers, indicate builder and location of Yard in the following manner :—
A.S. = Gio. Ansaldo & C., Sestri-Ponente.
C.P = Cantiere Navale Riuniti, Palermo.
O.L. = Fratelli Orlando & Co., Leghorn.
O.L.T. (T. added to turbine-driven boats.)
O.S. = Odero & C., Sestri-Ponente.
P.N. = Pattison & C., Naples.
R.M. = Regia Marina (built in Navy Yard).
S. = Schichau (Germany).

Photo by courtesy of Flli, Orlando.

2 *Orlando* boats : **74 O.L.T., 75 O.L.T.,** Built at Leghorn. Begun 1917. Launched Oct., 1917–Jan., 1918., finished June–Sept., 1918. 200 tons. Guns : 1 or 2—14 pdr. AA. Torpedo tubes : 2—18 inch. S.H.P. 4500 = 29 kts. 2-shaft turbines and 2 water-tube boilers.

Photo wanted.

4 *Cantiere Navale Riuniti* boats : **70 C.P.-73 C.P.** Built at Palermo. Begun 1917, launched 1918. finished 1919. Details as 12 Pattison boats in next column, except that these boats are (*a*) 169 tons displacement, and have (*b*) *two* 14 pdr. AA. and (*c*) 2—18 inch torpedo tubes in *two single* deck mountings, (*d*) Speed : 28 to 31 kts.

Photo by courtesy of Flli. Orlando.

6 *Orlando* boats : **58 O.L-63 O.L.** Built at Leghorn. Begun 1915-16, launched April–Sept., 1916. Completed May–Oct., 1916. Details generally as 12 Pattison boats in next column. But I.H.P. 3700 = 28.1 kts.

Photo wanted.
(1 funnel. 1 mast.)

6 *Ansaldo* boats : **52 A.S.-57 A.S.** Built 1915-16 at Sestri-Ponente. Details as 12 Pattison boats below

Photo wanted.

6 *Odero* boats : **46 O.S.-51 O.S.** Built 1915-16 at Sestri-Ponente. Details as 12 Pattison boats below.

Photo wanted.

12 *Pattison* boats : **40 P.N.-45 P.N.** (begun 1915, launched and completed 1916), **64 P.N.-69 P.N.** (begun 1916 and completed 1917-18). All built at Naples. About 160-165 tons. Dimensions - 139½ × 15 × — feet. Guns 1—14 pdr. AA. Tubes : 2—18 inch in one twin mounting. I.H.P. 3500 = 28 to 29 kts. Machinery - 2 sets recipro. triple expansion. Boilers : Thornycroft.

Coastal Torpedo Boats (*Continued*.)

Official photo.

Appearance of all boats as above.

1 *Navy Yard* boat : **39 R.M.** (Spezia Navy Yard).

16 *Pattison* boats :
- **33 P.N.—38 P.N.**
- **6 P.N.—12 P.N.**
- **1 P.N.—4 P.N.**

11 *Odero* boats :
- **18 O.S.—24 O S.**
- **13 O.S.—16 O.S.**

8 *Ansaldo* boats : **25 A.S.—32 A.S.**

36 boats in all. Launched 1911-13. Completed 1911-14. Average 125 tons. Dimensions : 139½ × 15 × 5 feet. Guns : 1—6 pdr. Tubes : 2—18 inch. I/S.H.P. 2700-3200 = 27·5-31·5 kts. Oil : 15 tons.

Boilers : 2 Thornycroft oil-burning, except *39 R.M.* with special type. Machinery : 2 sets triple expansion, except (*a*) *39 R.M.* with 3 sets triple expansion and 1 B.P. turbine to 3 screws ; (*b*) *31 A.S.* with 3-shaft Parsons turbines ; (*c*) *32 A.S.* with 2-shaft Bergmann turbines. *5 P.N., 17 O.S. 36 P.N.*, lost in War.

Now has pole mast just abaft fore bridge.

1 *ex-Austrian* boat : **Francesco Rismondo** (ex-Austrian *No. 11*). Armed with 2—3 pdr. and 2—17·7 inch tubes. Oil fuel only. White-Forster boilers. Deserted to Italian Navy, October, 1917.

(*All relegated to Harbour Duties.*)

7 *Schichau* type : **134 S, 128 S, 115 S, 114 S, 113 S, 102 S, 68 S.** 80-85 tons. Speed : 17-19 kts.

Armament : 2—1 pdr., 2—14 inch tubes. (*Several have been re-boilered.*)

(M. A. S. Boats with torpedo tubes described on a later page.)

A.—Summary of Submarines (*Sommergibili*).

Note.—This Table only includes boats given in the Official List furnished by the Ministry of Marine. Other Submarines, not mentioned in Official List, but believed to be in existence are relegated to a second Table B.

No.	Type.	First begun.	Com-pleted.	Dis-place-ment	B.H.P. Kw.	Speed. kts.	Endurance.	Tubes.	Com-ple-ment	Max. draug't
										feet.
*	*Ocean-going :*			*	*	*		*		
6	P. Micca (C)	1914	'17-'19	840 / 1244	2600 / 900	17 / 10	...	6	32	14
4	A. Barbarigo (FL)	1913	'17-'18	747 / 925	2600 / 900	17·5 / 10	3000 at 12 kts.	6	32	13¼
1	G. Pacinotti (FL)	1913	1916	700 / 870	2600 / 900	18 / 10	3000 at 12 kts.	5	32	..
	Coastal :—									
2	N5 N6 (B)	1917	'18-'19	276 / 357	620 / 330	13·6 / 8	...	2	21	10
4	N1—N4 (B)	1915	'17-'18							
7	H1—H8 (H)	1916	1917	361 / 441	480 / 500	12·6 / 11	2000 at 13 kts. 30 at 6 kts.	4	22	12⅓
(21)	F1—F21 (FL)	1915	'16-'17	260 / 318	700 / 238	13 / 8	1600 at 8·5 kts. 80 at 4 kts.	2	21	10¼
1	Nautilus (B)	1912	1913	225 / 303	600 / 260	13·2 / 8	...	3	19	9¼
	Mine-Laying									
2	X2, X3 (B)	1916	1917	403 / 468	660 / 235	9·2 / 6·3	1200 at 12 kts.	(†) 6 or 9	..	13
1	X1 (ex-German)	1915	1915	182 / 210	80 / 100	6·8 / 5·2	1100 at 4 kts. 50 at 2·5 kts.	6	14	9⅔

(C)=Cavallini design ; (FL)=Fiat-Laurenti design ; (B)=Bernardis design ; (H)="Holland" (Electric Boat Co.) design.

* Details in these columns are all official, with the reservation that the Ministry of Marine gives a total of *six* boats for "F" class. Since *F 13, 15, 17* have been built by Flli Orlando, the official total is probably a mistake.

† Total of mine-discharge chutes ; figures are *not* official.

(*Description by classes on following pages.*)

11 Ocean-going Boats—(*Somnergibili d'alto mare*).

Photo wanted.

(*See Silhouettes for appearance*).

---

6 *Cavallini* type : **Angelo Emo,* Lorenzo Marcello,* Lazarro Mocenigo,° Galvani, Pietro Micca, Torricelli** (Spezia Navy Yard). Dimensions : 206¾ × 19¾ × 14 feet. Guns : 2—14 pdr. (40 cal.) AA. 6—17·7 inch torpedo tubes. Machinery : In first three, 2 Tosi Diesel motors *on surface* and 2 Savigliano electric motors *when submerged* ; last three have 2 Ansaldo Diesel and 2 Ansaldo electric motors. Carry 60 tons oil fuel. Other details as Table. Completed 1917-1919.

*These 3 boats begun at Venice D.Y., Aug., 1914. They were dismantled and taken to Spezia in the summer of 1915 and laid down for a second time.

Photo wanted.

(*See Silhouettes for appearance*).

---

4 *Fiat-Laurenti* type : **Agostino Barbarigo,·** (1914), **Andrea Provana** (—), **Sebastiano Veneiro** (—), **Giacomo Nani** (Fiat-San Giorgio Co., Spezia). Dimensions : 213¼ × 19¾ × 13¼ feet. Guns : 2—14 pdr. AA. 6—17·7 inch torpedo tubes. Machinery as *G. Pacinotti* below. Carry 60 tons oil. Completed between Dec., 1917 and Dec., 1918. Other details as Table.

Photo, Ansaldo-San Giorgio Co.

1 *Fiat-Laurenti* type : **G. Pacinotti** (Spezia, 1915 or 1916). Dimensions : × × feet. Guns : 2—14 pdr. (40 cal.) AA., 5—17·7 inch torpedo tubes (3 bow, 2 stern). Machinery : 2 Fiat Diesel engines *on surface*, 2 Savigliano electric motors *when submerged*. Other details as Table. A sister boat, *Alberto Guglielmotti*, was mistaken for a German U-boat by a British Auxiliary and destroyed.

37 Coastal Boats—(*Somnergibili Costieri*).

N 5.   *Photo by courtesy of the Ministry of Marine.*

2 *Bernardis* type : **N 5** (1917), **N 6** (1918). Both built by Tosi, Taranto. Dimensions : 152¼ × 14¾ × 10 feet. Machinery : 2 Tosi Diesel engines *on surface*. Guns, tubes and electric motors as N 1—4 below. Other details as Table.

N 1—4.   *Photo, Ansaldo-San Giorgio Co.*

4 *Bernardis* type : **N1—4** (Ansaldo-San Giorgio Co., Spezia, 1916-17). Dimensions : 150¼ × 14¾ × 10 feet. Guns : 1—14 pdr. (30 cal.) AA. 2 bow 18 inch tubes. Machinery : 2 Sulzer-Ansaldo Diesel engines *on surface* ; 2 Tecnomasio Italiano electric motors *when submerged*. Oil : 9-10 tons. Are an " Improved *Nautilus* " class. Other details as Table.

(*Continued on next page*).

Coastal Boats (*Continued*).

H 2.

7 *Holland* type : **H1, H2** (1916) **H3—H8** (1917). All built by Canadian Vickers Co., Montreal. Dimensions : 150¼ × 15¾ × 12½ feet. Guns : 1—14 pdr. (30 cal.) AA. 4—18 inch bow tubes. Machinery : 2 Nlseco Diesel engines *on surface* ; 2 Dynamic Electric Co. motors *when submerged*. Oil : 14 tons. Other details as Table. *H5* War Loss.

F 7.

21 (or less) *Fiat Laurenti* type : **F1, F2, F3, F5, F7—12, F14, F16. F18—21,** built by Fiat-San Giorgio Co., Spezia and Odero, Sestri-Ponente : **F4, F6, F13, F15, F17,** built by Orlando, Leghorn. Launched and completed 1916-17. Dimensions : 149½ × 13¾ × 10¼ feet. Guns : 1—14 pdr. (30 cal.) AA. 2—17.7 inch bow tubes. Machinery : 2 Fiat Diesel *on surface* ; 2 Savigliano electric motors *when submerged*. Oil : 12 tons. Are an " Improved *Medusa* " type. Other details as Table.

1 *Bernardis* type : **Nautilus** (Venice Navy Yard, 1913). Dimensions : 134½ × 14 × 9½ feet. 2—18 inch bow tubes and 1 revolving 18 inch deck tube. Machinery : 2 Sulzer-Diesel engines *on surface* ; 2 Ansaldo electric motors *when submerged*. Carries 6 tons oil. Other details as table. A sister-boat, *Nereide*, lost in the War.

3 Mine Laying Boats (*Somneergibi—Affondamine*).

Photo wanted.

2 *Bernardis* type : **X2, X3** (Ansaldo. Spezia, 1916). Dimensions about 140 × 18 × 13 feet. Guns : 1—14 pdr. (30 cal.) A.A. Carry 18 mines in 6 or 9 discharge chutes. Machinery : 2 Ansaldo Diesel *on surface* ; 2 Ansaldo electric *submerged*. Carry 14½ tons of fuel. (Other details as Table.)

X 1, AS REPAIRED FOR ITALIAN NAVY.

1 (*type unknown*) : **X1** (ex-German *UC* 12, ex-Austrian *XVI*). Launched by Weser Co., Bremen, May, 1915. Ceded to Austria by Germany, transported in sections by rail to Pola, June, 1915, and there assembled in four days. Engaged in mine-laying operations in the Adriatic 1915-16, and in December, 1915, she transported rifles and munitions from Cattaro to rebel Arab tribes in Northern Africa. Destroyed during 1916 off Taranto, raised in two parts from 100 feet depth, placed on slip, re-built and re-commissioned for service in Italian Navy. Dimensions : 110¼ (*o.a.*) × 10½ × 9¾ feet. Machinery : 1—4 cyl. Benz motor *on surface* ; 1 Siemens-Schukert electric motor *submerged*. One M.G. Carries 12 mines in 6 discharge chutes.

Note.

None of the Submarines tabulated below and described on this and the next two pages are included in the Official List, furnished by the Ministry of Marine. The majority of these boats may have been paid off and placed out of commission. "Argonauta," "S" class and the "W" boats, being of fairly modern construction, may be retained for Training Duties or Local Defence Flotillas; the other boats will probably be condemned or broken up in the near future.

Table B.

No.	Class.	First begun.	Completed.	Displacement. tons. above below	H.P. above below	Kts.	Endurance.	T. Tubes.	Complement.	Max. draught
3	B1—B3	1915	1916	40/17	100	7/5	For 200 miles	2	..	8½
6	A1—A6	1915	1916	30·50	...	5/4	25 miles at 5 kts.	2	5	..
2	W2,W3(AL)	1913	1916	340/500	760/180	13/8·5	For 2500 miles 65 miles at 5 kts.	2	19	9½
1	W1 (AL)	1913	1915	310/508	710/180					
3	S1—S3 (SL)	1913	1915	255/390	600/400	13/8·5	1600 miles at 8·5 kts. 75 miles at 5 kts.	2	21	10
1	Argonauta (FL)	1914	1915	245/300	600/400	13/8·5	950 miles at 12 kts. 100 miles submerg'd	2	21	8½
2	G.Ferraris (B)	1911	1913	345/400	1500/...	15/9	For 1200 miles For 80 miles	6	20	12
1	Atropo (KG)	1911	1913	230/320	600/400	15/8	1300 miles at 12¼ kts 40 miles at 8 kts.	2	17	9
6	Velella class (FL)	1910	1912	245-252/300	600/400	13/8¼	650 miles at 12 kts. For 80 miles	2	19	9
1	Foca (FL)	1907	1908	185/230	600/260	10·7/7	875 miles at 8 kts. For 40 miles	2	10	8¾
5	Squalo class (FL)	1904	'05-'09	155-160/175-200	680-600/260	14/7—8	900 miles at 8 kts. 40 miles at 5 kts.	2	14	9
1	Delfino (P)	..	1894	100/110	150	8/6	...	1	10	9¼

(AL)=Armstrong-Laubeuf. (FL)=Fiat Laurenti. (C)=Cavallini. (KG)=Krupp-Germania. (B)=Bernardis. (SL)=Scott-Laurenti. (WH)=Whitehead-Holland. (P)=Pullino.

9 Small Coastal Boats.

Note.—Considering the small size and feeble radius of these boats, they are hardly worth maintaining in effective condition. They will probably be scrapped very soon—if they have not already been broken up.

No photo available.

3 boats (*type unknown*): **B 1—3** (Spezia D.Y., 1916). Dimensions: about 50 × 7½ × 8 feet. Endurance: 200 miles *on surface* at a low speed. 2—17.7 inch bow tubes. *B 4, B5* were begun, but work on them was stopped. They were never finished.

No photo available.

6 boats (*type unknown*): **A 1** (1915), 30 tons, **A2—4, A 5, A 6** (all 1916) 50 tons. Electric motors only for surface and submerged propulsion. Endurance: 25 miles at 5 kts. *on surface.* One torpedo tube. Were placed out of commission in 1918. Although they had a complement of 5, they were often referred to as "one man" submarines.

Note.

All boats listed on this page were acquired from Foreign Navies in 1915-1916. These seven submarines—although of fairly modern construction—do not appear in the Official List, furnished by the Ministry of Marine.

7 Coastal Boats.

W 3.

W 2.

2 *Armstrong Laubeuf* type : **W2** (1915, **W3** (1915), both built by Armstrongs at Selby, Yorks., for British Navy. Ceded to Italy about 1916. Dimensions : 149¾ × 17 × 9½ feet. Diesel engines of about 750 H.P. Otherwise as *W 1* below. *W 4* lost during War.

7 Coastal Boats (*Continued*).

No Photo available—See Silhouette.
Resembles Greek " *Delfin* " class but has large C.T.

1 *Armstrong-Laubeuf* type : **W 1** (1914), built by Armstrongs for British Navy, and ceded to Italy about 1916. Dimensions : 171½ × 15¼ × 9 feet. 1—3 inch A.A. gun. 2—18 inch bow tubes. Surface Diesel engines of about 700 H.P. Endurance : 2500 miles at 8 kts. *on surface*, 65 miles at 5 kts. *submerged*.

1 *Fiat-Laurenti* type : **Argonauta** (ex-Russian ———— ? ; Spezia, 1914). Dimensions : 147¾ × 13¾ × 8½ feet. 1 Q.F. gun. 2—18 inch torpedo tubes. Fiat-Diesel engines. Radii of action : 950 miles at 12 kts. *on surface* ; 57 miles *submerged*.

S 1

3 *Scott-Laurenti* type : **S1** (1914), **S2, S3** (1915), all built by Scotts S. B. & E. Co., Greenock, N.B., for British Navy as *S 2, 3, 4,* ceded to Italy about 1916. Dimensions : 148 × 13¾ × 9¾ feet. 1 Q.F. gun. 2—18 inch bow tubes. Fiat type Diesel engines. Endurance : 1600 miles at 8½ kts. *on surface* ; 75 miles at 5 kts. *submerged*.

Note.

None of the Submarines, listed on this page are included in the Official List furnished by the Ministry of Marine, At the end of the War, all the boats given in column or right were out of commission. Some may have been broken up, while the remainder will probably be sold and broken up in the near future.

1 *Cavallini* type: **Galileo Ferraris** (Spezia, 1913). Dimensions: 137·8×13¾×12 feet. 1—14 pdr. AA. gun. 6—18 inch tubes.

Also

1 *Cavallini* type: **Giacinto Pullino,** sister to *G. Ferraris* above. Captured Aug., 1916 and became Austro-Hungarian *XVIII*. Recovered by Italian Navy, Nov., 1916. Will probably not be re-commissioned for Italian Navy.

1 *Krupp-Germania* type: **Atropo** (Kiel, 1912). Dimensions: 146×14½×8⅚ feet. 2—18 in. tubes in bows. 2 sets 300-350 H.P. Krupp-Diesel engines. Radii of action: 1300 miles at 12½ kts. *on surface*; 40 miles at 8 kts. *submerged.*

VELELLA. *Official War Photo.*

6 *Laurenti* type: **Argo** (1912), **Velella** (1911), by Fiat Co., **Jantina** (1913), **Salpa** (1912), by Cantiere Riuniti, Spezia, **Fisalia** (1912), **Zoea** (1912), by Orlando, Leghorn. Dimensions: 147½×13¾×9⅝ feet. 1 small Q.F. or dismountable M.G. 2—18 inch tubes in bows. Fiat Diesel engines. 2 Siemens-Schuckert electric motors. Radii of action: 650—800 miles at 12—13½ kts. *on surface*; about 45—50 miles *submerged* at 6 kts. Some made 14·7 kts. *on surface* during first trials. *Jalea* and *Medusa* of this class lost in the war.

1 *Fiat-Laurenti* type, **Foca** (Spezia, 1908). Dimensions: 110×14×8¼ feet. 2—18 inch tubes in bows. Fiat petrol motors. Radii of action: 875 miles *on surface*; 40 miles *submerged.*

5 *Fiat-Laurenti* type: **Glauco** (1905), **Squalo** (1906), **Narvalo** (1907), **Otaria** (1908), **Tricheco** (1908). All built at Venice Navy Yard. Dimensions: 120¾×14¾×8¼ feet. 1 dismountable M.G. 2—18 inch tubes. First three have 680 H.P. Thornycroft petrol motors, and displace 150 tons *on surface*, 175 tons *submerged*. Last two have 700 H.P. Fiat heavy oil motors, and displace 175 tons *on surface*, 200 tons *submerged*. Radii of action: 900 miles at 8 kts. *on surface*; 40 miles at 5 kts. *submerged.*

1 old *Pullino* type **Delfino** (1894). Electric Motor only of 150 H.P. 1 tube.

ITALIAN "MOBILE BATTERIES." (*Batteria semovente.*)

Not completed by June, 1919.

THREE " MOBILE BATTERIES," building or completing. 630 tons. Guns : 1—15 inch 40 cal. and some smaller AA. guns. No other details communicated by Ministry of Marine.

No photo available.

CARSO, CUCCO, MONFALCONE and **VODICE.** Some (or all) built at Venice D.Y. about 1916-17. Displacement, dimensions, H.P., not known, but design similar to *Faa' di Bruno.* Speed : 6 kts. Guns : in *Carso* only, 2—7.5 inch ; in *Cucco, Monfalcone* and *Vodice,* 1—12 inch in each.

Photo by courtesy of the Ministry of Marine.

FAA' DI BRUNO (Venice D.Y., 1916-17). 2,500 tons. Dimensions : 220 (*o.a.*) × 65½ × 6 feet. Complement, —. Guns : 2—15 inch, 40 cal., 2—14 pdr. AA., 2—1½ pdr. AA. Armour : —" Barbette, —" Deck. H.P. 100 = 4 kts. Has only a small engine and 1 screw to raise enough speed to move ship. Hull is box-shaped, without bow or stern.

ITALIAN GUNBOATS.

Lagoon Gunboats (*Cannoniere lacunari*).

No photo available.

APE, VESPE. Built at Venice D.Y. 1918. About 50 tons. Dimensions : 60 × 10 × 2¼ feet. Guns : 1—14 pdr. and 10 machine. H.P. and speed unknown.

No photo available.

(*For Venetian Lagoons.—Have served as Mine Layers.*)

BRONDOLO (1909), **MARGHERA** (1909). 120 tons. Dimensions : 125 × 11 × 2¼ feet. Guns : 1—14 pdr. During War, each fitted to carry and lay 60 mines. Designed H.P., 450 = 13 kts. Coal : 12 tons. Complement, 17.

There are also about 62 small ships under 200 tons *gross* for service in Venetian Lagoons.

Colonial and River Gunboats.

No photo available.

SEBASTIANO CABOTO (Palermo, 1913). Colonial gunboat (*Cannoniera per Servizio Coloniale*). 1050 tons. Complement, 111. Dimensions : 196.8 × 31.8 × 9.2 feet. Guns : 6— 14 pdr., 4 machine. Designed H.P., 1200 = 13 kts. 2 screws. 2 cyl. (direct flame) boilers. Coal : 100 tons. Was built for S. American Station.

No photo available.

(*For service on Chinese Rivers.*)

ERMANNO CARLOTTO (Shanghai, 1914). Shallow-draught river gunboat (*Cannoniera fluviale per la Cina*). 220 tons. Dimensions : 140 × 24½ × 3 feet. Guns : 2—14 pdr., 4 machine. Designed H.P., 1100 = 14 kts. 2 Yarrow boilers. Complement, 73.

Convoy Gunboats (*Cannoniere di scorta*).

Not completed by June, 1919.

SIX CONVOY GUNBOATS, building or completed. 230 tons. Guns : 2—4 inch, 50 cal. and some small AA. H.P., 2800 = 23 kts. No further details communicated by the Ministry of Marine.

M. A. S. 1—434 (*Motobarche Armate*).

Note.—Correspond to British C.M.B. and M.L. types. May carry Depth Charges, Hydrophones, Smoke Boxes, etc.

Photo, Messrs. Ansaldo & Co.

"TIPO VELOCISSIME." 12 BUILT (1917-19) + 4 ON TRIALS. 18 tons. Length : 59 feet. Motors (Isotta Fraschini) : 1600 B.H.P. = 35 kts. Guns : 3 M.G. Torpedo tubes : 2.

"TIPO VELOCI." 14 BUILT (1917-19) — 1 ON TRIALS. 30 tons. Length : 72.2 feet. Motors (Isotta Fraschini) : 1900 B.H.P. = 30 to 33 kts. Guns : 1—14 pdr., 30 cal., 1 M.G. Torpedo tubes : 2—18 inch in some.

Same appearance as British M.L.

TYPE C : 127 BUILT (1916-19) + 35 *BUILDING.* 40 tons. Length : 80 feet. Motors (Standard) : 450 B.H.P. = 19 kts. Guns : 1—14 pdr., 40 cal. (A.A.) and 1 M.G. Are much the same as British *ML* 1—151.

TYPE B : 46 BUILT (1916-19) + 8 *BUILDING.* 19 tons. Length : 59 feet. Motors (Isotta-Fraschini) : 500 B.H.P. = 18 kts. Guns : 1—14 pdr., 30 cal. and one or two M.G.

M. A. S. (*Continued*).

M.A.S. 91—102, 218—232 (built by Orlando).

With two torpedoes.

TYPE A : 175 BUILT (1916-19) + 11 *BUILDING.* 12 tons. Length : 52½ feet. Motors (Isotta-Fraschini or Sterling, or F.I.A.T.) : 400 to 500 B.H.P. = 24 to 26 kts. Guns : (*a*) 1—3 pdr., 40 cal. and 1 M.G., or (*b*) 1—6 pdr., 43 cal. and 1 M.G. Several have 2 torpedo tubes or dropping gears.

"Grillo" Boats.

No photo available.

TOTAL NUMBER NOT KNOWN. About 20 tons. Dimensions : 36 × 6 × — feet. 1—15 H.P. electric motor and tunnel screw = 5 kts. 1—30 H.P. electric motor driving endless climbing chains for surmounting booms. 2—18 inch torpedoes carried in dropping gears. Complement, 3. Designed by Gen. Prunieri.

"Subsidiary Ship" (*Nave Sussidiaria*).

Not completed by June, 1919.)

NAME AND TYPE UNKNOWN. Is building at Riva Trigosa. 10,500 tons. Dimensions : 328.1 × — × — feet. Estimated speed : 10 kts. Has special underwater protection.

Seaplane Carrier & Submarine Depot Ships.

(*Nave per trasporto idrovolanti e appogio Sommergibili.*)

EUROPA (ex-liner of La Veloce Nav. Italiana) (1907). 8800 tons. Dimensions : 454.7 × 53.4 × 20.5 feet. Speed : 15 kts. 1 screw. 2 cyl. boilers. Guns : 2 or more small Q.F. For Seaplanes and Kite Balloons.

Note.—Old Cruiser *LOMBARDIA* (described on an earlier page) served during War as a Submarine Depot Ship. Uncertain if she is still so employed.

Submarine Salvage Ship.

(*Pontone per ricupero Sommergibili.*)

ANTEO (Smulders, Schiedam, 1914). Special Salvage Ship for Submarines. 2100 tons. Dimensions : 164 × 73¾ × — feet. I.H.P., 750 = 8 kts. 2 screws. 2 cyl. boilers. 2 cranes, each lifting 200 tons.

ITALIAN MISCELLANEOUS.

Mine Layers (*Navi Affondamine*).

Note.—All vessels in section A—F are fully described and illustrated on preceding pages.

A :—Light Cruisers.

NINO BIXIO, MARSALA } Carry 200 mines each.
QUARTO.

B :—Old Cruisers.

LIGURIA, PUGLIA. Carry 60 mines each.

C :—Flotilla Leaders.

4 *Aquila* class : **Aquila, Falco, Nibbio, Sparviero.** Carry 50 mines each.

2 *Mirabello* class : **Augusto, Riboty, Carlo Mirabello.** Carry 100 mines each.

D :—Destroyers.

7 boats of *G. Sirtori* class, viz : **Angelo Bassini, Agostino Bertani, Giacinto Carini, Giacomo Medici, Giuseppe la Farina, Giuseppe la Masa, Nicola Fabrizi.** Each carries 10 mines.

E :—Submarines.

X1, X2, X3, described in Submarine Section, 18 mines each.

F :—Lagoon Gunboats.

BRONDOLO, MARGHERA. 60 mines each.

G :—Old Torpedo Gunboats.

(May no longer be Mine Layers).

AGORDAT (1899) & **COATIT** (1899). 1313 tons. Complement, 175. Dimensions : $287\frac{1}{2} \times 30\frac{1}{2} \times 12$ feet. Armament : 2—4·7 inch, 4—14 pdr. AA., 2—14 inch tubes (*above water*). Deck, $\frac{3}{4}''$. Designed H.P., 8000 = 23 kts. 8 Blechynden boilers. Coal : *normal* 180 tons ; *maximum* 300 tons.

Has mainmast now. *(May not be Mine Layer now.)*

Photo, Spartiali.

IRIDE (1891). 946 tons. Complement, 115. Guns : 6—14 pdr. AA. Tubes : 2. I.H.P., 4240 = 20·7 kts. 2 screws. 4 loco. boilers. Coal : 130 tons.

Mine Layers (*Old Torpedo Gunboats*)—*continued.*

No photo available.
Almost same in appearance as *Iride* in preceding column.

MINERVA (1892). 940 tons. Complement, 83. Length : 246 feet. Beam : 27 feet. *Max.* draught : $12\frac{1}{2}$ feet. Guns : 3—14 pdr., 1—14 pdr. AA. 2—1 pdr. AA. Carries 60 mines. Armour : $1\frac{1}{2}''$ deck. Designed H.P., 4000 = 19 kts. 4 Blechynden boilers. Oil fuel : 80 tons.

GOITO (1887, rebuilt 1906). 857 tons. Complement, 83. Guns : Removed during War. Deck $1\frac{1}{2}''$. Designed H.P., 2600 = 18 kts. 3 screws. 6 loco. boilers. Oil fuel : 72 tons.

TRIPOLI (1886, rebuilt 1906) (1898). 860 tons. Complement, 83. Guns : 1—14 pdr., 1—14 pdr. AA. Carries 60 mines. Designed H.P., 2400 = 18 kts. 3 screws. 6 loco. boilers. Oil fuel : 72 tons.

Fuel Ships (*Navi riforminento carbone e naftetine*).
Oil Tankers (*Cisterne per nafta*).

Not completed, May, 1919.

SIX OIL TANKERS building or completing, of "Improved Acheronte" class. No details available.

ACHERONTE, COCITO, FLEGETONTE, LETE, STIGE (all 1914-15). Oil tankers. 1204 tons. Armament : ? H.P., 400. Fiat Diesel engines = kts. Cargo : 760 tons oil fuel.

No photo available.

GIOVE* (——), **NETTUNO*** (——). Oil tankers. 10,310 tons. Dimensions : $416\frac{1}{2} \times 50\frac{3}{4} \times 24$ feet. Armament : 6—14 pdr. H.P. and speed not known. Cargo : 6000 tons oil fuel.

*These two Ships are not mentioned in Official List furnished by the Ministry of Marine, Rome. They may have been (*a*) sunk during the War, or (*b*) transferred to Mercantile Marine.

Fuel Ships (Continued.)

BRONTE (1904). Fleet Collier, Oil Tanker and Transport. 9460 tons. Complement, 79. Guns: 4—6 pdr. With full cargo, 3700 I.H.P. = 11·5 kts.; with reduced cargo, 4300 I.H.P. = 14·5 kts. 2 screws. 4 cyl. boiler. Carries 6,000 tons coal or 4000 tons oil + 2000 tons coal. Own coal: 550 tons. *Sterope* (sister ship) lost during War.

Note.—*Garigliano* (see third column) can also carry a small cargo of oil fuel.

Repair Ship (*Nave Officina*).

VULCANO (ex *Savoia*, 1885). 3260 tons. Complement, 199. Guns: 4—6 pdr. I.H.P., 3340 = 15·2 kts. 1 screw. 8 loco. boilers. Coal: 600 tons.

Transports (*Trasporti*).

Note.—*Bronte* (see above) is rated as a Transport.

Transports (*Continued.*)

> No photo available.

ERITREA (ex *Kaiseri*, captured from Turkey, 1911). 4350 tons. Guns: 6—6 pdr. I.H.P., 1000 = kts. 1 screw. 2 cyl. boilers. Can carry 1700 tons cargo.

> No photo available.
>
> (See Silhouettes.)

ZENSON (ex-cruiser *Carlo Alberto*, 1896). 7200 tons. Disarmed during War. I.H.P., 13,000* = 20 kts.* 2 screws. 6 cyl. boilers. Coal: 1000 tons.*

*These figures probably reduced on conversion to Naval Transport.

Official photo.

CORTELLAZZO (ex-cruiser *Marco Polo*, 1892). 4900 tons. Guns: Not known. Armour removed during War. I.H.P., 10,650* = 17·8 kts. 2 screws. 4 cyl. boilers. Coal: 720* tons.

*These figures probably reduced on conversion to Naval Transport.

Transports (*Continued.*)

BENGASI (ex-*Derna*, captured from Turkey, 1911). Built 1890. 3560 tons. Complement, 64. Guns: 2—6 pdr., 4—3 pdr. I.H.P., 2000 = 13.6 kts. 1 screw. 4 cyl. boilers. Can carry 1050 tons as cargo.

(*Also Oil Tanker.*)

GARIGLIANO (1887). 1300 tons. Complement, 42. Armament: 2—12 pdr. H.P., 537 = 11 kts. 1 screw. 1 cyl. boiler. 120 tons coal. Can carry 200 tons cargo and 35 tons oil (as cargo).

Small Mine-Sweeping Tugs.

> *Appearance much as " Tevere " on next page.*

RD 1—RD 29 (builders unknown, 1916-18). **RD 30—RD 44** (builders unknown, 1918-19). **RD 45—49** (Pattison, Naples, 1918-19). No details known of these vessels.

(*For other Tugs, see next page.*)

Tugs (*Rimorchiatori*), Tanks (*Cisterna*), Distilling Ships (*Navi Distillatrice*).

No photo available.

TITANO (1913). High Sea Tug. 970 tons. Guns : 2—6 pdr. H.P., 1970 = 15 kts. 2 screws. 2 Gennardini boilers. Coal : 160 tons.

No Photo available.

ERIDANO (1911). Tank. 1260 tons. Guns : 2—3 pdr. Designed H.P., 1200 = 12.7 kts. 2 screws. 2 Yarrow boilers. Coal : 120 tons. Carries 400 tons water.

Official photo.

CICLOPE (1903). High Sea Tug. 850 tons. Dimensions : 177 × 29½ × 12 feet. Armament : 2—6 pdr. H.P., 1900 = 13.6 kts. 2 screws. 4 Thornycroft boilers. Coal : 195 tons.

TEVERE (1897). Tank. 960 tons. Guns : 2—1 pdr. H.P., 620 = 11 kts. 1 screw. 2 Thornycroft boilers. Coal : 150 tons. Carries 320 tons water.

Armed Tugs, Tanks, &c.—*Continued.*

ATLANTE (1892), 776 tons, and **ERCOLE** (1892). High Sea Tugs. 853 tons. Armament : 2—6 pdr. Designed H.P., 1830 and 1700 = 13 kts. 2 screws. 4 cyl. boilers. Coal : 150 tons.

GIOVANNI BAUSAN (1883). Distilling Ship, late Cruiser. 3500 tons. Complement, 152. No guns. I.H.P., 6470 = 17.4 kts. 2 screws. 4 cyl. boilers. Has 4 Spampani distillers for 200 tons water per 24 hours. Coal : 590 tons.

No photo available.

(**VERDE & PAGANO** (1877). Tanks. 390 tons. Armament : 2—1 pdr. Original speed : 9 kts. Coal : 35 tons. Carry 105 tons water.

Also 232 other Tugs, 33 Harbour Tanks. 12 Lagoon Tugs are *building.*

Royal Yacht.

Photo, Seward, Weymouth.

TRINACRIA (ex *America*), 1884. 9200 tons. Complement, 180. Dimensions : 441⅔ × 51¼ × 27 feet. Armament : 4—6 pdr., 2—1 pdr. Designed H.P., 6000 = 15 kts. 1 screw. 6 cyl. boilers. Coal : 1500 tons.

Armed Yachts (*Yacht Armato*).

No photo available.

TOBRUK (1897). 700 tons. Complement, 38. Dimensions : 184 × 25 × 15½ feet (*mean*). Guns : 2—14 pdr. (*A A*). I.H.P., 560 = 11.5 kts. 1 screw. 1 cyl. boiler. Coal : 170 tons.

No photo available.

MISURATA (1894). 700 tons. Complement, 33. Dimensions : 191⅓ × 25½ × 14 feet (*mean*). Guns : 2—14 pdr. (*A A*). I.H.P., 780 = 12.5 kts. 1 screw. 1 cyl. boiler. Coal : 120 tons.

No photo available.

GIULIANA (1893). 1100 tons. Complement, 46. Dimensions : 22½ × 28 × 15 feet (*mean*). Guns : 4—6 pdr. I.H.P., 700 = 11.9 kts. 1 screw. 1 cyl. boiler. Coal : 180 tons.

(*Continued on next page.*)

Armed Yachts (*continued*).

> *No photo available.*

CUNFIDA (ex-*Shipka*, 1892, captured during Turko-Italian War). 560 tons. Complement, 36. Dimensions : $151\frac{1}{3}$ × $22\frac{1}{2}$ × — feet. Guns : 1—14 pdr., 1—14 pdr. (AA). I.H.P. 700 = 12·9 kts. 1 screw. 2 cyl. boilers.

> *No photo available.*

ARCHIMEDE (——). 815 tons. Guns : 4—6 pdr. I.H.P. —— = 13 kts. 1 screw. 1 cyl. boiler.

Note—Captured by Germans at Odessa, June, 1918. Re-captured December, 1918.

> *No photo available.*

CAPITANO VERRI (ex-*Thetis*, captured during Turko-Italian War). 640 tons. Guns : 3—6 pdr. I.H.P., 355 = 10.5 kts. 1 screw. 1 cyl. boiler.

Surveying Ship (*Servizio Idrografico*).

> *No photo available.*

AMMIRAGLIO MAGNAGHI (Ansaldo, –/8/14). 2050 tons. Complement, 137. Dimensions : $229\frac{1}{2}$ × $37\frac{1}{2}$ × $12\frac{1}{4}$ feet. Guns : 4—14 pdr. I.H.P., 2000 = 14 kts. Machinery : 2 sets vertical triple expansion. Boilers : 4 cylindrical.

Training Ships (*Navi Scuola*).

For Cadets :

Cruiser **ETNA,** described on a previous page.

Also

AMERIGO VESPUCCI (1882). 2660 tons. Complement, 279. Armament : 4—4·7 inch.* Armour : $1\frac{1}{2}''$ deck amidships. H.P., 3340 = 14 kts. 1 screw. 8 locomotive boilers. Coal : 500 tons.

*Removed during War.

FLAVIO GIOIA (1881). 3016 tons. H.P., 4156 = 15 kts. All other details as *Amerigo Vespucci*.

Training Ships (*continued*).

(*Stokers' Training Ship*).   *Official photo.*

MONTEBELLO (1887). Late Torpedo Gunboat of 820 tons. Complement, 108. Guns : 4—6 pdr.* Armour : $1\frac{1}{2}''$ deck. I.H.P. 4240 = 20·7 kts. (*trials*). Machinery : 2 sets vertical triple expansion. Boilers : For training duties, (*a*) 6 water-tube types, and (*b*) 3 of mixed types. Coal : 100 tons.
*Removed during War.

(*Boys' Training Ships*).

MISENO (1886), **PALINURO** (1886). 552 tons. Armament : 2—14 pdr. (Anti-aircraft). I.H.P., 430 = 10 kts. 1 screw. 1 cylindrical boiler. Coal : 52 tons.

2 A

ESTHONIAN FLEET.

Compiled, 1919, from details supplied by courtesy of the Naval Staff, Reval.

NAVAL & MERCANTILE ENSIGN.

PALE BLUE.

BLACK.

WHITE.

Note.—The top bar of Ensign is *pale* blue.

Commander-in-chief of the Navy and Naval Defences : Captain Johann Pitka.

Mercantile Marine consists of (*a*) 80 steamers, total gross registered tonnage 30,000 tons ; and (*b*) Sailing ships 177, total gross registered tonnage 20,000 tons.

Coinage : Marks and pennies (Finnish system). Present rate of exchange, 45 marks = £1. (Normal rate of exchange, 25 marks = £1.)

Naval Officers and Men : 2,100.

RECOGNITION SILHOUETTES.

Scale : 1 inch = 160 feet.

Lembit (*Gunboat*).

Wambola (*T.B.D.*)

Lennuk (*T.B.D.*)

Naval Base, Ports, Harbours, etc.

ROHUKULA (*Naval Base*). (About 3 miles to the S.W. of Hapsal.) Extended and built in 1914-16. Entrance to harbour, 18-20 feet. Depth in harbour, up to about 18 feet. Railway running on quays. Capable of accommodating at present 6 steamers, when completed and repaired, 15 to 20 steamers. Good anchorage in the roadstead. Warehouses, Ship Repairing Shops. Was partly destroyed by fire and bombardment when the Russian Army retired, but now being rebuilt and repaired by Esthonians.

REVAL. (A late Naval Base of the Russian Navy, dredged to take Dreadnoughts.)

A : **HARBOUR.** Depth at the entrance of the port, up to 35 feet. Depth in the port, 30 feet. There is room to berth in the harbour, under present conditions, 30 large steamers and 10 smaller steamers, besides sailing coasters. Good anchorage in the roads, no tides. The new modern mole in the place of the old wooden jetty, is in the course of completion, but owing to the disturbances which Esthonia has experienced, this work has been temporarily stopped. The Esthonian Government proposes to finish this work on the first possible opportunity, and contemplates making the Port of Reval a modern free port, with all the up-to-date appliances, to accommodate the enormous amount of shipping which will have to pass over Reval in the future, when Reval (being the nearest point to the Russian Moscow district and Siberia) will be used as a transit port for Russian trade. Large cold storage buildings are in the course of construction. Port of Reval has 8 large grain elevators with capacity for 750,000 poods (about 12,000 tons) and one small elevator. Also three floating cranes to lift from 40 to 60 tons, and one wooden crane. Besides this, 4 floating dry docks, capable of lifting 2,000, 1,250 and 3,000 tons are available. The cranes and floating docks belong to the Esthonian Government, while the elevator, to the town. *Navigation School.* Floating Ships' Repairing Workshops. Also Salvage Steamers belonging to the Esthonian Baltic Salvage Association. Three extensive Shipbuilding Yards (belonging to the Baltic Shipbuilding Co., Ltd., Bekker & Co., Ltd., and the Peter Wharf (late Noble & Lessner) at Telliskoppel). The Telliskoppel Bay being an excellent site for a harbour, the Esthonian Government has decided to build an extensive harbour there.

B : **NEW HARBOUR or MINE HARBOUR (MIINI Sadam).** This harbour, being situated a short distance from the Harbour of Reval (approximately one mile), is also under construction, and can already accommodate several small coasting vessels. There is a slipway here.

PERNAU. The normal depth on the bar and thence up to 2 miles above, floating Bridge, owing to not being dredged during the War, is about 15 feet. This depth can easily be increased by dredging up to 20 feet, that is, level with the roadstead. Accommodation for 6 steamers in the harbour. Three berths, with electric cranes, at the Waldhof Works, situated on the left side of the river. There is also a private quay on the right side of the river.

BALTIC PORT. Depth at entrance to port, 16 to 20 feet. Depth in port, 16 to 20 feet. There is room for two steamers alongside the quay, but as many as four have been accommodated at one time. No tides. Difference in depth caused by the winds. The entrance to port is narrow and difficult. The best anchorage is under the Island of Rogor. *Navigation School.*

NARWA. Average depth on the bar : in spring, 12 feet ; in summer, 18-21 feet. Draft : for entering harbour, 18-21 feet ; for coming to the town, 9-10 feet. Length : of private quays, 2,850 feet ; of public quays, 1,600 feet ; of quays at the mouth of river, 1,100 feet. Anchorage in the roads outside the bar. Four Mooring Buoys. Esthonian Government proposes to improve the harbour arrangements in Narwa, especially for the timber trade, as much as possible. *Navigation School.*

(*Continued on next page.*)

HAPSAL. Depth at entrance to port (average), 10 feet. No docks. One wooden jetty, about 250 feet long, with the same depth alongside.

PORT LOKSA. Open coast port, protected by breakwater. Slipway capable of lifting 6–700 tons, also at the same time two or three 400 ton vessels. Depth at entrance, 20 feet. Inside breakwater, 17–18 feet. Alongside quay, 14 feet. Length of quayside, about 500 feet. Capable of accommodating 3 coasting steamers and at the same time small sailing craft. Good anchorage in the roads.

HEINAST (Hainasch). Port protected by breakwater. Draft, 14 feet. Railway. Open port all year round practically. Proposed to be extended to cope with future traffic of Esthonia. *Navigation School.*

KURESAAR (Arensburg). On Island Esel (Oesel). Draft, 12 feet. Quay about 1 mile long. Good anchorage on roads. Protected by Isle Abroka. About 1½ miles from town is a small harbour for small coasting vessels. This will be rebuilt and extended to accommodate larger ships. *Navigation School.*

KERDLA (Kertel). Draft, 12–14 feet. Situated on the Isle of Dago in Bay. Good natural harbour. Capable of accommodating alongside quay 2 or 3 coasting steamers.

PORT KUNDA. Natural harbour in Bay. Good anchorage. Depth, 10–30 feet. Alongside quay, up to 10 feet.

WIRTS (Werder). On the N.W. Coast of Isle Wirts (Schildau). Quay for coasting passenger steamers, also for small sailing craft.

KIHELKOND. Very good natural site for a Naval Base and Wireless Station. Open practically all year round. There is a small harbour for local vessels, also the harbour especially built by the Russians to accommodate torpedo boats.

SPITHAM. A harbour of refuge under construction.

KAESMU (Kaspepwik). Good anchorage. *Navigation School.*

ASSERIN. Quay for small coasting steamers and sailing vessels.

ESTHONIAN DESTROYERS. (*Miini istlejad.*)

1 *Isyaslav* type : **Lennuk** (ex-Russian *Avtroil*, launched by Reval S.B. Co., 1915, completed 1917). 1800 tons. Dimensions : 344½ × 31¼ × 9⅝ feet. Guns : 5—4 inch, 1—9 pdr. anti-aircraft, 2 machine. Torpedo tubes : 9 —18 inch, in 4 triple-deck mountings.* Also designed to carry and lay 80 mines. Designed S.H.P. 32,700 = 32 kts. A.E.G.-Curtis turbines. Oil fuel : 400 tons = 2400 miles at 15 kts. Complement, about 100-110. Captured (with *Wambola*) from Bolshevists by British Light Cruisers and Destroyers in the Baltic, 1919, and transferred to Esthonian Navy.

* Tubes reported removed, October, 1919.

1 *Gavryil* type : **Wambola** (ex-Bolshevist *Spartak*, ex-Kerensky *Mikula Maklej*, ex-Czarist *Kapitan 2r Kingsbergen*). Launched by Putilov Works, Petrograd, 1915 and completed 1918. 1585 tons. Dimensions : 314¾ × 30¼ × 9¾ feet. Guns : 4—4 inch (1—2 pdr. anti-aircraft ? 2 M.G. ?) Torpedo tubes : 9—18 inch, in 3 triple-deck mountings. Also designed to carry and lay 80 mines. Designed S.H.P. 30,000 = 29 kts. A.E.G. Curtis turbines. Oil fuel : about 150 tons. Captured by British Light Cruisers and Destroyers in the Baltic, 1919 (with *Lennuk*) and transferred to Esthonian Navy.

Gunboats.

Note.—Mainmast has been removed.

LEMBIT (ex-German ————, ex Russian *Bobr*, 1907). 875 tons. Dimensions : 218¼ (*o.a.*) × 36 × 8 feet (*max.* draught). Guns : 2—4·7 inch, 4—11 pdr. Used to carry about 50-60 mines. I.H.P. 900=12 kts. (*trials*, 1029 = 11·5 kts.) Coal : 130 tons.

Note.—Above Gunboat was captured by Germans at Helsingfors in 1918 and served for a short time in German Navy.

No photo available.

LAINE (————). About 400 tons. Guns : 2—3 pdr. and some machine. Speed : 12 kts.

Mine Layers.

No photo available.

KALEW, OLEW (ex-Russian Motorships *No. 2* and *No. 8*). 50 tons *gross*. Guns : 1—3 pdr. Speed : 9 kts. Have motor engines.

Mine Sweepers.

No photo available.

| **ALICE.** | **KAETHE.** | } All four are |
| **EDITH.** | **UNA.** | } Converted Tugs. |

Also 10 small Mine Sweepers with motor engines.

Transport.

No photo available.

KALEWI POEG (ex-*Aleksei*). 800 tons *gross*. Gun : 1—3 pdr. Speed : 12 kts.

Ice Breaker.

No photo available.

HERCULES (————). 900 tons. Guns : 1—5·1 inch, 1—11 pdr. Speed : 12 kts.

Peipus Lake* Flotilla.

Gunboats.

No photo available.

| **TAARA.** | **UKU.** |
| **TARTU.** | **WANEMUINE.** |

All above ships converted from Passenger Steamers during the War by the Russian Navy. Displacement : 100-200 tons. Speeds : 12-9 kts. Guns : *Taara*, 3—11 pdr. ; *Tartu*, 2—1 pdr. machine ; *Uku*, 1—11 pdr. ; *Wanemuine*, 2—11 pdr.

*Lake Peipus is referred to in Bolshevist Naval Staff reports as Lake Chudakoë, Tchudakoye, &c.

Transport (on Lake Peipus).

No photo available.

KAJAK (ex-*Severnaja Komuna*, ex-*Gagara*, captured from the Bolshevists). 5,100 tons *d.w.c.* Speed : 9 kts.

Also various tugs, small launches and motor-engined craft ; some on Lake Peipus.

MINOR EUROPEAN NAVIES.

ADDENDA AND CORRECTIONS.

DENMARK.

NIELS JUEL:—Reports were current during the summer of 1919, that this Coast Defence Ship would be completed as a Cruiser. Armaments ascribed to the revised design are : (*a*) 2—9.4 inch and 5—5.9 inch guns, or (*b*) 2—5.9 inch and 8 to 10—14 pdr. guns. It appears more likely that the construction of this ship may be completely given up in the near future.

Torpedo Boats.

The ten new boats of the *Söhunden* Class are generally of the same design and appearance as *Ormen*. The Normand type of T.B. has proved very suitable for Danish requirements and is very economical to build. The last two boats of the class, given as building, were launched during June, 1919, but their names have not yet been reported to us. Torpedo Boat **Narhvalen** now has a raised fore funnel and a short pole mainmast aft. Photograph held over to next year.

Mine Layers.—The two small vessels, given as building or completing, are now in service. Details as follows : **MINEKRAN FEM** * (1917), **MINEKRAN SEX** † (1918), both built at Copenhagen D.Y. 200 metric tons. Dimensions : 88 (*p.p.*) × 20.5 × 6.3 feet (*mean* draught). Guns : 2—1 pdr. Machinery : in each, 2 sets of Bergsund surface-ignition, heavy-oil motors and electric drive. B.H.P. 290 = kts. Complement, 23.

Repair Ship **GRÖNSUND** has been re-engined with Submarine type of propulsion (internal combustion motors and electric drive), and now serves as Depot, Repair and Training Ship to Submarines, particularly those operating in the Great Belt.

The Old Cruiser *Hekla* (1890), of 1300 tons, serves as a Parent Ship to Submarines and Seaplanes, but only for Harbour Duties.

* *Fem = V.* † *Sex = VI.*

GREEK.

T.B.D. Leon, as re-built with *three* funnels.

Photo, Spartiali.

BELGIUM.

The two German Submarines **U 91, U 112** have been presented to Belgium and left British ports in November, 1919, under tow for Antwerp.

POLISH NAVY.

All details relate to status as German Naval Base.

GDANSK (DANZIG). Three small floating docks and three patent slips. Salvage dock, to raise 1200 tons. All for torpedo craft. One building slip (328 feet). Base and Training School for Seaplanes and Navy Airships, Kite Balloons, &c., at Putzig, near Danzig. Men employed : 4000 before war. Machinery: 13 of 1355 H.P., before war.

NEUFAHRWASSER (which was also a minor German Naval Station) and DANZIG, trade about 850,000 tons of shipping cleared annually—over a million tons or more now.

Admiralty Chart No. 3503.

Shipyard.

(Late) SCHICHAU (DANZIG). Eight *Slips* (some 885 × 115 feet, three about 500 feet, two smaller). *Docks* : Four floating. *Employees* : About 5000. *Machinery* : About 2000 H.P.

At present the Polish Fleet is only a project, providing for an Establishment of

4 Armoured Cruisers,
12 Large Destroyers,

and a *personnel* of 3500 officers and men.

Personnel, in 1919, reported to be 1500 ex-officers and bluejackets from the late Austrian and Russian Navies.

Vistula Flotilla.

There is a heterogeneous flotilla on the Vistula, composed of armed steamers, launches, &c. No details are available of these craft.

FINNISH FLEET.

RECOGNITION SILHOUETTES.

AVANCE.   ELÄKÖÖN.   POSADNIK *class* (2 ships).

GILYAK.   MURTAJA.   SAMPO.

TORPEDO CRAFT.

PODVISHNI *class* t.b.d. '(5).   Nos. 212--222 t.b. (5).

Ports.—Abö, Hango, Helsingfors (last with dock 314 × 56 × 18½ feet).

5 Destroyers.

No Photo available.

5 *Yarrow* type : ***Podvishni, Poslushni, Prosorlivi*** (Izhora Works, Petrograd, 1899–1900). ***Ryezvi, Ryani*** (Nevski Works, Petrograd, 1901). 220 tons. 190 × 18½ × 7½ feet. Guns : 2—11 pdr., 2 machine. Tubes : 1—15 inch. Carry 14 mines. I.H.P. 3800 = 27 kts. Boilers : 4 Yarrow. Coal : 60 tons. Complement, 52. Captured from Russia, 1918.

5 Torpedo Boats.

5 *Normand* type : ***Nos. 212, 215, 216, 218, 222*** (1902–4). 150 tons. 147¾ × 16 × 4¾ feet. Guns : 2– 3 pdr., 1 M G. Tubes : 2—15 inch in twin mounting. I.H.P. 3700 = 29 kts. Coal : 30 tons. Complement, 28. Captured from Russia, 1918. Fitted as Minesweepers.

Gunboats.

Note:—Mainmast has been removed.

GILYAK (ex-Russian *Gilyak*, 1907). 875 tons. Dimensions : 218¼ (*o.a.*) × 36 × 8 feet (*max.* draught). Guns : 2—4·7 inch, 4—11 pdr. Used to carry about 50-60 mines. I.H.P. 900 = 12 kts. Coal : 135 tons. Captured, 1918, from Russia.

POSADNIK (1892) and **VOEVODA** (1893), 400 tons. Armament : 2 or 3—11 pdr., 2 M.G. Designed H.P. 3500 = 21 kts. (about 17 now). Coal : 80 tons. Captured from Russia, 1918.

Ice Breakers.

SAMPO (Armstrong, Elswick, 1898). 1339 tons *gross*. Dimensions : 201·8 × 42·9 × 15 feet. *Nominal* H.P. 357 = (10 ?) kts.

Ice Breakers (*continued*).

AVANCE (Howaldt, Kiel, 1899). 568 tons *gross*. Dimensions : 136 (*o.a.*) × 35·5 × 13½ feet. *Nominal* H.P. 239 = (10 ?) kts.

MURTAJA (Stockholm, 1890). —— tons. Dimensions : 155·8 × 36 × 18 feet. I.H.P. 1126 = (9 ?) kts.

Mine Sweepers.

During 1919, estimates were prepared for the construction of a Mine Sweeping Flotilla at a cost of £320,000. The Finnish Government has offered to buy three Swedish vessels, building in Finnish Yards, for use as Mine Sweepers.

Revenue and Coastguard Cruiser.

ELÄKOÖN (Stockholm, 1886). tons. Dimensions ; 155 × 19½ × 9¼ feet. I.H.P. 670 = kts. Guns : Used to have 1—14 pdr.

Service Unknown.

No photo available.

KARJALA (ordered by Russian Government, 1916, completed at Crichton's Yard, Abö, 1918, and taken over by Finnish Government). 350 tons. Speed, 14 kts.

Note.—The following Russian Fleet Auxiliaries were abandoned on the evacuation of Abö and Helsingfors, 1918. Not certain if they have been taken over for Finnish Navy :—*Lakhta, Merkuri, Mitava, Pallada, Tovarisch, Zhula* (all Hospital Ships); *Ilmen, Msta, Svir* (Minelayers) : *Zapal, Minrep* (Minesweepers) ; *Kobchik* (Patrol Boat).

Lake Ladoga Flotilla.

Various armed vessels are in service on Lake Ladoga, of which the Bolshevits claim to have sunk "one armed ship" by gunfire early in May, 1919. During July, 1918, small German Submarines appeared on Lake Ladoga, flying the Finnish flag. It is doubtful if these boats are now in service.

(ROYAL) SWEDISH NAVY.

Revised from the 1919 Edition of the Official Handbook "Svenska Marinens Rulla."

Illustrated from photos taken or collected by S. Anderson, Esq.

ENSIGN & JACK — ADMIRAL — VICE ADMIRAL — REAR ADMIRAL

COMMODORE — SQUADRON COMMANDER — OFFICER COMMANDING DIVISION — MERCANTILE

Blue — *Yellow*

ROYAL STANDARD — MINISTER OF MARINE

Minister of Sea Defence:
Baron Palmstierna, Commander, R.N.R.

INSIGNIA OF RANK ON SLEEVES.

Vice-Am.	Konter-Am.	Kommendör.	Kommendörkapten.		Kapten.	Löjtnant.	Under-Löjtnant.
			1 graden.	2 graden.			

British or U.S.A. : Rear-Ad. — Commodore. — — Captain. — Commander & Lieut.-Com. — Lieutenant. — Sub-Lieut.

Note.—Full Admirals have 3 stars (as for Vice and Rear combined).

Reserve officers have *blue* above the stripes. All civilian officers have stripes without the curl, and colour between stripes as follows :—Constructors and Engineers, *violet blue*; Doctors, *red*; Paymasters, *white.*

Swedish Arsenals.

KARLSKRONA. One t.b. slip. Dry docks: (Oscar II.), 410×69×24¾; (No. 1), 203×50×19¾; (No. 2), 265×50×19¾; (No. 3), 209×50×19¾; (No. 4), 236×50×19¾; (No. 5), 212×50×19¾; (No. 6), 233×50×19. Submarine Station. Is fortified.

STOCKHOLM. One t.b. slip. One dry dock, 410×58½×22¾ feet. There are also two private docks (Beckholmen), at Stockholm. (No. 1), 328×55×18 feet; (No. 2), 321½ × 35½ × 11½ feet. Mining and Torpedo Craft Station. Is fortified.

Swedish Private Yards

(that build warships).

LINDHOLMEN (Lindholmens Mekaniska Verkstad och Varf) Gothenburg. Two slips, 220 and 187 feet long. One dry dock, 402×58½×20 feet. One 60-ton crane. Electric and pneumatic plant. Total employees 900.

GÖTAVERKEN. Gothenburg. One or two slips (up to 8000 tons), and two slips (2500 and 1200 tons). No docks. Employees 700. 12,000-ton Floating Dock at this port.

BERGSUND (Bergsunds Mekaniska Verkstad och Varf) Stockholm. One slip, 151 feet long. No docks. One 40-ton crane. Employees 600.

FINNBODA (same firm as above) Stockholm. One slip, 226 feet long. 60-ton crane. Employees 700. One large floating dock, one small.

KOCKUM (Kockums Mekaniska Verkstads Aktiebolag) Malmö. One slip, 400 feet or over, and another, 275 feet long. Two dry docks (Harbour Commissioners) 502×66×23¾ feet and 236×34×12½ feet. 45-ton crane. Electric, pneumatic, and hydraulic power throughout yard. Employees 1000. One large dry dock building or completed.

At ORESUND (Landskrona) there is a dock suitable for ships up to 15,000 tons.

Mercantile Marine.

—— steamers of 917,000 tons *gross.*
1174 sailing of 175,891 tons *gross.*

Principal Trade Ports.

Gothenburg, Stockholm, Malmö, Norrköping, Helsingborg, Gefle and Sundervall.

Coinage.

1 krona = about 1s. 1¼d. British, 25 cents U.S.A. (18 kronor = £1).

General Notes.—Personnel: About 4,000. *Colour of Ships:* Grey.

Modern Swedish Guns (Bofors).

(All details are unofficial).

Notation	Designation		Length in calibres	Model	Weight of Gun	Weight of A.P. shot	Initial velocity	Max. penetration firing A.P. capped at K.C.			Danger Space against average warship, at			Nom. per minute
								8000 yds.	5000 yds.	3000 yds.	10,000 yards	5000 yards	3000 yards	
	c/m	inches			tons	lbs.	ft.secs.	in.	in.	in.				
A⁵	28	11	45	'11	41	760½	2576†	10½	15	18	..	..	..	1·2
AA	25.4	10	42	'94	29	450	2362	..	8	11	125	340	675	1
A	21	8.3	44	'98	17	275½	2460†	..	7	9½	100	425	600	2
C	15.2	6	50	'03	7½	100	2789†	..	..	7	75	230	460	6
E	15.2	6	45	'98	6	100	2460	..	..	6	60	200	410	6
	12	4.7	50	'11	3½	46½	2822	..	..	..	..	..	..	8
F	12	4.7	45	'94	2	46½	2430	..	..	3½	..	..	..	8

Guns marked † in the velocity column fire Bofors special nitro-compound.

Torpedo.

Whiteheads. *Submerged* tubes (Elswick pattern), except in *Oden & Svea* class. Torpedoes, 18 in., 15 in. and 14 in. Since 1911 torpedoes have all been manufactured at Karlskrona.

Wireless. Marconi.

ONE FUNNEL.

BJÖRN, GERDA.
(Monitors.)

THORDÖN, TIRFING.
(Monitors).

THOR, NIORD & ODEN.

SVENSKSUND.
(Special Service).

TWO FUNNELS.

EDDA.
(Mine Layer).

SKÄGGALD.
(Depot Ship.)

BLENDA & ROTA (Depot Ships.)
SKULD (Mine Ship.)

VERDANE.
(Hospital Ship.)

DISA (Depot Ship)
& SKAGUL.

DROTT.
(Royal Yacht).

PSILANDER.

J. BAGGE & CLAES HORN.

ÄRAN class (4 ships).

DRISTIGHETEN.

GÖTA, THULE.
(SVEA, Depot Ship, has no turrets).

ORNEN.

CLAES FLEMING.
(Mine Layer).

SVERIGE class (3 ships.)

TORPEDO CRAFT.   Scale : 1 inch = 160 feet.

WRANGEL class t.b.d. (2).

WALE class (1), HUGIN class (2).
MAGNE, MODE—all t.b.d.

PLEJAD class t.b. (17)

BLIXT class t.b. (11).

N : r 5—15 t.b

THREE FUNNELS.

SUBMARINES.   Scale : 1 inch = 80 feet.

Hajen N : r 1.

N : r 10 Delfinen.

N : r 3—N : r 7.

Hvalen N : r 2.

FYLGIA.

OSCAR II.

SWEDISH COAST DEFENCE BATTLESHIPS (*Kustpansarfartyg*)

From *Sverige* class, down to and including *Svea* class, officially rated as *1 kl. Pansarbåtar*.

(SVERIGE CLASS—3 Ships.)

SVERIGE (May, 1915), **DROTTNING VICTORIA** (Sept., 1917) and **GUSTAV DEN FEMTA** (Feb., 1918).

Displacement : *Sverige*, 7185 tons ; *D. Victoria* and *Gustav V about* 7,400 tons.   Complement, 408.

Length (*w.l.*) { *Sverige*, 392·8 feet / *D.V.* & *G.V*, 396·6 feet } Beam, 61 feet.   *Max.* draught, 21 feet.

Guns (Bofors) :
4—11 inch 45 cal. (A⁵)
8—6 inch, 50 cal.
6—14 pdr.
2—6 pdr.
2 machine.
Torpedo tubes (18 inch) :
2 *submerged* (broadside).

Armour : (Carnegie).
8″ Belt (amidships)......
6″ Belt (ends)........
1¾″ Deck (slopes) .....
4″ Redoubt..............
8″ Big gun turrets......
5″—3″ Small turrets ....
8″ Conning tower .. ...

Broadside : 4—11 inch, 5—6 inch.

Ahead :
2—11 in.
4 to 6—
6 in.

Astern :
2—11 in.
4—6 in.

Photos by courtesy of S. Anderson, Esq.

Machinery : In *Sverige*, Curtis turbines by Bergsund Co., 4 screws ; in *Gustav V* and *Drottning Victoria*. Westinghouse geared turbines by the Motala Company. 2 screws. Boilers : 12 Yarrow. Designed S.H.P. 20,000 in *Sverige*, 22,000 in *D. Victoria* and *Gustav V* = 22·5 kts.   Coal : *Normal* 350 tons ; *maximum* 700 tons + 100 tons oil.

Engineering Notes.—In *D. Victoria* and *Gustav V*, Westinghouse turbines consist of 2 sets on each shaft, each containing two turbines of the " divided-flow " type, driving propellers through double-pinion reduction gears (total weight of turbines and reduction gears about 120 tons) :

Shaft H.P.	22,000	15,000	3,150
R.P.M. (turbines)	3,600	3,186	2,070
R.P.M. (propellers)........	200	177	115
Speed (knots)	22·5	20	12·5

General Notes.—*Sverige* was sanctioned 1911 ; but upon a change of Government was cancelled by the Liberals. The nation then voluntarily subscribed a sum which at the end of April, 1912, amounted to nearly £970,000 for the building of this ship, which was estimated to cost £670,000 ; the balance was devoted towards commencement of *D. Victoria* and *Gustav V* under the 1915-19 Naval Programme.

Name.	Builder.	Machinery.	Laid down.	Completed.	Trials.	Boilers.	Best recent speed.
Sverige	Götaverken, Gothenburg	Bergsund Co. Motala Co.	Feb. '13	May, '17		Yarrow in all	
D. Victoria			?	'18-'19			
Gustav V	Kokum Co., Malmö	Motala Co.	Dec. '14	'18-'19			

Oscar II : Present appearance.

OSCAR DEN ANDRA (1906).

Displacement, 4660 tons. Complement, 329.
Length (*w.l.*) 316⅓ feet. Beam, 50½ feet. *Maximum* draught, 18 feet.

Guns :
2—8·3 inch, 45 cal. (*A*).
8—6 inch, 50 cal.
10—6 pdr.
1—1 pdr.
Torpedo tubes (18 inch) :
2 *submerged* (Elswick).

Armour (Krupp) :
6"—4" Belt (amidships)
2" Deck (slopes) ....
6" Bulkheads ....
4' Lower deck redoubt ......
7½"—5" Big gun
" turrets (N.C.) ......
7' Hoists to these...............
5"—3" Small tur-
rets (N.C.)...
7" Conning tower..............

Ahead :
1—8·3 in.
4—6 in.

Astern :
1—8·3 in.
4—6 in.

Broadside : 2—8·3 in., 4—6 in.

Machinery : 2 sets triple expansion. 2 screws. Boilers : 12 Yarrow. Designed H.P. 9000 = 18·3 kts.
Coal : *normal* 350 tons ; *maximum* 500 tons = 2950 miles at 10 kts.

Notes.—Four searchlights carried—one on each chart-house, and one on each mast. Built by Lindholmen Co. On *trial* : 9400 = 18·96 kts.

TAPPERHETEN.

(ÄRAN CLASS—4 SHIPS).

Photo, Karlsson, Karlskrona.

Note.—Appearance now as plans below and silhouettes. Ventilators removed and searchlights now on masts.

ÄRAN (1902), VASA (Dec., 1901), TAPPERHETEN (1902) & MANLIGHETEN (Dec., 1903).

Displacements : *Aran*, 3650 tons ; *Vasa*, 3745 tons ; *Tapperheten* and *Manligheten*, 3840 tons.
Length, (*w.l.*) 287 feet. Beam, 49¼ feet. *Maximum* draught, 16¾ to 17⅓ feet.
Complement, 301. (*Manligheten* 285).

Guns :
2—8·3 inch, 45 cal. (*A*).
6—6 inch, 45 cal.
10—6 pdr.*
1—1 pdr.
Torpedo tubes (18 inch) :
2 *submerged* (Elswick).

*Tapperheten and Manligheten have only 8—6 pdr.

Armour (Krupp) :
7" Belt (amidships) ....
2" Deck (flat on belt) ....
7" Bulkheads ....
7½"—5" Turrets ......
8" Supports ....
5½"—2½" Small turrets (N.C.)
" Hoists, etc. ....
8" Conning tower ....

Ahead :
1—8·3 in.
4—6 in.

Astern :
1—8·3 in.
4—6 in.

Broadside : 1—8·3 in., 3—6 in.

Machinery : 2 sets triple expansion. 2 screws. Boilers : 8 Yarrow. Designed H.P. 7400 for *Manligheten*, 6500 for others = 17 kts. Coal : *maximum*, 300 tons. Endurance : 2000 at 10 kts.

Notes.—Where built : *Aran*, Lindholmen ; *Vasa*, Bergsund ; *Tapperheten* and *Manligheten*, Kockum. These ships carry 4 searchlights.

Photo, Karlsson. Karlskrona.

THOR, as rebuilt, 1916.   **THOR** (1898), & **NIORD** (1898).   *Photo, Karlsson, Karlskrona.*

DRISTIGHETEN (1900).

Displacement, 3620 tons.   Complement, 262.

Length (*w.l.*), 285 feet.   Beam, 48½ feet.   *Maximum* draught, 17 feet.

Guns :
  2—8·3 inch, 45 cal. (A).
  6—6 inch, 45 cal.
  10—6 pdr.
  1—1 pdr.
Torpedo tubes (18 inch) :
  2 submerged (Elswick).

Armour (Krupp) :
  8″ Belt (amidships) ....
  2″ Deck (flat on belt)......
  8″ Turrets ....
  8″ Turret supports ......
  3¾″ Battery.................
  3¾″ Hoists ....
  8″ Conning tower ....

Displacement : *Thor*, 3690 tons ; *Niord*, 3700 tons.   Complement, 254.
Length, (*w.l.*) 278¼ feet.   Beam, 48½ feet.   *Maximum* draught, 18 to 18⅓ feet.

Guns (*see Notes*) :
  2—10 inch, 42 cal. (AA).
  6—4·7 inch, 45 cal.
  8—6 pdr.
  1—1 pdr.

Armour (Harvey-nickel) :
  9½″ Belt ....
  2″ Deck (flat on belt)......
  8″ Turrets ....
  8″ Supports and hoists ...
  3¾″ Battery...............

Ahead :
  1—8·3 in.
  2—6 in.

Astern :
  1—8·3 in.
  2—6 in.

Broadside : 2—8·3 in., 3—6 in.

Machinery : 2 sets triple expansion.   Designed H.P. 5000=16 kts. *natural* draught.   2 screws.
Boilers : 8 Yarrow.   Coal : *normal* 280 tons ; *maximum* 310 tons = 2040 miles at 10 kts.
First trials : I.H.P. 5557=16·8 kts.

Built by Lindholmen Co.   4 searchlights.   Fire control and tripod fore-mast, fitted 1911-12.

Ahead :
  1—10 in.
  2—4·7 in.

Astern :
  1—10 in.
  2—4·7 in.

Broadside : 2—10 in., 3—4·7 in.

Machinery : 2 sets, vertical triple expansion. 2 screws.   Boilers : 6 Cylindrical.   Designed H.P.
5000 = 16 kts.   Coal : *normal*, 280 tons ;   *maximum*, 300 tons = 2530 miles at 10 kts.

Name	Builder	Machinery	Laid down	Com-pleted	Last refit	First trials (f.d.) :—	Boilers	Best recent speed
Thor	Bergsund	{ By builders	1896	1899	1916	=16·7	Cylindrical	
Niord	Lindholmen	{	1896	1900	1917	=16·5	Cylindrical	

Notes.—The big guns of *Thor* are Canet, those of *Niord* are Bofors.   4 searchlights.   *Thor* was rebuilt in 1916 and *Niord* in 1917, their appearance being greatly altered.   As originally built, they had two masts and two funnels, like *Svea* class, on next page.   Now they are almost identical with the re-built *Oden*, also given on next page.

Photo, Karlsson, Karlskrona.

ODEN as re-built 1915. Appearance is now almost the same as that of *Thor* and *Niord* on preceding page, but note that there is no ventilator abeam of the conning tower; chart house is slightly deeper fore and aft, and small topmast to stump of old mainmast is much higher. As will be seen by comparing photos and plans the 4·7 inch guns are differently arranged. Has plain top on tripod mast. *Thor* and *Niord* have a ringed top.

ODEN (March, 1896).

Normal displacement, 3715 tons. Complement, 243.

Length (*w.l.*), 278¼ feet. Beam, 48½ feet. *Maximum* draught, 18¼ feet.

Guns (Canet and Bofors) :
2—10 inch, 42 cal. (A.A) Canet.
6—4·7 inch, 45 cal. Bofors.
8—3 pdr.
1—1 pdr.

Armour (Harvey-nickel) :
10″ Belt (amidships) ......
2″ Deck (flat on belt)
10″ Turrets ....
10″ Supports and hoists
3¾″ Battery ....
9¾″ Conning tower ......

Ahead :
1—10 in.
2—4·7 in.

Astern :
1—10 in.
4—4·7 in.

Machinery : 2 screws. Boilers : 6 cylindrical. Designed H.P. 5000 = 16 kts. Coal : *normal* 275 tons ; *maximum*, 300 tons. Endurance : 2530 miles at 10 kts.

Laid down by Bergsund Co., 1894. Completed 1898. 4 searchlights. Re-constructed 1915, when appearance was greatly changed. Appearance was originally like *Svea* class in next column.

THULE.
Forebridges run to tripod legs ; no funnel caps.
(*Old Gunboat with raking masts and funnels.*)

(SVEA).*

Photo by courtesy of S. Anderson, Esq.
GÖTA.
Still has derricks just before fore funnel.

SVEA* CLASS—2 SHIPS.

GÖTA (1889), & THULE (1893).

	Length (*w.l.*) (feet)		Beam (feet)		Draught (feet)		Displacement.
Göta.....	258·5	×	47·9	×	17	=	3393 tons.
Thule ...	260·8	×	47·9	×	18·4	=	3305 tons.

Guns :
1—8·3 inch, 45 cal. (A),
7—6 inch, 45 cal.
9—6 pdr.
1—1 pdr.
Torpedo tubes : (15 inch) :
1 *submerged* (bow), but *Thule* has none.

Complement 265 and 269.

Armour (Creusot) :
11¾″—8″ Belt..........
2″ Deck (flat on belt) ...
2″ Deck (at ends) ....
10½″ Conning tower .....
Armour (Krupp) :
7½″ fore turret (N.C) ...
5″ Hoist to this (N.C.) ...
5″ Secondary turrets (7) ...
4″ Hoists to these ....

Ahead :
1—8·3 in.
4—6 in.

Astern :
5—6 in.

Broadside : 1—8·3 in., 4—6 in.

Machinery : 2 sets horizontal triple expansion. 2 screws. Boilers : 6 cylindrical. Designed I.H.P. 4650 = 15 kts. Coal : *normal* 200 tons ; *maximum* 288 to 300 tons.

Notes.—Completely reconstructed, 1901—04. *Göta* built by Lindholmen Co., *Thule* by Bergsund Co. *Göta* has square funnels, *Thule* round ones. 4 searchlights. Tripods fitted 1911-12.
Svea of this class transferred to Depot Ships.

THORDÖN AND TIRFING.

THORDÖN, 1505 tons, & **TIRFING**, 1524 tons, (launched 1866—67, and reconstructed 1903—1905). Complement 91.

Guns : *Thordön*. 2—4·7 inch, 8—3 pdr.   Armour (iron), 4½″ belt, 18″ turret
Tirfing. 2—4·7 inch, 8—6 pdr.,   ,,   4½″ ,, 10¾″ ,,

Both have a 9½″ conning tower. 1 screw. H.P. 380=6—7 kts. Coal : 115—120 tons.

Official Illustration.

BJÖRN & **GERDA** (built 1873—74, and reconstructed 1909—1910).   459 tons.   Complement 48.
Guns : 1—4·7 inch, 3—6 pdr., Armour (iron), 2½″ belt, 16½″ casemate.   H.P., 155=8 kts., but
Gerda only, 133 H.P. for 7 kts. 2 screws. Coal : *maximum* 25 tons.

FYLGIA (Dec., 1905).

Displacement, 4810 tons.   Complement, 362.

Length (*w.l.*), 377⅔ feet.   Beam, 48½ feet.   *Max.* draught, 19⅓ feet.

Guns (M. '00) :
  8—6 inch, 45 cal.
  14—6 pdr.
  2—1 pdr.
Torpedo tubes (18 inch) :
  2 *submerged.*

Armour (Krupp) :
  4″ Belt ....
  2″ Deck (slopes) ......
  5″—2″ Turrets
  4″ Hoists and supports
  4″ Conning tower......

Ahead :
6—6 in.

Astern :
6—6 in.

Broadside : 6—6 in.

Machinery : 2 sets triple expansion. 2 Screws. Boilers : 12 Yarrow. Designed H.P. 12,000=21·5 kts.
Coal : *normal* 350 tons ; *maximum* 900 tons=5770 miles at 10 kts.

General Notes : Laid down by Bergsund Co.. at Finnboda in 1903 and completed 1907. Trials :
12,440 H.P.=22·7 kts. Machinery by builders. (There are no sponsons under beam 6-inch turrets, as
incorrectly shown on elevation, plan and section above.)

10 Destroyers.

No.	Type	Date	Displacement tons	H.P.	Max. speed	Fuel	Complement	T. tubes	Max. draug't feet.
2	*Wrangel*	'15—'18	498	13000*t*	kts. 27	tons ...	...	2 or 4	9½
2	*Hugin*	'10—'12	460	8000*t*	30	80 + 3 oil	69	2	8½
4	*Wale*	'06—'10	460	8000	30	80	63	2	8½
1	*Magne* (T)	1905	460	7700	30·7	80	63	2	9½
1	*Mode* (Y)	1902	453	6500	31	86	63	2	9

T = Thornycroft. Y = Yarrow. *t* = turbines.

4 *Wale* class:— **Wale** ('06), **Ragnar** ('07) **Sigurd** ('07), **Vidar** ('09). 460 to 462 tons. Dimensions : 216 × 20¼ × 8¾ feet. Armament : *Wale*, 2—14 pdr., 4—6 pdr., 2 machine; other boats, 4—11 pdr., 2 machine ; 2—18 inch tubes in all. 4 Yarrow boilers. Hull on Thornycroft lines. All built in Sweden. Coal : 80 tons. Radius of action : 920 miles at 15 kts.

WRANGEL AND WACHTMEISTER completing.   *Photo, S. Anderson, Esq.*

2 *Wrangel* class : **Wrangel** and **Wachtmeister** (Lindholmen Co., Gothenburg, both launched 1917.) Dimensions : 236¼ × 21⅔ × 9¼ feet. Armament : 4—14 pdr., 2 machine guns, 2 or 4 torpedo tubes (size unknown.) Designed S.H.P., 11,000 (*n.d.*), 13,000 (*f.d.*) = 26-27 kts. Have de Laval turbines. Completed, early 1918.

1 *Thornycroft:* **Magne** (1905), Dimensions : 215¾ × 20¼ × 9 feet. Armament : 6—6 pdr., 2 machine, 2 single 18 inch tubes aft. 4 Thornycroft boilers. Endurance : 920 miles at 15 kts.

No *photo available.*

Appearance same as *Wale* class in next column.

---

1 *Yarrow:* **Mode** (1902). Dimensions : 220 × 20¼ × 8¾ feet. 4 Yarrow boilers. Armament : 6—6 pdr., 2 machine. Tubes : 2 single, aft. (18 inch). Endurance : 980 miles at 15 kts.

2 *Hugin* class : **Hugin** (1911), **Munin** (1912). 460 tons. Dimensions : 216¾ × 21¼ × 8¼ feet. Guns : 2—14 pdr., 2 machine. Torpedo tubes : 2—18 inch. 4 Yarrow boilers. Curtis turbines. S.H.P., 8,000 = 30 kts. Fuel : 80 tons coal + 3 tons oil. Endurance : 800 miles at 15 kts. *Hugin* built by Goteborg Co., and *Munin* by Kockum Co., Malmö.

38 Torpedo Boats.

No.	Type	Date	Displacement	H.P.	Max. speed	Fuel	Complement	T. tubes	Max. draug't
	(First class)		tons		kts.	tons			feet
17	Plejad (N)	'05—'10	106-122	2000	25-26	18	18	2	8¼
11	Blixt (S)	'96—'04	94-117	1300	23	20 to 13	18-15	2	7¼
	(Second class)								
10	N:r 5—15	'04—'08	58-61	800	21	22	14	2	6¼

(N)=Normand type. (S)=Schichau type.

BLIXT

Photo. S. Anderson, Esq.

11 *Blixt* class: **Blixt** ('98), **Bris** ('00), **Kapella** ('01), **Meteor** ('99). **Mira** ('02), **Orion** ('03), **Orkan** ('00), **Stjerna** ('99). **Sirius** ('03). **Virgo** ('02), **Vind** ('00). Guns: 2—1 pdr. Torpedo tubes: 2—15 inch. All built in Sweden.

SECOND CLASS :—

No 11.

10 second class boats : **N:r 5—15** (No. 13 vacant) Armament: 1—1 pdr., 2—18 inch tubes.

(Vedette Boats of 23–83 tons are listed on a later page, with Swedish Miscellaneous Ships.)

FIRST CLASS :—

CASTOR doing 28·3 kts.

17 *Plejad* class : **Astrea** ('07), **Castor** ('07), **Iris, Plejad** ('05), **Pollux** ('07), **Thetis** ('07), **Spica** ('07), **Vega** ('07) **Vesta, Argo, Antares, Arcturus, Altair, Polaris, Perseus, Regulus, Rigel** ('09-'10). Armament: (except for *Plejad, Castor* and *Pollux*, which have 2—3 pdr.), 2—6 pdr., 2—18 inch tubes. Except *Plejad* (by Normand, Le Havre), all built in Sweden.

10 (+6 ? *building*) Submarines.

Note.— No particulars of Submarines are published by the Ministry of Sea Defence. The following table and description by classes are *not* from any official data.

No.	Type	Date	Displacement	H.P.	Max. speed	Fuel or Battery Endurance.	Complement	T. tubes	Max. draug't
			tons		kts.				feet
6	First Class :— N : r 11—N : r 18 (L)	'15—?	...	...	...	...	...	...	...
1	N : r 10 (N)	1915 ⎫	250	800	15	...	17	2	...
2	N : r 9, N : r 8 (L)	1914 ⎭	370		9				
6	Second Class :— N : r 3—N : r 7 (N)	'09—'12	180 / 230	1000 / 290	15 / 8	1500 miles at 10 kts. / 40 miles at 5 kts.	17	2	...
1	N : r 2 (L)	1909	180 / 230	900 / 290	15 / 8	1500 miles at 10 kts. / 40 miles at 5 kts.	17	2	7
1	N : r 1 (H)	1904	107 / 127	200	9·5 / 7	...	8	1	9¾

(L) = Laurenti type. (N) = Navy type. (H) = Holland type.

1st Class Submarines.

> Uncertain how many of these boats have
> been completed.

6 *Laurenti* type : **N : r 11 Aborren** (1917), **N : r 12 Gäddan** (1918), **N : r 13 Laxen** (1918), **N : r 17 Otter** (——),
N : r 18 Sälen (——), all built by Kockum Co., Malmö ; **N : r 14 Bavfer** (——), **N : r 15 Hvalrossen** (——),
N : r 16 Iller (——), all built by Karlskrona D.Y.   No details yet known.   The conjunction of numbers and names
given above is more or less conjectural and open to future correction.

Photo, Karlsson, Karlskrona.

1 *Navy* type : **N : r 10 Delfinen** (Bergsund Co., Stockholm, 1915).   Armament : 1 machine gun, and 2—18 inch
bow tubes.

> **Photo wanted.**

2 *Laurenti* type : **N : r 9 Svärdfisken, N : r 8 Tumlaren** (Kockum Co., Malmö, 1914).   2—18 inch bow tubes.

2nd Class Submarines.

5 *Navy* type : **N : r 3, N : r 4,** both built by Stockholm D.Y., **N : r 5, N : r 6,** Kockum Co., **N : r 7,** Bergsund
Co., all built 1910-11.   Dimensions : 139½ × 14¾ × 9¾ feet.   2—18 inch tubes.   These are improved *Hajens*.   Radius of
action at full speed (15 kts.), 475 miles.

1 *Laurenti-Fiat* type : **Hvalen N : r 2** (Spezia, 1909).   Dimensions : 139 × 14 × 9¾ feet.   2—18 inch bow tubes.   3 sets of
8-cyl. Fiat petrol engines.   3 screws.

When running on surface may have two masts raised, one right in bow and other right at stern.

1 *Holland* type : **Hajen N : r 1** (Stockholm D.Y., 1904).   Dimensions : 65 × 12 × 9¾ feet.   1—18 inch bow tube.   3 torpedoes
carried.   Petrol motor.   1 screw.

Torpedo Gunboats (*Torpedkryssare*).

PSILANDER.

JAKOB BAGGE and CLAS HORN.

ORNEN.

PSILANDER (1900), 814 tons, **JAKOB BAGGE,** 835 tons, **CLAS HORN** (1898), 846 tons, **ORNEN** (1896), 844 tons. Designed H.P. 4000 = 20 kts., *natural draught.* Coal, 100 tons. Armament : 2—4·7 inch, 4—6 pdr., 1—15 inch *submerged* bow tube.

General Notes : To distinguish between these ships compare relative positions of foremast, bridges, and fore funnel. In 1917, some (or all) of these four ships had extremely high top-gallant masts for W/T., and appeared to have a single stiffening strut to foremast, giving the appearance of a fore tripod mast when seen full broadside.

Gunboat (*Kanonbat*).

Photo, S. Anderson, Esq.

SKAGUL (1878). 589 tons. Guns : 2—4·7 inch, 4—6 pdr Speed : 13 kts. Coal: 94 tons.

Note.—Present employment of above ship not known.

Depot Ships (*Depotfartyg*).

Note :—Gunboat *Rota,* given on next page as a "Mine Ship" is officially rated as a "Depot Ship." Other old Vessels used as Parent Ships are *Stockholm* (for T.B. at Karlskrona), *Saga* (for Submarine at Karlskrona) and *Freja* (for Torpedo Craft at Stockholm).

> *Is included in Illustration of "Gota" and "Thule" on a preceding page.*

SVEA. Old Coast Defence Battleship, built by Lindholmen Co., 1886, rebuilt 1904. 3273 tons. Dimensions : 248·4 × 48·5 × 17·4 feet. Guns : 4—4·7 inch, 2—6 pdr. Armour : 11¾"—8" Belt, 2" Decks, 10½" C.T. 2 screws. 6 cyl. boilers. I.H.P. 4650 = 15 kts. Coal: 290 tons.

Depot Ships—*continued.*

As rebuilt. (*Submarine Depot Ship.*) *Photo, Karlsson, Karlskrona.*
SKAGGALD (1879, rebuilt 1913). 670 tons. Guns : 4—14 pdr. Speed : 13 kts. Coal: 94 tons.

Photo, S. Anderson, Esq.
DISA (1877, rebuilt 1908). 512 tons. Guns : 1—5·9 inch, 1—4·7 inch, 2—6 pdr., 2 machine. Speed : 11 kts. Coal: 98 tons.

Photo, S. Anderson, Esq.
BLENDA (1874, re-built 1908). 464 tons. Guns : 2—6 pdr. Speed : 11 kts. Coal: *about* 95 tons.

Balloon Ship (*Ballongfartyget*).

> *No Photo available.*
> No funnels; no masts.

N : r 1 (1902). 264 tons. Assigned to Coastal Defence.

Mine Ships (*Minfartyg*).

Official photo.

*CLAES FLEMING** (1914). 1,748 tons. Dimensions: 262 × 32·8 × 13·7 feet. Guns: 4—4·7 inch (50 cal.), 6 machine. Speed: 20 kts. Parsons turbines.

*EDDA** (1885) (1907). 662 tons. Guns: 4—6 pdr. Speed: 13·5 kts. Coal: 80 tons.

* These are the only two Swedish warships officially rated as " Mine Ships." *Skuld* and *Rota* are not so rated officially.

Mine Ships—*Continued.*

Photo, Karlsson, Karlskrona.

SKULD (1879). Old Gunboat, 604 tons. Guns: 4—6 pdr. Speed: 13½ kts. Coal, 94 tons.

Note.—In 1919, the 2nd Mining Division consisted of *Skuld* (above), *Svensksund* (*v.* next page), and Vedette Boats N : r 23, 24, 25 (see N : r 26—23 on next page).

Photo, S. Anderson, Esq.

(Is also rated as a "Depot Ship.")

ROTA (1878). 540 tons. Guns: 2—6 pdr. Speed: 13 kts. Coal: about 95 tons.

Note.—In 1919, the 1st Mining Division consisted of *Rota* (above) and Vedette Boats *Sökaren*, N : r 20, 21, 22 (all listed on next page).

Hospital Ship (*Lasarettsfartyg*).

VERDANDE (1879). 514 tons. Speed : 13½ kts. Coal : 94 tons.

Royal Yacht.
(Is officially rated as "Chefsfartyg" or "Flagship.")

DROTT (1877). 633 tons. Guns: 4—3 pdr. Designed H.P., 960 = 13 kts. Coal : 100 tons.

Surveying Ships (*Sjökarteverkets fartyg*).
SVENSKUND (see next page) is occasionally used as a Surveying Ship.
Five small vessels are employed on this service, viz. :—*Ejdern* (1916), 93 tons : *Tarnan* (1889, rebuilt 1909), 54 tons ; *Falken* (1888), 157 tons : *Svalan* (1881), 127 tons, and *Ran* (1857) of 199 tons.

Pilot Vessels (*Lotsverketsfartyg*),
There are ten of these vessels, the largest and most modern being :—*Vega* (1901), of 285 tons ; *Malmö* (1897), of 138 tons ; *Göteborg* (1894), of 132 tons ; and *Gäfle* (1892), of 110 tons. The remaining six, built 1885—1866, are under 100 tons.

(Continued on next page.)

2 B 2

Patrol or Coastguard Ships (and Mine Sweepers ?).

> *Building or Completing.*

SÖKAREN, SVEPAREN, SPRÄNGAREN (1918, Motala Co.), 227 tons. Dimensions : 85·3 × 23 × 9·8 feet. Guns : 1—6 pdr.

Note.—These ships may be fitted out as Mine Sweepers. *Sprängaren* is officially rated as a " Vedette Boat."

Vedette Boats (*Vedettbatar*).

> *No photo available.*

N : r 19 (1918). 67 tons. No guns. Speed unknown. Officially rated as " Lysmaskinbåt." (" Searchlight Boat.")

Photo, S. Anderson, Esq.

N : r 26—23 (ex-T.B. *79, 81, 83, 85*, 1903). 62—55 tons. Speed, 20 kts. Guns : 1—1 pdr. May still have 2—15 inch tubes.

> *No photo available.*

N : r 20 (ex-T.B. *Komet*, 1896). 104 tons. Speed, 23 kts. Guns : 1—1 pdr. May still have 2—15 inch tubes.

Vedette Boats—*Continued.*

> *No photo available.*

N : r 22 (ex-T.B. *Gudur*, 1894). 73 tons. **N : r 21** (ex-T.B. *Gondul*, 1894). 83 tons. Speeds, 19½ kts. Guns : 2—1 pdr. May still each have 2—15 inch torpedo tubes.

Photo, Karlsson. Karlskrona.

N : r 18—N : r 15 (1887-4), 86—72 tons ; **N : r 14—N : r 9** (1891-1886), 55—51 tons ; **N : r 8—N : r 5** (1885-1880), 49—43 tons ; **N : r 5—N : r 1** (1880-1879), 23 tons. Speeds, 19 to 17 kts. All armed with 1—1 pdr. gun. *N : r 5—N : r 1* for Coastal Defence. *N : r 14—9* and *N : r 8—5* are ex-Torpedo Boats *77—61* (alternate numbers) ; *N : r 18—15* are ex-T.B. *4, 3. 2* and *1*.

For Various Special Services.

SVENSKSUND (1891). 394 tons. Guns : 2—6 pdr. Speed : 12½ kts. Coal : 50 tons.

Note.—This ship is employed as (*a*) a Mine Layer, (*b*) a Surveying Ship, (*c*) a Fisheries Protection Vessel, (*d*) an Ice Breaker, and (*e*) a Repair Ship, according to season of the year and when necessity arises for her use on any of these duties.

Training Ships (*Ovningsfartyg*).

JARRAMAS.   *Official illustration.*

JARRAMAS (1900). 337 tons. Speed, 11 kts.
NAJADEN (1897). 355 tons. Speed, 11 kts.

GLADAN.   *Photo, S. Anderson, Esq.*

GLADAN (1857). 327 tons. Speed, 10 kts.
FALKEN (1877). 138 tons. Speed, 8½ kts.
The old Corvette *Saga* (1878), of 1,777 tons, is also officially listed as a Training Ship, and is attached to the Karlrona Submarine Station.

Lastly, there are five very old " Accommodation and other vessels " (*Logements—och andra fartyg*), all probably being useless for fighting purposes.

NORWEGIAN FLEET.

(Revised, 1918, from information supplied by courtesy of H. E. the Minister of Defence.)

ENSIGN · ADMIRAL · VICE ADMIRAL · REAR ADMIRAL

MERCANTILE & JACK · ROYAL STANDARD

Red · Blue · Yellow · White

Arsenal.

HORTEN. One dry dock, $346 \times 60 \times 20\frac{1}{2}$ feet.

Principal Private Yards.

FREDRIKSSTAD: Fredriksstad Mek. Verksted. Docks: 1 small floating.
KRISTIANIA: (*a*) Nylands Verksted. Docks: 1 floating ($320 \times 61 \times 19$ feet), 2 smaller floating.
      (*b*) Akers Mek. Verksted. Docks: 1 dry, 1 floating (both small).
SANDEFJORD: Framnes Mek. Verksted. Docks: 1 floating ($360 \times 65 \times 21$ feet), 2 smaller floating.
KRISTIANSAND: Kristiansands Mek. Vervsted. Docks: 1 dry, $330\frac{1}{2} \times \frac{36}{52\frac{1}{4}} \times 18$ feet. 3 small slips.
BERGEN: (*a*) Laxevaags Dokkompagni. Docks: 1 dry, $365 \times 68 \times 18$ feet.
      (*b*) Bergens Mek. Verksted. Docks: 1 small dry.
      (*c*) Bergens Dokkompagni. Docks: 1 small dry.
      (*d*) Laxevaags Maskin-og Jernskibsbyggeri. Docks: *none*.
      (*e*) Mjellem & Karlsen Mek. og Patentslipper. Two slips. Docks: *none*.
TRONDHJEM: Trondhjems Mek. Verksted. Docks: 2 small dry.
STAVANGER: Stavanger Stöberi og Dok. Docks: 2 small dry.
PORSGRUND. Porsgrund Mek. Verksted. One small floating dock. One slip.

Mercantile Marine.

—— steamers of 1,597,000 tons *gross*.
987 sailing of 556,057 tons *gross*.

Principal Trade Ports.

Kristiania, Bergen, Trondhjem.

Coinage.

Same as Swedish.

Modern Guns (Elswick).

(All details are *unofficial*)

Nota-tion.	Designation		Length in calibres	Model.	Weight of Gun.	Weight of A.P. shot.	Initial velocity	Max. penetration firing A capped at K.C.		Danger Space against average warship, at			Nom. Rounds per minute.
	c/m.	inches.			tons.	lbs.	ft. secs.	5000 yards.	3000 yards.	10,000 yards.	5000 yards.	3000 yards.	
B	20·9	8·2	45	...	$18\frac{1}{2}$	309	2300	$6\frac{1}{2}$	$9\frac{1}{4}$	100	405	594	...
E	15	6	45	...	7	100	2625	3	$4\frac{1}{2}$	67	215	440	8
F	12	4·7	44	...	$2\frac{3}{4}$	44	2570	...	...	...	...	...	10
F	10	4	...	...	...	...	...	...	...	...	...	...	
F	7·6	3	40	...	$\frac{3}{5}$	12	2210	...	...	...	...	...	...

Minister of Defence.—C. T. Holtfodt.

Colour of Ships: Coast Defence Ships, Destroyers, Torpedo Boats, Gunboats, &c., all light grey.

INSIGNIA OF RANK ON SLEEVES.

Admiral. · Vice-Am. · Kontre-Am. · Komman-dör. · Kommandör-Kaptein. · Kaptein. · Premier-Löitnant. · Sekond-Löitnant.

British or U.S.A. } ,,   *Vice-Ad.*   *Rear-Ad.*   *Commodore.*   *Captain.*   *Commander.*   *Lieutenant.*   *Sub-Lieut.*

In relative rank Engineers have the same *without curl*.
  ,,   ,,   Doctors   ,,   ,,   ,,   and a *red* passepoil above upper stripe.
  ,,   ,,   Paymasters   ,,   ,,   ,,   ,,   *blue*   ,,   ,,   ,,

General Notes.—Personnel: About 1400 permanent, 1000 yearly conscripts, all seafaring men in reserve.

NORWEGIAN RECOGNITION SILHOUETTES.

Scale : 1 inch = 160 feet.

ONE FUNNEL.

Old Gunboats (7).
Minelayers

GLOMMEN, LAUGEN.
(Minelayers).

AEGER.
(Gunboat).

Ellida.
(Repair and Depot Ship).

Coastguard Vessel.
(ex Whaler.)

SARPEN & RJUKAN.
(Special Service.)

HEIMDAL.
(Special Service).

VIKING.
(Gunboat).

FARM.
(Transport).

HARALD HAARFAGRE *class* (2 ships).

TWO AND THREE FUNNELS.

FROYA. (Minelayer).

NORGE *class* (2 ships).

FRITHJOF. (Gunboat).

TORPEDO CRAFT.   **Scale : 1 inch = 160 feet.**

Myg t.b.

Delfin *class* t.b. (9.)

Orn *class* t.b. (5)

Hvas *class* t.b. (4.)

Snogg *class* t.b. (3.)

Scale 1 inch = 80 feet.

Valkyrjen.

Draug *class* t.b.d. (3.)

A 1 *(Submarine.)*

390

NORWEGIAN COAST DEFENCE BATTLESHIPS. *(Panserskibe.)*

Photo, Wilse, Christiania.

NORGE (March, 1900), **EIDSVOLD** (June, 1900).

Displacement, 4166 tons.   Complement, 270.

Length (*p.p.*), 290 feet.   Length (*over all*), 301¼ feet.   Beam, 50½ feet.   *Max.* draught, 17⅔ feet.

Guns :
2—8·2 inch, 45 cal. (*A*).
6—5·9 inch, 45 cal.
8—12 pdr.
6—3 pdr.
Torpedo tubes (18 inch) :
2 *submerged.*

Armour (Krupp) :
6″ Belt..............
2″ Deck slopes ...
8″ Turrets ....
6″ Bases ....
5″ Casemates (NC)
6″ Conning tower

Ahead :
1—8 in.
2—6 in.

Astern :
1—8 in.
2—6 in.

Machinery : 2 screws.   Boilers : 6 Yarrow.   Designed H.P. 4500 = 16·5 kts.   Coal : *normal* 440 tons ; *maximum* 550 tons.

Notes.—Built at Elswick.   Completed 1900–1901.   Machinery by Hawthorn, Leslie & Co.   Excellent seaboats.

Coast Service Battleships (*Panserskibe*).

TORDENSKJOLD. (Both exactly alike.)

HARALD HAARFAGRE (Jan. 1897), TORDENSKJOLD (March, 1897).

Displacement, 3858 tons. Complement, 249.

Length (*p.p.*), 279 feet. Length (*over all*), 304 feet. Beam, 48¼ feet. *Maximum* draught, 17⅔ feet. *Mean* draught, 16½ feet.

Guns (Elswick) :
  2—8·2 inch, 45 cal. (*A*)
  6—4·7 inch, 44 cal.
  6—12 pdr.
  6—1 pdr. (Hotchkiss)
Torpedo tubes* :
  2 *submerged*.

Armour (Harvey) :
  7″ Belt (amidships)
  4″ Belt ends ......
  2″ Deck (flat on belt)
  8″ Bulkheads ......
  8″—5″ Turrets ...
  6″ Bases of turrets
  6″ Conning tower

Ahead :
  1—8 in.
  2—4·7 in.

Astern :
  1—8 in.
  2—4·7 in.

Machinery : Boilers : 3 cylindrical. 2 screws. Designed H.P. 4500 = 16·9 kts. (made 17·2 on trial, 1897-8) Coal : *normal* 400 tons ; *maximum* 540 tons.

Notes.—Built at Elswick, and completed 1897-8. Engines by Hawthorn, Leslie & Co. Belt is 174 feet long by 6½ feet deep. Excellent seaboats.

° Tubes are 18 inch in *H. Haafagre* and 17·7 inch in *Tordenskjold.*

4 Destroyers (*Torpedobaatsjagare*).

No.	Type	Date	Displacement	H.P.	Max. speed	Coal or Oil	Complement	T. tubes	Max. draug't
			tons		kts.	tons			feet
3	*Draug*	'08-'14	540	7500	27	95 coal	71	3	9½
1	*Valkyrjen** (S)	1896	410	3300	23	90 coal	59	2	8½

(S) = Schichau.

Valkyrjen is not officially listed with Destroyers, but separately as a "Torpedodivisionsbaat " or Torpedo Division Boat.

Garm (1913), **Draug** (1908), and **Troll** (1910). All built at Horten. 540 tons. Dimensions : 227 × 23¼ ×8¾ feet. Armament : 6—12 pdr., 3—18 in. tubes. H.P. 7500 (8000 in *Garm*) = 27 kts. Reciprocating engines in last two, turbines in *Garm*. Coal : 95 tons. Complement 71.

Photo, Wilse, Christiania.

1 Schichau type : **Valkyrjen** (1896). 410 tons. Dimensions : 190 × 24¼ × 8½ feet. Complement 59. Guns : 4—12 pdr., 2 torpedo tubes (18 in.) 2 screws. Boilers : Thornycroft. Designed H.P. 3300 = 23 kts. Coal : 90 tons.

40 Torpedo Boats.

(Details in table are by averages.)

No.	Type	Date	Displacement	H.P.	Max. Speed	Coal	Complement	T. Tubes	Max. draug't
			tons		kts.	tons			feet
3	Sea-going— *Snögg*	'16—'17	220	3500	25	30 *with oil*	32	4	5¼
9	1st class— *Delfin*	'96—'02	90—79	1000	20	17	19	2	7
	2nd class—								
3	*Skarv*	'07—'13	92	1700	25	16	18	2	7¼
3	*Grib*	1906-3	70	1100	22¼	13	15	2	6½
2	*Ravn*								
2	*Hauk*								
2	*Hvas*	'03—'98	65	700	19¼	12—14	14	2	6
3	*Djerv*								
3	*Lyn* and	'96—'82	40	650	18¼	12—11	14—11	2—1	5¼
9	Older boats								
1	3rd class— *Myg*	'99	27	290	17¼	3	8	1	5

"Large Torpedo Boats" *(Större Torpedobaater).*

3 new boats: **Snögg, Stegg, Trygg** (1916-17). 220 tons. Dimensions : 173·9 × 18 × 5·2 feet. Guns : 2—12 pdr. Tubes : four (size not known). Designed H.P. 3500 = 25 kts. Fuel capacity : 30 tons coal *and* oil. Complement, 32.

1st Class Torpedo Boats.

9 boats : **Laks, Sild, Sœl Skrei,** (1900). 90 tons and 21 kts.
Brand, Storm, Trods (1899). 20 kts. }
Delfin, Hval (1896). 19 kts. } 79 tons.
All armed with 2—1 pdr. guns and 2 tubes on deck. Complement, 19. Last two built by Schichau, Elbing.

Photo, Wilse, Christiania.

2nd Class Torpedo Boats.

GRIB, JO, LOM, ORN, RAVN, as above photo.
Appearance of KJELL, SKARV, TEIST, not known.

Photo, Wilse, Christiania.

8 { **Kjell** (1912), 94 tons ; **Skarv, Teist** (1907-08). 92 tons. All 2—3 pdr. guns. Speed of all 3 boats, 25 kts. Complements, 18.
Grib, Jo, Lom (1906) and **Orn, Ravn** (1904). All 70 tons, and about 22—23 kts. Guns : 2—1 pdr., but *Lom* has 2—3 pdr. Complements, 16.

Note.—All above 8 boats have 2 tubes, viz., 1 bow and 1 deck.

Photo, Wilse, Christiania.

4 boats : **Hauk, Falk** (1903). 63 tons ; **Hvas, Kjœk** (1900). 64 tons. All have 2—1 pdr. and 2 tubes (1 bow and 1 deck). First two 20 kts., others 19 kts. Complements, 14.

(Same appearance as above but shorter funnels).

8 boats : **Djerv, Dristig, Kvik** (1897-98). 67 tons. Guns : 2—1 pdr. **Blink, Glimt, Lyn** (1896). 45 tons. Guns : 2—1 pdr. **Raket, Varg** (1894). 45 tons. Guns : 1—1 pdr. All 19 kts. speed, and 2 tubes (1 bow, 1 deck). Complements : 14 for all, except last two with 12.

Appearance uncertain. Some may have two funnels abreast with mast between.

7 { **Orm, Oter** (1888). 41 tons.
Snar (1887), 39 tons ; **Pil, Rask** (1886), 34 tons.
Springer, Od (1882-3). 36 tons.

Notes.—All 1—1 pdr. All have 2 tubes, except *Od*, with only one. All 19 kts., except *Springer* and *Od*, 18 kts. Complements : 12 for first two, and 11 for last five boats.

3rd Class Torpedo Boat.

Myg (1899). Armed with 1—1 pdr. and 1 deck torpedo tube.

4 + ? Submarines *(Undervandsbaater)*.

Note.—The only information officially published concerning Norwegian Submarines is : the *A* class, built between 1909 and 1914, and the *B* and *C* classes, not yet completed. No details are publicly communicated. The details given in following table and description of classes are *not* from any official data.

No.	Type.	Date.	Dis-place-ments.	H.P.	Max. speed	Fuel or Battery Endurance.	Com-ple-ment	T tubes	Max. draug't
			tons.		kts.	miles			feet
2 ?	*C2 ? C1 ?*	Bldg.	420/515	...	14/9	...	...	4	10
2 ?	*B2 ? B1 ?*	Bldg.	...	...	...	...	...	...	...
3	*A4—A2* (K)	1913	250/335	900/650	14/9	...	15	3	9¼
1	*A1* (K)	1909	205/255	440/250	11·7/9	1450 at 9 kts./45 at 6·5 kts.	14	3	9¼

(K)=Krupp-Germania type.

Building ?

2 *Holland* type : *C2; C1*, ordered from Electric Boat Co., U.S.A., about 1915. Dimensions : about 160 × 17 × 10 feet. Armament : 1—12 pdr., 4—18 inch tubes.

Note.—Doubtful if either of the above boats has ever been commenced. The contract may have been cancelled.

Submarines—*Continued.*

Building ?

2 *Type unknown* : *B2, B1*, assigned to Kaldnaes Yard, Tonsberg, for construction. No details known.

Note.—Four further boats of this class, *B6, B5, B4, B3*, reported to be projected. It is doubtful if any of these six boats have yet been begun.

No Photo available—generally similar to A 1 below.

3 *Krupp-Germania* type : **A4-A2** (all 1913). Dimensions : 152¼ × 16½ × 9½ feet. Surface engines : Krupp-Diesel. 3—18 inch tubes. 4 torpedoes carried.

Note :—A5 of this class completing at Kiel, was appropriated by Germany on outbreak of war.

1 *Krupp-Germania* type : **A1** (ex-*Kobben*) (1909). 205 tons./255 tons. Speed : 11·7 kts./9 kts. 3—18 inch tubes. 4 torpedoes carried. Körting paraffin engines. Dimensions : 129 × 12 × 9¼ feet.

Patrol Boats (*Patruljebaater*).

No photo available.

FIVE NEW BOATS (names or numbers not known, completed 1917). Are 39⅓ feet long. **135** H.P. Van Blerck petrol engines = 17 kts. No other details known.

Note.—Above details are not from any official source.

No photo available.

Nos. **1** and **2** (1893). 25 tons. Guns : 2—1 pdr. Speed, 12 kts.

1st Class Gunboats (*Kanonbaater av I. Kl.*).

Photo, Wilse, Christiania.

FRITHJOF (1895). 1382 tons. Complement 166. Dimensions : 223⅔ × 32¾ × 13½ feet. Guns : 2—4·7 inch, 4—12 pdr., 4 M.G. Tube (18 inch), 1 *sub.* (bow). Designed H.P. 2800 = 15 kts. Coal : 160 tons.

Photo, Wilse, Christiania.

VIKING (1891, rebuilt 1903). 1123 tons. Complement 153. Dimensions : 206 × 30½ × 12 feet. Armament : 1—4·7 inch forward, 1—5·9 inch aft., 4—12 pdr., 4 M.G. Torpedo tube (18 inch), 1 *sub.* (bow). Designed H.P. 2200 = 15 kts. Coal : 140 tons.

2nd Class Gunboat (*Kanonbaat av. 2 Kl.*).

Photo, Wilse, Christiania.

AEGER (1893). 383 tons. Complement 43. Guns : 1—8·2 inch, 1—10 pdr., 2—4 pdr. H.P. 370 = 9·8 kts. Coal : 25 tons. *Max.* draught : 7¾ feet.

Gunboats.

(*Class not known.*)

Photo wanted.

ORKLA (1917), **RAUMA** (1917). 270 tons. Complement —— Dimensions : 124·7 × 23 × 5·8 feet. Guns : 2—4·7 inch. Designed H.P. 360 = 10 kts. Oil : tons.

Mine Layers (*Mineutlæggere*).

Plans by courtesy of the Ministry of Defence.

FRÖYA (1916). 755 tons. Complement, 79. Dimensions : 248·7 × 27 × 8·2 feet. Guns : 4—4 inch q.f. Designed H.P. 7000 = 22 kts. Coal : 95 tons, + 60 tons oil. Carries about 200 mines.

Plans by courtesy of the Min

GLOMMEN (1917), **LAUGEN** (1917). Both built at Kaldnaes Yard, Tonsberg. 335 tons. Complement 35. Dimensions : 137·8 × 27·9 × 6·2 feet. Guns : 2—14 pdr. Designed H.P. 170 = 9·5 kts. Coal : 21 tons. Each carries about 50 mines.

Mine Layers—(continued).

Vale (as Minelayer) on right.

Photo, S. Anderson, Esq.

Name.	Date.	Tons.	Crew.	Guns.		Speed kts.
Tyr ...	1888	281	44	1—10·2 in., 1—6,+2—1 pdr.		10·5
Gor ...	1885	276	44	1—10·2 in.	3—1 pdr.	10·5
Vidar ...	1881	254	41	1—4·7 in.	3—1 pdr.	9·5
Brage ...	1876					8·5
Nor ...	1878	254	38	1—6 in.	3—1 pdr.	8·5
Vale ...	1878	233	41	1—4·7 in.	3—1 pdr.	8
Uller ...	1874					

(All fitted as Minelayers).

For Special Service.

Photo, Wilse, Christiania.

HEIMDAL (1892). 640 tons. Complement 62. Guns : 4—9 pdr., 2—1 pdr. H.P. 625=12 kts. Coal : 92 tons.

Photo, Wilse, Christiania.

SARPEN (1860), **RJUKAN** (1861). 187 tons. Complement : 48. Guns : 2—9 pdr., 2—1 pdr. H.P. 220=10 kts. Coal : 26 tons.

NORWEGIAN MISCELLANEOUS—(continued).

Coastguard Vessels.

Photo, S. Anderson, Esq.

————— (name not known.) Is an armed whaler used for patrolling and watching Norwegian territorial waters, during the war.

Patrol Boat : *Morelos.*

Armed Auxiliaries : *Brim, Michael Sars, Ranen, Sivert Nielsen.*

Auxiliaries : *Harris, Sir Samuel Scott.*

Armed Trawlers : Three.

Fuel Ships.

Photo wanted.

————— (name not known, launched 1916). Oil Tanker. No particulars available.

Fuel Ships—(continued).

Photo wanted.

————— and ————— (names not known, built 1911). Are Oil Tankers, each carrying 300 tons oil as cargo. Have internal-combustion motors. No other details known.

Transport (*Transportskib.*)

Photo, Wilse, Christiania.

FARM (1900). 300 tons. Complement : 32. Guns : 2—9 pdr., 2—1 pdr. Speed : 10 kts.

Workshop and Mother Ship.
(*Jerksteds-og-Moderskib.*)

Photo, S. Anderson, Esq.

ELLIDA (1880). 1,045 tons. Guns : 4—9 pdr., 2—1 pdr. Speed 10·5 kts.

(ROYAL) DANISH NAVY.

(Officially revised, 1918, by courtesy of H.E. the Minister of Marine. Corrected, 1919, from the Official List "Danmarks og Islands Skibsliste.")

Red ▨
White □
Blue ▤
Green ▧
Yellow ▦

ENSIGN & JACK

MINISTER OF MARINE

VICE ADMIRAL

REAR ADMIRAL

SENIOR OFFICER

COMMODORE

ROYAL STANDARD

MERCANTILE ENSIGN

Note.—Division flag pennant, otherwise as commodore.

INSIGNIA OF RANK ON SLEEVES.

	1	2	3	4	5	6	7	8	9
	Admiral.	Vice-Admiral.	Kontre-Admiral.	Kommandör.	Kaptejn.	Premier-löjtnant.	Löjtnant.	Second-löjtnant.	Kadet.

British or U.S.A. — Admiral. Vice-Admiral. *Rear-Admiral* Captain. Commander. Lieut-Commander. Lieutenant. Sub-Lieut. Midshipman.

Band between stripes:—   Branches (*with, but after Executive.*)
Crimson   ...   ... Ingeniör (*Engineer*). Officers of the Technical Department have rafters (?) } Without curl,
                    in the stripes.   but with Corps
Blue   ...   ... Intendant (*Paymaster ?*)   emblem.
Ponceau Red   ... Læge (*Surgeons*).   }

The broad stripes in ranks 1—3 are 2·7 cm. wide.
The narrow " 7 & 9 are 0·7 "
The other stripes are 1·4 cm. wide.   Distance between stripes is 0·7 cm.

Personnel: About 4000, all ranks.
Mercantile Marine: —— steamers of 631,000 tons *gross.* 783 sailing of 109,258 tons *net,* Sea trade chiefly with England, Sweden and Norway.
Oversea Possessions: Iceland, Greenland, Faroes Islands.
Coinage: Krone (100 ore) = about 1s. 1d. British; 50 cents U.S.A.
Minister of Marine: M. Peter Munch.

Naval Guns. (All details unofficial.)

Bore:		Length in Calibres.	Make and Date of Model.		Weight of Gun	Weight of Projectile.	Muzzle Velocity.	Mounted in:
ins.	cm.				metric tons.	lbs.	ft.-secs.	
9·4	24	43	Bofors	M. '06	24·5	352	2806	*P. Skram*
9·4	24	43	Bofors	M. '01	24·3	353	2477	*O. Fisher*
9·4	24	40	Canet	M. '96	22·9	353	2362	*H. Trolle*
9·4	24	40	Krupp	M. '93	25·4	353	2362	*Skjold*
5·9	15	50	Bofors	——	7·5	112	2690	*P..Skram (& Valkyrien?)*
5·9	15	43	Bofors	M '96/'01	5·5	112	2296	*O. Fisher, H. Trolle*
4·7	12	40	Krupp	——	2·3	44	2362	*Skjold, Hejmdal, Gejser*

Arsenal.

COPENHAGEN. One slip. One dock (lengthened, 1912), 316½ × 59½ × 20½ feet. Floating docks: No. 1, 157½ × 28½ × 12¾ feet. No. 2, 113 × 31 × 11¾ feet. Coast Defence Battleships, Torpedo Boats, and Submarines built here.

Private Establishments.

COPENHAGEN. (BURMEISTER & WAIN). Several large building slips. Dry dock, 469 × 66 × 23 feet, and three patent slips. Floating dock: 492 × 77 × 25 feet. Construct submarines and specialise in the building of large Diesel-engined mercantile ships. (*Note*: These details refer to conditions before the war. The shipbuilding establishment is believed to have been greatly enlarged in 1915-17.)

GAMLE. One slip. One dry dock, 232 × 52 × 15¼ feet.

COPENHAGEN FLOATING DOCK CO. One dry dock (Gamle), 246 × 52 × 15¼ feet. Floating docks: No. 1, 296 × 50 × 16½ feet. No. 2, 130 × 45 × 12 feet. No. 3, 310 × 55½ × 16 feet. There are also at Copenhagen two small patent slips.

ELSINOR. Dry docks (a) 379 × 57 × 18 feet (New Dock);
    (b) 335 × 43 × 14 feet (Elsinor Dry dock);
    Also a patent slip.

AARHUS. Patent slip, able to take a small torpedo boat.

Other private shipbuilding companies are; Elsinore Co., Elsinore; Copenhagen Co., at Copenhagen and Elsinore; Stuhr, at Aalborg and the Frederikshavn Co., Frederikshavn.

Note.

All displacements given in metric tons. Where measurement of length is not stated, it can be taken as between perpendiculars (*p.p.*) All draughts *max. load aft.* unless otherwise stated.

DANISH WARSHIPS : RECOGNITION SILHOUETTES.

Scale : 1 inch = 80 feet.

* These Silhouettes are from drawings furnished by courtesy of the Ministry of Defence.

ONE FUNNEL.

FALSTER. (Gunboat).

LOSSEN.* (Mine-Layer.)

SKJOLD.*

KRIEGER class (3). (Surveying Ships.)

HJÆLPEREN. (Mine Layer.)

GULDBORGSUND. (Gunboat.)

BESKYTTEREN.

ABSALON.

ISLANDS FALK.

(Fisheries and Coast Guard Vessels.)

HEJMDAL.* (Training Ship).

VALKYRIEN.*

O. FISHER & H. TROLLE.

P. SKRAM.

INGOLF* (Training Ship).

TWO FUNNELS.

(Yacht bow, 2 masts raking, two bell-topped funnels raking, paddle wheels.)

DANNEBROG (Royal Yacht).

GEJSER.*

TORPEDO CRAFT. Scale ; 1 inch = 160 feet.

Tumleren class t.b.* (3).

Nos. 4 & 5 t.b. (2).

Ormen t.b.*

Hvalrossen class t.b. (3). Fore funnels now raised.

Havörnen class t.b. (3).

Söridderen class t.b.* (3)

SUBMARINES. Scale : 1 inch = 80 feet.

Aegir class (5 or 6).

Havfruen class (6).

DANISH COAST SERVICE BATTLESHIP. (Kyst forsvarsskib.)

Note.
This ship was laid down in February, 1914, and was only launched in 1918. Very little work is being done on her at present, and it is impossible to state when she will be finished.

NIELS JUEL (July, 1918.)

Displacement, 3,900 tons. Complement,
Length (o.a.), 295·1 feet. Beam, 53·5 feet. Draught (full load, aft), 15·8 feet. Length (p.p.), 285·4 feet.

Guns (Krupp) :
2—12 inch, 45 cal. (A⁵).
8 or 10—4·7 inch, 45 cal.
2—12 pdr., 55 cal. (anti-aircraft)
Torpedo tubes :
2 submerged (broadside).
1 „ bow).
1 „ (stern).

Armour (Krupp) :
7″ Belt (amidships) ...
4″ Belt (ends)...........
7″ Turrets ....
6″ Casemates (KNC)...
7″ Bulkhead ....
7″ Conning Tower......

(No plans available, but similar to "Pedr Skram.")

Machinery : 2 screws. Boilers : Thornycroft. Designed H.P. 5500 = 16 kts. Coal : tons.
Notes.—Laid down at Copenhagen Royal Yard in Feb., 1914.

P. SKRAM, O. FISHER, H. TROLLE.

For Tabulated details see next page.

Armour (*see Notes*) :
7″ Belt (amidships) ...
4″ Belt (aft) ... ...
3″ Deck (forward) ...
[Deck flat on belt.]
7″ Turrets ... ...
6″ Casemates (KNC)...
7″ Bulkhead ... ...
7″ Conning tower ...

Ahead :
1—9·4 in.
2—5·9 in.

Astern :
1—9·4 in.
2—5·9 in.

Machinery : 2 sets, triple expansion, 2 screws. All are fitted with 6 Thornycroft boilers. Coal (*maximum*) : 255 tons in *O. Fisher* and *P. Skram* ; 245 tons in *H. Trolle.*

Gunnery Notes.—Bofors 1896 models in *P. Skram* ; Bofors 1896-1901 models in *O. Fisher.* In *H. Trolle* 9·4 inch are Canet 1896 model, and 5·9 inch are Bofors 1896 model.

Armour Notes.—Krupp armour in *P. Skram,* Creusot in other ships. Belt is 7 feet deep, 3½ feet above, and 3½ feet below water-line.

Torpedo Notes.—All tubes 18 inch and submerged : 1 bow, 1 stern, 2 broadside in *P. Skram,* 1 bow and 2 broadside in *O. Fisher* and *H. Trolle.*

Engineering Notes.—Trial : H.P. and speeds given in Table on next page as *O. Fisher* and *H. Trolle* did not reach designed speed of 16 kts. with 4200 I.H.P. on trials. Endurance is about 2000 miles at 10 kts. and 1050 miles at 14¾ kts.

General Notes.—All built at Copenhagen Dockyard. In plan above for *O. Fisher,* 6 pdrs. amidships are now 12 pdr. In all 2—12 or 6 pdr. anti-aircraft guns mounted on crowns of 9·4 inch barbettes.

Photo, Ebessen, Aarhus.

OLFERT FISHER. Fore chart house aft of bridges, also chart house at foot of mainmast. Searchlights on towers between foremast and funnel. Ventilators before funnel *high.*

Photo, Ebessen, Aarhus.

PEDER SKRAM. *No* ventilators and *no* yard on mainmast. Funnel rather shorter and thicker than in other 2 ships. Three searchlights round foot of foremast. Also note 12 pdr. guns on roof of 9·4 inch barbettes (are anti-aircraft type now).

Photo, Ebessen, Aarhus.

HERLUF TROLLE. Has only two searchlights at feet of masts. Ventilators before funnel *low.*

(HERLUF TROLLE CLASS—3 SHIPS.)

The three differ in dimensions and armament as follows:—

	PEDER SKRAM.	OLFERT FISHER.	HERLUF TROLLE.
Launched	May, 1908	1903	1899
Displacement (tons)...	3735	3650	3595
Complement	257	255	255
Length (ft.)	275⅗ (*p.p.*)	271⅔ (*p.p.*)	271⅓ (*p.p.*)
Beam (ft.)	51¾	50½	49½
Max. draught (ft.) ...	16⅓	16¾	16½
Armament	2—9·4 inch, 43 cal. 4—5·9 in., 50 cal. 6—14 pdr.* 2—6 pdr.✷ 2—1 pdr. 2 Machine	2—9·4 inch, 43 cal. 4—5·9 inch, 43 cal. 6—12 pdr. 2—6 pdr.✷ 2—1 pdr. 2 machine	2—9·4 inch, 40 cal. 4—5·9 inch, 43 cal. 12—6 pdr.✷ 2 machine
All 18 inch tubes.	4 tubes (*submerged*)	3 tubes (*submerged*)	3 tubes (*submerged*)
H.P. } Trials { Speed } Trials {	5400 15·9	4600 15·8	4400 15·6

* 2 of these guns anti-aircraft type.

(**For plans and illustrations, v. preceding page.**)

VALKYRIEN, as re-constructed.   *Photo, Ebessen, Aarhus.*

VALKYRIEN (1888 re-built, 1913). 3020 tons. Complement, 282. Dimensions: 265¾ *p.p.* × 43¼ × 18 feet (*maximum* draught). Guns: 2—5·9 inch (Bofors, 50 cal.), 2—12 pdr. (Danish), 2—6 pdr. AA., 2 machine, 3—15 inch *above water* tubes (2 bow, 1 stern). 2½ inch deck. Designed H.P. 5300 = 17·4 kts. Coal: 496 tons. Now used as a Training Ship.

DANISH COAST SERVICE SHIP

(*Kystforsvårsskibe*).

1918 *Photo.*

SKJOLD (1896). Laid down at Copenhagen 1893, and completed 1899. Displacement, 2200 tons. Complement, 137. Dimensions: 227½ × 38 × 13¾ feet. Guns (Krupp): 1—9·4 in., 40 cal., 3—4·7 in., 40 cal., 4—6 pdr., 1 Machine. Armour (Harvey): 10″ Belt, 3″ Belt (aft), 2″ Deck (bow), [Deck flat on belt amidships.], 8″ Big turret, 5″ Small turrets, 7″ Bulkhead, 8″ Conning tower. Machinery: I.H.P. 2400 = 13·4 kts. Boilers: 4 Thornycroft. Coal capacity: 110 tons (*maximum*).

Photo, Ebessen, Aarhus.

HEJMDAL (1894, rebuilt 1909). 1313 tons. Complement, 156. Dimensions: 231¾ (*p.p.*) × 34 × 11¾ feet. Guns (Krupp): 2—4·7 inch, 4—20 pdr., 4—6 pdr. (1 converted to AA.), 2 machine, 2 torpedo tubes. (1—18 inch, 1—15 inch). 1¼″ deck amidships. 6″ engine hatches. H.P. 3100 = 17 kts. Thornycroft boilers. Coal: 150 tons.

(*Continued on next page.*)

GEJSER.   HEJMDAL.   *Photo, Ebessen, Aarhus.*

GEJSER (1892, rebuilt 1907). 1282 tons. Complement, 156. Dimensions : $231\frac{3}{4}$ (p.p.) $\times 34 \times 11\frac{1}{4}$ feet.
Guns (Krupp) : 2—4·7 inch, 4—20 pdr., 4—6 pdr.* 2 machine. 2 torpedo tubes (1—18 inch, 1—
15 inch) *above water.* $1\frac{3}{4}''$ deck amidships. 6″ engine hatches. H.P. 3100 = 17·1 kts. Coal : 150
tons. Boilers, 8 Thornycroft (first ship to be so fitted). Training Ship for Boys.

* 1—6 pdr. converted to AA.

20 *(+ 10)* **Torpedo Boats.** *Torpedobaade.*

No	Class	Date.	Displacement	H.P.	Max. speed	Fuel	Complement	T tubes	Max. draug't
			tons		kts.	tons			feet
10	Söhunden (Ny)	'15—'19	108	2000	24·3	...	22	...	9
3	Hvalrossen (Ny)	1913	187	3500	26	...	30	4	7
3	Söridderen (Y)	1911	271	5000	27·5	80 tons coal	33	5	$6\frac{1}{4}$
3	Tumleren (S)	1911	295	5000	27·5	,, ,,	33	5	$7\frac{1}{4}$
1	Ormen (No)	1907	105	2100	26·2	11 tons coal	21	3	$8\frac{1}{4}$
3	Havörnen (Ny)	'98—'97	138	2100	23·5	16 tons coal	24	4	$7\frac{1}{4}$
2	T 6, T 7 (Ny)	1893	128	1400	20	13 tons coal	20	4	$7\frac{1}{4}$
1	No. 1	1891	90	810	18	13 tons coal	17	2	7
2	No. 5, No. 4 (T)	1888	115	1200	21	15 tons coal	20	1—2	$7\frac{1}{2}$
2	No. 2, No. 3 (T)	1887	110	1300	22	14 tons coal	20	1—2	$7\frac{1}{2}$

(Ny)=Navy type. (S)=Schichau type. (Y)=Yarrow type. (No)=Normand type. (T)=Thornycroft type.

(Continued in next column)

Photo wanted.

10 *Söhunden* class : **Havhesten, Makrelen, Narvhalen, Nordkaperen, Söhunden** (all launched
1917), **Söloven, Springeren, Stören,** (launched 1916), and *two others* (names not known) *building.*
All by Copenhagen D.Y. Dimensions : 126·3 (o.a.) $\times 13\cdot9 \times 8\cdot8$ feet *normal* draught (9 feet *full load* draught.)
Armament : 2—6 pdr., 30 cal. (anti-aircraft) ; 2—18 inch tubes.

Now have raised fore funnels.   *Photo, Ebessen, Aarhus.*

3 *Hvalrossen* type : **Delfinen, Hvalrossen, Svaerdfisken** (all 1913), built at Copenhagen Dockyard.
Dimensions : $148\frac{1}{4} \times 17 \times 7$ feet. Armament : 1—14 pdr. (aft.), 4—18 inch tubes in 2 twin-deck mountings amidships.

FLYVEFISKEN.   *Photo, Ebessen, Aarhus.*

3 *Yarrow* type : **Söridderen, Soulven, Flyvefisken** (all 1911). First built by Yarrow, others by
Burmeister & Wain, Copenhagen. Dimensions : $181\frac{1}{4} \times 18 \times 6\frac{1}{4}$ feet. Armament : 2—14 pdr., 5—18 inch tubes.
There are 10 w.t. compartments. On trial did 5300 I.H.P. = 28·2 max. Curtis turbines in *Söridderen.* Yarrow
boilers in all.

(Continued on next page.)

(Plan as *Söridderen* class on previous page.)

Old Torpedo Boats.

VINHUNDEN. *Photo, Ebessen, Aarhus.*

3 *Schichau* type: **Tumleren, Vindhunden, Spœkhuggeren** (all 1911). First by Schichau, others by Copenhagen Dockyard. Dimensions: 185×19×7·3 feet. Armament· 2—14 pdr., 5—18 inch tubes, 1 in bows *above water,* other 4 on deck. Turbine engines and Normand boilers in all. Radius of action : 1400 miles at 14 kts.

HAJEN. *Photo, Ebessen, Aarhus.*

3 *Havörnen* class named **Havörnen** (1897, rebuilt 1902). **Hajen** (1896, rebuilt 1908). **Söbjörnen** (1898, rebuilt 1908.) All built at Copenhagen D.Y. Armament: 1—3 pdr., 1 M.G., 4 tubes (all 18 inch in *Havörnen* and *Söbjörnen* : 2—18 inch + 2—15 inch in *Hajen.*

2 *Makrelen* class: **T 6** (ex-*Makrelen*), **T 7** (ex-*Nordkaperen*), built at Copenhagen, D.Y., 1893. Guns : 2 machine, 4 tubes (2—18 inch, 2—15 inch.)

Following five T.B. all used for Subsidiary Service.

Photo wanted.

1 *Navy* type: **No. 1** (ex *Springeren*), built at Copenhagen D.Y., 1891, rebuilt 1902. Armament: 2 machine guns and 2—18 inch torpedo tubes.

Photo, Ebessen, Aarhus.

1 *Normand* type: **Ormen** (Copenhagen D.Y. 1907). 124·7 × 14 × 8·5 feet. Armament: 2—1 pdr., 1—18 inch tube (bow, *submerged*), 2—18 inch amidships.

No. 4. *Photo, Ebessen, Aarhus.*

2 *Thornycroft* type : **No. 4** (ex *Havhesten*, 1888, rebuilt 1904-5), **No. 5** (ex *Narvhalen*, 1888, rebuilt 1897). Armament: 2 machine guns. Originally had 4 tubes, but now have only 1 or 2—15 inch tubes.

2 *Thornycroft* type: **No. 2** (ex *Sölöven*), **No. 3** (ex *Stören*, both 1887, and rebuilt 1897). Armament and tubes as Nos. 4 and 5 above.

(Patrol Boats listed on next page.)

12 + 6. Submarines (*Undervandsbaade*).

No.	Type	Date.	Dis-place-ment	H.P.	Max. speed	Fuel or Battery Endurance.	Tubes	Com-ple-ment	Max. draug't
			tons						feet
6	*Bellona* (N)	'15-'18	$\frac{301}{369}$	$\frac{1000}{650}$	$\frac{15}{10\frac{1}{2}}$	...	4	...	$8\frac{3}{4}$
5	*Aegir* (HW)	'12-'15	$\frac{185}{235}$	$\frac{450}{340}$	$\frac{13.5}{8}$	1400 miles at 10 kts.	3	11	8
6	*Havmanden* (HW)	'11-'14	$\frac{164}{204}$	$\frac{450}{275}$	$\frac{13\frac{1}{2}}{8}$	For 920 at 12 kts. ...	2	11	8

(N) = Navy type.   (HW) = Hay-Whitehead type, designed by Marley F. Hay and Messrs. Whitehead, Fiume, Austria.

Building or Completing.

6 *Navy* type: **Bellona** (1918), **Flora** (1918), and **Rota** (1917), and *three others,* (names not known.) All built at Copenhagen D.Y. Burmeister & Wain 6-cylinder, 4-cycle Diesel engines. Dimensions: 155.7 × 14.4 × 8.8 feet. Armament: 1—6 pdr. anti-aircraft gun; 4—18 inch torpedo tubes.

HAVFRUEN.   *Photo, Ebessen Aarhus.*

6 *Hay-Whitehead* type:—**Havmanden** (1911) and **Havfruen** (1912), **Thetis** (1912), built by Whitehead & Co., Fiume, and **Najaden** (1913), **Nymfen** (1914), **Den Andra April** (1913), built at Copenhagen D.Y. 1 set 6-cyl. Diesel engines. Dimensions: 118¾ × 11·9 × 8 feet. 2—18 inch torpedo tubes. Radius of action: *on surface* (additional to that given in table) 1400 miles at 10 kts ; *submerged* 2 hrs. 50 mins. continuous running at 8 kts.

RAN : (now has an anti-aircraft gun, probably before C.T.)   *Photo, Ebessen, Aarhus.*

5 *Hay-Whitehead* type :—**Aegir** (1914), **Galathea** (1914), **Neptun** (1914), **Ran** (1915). **Triton** (1914), all built at Copenhagen D.Y. Diesel motors. Dimensions : 133½ × 12 × 8 feet. Armament : 1—1 pdr. anti-aircraft, and 3—18 inch torpedo tubes. These boats are an enlarged and slightly improved *Havmanden* design.

Patrol Boats.

No.	Date.	Tons.	H.P.	Kts.	Guns.	T.T.
9, 8 ...	'94—'95	47	330 =	13	1—3 pdr., 1 M.G.	1—14 inch.
7, 6, 5, 4	'89—'90	22	180 =	12	2 M.G.	2 Spar.
13, 12 ...	1889	25	350 =	17		
10, 11 ...	1888	17	180 =	15	All have	
15, 14 ...	1886	16	170 =	13	1—1 pdr.	2—14 inch.
3, 2 ...	1884	16	150 =	15		
1 ...	1879	39	350 =	20	1—1 pdr.	1—14 inch.

DANISH MISCELLANEOUS.

Mine Ships—(*Mineskibe*).

> *Building or Completing.*

TWO SMALL MINELAYERS of 200 tons, building or completing.

> *No photo available.*
>
> (*See Silhouettes.*)

LOSSEN (1910). 628 tons. Complement, 53. 149·3 (*p.p.*) × 28 × 9·5 feet. Guns: 2—14 pdrs. I.H.P. 900 = 13 kts. Coal: 20 tons. Carries about 150—180 mines

HJÆLPEREN (1890). 283 tons. Complement, 40. 125·6 (*p.p.*) × 22·2 × 7·5 feet. 3 M.G. I.H.P. 330 = 11 kts.

Gunboats (*Kanonbaade*).

(*Employed on Special Service.*)

GULDBORGSUND (1884, re-built 1903). 270 tons. Complement, 46. 119 × 20 × 8·1 feet. Guns: 2—3 pdr., 4 M.G. H.P. 400 = 11·6 kts.

> *No photo available.*

LILLE BELT (1875, re-built 1894). 250 tons. Complement, 30. 85·6 (*p.p.*) × 26·2 × 7·3 feet (*mean* draught). Guns: 2—3 pdr., 4 machine. H.P. 200 = 7·6 kts.

(*Training Ship for Engineers.*)

FALSTER (1873, re-built 1906). 380 tons. Complement, 50. 112·5 (*p.p.*) × 29 × 8·7 feet. Guns: 2—3 pdr., 4 machine. H.P. 500 = 9·8 kts.

Torpedo Transport (*Torpedo Transportbaad*).

> *No photo available.*

SLEIPNER (——) 80 tons. 73 × 14·8 × 5·9 feet (*mean* draught). Guns: not known. I.H.P. 110 = kts.

Repair Ship (*Vaerkstedsskib*).

> *No photo available.*

GRÖNSUND (1883, re-built 1905-6). Old gunboat of 260 tons. Complement, 49. 119 × 20 × 8·1 feet. Guns: 2 M.G. (B?)* H.P. 260 = 11·6 kts.

*Not certain if this ship has been re-built with Diesel engines, or not.

Surveying Ships (*Opmaalingsskibe*).

KRIEGER, MARSTRAND, 170 tons, **WILLIMOËS,** 160 tons. d14 × 17·5 × 6·4 feet (*mean* draught). All launched 1861. Complements, 28 to 39. I.H.P. 240 to 260 = 13 kts., now 11 kts. (*or less*). Guns: 2 machine.

(*Continued on next page.*)

2 c 2

Fishery Cruiser (*Fiskerriinspektiouskib*).

ISLANDS FALK (1906). 760 tons. Complement. 52. 170·6 (*p.p.*) × 29·3 × 14·7 feet. Guns : 2—3 pdr. I H.P. 1100 = 13 kts.

Coastguard Vessels (*Inspektionsskibe*).

BESKYTTEREN (1900). 447 tons. Comp. 36. 134 × 24·5 × 11·5 feet. Guns : 2 –3 pdr. I.H.P. 620 = 11 kts.

Coastguard Vessels—(*Continued*).

Photo, S. Anderson, Esq.

ABSALON (1877). 292 tons. Complement, 26. 125 (*p.p.*) × 20·1 × 8·8 feet. Guns : 2—3 pdr. H.P. 390 = 10 kts.

No photo available.

DIANA (Holland, 1916). 260 tons. 116·5 (*p.p.*) × 21·6 × 8·8 feet. Guns : 2—3 pdr. I.H.P. 400 = 10·5 kts. Complement, 27.

No photo available.

FENRIS (Holland, 1915). 190 tons. 86·4 (*p.p.*) × 20·7 × 9·2 feet. Guns : 2—3 pdr. I.H.P. 420 = 12 kts. Complement, 18.

No photo available.

SALTHOLM (Copenhagen, 1882). 300 tons. 135·6 (*p p.*) × 22·4 × 8·4 feet. Guns : 2—3 pdr. I.H.P. 380 = kts.

Training Ship for Boys (*Skoleskib*).

INGOLF (1876) 1000 tons. Complement, 125. 193·6 (*p.p.*) × 28 × 13·6 feet. Guns : 3 machine. I.H.P. 600 = 10·5 kts.

Cruiser **VALKYRIEN** (described on a previous page) is also used as a Training Ship for cadets, and gunboat **FALSTER** (*v.* preceding page) as a Training Ship for engineers. Cruiser **GEJSER** to replace *Ingolf* as Training Ship for boys. Also three Cutters, *Bacchus, Svanen* and *Thyra*.

Royal Yacht (*Dampskib til Hs. Majestæt Kongens Brug*).

Photo, Ebessen, Aarhus.

DANNEBROG (1879). 1190 tons. 235 (*p.p.*) × 26·8 × 10·4 feet. Guns : 2 small. I.H.P. 940 = 13 kts.

Also *C. F. Grove, Kattegat, Nordsöen* and *Lerenörn*, all small unarmed vessels of 400-470 tons, used as Light and Beacon Inspection Ships, &c.

(ROYAL) NETHERLANDS NAVY.

Revised from the 1919 Edition of the Official Year Book "Koninklijke Marine."

ENSIGN. JACK. & MERCANTILE — ADMIRAL OF THE FLEET — ADMIRAL — VICE-ADMIRAL — REAR-ADMIRAL — CAPTAIN COMMANDING A DIVISION — SENIOR NAVAL OFFICER — ROYAL NAVAL RESERVE. — ROYAL STANDARD H.M. THE QUEEN — H.R.H. THE PRINCE CONSORT — RED — BLUE — WHITE — ORANGE

Netherlands Uniforms.

	1	2	3	4	5	6	7	8	9
	Admiraal	Luitenant-Admiraal	Vice-Admiraal	Schout-by-nacht	Kapitein ter Zee	Kapitein Luitenant ter Zee	Luitenant ter Zee 1e Kl.	Luitenant ter Zee 2e Kl	Luitenant ter Zee 3e Kl.
Corresponding British or U.S.	Admiral of the Fleet	Admiral	Vice-Admiral	Rear-Admiral	Captain	Commander	Lieut. (over 11 years)	Lieut. (under 11 years)	Sub. Lieut.

In relative ranks—

Doctors have insignia 4 to 8 without the curl.
Paymasters   ,,   5 to 9   ,,   in silver.
Engineers   ,,   5 to 8 with the curl with blue velvet between stripes.

The broad stripes in ranks 1—4 are 2 inches wide (5 c/m); 5—8, $\frac{2}{5}$ inch (1 c/m); No. 9, $\frac{1}{5}$ inch. Distance between stripes is $\frac{1}{5}$ inch (5 m/m).

Naval Construction.

None of the Royal Naval Yards in Holland appear to have built any warships for some years past. Warship construction is carried out by three firms : (1) Koninklijke Maatschaapij "de Schelde" (the Royal Company "de Schelde") at Flushing; (2) Maatschaapij "Fijenoord" Rotterdam, and (3) Nederlandsche Scheepsbouw Maatschaappij, Amsterdam. All these firms built warships of all types, except the last named, which does not build submarines. Werf Gusto (A. F. Smulders), Schiedam, and the Conrad Co., Haarlem, have also built special Submarine Depot Ships for foreign Navies. In the Dutch East Indies, some small auxiliaries have been built at Surabaya, Batavia, &c.

Notes :

For Arsenals, Docks, Slips, &c., in Holland and Dutch East Indies, a revised and extended list is given on the next page but one.

All displacements are given in *metric* tons. Regarding the two sets of figures given for complements on later pages, (H) denotes complement when serving in home or European waters; (A) denotes complement when serving in Dutch East Indies or abroad.

Personnel : About 11,000 all ranks, navy and marine infantry (enlisted men).
Mercantile Marine : —— steamers of 1,574,000 tons *gross*; 468 sailing of 60,364 tons *gross*.
Principal Trade Ports : Rotterdam, Amsterdam, Flushing.
Coinage : Guilder (or florin) (100 cents) = 1s. 8d. British, or 40 cents U.S.A.
Oversea Possessions : Dutch East Indies (Sumatra, Java, Borneo, etc.); Dutch Guiana (Surinam) Curaçoa.
Minister of Marine :
Colour of Ships : Grey Ships serving in East Indies are white. Submarines have national colours (red, white, blue) painted in vertical stripes over bows.

Naval Guns (Krupp Models). All details unofficial.

Notation	Calibre		Official Mark	Long.	Weight of Gun.	Weight A. P. Shell.	Initial Velocity.	Max penetration with A. P. capped against K. C.		
	in.	c/m.		cals.	tons.	lbs.	ft. secs.	8000 in.	5000 in.	3000 in.
A³	11	28	...	42½	31	595	2920	8	13	15½
A	9·4	24	"No. 2"	40	24½	375	2788	3½	7½	10¼
AA	9·4	24	"No. 1"	40	24¼	375	2690	4	8½	10¾
E	8·2	21	"A"	35	16	308½	1740	—	—	3½
F	5·9	15	"No. 6"	50	5⅔	101½	3084	—	—	—
F	5·9	15	...	50	5½	101½	3084	—	—	—
F	5·9	15	"No. 5"	40	5	90⅓	2788	—	—	—
F	5·9	15	"No. 4"	40	4¾	90⅓	2444	—	—	—
F	5 9	15	"No. 2"*	40	4¼	100	2231	—	—	—
F	4·7	12	{ "No. 2" } { "No 1" }	40	2	52½	2231	—	—	—
F	4·1	10·5	"A"	50	...	40	2897	—	—	—

Velocities of 40-calibre guns are not service ones. In addition, there are 40 and 55 calibre (semi-automatic and anti-aircraft) models of 7·5 c/m. (3 inch, 13 pdr.) guns, a 9 pdr., (7·6 c/m.) Mark "A" mortar, a 5 c/m. 4 pdr., 3·7 c/m. 1 pdr., and various old types.

*"No. 3" model of the 5·9 inch/15 cm. is the same as the "No. 2" model.

NETHERLANDS RECOGNITION SILHOUETTES.

ONE FUNNEL.

DOLFIJN.
(*Fishery Patrol.*)

ZEEHOND.
(*Fishery Patrol.*)

KOETEI *class* (5).
("*Assahan*," "*Serdang*" & "*Siboga*" are Mine Layers ; have no gun aft.) **All E. I.**

BRINIO *class* gunboats (3).

BELLONA.
(*Gunnery Tender.*)

HYDRA
MEDUSA
(*Mine Layers.*)

C. DREBBEL.
(*Submarine Depot Ship.*)

M. H. TROMP.

J. V. HEEMSKERK.

DE RUYTER, H. HENDRIK (*plain funnel*)
and K. REGENTES. **All E. I.**

BORNEO.
(*Surveying Ship.*)

Aft barbettes normally hidden behind lowering bulwarks. With bulwarks raised, these ships appear to be flush-decked from stem to stern, and to have no aft barbettes.

TWO FUNNELS.

HOLLAND *class* (4 ships).
("*Holland*" and "*Gelderland*" *Training Ships.*)

DE ZEVEN PROVINCIEN.

SUBMARINES. **Scale : 1 inch = 80 feet.**

K 1.—(**E. I.**)

O 8.

O 7.

O 6.

O 2—O 5 class (4).

M 1

O 1.

TORPEDO CRAFT. **Scale : 1 inch = 160 feet.**

EMPONG
CERBERUS.—**E.I.**

(*T.B.—Identity
uncertain.*)

G 1—12 type (11).
(*Some have 2 masts.*)

TANGKA and OPHIR
types (6).

DRAAK 1st class t.b. (8). **All E. I.**
M. GARDEYN class (3)
same but smaller.

G 13—16 type (4).

Z 1—4 type (4).

Z 5—8 type (4).

WOLF class (8) t.b.d.
(*Vary a little in details.*)
All E. I.

DOCKS.

Note.—All the following particulars have been communicated to "Fighting Ships" by courtesy of Koninklijke Nederlandsche Vereeniging, "Onze Vloot" (Royal Netherlands Association, "Our Fleet") during 1918.

Arsenals.

WILLEMSOORD (Nieuwediep).—No slips. Dry dock No. 1 : 360¾ × 68¾ × 19½ ft. No. 2 : 262¼ × 65½ × 15 ft. Floating dock : 131½ × 23 × 7¾ ft.

HELLEVOETSLUIS.—One slip. Dry dock No. 1 : 239½ × 51¾ × 14 ft. No. 2 : 231½ × 51¾ × 7½ ft.

Private Establishments.

AMSTERDAM :—

Amsterdam Dry Dock Co.—Juliana-dock : Length, 615 ft. ; breadth, 118¼ ft. For ships with a draught of 20 ft. Carrying capacity, 16,500 tons. Wilhelmina-dock : Length, 424½ ft. ; breadth, 96 ft. For ships with a draught of 18¾ ft. Carrying capacity, 7500 tons. Koninginne-dock : Length, 400 ft. ; breadth, 92 ft. For ships with a draught of 17 ft. Carrying capacity, 4000 tons. Koningsdock : Length, 400 ft ; breadth, 72 ft. For ships with a draught of 15 ft. Carrying capacity, 3000 tons.

Floating Dry Dock Co., Ltd.—No. 1 : 213¼ × 62½ × 20½ ft. No. 2 : 200 × 62½ × 20½ ft. No. 3 : 164 × 62½ × 18½ ft.

MIDDELBURG :—

The Royal Co. : "De Schelde" (Koninklijke Maatschaapij de Schelde).—Dry dock, 413½ × 65½ × 13—15 feet.

ROTTERDAM :

Municipal Floating Docks.—No. 1 : *Length, 157½ ft. ; breadth, 69 ft. Carrying capacity, 2000 tons. No. 2 : Length, 295½ ft. ; breadth, 69 ft. Carrying capacity, 4000 tons. For ships with a draught of 18¾ ft. No. 3 : Length, 361 ft. ; breadth, 69 ft. Carrying capacity, 6000 tons. No. 4 : Length, 567½ ft. ; breadth, 95 ft. Carrying capacity, 15,000 tons.

* Dock No.1 can be coupled to dock No.2.

Ships of 229½ ft. length can be taken into dock No 1, ships of 377¼ ft. length into dock No. 2, ships of 459 ft. length into dock No. 3, and ships of 656 ft. length into dock No. 4.

ROTTERDAM (*continued*) :—

Rotterdam Dry Dock Co.—Prins Hendrikdock No. 1 : Length, 439¾ ft. ; breadth, 95 ft. For ships with a draught of 19¾ ft. Carrying capacity, 7500 tons. Prins Hendrikdock No. 2 : Length, 300 ft. ; breadth, 70½ ft. For ships with a draught of 18¼ ft. Carrying capacity, 3000 tons.

Shipbuilding Co. : "New Waterway." — Dockharbour : 1312 × 656 × 29½ ft. Slips—No 1 : Length, 406¼ ft. ; breadth, 19¾ ft. For ships up to 8000 tons. No 2 : Length, 400 ft. ; breadth, 19¾ ft. For ships up to 8000 tons. No. 3 : Length, 406½ ft. ; breadth, 23 ft. For ships up to 12,000 tons. No. 4 : Length, 400 ft. ; breadth, 23 ft. For ships up to 12,000 tons. No. 5 : Length, 886 ft. ; breadth, 39½ ft. For ships up to 18,000 tons.

Wilton's Engine Works & Shipbuilding Yard, Ltd.—Docks—No. 1 : Length, 426½ ft. : breadth, 70 ft. For ships up to a length of 492 ft. Carrying capacity, 8500 tons. No. 2 : Length, 367½ ft. ; breadth, 58 ft. For ships up to a length of 426½ ft. Carrying capacity, 4500 tons. Side slip : 347½ ft. long, for ships to 3000 tons. Wilhelmina-dock : Length, 510 ft. ; breadth, 81 ft. For ships up to a length of 574 ft. Carrying capacity, 14,000 tons.

VLISSINGEN (Flushing) :—

The Royal Co. : "De Schelde" (K. M. de Schelde.)—Dry dock : 243 × 52½ × 11 ft.

DUTCH EAST INDIES.

Arsenals.

SOERABAIA or SURABAYA (Java).—Two floating docks : 328 × 62 × 22¾ ft. and 197 × 59 × 17½ ft.

BATAVIA (Java).—Floating dock : 324 × 67 × 22 ft.

SABANG (Sumatra).—Dry dock : 295¼ × 78¾ × 34½ ft.

Private Establishments.

Floating dock : 460 × 82 × 24½ ft. (property of the Netherlands Government) and another 320 × 57½ ft. (1400 tons).

Photo, Fotopersbureau " Holland," Amsterdam.

DE ZEVEN PROVINCIEN (March, 1909).

Displacement, 6530 tons. Complement, 447 (A), 407 (H).
Length (o.a.), 333 feet. Beam, 56·1 feet. *Maximum* draught, 20·2 feet.

Guns (Krupp) :
2—11 inch, 42½ cal. (A³)
4—5·9 inch, 40 cal. "No. 5."
10—13 pdrs., 55 cal. S.A. "No. 1"
1—9 pdr. mortar.
4—1 pdr.
2 machine.
Torpedo tubes :
None.

Armour (Krupp) :
6" Belt (amidships) ......
4" Belt (ends) ....
2" Deck (on slopes) ......
9¾" Main Barbettes (N.C.)
9¾" Shields ....
4" Small Barbettes
9¾" Conning Tower (N.C.)

Machinery : 2 sets triple expansion. 2 screws. Boilers : 8 Yarrow. Designed H.P. 8000 = 16 kts. (Trials : 8516 = 16·3 kts.) Coal : *normal*, 700 tons ; *maximum*, 1030 tons. Radius of action, 2100 miles at 15·3 kts. ; 5100 miles at 8 kts.

Notes.—Main belt is 7 feet wide. Laid down Feb., 1908, at Amsterdam D.Y.

Note.—Aft barbette is hidden behind lowering bulwarks.

Photo, Fotopersbureau "Holland," Amsterdam.

JACOB VAN HEEMSKERCK (September, 1906).
Displacement, 5000 tons. Complement, 351.

Length (*o.a.*), 321½ feet. Beam, 49·9 feet ; Beam outside sponsons 55·4 feet. *Max.* draught, 18¾ feet.

Guns (Krupp) :
2—9·4 in., 45 cal. (*AA*). 'No. 2.'
6—5·9 in., 40 cal. 'No. 5.'
6—13 pdrs.
1—9 pdr. mortar.
4—1 pdr.
2 machine.
Torpedo tubes (18 inch) :
1 *submerged* (bow).
1 *submerged* (stern).

Armour (Krupp) :
6″ Belt (amidships) ...
4″ Belt (ends) ....
2″ Deck (reinforcing belt)
7¾″ Main Barbettes ...
4″ Hoods to these ...
6″ Small Barbettes ...
8″ Conning tower (K.C.)

Ahead :
1—9·4 in.
2—5·9 in.

Astern :
1—9·4 in.
2—5·9 in.

Broadside : 2—9·4 in., 3—5·9 in.

Machinery : 2 sets triple expansion. 2 screws. Boilers : 6 Yarrow. Designed H.P. 6400 = 16·5 kts. Coal : *normal* — tons ; *maximum* 610 tons.

Notes.—Main belt is 6 feet wide and about 220 feet long. Begun at Amsterdam D.Y., 1905, and completed, May, 1908. *Trials* : I.H.P. 6600 = 16·7 kts. Radius of action : 3300 miles at 10 kts

Note.—Aft barbette is hidden behind lowering bulwarks.

Photo, Geiser.

MARTEN HARPERTZOON TROMP (1904).
Displacement, 5300 tons. Complement, 349 (H), 377 (A).

Length (*o.a.*), 330·7 feet. Beam, 49·8 feet. *Maximum* draught, 18·7 feet.

Guns—(M. '01) :
2—9·4 inch, 40 cal. (*AA*). 'No. 2.'
4—5·9 inch, 40 cal. 'No. 5.'
8—13 pdr. "No. 3 "
1—9 pdr. mortar.
4—1 pdr.
2 machine.
Torpedo tubes (18 in.) :
3 *above water.*

Armour (Krupp) :
6″ Belt (amidships) ......
4″ Belt (ends) ....
2″ Deck (reinforcing belt)
7¾″ Barbettes (N.C.) ......
4″ Hoods to these ......
3″ Small turrets ....
7¾″ Conning tower ......

Ahead :
1—9·4 in.
2—5·9 in.

Astern :
1—9·4 in.
2—5·9 in.

Machinery : 2 sets triple expansion. 2 screws. Boilers : 6 Yarrow. Designed H.P. 6400 = 16 kts. Coal : *normal* 680 tons ; *maximum* 830 tons. Radius of action : 1600 miles at 14½ kts., 4100 miles at 9¼ kts. *Trials* ('06).—6,405 I.H.P. = 16·7 kts. Begun at Amsterdam D.Y., 1903, and completed 1906.

All on East Indies Station.

KONINGIN REGENTES (1900), **DE RUYTER** (1901), & **HERTOG HENDRIK** (1902).

Length (o.a.), 316·9 feet.   Beam, 49·8 feet.   *Maximum* draught, 19 feet.

Displacement, 5080 tons.   Complement, 375 (A), 342 (H).

Guns—(M. '99) :
  2—9·4 inch, 40 cal. (A). 'No. 1.'
  4—5·9 inch, 40 cal. 'No. 4.'*
  8—13 pdr.†
  1—9 pdr. mortar.
  2—1 pdr.
  2—1 pdr. (anti-aircraft).
  2 machine.
Torpedo tubes (18 in.) :
  2 *above water*.‡
  1 *submerged* (bow).‡

Armour (Krupp) :
  6″ Belt (amidships) ...... ▨
  4″ Belt (ends) .... ▥
  2″ Deck (reinforcing belt)
  9¾″ Barbettes .... ▨
  4″ Hoods to these .... ▥
  9¾″ Conning tower (fore) ▨

Ahead :
1—9·4 in.
2—5·9 in.

Astern :
1—9·4 in.
2—5·9 in.

Broadside : 2—9·4 in., 2—5·9 in.

Gunnery Notes.—} * Number of 5·9 inch guns may be increased to *six*.
               † Number of 13 pdrs. may be reduced to *four*.

‡ *Torpedo Notes*.—In H. Hendrik all three tubes are *above water*.

Armour Notes.—The belt is 5¾ feet wide and four feet of it is below the waterline.

Machinery : 2 sets triple expansion. 2 screws. Boilers : 6 Yarrow. Designed H.P. 6300 (6400 in K. R.) =16 kts.   Coal : *normal* 680 tons ; *maximum* 830 tons.   Same radius of action as *M. H. Tromp*.   *K. Regentes* begun 1898 and *H. Hendrik*, 1900, both at Amsterdam D.Y. : *De Ruyter* begun 1900, by Fijenoord Co., Rotterdam.

DE RUYTER.   *Photo, Fotopersbureau "Holland,"*
Note.—H. Hendrik has *plain* funnel.   In these ships after barbette may be hidden behind lowering bulwarks.

Photo, Fotopersbureau, "Holland."

JAVA (building) & SUMATRA (building).

Normal displacement, 7050 tons.   Complement, 474 (h), 482 (a).

Length (*o.a.*), 509·5 feet.   Beam, 52½ feet.   *Max.* draught, 18 feet.

Guns (Krupp) :
10—5·9 inch (50 cal.) " No. 6 "
4—13 pdr. S.A. (anti-aircraft)
4 machine.
Torpedo tubes :

Armour (Krupp) :
3″ Belt ....
 ″ Deck... ....
 ″ Gun shields .....
 ″ Funnel bases ...
 ″ Conning tower

Ahead :
4—5·9 in.

Broadside : 7—5·9 in.

Astern :
4—5·9 in.

Machinery : 3 sets Krupp-Germania turbines.   3 screws.   Boilers : 8 (*type unknown*).   Designed H.P., 65,000 = 30 kts.   Fuel, oil only : *normal*,   tons; *maximum*,   tons.   Radius of action : 5000 miles at 12 kts.

Name	Builder	Machinery	Laid down	Com-pleted	Trials.	Boilers	Best recent speed.
Sumatra	Nederlandsche Scheepsbouw Maatschappij, Amsterdam	Krupp, Germania	July,'16	1920			
Java	K. M. de Schelde, Flushing	Krupp, Germania	May,'16	1920			

* Contracted for, June, 1917.

General Notes.—These cruisers are being built in Dutch Yards from plans supplied by Krupp.   The German firm supplies materials, technical supervision, and a certain amount of skilled labour.   The shortage of certain metals and alloys in Germany may result in very slow construction of these ships, so long as the war lasts. Date of completion was first intended to be in 1918.   Belong to 1915-16 Naval Programme.   A third unit, *Celebes,* was provided by 1917-18 Programme, and her construction was contracted for by Fijenoord Co., Rotterdam.   In 1919 it was decided that *Celebes* should not be proceeded with.

GELDERLAND   (See next page.)

Photo, Fotopersbureau " Holland," Amsterdam.

NOORDBRABANT.   (See next page.)

Photo, Fotopersbureau " Holland," Amsterdam.

Old Protected Cruisers. (*Pantserdekschepen.*)

For Illustrations, see preceding page.

Gelderland has top on foremast *low*. The upper portions of funnels have steam-pipes run inside and are slightly thicker than lower portions. Ventilators between funnels rather prominent.

Noordbrabant has top on foremost fairly high. Compare her funnels with those of *Gelderland*.

(HOLLAND CLASS.)

GELDERLAND (1898), & **NOORDBRABANT** (1899). Displacement 4030 tons. Complement 381 (A), 325 (H). Length, (*o.a.*) 310·7 feet. Beam, 48½ feet. *Maximum* draught, 17¾ feet.

also

HOLLAND (1896) & **ZEELAND** (1897). Displacement 3900 tons. Complement 381 (A), 325 (H). Length, (*o.a.*) 306·1 feet. Beam, 48½ feet. *Maximum* draught, 17¾ feet.

Armour (Harvey and steel): 2″ Deck (steel). 4″ Engine hatches, 6″ Gun shields, 4″ Conning tower.

Guns: Re-armed during 1914-15 as follows:—

Gelderland.	*Noordbrabant.*	*Holland.*	*Zeeland.*
4—5·9 inch "No. 3."	10—4·7 inch (viz.:	10—4·7 inch "No. 2"	2—5·9 inch "No. 2."
8—13 pdr. "No. 2."	2—4·7 inch	2—13 pdr. "No. 1."	8—4·7 inch "No. 1."
	"No. 3" + 8—4·7		2—13 pdr. "No. 1."
	inch "No. 2.")		
	2—13 pdr. "No. 1."		

and in all, 1—9 pdr. mortar 4—1 pdr., 2 machine.
Torpedo tubes: 1 *submerged* in *Gelderland* and *Noordbrabant* only.

Machinery: 2 sets 3 cylinder triple expansion. 2 screws. Boilers: *Gelderland* class, 12 Yarrow; *Holland* class, 8 Yarrow and 2 cylindrical. Designed H.P. (*n.d.*) 6400 = 17 kts. in *Holland*; 8400 = 18·5 kts. in other three ships; (*f.d.*) about 10,000 = 20 kts. Coal: *normal* 470 tons, *maximum* 930 tons in *Gelderland* and *Noordbrabant*; 1000 tons in *Holland* and *Zeeland*. Radius of action: 2100 miles at 16 kts., 4500 miles at 9·7 kts.

Name	*Builder*	*Machinery*	*Laid down*	*Com-pleted*	*First Trials:*	*Boilers*	*Best recent speed*
Holland	Amsterdam	...	'95	'98	10,836 = 19·75	} Yarrow,	
Zeeland	Flushing	De Schelde	'95	'98	9818 = 19·5	+ 2 cyl.	
Gelderland	Rotterdam	Fijencord	Feb.'97	'00	9867 = 20	} 12 Yarrow	
Noordbrabant	Flushing	De Schelde	Mar.'97	'99	10,070 = 20·1		

Notes.—*Holland* now serves as a Gunnery Training Ship, and *Gelderland* is employed as a Training Ship for Midshipmen and Cadets. *Zeeland* was to have proceeded to Dutch East Indies during the summer of 1919.

---

8 Destroyers (*Torpedobootjagers*).

No.	Type	Date	Dis-place-ment	H.P.	Max. Speed	Coal	Comp-lement	T. tubes	Max. Dra'ght
2	*Panter* (Y)	'12–'14	tons	8000—	30	tons	64	2	feet
2	*Lynx* (Y)	'12–'13	} 510	8500		120*			9¼
4	*Fret* (Y)	'09–'12							

Y = Yarrow design.　*+12¼ tons oil in 4 later boats.

HERMELIJN.　　　*Photo, Fotopersbureau " Holland," Amsterdam.*

(ALL ON EAST INDIES STATION.)

8 *Yarrow* type: **Fret** (1910), **Wolf** (1910), **Jakhals** (1911), **Bulhond** (1911), **Hermelijn** (1913), **Lynx** (1913), all built by K. M. " de Schelde," Flushing, **Panter** (1913), **Vos** (1913), both built by Fijenoord Co., Rotterdam. 510 tons. Dimensions: 230 (*o.a.*) × 22 × 6½ feet *normal* draught, *max.* draught 9¼ feet. Armament: 4—13 pdr. (55 cal., semi-auto.) "No. 2," 4 machine, 2—18 inch tubes. Designed H.P. 8000 to 8500 = 30 kts, (30 to 30·3 on trials). 4 Yarrow boilers. Radius of action: 2360 miles at 8½ kts. Last four carry 12¼ tons oil fuel.

42 Torpedo Boats (*Torpedobooten*).

No.	Type	Date	Displacement	H.P.	Max. Speed	Fuel	Complement	T. tubes	Max. Dra'ght
			tons			tons			feet
	29 Sea-going class—								
4	Z 8—Z 5	'14—'16	310	5600	27	52	39	4	5½
4	Z 4—Z 1	'15—'19	322	5500 (t)	27	53	39	4	
4	G 16— G 13	'12—'14	180	2600	25	44	27	3	8
3	)	'07—'09	)						
4	} G 12 - G 1	'05—'08	} 140	1900	25	30	25	3	7½
4	)	'03—'06	)						
3	)	'02—'04	)						
3	} Ophir	'00—'02	} 114	1900	25	40	25	3	7½
	10 1st class—								
3	Draak	'05—'07	)						
3	Sphinx	'01—'04	} 103	1200	24	21	14-6	3	6⅔
2	Hydra	'00—'01	)						
1	Empong	'88—'89	90	1000	22	16	16	...	6¼
1	Cerberus	'86—'88	84	800	21	12	14-6	3	7
	3 2nd class—								
3	M. Gardeyn	'04—'06	48	450	18	5	12	...	5⅘

Ophir class, 1st class and 2nd class boats are all Yarrow types.   (t) = Turbines.

Note.—*G 13-16, Z 1-8* may have 1—1 pdr. anti-aircraft guns.

4 *322 ton* boats, **Z 4—Z 1** (Ned. Scheepsb. Mij., Amsterdam, 1916-18.). 322 tons. Dimensions : 201 × 20½ × 6 feet. Guns : 2—13 pdr., 2 machine. Torpedo tubes : 4—17·7 inch (one twin deck mounting + 2 single ditto). Curtis type turbines. Boilers fitted to burn coal or oil. Carry 46 tons coal + 7 tons oil. Radius of action : 425 miles at 20 kts.

Note.—The original boats, Z 4—Z 1, building by the German Vulkan Co. in 1914, were appropriated by the German Navy, and are now the German Destroyers *V108—105*. These four "replace" boats were begun by the Nederlandsche Scheepsbouw Maatschappij, Amsterdam, in 1914, but owing to lack of materials they were not finished until 1919, or *after* the *Z8—Z5* boats listed above.

Z 8.   *Photo, Fotopersbureau " Holland," Amsterdam.*

4 *310 ton* boats, **Z 8, Z 7** (K. M. de Schelde, Flushing, 1915), **Z6, Z5** (Fijenoord Co., Rotterdam, 1915). 310 tons. Dimensions : 193 × 19⅔ × 5½ feet. Guns : 2—13 pdr., 2 machine. Torpedo tubes : 4—17·7 inch (one twin deck mounting + 2 single ditto). Designed H.P. 5700 to 5500 = 27 kts. (made about 27·4 on trials). Machinery : Reciprocating. Boilers fitted to burn coal or oil. Carry 45 tons coals + 7 tons oil. Radius of action : 425 miles at 20 kts. Completed 1916.

G13.   *Photo, Fotopersbureau, " Holland." Amsterdam.*

4 *180 ton* boats ('12-'14): **G 16, G 15** (Fijenoord Co., Rotterdam, 1914), **G 14, G 13** (K. M. de Schelde, Flushing, 1913), 180 tons. Dimensions : 162·4 × 17 × 4·6 feet. Armament : 2—13 pdr. "No. 4," 3—17·7 inch deck tubes. Designed H.P. 2600 = 25 kts. (26 kts. on trials.) Fuel : 44 tons. Boilers burn coal or oil fuel.

G5 (2 masts).

Photo, Fotopersbureau "Holland" Amsterdam.
G6 (1 mast).

3 ('07-'09 boats):—**G 9, 10 & 12.**
4 ('05-'08 boats):—**G 8—5.**
4 ('03-'06 boats):—**G 4—1.**

Armament: 2—4 pdr., 3—17·7 inch deck tubes (*93·5* 1 bow *submerged*, 2 deck tubes).
Radius : 1230 miles at 8 kts.

Note.—Names of **G8—G1** are *Cornelius Janssen de Haan,* (*G 8,*) *Jacob Cleydijck,* (*G 7*) *Pieter Constant* (*G 6*), *Roemer Vlacq* (*G 5*), *Willem Willemsze* (*G 4*), *Meijndert Jentjes* (*G 3*), *Jan Danielzoon van de Rijn* (*G 2*), and *Johan van Brakel* (*G 1*). They still bear these names, *G 8—G1* only being their identification marks. *G 11* mined and sunk off Vlieland, March, 1918. G 2 mined Feb., 1918 and salved in sections May be rebuilt.

Identity of above T.B. not exactly known, but she is believed to be one of the six boats given below, reconstructed at an unknown date.

Photo, Alfieri.

3 ('02-'04 boats) named :—**Tangka, Smeroe, Wajang.**
3 ('00-'02 boats) named :—**Ophir, Pangrango, Rindjani.**

Armament: 2—4 pdr., 3—17·7 inch deck tubes.
Radius : 1630 miles at 8 kts,

(IN EAST INDIES).

3 *Draak* class :—**Draak, Krokodil, Zeeslang.** (1906-7).
3 *Sphinx* class :—**Minotaurus, Python, Sphinx.** (1902-3).
2 *Hydra* class :—**Hydra, Scylla.** (1900).

Armament: 2—1 pdr., 3—17·7 inch deck tubes.
(3 *Draak* Class ; 1 bow *submerged*, 1 deck tube).

(*Nominal* radius of all these class boats about 1500 at 8½ kts.)
Note.—All these 8 belong exclusively to the East Indies Marine.

1 *Empong* class : **Empong** (1888). 86 tons.
1 *Ardjoeno* class : **Cerberus** (1888), 84 tons*

Armament : 2—1 pdr., *Empong,* no tubes. 2—17·7 inch deck tubes
+ 1 *submerged* bow in *Cerberus.*

* *Cerberus* belongs to East Indies Marine.

No photos available.

These are just like *Draak* class but much smaller.

3 *M. Gardeyn* class : **Michel Gardeyn (K1), Christiaan Cornelis (K2), Willem Warmont (K3).**
Armament: 2—1 pdr, 2/1 M.G. Tubes removed. Radius : 5100 miles at 9 kts.

Tabulated Details.

Owing to shortage of materials caused by the war, the completion and commencement of many submarines has been (and will be) much delayed. The total number of completed boats is uncertain. About 10 or 11 boats are finished, or nearly ready ; 8 or 9 boats are building or not yet launched, and 6 or 9 are projected or ordered but not begun. The following details are not derived from any official source, but are based on very reliable details, specially furnished to "Fighting Ships."

No.	Type	Date	Displacement	H.P.	Max. speed	Extreme endurance.	Complement	T. tubes	Max. draug't
			tons.		kts				feet
3	O 14—O 12	⎫ Pro.	...	...	...	...	...	...	...
3	K 13—K 11	⎭							
3	O 11—O 9	Bldg.?	...	...	...	...	...	...	...
1	M 1 ( )	1915†	180 / 191	80 / 155	6 / 5	900 miles at 4 kts. / 50 miles at 2·5 kts.	15	6*	9
1	O 8 (H)	1915†	441 / 510	480 / 320	12 / 10	1350 miles at 12 kts.	22	4	12⅓
3	K 10—K 8 (H)	'17-?	550 / 836	1900 / 630	17·5 / 9	...		6	...
2	K 4—K 3 (H)	'15-'19							
4 ⎰	K 7—5 (HD)	'15-'20	550 / 800	1740 / 700	16 / 8·5	5500 miles at 11 kts. / 25 miles at 8·5 kts.	...	6	11½
⎱	K 2 (HD)	'15-'19							
1	O 7 (HD)	'13-'16	176 / 230	560 / 185	11·5 / 8·5	750 miles at 10 kts. / 25 miles at 8½ kts.	12	3	9¼
1	O 6 (H)	'13-'16	170 / 208	560 / 185	12 / 9	...	12	3	9¼
1	K 1 (HW)	'11-'14	330 / 390	900 / 650	17 / 9	2250 miles at 11 kts. / 23 miles at 9 kts.	17	3	9⅓
4	O 5—O 2 (HW)	'09-'13	131 / 150	300 / 200	11 / 8·6	760 miles at 10 kts. / 26 miles at 8 6 kts.	10	2	9
1	O 1 (H)	'05-'08	120	210 / 80	7·2 / 5·5	400 miles at 7 kts.	10	1	9¼

* Mine-laying tubes.   † Taken over in 1917.

Notes on above Table.

All boats with letter K (K 13 to K 1) are for Colonial Service in East Indies. (H) submarines are "Holland" type, and all boats of this design are built by the Koninklijke Maatschappij de Schelde, to plans by Electric Boat Co., U.S.A. (HD) submarines are of the Hay-Denny type, all now being built by the Maatschappij Fijenoord, Rotterdam, to plans by Marley F. Hay and Messrs. Denny & Co., Dumbarton. (HW) submarines are of the Hay-Whitehead type, built by the K. M. de Schelde, to plans by Marley F. Hay, and Messrs. Whitehead & Co., Fiume, Austria ; no further boats of this type are now being built.

(*Projected*).

O 14, O 13 and O 12 ⎱ Types not yet settled.
K 13, K 12 and K 11 ⎰ Provided for by 1918 Naval Programme. Will have 20·8 inch torpedo tubes.

Note.—According to the 1918 edition of an enemy Naval Annual, 3 further Colonial submarines, provided for by the 1917 Naval Programme, were begun by an American private company, but the U.S. Government stopped their construction.

Building or Projected.

3 boats, *type unknown* : O 11, O 10 and O 9, provided for by 1917 Naval Programme. No details known.

M 1. Appearance generally as above.   *Photo, Alfieri.*

1——type : **M 1** (ex-German mine-laying submarine *UC 8*, Vulkan, Hamburg, 1915, stranded on Terschelling Island, Nov., 1915, salved, interned and purchased by Dutch Government, 1917). Displacements : 180 tons *surface*, 191 tons *submerged*. Dimensions : 111½ × 10½ × 9 feet. Guns : 1 machine. No torpedo tubes but carries 12 mines in 6 mine-laying tubes before conning tower. Machinery : 1 —4 cyl. oil engine= 6 kts. (7·5 kts. for short periods with electric motors), on *surface* : max. *submerged* speed : 5 kts. (1 hour). Endurance : 900 miles at 4 kts. on *surface* ; 50 miles at 2½ kts. *submerged*.

O 8.   *Photo, Fotopersbureau " Holland."*

1 *Holland* type : **O 8** (ex-British submarine *H 6*), built by Canadian Vickers Co., Montreal, 1915, wrecked on Schiermonnikoog Island, Jan., 1916, salved Feb., 1916, interned at Nieuwediep, and subsequently purchased by Dutch Government. Displacements : 441 tons on *surface*, about 510 tons *submerged*. Dimensions : 150½ × 15¾ × 12⅓ feet. Armament : 4—17·7 inch torpedo tubes. Machinery : 2 sets 6 cyl. Niseco Diesel engines= 12 kts. on *surface*. Max. *submerged* speed 10 kts. Endurance : 1350 miles at 12 kts. on *surface* (16 tons oil carried).

Building.

3 *Holland* type : **K 10**, K 9 and K 8, building by K. M. de Schelde. No details known, but are practically the same as K 4 and K 3, described below. Provided for by the 1916 Naval Programme.

Completing or building.

2 *Holland* type : **K 4** and **K 3** (K. M. de Schelde, Flushing). Displacement : about 550 tons on *surface*, 825-836 tons *submerged*. Dimensions : 211½ × 18½ × 11½ feet. Armament : 1 gun (calibre unknown, but probably a 13 pdr.) and 6—17·7 inch torpedo tubes. Have Diesel engines. K 4 was to have been completed in 1918 and K 3 by the end of 1917, but both have been greatly delayed owing to shortage of building materials.

Building or Completing.

4 *Hay-Denny* type: K 7, K 6, K 5 (*building*) and **K 2** (launched 1917.) All by M. Fijenoord, Rotterdam. Displacements: 550 tons *on surface*, 800 tons *submerged*. Dimensions: 177 × 16½ × feet. Armament: 1—13 pdr. (anti-aircraft) and 6—17·7 inch torpedo tubes, of which two are *broadside* tubes. Machinery: 2 sets, 8-cyl. Diesel engines = 16 kts. *on surface*. Max. *submerged* speed 8½ kts. Endurance: 3500 miles (*normal*), 5500 miles (*extreme*), at 11 kts. *on surface*; 3 hours continuous running at 8½ kts. *submerged*.

K 7, K 6, and K 5 are an improved K 2 type.

Photo. Fotopersbureau " Holland."

1 *Hay-Denny* type: **O 7** (M. Fijenoord, Rotterdam, 1916). Displacements: 176 tons *on surface*, 230 tons *submerged*. Dimensions: 105 × 12 × 9½ feet. 3—17·7 inch torpedo tubes (2 bow, 1 stern). Machinery: 1 set 6-cyl. Diesel engines = 11½ kts. *on surface*. Max. *submerged* speed 8½ kts. Endurance: 750 miles at 10 kts. *on surface*; 3 hours continuous running *submerged* at 8½ kts.

Photo, Fotopersbureau " Holland."

1 *Holland* type: **O 6** (K. M. de Schelde, Flushing, 1916). Displacements: about 170 tons *on surface*; 208 tons *submerged*. Dimensions: 112½ × 12 × 9½ feet. 3—17·7 inch torpedo tubes. 1 set of 6-cyl. Diesel engines = 11·5 kts. *on surface*; max. *submerged* speed, 8½ kts.

(On East Indies Station.) *Photo by courtesy of Marley F. Hay, Esq.*

1 *Hay-Whitehead* type: **K 1** (K. M. de Schelde, Flushing, 1913). Displacements: 330 tons *on surface*, 390 tons *submerged*. Dimensions: 148·3 × 14·2 × 9⅜ feet. 3—17·7 inch torpedo tubes (2 bow, 1 stern). Machinery: 2 sets 8-cyl. Diesel engines = 17 kts. *on surface*. Max. *submerged* speed 9 kts. Endurance: 1700 miles (*normal*), 3250 miles (*extreme*), at 11 kts. *on surface*; 3¾ hours continuous running at 8·9 kts. *submerged*.

4 *Hay-Whitehead* type: Nos. **O 2** (1911), **O 3** (1912), **O 4** and **O 5** (both 1913.) All built by K. M. de Schelde, Flushing. Displacements: 133 tons *on surface*, 150 tons *submerged*. Dimensions: 98·4 × 9½ × 9 feet. Armament: 2—17·7 inch tubes (a spare torpedo carried for each). Machinery: 1 set 6-cyl. Diesel engines = 11 kts. *on surface*. Max. *submerged* speed 8¾ kts. Endurance: 760 miles at 10 kts. *on surface*; 3 hours continuous running at 8¾ kts. *submerged*.

No Photo available of " O 1 "—see Silhouettes.

1 *Holland* type: **O 1** (ex *Luctor et Emergo*, K. M. de Schelde, Flushing, 1905). Dimensions: 67 × 13½ × 9½ feet. 1—17·7 inch bow torpedo tube. Designed speed was 9 kts. *on surface* and 7 kts. *submerged*, but on trials she only made 7·2 kts. *on surface* and 5·5 kts. *submerged*. Is of little practical worth now.

(All these photographs by Fotopersbureau "Holland," Amsterdam.)

BRINIO. Ventilators used as stanchions to forebridge. After bridge stands *abaft* mainmast. Small uncapped funnel.

FRISO. Thin and tall funnel.

GRUNO. Capped funnel and ensign gaff to mainmast.

BRINIO (1912), **FRISO** (1912), **GRUNO** (1913). All built by Amsterdam D.Y. 540 tons. Complement 52. Dimensions: 172·2 (*o.a.*) × 27·9 × 9·1 feet *max.* draught. Armament: 4—4·1 inch semi-automatic, 2 machine. Armour: 2″ Belt, ⅔″ Deck, 2″ Conning tower. Machinery: 2 sets of Diesel engines (Kromhout, M.A.N., or Werkspoor types). B.H.P. 1200 = 14 kts. Oil, 25 tons.

Gunboats (*Kanonerbooten*).

Mine Layers (*Minjenleggers*).

(All on East Indies Station.)

ASSAHAN✻ (1900), **KOETEI**✻ (1898), **SIBOGA**✻ (1898), **SERDANG**✻ (1897), **MATARAM** (1896). About 810 tons *average.* Armament: 2—4·1 inch (in *Mataram* and *Koetei* only) 1—4·1 inch in others, 1—9 pdr. mortar, 4—1 pdr. H.P. 1350—1400 = 13 kts. Coal: 130—150 tons. Complement, 55. *Max* draught, 12 ft.

*✻**Note.**—Assahan, Serdang* and *Siboga* are mine-layers. Other two ships officially rated as "Flottielje-vaartuigen" or "Flotilla Vessels."

No photo available.

BRAGA, HEFRING, NJORD, THOR, TYR, WODAN. Are old iron twin-screw Gunboats, built 1876-79. 280 tons (*Hefring* and *Njord* = 270 tons). Complements, 34—30. Dimensions: 91·5 to 91·8 (*o.a.*) × 26·9 × 7·8 to 8·1 feet (*max.* draught). Guns: In *Braga, Hefring, Wodan*, 1—4·7 inch "No. 3" or "No. 1," 2—1 pdr., 1 machine; in *Njord* and *Tyr*, 1—5·9 inch "No. 2," 3—1 pdr.; in *Thor*, 1—13 pdr. "No. 1," 3—1 pdr, 1 M.G., but is to be re-armed as *Njord* and *Tyr*. H.P. 100 to 170 = 7½ to 8⅓ kts. Coal: 30 tons.

Building or completing.

TWO NEW MINE LAYERS; first begun under 1917 Naval Programme and the second begun under 1918 Naval Programme. Both laid down by Werf Gusto, Schiedam, 1918. 748 tons. Dimensions: 179·8 × 28·5 × 10·4 feet. Guns: 3—13 pdr. semi-auto. "No. 3." Twin screws. No other details known.

Will be of the same type as *Hydra* and *Medusa* (see next page), but will be faster and carry more mines.

(Mine Layers continued on next page).

Mine Layers—*continued.*

Photo, Fotopersbureau " Holland."

HYDRA (1911) & **MEDUSA** (1911). Both built at Amsterdam D.Y. 670 tons. Complement 60. Dimensions : 163 × 29·5 × 9 feet. Guns : 3—13 pdr. S.A. "No. 2" 1—1 pdr., 1 M.G. Designed H.P. 800 = 11·5 kts. Coal : 72 tons. Radius of action : 1440 miles at 6 kts. Each carries double laying gears for 80 mines.

Note.—There is also a T.B. named *Hydra*, but she is on the East Indies Station.

> ### Photo wanted.

TRITON (N. Shields, 1906). Ex-trawler of 277 tons. Complement 34. 120·5 × 21·5 × 11·6 feet. Guns : 2—1 pdr., 1 M.G. Coal : 120 tons. Double mine-laying gear.

> ### Photo wanted.

VULCANUS (Grimsby, 1902). Ex-steam trawler, 410 tons. Complement, 34. 123·7 × 21·6 × 10·5 feet. Guns : 2—1 pdr., 1 M.G. Double laying gear for mines.

Mine Layers—*Continued.*

> *No photo available.*

BALDER (1878), **VIDAR** and **HADDA** (1879), ex-gunboats of 270 tons. Complement 36. Carry 19 mines each (double mine-laying gear.) Guns : 2—4 pdr. (semi-auto.) in *Balder* and *Hadda*, 2—1 pdr. in *Vidar*. ; 1 M.G. in all three. Speed : 7 kts. Coal : 30 tons.

> *No photo available.*

DAS (1873), **HAVIK** (1875). Ex-gunboats of 210 tons. Guns : 2—1 pdr., 1 M.G. Speeds : About 6½–7 kts. Complement, 32.

Notes.—For *Serdang* and *Siboga*, gunboats used as mine layers in East Indies, see first column on preceding page.

Mine Sweepers. (*Mijnenvegers.*)

> ### Photo wanted.

I (v.d. Kuyck en van Ree, Rotterdam), **II** (Koopman, Dordrecht), **III, IV** (v.d. Schuigt, Papendrecht). Completed and taken over in 1918. — tons. Steel. Dimensions : (*I*) 92·5 × 20·6 × feet ; (*II*) 100·7 × 20·5 × feet ; (*III & IV*) 90·2 × 20 × feet. Guns : 1 machine. Complement, 16. No more details available.

Submarine Depot Ships (*Depotschepen*).

Photo, Fotopersbureau, " Holland."

CORNELIS DREBBEL (1915). 800 tons. Guns : 1—1 pdr. Complement 73. Has Diesel engines.

> *No photo available.*

VALI (1878). 840 tons. Guns : 1—1 pdr. Speed : 9 kts.

Fuel Ship. (*Brandstvfvoorraadschip.*)

> *No Photo available.*

ULFR. No details known.

(Continued on next page).

NETHERLANDS MISCELLANEOUS.

Surveying Ships (*Opnemingsvaartuigen*).

NEW SURVEYING SHIP, building, under 1915 Naval Programme, to replace old *Raaf* and *Geep.*

> *Building or completing.*

ELLERTS DE HAAN, building by Fijenoord Co., at Rotterdam, to replace old gunboats *Raaf* and *Gup.* No details known.

> *No photo available.*

(On East Indies Station.)

TYDEMAN (1916). No details known.

> *No photo available.*

HYDROGRAAF (1911). 300 tons. Draught 6¼ feet. Speed, 9 kts.

> *No photo available.*

(In East Indies.)

VAN DOORN (1901) **VAN GOGH** (1898). Composite and zinced. 700 tons. Complements, 57 (A), 26 (H). H.P. 390 to 370 = 10 to 9 kts. Coal: 100—110 tons.

> *No photo available.*

BORNEO (Clydebank, 1892). Composite and coppered. 800 tons. Complement, 57 (A), 26 (H). Speed: 13¼ kts. Coal: 160 tons.

Surveying Ships.—*continued.*

> *No photo.*

"Sumbawa." (In East Indies.)

LOMBOK, SUMBAWA (1891). 600 tons. Complement, 57 (A), 26 (H). Speed: 12½ kts. Coal: 90—120 tons.
Old Gunboats *Raaf* (1889) and *Geep* (1875) are employed as Surveying Ships in the East Indies, but are to be replaced by new Surveying Ship, *Ellerts de Haan,* as noted in preceding column. Both 200 tons and 7 kts. speed.

Gunnery Tender.

BELLONA (1892). Gunnery tender. 930 tons. For Training duty. carries 1—4·7 inch, 4—13 pdr., 2—4 pdr., 8—1 pdr., 2 M.G., of various models. Speed: 8 kts.

Fishery Patrols.

(Mainmast now removed.)

ZEEHOND (1892). 720 tons. Complement, 72. Armament: 2—1 pdr. Speed: 11 kts. Coal: 78 tons.

Fishery Patrols—*continued.*

DOLFIJN (1889). 290 tons. Complement, 42. Armament: 2—1 pdr. Speed: 10·7 kts. Coal: 29 tons.

Miscellaneous.

About 20 obsolete old vessels, used as harbour training ships, store hulks, barracks, transports, &c. All are practically worthless for military purposes.

Dutch East Indies Marine.

Consists of the 4 gunboats of *Assahan* class, 8 torpedo boats of the *Draak* class (and old torpedo boat *Cerberus*), surveying ships, *van Doorn, van Gogh, Borneo, Lombok* and *Sumbawa.*
All these ships described on this and preceding pages.

Miscellaneous Vessels belonging to the East Indies Government.

No photographs are available of any of the following ships. It is not definitely known which are armed and which are not.

DENEB (1914), **BELLATRIX** (1913), **CANOPUS** (1913), **ALDEBAREN** (1912), **ALBATROS** (1910), **ZWALUW** (1910), **SPEURDER** (1908).

KWARTEL (1901). Old Gunboat. 355 tons. May have 4—6 pdr. and 4—1 pdr. guns. Armour: 1″ deck. H.P. 550=12 kts. Coal: 23 tons.

SPITS (1899), **TELEGRAAF** (1899), **BRAK** (1898), **DOG** (1898) **HAZENWIND** (1898), **EDI** (1896), **NIAS** (1894), **ARGUS** (1892), **CYCLOOP** (1892).

GLATIK (1894), **FLAMINGO** (1891), **PELIKAAN** (1891), **ZWAAN** (1891). All old Gunboats. 400 tons. Guns: probably a few 13 and 1 pdr. H.P. 480=11·3 kts. Coal: 45 tons.

ZEEDUIF (1890). Old Gunboat. 420 tons. Guns: may have 2—13 pdr. and 2—4 or 1 pdr. Speed: 10½ kts. Coal: 40 tons.

REIGER (1887). Old composite-built Gunboat. 390 tons. Guns: may have 2—13 pdr. and 2 machine. Speed: 10 kts. Coal: 43 tons.

CERAM (1886), **JAVA** (1885), **WACHTER** (——).

ROYAL BELGIAN NAVY.

Flags.

Uniforms.

Minister of Defence:

Personnel: officers and   men, active list.   officers and men, reserve list.

Mercantile Marine: steamers of   tons gross,   sailing vessels of tons gross, also about   trawlers and fishing craft.

Colonies:

Coinage: =   s.   d. British currency.

(Uniform scale. Divided into 2000 yard squares. Soundings in fathoms).

ZEEBRUGGE.—Small port on Belgian coast, occupied and fortified by Germany during the war. Connected to Bruges by canal ($6\frac{1}{4}$ miles) 230 feet wide at water level, $72\frac{1}{4}$ feet wide at bottom × $26\frac{1}{4}$ feet deep. 5154 feet of quayage. Lock 840 feet between gates × $65\frac{2}{3}$ feet at entrance × 18 feet depth at low tides. Oil tanks situated in Inner Port. Mole 1970 yards long, where the Germans established batteries and depôts for torpedo craft, submarines, and seaplanes. Coast was heavily fortified by Germans, batteries including naval guns of 15 inch calibre and downwards, the largest guns ranging up to 25,000 yards. Port works, &c., wrecked by Germans on evacuation. Small wet dock at Blankenberghe (14 feet depth of water). Admiralty Chart No. 120.

OSTEND. Is connected by canal with Bruges. During German occupation coast was heavily fortified. Bomb proof Submarine shelters, also slips for building and repairing small submarines, repair workshops, &c. German Destroyer and Submarine basin lay between the Old and New Bassins de Chasse. Old Bassin de Chasse said to be partly filled in by Germans for use as an Aerodrome. One or two floating docks existed to take 1 large T.B.D. or two small Submarines, and perhaps one or two small graving docks were built. All port works &c. were wrecked by the Germans on evacuation. The Tirpitz battery at Hamilton Farm, near Mariakerke consisted of 4—11·2 inch guns and could range up to 30,000 yards *extreme*.

BELGIAN NAVY.

Following Ports within Belgium are connected with sea :—

ANTWERP. Eight Dry Docks. Municipal: No. 1, 506 × 81¼ × 23 feet ; No. 2, 248 × 39¼ × 14 feet ; Nos. 4, 5, & 6, 440½ × 49¼ × 16 feet. J. Cockerill : 400 × 41 × 17½ feet. Also 2 others 330 × 42 × 14 and 300 × 36 × 13 feet. About 12 wet docks, coaling basin, and 11 quays, all well equipped, with fixed and moveable cranes, and lit by arc lamps.

BRUGES. Connected to Ostend and Zeebrugge by canals. 5 wet docks. Was extensively used by Germans as a naval base during the war. Various bomb-proof shelters for Submarines were built here.

GHENT. Two dry docks, No. 1, 446 × 42⅔ × 18 feet. No. 2, 255 × 36 × 15 feet. 7 wet docks. Carels Works located here.

Shipbuilders.

Messrs. JOHN COCKERILL & CO., Hoboken, near Antwerp. Works looted or destroyed by Germans.

RECOGNITION SILHOUETTES: TORPEDO BOATS.

Scale: 1 inch 160 = feet.

A1—A3.

3 Torpedo Boats.

3 boats : **A1** (ex-German A14), **A2** (ex-German A12) and **A3** (ex-German A4) Built 1915. Displace about 80 tons. Dimensions 140 × 19½ × 8 feet. Guns : 1—4 pdr. (aft.), 1 M.G. Torpedo tubes : 1 or 2 deck 17·7 inch. Speed about 15 knots. Complement about 30.

Note : Above three boats abandoned by Germans on evacuation of Flanders and captured. A fourth Torpedo boat of above type salved and used as Patrol and Police Boat by Port Authorities at Antwerp.

Belgian Congo.

Photo wanted.

(Both on Lake Kivu).

PAUL RENKIN, Gunboat, launched during the War. No details available.

One Motor Patrol Boat (name unknown), launched during the War. No details known.

No photo available.

(On Lake Tanganyika).

NETTA (launched December, 1915). Torpedo Boat. No details known.

(ROYAL) SPANISH NAVY.

(Corrected, 1919, from the "Lista Official de los Buques de Guerra y de los Mercantes," issued by the Ministry of Marine. Illustrations and other information furnished by the courtesy of Alferez de Nairo M. Mille).

ROYAL STANDARD

ENSIGN

MINISTER OF MARINE

ADMIRAL OF THE FLEET.

ADMIRAL.

VICE-ADMIRAL

JACK & MERCANTILE.

VICE-ADMIRAL SUBORDINATED

REAR-ADMIRAL

REAR-ADMIRAL SUBORDINATED

RED
YELLOW
BLUE
PURPLE

Uniform Insignia.

	Capitan-General de la Armada. *Admiral of the Fleet*	Almirante. *Admiral.*	Vice-Almirante. *Vice-Admiral*	Contra Almirante. *Rear-Admiral.*	Capitan de Navio. *Captain.*	Capitán de Fragata. *Commander.*	Capitán de Corbeta. *Lieutenant-Commander.*	Teniente de Navio. *Lieutenant.*	Alferez de Navio. *Sub-Lieutenant.*

As Almirante but *four* upper stripes.

Other branches, *without the curl*, have distinguishing colours as follows :—

Engineers	...	*green.*		
Constructors	...	*blue.*	Astronomical ...	*green brown.*
Doctors	...	*red.*	Pharmaciens ...	*yellow.*
Paymasters	...	*white.*	Chaplains ...	*violet.*

Personnel: about 11,000 officers and men, 5000 marines—16000 in all. *Minister of Marine*: Admiral Lobaton (May, 1919).

Colour of Ships: Light grey.

General.

Naval School is at Cadiz on land. At Ferrol, the old frigate *Villa de Bilbao* (1843, 1313 tons, is a school for quartermasters, (*Escuela de Marineria*): also corvette, *Nautilus* (*Escuela de cabos de mar*), built 1868. 1700 tons. Guns: 1—6 inch, 6—5 pdr. Complement 221. The battleship *Pelayo* is training ship for gunnery, and cruisers *Reina Regente* and *Carlos V* are training ships for midshipmen and cadets. *Carlos V* is Flagship of the Training Squadron.

(All details unofficial).

Principal Naval Guns in Service.

Nota-tion.	Nominal Calibre.		Model.	Length in calibres	Weight of Gun.	Weight of A.P. shell.	Initial velocity	Max. penetration A.P. capped direct impact at K.C. at		Danger Space against average ship, at			Rounds per minute.
	c/m.	inches.						5000 yards.	3000 yards.	10,000 yards.	5000 yards.	3000 yards.	
	c/m.	inches.	V'09		tons.	lbs.	ft. secs.	inches.	inches.				
A^5	30·5	12	V'09	50	66	850	3010	17	20	...	...	...	2
AA	32	12·5	...	35	47½	1036	2034	8	11	...	...	...	...
B	28	11	...	35	32½	837	2034	5½	8	...	...	...	...
AA	28	10·8	...	40	30	507	2625	8½	11¾	110	420	720	0·5
A	24	9·4	...	40	17	318	2625	7¼	9½	110	350	620	1
D	24	9·4	...	35	21	439	2034	4	6¼	60	250	500	0·5
D	15	6	V.	50	7¾	100	3100	...	8¾	...	...	...	10
F	15	5·9	...	45	4½	88	2625	...	3	25	200	430	5–6

V = Vickers.

Naval Yards, &c.

FERROL. Dry docks. (1) "Victoria Eugenia," 573×82×37 feet (completed 1913), (2) "San Julian," 437½×72¼×29 feet. Ferrol is the big shipyard. It has a large coal depôt, good bay, well fortified.

CARTAGENA. One dry dock, 492×82×31½ feet. One floating, 6000 tons. Cruisers, gunboats and torpedo craft building yard. Very strongly fortified.

LA CARRACA (Cadiz). Dry docks. (1) 238½×55½×23¾ feet, (2) 328×70½×23½ feet, (3) 192½×57×18½ feet, (4) 925×85×34 feet (in two lengths). No slips. Only used as base for Morocco coast gun boats. S.E.C.N. ordnance and munitions factory located here.

MAHON. Very small yard.

Private Establishments.

Warship building is carried out in the Naval Yards by the "Sociedad Española de Coustrucion Naval," (S. E. C. N.), an Anglo-Spanish shipbuilding syndicate in which the British firms of Sir W. G. Armstrong-Whitworth, Ltd., Vickers, Ltd., and John Brown & Co. have a large interest. In carrying out Naval Programmes these three firms supply materials, ordnance, armour, etc., and skilled supervision of work. The S. E. C. N. has built large Ordnance factories for the production of guns, gun-mountings, shells, &c., at the Arsenal of La Carraca (Cadiz), and in Reinosa. S.E.C.N. Shipbuilding Yards have been created at Ferrol, Cartagena, Matagorda, and Sestao (Bilbao). A new yard at Cadiz is projected by the Asociacion Hispano-Britanica.

Private Docks.

BARCELONA (Los Astilleros de Euskalduna) Floating dock, 367×68×20 feet.
CADIZ. Compania Trans-Atlantica dock, 512×64×23 feet.
BILBAO. Compania Euskalduna dock, 605×60×25 feet. **Two** smaller.
SANTANDER. Gamazo dock, 445×57×23½ feet.
GIJON. Cifuentes Co. dock, 288×46×12 feet.

Mercantile Marine : —— steamers of 709,000 tons *gross*; 270 sailing vessels of 35,942 tons *gross*. About 400,000 tons is said to be building.

Coinage: Peseta (100 centimes) = 9½d. Ps. 29 = £1.

Colonial Possessions, &c.: Rio de Oro. Adrar, Rio Muni (or Spanish Guinea), Annobon, Fernando Po, Corisco Islands, Great and Little Elobey; all on Atlantic Coast of Africa. Canary Islands (Atlantic), *Ceuta (Straits of Gibraltar), and Spanish Morocco. There is a Protectorate in the north and west of Morocco, with controlled Ports at Ceuta, Melilla, Alhucemas, Gomera, and Chafarina.

* Administered as a province.

ONE FUNNEL.

ANTELO.
(Mining Vessel).

MacMahon.

H. Cortes class (2 ships).

Marques de Molins.

M. de la Victoria.

Bonifaz class (4 ships).

Delfin class (3 ships).

Almirante Lobo.
Now has W/T top gallant masts.

Espana class (3 ships).

Urania
(Surveying Ship).

Inf. Isabel.

TWO FUNNELS.

D. M. de Molina.

D. A. de Bazan.

Extremadura.

Rio de la Plata (Mine Layer).

Pelayo (Training Ship).

Cataluna class (2 ships).

THREE FUNNELS.

Reina Regente.
(Training Ship).

Carlos V.
(Flagship, Training Squadron).

TORPEDO CRAFT.　Scale : 1 inch = 160 feet.

No. 1—24 (t.b.)
(Some have no tubes.)

Bustamante class t.b.d. (3)

Audaz class (4).
"Terror" has mainmast.
(Mine Layers).

SUBMARINES.　Scale : 1 inch = 30 feet.

"A" or Monturiol class (3).
(Have 1—3 pdr. gun.)

Isaac Peral.
(Has a 3 inch gun just before C.T.)

ESPAÑA (Feb., 1912), **ALFONSO TRECE** (May, 1913), & **JAIME PRIMERO** (Sept., 1914).

Normal displacement, 15,452 tons. Complement, 735.

Length (*waterline*), 435 feet. Beam, 78¾ feet. *Max.* draught, 25½ feet. Length (*over all*), 459⅙ feet.

Guns (Vickers) :
8—12 inch, 50 cal. (A⁶).
20—4 inch. 50 cal.
2—3 pdr.
2 Maxims.
(2 landing).
Torpedo tubes :
none.

Armour (Krupp) :
8″ Belt (amidships) ......
3″ Belt (bow) ....
4″ Belt (aft) ....
1½″ Deck ....
6″ Lower deck side ......
8″ Turrets (N.C.) ....
10″ Turret bases (N.C.) ...
3″ Battery (N.C.) ....
10″ Conning tower ....
6″ After C.T. (Hadfield)

Ahead :
6—12 in.
4—4 in.

Astern :
6—12 in.
4—4 in.

Broadside : 8—12 in., 10—4 in.

Machinery : Parsons turbine. 4 screws. Boilers : 12 Yarrow. Designed H.P. 15,500 = 19·5 kts. Coal : *normal* 900 tons ; *maximum* 1850 tons + 20 tons oil fuel = nominal radius of 5000 miles at 10 kts., and 3100 miles at 16¾ kts.

Gunnery Notes.—12 inch manœuvred by hydraulic power ; all-round loading at any angle of elevation. Magazine capacity is 80 rounds per 12 inch gun, but there is ample storage for more than this. Arcs of fire : end, 12 inch, *about* 270° ; echelon, 12 inch. 180° own beam (*nominal*) and about 80° far beam. Heights of guns over normal waterline : 12 inch, 24¼ feet ; 4 inch, 13¾ feet. Total weight *about* 2550 tons. (These notes are not from any official source).

Armour Notes.—Main belt is 6 feet 7 inches deep, 4 feet 7 inches of this being below waterline and 2 feet above. On plans 8 inch belt amidships should extend to bases of end barbettes. Hull without armour = 5600 tons.

Machinery Notes.—Engines = 1320 tons.

Torpedo Notes.—Bullivant net defence. No torpedo tubes installed.

Name	Builder	Machinery	Laid down	Completed	Trials (Full Power)	Boilers	Best recent speed
Espana Alfonso XIII Jaime I	} Ferrol Yard	S. E. C. N.	{ Dec. '09 Feb. '10 Feb. '12	1914 1915 1919*	21,582 = 20·2 = 20·36 =	} Yarrow in all.	

* By April, 1919, only 5—12 inch guns had not been delivered for *Jaime I.* She was still short of various other special fittings, but was otherwise complete.

ESPAÑA.

Photo (1919), A. de N. M. Mille.

ALFONSO XIII.

Photo (1919), A. de N. M. Mille.

2nd Class Battleship.

(Acorazado de 2ª Clas.)

(1st Class Cruisers.)

Cruçeros de 1ª Clas.

(Gunnery Training Ship.)

PELAYO (1887) (1897) (1910.)

Photo (1918), Casau; Cartagena.

Length (o.a.) 341⅚ feet. Beam, 65¼ feet. *Maximum* draught, 25⁵⁄₁₂ feet.
Displacement, 9733 tons. Complement, 621.

Guns :
2—12·6 inch, 35 cal.
2—11 inch, 35 cal.
9—5·5 inch, 35 cal.
12—6 pdr.
9 or 5—1 pdr.
2 landing.
Torpedo tubes :
removed.

Armour (steel) :
16″ Belt (amidships) ...
12″ Belt (ends) ....
3½″ Deck (flat below belt).
16″ Barbettes............
2″ Hoods to these .....
3″ Battery (Harvey)...

Machinery : 2 sets vertical compound. 2 screws. Boilers : 16 Niclausse (in 4 groups). Designed H.P.
6800 = 15 kts. Coal : *normal* 500 tons ; *maximum* 676 tons. Built at La Seyne. Reconstructed there in 1897. Was partially rebuilt in 1910.

(CATALUNA CLASS—2 SHIPS).

Photo, Casau, Cartagena.

PRINCESA DE ASTURIAS (1896) & **CATALUNA** (1900)

Displacement, P. de A. 7427 tons, C. 7405 tons. Complement, 546.
Length (o.a.), 347¾ feet. Beam, 60¾ feet. Max. draught, 23⅓ to 23⅔ feet.

Guns :
2—9·4 inch, 40 cal. Guillen.
8—5·5 inch, 40 cal. Canet.
8—6 pdr.
10—1 pdr.
2 landing.
Torpedo tubes :
Removed.

Armour (Harvey) :
12″ Belt (amidships) ....
6″ Belt (forward) ....
8″ Belt (aft) ....
2¾″ Deck (flat on belt)......
12″ Bulkheads ....
8″ Barbettes ....
4″ Hoists to these...........
2¾″ Casemates (chrome steel)
8″ Conning tower (fore) ...

Ahead :
1—9·4 in.
2—5·5 in

Astern :
1—9·4 in.
2—5·5 in.

Broadside : 2—9·4 in., 4—5·5 in.

Machinery : 2 sets horizontal triple expansion. 2 screws. Boilers : 6 cylindrical. Designed H.P. *natural*
10,500 = 18 kts. Coal : *maximum* 1178 tons in *C.* and 1007 in *P. de A.*

(1st Class Cruisers continued on next page.)

1st Class Cruiser (*Cruçero de 1ª Clas*).

CARLOS CINCO (1895). 9903 tons. Comp., 583. Dimensions: $404\frac{3}{4}$ (*o.a.*) × 67 × $27\frac{2}{3}$ feet, *max.* draught; *mean* draught, 25 feet. Armament (Hontoria, 35 cal.): 2—11 inch, 8—5·5 inch, 4—4·1 inch, 10—6 pdr., 8—1 pdr., 2 Machine. Torpedo tubes (14 inch): 2 *above water.* Armour: $2\frac{1}{2}''$ Deck, 10″ Barbettes with 4″ Hoods and 8″ Hoists, 2″ over Battery, 12″ C.T. Boilers: 12 cyl. Designed H.P. 15,000, made 19 kts. on trial. Coal: *max* 2008 tons.

2nd Class Cruiser (*Cruçero de 2ª Clas*).

(1919 Photo, A. de N. M. Mille).

REINA REGENTE (Sept., 1906) 5778 tons. Complement, 452. Dimensions: 337 × $52\frac{1}{2}$ × $16\frac{1}{4}$ feet. Guns: 10—5·9 inch, (45 cal.), 12—6 pdr., 8—1 pdr., 2—3 inch Field. Armour: $3\frac{1}{4}''$ Deck and C.T., 3″ Gun Shields. Machinery: Reciprocating. 2 screws. Boilers: Belleville. Designed H.P. 11,000 = 19·5 kts. Coal: 1178 tons.

(New) Light Cruisers (*Cruçeros de—Clas*).

Building.

No. 6 (building) and No. 7 (building).

Normal Displacement : $\begin{cases} (a) & 4825 \text{ } metric \text{ tons.} \\ (b) & 4650 \text{ } English \text{ tons.} \end{cases}$

Length, $439\frac{1}{2}$ feet. Beam, 46 feet. Draught, $\begin{cases} (a) & 14\frac{1}{3} \text{ feet } mean. \\ (b) & 15\frac{1}{2} \text{ feet } max. \end{cases}$

Guns :
 6—6 inch, 50 cal.
 4—3 inch anti-aircraft.
 (1—12 pdr. landing.)
 4—M.G.
Torpedo Tubes (21 inch),
 4 *above water* (twin mountings).

Armour :
(Not known).

6—6 inch guns mounted on centre line.

Machinery: Parsons turbines. Boilers: 10 Yarrow; to burn oil fuel only. Designed H.P. = 29 knots. Fuel (oil only): *normal,* tons; *maximum,* 840 tons.

Name	Builder*	Machinery	Laid down	Completed	Trials	Boilers
No. 6	Ferrol D.Y.	S. E. C. N.	9 April '17	To be 1920		Yarrow
No. 7	Ferrol D.Y.		28 Sept.'17			

General Notes.—On account of the great shortage in shipbuilding materials construction of these vessels is proceeding very slowly. Two further ships of this class, previously projected, were cancelled in 1919.

(New) **Light Cruiser** (*Cruçero de —a Clas*).

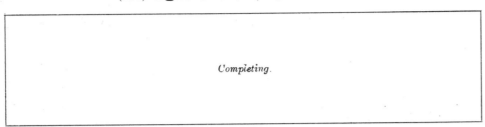

Completing.

REINA VICTORIA EUGENIA (27th August, 1919).

Displacement 5550 tons. Complement —.

Length (*p.p.*) 440 feet. Beam, $49\frac{2}{3}$ feet. *Max.* draught, $16\frac{3}{4}$ feet. Length *over all*, 462 feet.

Guns (Vickers) :
  9—6 inch, 50 cal.
  4—3 pdr.
  1—12 pdr. (Field)
  4 Machine
Torpedo tubes : (21 inch).
  2 *submerged.*

Armour :
  3″ Side .... ▨
  ″ Ends .... ▨
  3″ Deck ....

Ahead :
4—6 in.

Astern :
3—6 in.

Broadside : 5—6 in.

Machinery : Parsons turbines. 2 screws. Boilers : 12 Yarrow, in 3 rooms. Designed H.P. 22,500 = 25·5 knots. Coal : *normal* tons ; *maximum* 660 tons (inclusive of oil fuel).

Gunnery Notes.—Forecastle 6 inch have 180° arc of training, *i.e.*, 30° inboard and 150° on own beam. One or two anti-aircraft guns will be mounted, either as additional guns or in place of 3 pdr. guns.

Name	Builder	Machinery	Ordered	Laid down	Completed	Trials	Boilers	Best recent speed
R.V. Eugenia	Ferrol DY.	S. E. C. N.	Aug. '14	Mar. '15	1920*		Yarrow.	

General Notes.—Design is practically identical with British Light Cruisers of *Birmingham* class.

* Construction of this ship has been (and will be) greatly delayed owing to shortage of materials caused by the war.

3rd Class Cruisers (*Cruçeros de 3a Clas*).

Photo (1918), A. de N. M. Mille.

EXTREMADURA (Cadiz, 1900). 2100 tons. Complement, 266. Dimensions : $288\frac{2}{3} \times 36\frac{1}{4} \times 16\frac{1}{3}$ feet. Guns : 8—4 inch (50 cal. Vickers), 4—6 pdr., 4—1pdr., no tubes. Armour : $1\frac{1}{4}$″ Deck. Machinery : 2 screws. Boilers : Thornycroft. H.P. 7000 = 19 kts. Coal : *max.* 425 tons.

(*Is now equipped as a Mine Layer*). *Photo (1919), A. de N. M. Mille.*

RIO DE LA PLATA (Havre, 1898). 1920 tons. Comp., 213. Dimensions : $250\frac{1}{3} \times 35\frac{1}{3} \times 15\frac{1}{2}$ feet, *maximum* draught ; *mean* draught, $14\frac{1}{4}$ feet. Guns : 2—5·5 inch, 35 cal., 4—4·1 inch, 6—9 pdr., 4—1 pdr. No tubes. Armour : $1\frac{1}{4}$″ Deck. Machinery : Reciprocating. 2 screws. Boilers : Normand-Sigaudy. H.P. 7000 = 19 kts. Coal : *max.* 370 tons.

SPANISH DESTROYERS.

7 + 3 Destroyers (*Destroyers*).

No.	Type	Date	Displacement	H.P.	Max. speed	Fuel	Complement	T. tubes	Max. draug't
			tons		kts.	tons			feet
3	New	*Bldg*	1145	33,000(*t*)	34	265 oil	...	4	10⅓
3	*Bustamante* (V)	'12-'17	364	6250 (*t*)	28	79	70	2	5½
1	*Proserpina* (C)	1897	457	7200	30	94	74	2	9¾
2	*Audaz* (C)	1897	457	7700	·30	94	74	2	9¾
1	*Terror* (C)	1896	450	6000	28	104	74	2	9¾

C = Clydebank.   V = Vickers, etc., built in Spain by S.E.C.N.

3 New Boats.

Building ?

3 *New* Ocean-going Destroyers (names not known) 3 building at Cartagena by S.E.C.N.   Displacement : 1145 tons, (*normal*) 1325 tons (*full load*).   Dimensions : 275 × 27 × 10¼ feet.   Designed H.P. 33,000 = 34 kts.   Will have Parsons turbines and 4 Yarrow boilers.   Guns : 3—4 inch (40 cal.), 2—2 pdr. anti-aircraft.   Torpedo tubes : 4—21 inch in 2 twin deck mountings.   Full 265 tons oil only.   To be finished in 1920-21.

3 Bustamante Class.

BUSTAMANTE.

Photo, Casau, Cartagena.

3 *Bustamante* class : named **Bustamante** (1913), **Villaamil** (1913), **Cadarso** (ex *Requesens*, 1914).   All built at Cartagena D.Y., 364 tons.   Dimensions : 221¼ × 22 × 5¼ feet.   Armament : 5—6 pdr.   S.H.P. 6250 = 28 kts. Tubes : 2—18 inch in first two and 2—15 inch in *Cadarso* only.   Yarrow or Normand boilers.   Parsons turbine. 3 screws.   Coal : 79 tons = 900 miles at 15 kts.   Complement 70.

4 Audaz Class.

AUDAZ.

OSADO   (PROSERPINA, rebuilt 1916, appearance may be changed.)

1st, 2nd, and 3rd boats of the *Audaz* class :—**Audaz, Osado,** and **Proserpina,** Clydebank, 1897, *Proserpina* rebuilt 1916).   457 tons.   229 × 22¼ × 9¾ feet.   I.H.P. 7200 (7950 in *Osado*) = 29·3 to 31 kts. on trials.   Guns : 2—14 pdr., 2—6 pdr., 2—1 pdr   Topedo tubes : 2—15 inch.   Coal : 93 tons = 1020 miles at 15 kts.   Complement 74.

Photo (1919), A. de N. M. Mille.

4th boat of *Audaz* Class : **Terror** (Clydebank, 1895).   450 tons.   221 × 22 × 9¾ feet.   I.H.P. 6000 = 29.5 kts.   Guns : 2—6 pdr., 2—2½ pdr.   Torpedo tubes : 2—15 inch.   Coal : 104 tons = 1100 miles at 15 kts.   Complement 73.

(All above 4 boats fitted for Mine Laying).

18 *(+ 4)* 1st Class Torpedo Boats *(Torpederos de 1ª Clas).*

Photo (1919), A. de N. M. Mille.

22 Vickers-Normand. *2* (1911), *1, 3, 5, 6* (1912), *4* 1912, rebuilt 1916), *7, 8, 13* (1914), *9, 11, 12, 14* (1915), *10, 15, 16* (1916), *17, 18, 19,* 20** (1918), *21,* 22** (1919). 177 tons. Dimensions: 164 × 16¼ × 4⅚ feet (*max.* draught).
Armament: 3—3 pdr., 3—18 in. tubes, twin amidships and single aft. (Nos. *1, 4, 5, 17, 18* no tubes; *15* and *16* only 2 tubes.) H.P. 3750=26 kts. Parsons turbines and Normand boilers. Coal: 33 tons. 3 screws (Nos. 1—7). 2 screws (Nos. 8—22). Complement 31. Nos. *23* and *24* abandoned 1919.

Note.—Following three old T.B. may still exist: *1—1st Class* boat, **Halcon (No. 41)**, built 1887, rebuilt 1905. 235 tons. I.H.P. 1650=20 kts. Armament: 2—2¼ pdr., 2 tubes. Coal: 25 tons. *2—2nd Class* boats; **Habana (No. 45)**, built 1886. 61 tons. I.H.P. 780=19 kts. Armament: 1 M.G. and 2 tubes. Coal: 25 tons; **Orion (No. 42)**, built 1885. 89 tons. I.H.P. 1000=21 kts. Armament: 2—1 pdr., 2 tubes. Coal: 18 tons.

* Not yet finished.

4 *(+ 6)* Submarines *(Submarinos.)*

Note.—All details given on this page are *not* based on any official information.

No.	Type	Date	Displacement	H.P.	Speed	Radius of Action.	T. tubes	Complement	Max. draug't
			tons		kts.				feet
12	—— (H)	?	...	...	...	...	...	...	...
6	"Improved Peral" type (H)	'16-'20	610 / 740	1400 / 850	16 / 10½	...	4-6	...	11¼
3	*Monturiol* or *A* class (FL)	'15-'17	260 / 382	700 / 500	13 / 8½	1600 miles at 8·5 kts. / 85 miles at 4 kts.	2	17	10½
1	*Peral* (H)	'15-'16	488 / 750	1200 / 680	15 / 10	3700 miles at 11 kts. / 100 miles at 5 kts.	4	32	11

(H)=Holland type   (FL)=Fiat-Laurenti type.

The 1915 Naval Programme provides for 28 submarines, out of which 4 boats have been completed, and 6 are building.

Submarines *(continued.)*

Building ?

12 *Holland* type: Names and numbers not known. May be the same as British, Italian, and Chilean "H" Classes of Submarines. Uncertain if these boats will be built in U.S.A. or in Spain by S.E.C.N.

Building.

6 *Holland* type: Names and numbers not known. Began at Cartagena, July, 1916. Are an improved and enlarged *Isaac Peral* type. Displacements: 610 tons *on surface*, 740 tons *submerged*. Dimensions about 210 × 18½ × 11¼ feet. Machinery: *on surface*, 2 sets Diesel engines, totalling 1400 B.H.P.=16 kts.; *when submerged*, electric motors and batteries of 850 H.P.=10-10½ kts. Guns: 2 (calibre unknown, but one is A.A. type). Torpedo tubes: 4 or 6 (size uncertain).

Photo (1919). A, de M, N, Mille.

MONTURIOL (A1). These boats have a tall telescopic mast for W/T. abeam of after periscope on port side of C.T. also 1—3 pdr. gun mounted, now shown in above view.

Laurenti-Fiat type: **Narciso Monturiol (A1), Cosmo Garcia (A2)** and **A3,** (all built by Fiat San Giorgio Co., Spezia. 1915-17). Displacements: 260 tons *on surface*, 382 tons *submerged*. Dimensions: 149·6 × 13·8 × 10·2 feet. Machinery: *on surface*, 2 sets of 350 H.P., 6-cylinder., 2-cycle Fiat Diesel engines= 700 H.P.; when *submerged*, 2 electric motors of 250 H.P.+batteries of 500 H.P. Maximum speeds: 13 kts. *on surface* and 8½ kts. *submerged*. Radii of action: *on surface*, 650 miles at full speed and 1600 miles at 8½ kts; when *submerged*, 18 miles at 8 kts. and 85 miles at 4 kts. Guns: 1—3 pdr. Torpedo tubes: 2—18 inch in bows. Complement 17.

Note : Each boat is internally sub-divided into 8 w.t.c. Maximum diving depth 130 feet (about 22 fathoms). Detachable lead keel, weighs 9½ tons. Fitted with telephone buoy, Fessenden submarine signalling and receiving apparatus, and Marconi W/T. For rescue and salvage work there are 6 lifting rings outside hull, and 3 escape hatches within hull, for crew. 2 Periscopes about 3¼ inches diameter.

(Continued on next page.)

Submarines—*(Continued).*

Photo (1919), A. de N. M. Mille.

ISAAC PERAL : Has a tall folding mast for W/T. just before conning tower; two ventilators on top of C.T. may also be raised, when on surface. These details are not shown in above illustration.

1 *Holland* type : **Isaac Peral** (Fore River Co., U.S.A., July, '16). Displacement : 488 tons *on surface*, 750 tons *submerged*. Complement 32. Dimensions : 197 × 19 × 11 feet. Machinery : *on surface*, 2 sets of 600 H.P. Nlseco Diesel engines = 1200 H.P. for 15 kts. speed (made 15·36 on trials) ; *submerged*, electric motors + batteries of 680 H.P. = 10 kts. speed. Radii of action : 3700 miles *on surface*, at cruising speed of about 11 kts. ; 100 miles *submerged*, at 5 kts. Armament : 1–3 in. Q.F. (anti-aircraft and disappearing mounting), 4 torpedo tubes in bows.

1st Class Gunboats *(Cañoneros de 1ª Clas).*

> *Projected.*

"A," "B" and "C," building by S.E.C.N., at Cartagena. Displacement, 1500 tons. Speed, 18 kts. Provided for by 1915 Naval Programme. No other details known.

1st Class Gunboats—*(Continued).*

RECALDE.   *Photo (1919), A. de N. M. Mille.*

BONIFAZ (1911), **LAURIA** (1912), **LAYA** (1910), **RECALDE** (1910). 787 tons. Complement, 121. Dimensions : 213¾ × 30 × 9½ feet (*max*) draught. Guns : 4—14 pdr. 2 machine. Designed H.P. 1100 = 14 kts. Made 14·5 kts. on trial. Yarrow boilers. Coal : 148 tons. Radius, 3000 at 10 kts.

Photo (1919), A. de N. M. Mille.

DON ALVARO DE BAZAN (1897). 810 tons. 236 × 27 × 11¼ feet. Guns : 6—6 pdr., 2—2½ pdr., 2 M.G. I.H.P. 3500 = 19 kts. Coal : 168 tons. Complement 121.

(Continued on next page).

First Class Gunboats.—Continued.

Photo (1918), Alferez de Navio, M. Mille.

MARQUES DE LA VICTORIA (1897, reconstructed 1917-18), 810 tons. 233×27×10¾ feet. Guns: 8—6 pdr., 2 M.G. I.H.P. 3500=19 kts. Coal: 168 tons. Complement, 121.

Photo (1916), Alferez de Navio, M. Mille.

DOÑA MARIA DE MOLINA (1896) 810 tons. 236×27× 11¼ feet. Guns: 8—6 pdr., 2 M.G. H.P. 3500=19 kts. Coal: 183 tons. Complement, 121.

Photo (1914), Alferez de Navio, M. Mille.

INFANTA ISABEL (1885, reconstructed 1911). 1136 tons. 221½× 32×15 feet. Guns: 1—9 pdr., 10—6 pdr. I.H.P. 1500=12 kts. 1 screw. Coal: 194 tons. Complement, 194.

Second Class Gunboats. (Cañoneros de 2a clas.)

VASCO NUNEZ DE BALBOA (1895) & **HERNAN CORTES** (1895). 295 tons. 155×21½×7 feet. Guns: 2—3 pdr., 2—1 pdr. or Maxims. I.H.P. 500=10 kts. 1 screw. Coal: 61 tons. Complement, 54.

As re-boilered with one funnel.   *(1919 photo, A. de N., M. Mille.)*

MARQUES DE MOLINS (1893). 560 tons. 177¼×23×10½ feet. Guns: 4—6 pdr., 3—machine. Speed, 13 kts. Coal: 134 tons. Complement, 93.

Third Class Gunboat. (Cañonero de 3a clas.)

Photo (1916) Alferez de Navio, M. Mille.

MACMAHON (1887). 114 tons. 91½×16×5 feet. Guns: 2—2½ pdr., 1—1 pdr. I.H.P. 150=7 kts. Coal: 10½ tons.

River Gunboats. (Lancha-Cañoneros.)

1919 Photo, Alferez de Navio, M. Mille.

CARTAGENERA (1908). 27 tons. Complement, 12. 53·5 × 11·8 × 3·9 feet. Guns: 1 pom-pom. I.H.P. 120=12 kts.

No photo available.

PERLA (1887). 42 tons. 7 kts. 1 machine gun.

Submarine Salvage Vessel.
(Buque para salvamento de submerinos.)

(Photograph wanted.)

KANGARU (1917). Double hulled type, with interior docking space. Built by Werf Conrad, Haarlem, Holland. About 3000 tons. Length, 275·4 feet; beam, 65·4 feet; draught (with submarine docked), 13 feet. Can dock submarine up to 151 feet long. Salvage power: Can raise 650 tons, from 27⅛ fathoms. H.P. 1000=10 kts.

430

SPANISH MISCELLANEOUS.

Mining Vessels.

Mine Layers.

Old Cruiser **RIO DE LA PLATA** and old Destroyers of the *Audaz* class have been equipped for this duty. Also some (or all) of the 15 Coastguard and Fisheries Vessels of the *Esmeralda* type (see third column of this page) can be used as Mine Layers.

Auxiliaries.

Hercules (Repair Ship), *Bermea, Donestierra, Guipozcoa, Mariano, Primero de Meiro,* and three others.

Photo (1919), A. de N. M. Mille.

ANTELO (1903). Ocean-going Tug, Mine Layer, Mine Sweeper and Training Ship for Mining Service. 342 tons. 131·2 × 21·6 × 6·8. feet. I.H.P. 650 = 11 kts. Coal : 32 tons. Carries 40 mines.

Transport. (*Transporte.*)

Photo (1919), A. de N. M. Mille.

ALMIRANTE LOBO (1909). 2545 tons. Guns : 2—5 pdr. Designed H.P. 4300 = 12 kts. *Nominal* radius, 4540 at 10 kts.

Surveying Ship. (*Comtsión Hidrografica.*)

URANIA (1895). 801 tons. 195 × 26 × 10½ feet. Guns : 2—6 pdr. 2 screws. I.H.P. 350 = 10 kts. Coal : 200 tons. *Nominal* radius, 6400 at 8 kts.

Coastguard and Fisheries Vessels. (*Guardapescas.*)

No photo available.

ESMERALDA, INTREPIDA, PRONTA (Malaga) (——), **LIEBRE, SANTA MARIA** (Cadiz) (——), **SERPIENTE** (Algeciras) (——), **CUERVO** (Alicante) (——), **CEDIDA** (Valencia) (——), **RADIANTE** (Barcelona) (——), **FLECHA, GARZA, PEZ** (Balearic Islands) (——), and *3 others building,* provided for under new Naval Programme. All equipped for mine-laying and sweeping in war-time. 300 tons. Dimensions : 114·8 × 19·7 × feet. Speed, 16 kts. Machinery : 2 sets Diesel engines. Complement, 70.

Note.—Ports given are *not* building yards but stations to which these ships will be assigned, when completed.

"*Delfin*"

Photo, Alferez de Navio, M. Mille.

DELFIN, DORADO, GAVIOTA (1910-11). 158 tons. Guns : 1—5 pdr. Speed, 11 kts.

PORTUGUESE FLEET.

Portuguese Navy.—Re-illustrated 1919, from photographs furnished by courtesy of Captain Ernest Vasconcellos. and A. W. Paterson, Esq., of Lisbon.

Revised 1919, from Official "Lista dos Navios da Marinha de Guerra e da Marinha Colonial." Also corrected from information furnished by courtesy of the Portuguese Naval Attache, and Lieut. H. Reuterdahl, U.S.N./R.F. All armaments list are not from any official data. Ships marked with asterisk (*) form part of the Colonial Navy. All displacements in English tons unless otherwise stated.

Naval Uniforms.

Almirante.*	Vice-Almirante.†	Contra-Almirante.	Capitao de Mar e Guerra.	Capitão de Fregata.	Capitão Tenente.	Primeiro Tenente.	Segundo Tenente.	Guarda Marinha.
Admiral.	Vice-Admiral.	Rear-Admiral.	Captain.	Commander.	Lieut-Commander.	Lieut.	Sub-Lieut.	Midshipman.

British or U.S. rank.

* Admiral has four *gold* stars. † Vice-Admiral has four *silver* stars.
Staff officers same but *without* executive curl. Colour between stripes—*Surgeons*: red; *Engineers*: violet; *Paymasters*: blue; *Constructors*: purple red. On visor of cap, *Admirals*: 2 oak leaves; *Captains*: 1 oak leaf; *Commanders*: 1 narrow stripe. Uniforms like British Navy. Chin strap of gold cord, but officers of lieutenant's rank and below have black chin straps.

Personnel :

Mercantile Marine : 162 steamers of 319,954 tons *gross*, 219 sailing of 49,547 tons *gross*.

Trade Ports : Lisbon and Oporto.

Oversea Possessions : Cape Verde Islands, Madeira and Azores, Guinea (Senegambia), St. Thomas and Prince Islands (Gulf of Guinea), Timor (East Indies), Goa, Damao and Diu (India), Macao (China), Angola (Congo), Portuguese East Africa.

Coinage : Escudo (1000 reis) = 4s. 5d. British, $1.06 U.S.A. ; 4500 reis = £1 English.

Colour of Ships : Dark grey.

Naval Bases.

LISBON. Some small slips. Government dry dock: $258 \times 56\frac{3}{4} \times 12$ feet. Harbour Board dry docks : No. 1, $549 \times 82 \times 32\frac{1}{2}$ feet ; No. 2, $328 \times 49 \times 27$ feet. Private dock, H. Parry & Sons (Cacilhas) : No. 1, $225 \times 37 \times 9$ feet. There are also two smaller docks (H. Parry & Son).

S. PAULO DE LOANDA (Angola). There is a small floating dock here of 1,100 tons capacity, capable of taking any of the gunboats employed on this station.

Note.— During war, batteries and other defences were erected at Porto Delgada in the Azores, while the port was used by U.S. troopships, &c. If these new defences are turned over to Portuguese Navy, Porto Delgada can serve as a defended anchorage and coaling base for War Vessels.

Scale: 1 inch = 160 feet. **RECOGNITION SILHOUETTES.**

ONE FUNNEL.

RIO MINHO.   MACAU.   *(Mining Vessel).*   LIDADOR. *(Tug).*   SAVE *class* (2).

River Gunboats.

BERRIO. *(Tug).*   ACOR.   LIMPOPO.   CHAIMITE.   SALVADOR CORREIA. *(Transport.)*

VULCANO *(Mine Layer).*   BEIRA *class* (5).   SÃO GABRIEL.

SADO (2). *(Mine Layer.)*   PEDRO NUNEZ. *(Auxiliary Cruiser).*

SADO (1). *(Gunboat).*   ZAMBEZE.

For :—
Two Funnel Types ;
Torpedo Craft ;
Submarines ;
See next page.

Scale : 1 inch = 160 feet.   RECOGNITION SILHOUETTES—*Continued.*

TWO FUNNELS.

PATRIA.

VASCO DA GAMA.

ADAMASTOR.

5 DE OUTUBRO.
(Has W/T. top gallant masts now.)

ALMIRANTE REIS.
(Dismantled at present; has no funnels, guns, topmasts, or boats.)

TORPEDO CRAFT.   **Scale : 1 inch = 160 feet.**

No. 2, No. 3 (t.b.)

TEJO t.b.d.
(as reconstructed).

DOURO *class* t.b.d. (2).

SUBMARINES   **Scale : 1 inch = 80 feet.**

FOCA *class* (3).

ESPADARTE.

Old Battleship *(Cruzador).*

VASCO DA GAMA (Blackwall, 1876, reconstructed and lengthened by Orlando 1902). 2982 tons. Comp., 259. Dimensions: $232 \cdot 9 \times 40\frac{1}{4} \times 18\frac{1}{4}$ feet. Guns (new in 1902): 2—8 inch, 1—6 inch, 1—12 pdr., 8—3 pdr. No torpedo tubes. Armour (iron): 9″—7″ Belt, $7\frac{3}{4}''$ (Terni) Barbettes. Machinery: 2 sets triple expansion. 2 screws. Designed H.P. (new): $6000 = 15 \cdot 5$ kts. Boilers: Cylindrical. Coal: 300 tons.

Protected Cruisers *(Cruzadores).*

Photo by favour of Major Maunsell, R.A.

ALMIRANTE REIS (ex *Dom Carlos I.,* Elswick, 1896). 4186 tons. Comp., 418. Dimensions: $360 \cdot 8 \times 46\frac{1}{2} \times 17 \cdot 5$ feet. Guns (Elswick): 4—6 inch, 45 cal., 8—4·7 inch, 45 cal., 14—3 pdr., 2—1 pdr., 3 Machine. Torpedo tubes (14 inch): *2 above water.* Deck, $4\frac{1}{2}''$. Machinery: 2 sets triple expansion. 2 screws. Boilers: 12 Yarrow. H.P. $12,000 = 19 \cdot 5$ kts. Coal: 820 tons.

Note.—Dismantled 1918 for re-construction and long refit.

2 E

Protected Cruisers—(*Continued*).

Photo, Abrahams & Sons.

SAO GABRIEL (F. & C. de la Med., 1898). 1809 tons. Comp., 242. Dimensions: 246 × 35·5 × 14·3 feet. Guns (Canet): 2—5·9 inch, 4—4·7 inch, 8—3 pdr., 2—1 pdr., 3 machine. Torpedo tubes: 1—18 inch (bow) *above water*. 1″ Deck, 2½″ C.T. Machinery: 2 sets triple expansion. 2 screws. H.P. 3000 = 15 kts. Coal: 289 tons. Boilers: 4 Normand-Sigaudy.

*ADAMASTOR (Orlando, 1896). 1729 tons. Comp., 206. Dimensions: 242·1 × 35·1 × 15·3 feet. Guns (Krupp): 2—old 5·9 inch, 4—4·1 inch, 4—9 pdr., 2—1 pdr., 3 machine. Torpedo tubes (14 inch): 3 *above water* (bow and broadside). Armour: 1¼″ Deck, 2¾″ C.T. Machinery: 2 sets triple expansion. 2 screws. Boilers: 8 cylindrical. H.P. *forced* 4000 = 18·19 kts. Coal: 420 tons.

3 + 2 Destroyers. (*Contra-torpedeiros*).

No.	Type	Date	Displacement	H.P.	Max. speed	Coal	Complement	T. tubes	Max. draug't
			tons		kts.	tons			feet
2	*Vouga* (Y)	'14—?	} 660	11,000	27t	146	73	2	7⅔
2	*Douro* (Y)	'11-'13							
1	*Tejo*	'01-17*	526	7000	27	140	73	2	10⅓

(*t*) = turbine.   (Y) = Yarrow.   * Rebuilt by this date.

4 *Yarrow* type. *Vouga* and *Tamega* (both building at Lisbon D.Y.), **Douro** (1913) and **Guadiana** (1914). 660 tons. Dimensions: 240 × 23½ × 7¾ feet, *max.* draught. Armament: 1—4 inch, 2—12 pdr., 2 tubes. Parsons turbines; 3 Yarrow boilers. Coal: 146 tons = 1600 miles at 15 kts. Built by Yarrow and assembled at Lisbon. On trials, *Douro* made 30·3 kts., good for 27 now.

1 *Navy* type. **Tejo** (Lisbon D.Y. 1901, rebuilt 1917). 526 tons. Dimensions: 229⅔ × 23 × 8·2 feet. Armament: 1—3·9 inch (aft), 1—3 inch (forward). 2—14 inch tubes. Machinery: 2 sets triple expansion. 2 screws. Boilers: White-Forster. H.P. 7000 = 27 kts. (*estimated*). Wrecked in 1910, salved, but reconstruction not finished till 1917.

Torpedo Boats. (Torpedeiros).

(For appearance see Silhouettes.)

2 old *Yarrow* type. **No. 2** and **No. 3** (Poplar, 1886). 66 metric tons. Dimensions: $119\frac{2}{3} \times 12\frac{2}{3} \times 3.4$ feet. Armament: 2 M.G. and 2 tubes. Designed H.P. 700=19 kts. (much less now). 1 screw. Coal: about 18 tons. Complement, 22.

4 Submarines. (Submersereis).

No.	Class	Date	Displacement	H.P.	Speed	Endurance (miles)	T. tubes	Complement	Max. draug't
3	*Foca* class	'15-'17	tons $\frac{260}{389}$	$\frac{600}{450}$	kts. $\frac{13}{8\frac{1}{4}}$	$\frac{1500 \text{ miles at } 8\frac{1}{2} \text{ kts.}}{18-85 \text{ miles.}}$	2	20	$11\frac{1}{2}$
1	*Espadarte*	'11-'13	$\frac{245}{300}$	$\frac{600}{300}$	$\frac{13.8}{8}$	(About the same.)	2	20	...

All above boats are of the Laurenti type. Displacements in metric tons. All have Fessenden submarine signalling gear.

Photo wanted.

Resemble Spanish *Monturiol* type.

Laurenti-Fiat type: **Foca, Golfinho,** and **Hidra** (all built at Spezia, 1916- 1917) Dimensions: $147\frac{2}{3} \times 13.8 \times 10\frac{1}{4}$ feet. Armament: 2—18 inch bow torpedo tubes. 4 torpedoes. Machinery: 2 sets of 300 H.P. 6-cylinder Fiat-Diesel engines *on surface*; electric motors + batteries *submerged*. Maximum speeds: 13 kts. *on surface* and $8\frac{1}{4}$ kts. *submerged*. Radius of action: about 650 miles at full speed, and 1500 miles at 7-8 kts. *on surface*: about 15-20 miles at $9\frac{1}{4}$ kts. and 80-85 at 4 kts. *submerged*.

1 *Laurenti-Fiat* type: **Espadarte** (Spezia, 1912). Displacement, $\frac{245}{300}$ tons. Dimensions: $148 \times 13\frac{1}{4} \times 9.7$ feet. Torpedo tubes: 2—18 inch (bow). 4 torpedoes carried (4000 yds at kts.) Machinery: 2 sets 300 H.P. 6-cyl. Fiat-Diesel engines *on surface*; electric batteries + motors *submerged*. Maximum speeds, $13\frac{3}{4}$ kts. *above* and 8 kts. *below* water. Radius of action: About same as for *Foca* class above.

Auxiliary Cruiser (Cruzador auxiliar).

No photo available.

PEDRO NUNEZ (ex-s.s. *Melange* of Empraza Naçional, Lisbon, 1889). 5574 metric tons. $356 \times \quad \times \quad$ feet. Guns: several 4.7 inch and smaller Q.F. I.H.P 2300=about 16 kts. 1 screw. Complement 209.

"Aviso," or Despatch Vessel.

CINCO DE OUTUBRO (ex *Amelia*, ex *Banshee*; Ramage & Ferguson, Leith, 1900). 1343 tons. $226.9 \times 28.9 \times 14$ feet. Guns: 2—3 pdr., 4—1 pdr. H.P. 1800=15 kts. 2 screws. Cylindrical boilers. Coal: 230 tons. Complement, 225.

Gunboats (Canhoneiras).

Photo, R. E. Forrest, Esq.

BENGO (1917), **MANDOVI** (1917), **QUANZA** (1918), **BEIRA** (1910) and **IBO** (1910). All built at Lisbon D.Y. 463 tons. Dimensions: $147\frac{2}{3} \times 27\frac{1}{4} \times 6.8$ feet. Guns: in *Bengo, Mandovi,* and *Quanza*, 4—3 pdr.: in *Beira* and *Ibo*, 2—3 pdr., 2 M.G., 2 field. H.P. 700=13 kts. Coal: 85 tons. Radius: 3200 miles at 9 kts. Boilers: Cylindrical. 2 screws. Complement 71.

(Gunboat types continued on next page).

PORTUGUESE GUNBOATS AND MINE LAYERS.

Gunboats (continued).

*SAVE (1908) and *LURIO (1907). Both built at Lisbon D.Y. 305 tons. Dimensions: 140·4 × 23·6 × 5·9 feet. Guns: 2—3 pdr., 1 machine. H.P. 500 = 12½ kts. Boilers: Cylindrical. 2 screws. Coal: 61 tons. Complement 51.

ZAMBEZE (Lisbon, 1886). Wood. 606 tons. 146 × 26¼ × 11 feet. Guns: 3—3·9 inch (old), 1—1 pdr., 1 M.G. H.P. 460 = 10 kts. Cylindrical boilers. Coal: 90 tons. Complement, 65.

VULCANO (1910). Built by Thornycroft. 151 tons. 110 × 19½ × 4½ feet. 2 dropping gears forward. H.P. 412 = 12 kts. 2 screws. Cylindrical boiler. Complement, 24.

*PATRIA (Lisbon D.Y., 1903). 626 tons. Dimensions: 196·8 × 27·5 × 8·4 feet. Guns: 4—3·9 inch, 6—3 pdr., 1 machine. ½″ waterline belt. H.P. 1890 = 16·7 kts. Cylindrical boilers. 2 screws. Complement 88.

No Photo available.

CHAIMITE (Parry & Sons, Lisbon, 1898, rebuilt 1913). 335 tons. 134 × 26¼ × 6·6 feet. Guns: 2—3 pdr., 2 machine. H.P. 480 = 11 kts. Cylindrical boilers. Coal: 120 tons. Complement, 25.

Photo, Sub-Lieut. Poyntz, R.I.M.

SADO (1) (Birkenhead, 1875). 635 tons. 149¼ × 28¼ × 10⅔ feet. Guns: 2—4·1 inch, 2—9 pdr., 1—1 pdr., 1 machine. H.P. 500 = 11 kts. Cylindrical boilers. Coal: 84 tons. Complement, 30.

For appearance, see Silhouettes.

SADO (2) (1905). 2558 metric tons. 229·6 × 36 × 14·8 feet. Guns: 1 M.G. aft. H.P. 500 = 11 kts. 1 screw. Cylindrical boilers. Coal: 100 tons. Complement 69.

LIMPOPO (Poplar, 1890). 288 tons. 124 × 21 × 6½ feet. Guns: 2 —3 pdr., 1 machine. H.P. 523 = 11·3 kts. Complement, 54.

ACOR (ex-s.s. *Gomes VII*, 1874). 330 tons. 136·1 × 19 × 9 feet. Guns: 1—3 pdr. I.H.P. 360 = 9 kts.; could make 11 with sail out. Complement 53. Has been employed on fisheries and surveying duties. Will probably be condemned soon.

For River Gunboats, see next page.

MINING VESSEL (name and details not known).

Small River Gunboats. *(Lancha Canonheiras.)*

No photo available of *Tete.*

TETE (Yarrow, Scotstoun. Begun Feb., 1918, completed Mar., 1919). Stern wheel type for Zambese River. 70 ton. 89 *(o.a.)* × 20 × 4 feet. Guns: 2—1 pdr. Hotchkiss, 2 M.G. I.H.P. 80 = 9 kts. Boiler: locomotive. Fuel: wood.

*MACAU (Yarrow, 1909). 133 tons. $119\frac{2}{3}$ × 19·8 × 2 feet. Guns: 2—6 pdr., 3 machine. H.P. 250 = 11·8 kts. Boilers: Yarrow. Complement. 24.

No Photo available.

*FLECHA, is also given in Official Navy List as **FLEXA** (1909). tons. 68·8 × 13·1 × 2·2 feet. Guns: 1 or 2 small. 1 screw. Speed 10 kts. Complement 7.

Note.—There is also a Flotilla of 7 launches for River Service in Portuguese India, with civilian crews. They are under the command of the " Captain of Ports."

*RIO MINHO (Lisbon D.Y., 1904). 38 tons. Paddle wheel. 80·7 × 13·1 × 1·9 feet. H.P. 64 = $7\frac{1}{2}$ kts. Guns: 2—1 pdr. Complement 68, are nominally borne on her books, the majority of these ranks and ratings being actually at various shore stations on the Portugese bank of the river Minho, for fisheries, customs duties, &c.

Naval Transports. *(Transportes.)*

No Photo available.

*CHINDE (1911) tons. 240 *(p.p.)* × 33·5 × feet. I.H.P. 950 = kts. 1 screw.

Naval Transports *(continued)*.

No Photo available.

*PÈBANE. 148 H.P. 1 screw. Complement 37. No other details known.

No Photo available.

*PUNGUÉ (1895). tons. 232 *(p.p.)* × 34·1 × feet. I.H.P. 424 = kts. 1 screw.

(Transports continued on next page.)

Transports (continued.)

SALVADOR CORREIA (Birkenhead, 1895). 300 metric tons. 140×21×7 feet. Guns: 2 M.G. H.P. 450=11 kts. 1 screw. Cylindrical boilers. Coal: 80 tons. Complement, 19.

Also

Bissau (1913). 300 metric tons.

Massabi (1886). 266 metric tons.

Vilhena.

Above three vessels serve as Transports in the Colonies of Guinea and Angola; they have mixed complements of naval officers and civilians.

Auxiliaries.

Capitanio, Salvation, for Colonial Service.

Tugs. *(Reboreadores.)*

BERRIO (1898). 498 metric tons. 132·9×22·5×10·5 feet. Guns: 1. M.G. in bows. H.P. 1070=12 27 kts. 2 screws. Complement 44.

LIDADOR (1884). 252 metric tons. Iron. 113·8×20×6·9 feet. H.P. 400=11 kts. 2 screws. Complement, 41.

Salvage Vessel. *Vapor de Salvação).*

PATRÃO LOPEZ (——). 1109 metric tons. 157·5 (p.p.)×26·2 ×14·6 feet. Complement. 53.

For Fisheries Protection.

CARREGADO (1912). 107 metric tons. 80 (p.p.)×18× feet. Guns: not known. I.H.P. 300= kts. 1 screw. Is stationed at Algarve.

Note.—Gunboat *Acor* and River Gunboat *Rio Minho* may be employed on this service, from time to time.

For Various Duties.

*DILLY (is also referred to in Official Navy List as **DILI**). 500 metric tons. 140 (p.p)×25×10·3 feet. I.H.P. 500=11 kts. 1 screw. Complement 12.

LINCE (1911). 78 metric tons. 88·5 (p.p.)×14×5·5 feet. I.H.P. 300= kts. 2 screws. Complement (nominally) 53.

Trawlers, Patrol Vessels and Armed Launches.

The following Vessels were in Naval Service in May, 1919, but were probably only requisitioned for the duration of the war. They are not included in Official Navy List. *Manuel Azevedo* and *H. Capello* may be permanently retained by the Navy; the other vessels will probably revert to private use.

Trawlers:—

A. de Castilhos.	Manuel Azevedo.
A. P. de Arcos.	M. Victoria.
C. Sores.	P. Lopez.
H. Capello.	

Patrol Vessels:—

Galco.	T Andres.
Republica.	Tresirmos.

Armed Launches:—

Guarda Marinha Janeira.	Tenente Roby.

Also the old wooden sailing frigate *Dom Fernando* (1842), of 1849 tons; is totally non-effective for fighting purposes. Used as Gunnery Training Ship.

NAVY OF THE SERBS, CROATS AND SLOVENES.

Scale :— 1″ = 160 feet.

Danube Monitor.

BODROG.

Note.

Reported that various Austrian Warships interned at Cattaro and Sebenico will be assigned to the Serbs, Croats and Slovenes.

Various Hungarian Monitors and River Craft have surrendered to the British and Serbs, and are interned at Belgrade. These ships are listed in Hungarian Danube Flotilla Section, but their names are :

Danube Monitors :—Bosnia, Enns, Köros, Leitha, Maros, Sara, Temes.

Scouts :—Barsch, Fogos, Isuka, Vels.

All the above will probably be transferred to the Navy of the Serbs, Croats and Slovenes.

BODROG (1904). 433 tons.   Dimensions : $183\frac{3}{4} \times 31\frac{1}{4} \times 4$ feet. Designed H.P. 1400 = 13 kts. Boilers : Yarrow. Armament : 2—4·7 inch (45 cal.) + 1—4·7 inch howitzer, 2—3 pdr., 1 or 3 machine.   Armour : $1\frac{1}{2}″$ Belt and Bulkheads, 1″ Deck, 3″–$1\frac{1}{2}″$ Turrets and Conning tower. Complement, 79. Coal : 62 tons.

Official Photo, L.N.A.

SERBIA. (Purchased 1916.) Under 100 tons. Speed : 12 kts. Is unarmed. National colours painted on funnel. Mainmast now removed.

ROYAL HELLENIC NAVY.

(GREEK FLEET.)

Officially Revised, 1919, by courtesy of H.E. The Minister of Marine.

VICE ADMIRAL.

Note to Flags. — Royal Standard and Admirals' flags were altered about two years ago, but their present design cannot be ascertained.

ENSIGN

MERCANTILE

CAPTAIN COMMANDING A DIVISION

SENIOR OFFICER

Blue

White

Red

Nauarkos.	Antinauarkos.	Yponauarkos.	Ploiarkos.	Antipliarkos.
Admiral.	Vice-Admiral.	Rear-Admiral.	Captain.	Commander. 1st class

Other branches, without the curl :—

Surgeons : *purple velvet.*
Apothecaries : *green velvet.*
Constructors : *black velvet.*
Engineers : *violet velvet.*
Paymasters : *scarlet cloth.*

Plotarkis.	Ypoploiarkos.	Anti-poploiarkos.	Simaiophoros.
Comdr.	Lieutenant-Commander.	Lieutenant.	Sub-Lieut.

For details of Docks, Canal of Corinth, Fleet Anchorages, &c., See next page.

SALONIKA. Port has the shape of square wet dock and is very safe, with good anchorage. Ample quayage, which may have been further enlarged during the Allied use of this port. Was netted, mined and patrolled during War, and aircraft stations established here. No dry docks. Admiralty Chart No. 2070.

Mine Layers.   Old Gunboats.   Achelaos *class* (4).

Helle.   Kanaris.   Amphitrite.

Spetsai & Hydra.   Psara.

Kilkis *class* (2 ships).   Giorgios Averoff.

TORPEDO CRAFT.   Scale : 1 inch = 160 feet.

Nikopolis t.b.   V 12, 14, 15, 16, t.b.   Aigli *class* t.b. (6).   Keravnos *class* t.b.d. (2).

Thyella *class* t.b.d. (4).   Nike *class* t.b.d. (3).   Leon t.b.d.

Scale : 1 inch = 80 feet.

Delfin *class* submarines (2).   Aetos *class* t.b.d. (3).

Docks. *(For Salonika, see preceding page.)*

SALAMIS (Arsenal). Government floating, 311 × 59 × 23 feet (3,000 tons).
Private Docks: There are two dry docks at Piræus (Harbour Trust), viz., "Vasilefs Giorgios,"
    460 × 69 × 29½ feet ; "Vasilissa Olga," 320 × 51 × 26 feet.
Mercantile Marine: 334 steamers of 695,105 tons *gross*, 585 sailing of 108,685 tons *gross*.
Chief Ports: Piræus, Syra, Volo, and Salonika.
Oversea trade chiefly with England, Russia, and Austria.
Coinage: Drachma (100 lepta) = about 9½d. British, 18 cents U.S.A.
Personnel: About 4000 (conscript 2 years or enlistment).
Minister of Marine: Admiral Condouriotis.

Fleet Anchorages.

During the War, the Allied Fleets made extensive use of Greek Harbours and Anchorages.
MUDROS BAY (Lemnos) became the chief base of the British Eastern Mediterranean Fleet
and Allied Squadrons during the War, being netted, mined and patrolled A R.N. Airship
Station was established at Mudros for anti-submarine service, with an outlying station at Kassandra.
R.A.F. Stations were also created at Bessonreau, Imbros, Romanos, Syros, Stavros, Skyros, Syra,
Thasos, Talikna, and Thermi-Mitylene (all under C.-in-C., Mediterranean & R.A. Aegean).
IMBROS and **SUDA BAY** (latter with R.A.F. Station) were also used as Fleet Anchorages.
CORFU became the principal base of the French Fleet, being netted, mined and patrolled by
British R.N. Trawlers from N.E. of Corfu to Sasseno Island near Valona. Milo, Salomina and
the Gulf of Patros were also netted. It is possible that some of the permanent works at these
bases and stations may become the property of the Greek Government, and be used by the Greek
Navy in the future.

Canal of Corinth.

Length : 6 kilometres = 3¾ miles *approx*.   Breadth : (a) at surface 24·6 metres = 80·7 feet, (b) at
    bottom 21 metres = 68·9 feet. Depth : 8 metres = 26¼ feet. Not navigable by Dreadnoughts
    and Battle Cruisers.

(1904) Battleships.

(1887-8) Coast Defence Ships.

SPETSAI.

Photo, Mons. C. B. Rontiri.

LEMNOS.

KILKIS (*ex Idaho*) (December, 1905), & **LEMNOS** (*ex Mississippi*) (September, 1905). *Normal* displacement, 13,000 tons. *Full load* displacement, 14,465 tons. Complement, 802. Length (*waterline*), 375 feet. Beam, 77 feet. *Max* load draught, $24\frac{2}{3}$ feet. Length *over all*, 382 feet. Guns: 4—12 inch, 45 cal. (A^5), 8—8 inch, 45 cal., 8—7 inch, 45 cal., 12—3 inch, 13 pdr., 4—6 pdr. (saluting), 2—6 pdr. (anti-aircraft), 4—1 pdr., 8 M.G. (landing). Torpedo tubes (21 inch): 2 *submerged*. Armour (Midvale): 9″ Belt (amidships), 4″ Belt (ends), 3″ Armour deck, 12″—8″ Turrets, 10″—$7\frac{1}{2}$″ turret bases (N.C.), $6\frac{1}{2}$″-6″ Secondary turrets (N.C.), 7″ Lower deck (redoubt), 7″ Battery (redoubt), 9″ Conning tower. Machinery: 2 sets vertical 4 cylinder triple expansion. 2 screws. Boilers: 8 Babcock. Designed H.P. 10,000=17 kts. (can only make 12 kts. now). Coal: *normal*, 750 tons; *maximum*, 1824 tons = 6920 miles at 10 kts. Authorised 1903 for U.S. Navy; laid down at Cramp's, Philadelphia, May, 1904, and completed early in 1908. Sold to Greece early in 1914.

PSARA.

Photo, Mons. C. B. Rontiri.

Spetsai. Re-fitting, 1919.

Psara. Stokers' Training Ship.

PSARA (1890, rebuilt 1897), **SPETSAI** (1889, rebuilt 1900), **HYDRA** (1889, rebuilt 1900). Displacement, 4808 tons. Complement, 440. Length (*o.a.*) $344\frac{1}{2}$ feet. Beam, $51\frac{5}{6}$ feet. *Mean* draught, 18 feet. Guns (Canet): 2—10·6 inch, 36 cals., 1—10·6 inch, 30 cals., 3—5·9 inch, 45 cals, 1—3·9 inch, 50 cals., 8—9 pdr., 4—3 pdr., 8 to 6—1 pdr. Torpedo tubes: 1—15 inch, 2—14 inch (all *above water*). Armour (Creusot steel): 12″—$4\frac{3}{4}$″ Belt (lower), 3″ Belt (upper), $2\frac{1}{4}$″ Deck (flat), $13\frac{3}{4}$″ Battery redoubt. 12″ Barbette (aft), 6″ Hood, 6″ Hoists (main guns), 12″ Conning tower. Machinery: 2 sets vertical triple expansion. 2 screws. Boilers: Belleville (1914-15). H.P. 6700 =17 kts. Coal: *normal* 400 tons; *maximum:* others, 690 tons. Built by F. & C. de la Med., 1887–1892. All three are now fitted with flying topmasts, as *Hydra*. Appearance of *Spetsai* and *Psara* has been slightly changed by removal of the thin " auxiliary funnel " before fore funnel.

HYDRA.

GREEK NAVY.

(1907) Armoured Cruiser.

Photo by favour of M. C. B. Rontiri.

GIORGIOS AVEROFF (March, 1910).

Normal displacement, $\left\{\begin{array}{l}9,960\text{ tons.}\\10,118\text{ metric tons.}\end{array}\right\}$ Complement, 550:

Length (*over all*), 462 feet. Beam, 69 feet. *Maximum* draught, 24¾ feet. Length (*p.p.*), 426 feet.

Guns (Elswick) :
4—9·2 inch, 45 cal. (A³).
8—7·5 inch, 45 cal. (A).
16—14 pdr.
1—12 pdr. (anti-aircraft)
4—3 pdr.
2 M.G.
Torpedo tubes (18 inch) :
2 *submerged* (broadside).
1 „   (stern).

Armour (Terni) :
8″ Belt (amidships) ....
3¼″ Belt (ends) ....
2″ Deck ....
7″—6″ Upper belt ....
4″ Upper belt (ends).........
8″ Main barbettes (N.C.) ...
6½″ Turrets to these (N.C.)
7″ Citadel ....
7″ Secondary turrets (N.C.)
7″ Conning towers (4) ......

Ahead :
2—9·2 in.
4—7·5 in.

Astern :
2—9·2 in.
4—7·5 in.

Broadside : 4—9·2 in., 4—7·5 in.

Machinery : 2 sets 4 cylinder triple expansion. 2 screws. Boilers : 22 Belleville. Designed H.P. 19,000 = 22·5 kts. Trials : 21,500 = 23·9. Coal : *normal* 660 tons ; *maximum* 1500 tons = 7125 miles at 10 kts. ; 2489 miles at 17¾ kts. Built by Orlando, 1905-11.

Gunnery Notes—All big guns electrically controlled. 12 pdr. anti-aircraft gun mounted on after superstructure.

General Notes.—Cost £950,750. Sister to Italian *Pisa* with certain modifications as to armament and rig. This is the Italian ship formerly known as "X." Under the will of a deceased Greek millionaire. M. Giorgios Averoff, about £300,000 was left for increasing the Navy. This sum was devoted towards the part purchase of the above vessel, the balance of her cost being defrayed by the State. Still has shell holes in funnels from Balkan war.

(1912) Light Cruiser.

HELLE.

HELLE (May, 1912).

Normal displacement, 2600 tons. Complement, 232.

Length (*over all*), 322 feet. Beam, 39 feet. Draught, 14 feet.

Guns (Armstrong) :
2—6 inch.
4—4 inch.
2—14 pdr., 3 inch.
1—6 pdr. anti-aircraft.
2—3 pdr.
2—1 pdr.
Torpedo tubes (18 inch) :
2 *above water.*

Armour (steel):
2″ Deck on slopes ...
1″ Deck on flat.........

Machinery : Parsons turbine. 3 screws. Boilers : Thornycroft. Designed H.P. 6000 = 20 kts. Coal : *normal*, 400 tons ; *maximum*, 600 tons + 100 tons of oil fuel. = 5250 miles at 10 kts. ; 3320 miles at 17¾ kts.

Name	Builder	Machinery	Laid down	Completed	Trials: 4 hours.	Full Power.	Boilers	Best recent speed
Helle	N.Y. Shipblg.	N.Y. Shipblg.	1910	Nov.,'13	7500 = 20·3	8650 = 21	Thornycroft	

General Notes.—Built as the *Fei-Hung* for China. Purchased 1914.

Note:—All boats reported to have been re-armed by French Navy during War. Armaments may now be different to those given below.

13 Destroyers.

No.	Type	Date	Displacement tons	H.P.	Max. speed kts.	Fuel	Complement	T. tubes	Max. draug't
4	*Aetos* (L)	'10-'12	980	19,750 (t)	32	For 3000 at 15 kts.	102	4	10
2	*Keravnos* (V)	'11-'12	562	16,500 (t)	32·5	For 2000 at 15 kts.	83	2	10
4	*Thyella* (Y)	'06-'07	350	6700	30	From 1140 to 1250 miles at 15 kts.	70	2	9
3	*Nike* (V)	'06-'07	350	6600	30·5		70	2	9

(L)=Cammell Laird.   (V)=Vulkan Co.   (Y)=Yarrow.   (t)=Turbines.

Note.—Russian T.B.D. **Zvonki** taken over. For details *v.* Russian (Black Sea) Section.

Now have high foremast for W/T. rig.

2 *Vulkan* type : **Keravnos, Nea Genea** (ex-German V5, V6, (both launched 1912, re-built 1918). 562 tons. Dimensions : 233¼ × 25 × 10 feet. Armament : 4—3·4 inch (15 pdr.), 2—18 inch tubes. A.E.G.-Curtis turbines. S.H.P. 16,500 = 32·5 kts. (about 26 now). Schulz boilers. Fuel : 137 tons coal + 80 tons oil = 2000 miles at 15 kts.

Photo wanted.

Has *three* funnels.

Leon only of the *Aetos* class.

4 boats : **Kriti, Lesvos, Chios, Samos** (——1915).

Notes to Plans.—*Aetos, Jerax,* & *Panther* have 5 funnels, being set to port and starboard of centre line. *Leon* has *three* funnels. In all boats the 6 pdr. AA. gun mounted on "bandstand" abaft last funnel.

AETOS

Now have short pole mainmast at stern.

4 *Thyella class.* Yarrow type : **Thyella, Sphendoni, Navkratousa** and **Lonkhi** (1906-07). 350 tons. Dimensions : 220¼ × 20¼ × 6 feet, *mean* draught ; *max.* draught, 9 feet. Armament : 2—14 pdr., 4—6 pdr. 2 tubes (18 inch). Speed : 30 kts. (about 28 *max.* now). Coal : 80 tons. Endurance : 1140 to 1250 miles at 15 kts. Complement 70.

AETOS, JERAX, & PANTHER as above view.

4 *Cammell-Laird* type : **Aetos, Jerax, Leon, Panther** (all launched 1911). 980 tons *normal*, 1175 *full load*. Dimensions : 293 × 27¾ × 8¼ feet, *normal* draught ; *full load* draught, 10 feet. Armament : 4—4 inch Bethlehem, 1—6 pdr. AA. 4—18 inch tubes. 4 spare torpedoes in carriers on upper deck. 2 searchlights. S.H.P. 19,750 = 32 kts. (30 about *max.* now). Combined Parsons and Curtis turbines. 5 White-Forster boilers. Coal : 243 tons + 84 tons oil = 3000 miles at 15 miles. These were 4 boats, *San Luis, Santa Fé, Tucuman,* and *Santiago,* built for the Argentine. Purchased by Greece, Oct., 1912.

3 *Nike class.* Vulkan Stettin type : **Aspis** (1906), **Niki** (1905), and **Velos** (1906), 350 tons. Dimensions : 220¼ × 20¼ × 6 feet, *mean* draught ; *max.* draught, 9 feet. H.P. 6700 = 30 kts. (about 28 now). Armament : 2—12 pdr. 4—6 pdr. 2 tubes (18 inch). Coal : 90 tons. Complement 70. Endurance : 1140 to 1250 miles at 15 kts.

Doxa of this class was lost during the War.

11 Torpedo Boats.

No.	Type	Date	Displace-ment tons	H.P	Max. speed kts.	Fuel	Com-ple-ment	T tubes	Max. draug't
6	*Aigli* class (V)	'12-'13	120	2400(t)	25	tons coal + oil	...	3	...
1	*Nikopolis* (A)	1905	160	2700	24	60 tons coal	20	1	...
4	*16—11* (V)	1885	85	1000	18	22 tons coal	20	2	...

(A)=Ansaldo.   (V)=Vulkan Co.   (t)=Turbines.

6 *Vulkan* type: **Aigli, Alkyone, Arethousa, Dafni, Doris, Thetis** (all launched 1913). 120 tons. Dimensions: 147¾×9½×4 feet. Armament: 2—6 pdr. Bethlehem, 3—18 inch tubes. S.H.P. 2400=25 kts. Trials: *Aigli* 26·2, *Doris* 25·7.

1 *Ansaldo* type: **Nikopolis** (ex-Turkish *Anatolia*, 1905). 160 tons. Dimensions: 167×18×6 feet (*mean draught*). Armament: 2—1 pdr. Bethlehem (1913). 1—18 inch tube. H.P. 2700=24 kts. Coal: 60 tons. Complement 20. Captured, 1912

4 *Vulkan* type: **V16, V15, V14,** and **V12** (1885) (re-engined, etc., 1905). 85 tons. Dimensions: 128×15¼×6¼ feet. Guns: 1—1 pdr., 1 M.G. 2 -14 inch bow tubes. H.P. 1000=18 kts. Coal: 22 tons. Complement 20.

2 Submarines.

No.	Type	Date	Displace-ment tons	B.H.P.	Max. speed kts.	Fuel	Com-ple-ment	T. tubes	Max draug't
2	*Delfin*	'10-'12	295 / 452	1850	15 / 8	...	...	5	...

2 *Laubeuf-Schneider* type: **Delphin** (8/11) and **Xiphias** (6/12). Dimensions: 164× × feet. 1—18 inch bow tube and 4 torpedoes, carried in dropping gear on beam. Carry 6 torpedoes. Machinery: 2 sets, Schneider-Carels Diesel engines *on surface*; electric motors and batteries *submerged*. Cost of both boats defrayed by a national and voluntary subscription. For other details see Table.

Torpedo Depot Ship.

KANARIS (1870). 1083 tons. Dimension: $298\frac{1}{2} \times 20\frac{5}{6} \times 10\frac{1}{2}$ feet. Guns: 1—4 inch, 2—14 pdr., 2—6 pdr., 2 machine. H.P., 1200 = 14 kts. Coal: 200 tons. Complement 190.

Hospital Ship.

AMPHITRITE (Birkenhead, 1864, 1885). 1950 tons. Dimensions : $298\frac{1}{2} \times 26 \times$ feet. Guns: 4—1 pdr. H.P., 1200 = 14 kts. (Funnels have been lengthened since this photo was taken.)

Mine Layers.

MONEMBASIA, AIGIALIA, NAUPLIA (1881). 290 tons. Dimensions : $75\frac{1}{2} \times 13\frac{1}{4} \times 8\frac{1}{2}$ feet. H.P. 60 = 9 kts. Coal : 60 tons. Carry about 20 mines each.

ACHELAOS, ALPHIOS (Blackwall, 1884), **PENEIOS, EUROTAS** (Dumbarton, 1884). All rebuilt 1895-7. 404 tons. Dimensions : $131\frac{1}{4}$ (p.p.) $\times 24\frac{1}{3} \times 11$ feet. Guns: 2 old 3·7 in., in first three (+4 M.G. in *Eurotas*.) *Peneios* has only 4 M.G. H.P. 400 = 11 kts. Complement 60.

AKTION.   *French official War Photo.*

AKTION & AMBRAKIA (Blackwall 1881, re-built 1910). 433 tons. Dimensions : 128 (p.p.) $\times 25 \times 9\frac{1}{2}$ feet. Guns: 1—old 10·2 inch, 2—14 pdr. (in *Aktion* only), 1—1 pdr. H.P. 380 = 11 kts. Complement 70.

Note.—Foremast in one or both ships now removed.

Old Gunboats (continued.)

SALAMINIA (1858), and **SYROS** (1858). 374–300 tons. Guns: not known. *Nominal* speeds: 10 kts. Coal: 62–42 tons. Complement 55–42.

Used only for transferring crews and officers from the Naval Arsenal.

Submarine Depot Ship.

> *1 funnel, schooner-rigged.*

SPHAKTERIA (1885). 1000 tons. H.P., 2400 = 16 kts. Guns: 2—1 pdr.

Oil Tanker.

> **Photo wanted.**

PROMETHEUS. No details known. Can carry up to 4125 tons of oil fuel.

Salvage Tug.

> *(1 funnel, 2 masts, schooner-rigged, swan bow.)*

TENEDOS (——). 100 tons.

Gunnery Training Ship.

> *1 funnel, barque-rigged, ram bow.*

NAUARKOS MIAULIS (La Seyne, 1879). 1770 tons. Guns: various, from 12 pdr. downwards, and including 6 pdr. anti-aircraft for training purposes.

RUMANIAN NAVY.

RECOGNITION SILHOUETTES.

Scale : 1 inch = 160 feet.

ENSIGN

MERCANTILE

I. BRATIANU *class*.

ELISABETA.

SIRETUL *class*.

Naluca t.b.

MIRCEA.

ALEXANDRU CEL BUN.

Personnel : ?

Mercantile Marine : In 1916-17, 41 steamers of 75,174 tons *gross*. Some of these may have been destroyed during war.

Docks : At Galatz, on the Danube River, there used to be a floating dock in two sections, 264 × 56 × 16½ feet (2400 tons). May have been destroyed during war.

Addenda.

Following additional Rumanian Warships reported just before going to Press :—

Patrol Boats. **ARGESUL, FROTUGUL, GRANICERUL, ILEANA, PANDURUL, PORUMBITSA, POTERAZUL, RANDUNICA, SENTINELA, SILISTRIA, SRUTUL, SVIMULET, TROTUS, TELERMAN, VEDEA, VEGHETORUL.**

Six Motor Boats, lettered *A* to *F*.

Training Ship. **STEFAN CEL MARE.**

Hospital Ship. **PRINCEPO MIRCEA** (and 10 Hospital Barges).

Cruiser.

ELISABETA (Elswick, 1887, rebuilt 1905). 1380 tons. Complement 150. Length, 239½ feet. Beam, 33½ feet. *Mean* draught, 12¼ feet. Guns : (4—4·7 inch have been landed for service ashore during war and may not be re-mounted), 4—12 pdr. (modified for anti-aircraft fire), 4 machine, 2 S.L. Torpedo tubes (14 inch) : 4, *above water*. Armour (Steel) : 3½″ Deck (amidships), 1¾″ Deck (ends). Designed H.P. 4700 = 17·3 kts. Coal : 300 tons.

Danube Monitors.

ION BRATIANU (1907), **MIHAIL COGĂLNICEANU** (1908), **ALEXANDRU LAHOVARI** (1908), and **LASCAR CATARGIU** (1907). Displacement 670 tons. Complement, 110. Dimensions : 208¼ × 33⅓ × 5¼ feet. Guns : 3—4·7 inch, 2—3 pdr. anti-aircraft, 2 machine, 2—14 inch S.L. Armour : 3″ Belt, 3″ Deck, 3″—2″ Turrets. H.P., 1800 = 13 kts. Coal : 60 tons. Built by Stabilimento Tecnico, Trieste.

Coastguard Cruisers.

BISTRITSA.

BISTRITSA, OLTUL, SIRETUL (Blackwall, 1888). 96 tons.
Dimensions : $100 \times 13\frac{1}{2} \times 5\frac{3}{4}$ feet. Guns : 1—6 pdr., 1—1 pdr.
H.P., 380 = 12 kts. Coal : 12 tons. Complement, 30.

1 funnel.

GRIVITZA (1880). 104 tons. Dimensions : $198\frac{1}{2} \times 17 \times 5\frac{5}{6}$ feet.
Armament : 2—6 pdr., 2—1 pdr., 2 machine. H.P., 180 = 9 kts.
Coal : 18 tons. Complement, 30.

No Photo available.

FULGERUL (1873). 85 tons. Dimensions : $82 \times 15\frac{2}{3} \times 4\frac{1}{4}$ feet.
Guns : 1—6 pdr., 1—1 pdr. H.P., 100 = $7\frac{1}{2}$ kts. Coal : 10 tons.
Complement, 18.

Mine Layer.

(v. Silhouette).

ALEXANDRU CEL BUN (1882). 104 tons. Dimensions :
$75\frac{1}{2} \times 15 \times 5\frac{3}{4}$ feet. Guns : 2—1 pdr., 2 machine. H.P. 100 = 9 kts.
Coal : 12 tons. Complement, 20.

Training Ship.

MIRCEA (1882). 360 tons. Guns : 4 machine. Speed : about 6 kts.

Patrol Boats.
(All armed with 2 machine guns).

Opanez, Rahova, Smardan (1882). 45 tons. 1—1 pdr. Speed : 9 kts.
Romania (1862, 1883, 1890). 111 tons. Speed : 9 kts.
Prutul (1893). 31 tons. Speed : 8 kts.

---

11 Torpedo Boats.

No.	Type	Date	Displacement	H.P.	Max. speed	Fuel (Coal)	Complement	Tubes or Gears } + { Spar T	Max. draug't
			tons		kts.	tons			feet
8	*Major G. Sontzu* (T)	1906	50	600	18	7	20	2 + 2	3
3	*Naluca* (F)	1888	60	540	16	7	20	2 + 2	7

(F) = Forges et Chantiers de la Med.   (T) = Thames Ironworks.

No photo available. 2 funnels abreast.

8 *Major Sontu* class : **Capt. Nicolae Lascar Bogdan, Capt. Romano Mihail, Capt. Valter
Maracineau, Lieut. Demetre Calinescu, Major Constantine Ene, Major Demetre
Giurescu, Major Nicolae Ivan, Major Giurge Sontzu** (Thames Iron Works, 1906). Dimensions :
$100 \times 13 \times 2\frac{3}{4}$ feet. Armament : 1—3 pdr., 1 machine, 2 sets of dropping gears and 2—14 inch spar torpedoes. 1—20
inch S.L. For other details, see Table.

2 *Naluca* class. **Naluca, Sborul** (1888, reconstructed, 1907). Dimensions : $120\frac{5}{6} \times 11\frac{1}{4} \times 6\frac{5}{8}$ feet. Armament : 1 machine
gun. 2 tubes. 1 spar torpedo. For other details see Table.

SOUTH & CENTRAL AMERICAN NAVIES.

(ARRANGED ALPHABETICALLY).

ADDENDA AND CORRECTIONS.

BRAZIL.

Photo, N. G. Moser.

Sao Paulo, refitting at New York Navy Yard, 1919.   Note U.S. Navy type of V-faced bridges and control top.

CHILE.

Flag for Minister of Marine should be shown as a white foul anchor vertical on a blue ground, and four white stars, one in each corner of flag.

Cruiser **O'HIGGINS** reported to be re-building for service as a Seaplane Carrier.

Following Notes contributed by Senor Roberto Kelly G., of Valparaiso :—

Training Ships.—**PRESIDENTE ERRAZURIZ, ALMIRANTE COCHRANE** for gunnery.   **TOME, TALCAHUANO** (Torpedo and Engineering Schools).   Torpedo Boats of the *Ingeniero Hyatt* class, are Tenders to Torpedo Schools.   Corvette *Abtao*, Navigation School Ship, Frigate *Lautaro*, for Boys.

Transports.—*Angamos, Maipo, Rancagua,* have been chartered to private firms.   Following Steamers of the Compania Sud-American de Vapores are subventioned for use as Transports in case of war : *Aysen, Huasco, Cachapoal, Cautin, Imperial, Maipo, Mapocho, Palena.*

CHILEAN NAVY—*(continued)*.

Sea-going Tugs.

Name	(Built)	Tons.	kts.	Name.	(Built)	Tons.	kts.
Porvenir	(1909)	350	8	Lautaro	(1881)	250	6
Yelcho	(1909)	300	8	Toro	(1874)	180	8
Valdivia	(1905)	250	9	Pisagua	(1873)	540	8
Galvez	(1897)	475	9	Aguila	(?)	600	10
Condor	(1889)	145	8	Artillero	(?)	80	5
Huemul	(1889)	145	8	Galvarino	(?)	335	8
Yanez	(1888)	130	8	Ortiz	(?)	400	8

PARAGUAY.

Following Warships reported to exist, 1919 :—
Despatch Vessels.— **TRIUMFO** and another.
Presidential Yacht.—**ADOLFO RIQUEILME.**
Miscellaneous.—*Constitucion, Independencia,* 2 Armed Steamers

---

PERU.

River Launches.—*Cahaupanas, Francisco Pizarro, Iquitos, Orellana, Requena.*
Vedette Boats.—*Cuzco, Puno.*
Transport.—*Chalaco* is still chartered out to a private company.

ARGENTINE FLEET.

Note.—The Ensign, Jack and Mercantile blue is *sky blue*, not ordinary flag blue.

ENSIGN   JACK   PRESIDENT OF THE REPUBLIC   MINISTER OF MARINE   ADMIRAL

VICE ADMIRAL   REAR ADMIRAL   VICE ADMIRAL SUBORDINATE   REAR ADMIRAL SUBORDINATE   CAPTAIN COMMANDING SQUADRON   CAPTAIN COMMANDING SQUADRON SUBORDINATE

SENIOR OFFICER   REAR ADMIRAL COMMANDANT NAVY YARD   CAPTAIN COMMANDANT NAVY YARD   MERCANTILE ENSIGN

BLUE   WHITE   RED   YELLOW

ALMIRANTE *Admiral*   VICE ALMIRANTE *Vice-Admiral*   CONTRA ALMIRANTE *Rear-Admiral*   CAPITAN DE NAVIO *Captain*   CAPITAN DE FRAGATA *Commander*   TENIENTE DE NAVIO *Lieut.-Comm'r.*   TENIENTE DE FRAGATA *Lieut.*

ALFEREZ DE NAVIO   ALFEREZ DE FRAGATA   GUARDIA MARINA *Midshipman*   CADETE *Cadet*

Sub-Lieutenant.

Note :—Coloured velvet cloth between sleeve and cap stripes as follows :—

Engineers : Purple.
Electrical Engineers : Emerald green.
Surgeons : Red.
Paymasters : Grey-blue.
Constructors : Dark green.

Nota-tion.	Nominal Calibre.		Maker.	Length in Calibres.	Muzzle Velocity.	Weight A.P. Projectile.	*Max.* penetration against K.C. with capped A.P. at		Danger Space against average warship, at			Service Rounds per minute.
							5000 yards.	3000 yards.	10,000 yards.	5000 yards.	3000 yards.	
	inches.	c/m.		calibres.	ft. secs.	lbs.	inches.	inches.				
A^6	12	30·5	B	50	2900	870	19	23				2
A	10	25·4	E	40	2207	500	7	9½				·6
C	9·4	24	K	35	{ 2300 2133 }	352	4½	6				·4
A	8	20·3	E	45	2660	210	6½	9				1
B	8	21	E	40	2286	210	4	6				
E	8	20	K	35	2120	200	3	5				
D	6	15	B	50	2600	105		8¼				
D	6	15	C	50	2625	88	4	6	74	240	465	5
E✻	6	15		45	2500	100	3	4½	66	210	435	
F✻	6	15		40	2200	100	3	3¾	37	150	360	
F✻	4·7	12	C	50	2600	46·3	...	3½				
F✻	4·7	12	E	45	2570	45	...	2¾				
F✻	4·7	12	E	40	2230	45	...	...				

✻ = Brass cartridge case used.

In the Maker's column B = Bethlehem   E = Elswick ; K = Krupp ; C = Canet ; V = Vickers.

The above details of Argentine Naval Ordnance are not taken from any official source and must be regarded as merely approximate.

Arsenals.

(1) **BUENOS AIRES.** Dry docks : (Eastern) 590½ × 65½ × 25 feet, and (Western) 492 × 65½ × 25 feet.

(2) **PUERTO BELGRANO** (Bahia Blanca). Dry docks : (1) 683 × 84 × 32½ feet, (2) 683 × 114 × 43.

(3) **RIO SANTIAGO.** New dock, 672 × 114 × 36 feet. Two floating docks, (1) 1500 tons lift (2) 300 tons lift.

General Notes.

Mercantile Marine : 317 steamers of 222,533 tons *gross*, including sailing vessels and ships over 100 tons

Personnel : about 9500 all ranks. *Reserve :* about 8000 *Special reserve :* 10,000.

Minister of Marine :

449

2 F

Scale: 1 inch = 160 feet.

ONE FUNNEL.

INDEPENDENCIA.
LIBERTAD.

ROSARIO.
PARANA.

ALMIRANTE BROWN.
(*Training Ship.*)

A. DEL VALLE.
(*Oil Tanker.*)

URUGUAY.
(*Surveying Ship.*

TWO FUNNELS.

GENERAL SAN MARTIN.

GENERAL BELGRANO.

GARIBALDI.
PUEYRREDON.
(*Training Ship*).

MORENO.
RIVADAVIA.

PATRIA.
(*Surveying Ship.*)

NUEVE DE JUILIO.

BUENOS AIRES.

PRESIDENTE SARMIENTO.
Training Ship.)

TORPEDO CRAFT. (**Scale: 1 inch = 160 feet.**)

Yarrow t.b. (3)

Thornycroft t.b. (2)

CORRIENTES.
ENTRE RIOS.
MISIONES. } Yarrow t.b.d.

CORBOBA.
LA PLATA. } t.b.d.

CATAMARCA.
JUJUY. } t.b.d.

450

RIVADAVIA (26 Aug., 1911) & MORENO (23 Sept., 1911).

Normal displacement, 27,940 tons. *Full load*, 30,600 tons. Complement, 1215.

Length (*w.l.*), 577½ feet. Beam, 95 feet. *Max* load draught, 28 feet. Length *over all*, 585 feet.

Guns (Bethlehem):
12—12 inch, 50 cal. *Dir. Con.* ?
12—6 inch, 50 cal.
16—4 inch, 50 cal.
4—3 pdr.
6 M.G.
(4 landing).
Torpedo tubes (21 inch):
2 *submerged*
(broadside).

Armour (Krupp):
11″—8″ Belt (amidships)
5″ Belt (bow) N.C.
4″ Belt (stern) N.C.
3″ Deck (slopes)
9″—8″ Side above belt
12″—9″ Big gun turrets
6″ Secondary battery (N.C.)
12″ Conning Tower (forward)
9″ Do. (aft.
Total weight: 7600 tons.

Ahead:
8—12 in.
2—6 in.

Astern:
8—12 in.
2—6 in.

Broadside: 12—12in., 6—6 in.

Machinery: Curtis Turbines. 3 screws. Designed S.H.P. 39,500=22·5 kts. Boilers: 18 Babcock. Coal capacity: *normal*, 1600 tons; *maximum*, 4000 tons. Oil: 660 tons. *Nominal* radius: 3930 miles at full speed, 7740 miles at 10 kts. (see *General Notes*).

Gunnery Notes.—Heights of barbettes over normal draught w.l.: No. 1, 29¼ feet; No. 2, 37¼ feet; Nos. 3 and 4 (echelon), and No. 5, 29 feet; No. 6, 20 feet; 6 inch guns, 19¼ feet above w.l. Arcs of fire: end barbettes, Nos. 1 and 6, 270°; Nos. 2 and 5 (super-firing), 300°; Nos. 3 and 4 (echelon) 180° own beam and 100° far beam. R.F. on heads of derrick posts.

Armour Notes.—Main belt is 8 feet deep, 4½ feet above water-line and 3½ feet below same at normal draught. It is 240 feet long, but 11″ section is only 2 feet deep from top edge of belt, and then tapers to 5″ on lower (under-water) edge. Belt under end barbettes is 10″ tapering to 5″ as main belt. Upper belt 400 feet long, 9″ lower edge, 8″ top edge, 6″ battery above this. Funnel bases, 1½″ nickel steel for 15 feet above deck. Protective decks, 1½″ upper, 3″ lower. Two Director stations behind upper belt at bases of C.T. communication tubes. Barbettes: bases are 9″ where exposed. Shields to these: 12″ port-plate, 9″ sides, 11″ back, 3″ roof.

Anti-Torpedo Defence—3″ longitudinal wing bulkheads in way of machinery and magazine spaces. ¾″ nickel steel flats under magazines, boilers, and engine rooms. Total weight, 680 tons (included in 7,600 tons total weight of armour given above). 12 searchlights.

451

RIVADAVIA.   *Photo by courtesy of the Ministry of Marine.*

General Notes.—Built under 1908 Programme. Gave considerable trouble on trials, as steam consumption exceeded contract rate. Turbines were re-bladed completely before these ships got through their trials. They are said to have so heavy a coal consumption, plans are being prepared for conversion to "all oil fuel." On a voyage, Buenos Ayres—New York—Buenos Ayres, in 1918, one of these ships consumed 15,000 tons of coal, or 4000 tons more than the estimated normal cruising consumption with auxiliaries running.

RIVADAVIA.

Torpedo Notes.—Bullivant net defence. 12—38 inch searchlights. Electric installation at 115 volts.

Name	Builder	Machinery	Laid down	Completed	Trials	Boilers	Best recent speed
Rivadavia Moreno	Fore River Co. N.Y. Ship- building	Fore River Co.	May, '10 July, '10	Dec., 1914 Mar. 1915	39,750=22·5	Babcock Babcock	

ARGENTINE ARMOURED SHIPS.

GEN. BELGRANO: Searchlight on mast now on tower abaft 2nd funnel. Small Q.F. in fighting top on mast removed.

GEN. SAN MARTIN: One fighting top has been removed from mast. This ship is now almost of same appearance as *Belgrano.*

Photo by courtesy of the Ministry of Marine,
(LIBERTAD).

GARIBALDI.

Photo by courtesy of Ministry of Marine.

GENERAL BELGRANO (July, 1897), **GENERAL SAN MARTIN** (1896), both by Orlando, Leghorn, **GARIBALDI** (1895), by Ansaldo, Sestri, Ponente. All 6840 tons. Length (*o.a.*), 328 ft. Beam, $59\frac{7}{12}$ feet. *Max.* draught, $23\frac{1}{8}$ feet. Complements, (*G.B.*) 425, (*G.S.M.*) 431, (*G.*) 414. Armament: *Belgrano* 2—10 inch, 14—6 inch, 4—12 pdr., 4—6 pdr., 4—18 inch tubes *above water.* *San Martin*: 4—8 inch, 10—6 inch, 6—4·7 inch. 2—12 pdr., 6—6 pdr., 4—18 inch tubes *above water. Garibaldi*: 2—10 inch, 10—6 inch, 6—4·7 inch, 2—12 pdr., 4—6 pdr. Armour: (Krupp in *G.B.*, Harvey Nickel in *G.S.M.*, Harvey in *G.*), 6″ Belt with 3″ at ends and $1\frac{1}{2}$″—2″ deck, 6″ Lower deck side, 6″ Battery, 6″ Barbettes, 6″ Bulkheads, 3″ Gunhouses, 6″ C·T. Machinery: 2 sets triple expansion. Boilers: 8 cylindrical, single-ended. H.P. 13000 = 20 kts. Coal: *normal*, about 400 tons; *maximum* (*G.B.*) 1150 tons, (*G.S.M. & G.*) 1137 tons. Endurance: about 6000 miles at 10 kts.

Note.—A fourth ship of this type, **PUEYRREDON**, now employed as a Training Ship, will be found on next page.

ARGENTINE COAST DEFENCE BATTLESHIPS.

INDEPENDENCIA.

Photo by courtesy of the Ministry of Marine.

INDEPENDENCIA (1891), & **LIBERTAD** (ex-*Nueve de Julio*) (1890). Both built at Laird's, Birkenhead. Displacement 2300 tons. Complement 196. Length (*p.p*) 240 feet. Beam, 43 feet. *Max.* draught, $13\frac{3}{4}$ feet. Guns : 2—9·4 inch, 35 cal. (Krupp), 4—4·7 inch, 40 cal. (Elswick), 6—3 pdr. Armour (compound): 8″ Belt (amidships), 2″ Deck (flat on belt,) 8″ Bulkhead (forward), 6″ Bulkhead (aft), 8″ Barbettes and bases, 5″ Shields to big guns (fronts), 4″ Conning tower. Machinery: Compound vertical. 2 screws. Boilers: 4 double cylindrical. Designed H.P. 3000 = 14 kts. Coal : *normal* 230 tons ; *maximum* 356 tons. Endurance: 3000 miles at 10 kts.

Old Protected Cruisers.

Training Ships.

Now has W/T. aerials from truck of mast to bow and stern, as *Garibaldi* on preceding page.

PUEYRREDON (Ansaldo, 1897). Armoured ship. *Normal* displacement, 6840 tons. Complement, 427. Guns (Elswick): 2—10 inch, 40 cal. (A)., 10—6 inch, 40 cal., 6—4·7 inch, 40 cal., 2—12 pdr. 4—6 pdr., Torpedo tubes (18 inch): 4 *above water* (behind armour). All other details as *General Belgrano*, described on a preceding page, except :—(a) Armour (Terni); (b) 16 Belleville boilers. (*c*) *maximum* coal capacity 1000 tons = 4800 miles at 10 kts. Laid down 1896, completed 1901. Made 19·94 kts. on first trials. Machinery :—Ansaldo-Maudslay.

Photo, Abrahams & Son, Devonport.

BUENOS AIRES (Elswick, 1895). Displacement 4780 tons. Sheathed and coppered. Complement 375. Length (o.a.), 403½ feet. Beam, 47⅞ feet. *Maximum* draught, 19 feet. Guns (Elswick): 2—8 inch, 45 cal. (A), 4—6 inch, 45 cal., 6—4·7 inch, 45 cal., 12—3 pdr. Torpedo tubes : 5 *above water*. Armour (steel) : 5″ Deck (amidships), 5″ Engine hatches, 4½″ Gun shields, 3″ Hoists to guns, 6″ Conning tower (Harvey). Machinery : 2 sets vertical 4-cylinder (2 low-pressure cylinders). 2 screws. Boilers : 4 double-ended and 4 single-ended. Designed H.P. 13,000 = 23 kts.; 17,000 = 24 kts. Coal : *normal* 400 tons ; *maximum* 1000 tons. Endurance : 6400 miles at 10 kts.

(Gunnery Training Ship.)

Photo by courtesy of the Ministry of Marine.

NUEVE DE JULIO (Elswick 1892) Displacement 3540. Complement 315 Length, (o.a.) 354¾ feet. Beam, 44 feet. *Maximum* draught, 19¼ feet. Guns (Elswick): 4—6 inch, 40 cal., 8—4·7 inch, 40 cal.,10—3 pdr. Torpedo tubes : 3 *above water*. Armour (steel): 4½″ Deck, 5″ Glacis to engines, Cofferdam amidships. Machinery : 2 sets vertical 4 cylinder (2 low-pressure cylinders). 2 screws. Boilers : 8—single-ended. Designed H.P. (*forced*) 14,500 = 22·5 kts. Coal : *normal* 300 tons ; *maximum* 770 tons. Endurance : 5500 miles at 10 kts.

ALMIRANTE BROWN (Samuda, Poplar, 1880, reconstructed at La Seyne, 1907). Old Coast Defence Battleship. 4200 tons. Dimensions : 240 (p.p.) × 50 × 20½ feet. Complement, 290. Guns : 10—6 inch (50 cal.), 4—4·7 inch (50 cal.), 8—6 pdr. Torpedo tubes : 2—18 inch *above water*. Armour (compound) : 9″ Belt with 7″ Bulkheads and 1½″ Flat Deck, 8″ Central battery. Designed H.P. 4500 = 14 kts. (present speed, 11 kts.) Boilers : Cylindrical. Coal : 622 tons.

[*Continued on next page.*

Training Ships *continued.*

PRESIDENTE SARMIENTO (1898). Built at Birkenhead. 2850 tons. Complement 294. Dimensions: $251\frac{5}{12} \times 43\frac{1}{4} \times 23\frac{1}{4}$. Guns: 2—4·7 inch, 50 cal.; 2—4 inch, 2—6 pdr., 2—3 pdr. Torpedo tubes: 3 *above water*. Designed H.P. 2800=15 kts. Coal: 330 tons. Boilers: 1 Niclausse, 1 Yarrow, 2 cylindrical single-ended.

Armoured River Gunboats.

Official photo, 1918.

PARANA (April, 1908) & **ROSARIO** (July, 1908). Both built at Elswick. Displacement, 1055 tons. Complement, 142. Length, $329\frac{2}{3}$ feet. Beam, $32\frac{2}{3}$ feet. Draught, $7\frac{5}{12}$ feet. Guns: 2—6 inch Howitzers, 6—12 pdr., 8 Machine, 2 landing. Armour: 3″ Belt (amidships), $1\frac{1}{2}$″—1″ Deck, 3″ Conning tower. H.P. 1600=15 kts. 2 Yarrow boilers. Coal: 120 tons. *Nominal* radius, 2400 miles at $10\frac{1}{2}$ kts.

Surveying Ships.

Photo wanted.

ALFEREZ MACKINLAY (1914). 783 tons. H.P., 520=10 kts.

(Gunboat.)

PATRIA (Birkenhead, 1893). Displacement, 1070 tons. Dimensions: $251\frac{5}{12} \times 30\frac{2}{3} \times 11\frac{1}{4}$ feet. Complement, 156. Guns: 2—4·7 inch, 40 cal., 4—6 pdr., 2—3 pdr. Machinery: 2 sets triple expansion. 2 screws. Boilers: 4 double-ended Yarrow. Designed H.P. 4500=20·5 kts. Coal: 260 tons. Endurance: 3200 miles at 10 kts.

See Silhouettes.

URUGUAY (Birkenhead, 1874). 550 tons (sheathed). Original speed: 11 kts. Coal: 90 tons. Is an old iron Gunboat. Loaned 1918 to a Meteorological Surveying Expedition.

Oil-Tankers.

No photo available.

INGENERIO LUIS A. HUERGO (1917). 7378 tons. Dimensions: × × 22·5 feet. Designed H.P. 1600=10 kts.

Oil-Tankers—*continued.*

Official photo.

ARISTÓBULO DEL VALLE (1917). 5,400 tons. Dimensions: × × 21·6 feet. Designed H.P. 1400=9·5 kts.

Photo wanted.

MINISTRO EZCURRA (1914). 2600 tons. H.P., 1243=$10\frac{1}{2}$ kts.

Transports, &c.

VICENTE-FIDEL-LOPEZ (1906). 725 tons. H.P., 480=9·3 kts.
GUARDIA-NACIONAL (1890). 6500 tons. H.P., 1850=14 kts.
PIEDRABUENA (1874). Old iron Gunboat, sister to *Uruguay* in preceding column. Guns: 1 machine.

Also *Azopardo* and *Ingenerio Iribas*, both detached on Surveying Service, *Chaco, Guarda-Nacional, Pampa, Primeiro de Mayo.*

Tugs.

ONA (1913), **QUERANDI** (1914). Both built by Thornycrofts. These are large sea-going vessels and powerful salvage craft of 615 tons, 1200 H.P. and 11 kts. speed. During war, they performed more patrol work than any other ships of the fleet. In 1914, the Admiralty wished to take them over, but the Argentine Government insisted on delivery.

There are 7 other Tugs, built about 1900, the largest being **TECHUELCHE** and **FUEGUINO** of 310 tons and $11\frac{1}{2}$ kts. speed. Also *Fulton.*

Old Monitors.

(On Subsidiary Service).

EL PLATA, LOS ANDES (1874). 1535 tons. H.P., 750=9 kts. *nominal.* Guns: 2—8 inch, 1—4·7 inch, 1—12 pdr., 4 or 2—6 and 3 pdr.

7 Destroyers. (Cazatorpederos.)

No.	Type	Date	Displacement	H.P.	Max. speed	Fuel	Complement	T. tubes	Max. draug't
			tons		kts.	tons			feet
2	*Cordoba* (S)	'10-'12	950	20,000	32	290 coal + 50 oil	99	4	8
2	*Catamarca* (K)	'10-'12	950	18,000	32	250 coal + 100 oil	99	4	8½
3	*Corrientes* (Y)	'96-'98	340	4000	26	80 coal	66	3	8¼

K = Krupp. S = Schichau. Y = Yarrow

Photo by courtesy of the Ministry of Marine.

2 (*German*) type: **Cordoba** (Schichau, Nov., 1910), **La Plata** (Germania, Jan., 1911). 950 tons. 295 × 29½ × 7¾ feet. Armament: 4—4 inch (Beth.), 4—21 inch tubes. Curtis (A.E.G.) turbines. Boilers: 5 Schulz-Thornycroft. Designed S.H.P. 20,000 = 32 kts. Coal: 290 tons. Oil: 50 tons. Endurance: 2700 miles at 15 kts., 715 miles at full Speed Trials (*max.*): Cordoba, 34·2; La Plata, 34·7.

Photo by courtesy of the Ministry of Marine.

2 (*German*) type: **Catamarca** (Schichau, Jan., 1911), **Jujuy** (Germania, March, 1911). 950 tons. 288⅔ × 27 × 8½ feet. Armament: 4—4 inch (Beth.), 4—21 inch tubes. Curtis (A.E.G.) turbines. Boilers: Schulz-Thornycroft. Designed S.H.P. 18,000 = 32 kts. Coal: 250 tons. Oil: 110 tons. Endurance: 3000 miles at 15 kts. 800 miles at full speed.

Destroyers *Continued.*

3 *Yarrow* type: **Corrientes, Entre Rios, Misiones** (—1896). Dimensions: 190 × 19½ × 8½ feet. 1" armour protection amidships. Armament: 1—14 pdr., 3—6 pdr., 2—1 pdr., 3 tubes (18 inch). 6 Yarrow boilers. Coal: 80 tons. Endurance: 900 miles at 15 kts. Other details as table.

5 Torpedo Boats. (Torpederos).

No.	Type	Date	Displacement	H.P.	Max. speed	Fuel	Complement	T. tubes	Max. draug't
			tons		kts.	tons			feet
2	*Comodoro Py* (T)	'90-'91	110	1700	24·5	24	43	3	3½
3	*Buchardo* (Y)	'90-'91	85	1200	23	22	28	2	6

T = Thornycroft. Y = Yarrow.

2 *Thornycroft* type **Comodoro Py** (1891) and **Murature** (1890). Dimensions: 150 × 14½ × 3½ feet. Armament: 2—3 pdr., 1 M.G., 3—18 inch tubes. Thornycroft boilers. Endurance: 1200 miles at 15 kts. Other details as Table above.

3 *Yarrow* type: **Buchardo, Jorge, Thorne** (all 1890.) Dimensions: 130 × 14 × 6 feet. Armament: 2—3 pdr., 1 M.G., 3—18 inch tubes. Endurance: 1200 miles at 15 kts. For other details, v. Table above.

BRAZILIAN FLEET.

Almirante is only a war appointment : *Vice-Almirante* is the highest place rank.

Capitão di Corveta is equivalent to a British Lieut-Commander. *Capitão tenente* a lieutenant. *1° tenente* = sub-lieutenant. Civilian ranks have the same stripes-*without* the curl, and plus colours above top stripe and below bottom one as under :

Constructors.—No colour, but a ball above the stripes.

Engineers (Machinista).—Green.

Doctors (Cirurgiao).—Red.

Paymasters (Commissario).—White.

Shoulder straps for engineers carry a screw propeller, for doctors a stethoscope, for paymasters two quill pens crossed. These devices are also worn on the collar of tunic.

Caps.—Admirals have a broad gold band with oak leaf device, the other commissioned ranks narrow gold bands as on sleeves.

Warrant officers and men carry white distinctive sleeve badges, as follows :—*Torpedo*, torpedoes ; *gunnery*, two crossed guns ; *navigation*, two crossed anchors ; *signal*, two crossed flags ; *quartermasters*, a wheel ; *engine room complements*, a screw propeller.

Marine Infantry—Scarlet tunics with black insignia : five stripes for first sargento, four for second ditto, two for cabo. White helmets as the British. No commissioned officers.

Brazilian sailors enter as boys at about twelve years. They do three years in a school, then ten months special instruction, then serve twelve years with the fleet. Volunteers three to twenty years. There are nineteen schools for boys.

Arsenals.

RIO DE JANEIRO. 6 Docks. Government are " Guanabara " (Cobras Island), 423 × 70 × 20 feet ; " Santa Cruz," $258\frac{1}{2} \times 54\frac{2}{3} \times 18$ feet. Government Floating Dock, " Affonso Penna," lengthened in 1912 to $715\frac{2}{4} \times 102 \times 36$ feet (30,000 tons), requires 54 feet depth of water to dock ship of 30 feet draught. A seventh Floating Dock, 350 (*o.a*) × 136 feet (to lift 6000 tons), completing by Messrs. Vickers Ltd., 1919. This dock was taken over for British Navy during war, but released in 1919. 3 Private Docks, Mocangué No. 1, 400 × 60 × 16 feet ; Mocangué No. 2, 370 × 50 × 16 feet. Lage Bros. " Cruziero " (Vianna Island), 400 × 58 × 18 feet.

PARA. 2 Floating Docks, " Affonso Penna " and " Lauro Müller," each 235 × 45 × 12 feet (1700 tons).

LADARIO River.

Personnel.—About 10,000 of all ranks and ratings.

Minister of Marine—Senhor Raul Soares (July, 1919).

Mercantile Marine.

283 steamers, 266,605 tons *gross*.
79 sailing, 14,068 " "
49 German steamers, of 253,795 tons, have been seized and placed into service, two of which have been sunk.

Guns in Service.*

Nota-tion.	Calibre.		Length in calibres	Weight of A.P. shell.	Muzzle Velocity.	Max. penetration A.P. capped at K.C. at		Danger Space against average ships at			Service rounds per minute
						5000 yards.	3000 yards.	10,000. yards.	5000 yards.	3000 yards.	
	inch.	c/m.	cals.	lbs.	ft. secs.	inch.	inch.				
HEAVY	12	30·5	45	850	2800	...	...	...	...	...	2
MEDIUM	9·2	23	45	380	2700	9	11½	...	...	...	·8
LIGHT	6	15	40	100	2500	4	5	65	200	420	6
	6	15	50	100	2640	4¼	5½	72	240	460	6
	4·7	12	40	45	2150	..	..	...	...	...	8
	4·7	12	50	45	2630	...	...	...	...	...	8

° **Note.** = These particulars of the Brazilian Naval Ordnance are not derived from any official source and must be regarded as only approximate.

BRAZILIAN RECOGNITION SILHOUETTES.

ONE FUNNEL.

PERNAMBUCO.

ACRE *class*

OYAPOCK.

*1 funnel, 1 mast,
Clipper bow.*

J. BONIFACIO.
(*Yacht.*)

AMAPÁ.

M. HERMES.

JAGUARAYO.*

M. DO. CONTO.*

River Craft.

Tugs and Despatch Vessels.
(*Mining Vessels.*)

REPUBLICA.

C. COMEZ.
(*Mine Layer*).

DEODORO *class* (2 ships).

CEARA (*S/M. Depôt Ship*).
(*Double hulls at stern.*)

TIRADENTES.

BENJ. CONSTANT.
(*Training Ship.*)

TWO FUNNELS.

BAHIA *class* (2 ships).

MINAS GERAES *class* (2 ships).

TYMBIRA.

BARROSO.

TORPEDO CRAFT.

Scale : 1 inch = 160 feet.

Goyaz t.b.

Yarrow type, t.b.d. (10 Para *class*.)

SUBMARINES.

Scale : 1 inch = 80 feet.

F *class* (3).

(*May have one or two folding masts*).

(MINAS GERAES CLASS—2 SHIPS).

MINAS GERAES (Sept., 1908), **SAO PAULO** (April, 1909).

Normal displacement 19,200 tons.   *Full load* 21,200 tons.   Complement 850.

Length (*waterline*) 530 feet ; (*p.p.*), 500 feet.   Beam 83 feet.   *Max*. load draught, 25 feet.   Length *over all*, 543 feet.

Guns (Elswick) :
    12—12 inch, 45 cal.
    22—4·7 inch, 50 cal.
    8—3 pdr.
    4 M.G.
Torpedo tubes :
    Dropping gear for boats and carry torpedoes for this purpose.

Armour (Krupp) :
    9″ Belt ....
    6″—4″ Belt (bow) N.C. }
    6″—4″ Belt (aft) N.C. }
    2¼″ Deck (slopes) ....
    9″—6″ Upper belt.........
    9″ Bulkheads ....
    9″ Battery (main deck) ...
    12″—8″ Turrets (K.C.)... {
    12″ Conning tower (fore)
    9″ Conning tower (aft) ...

SAO PAULO.

Notes added in 1919.—In view of experiences gained by the war, the following remarks are added : (*a*) armouring is generally inadequate to give protection against the latest types of A.P. and H.E. shells ; (*b*) main deck 4·7 inch are not much use in any seaway ; (*c*) these ships lack any director systems of control for 12 inch or 4·7 inch guns but may have a few small-base R.F. ; (*d*) searchlights are uncontrolled and inadequate in number.

MINAS GERAES.

Ahead :
8—12 in.
6—4·7 in.

Astern :
8—12 in.
6—4·7 in.

Broadside : 10—12 in., 11—4·7 in.

Machinery : 2 sets triple expansion. 2 screws. Designed S.H.P. 23,500 = 21 kts. *f.d.* Boilers : 18 Babcock. Coal : *normal* 800 tons ; *maximum* 2360 tons + 350 tons oil.   Endurance : about 3600 miles at 19 kts., and about 8000 miles at 10 kts.

Gunnery Notes.—Arcs of fire : Centre-line 12-inch guns 270-280° ; beam 12-inch 180° *nominal*. Main deck, 4·7 inch 100° ; 4·7 inch in superstructure casemates, 90°.   3 pdr. guns can be transferred to landing mountings.

Torpedo Notes.—⅘ net defence (Bullivant). S.L. not controlled.

Engineering Notes.—66 revs. = about 10 kts ; 126 = 20 kts. ; 148 about 21·5 kts.   Heating surface, 55,370 sq. ft.   Grate area, 1868 sq. ft.

Armour Notes.—Main belt 22½ ft. deep, 5 ft. of this being below waterline. Belt does not run up to stern.

Name.	Builder.	Machinery.	Laid down.	Completed.	Trials. 30 hour at ¾	Full power	Boilers.	Best recent speed.
M. Geraes	Elswick	Vickers	1907	Jan.'10	16,177 = 19·13	25,519 = 21·2	Babcock	
S. Paulo	Vickers	Vickers	1907	July '10	16,067 = 19·85	25,517 = 21·2	Babcock	

General Notes.—Both ships were somewhat over normal displacement on trials. Have been in poor condition for several years past and cannot raise anything like full designed speed until machinery is fully overhauled.

* Not from any official source.

M. GERAES.

(1908) Light Cruisers (*Cruzadores*).

BAHIA.

BAHIA (Jan., 1909) & RIO GRANDE DO SUL (April, 1909).

Normal displacement 3000 tons.   Complement 320.

Length $\left\{ \begin{array}{l} (p.p.), \ 380 \ \text{feet.} \\ (o.a.). \ 401\frac{1}{2} \ ,, \end{array} \right\}$ Beam, 39 feet.   *Max.* draught, 13 feet. 5 ins.

Guns (Elswick):
  10—4·7 inch, 50 cal.
  6—3 pdr.
Torpedo tubes (18 inch):
  2 *above water*

Armour:
  1½″ Deck.....................
  3″ Conning tower ....

Ahead:
2—4·7 in.

BAHIA & RIO GRANDE DO SUL

Astern:
2—4·7 in.

Broadside: 5—4·7 inch.

Machinery: Parsons turbine.   3 screws.   Boilers: 10 Yarrow.   Designed S.H.P. 18,000 = 25 kts.   Coal: *normal* 150 tons, *maximum* 650 tons.   Endurance: about 1400 miles at $23\frac{1}{2}$ kts., 3500 miles at 10 kts.

Name	Builder	Machinery	Laid down	Com-pleted	Trials 6 hours ¾	Full power.	Boilers	Best recent speed
Bahia	Elswick	Vickers	1908	1910	= 24	20,101 = 27·02	Yarrow	
Rio G. do Sul	Elswick	Vickers	1908	1908	= 24	20,600 = 27·41	Yarrow	

General Notes.—Reported to be in poor condition up to 1917 and not capable of raising more than 18 kts.   But, during 1918, they may have been repaired and put in effective condition.

(1896) Coast Defence Vessels (*Encouraçados*).

DEODORO (ex-*Ypiranga*, 1898) & FLORIANO (1899).   Both built at La Seyne.   Displacement 3162 tons.   Complement 200.   Length (*p.p.*), $267\frac{1}{2}$ feet.   Beam, 48 feet.   *Max.* draught, $13\frac{1}{4}$ feet.   Guns: 2—9·4 in., 45 cal.; 4—4·7 in., 50 cal.; 4—6 pdr., 2 M.G. (2 field).   Armour (Harvey-nickel): $13\frac{3}{4}″$ Belt (amidships), 4″ Belt (ends), 1½″ Deck (reinforcing belt), 8″ Turrets, 3″ Casemates, 5″ Conning tower.   Machinery: 2 sets triple expansion.   2 screws.   Boilers: (1912), Babcock.   Designed H.P. 3400 = 15 kts.   Coal: 246 tons.   Radius of action: 2500 miles at 10 kts.   Reported to be in very bad condition.

(1895) Protected Cruiser.

BARROSO (Elswick, 1896).   3450 tons (sheathed and coppered).   Comp. 375.   Dimensions (*p p.*) $330 \times 43\frac{3}{4} \times 16\frac{5}{8}$ feet.   Guns (Elswick): 6—6 in., 50 cal.; 4—4·7 in., 50 cal.; 10—6 pdr., 4—1 pdr., 4 Maxims, (2 field.)   Armour: 3½″ Deck (amidships).   Machinery: 2 sets 3-cyl. triple expansion.   2 screws.   Boilers: cylindrical.   Designed H.P. *forced* 7500 = 20 5 kts.   Coal: *normal* 450 tons; *maximum* about 850 tons.   Endurance: 6500 miles at 10 kts.   Refitted 1916-17.   Two sister-ships, *Abreu* and *Amazonas*, were purchased by the U.S. for the Spanish-American War, and are now the U.S. *Albany* and *New Orleans*.

Gunboat.

REPUBLICA (Elswick, 1892). 1300 tons. Comp. 132. Dimensions: 210½ (p.p.) × 35 × 15 feet. Guns (Elswick): 6—4·7 inch, 4—6 pdr. 6 M.G. Torpedo tubes (18 inch), 4 *above w.* Armour: 2½″ deck. Designed H.P. 3800=16 kts. Cyl. boilers. Coal: 170 tons.

Note.—It is doubtful if the following two Ships are still in Service; they may have been scrapped during 1918-19.

Torpedo Gunboat.

TYMBIRA (ex-*Caramuru*, 1896). 1030 tons. Complement 110. Dimensions: 259 × 30 × 10¼ feet. Armament (Krupp): 2—4·7 inch, or 4·1 inch, 50 cal., 6—6 pdr., 2—1 pdr., 3—14 inch tubes. Armour: 1″ Deck. Designed H.P. 7000=23 kts. Coal: 260 tons. Built by Krupp.

Gunboat.

TIRADENTES (Elswick, 1892). 800 tons. Dimensions: 170½ × 29½ × 12 feet. Complement 100. Guns: 4—4·7 inch, 2—6 pdr., 5 Nordenfelts. Tubes: 2—14 inch. Designed H.P. 1200=14·7 kts. Coal: 140 tons.

River Craft.

Photo, Abrahams.

PERNAMBUCO (1909-10, River Monitor, built at Rio.) 470 tons. Dimensions: 146 × 24 × 5¼ feet. H.P., 800=11 kts. Coal: 45 tons. Guns: 3—4·7 inch, 10 machine. Armour: 6·6″—4″ belt, 4″ deck, 3½″ conning tower, 6″ turret. Took 20 years to build.

ACRE, MISSOES (Yarrow, 1904). 200 tons. Dimensions: 120 × 20 × 2 feet. Armament: 1—3·4 inch (15 pdr.) howitzer, 1—6 pdr., 4 maxims. H.P., 300=11 kts. Complement, 30.

No Photo available.

JUTAHY, TEFFE (1890-92, refitted 1917). River Gunboats of 33 tons. Dimensions: 90 (p.p.) × 15 × 5 feet. Guns: 1—3 pdr., 2 M.G. H.P.=11 kts. Coal: 7 tons.

Note :—These two Ships have also—but very doubtfully—been reported as vessels of "180 tons and 9 kts. speed, of much the same appearance as *Acre* and *Missoes*." Probably have been confused with Commercial River Steamers bearing same names.

River Craft—*continued*.

No Photo available.

(Present existence doubtful.)

OYAPOCK (—). Despatch Vessel of 195 tons, 14 kts. speed.

For Service with Seaplane.

The Brazilian Navy possess about ten Seaplanes of Curtiss and other types. It is not known if any Ship has been fitted out as a Seaplane carrier or as Tender to Seaplanes.

Mine Layers.

Photo wanted.

(See Silhouettes for appearance.)

CARLOS GOMEZ (ex-*Itaipu*, 1892). 1800 tons. Complement 100. Dimensions: 301 × 39 × 10 feet. Designed H.P. 4000=16 kts. (*less now*). Guns: *not known.* Coal: 400 tons. Can carry up to 550 mines *maximum.*

Mine Sweepers.

Tugs *Jaguarayo* and *Maria do Conto* (both listed on next page) are probably fitted out for this service.

Armed Merchantile Cruiser and Fleet Collier.

Photo wanted.

BELMONTE (ex-German S.S. *Valesia*, Rostock, 1912.) 5227 tons *gross*. Dimensions : 364¾×51× feet. Guns : 4—4·7 in. 6—6 pdr. H.P. 2700 = 12 kts. Can take about 6500 tons coal as cargo.

Note.—Above ship seized in Brazilian port, 1917, after declaration of war against Germany.

Tugs.

(Officially rated as Despatch Vessels).

No Photos available.

AMAPÁ (ex-Tug *Cayapo*). **GOYTACAZ.** No details known.
LAURINDO PITTA (1910). 304 tons.

Tugs (*continued.*)
(Officially rated as Despatch Vessels).

No Photo available.

MARECHAL HERMES. Sea-going Tug. No details known.

No Photo available.

JAGUARAYO. Sea-going Tug. No details known. Attached to Mining Flotilla ; may be Mine-Layer and/or Mine-Sweeper.

No Photo available.

MARIA DO CONTO. Sea-going Tug. No details known. Attached to Mining Flotilla ; may be Mine-Layer and/or Mine-Sweeper.

Training Ship.

Photo, Abrahams, Devonport.

BENJAMIN CONSTANT (La Seyne, 1892, reconstructed 1911). 2750 tons. Comp. 380. Guns (Elswick) : 8—4·7 inch, 45 cal. 2—12 pdr., 2—1 pdr. Torpedo tubes (14 inch), 1 *above w.* Armour : 2″ deck. Designed H.P. 4000 *f.d.* = 15 kts. Cyl. boilers. Coal : 260 tons.

Also Brigs *Caravellas, Cidade de Manaos* and *Recife.*

Yachts.

Photo wanted.
Appearance :—clipper bow, 1 mast, 1 funnel.

JOSÉ BONIFACIO. Ex-U.S. Yacht *Nourmaha* (?), 768 tons, 8½ knts. speed. No other details known.

No Photo available.

TENENTE ROSA, TENENTE RIBEIRO (1911). 152 tons. Speed : 12½ kts. One or two small guns.

SILVA-JARDIM. No details known.

10 Destroyers.

10 *Yarrow* type: **Amazonas, Matto Grosso, Piauhy, Pará** (all launched 1908), **Rio Grande do Norte, Parahyba, Alagoas, Santa Catharina** (all launched 1909), **Parana, Sergipe** (both launched 1910). Displacement 560 tons. Dimensions: 240 × 23½ × (*Mean* draught) 7⅝ feet. Armament: 2—4 inch, 4—3 pdrs., 2—18 in. tubes. Designed H.P. 8000 = 27 kts. Machinery: 2 sets triple expansion reciprocating. 2 double-ended Yarrow boilers. Majority of these boats retubed 1917-18. Coal: 140 tons. Nominal radius: 1600 miles at 15 kts. On acceptance trials with 6563 to 8877 H.P. they made 27·1 to 28·7 kts. Hulls of several are said to be in bad condition.

Note :—The numbers on after funnel are thus : 1, *Amazonas* ; 2, *Para* ; 3, *Piauhy* ; 4, *R. G. do Norte* ; 5, *Parahyba* ; 6, *Alagoas* ; 7, *Sergipe* ; 8, *Parana* ; 9, *S. Catherina* ; 10, *Matto Grosso*.

1 Torpedo Boat.

1 *Yarrow* type: **Goyaz** (1907) 150 tons. Dimensions: 152 × 15¼ × 4¼ feet. Guns: 2—3 pdr. Torpedo tubes: 2 single 18-inch. Turbine and reciprocating engines. Designed speed, 26¼ kts. Yarrow boilers. Worn out and practically unfit for futher service.

3 Submarines.

3 *Laurenti-Fiat* type : **F 5, F 3, F I** (Spezia, 1913-14). Built by Fiat-San Giorgio Co. Dimensions : 150 × 13·8 × 9·8 to 12 feet draught. Displacement : 250 tons *on surface* ; 305 tons *submerged*. Machinery : 2 sets 350 H.P. 6-cylinder, 2-cycle Fiat Diesel engines *on surface*=700 H.P. 2 sets 250 H.P. electric motors+batteries=500 H.P. *submerged*. Speeds: (maximum) 13¼ kts. *on surface*, 8 to 8½ kts. *submerged*. Radii of action : *on surface* about 800 miles at full speed, 1600 miles at 8½ kts ; when *submerged*, 18 miles at full speed, or 100 miles at 4 kts. Torpedo tubes : 2—18 inch in bows. Complement about 20.

Submarine Carrier, Depot, Docking and Salvage Ship.

(Also serves as Training Ship for submarine service.)

CEARA (Spezia, 1915). Length (*p.p.*) 328 feet. Beam, 52 feet. Draught and displacement (with all stores) vary thus : (*a*) with dock empty and dock-gate closed 4100 tons at 14 feet draught ; (*b*) with dock-gate open and dock flooded to float submarine in, 4130 tons at 17½ feet ; (*c*) with gate closed and submarine docked, 4560 tons at 15 feet ; (*d*) with gate closed and submarine under hydraulic pressure test in dock, 6460 tons at 20¼ feet ; (*e*) with dock empty and gate closed, and when raising submarines by double cranes at stern, 4615 tons at 15 feet. tons for submarines (sufficient fuel carried to fill tanks of six submarines four times). Radius of action : Machinery : 2 sets 6-cylinder, 2-cycle Fiat-Diesel engines. 4100 B.H.P.=14 kts. Fuel : 400 tons (own bunkers)+ 4000 miles at 10 kts. Guns : 4—4 inch, 2 smaller. Built by Fiat-San Giorgio Co. Completed 1916.

Note.—This ship has been specially designed and completely equipped to serve as a depot ship, salvage ship, and floating dock for a flotilla of 6 submarines. There is a central, circular caisson dock 216½ feet long (to dock submarines up to 198 feet length and 23¼ feet beam) between the double hulls, and two salvage cranes at stern for raising 400 tons deadweight. Equipment for service to submarines includes two 150 Kw. charging dynamos, two electric-driven and one steam-driven 75-150 atmos. air compressors, refrigerating plant, workshops, powerful pumps to empty dock in 2 hours, &c. ; carries spare batteries, torpedoes, stores, &c., for 6 submarines.

CHILEAN FLEET.

Revised and Re-Illustrated, 1919.

ENSIGN & MERCANTILE   JACK   MINISTER OF MARINE   DIRECTOR GENERAL & VICE-ADMIRAL COMMANDING   VICE-ADMIRAL SUBORDINATE

REAR-AD. COMMANDING   REAR-AD. SUBORDINATE   COMMODORE COMMANDING   COMMODORE SUBORDINATE   SENIOR OFFICER

|||| RED
☐ WHITE
☰ BLUE

Vice Almirante. | Contra-Almirante. | Capitan de Navio. | Capitan de Fragata. | Capitan de Corbeta. | Teniente 1° | Teniente 2° | Guardia Marina de 1a clase. | Guardia Marina de 2a clase.

Corresponding British or U.S.} Vice-Ad. Rear-Ad. Captain. Commander. Lieut. Comdr. Lieut.-Comm'r. Lieut. Sub. Lieut. Midshipman.

Other Branches the same without the star, and colours as follows :—Engineers (blue), Paymasters (white), Doctors (red).

Minister of War and Marine :

Personnel : About 7500, of whom about 1000 are conscripts, the rest volunteers.

Mercantile Marine : 87 steamers, of 89,515 tons *gross* ; 33 sailing vessels, 26,178 tons *gross.*

Bases : Talcahuano. One dry dock, 614 × 87 × 30½ feet. New dock *building*, 856 × 117 × 36 feet. One small floating dock, 216 × 42 × 15 feet.

Valparaiso. One small wooden floating dock, **and** two large *projected* in the Harbour Works.

TORPEDO CRAFT.   Scale : 1 inch = 160 feet.

I. Hyatt *class* t.b. (5)

Tomé *class* t.g.b. (2 ships).

Thompson t.b.d.

Orella *class* t.b.d. (4)
(Also with higher funnels).
O'Brien *class* t.b.d. (2)

Alm.-Lynch *class* t.b.d (2)
(Fore funnel in each now raised.)

Alm. Cochrane.
(*Torpedo School*)

P. Errazuriz.

General Baquedano.
(*Training Ship.*)

Ministro Zenteno.

Chacabuco.

Blanco Encalada.

Esmeralda.

Capitan Prat.

General O'Higgins.

SUBMARINES.   Scale : 1 inch = 80 feet.

H *class* (6 boats).

463

(1888) Battleship.

Copyright photo, G. Allan, Valparaiso.

CAPITAN PRAT (La Seyne, 1890). *Reconstructed 1909.* 6902 tons. Complement 500. Length (*p.p.*) 328 feet. Beam, 60⅔ feet. *Maximum* draught, 22⅗ feet. Guns (Canet): 4—9˙4 inch, 35 cal. (*A*), 8—4˙7 inch, 45 cal., 10—6 pdr., 4—3 pdr., 10—1 pdr., 1 Maxim. Torpedo tubes (18 inch): 2 *above water.* Armour (Creusot): 12″ Belt (amidships), 3″ Deck (flat on belt), 10½″ Barbettes, 2″ Barbette hoods, 4″ Redoubt (amidships), 2″ Small turrets. Machinery: 2 sets horizontal triple expansion. 2 screws. Boilers: new in 1909, 12 Babcock. H.P. 12,000 = 18 kts. (about 16 kts. now). Coal: *normal* 400 tons; *maximum* 775 tons = *circa* 4650 miles at 10 kts.

(1895) Armoured Cruiser.

Copyright photo, G. Allan, Valparaiso.

ESMERALDA (Elswick, 1896, re-fitted 1910). 7050 tons. Sheathed and coppered. Complement 500. Length (*p.p.*), 436 feet. Beam, 53 feet, 2 ins. Draught (*mean*), 20¼ feet. Guns (Elswick): 2—8 inch, 40 cal. (*B*), 12—6 inch, 40 cal., 12—12 pdr. (2 field). Torpedo tubes (18 inch): 2 *submerged.* Armour (Harvey): 6″ Belt, 2″ Deck, 6″ Bulkheads, 4½″ Shields to guns, 4½″ Hoists. Machinery: 2 sets 4 cylinder triple expansion. 2 screws. Boilers: 2-ended cylindrical. H.P. 18,000 = 22˙25 kts. (still steams well and can do 21 kts. now). Coal: *normal* 550 tons; *maximum* 1350 tons. Endurance: (*a*) 2400 miles at 24 kts., (*b*) 7680 miles at 10 kts.

Copyright photo, G. Allan, Valparaiso.

GENERAL O'HIGGINS (Elswick, 1897). 8500 tons. Sheathed and coppered. Complement 500. Length (*p.p.*), 412 feet. Beam, 62¾ feet. *Max.* draught, 22 feet. Guns (Elswick): 4—8 inch, 45 cal. (*A*), 10—6 inch, 40 cal., 8 *or* 10—12 pdr., 10—6 pdr., 4 M.G. Torpedo tubes (18 inch): 2 *submerged.* Armour (Harvey-nickel): 7″-5″ Belt (amidships), 2″ Deck (slopes), 7½″ Port plates to 8 inch gun turrets and front, 6″ Hoists to these, 6″ Gun houses, 6in. guns, 6″ Casemates (6), 9″ Conning tower. Machinery: 2 sets triple expansion. 2 screws. Boilers: 30 Belleville (in 3 groups). Designed H.P. *natural* 10,000 = 19 kts.; *forced* 16,000 = 21˙5 kts. (still steams very well and can do 21 kts. now). Coal: *normal* 700 tons; *maximum* 1200 tons. Endurance: (*a*) 2250 miles at 20 kts., (*b*) 6000 miles at 10 kts.

(1897) Protected Cruiser.

Copyright photo, G. Allan, Valparaiso.

CHACABUCO (Elswick, 1898, (purchased 1902). 4500 tons. Complement 400. Length (*p.p.*), 360 feet. Beam, 46½ feet. *Maximum* draught, 17 feet. Guns (Elswick): 2—8 inch, 45 cal. 10—4˙7 inch, 40 cal., 12—12 pdr., 6—3 pdr. Armour (Harvey nickel): 4½″ Deck (amidships), 1¾″ Deck (ends), 4½″ Fronts 8 in. gun shields, 2½″ Sides 8in. gun shields, 2½″ Shields 4˙7 in. guns, 5″ Conning tower. Machinery: Boilers, cylindrical. I.H.P. 15,500 = 24 kts. *forced.* Still steams well, and can do 23 kts. now) 2 screws. Coal: *normal* 300 tons; *maximum* 1028 tons. Electric training and elevating gear to 8 inch guns. Laid down at Elswick, 1897, as a speculation. Completed 1902, and purchased by Chile.

CHILEAN NAVY.

1896. Protected Cruisers (continued.)

Copyright photo, G. Allan, Valparaiso.

MINISTRO ZENTENO (Elswick, 1896.) 3420 tons. Complement, 350. Length, (p.p.) 330¼ feet. Beam, 43¾ feet. *Max.* draught, 16⅚ feet. Armament: 8—6 in., 10—6 pdr., 4—1 pdr., 4 Maxims. Armour: 3½" Deck, 4" Conning tower. Designed H.P. 7500=20 kts. (16 kts. now.) Cylindrical boilers. Coal: *maximum* 850 tons. Endurance: 6450 miles at 10 kts.

1893.

Copyright photo, G. Allan, Valparaiso.

BLANCO ENCALADA (Elswick, 1893). 4420 tons. Sheathed and coppered. Complement 427. Length (p.p.), 370 feet. Beam, 46½ feet. *Maximum* draught, 19½ feet. Armament: 2—8 inch, 40 cal., 8—6 inch, 40 cal., 2—4·7 inch. 4—12 pdr., 8—3 pdr., 4—1 pdr. Armour: 4" Deck, 6" Shields to 8" guns, 6" Conning tower. Boilers: cylindrical (retubed 1908-9). Designed H.P. *forced* 14,500= 22·75 kts. (about 21·5 kts. now.) Coal: *maximum* 850 tons. Endurance: 5000 miles at 10 kts.

1890. Protected Cruiser.

Copyright photo, G. Allan, Valparaiso.

PRESIDENTE ERRAZURIZ (La Seyne, 1890, refitted 1908). 2080 tons. Complement, 170. Dimensions: 268¼ p.p. × 35¾ × 14½ feet. Guns (new in 1908): 2—6 inch, 4—5·9 inch, 4—6 pdr., 4—1 pdr. Armour: 2¼" Deck, 3" shields to guns. Machinery: 2 sets horizontal triple expansion. 2 screws. Boilers: Belleville (1908). Designed H.P. 5400=19 kts. (12·5 kts. now.) Coal: 280 tons. Endurance: 2900 miles at 10 kts.

Sloop and Training Ship.

Copyright photo, G. Allan, Valparaiso.

GENERAL BAQUEDANO (1898). 2500 tons, sheathed and coppered. Armed with 4—4·7 inch guns, 2—12 pdr., and 2—6 pdr., I.H.P. 1500=13·75 kts. Belleville boilers. Coal: 300 tons. Built by Elswick. Best recent speed: 12 kts.

2 G

Torpedo Gunboats.

TOMÉ (ex *Almirante Lynch*, 1890) & **TALCAHUANO** (ex *Almirante Condell*, 1890). Displacement, 720 tons. Length, 240 feet (*o.a.*). Beam, 27½ feet. *Maximum* draught, 11 feet. Complement, 87. Guns: *Tomé*, 3—12 pdr., 2 M.G.; *Talcahuano*, 1—4·7 inch (aft), 2—12 pdr., 2 M.G. Torpedo tubes *in both*: 5—14 inch, viz., 1 bow, 4 broadside, all *above water*. Armour: Double skin (amidships), 1″ Bulkheads. Machinery: 2 sets triple expansion. 2 screws. Boilers: Belleville, *without* economisers. Designed I.H.P. 4500=20 kts. (exceeded on *trial*). Coal: 220 tons. Endurance : 3100 miles.

Laid down at Birkenhead, 1889. Completed 1892. Reconstructed 1900.

9 Destroyers.

No.	Type	Date	Displacement	H.P.	Max. speed	Fuel	Complement	T. tubes	Max. draug't
			tons.		kts.	tons			feet
2	*Lynch* (W)	'11-'14	1430	30,000	31t	427 coal, 80 oil	160	3	11
1	*Capitan Thompson* (E)	'98-'00	350	6500	30	120 coal	65	2	5⅓
2	*C. O'Brien* (L)	'00-'02	311	6000	30	90	65	2	8½
4	*C. Orella* (L)	1896	300	6000	30	90	65	3	8½

(E)=Elswick.   (L)=Laird.   (W)=White.   (t)=Turbines.

466

ALM. CONDELL (centre), AL. LYNCH (behind).   (Fore funnels now raised.)   *Copyright photo, G. Allan, Valparaiso.*

2 *White*: **Almirante Lynch** (1912), **Al. Condell** (1913). Dimensions: 320×32½×11 feet. *Normal* displacement: 1430 tons. *Full load*: 1850 tons. Armament: 6—4 inch, 4 M.G., 3—18 inch tubes. Designed H.P. 30,000=31 kts. Turbines: Parsons. Boilers: White-Forster. 3 screws. Fuel: 427 tons coal + 80 tons oil = 2750 miles at 15 kts. Trials: *Al. Lynch*, 31·8 kts. (6 hours); *Al. Condell*, 3·4 kts. Complement 160.

Note.—See British Navy Section for three other boats of this class, now H.M. ships *Botha, Broke* and *Faulknor.*

1 *Elswick*.   **Capitan Thompson** (1899). 350 tons. Dimensions: 213 (*p.p.*)×21½×5⅓ feet.   [*Photo, Abrahams.* Armament: 1—12 pdr., 5—6 pdr., 2—18 inch tubes. Designed H.P. 6500=30 kts. Coal: 120 tons=1150 miles at 15 kts.

CAPITAN O'BRIEN.   *Copyright photo, G. Allen, Valparaiso.*

2 *Laird*: **Capitan O'Brien** & **Capitan Merino Jarpa** (both 1901).   Armament: 1—12 pdr., 5—6 pdr., 2—18 inch tubes, one amidships, one aft. Boilers: Laird-Normand.   Other details as Laird boat below.

And as O'Brien except that the funnels are shorter :—

4 *Laird*: **Capitan Orella, Capitan Munoz Gamero, Teniente Serrano,** & **Guardia Marina Riquelme** (all 1896). 311 tons. Dimensions: 213 (*p.p.*)×21½×8½ feet. Armament: 1—12 pdr., 5—6 pdr., 3—18 inch tubes, Boilers: Normand. Designed H.P. 6500=30 kts., but some can only do 23 now. Coal: 90 tons. *Nominal* radius 900 miles at 15 kts. All reboilered and refitted 1909. Complement 65.   (*Torpedo Boats on next page.*)

CHILEAN TORPEDO BOATS, SUBMARINES AND MISCELLANEOUS VESSELS

5 (or 3) Torpedo Boats.

3 or 5 *Yarrow* type : **Injeniero Hyatt, Cirujano Videla** (Yarrow, Poplar, 1896). **Injeniero Mutilla,* Guardia Marina Contreras** and **Teniente Rodriguez*** (Balcachuamo, 1896-1901). 128 tons. Dimensions : 152½ × 15¼ × 7¾ feet. Armament : 3—6 pdr., 3—14 inch torpedo tubes. Designed H.P. 2000 = 25 to 27·5 kts. Yarrow boilers. Coal : 40 tons. Complement 28 and 32.

**Injeniero Mutilla* and *Rodriguez* may have been scrapped in 1918.

6 Submarines.

H 2.   *Copyright photo, G. Allan, Valparaiso.*

6 *Holland* : **H1, H2, H4, H5, H6** (Fore River Co., U.S.A., 1915-17). Displacements : ⅜⅝⅞ tons. Dimensions : 10¾ × 15¾ × 12¼ feet. H.P. ⁴⁸⁰⁄₃₂₀ = ¹¹⁄₅ kts. Machinery : *for surface* 2 sets 210 H.P. Nlseco Diesel engines. When *submerged* electric motors and batteries can develop 640 H.P. = 11 kts. for one hour only. Endurance : 2800 miles at 11 kts. *on surface* ; 30 miles at 5 kts. *submerged*. Oil : 17½ tons, Torpedo tubes : 4—18 inch (bow). Complement 22.

Notes.—These boats are believed to be units of the British *H 11—20* group of submarines, built by the Fore River Co., U.S.A., during 1915. The Admiralty intended to take them over and equip them with torpedo tubes at the Canadian Vickers Co. Yard at Montreal— provided that these boats could legally be delivered in an unarmed state. The U.S. Government decided the submarines could not leave any U.S. port, so long as the United States remained neutral, and all the boats were interned at Boston. They were released on the U.S. declaration of war, 1917. With the approval of the U.S. authorities, the above six boats were ceded to Chile by Great Britain, in part payment for the Chilian warships building in British yards in August, 1914, and appropriated for the British Navy.

Submarine Depot Ship.

Photo, Grimm, Valparaiso.

HUASCAR (1865, captured from Peru, 1870). Old Turret Ship of 1870 tons. Speed : 10 kts. *nominal*. Guns : 2—10 inch.

Gunnery and Torpedo School Ship.

Photo, Allen, Valparaiso.

ALMIRANTE COCHRANE (1874, reconstructed 1896). 3500 tons. Dimensions : 210 (*p.p.*) × 45¾ × 20½ feet. Guns : 4—4·7 inch, 2—12 pdr., 4—3 pdr., 2 M.G. Armour (iron) : 9"—4½" Belt, 8" Battery. H.P. 4300 = 12 kts. (not over 8 kts. now). Cylindrical boilers. Coal : 350 tons. Complement 306.

Other Ships.

A large armed transport *Angamos* was in service up to about 1918. She may have been sold out recently for Mercantile Service. No details are known of this ship.

Contramastor Ortiz and *Galvez* (1909), *Valparaiso* (1897). Tugs.

Meteoro, 800 tons, 14 kts. ; *Porvenir*, 350 tons, 12 kts., and *Yelcho*, 300 tons, 14 kts., are used as Lighthouse Supply Ships.

Condor and *Huemel* (1889), 11 kts. speed, and about 12 other very old ships are used for Harbour Duty and Subsidiary Service.

COLOMBIA.

ENSIGN

MERCANTILE

Gunboat.

Photo wanted.

CHERCINTO (1896). 643 tons. Dimensions: 185 (*p.p.*) × 31 × 12 feet. Guns: not known. Designed H.P. 400 = about 12 kts.

River Gunboats.

Photo wanted.

ESPERANZA (1897), **GENERAL NERINO** (1895), both built at Perth Amboy, U.S.A. Stern-wheelers of 400 tons. Dimensions: 140 (*p.p.*) × 9 × 3 feet. Guns: 3 M.G. Designed H.P. 430 = 15 kts. No other details known.

M. L. (*Motor Launches*).

No photo available.

Cauca (1913). 50 tons. Dimensions: 110 × 17 × 4 feet. Guns: none at present.* Speed, 12 kts.

Guarda Costas 1, 2, 3, 4 (Yarrow, 1913). 20 tons. Dimensions: 80 × 12½ × 3½ feet. Guns: *No. 3* has 1—1 pdr., no guns in others yet.* H.P. 160 = 12 kts. Fuel: 1800 galls. petrol = 2400 miles at 10 kts.

*Guns detained in Great Britain during the war.

Old Transport *Bogota* is still in service.

CUBA.

RED.
SKY BLUE

Mercantile Marine: 35 steamers of 29,286 tons *gross*; 146 sailing vessels of 15,132 tons *gross*; also 6 German steamers of 19,464 tons, seized on declaration of war, 1917.

A Government dockyard is projected in Havana Bay, near the Morro Castle. To have a 4000 ton Floating Dock. Naval Academy at Mariel to be transferred to vicinity of Dockyard.

RECOGNITION SILHOUETTES.

Scale : 1 inch = 160 feet.

E. VILLUENDAS.   HATUEY.

Revenue Cutters.

DIEZ DE OCTUBRE *class.*

BAIRE.

CUBA.   PATRIA.
(*Training Ship.*)

Light Cruisers.

CUBA (Cramp, 1911). 2055 tons. Dimensions: (*p.p.*) 260 × 39 × 14 feet. Armament:* 2—4 inch, 4—6 pdr., 4—3 pdr., 4—1 pdr., 2 machine. H.P. 6000 = 18 kts. Babcock boilers. Coal, 250 tons.

*Note.—Was re-fitted in U.S.A. during 1918, when her armament was altered. Present guns carried not known; armament given above is that mounted during 1911-18.

(*Training Ship*).

HABANA (1912), **PINAR DEL RIO** (1912). Both wooden vessels of 80 tons, built at Havana. Dimensions: 100 × 18 × 6 feet. Guns: 1—1 pdr. I.H.P. 200 = 12 kts. 1 screw. Coal: 20 tons.

Gunboats.

No photo available.

HABANA (1912) and **PINAR DEL RIO** (1912). Both wooden vessels of 80 tons, built at Havana. Dimensions: 100 × 18 × 6 feet. Guns: 1—1 pdr. I.H.P. 200 = 12 kts. 1 screw. Coal: 20 tons.

DIEZ DE OCTUBRE (Cramp), 1911), **VEINTE Y CUATRO DE FEBRERO** (Cramp 1911). 218 tons. Dimensions: 110 × 20 × 8 feet. Guns: 1—3 pdr., 2—1 pdr. Speed, 12 kts. Coal, 50 tons.

Photo by courtesy of the Ministry of War.

BAIRE (Schichau, 1906). 500 tons. Dimensions: 196 × 23 × 9 feet. Guns: 2—6 pdr., 2—3 pdr., 1 machine. H.P. 1200 = 14 kts. Babcock boilers. Coal, 120 tons.

Note.—Refitted in a U.S. Navy Yard, 1917; may now have a new armament.

Transport.

KYDONIA (ex-German ship). No details known.

Submarine Chasers.

4—*110 foot* boats, late U.S. *SC274, SC302, SC312, SC314.* For illustration and all details see U.S. Navy Section.

Note : 6 further boats reported ceded to Cuba; numbers not known.

Revenue Cutters.

MATANZAS (1912), **VILLAS** (1912). Details as *Habana* and *Pinar del Rio.*

HATUEY (ex U.S. *Pentooset,* 1903, bought 1907) 538 tons. 212 × 27 × 15 feet. Guns: 2—6 pdr., 2—3 pdr., 2—1 pdr. I.H.P. 1350 = 13 kts. Coal, 150 tons.

Photo by courtesy of the Ministry of War.

ENRIQUE VILLUENDAS (1899). 178 tons. 132 + 20 × 9 feet. Guns: 2—3 pdr., 1 M.G. I.H.P. 600 = 16 kts. Coal, 55 tons.

Revenue Cutters.—*Continued.*

No Photographs available of any of these ships.

MARTI (1898). 50 tons. Guns: 1—1 pdr. Speed 15 kts. Coal: 15 tons.

CESPEDES (ex-Spanish gunboat, 1896). 40 tons. Guns: 1—1 pdr. Speed, 12 kts. Coal: 110 tons.

MACEO (ex-Spanish gunboat, 1896). 35 tons. Guns: 1—1 pdr. Speed, 10 kts. Coal, 8 tons.

AGRAMONTE (ex-Spanish gunboat, 1895). 45 tons. Guns: 1—1 pdr. Speed, 11 kts. Coal, 10 tons.

VEINTE DE MAYO (Glasgow, 1895). 203 tons. 141 × 18·5 × 10·5 feet. Guns: 2—3 pdr., 2—1 pdr. I.H.P. 500 = 12 kts. Coal, 50 tons.

YARA (Glasgow, 1895). 449 tons. 155 × 26 × 13 feet. Guns: 2—6 pdr., 2—1 pdr. I.H.P. 600 = 12 kts. Coal, 150 tons.

ALFREDO (——) 40 tons. Guns: 1—1 pdr. Speed, 11 kts.

GUAIMARO. No details known.

ORIENTE (——). 210 tons. 160 × 21 × 13 feet. Guns: 2—6 pdr., 2—1 pdr. I.H.P. 700 = 12 kts. Coal, 80 tons.

ENSIGN

MERCANTILE

ECUADOR.

Silhouette Scale: 1 inch = 160 feet.

(Silhouettes revised, 1918.)

Minister of War and Marine: Sr. R. Pino y Roca.
Mercantile Marine: 7 steamers of 1942 tons *gross*;
4 sailing vessels of 1882 tons *gross*.

COTOPAXI.

PATRIA.

L. BOLIVAR.

Flag Notes.—To distinguish from Colombian flag, note that centre bar is *sky-blue.* Mercantile flag also has no badge, compared with Colombia.

Note :—The following three photographs have kindly been collected for "Fighting Ships" by Mr. George Chambers, Captain of the Port of Guayaquil.

Torpedo-Gunboat.

LIBERTADOR BOLIVAR (ex *A. Simpson*, 1896, purchased from Chile, 1907). Displacement 750 tons. Length, 240 feet. Beam, 27½ feet. *Maximum* draught, 10½ feet. Guns (Elswick): 4—3 pdr., 2 Maxims. Torpedo tubes (18 inch): 3 *above water.* Armour (Harvey): 1″ Belt, 4½″ Gun shields, 1″ Hood to steering gear, 1″ Bulkheads. Machinery: 2 sets triple expansion. 2 screws. Boilers: 4 Normand. Designed I.H.P. *forced* 4500 = 21·5 kts. Coal: 100 tons. Built by Laird.

Torpedo Boat (and Minelayer).

No photo available.

1 boat, *type unknown: Tarqui* (——). 20 tons. Carries 1 torpedo tube and is fitted as Minelayer. No other details known.

Gunboat.

*COTOPAXI (1884). 300 tons. 135 *(p.p.)* × 21 × 9 feet. Guns: **2** small Q.F. I.H.P. 175. *Max.* speed, 10½ kts. In 1917, is on commercial charter and may possibly have been outright.

Coastguard Vessel.

*PATRIA (ex-Yacht *Cavalier*, bought from G. & Q. Railway). 300 tons. Guns: 4 machine. No other details known.

*These two ships may no longer be Naval vessels.

(HAYTI.)

ENSIGN

MERCANTILE

RED

BLUE

YELLOW

GREEN

According to information received from Port-au-Prince, March, 1919, all Haytian Warships were sold out of service during 1915. This Republic now only maintains two unarmed Auxiliary Schooners for Coastguard Duties.

HONDURAS.

RECOGNITION SILHOUETTE.

Scale : 1 inch = 80 feet.

LIBERIA.

Gunboats.

No photo available.

TATUMBLA (——). 200 tons. Dimensions : not known. Complement, 44. Guns : 2 small. H.P. = 12 kts. Coal : 100 (?) tons.

By courtesy of " Motor Ship."

LIBERIA (ex Liberian *Mesurado*, Blandy Bros., Las Palmas, C.I., 1914). 24 tons. Dimensions : 85 × 12 × 4½ feet. Guns : 1 Nordenfelt, 1 M.G. H.P. 120 (2—60 H.P. Parsons paraffin engines) = 12–14 kts. Fuel : 500 galls. paraffin. 1 small searchlight. Built for Liberian Government as a Revenue Cutter, but never delivered. Purchased by Honduras.

MEXICAN NAVY.

Minister of Marine: Sr. Augustin Castro.

Mercantile Marine: 31 steamers of 33,975 tons *gross*; 16 sailing vessels of 2,630 tons *gross*.

RECOGNITION SILHOUETTES.

Silhouette Scale : 1 inch = 160 feet.

Vicente Guerrero.

Progreso.

Tampico and Vera Cruz.

Blanquet and Bravo.

Torpedo Gunboat.

Photo, J. Romanez, Esq.

BLANQUET (ex *Morelos*) and **BRAVO** (Odero, 1903). 1210 tons. Comp. 130. Dimensions: 240 (*p.p.*) × $32\frac{5}{6}$ × 10 (*mean*) feet. Armament (Bethlehem): 2—4 inch, 4—6 pdr., 1—14 inch tube (bow) *above water*. Designed H.P. 2500 = 17 kts. Blechynden boilers. 2 screws. Coal: 280 tons.

Torpedo Gunboats—*(Continued.)*

TAMPICO (1902) **VERA CRUZ** (1902). Both built at Elizabeth Port, N.J. 984 tons. Comp. 164 (*Vera Cruz*), 110 (*Tampica*). Dimensions: 200 × 33 × 11 feet. Armament: in *Tampica*, 2—4 inch, 4—6 pdr.; in *Vera Cruz*, 4—4 inch, 6—6 pdr. In both ships 1—14 inch tube (bow) *above water*. Designed H.P. 2400 = 15 kts. Mosher boilers. 2 screws. Coal: 200 tons.

Gunboats.

Photo wanted.

GENERAL JESUS CARRANZA. No details known.

Transports.

VICENTE GUERRERO (Vickers, 1908). 1850 tons. Dimensions: 245 × 35 × 17 feet. Guns: 6—4 inch, 2—3 pdr. Designed H.P. 1200 = 12 kts.

Transports—*(Continued.)*

Photo wanted.

(For appearance. see Silhouettes.)

PROGRESO (Odero, 1907.) 1560 tons. Complement 69. Dimensions: 230 × 34 × 10 feet. Guns: 4—6 pdr., 2 M.G. Designed H.P. 1400 = 13 kts. Sunk by insurgents in 1914 or 1915, but since salved and repaired.

No photo available.

PLAN DE GUADALUPE (ex *Dolphin*, Wilmington, 1892). 824 tons. Dimensions: 213 (*o.a.*) × 32 × 15 feet. Guns: not known. Designed H.P. = 14 kts.

Also *Bonita* and *Sonora*, subventioned merchantmen.

Armed Tugs.

No photo available.

PACIFICO. No details known.

Also two Revenue Cutters, names unknown.

NICARAGUA.

Gunboat.

Photo wanted.

MOMOTOMBO (——) 400 tons. Guns : 2—12 pdr., 1—6 pdr.
No other details known.

Also Auxiliaries **OMOTEPE** and **MAXIMO JERAZ** (ex s.s.
Venus). No details known.

PERU.

**(Revised, 1916, from particulars supplied by favour of H. E., The Minister
of War and Marine.)**

PERU ENSIGN

Mercantile flag the same but
without centre device.

PERUVIAN VICE-ADMIRAL

Rear Admiral has one sun.

PERUVIAN CAPTAIN

Colour of Ships : Brown grey.　　　　*Minister of War & Marine* : Col. C. A. de la Fuente.
Mercantile Marine : 12 steamers of 26,590 tons *gross* ; 40 sailing vessels of 10,950 tons *gross*.

PERUVIAN RECOGNITION SILHOUETTES.
Scale : 1 inch = 160 feet.

C. BOLOGNESI.

LIMA.

A. GRAU.

Scale : 1 inch = 80 feet.

T. RODRIGUEZ t.b.d.

FERRE and PALACIOS.
(Submarines.)

Uniforms.

Vice-Almirante.	Contra-Almirante.	Capitan de Navio.	Capitan de Fragata.	Capitan de Corbeta.	Teniente 1°.	Teniente 2°.	Alferez de Fragata.
		Captain.	*Commander.*		Lieut. Comm'r.	Lieut. Junior.	Sub. Lieutenant.

Engineers the same without the sun.

Other branches have the same stripes without the sun, and in addition colours as follows :—

Torpedo, *light blue* ; Constructor, *green* ; Electricians, *light green* ; Doctors, *red* ; Paymasters, *blue*.

Coronel Bolognesi. The *A. Grau* is identical *except* that she has a poop.

("*A Grau*" *Submarine Depot Ship*).

ALMIRANTE GRAU (March, 1906) & CORONEL BOLOGNESI (Nov., 1906).

Displacements: 3,200 tons. Complement, 315.

Length (*p.p.*): 370 feet. Beam, 40½ feet. *Maximum* draught, 14¼ feet.

Guns (Vickers):
2—6 inch, 50 cal.
8—14 pdr.
8—1 pdr.
Torpedo tubes (18 inch):
2 *submerged*.

Armour:
1½" Deck (amidships) =
3" Conning tower ..
3" Gun Shields ...

Ahead:
1—6 in.

Astern:
1—6 in.

Broadside: 2—6 in.

Machinery: 4 cylinder vertical triple expansion. 2 screws. Boilers: 10 Yarrow. Designed H.P. 14,000 = 24 kts. (not above 20 now, unless re-boilered). Coal: *normal,* tons ; *maximum,* 550 tons.

General Notes.—Built and engined by Messrs. Yarrow, Ltd., about 1905-7.

LIMA (Ex *S. S. Socrates*, Kiel, 1880). 1790 tons. H.P., 2000 = 10 kts. Coal : 300 tons = Guns : 4—4 inch, 8—3 pdr. Complement, 131.

Photo wanted.

AMERICA (1904). 100 tons. Guns : 2—3 pdr. No other details known.

Destroyer.

Photo by courtesy of Messrs. Schneider et Cie.

1 *Schneider-Creusot*:—**Teniente Rodriguez** (1909, ex-*Actée*). 490 tons. Dimensions : 212 × 21·3 × 14¾ feet. H.P. 8,600 = 28 kts. (much less now). Schneider-Zoelly turbines, du Temple boilers. Coal : 100 tons = 1200 miles at 10 kts. Armament : 6—9 pdr., 3—18 inch tubes, (2" deck amidships and 1 bow tube above water). Complement 60.

Submarines.

2 *Laubeuf* type : **Ferre** (1912), and **Palacios** (1913). Built by Schneider-Creusot. $\frac{300}{400}$ tons. Complement : 19. Schneider-Carels Diesel motors. H.P. $\frac{400}{200} = \frac{14}{9}$ kts. (present speed about 12–9 kts *on surface*, 7–5 kts. *submerged.*) Endurance : 2000 miles at 10 kts. 1 bow torpedo tube, 4 external dropping gears for torpedoes.

URUGUAYAN NAVY.

RECOGNITION SILHOUETTES.

Scale: 1 inch = 160 feet.

 Vanguardia *class.*

 Corsario *class.*

 B. de R. Branco.

18 DE JULIO.

 URUGUAY.

MONTE VIDEO.

Minister of War and Marine :—Dr. Arturo Gaze.   *Personnel* :—

Mercantile Marine :—27 steamers of 20,298 tons *gross* ; 48 sailing vessels of 24,537 tons *gross*.

Coinage : Gold Peso of 100 Centesimos = 4s. 3d.

Ports, Yards, &c.

MONTE VIDEO.—The National Dock (Dique Naçional) is operated by the Naval Authorities. Length, 459 feet. Breadth, 55 feet. Can take ships drawing up to 19 feet. Steam and electric pumps can empty dock in eight hours. This dock is said to be in need of repairs. Dique Maria (at Montes) 280 × 51 × 12 feet 4 inch to 15 feet 2 inch. Has 2 steam pumps and lifting engine of 30 tons, also fixed and moving cranes. The firm Varadero del Cerro have a yard, well equipped for repairs, with a small slipway. The National Port Administration has bought the Varadero Lussich, a repairing yard with a small slipway.

Old Cruiser.

Photo, A. J. Carbone.

MONTE VIDEO (ex-*24 de Agosto*, ex-*Dogali*, ex-*Salamina*, Elswick, 1890, purchased from Italy, 1908). 2050 tons. Complement, 250. Dimensions : 250 (*p.p.*) × 37 × 16¼ feet (*max.* draught). Guns : 6—6 inch, 9—6 pdr., 6 M.G. Torpedo tubes : 4 *above water*. Armour : 2″—1″ deck, 4½″ gun shields, 2″ conning tower. Machinery : 2 sets horizontal and 4 double-ended boilers. H.P. 7500 = 17 kts. Coal : 480 tons.

Torpedo Boat.

Photo wanted.

1 boat, type unknown : *Oriental* (launched 1907, builder not known). 80 tons. Dimensions : 107 (*p.p.*) × 12 × 7 feet. Guns and tubes not known. Speed : 18 kts. Coal : 8 tons.

(*Continued on next page.*)

Torpedo Gunboat & Training Ship.

URUGUAY (Vulkan, Stettin, 1910). 1150 tons. Complement, 125. Dimensions : $278\frac{3}{4}$ (*p.p.*) $\times 30\frac{5}{6} \times 12$ feet (*max.* draught). Guns (Skoda) : 2—4·7 inch, 45 cal., 4—12 pdr., 6—1 pdr. (Vickers). 4 M.G. Torpedo tubes : 2—18 inch *above water.* Armour : $\frac{2}{3}''$ nickel steel over boilers and engines. 4 Normand boilers. H.P. 8,000 = 23 kts. Coal : 210 tons = 3,000 miles at 10 kts.

Note.—Is fitted for service as Training Ship for midshipmen. Old Gunboat, *Gen. Suarez,* is a Harbour Training Ship.

Yacht.

DIEZ Y OCHO DE JULIO. 678 tons. Complement, 85. 4 small guns and 2 machine guns. Speed, 12 kts. Presidential Yacht.

Note.—May have been sold out for commercial service.

Surveying Ship.

Photo, A. J. Carbone.

BARON DE RIO BRANCO (ex-*Maldonado*). Old paddle-wheel gunboat, transferred to Ministry of Interior, 1912, for Surveying Duties. 300 tons. Carries 4 small Q.F. and 2 M.G. Speed, 12 kts.

Harbour Service Vessels.

Vanguardia class. *Photo, A. J. Carbone.*

Corsario class. *Photo, A. J. Carbone.*

INGENERIO, LA VALLEJA, OYARVIDE. These are three armed tugs for Naval Harbour Services, built about 1908, displace about 60 tons each. Guns : 3 pdr. or M.G. Speed, 13 kts. *Chapicuy, Corsario, Tangarupa, Yaguary,* also exist, but are believed to be Government and not Naval Vessels. No information has been supplied to assist in determining which of the seven ships named above belong to *Vanguardia* class or which to *Corsario* class.

VENEZUELAN NAVY.

(Revised in Venezuela, 1918,)

Gunboats.

Photo by courtesy of T. Ivor. Rees, Esq.

MARISCAL SUCRE (ex-Spanish *Isla de Cuba*, 1886, captured by U.S., 1898, and sold to Venezuela, 1912). 1125 tons. Dimensions : 192 × 30 × 12¼ feet. Guns : 2—4 inch, 2—6 pdr., 6—3 pdr., 2—1 pdr. H.P. 2000 = 13 kts. Coal : 200 tons. Endurance : 2640 miles at 10 kts. Complement 92.

GENERAL SALOM (ex-*Restaurador*, purchased 1900 ; built as U.S. private yacht *Atlanta*, 1884). 750 tons. Dimensions : 243 × 26 × 13 feet. Guns : 1—12 pdr., 4—6 pdr., 1 machine. H.P. 1900 = 14 kts. Coal : 200 tons. Endurance : 2200 miles at 10 kts. Complement 63.

Gunboats—*Continued.*

MIRANDA (Clydebank, 1895 ; purchased from Spain, 1898). 200 tons. Dimensions : 135 × 19 × 8 feet. Guns : 4—6 pdr. H.P. 315 = 12 kts. Coal : 36 tons. Endurance : 850 miles at 8 kts. Complement 45.

Armed Tug.

Photo by favour of Ellis Greu & Co., N.Y.

JOSÉ FELIX RIBAS (ex-*Zumbador*, built 1894). 300 tons. Dimensions : 127 × 23 × 12 feet. Guns : 2—6 pdr. Speed, 10 kts. Coal : 78 tons. Endurance : 1440 miles at 10 kts. Complement 44.

Transports.

> **Photo wanted.**

SALIAS (ex-S.S. *Julia*, transferred from Ministry of Hacienda to Navy, 1914). Only details known : H.P. 150. Complement, 18.

Brigantine **Antonio Diaz**, used as Naval Coal transport. 300 tons. Dimensions : 109 × 26 × 12 feet. Complement 16. Is armed to some extent.

ENSIGN   MERCANTILE

Personnel :

Minister of War and Marine : General C. Jiménez Rebolledo.

Warship Port : Puerto Cabello. Steel floating dock here (3000 tons capacity) built in four sections on self-docking system, and worked by electricity.

Mercantile Marine : 11 steamers of 5,298 tons *gross*, 8 sailing vessels of 1,097 tons *gross*.

RECOGNITION SILHOUETTES.

Scale 1 inch = 160 feet.

MIRANDA.

J. F. RIBAS.

GENERAL SALOM.

M. SUCRE.

MINOR ASIATIC NAVIES.

(ARRANGED ALPHABETICALLY.)

CORRECTIONS AND ADDENDA.

CHINESE FLEET.

Uniforms.

Colour between stripes :—*Engineers* (none) ; *Surgeons*, red ; *Paymasters*, white ; *Engine Constructor*, purple ; *Ship Constructor*, drab grey or ash colour ; *Navigating Officers*, light indigo blue.   All these branches *without* the curl or emblem over top stripe.

Secessionist Warships.

Following Warships are at Canton, under the Local Government, which has declared its independence of the Central Government at Peking :—

Light Cruisers :   **CHAO HO, HAI CHEN, HAI CHOU, HAI YUNG, HAI CHI.**

Destroyer :   *Tung An.*

Gunboats :   **YUNG PENG, YUNG HSIANG.**

River Gunboat :   **YUNG CHIEN.**

Despatch Vessel :   **WU FENG.**

Transport :   **FU AN.**

Gunboats.

FEI-HU, FEI-LUNG *and others ?* (built or building by Kiangnan Dock Co., at Shanghai).   Dimensions : 220 × 28 × 6½ feet.   1000 tons.   Speed : 14 kts. (*turbines*).

Note.—Above Gunboats do not appear in the Official Chinese Navy List.   They evidently do exist, but are probably not finished yet.   Nine boats of this class said to have been projected, of which the first three were launched by September, 1915.

SIAMESE NAVY.

New Programme.

PRA ROANG.   Projected Light Cruiser, to be built in Japan.   *About* 3000 tons.   Speed : 22 kts.   Cost has been already covered by a voluntary national subscription.

Armoured River Gunboats.—Several projected.

Torpedo Boat.—One under construction at Bangkok D.Y.   Believed to be the same as T.B. *No. 4.*

CHINESE FLEET.

(Revised 1919.)

NATIONAL FLAG.

ENSIGN.

MINISTER OF THE NAVY.

VICE MINISTER OF THE NAVY

ADMIRAL.

VICE ADMIRAL.

REAR ADMIRAL

COMMODORE

SENIOR NAVAL OFFICER.

GUARD SHIP

RED.   BLUE.   YELLOW.   WHITE.   BLACK.

Uniforms.

Admiral. | Vice-Admiral. | Rear-Admiral. | Captain. | Commander. | Lieut.-Comm'r. | Lieut. | Sub-Lieut. 1st Class. | Sub-Lieut. 2nd Class.

Personnel :

Minister of Marine—Lin Kueng Shung.

Mercantile Marine : (Exclusive of German and Austrian vessels seized during 1917) :—72 steamers of 95,560 tons *gross*; 7 sea-going sailing vessels of 865 tons *gross*. Also a large and unknown number of sailing craft (junks, etc.), for coastal trade and the larger rivers.

Shanghai is the principal port, about 4¼ million tons entering and being cleared per annum.

Docks.

FU-CHAU-FU. *Arsenal.* (See next page).

TAKU. *Arsenal.* Government Dock : 340×39×14 feet. Private Docks : No. 1, 335×36×10 feet. No. 2, 315×36×11 feet. No. 3, 300×28×11 feet. No. 4, 300×40×11 feet.

KIANGNAN (SHANGHAI). *Arsenal.* Government Dock, 390×70×19 feet. Private Docks (Kiangnan Dock & Engineering Co., Ltd.), New Dock, 473×74×21½ feet; Cosmopolitan, 560×77½×24 feet; Old Dock, 400×53×16 feet; Tunkado, 362×67×16 feet.

WHAMPOA. *Arsenal.* No Government Docks, but 2 Private : Cooper, 430×65×16 feet ; Locksun, 450×75×18 feet.

AMOY. Private Dock, 360×60×16½ feet.

Private Yards.

Small gunboats are built by the Kiangnan Dock & Engineering Co., Shanghai (12 building slips), and the Yangtse Works, Hankow.

Note on Spelling of Chinese Warship Names.

The transliteration of Chinese names depends first upon the dialect in which the characters happen to be spelt, and secondly, on the system used by the foreigner to represent that dialect. The official dialect in Pekingese and a widely adopted system of representing it is that known as "Wade's Spelling." In this Edition of "Fighting Ships," it has been thought advisable to adopt some standard form of spelling Chinese Warship Names. Accordingly, "Wade's Spelling" has been introduced, all aspirates, accents and tonic marks being omitted.

CHINESE IDENTIFICATION AND SIGNAL SILHOUETTES.

Scale : 1 inch = 160 feet.

RIVER GUNBOATS.

CHIEN CHUNG *class* (3).

LI CHIEH.

CHIANG HSI *class* (2)

LI SUI.

LIEN CHING.

CHIANG HENG *class* (4 ships).

CHU TAI *class* (6 ships).

YING JUI *class* (2 ships).

CHIEN WEI *class* (2 ships).

HAI YUNG *class* (3 ships).

HAI CHI.

TORPEDO CRAFT.

HU PENG *class*, or Nos. 7–10 (t.b.)

FEI YING.

CHAO-HO.

YING JUI (July, 1911) & CHAO HO (Oct., 1911).

Normal displacement $\left\{\begin{array}{l}\textit{Ying Jui}: 2,750 \text{ tons.} \\ \textit{Chao Ho}: 2,600 \text{ tons.}\end{array}\right\}$ Complement, 279.

Ying Jui: Length (*p.p.*) 330 feet. Beam, 42 feet. *Max.* load draught, 14 feet 11 inches.
Chao Ho: ,, 320 ,, ,, 39 ,, ,, ,, 14 ,,

Guns (*see Notes*):
2—6 inch, 50 cal.
4—4 inch, 50 cal.
2—14 pdr., 50 cal.
6—3 pdr.
2—1 pdr.
Torpedo tubes (18 inch):
2 *above water.*

Armour:
3″ Deck (amidships)
1½″ Deck (ends) ...
3″ Conning tower
″ Gun shields......

Ahead:
1—6 in.
2—4 in.

CHAO HO.

Astern:
1—6 in.
2—4 in.

Broadside: 2—6 in., 2—4 in.

Machinery: Parsons turbine. Boilers: see notes. 4 screws. Designed H.P. (6000 S.H.P.=20 kts.)
8000=22 kts. Coal: *normal*: 220 tons; *maximum*: 550 tons. Oil: 50 tons in *Ying Jui*, 100 tons in
Chao Ho. Endurance: about 4500—5000 miles at 10 kts., and about 2900 miles at 18 kts.

Gunnery Notes.—Vickers models in *Ying Jui*; Elswick in *Chao Ho*.

Name	Builder	Machinery	Laid down	Completed	Trials 4/5ths	Full power	Boilers
Ying Jui	Vickers	Vickers	1910	1912	5394=20·7	8797 = 22·23	White-F.+ cyl.
Chao Ho	Elswick	Hawthorn	1910	1912	...	8622 = 22·12	6 Yarrow

HAI YUNG (1897), HAI CHOU (1897) and HAI CHEN (1898). Displacement, 2950
metric tons. Complement 295. Length (*p.p.*) 314 feet. Beam, 40¾ feet. *Maximum* draught, 19 feet.
Guns (Krupp): 3—5·9 inch, 40 cal., 8—4·1 inch, 40 cal., 6—1 pdr., and 6 machine. Torpedo tubes
(14 inch): 1 bow (*submerged*). Armour: 2¾″ Deck (amidships), 1½″ deck (ends), 2″ gun shields, 1½″
conning tower. Designed H.P. 7,500 = 19·5 kts. 8 cylindrical boilers. Coal: *normal* 200-220 tons;
maximum 500-580 tons. All three ships built by Vulkan Co., Stettin.

Photo, Symonds & Co

HAI CHI (Elswick, 1898). Displacement, 4,300 tons. Complement, 431. Length (*p.p.*),
424 feet. Beam, 46⅝ feet. *Mean* draught, 16¾ feet; *max.* 19 feet. Guns (Elswick): 2—8 inch,
45 cal., 10—4·7 inch, 45 cal., 12—3 pdr., 4—1 pdr., 6 machine. Torpedo tubes (18 inch): 5 *above
water.* Armour (Harvey): 5″ Deck (amidships), 1½″ deck (ends), 4½″ gun shields, 4″ ammunition
hoists, 6″ conning tower. Designed H.P.: 17,000 (*f.d.*)=24 kts. Boilers: 12 cylindrical. Coal: *normal*
400 tons, *maximum* 990 tons.

Gunboats.

Photo wanted.

YUNG PENG, YUNG HSIANG (Kawasaki Co., Kobe, Japan, 1912—13). 830 tons. Dimensions: 205 (p.p.) × 29½ × 8 feet. Guns: 1—4·1 inch, 1—12 pdr., 4—3 pdr., 2—1 pdr. H.P. 1350 = 13·5 kts. Coal: 190 tons. Complement 105.

River Gunboats.

Photo wanted.

YUNG CHIEN, YUNG CHI. Begun 1915, by Kiangnan Dock Co., Shanghai. 900 tons. Dimensions: 215½ × 29½ × 10 feet. Guns: 1—4 inch, 1—12 pdr., 4—3 pdr., 2—1 pdr. Designed H.P. 1400 = 13·5 kts. Coal: 150 tons.

CHIEN CHUNG (6/15).   **YUNG AN** (1915).
KUNG CHEN (1915).

All built by Yangtse Works, Hankow. 90 tons. Dimensions: 110 × 18½ × 3 feet. H.P. 450 = 11 kts., but *Chien-Chung* made 13 kts. on trials in 1915. Guns: 1—3·4 inch howitzer. 4 M.G. Complement, 42.

River Gunboats—*Continued.*

CHIANG HSI (Krupp, 1911). **CHIANG KUN** (Vulkan, 1912). Dimensions: 146 (p.p.) × 24 × 3 feet. Displacement: 140 tons. H.P. 500 = 12 kts. Boilers: 2 Schulz. Coal: 30 tons. Guns: 1—3·4 (22 pdr.) howitzer, 4 machine. Complement, 42.

Note.—The three River Gunboats *Chiang Ku, Chiang Kung* and *Chiang Ta,* supposed to have been built at Hankow about 1908, are now reported as never having been commenced.

LI SUI (ex-German *Otter*, Tecklenborg, 1900. Interned in China, 1914, and taken over for Chinese Navy about 1917). 256 tons. Dimensions: 173·9 × 28·5 × 2·6 feet. Guns: 2—6 pdr., 3 M.G. Armour: 2″ on waterline, 2″ C.T. I.H.P. 1300 = 14 kts. Boilers: 4 Schulz. Coal: 79 tons. Complement (was 47).

LI CHIEH (ex-German *Vaterland*, Elbing, 1903. Interned at Nankin, August, 1914, and taken over for Chinese Navy, 1917). 217 tons. Dimensions: 157·5 × 26·2 × 2·6 feet. Guns: 1—3·4 inch (22 pdr.) howitzer, 1—4 pdr., 2 M.G. I.H.P. 1400 = 13 kts. Boilers: 2 Schulz. Coal: 79 tons. Complement (was 47).

River Gunboats—*Continued.*

CHU CHIEN.   **CHU TAI.**＊   **CHU YU** (1).
CHU KUAN.   **CHU TUNG.**   **CHU YU** (2).

All built by Kawasaki Yard, Kobe, 1906-07. 745 tons. Complement, 91. Dimensions: 200 × 29½ × 8 feet. Armament: 2—4·7 inch, 2—12 pdr., 4 machine. Machinery: 2 sets vertical triple expansion. 2 screws. Boilers: Water-tube. Designed H.P. 1350 = 13 kts. Coal: 150 tons.

CHIANG CHEN.   **CHIANG LI.**
CHIANG HENG.   **CHIANG YUAN.**

All built by Kawasaki Yard, Kobe, 1906-07. 550 tons. Complement, 91. Dimensions: 180 × 28 × 7 feet. Armament: 1—4·7 inch (bow), 1—12 pdr. (aft), 4—3 pdr., 4 Maxims. Machinery: 2 sets vertical triple expansion. 2 screws. Boilers: water-tube. Designed H.P. 950 = 13 kts. Coal: 113 tons.

CHINESE TORPEDO CRAFT.

Destroyers.

Photo wanted.

3 *Schichau* type: **Chien Kang, Tung An, Yu Chang** (— 1912), 390 tons. Dimensions: 198 × 21·3 × 6 feet. Armament: 2—12 pdr., 2—3 pdr., 2—18 inch tubes. Designed H.P. 6000 = 30 kts. Coal, 80 tons. Complement, 66.

First called *Fu Po, Fei Hung* and *Chang Feng* but names were altered by Yuan Shih Kai.

Torpedo Boats.

Photograph wanted of Kawasaki-Normand boats.

(See Silhouettes.)

4 *Kawasaki–Normand* type: **Hu Peng** or **No. 7, Hu E** or **No. 8, Hu Ying** or **No. 9, Hu Chun** or **No. 10** (Kobe, Japan, 1907-8). 97 tons. Dimensions: 135 × 15½ × 7½ feet. Armament: 2—3 pdr., 3 M.G., 3—18 inch tubes (1 bow *above water* and 2 deck). Designed H.P. 1200 = 23 kts. Coal, 28 tons *normal*. Complement: 34.

2 *Vulcan* type: **Su*** or **No. 4, Chen*** or **No. 2** (1895). 90 tons. 144 × 17 × 7 feet. Armament: 4 M.G., 3 torpedo tubes. H.P. 700 = 18 kts. Complement 38.

2 *Schichau* type: **Lieh*** or **No. 3, Chang*** or **No. 1** (1895), 62 tons. 130 × 15 × 5 feet. Armament: 6 M.G., 3 torpedo tubes. H.P. 600 = 16 kts. Complement 36.

* These four T.B. sometimes have suffix *Ting* (Boat) or *Tzu* (meaningless) added to their names.

Torpedo Gunboats.

CHIEN WEI (1902) and **CHIEN AN** (1900). Displacement, 850 tons. Complement, 139. Guns: 1—4·1 inch, 3—9 pdr., 6—1 pdr. Torpedo tubes: 2 *above water*. Armour: 1″ belt and deck (amidships). Designed H.P.: 6500 = 23 kts. (about 18 now). Coal: 180 tons. Built at Fu-Chau-Fu.

FEI YING (July, 1895). Displacement, 850 tons. Complement, 145. Guns (Krupp): 2—4·1 inch, 6—3 pdr., 4 M.G., 3 tubes (*above water*). Designed H.P. 5500 = 22 kts. Boilers: 8 Yarrow. Coal: 170 tons. Built at Stettin.

CHINESE MISCELLANEOUS.

Despatch Vessels.

Photo wanted.

WU FENG (Tsingtao, 1912). 200 tons. Dimensions: 124 × 20 × 7 feet. H.P. 300 = 10 kts. Guns: 4—3 pdr. Complement, 46.

LIEN CHING (Shanghai, 1910). Dimensions: 150 (*p.p.*) × 24 × 9½ feet (*mean*). 500 tons. I.H.P. 900 = 13·5 kts. Cylindrical boilers fitted with Howden's f.d. Coal: 95 tons. Guns: 4—6 pdr. Complement 61.

Training Ship.

No photo available.

(Barque rigged : one funnel).

TUNG CHI (1895). Steel. 1700 tons. Guns: 2—5·9 inch, 5—4 inch, 5—1 pdr., 2 M.G. Speed: 11·2 kts. 1 Screw. No other details known.

Transport.

No photo available.

FU AN. No details known.

Note.—These Ships do not belong to the Chinese Navy, but to the Water Police of the Provinces named. They might, however, be used for National Defence in the event of War.

Gunboats.

(All belong to Water Police of Kwang Tung Province.)

No photo available.

KUANG YU (1891). Wooden vessel of 600 tons displacement. Dimensions : 156 × 24 × 10 feet. Guns : 9 machine. Designed H.P. 400 = 11 kts. (never attained). Coal : 110 tons. Complement 72.

No photo available.

KUANG CHEN.   **KUANG LI.**
KUANG HENG.   **KUANG YUAN.**

Built 1886. Steel. 300 tons. Dimensions : 110 × 18 × 7 feet. Guns : one old Krupp, 4½ tons (5·9 inch), 1 old 3·5 inch. I.H.P. 78 = 7 kts.

No photo available.

KUANG CHIN (China, 1885—7). Wooden vessel of 560 tons. Dimensions : 250 × 34 × 10 feet. Guns : 2—4·1 inch, 1—12 pdr., 2—2 pdr. H.P. 312 = 9 kts. 1 screw. Coal : 110 tons. Complement 71.

Gunboats (Water Police of Kwang Tung Provence.)—*Continued.*

No photo available.

KUANG KENG (China, 1883). Composite vessel of 560 tons. Guns : 1—4·7 inch, 1—12 pdr. H.P. 400 = 11 kts.

River Gunboats.

(Both belonging to Water Police of Chechiang Province.)

CHE CHING *class* (2).

(Scale : 1 inch = 160 feet).

No photo available.

CHE CHING, CHE TING (Kiangnan Dock Co., Shanghai, 1914). Dimensions : 146 × 24 × 2 feet. 141 tons. H.P. 750 (*f.d.*) = 13 kts. Boilers : Yarrow. Guns : 1—3·4 inch howitzer, 2—3 pdr., 8 machine. Complement, 41.

Old Torpedo Boats.

(All belong to Water Police of Kwang Tung Province.)

No photo available.

5 *Schichau* type :

Lei Chung	*Lei Kan* (1)	*Lei Tui*
Lei Li	*Lei Kan* (2)	

All built in Germany, 1884-5. 26 tons. Armament : 1 or 2 M.G., 1 torpedo tube. H.P. 420 = 19 kts. (much less now).

No photo available.

4 type unknown :

Lei Chen	*Lei Ken*
Lei Kun	*Lei Sun*

All built 1884-5. No details known.

ROYAL SIAMESE NAVY.

(Revised, 1919.)

Flags (1919).

TRAIRANGA.
NATIONAL FLAG.

NAVAL ENSIGN.

NAVAL JACK.

RED. WHITE. BLUE.

Arsenal.

BANGKOK.—Dry dock: 474 feet (over blocks), 513 feet (over all) × 45 feet (at entrance) × 15 to 16 feet H.W.O.S. Sheer legs with lift of 40 tons and travelling crane with lift of 10 tons. Workshops and plant are modern and capable of effecting repairs for the whole fleet.

Private Docks. (Bangkok.)

Dry Dock Co., No. 1; 300 × 45 × 11½ feet. Samsen Dry Dock, 215 × 33 × 13 feet.

Personnel: 5000. Reserve: 20,000. Royal Naval Academy for Navigation and Engineering at Phra Rajwangderm, with accommodation for 120 cadets. There are about six Provincial Training Establishments, so that men recruited locally can receive preliminary training before being drafted to ships of the Royal Navy.

Naval W/T Stations: At Bangkok and Singora, with radius of 310 miles by day and 600 miles at night.

RECOGNITION SILHOUETTES.

Scale: 1 inch = 160 feet.

BHALI & SUKRIB.

MAHA CHAKRI.

Torpedo boats.
Nos. 1—4.

Sua Gamron Sindhu } t.b.d.
Sua Tayan Chol

Royal Yacht.

Photo, G. E. Bailey, Esq.

MAHA CHAKRI (Kawasaki Co., Kobé, Japan, 1918). About 2,400 tons *gross*. Complement, Length, 298 feet (*w.l*), 335 feet (*o.a.*). Beam, 40 feet. Draught, feet. Guns: Not known. Machinery (*see Notes*): 2 sets triple exp. Boilers: 4 (type unknown) coal and oil burning. I.H.P. about 2000 = 15 kts. Oil fuel: 200 tons = 2000 miles endurance.

Notes.—The hull of the old Royal Yacht *Maha Chakri* was sold to the Kawasaki Co. in 1917, but the engines and other fittings were removed, overhauled and renovated for installation in the new *Maha Chakri* described above.

Gunboats.

BHALI. Tops on *both* masts and yard on mainmast.

SUKRIB. Top on mainmast *only*.

BHALI (1901), **SUKRIB** (1901). 580 tons. 162 × 23 × 10 feet. Guns: 1—4·7 inch, 5—6 pdr., 4—1 pdr. Designed H.P. 500 = 11·4 kts. Complement, 83.

No photograph available.
1 funnel, 2 masts, with one military top.

MURATHA (1898). 530 tons. 145 × 23 × 10 feet. Guns: 1—4·7 inch, 4—6 pdr., 3—1 pdr. Designed H.P. 500 = 11·4 kts.

Transport.

> *No photo available.*

VIDU (   ).   850 tons. $176 \times 27\frac{1}{6} \times 13\frac{1}{2}$ feet.   Speed, 10 kts.

Also 10 other steamships serving as Despatch Vessels for Coastal and River Duties. No detailed information can be secured of these craft. There are 50 to 60 steamers and launches from 100 tons downwards for River Service.

2 Destroyers.

SUA-TAYAN-CHOL.   *Photo, G. E. Bailey, Esq.*

Sua-Gamron-Sindhu (1912), 385 tons, and **Sua-Tayan-Chol** (1908), 375 tons. Both built by Kawasaki Co,, Kobé, Japan. Dimensions: $227 \ (p.p.) \times 21\frac{1}{2} \times 6$ feet. H.P. 6000 = 27 kts. Coal: 100 tons = 1000 miles at 10 kts. Armament : 1—12 pdr.. 5—6 pdr., 2 M.G. ; 2—18 inch tubes. Complement: 75.

4 Torpedo Boats.

No. 2.   *Photo, G. E. Bailey, Esq.*

4 *Kawasaki* boats :—No. **1, 2** and **3** (1908), and No. **4** (1913), 120 tons. $131\cdot6 \times 16\cdot2 \times 3\cdot6$ feet. H.P. 1200 = 22 kts, Armament: 1—6 pdr., 1—3 pdr., 2—18 inch tubes. Complement: 29.

483

PERSIA.

ENSIGN

MERCANTILE

Silhouette Scale: 1 inch = 160 feet.

PERSEPOLIS.

Gunboat.

Photo, Lieut. Frewin, R.N.

PERSEPOLIS (1885). Dimensions : $207 \times 32\frac{3}{4} \times 19\frac{1}{2}$ feet. 1200 tons. H.P. 450 = 10 kts. Guns : 4 old 2·7 in., 2 machine.

Note : Gunboat *Mozaffir* served with and in H.M. Navy during the War. It is not known what has become of this ship.

SARAWAK.

> *No photos available.*

ALINE (1875). Gunboat of 175 tons. 2 small guns.

ADEN (1884). Steamer of 300 tons. Armed with 1 gun.

LORNA DOONE (1881). Steamer of 118 tons. 2 small guns.

AUSTRIAN, BULGARIAN, GERMAN, HUNGARIAN, RUSSIAN & TURKISH NAVIES.

LATE AUSTRIAN NAVY.

Modern Naval Guns.

| Notation. | Bore. | Official Designation. | | | Weight. | Weight, A.P. Shot. | Initial Velocity. | Maximum penetration A.P. capped against K.C. a'r at impact. | |
		Bore.	Length/ Calibres	Model.				11,000 yds.	5000 yds.
	in.	c/m.			tons.	lbs.	ft. secs.	in.	in.
A⁵	12	30·5	L/45		52	992	2625	10·6	19·6
A A	9·4	24	L/45		26·2	474	2625	4·2	10·9
A	9·4	24	L/40	S	27.5	474	2312	...	10·7
A	9·4	24	L/40	K.K/'97	30·2	474	2378	...	...
A	9·4	24	L/40	K.K/'94	27·8	474	2264	...	...
A	7·5	19	L/42		12·1	214	2625	3·5	7·1
	5·9	15	L/50	K/'13	...	100	...	...	...
	5·9	15	L/50		5·8	100	2887	...	4·3
	5.9	15	L/40	S	4·3	100	2264	...	...
	5·9	15	L/40	K	4·4	100	2264	...	...
	4·7	12	L/45		..	...	..	...	...
	4·7	12	L/40		2·1	52	2264	...	...
	3·9	10	L/50	K/'10	...	...	...	...	...
	3·9	10	L/50	K/'07	1·9	30	2954	...	...

In Model column S = Skoda; K = Krupp. In addition to the above there are 24 other models of older, smaller and Howitzer guns officially listed. Also new anti-aircraft guns, of which no particulars can be secured.

Torpedoes and tubes used: Whitehead-Fiume types (20·8, 17·7, and 14-inch).

Scale : 1 inch = 160 feet.

Note.—All interned at Cattaro, Sebenico, Pola and Venice.

ONE FUNNEL.

Dromedar.
(*Salamander* has shorter funnel.)

Sebenico.

Meteor.

Planet.

Trabant.

Blitz & Komet.
(*Chamäleon* similar but very thick funnel.)

Taurus.

Spalato & Zara.

Lussin.
(*May have no funnel now.*)

Monarch.

As "Monarch" but has no guns.

Budapest.

Pelikan.

Cyclop.

TWO FUNNELS.

Magnet.

K. E. Rudolf.

Mars.

Lakroma.

Leopard *class* (2 ships).

K. F. Josef.
(*Reported sunk.*)

Aspern *class* (2 ships).

K. ü K. Maria Theresia.

Habsburg *class* (3 ships).
(*Approximate* appearance after re-construction.)

Viribus Unitis *class* (2 ships).

Radetzky *class* (3 ships).

Miramar.
(*Continued on next page.*)

THREE FUNNELS.

Gäa (*Depot ship*)

Note :-

All interned at Cattaro, Sebenico, Pola and Venice.

SATELLIT.

KAISER KARL VI.

ERZHERZOG KARL *class* (3 ships).

SANKT GEORG.

TORPEDO CRAFT.　　　　**Scale : 1 inch = 160 feet.**

FOUR FUNNELS.

Old t.b.
(*Used for subsidiary duties.*)

Nos. 20–49 *class* t.b.
(*Reconstructed Schichau type.*)

Nos. 13–18 *class* t.b.

Nos. 1–12 *class* t.b.

Nos. 50–73 & 74–100 *classes* t.b.

ADMIRAL SPAUN and SAIDA *classes.*

Tatra *class* t.b.d. (9 or 10).

Huszar *class* t.b.d. (10), also Varasdinier.
(*Heights of funnels vary.*)

SUBMARINES.　　　　**Scale : 1 inch = 80 feet.**

V.　　　　XI., XVII.

XVII—XXXII.

XXI., XXII.

XL, XLVII.

(V. UNITIS CLASS—2 SHIPS).
PRINZ EUGEN (November, 1912), **TEGETTHOF** (March, 1912).

Displacement, 20,000 tons. *Full load,* 21,370 tons. Complement, 1,050.

Length (*w.l.*), 495¾ feet. Beam, 89½ feet. {*Mean* draught, 26¾ feet.} {*Max.* draught, 28 feet.} Length *over all,* 530 feet.

Guns (Skoda) :
  12—12 inch, 45 cal. (A⁵)
  12—5·9 inch, 50 cal.
  4—11 pdr. (anti-aircraft)
  2—3 pdr.
  (2—9 pdr. landing)
  4 machine
Torpedo tubes (20·8 inch) :
  4 *submerged*

Armour (special chrome nickel)
  11″ Belt (amidships) ......
  4¾″ Belt (ends) ...
  7¾″ Upper Belt (amidships)
  1¾″ Deck ....
  6¾″ Battery ....
  11″—7″ Turrets ... .
  11″ Barbettes ....
  11¾″ Conning tower (forward)

  9¾″ Conning tower (aft)
  6½″ Range-finding position

VIRIBUS UNITIS (now sunk, but *Tegetthof* and *Prinz Eugen* same).   *Photo Alfieri.*

Ahead :
6—12 in.
2—5·9 in.

Astern :
6—12 in.
2—5·9 in.

Broadside : 12—12 in., 6—5·9 in.

Machinery : Turbine, see *Notes.* 4 screws. Boilers : Yarrow. Designed H.P. 25,000 = 20 kts.
Coal : *normal* 900 tons ; *maximum* 1700 tons (+ oil : 200 tons).

Gunnery Notes—12-inch same model as in *Radetzky* class. Heights of guns above w.l. 29½ feet for end triples, 45 feet for super-firing triples. 5·9-inch battery about 20 feet above w.l. Arcs of fire 300° for end triples ; 320° for super-firing 12-inch. End 5·9 inch about 135°, others about 120°. 120 rounds per 12-inch and 200 per 5·9-inch gun carried. Magazine cooling controlled from central station. Range-finding positions are in upper parts of each C.T., and 2 amidships above 5·9-inch battery. Goerz R.F.

Torpedo Notes—Tubes are 2 broadside, 1 bow, 1 stern. Bullivant net defence right up to stern. 5 or 7—42½″ searchlights.

Armour Notes—Main and upper belts 15—16 feet deep. Usual internal protection against torpedoes by lateral bulkheads in way of magazine and machinery spaces, but it is not of much practical value. Austrian plans show armoured upper-works and funnel bases, but this is doubtful.

Name	Builder	Machinery	Laid down	Com-pleted	Trials	Turbines	Boilers	Best recent speed
P. Eugen	Stab. Tecnico	Stab. Tecnico	Jan., '12	May, '14	= 20·81	Parsons	12 Yarrow	
Tegetthof	Stab. Tecnico	Stab. Tecnico	Sep., '10	July, '13	= 19·75	Parsons	12 Yarrow	

Note.

TEGETTHOF interned at Venice. Reported refitting for service in Italian Navy.

PRINZ EUGEN interned at Cattaro.

General Notes.—These ships are very well designed, all details being carefully planned, but they are said to be unstable. Arcs of fire for all guns are large. Reports of first trials with the triple turrets are very contradictory, but they do not seem to have come up to expectation.

(RADETZKY CLASS—3 SHIPS).

ERZHERZOG FRANZ FERDINAND (Sept., 1908), **ZRINYI** (April, 1910), and **RADETZKY** (July, 1909).

Displacement, 14,500 metric tons.   Complement, 876.

Length *(waterline)*, 448 feet.   Beam, 80⅓ feet.   *Mean* draught, 26½ feet.   Length *over all*, 456 feet *(p.p.* 429¾).

Guns (Skoda) :
4—12 inch, 45 cal. (A^5)
8—9·4 inch, 45 cal. (A^3)
20—3·9 inch, 50 cal.
6—11 pdr., 45 cal.
2—3 pdr.
(2—9 pdr. landing)
3 machine
Torpedo tubes (17·7 inch) :
2 *submerged* (broadside)
1 *submerged* (stern)

Armour (Krupp) :
9″ Belt (amidships) ....
4″ Belt (ends) ....
2″ Deck on slopes, 1¾″ flat...
6″ Upper belt ....
3″ Upper belt (bow) ... ...
9¾″ Big gun turrets (N.C.) =
9¾″ Bases to these (N.C.) ...
8″ Secondary turrets (N.C.) =
4¾″ Battery ....
10″ Conning tower (N.C.).... =
(Total weight 3150 tons.)

Ahead :
2—12 in.
4—9·4 in.

Astern :
2—12 in.
4—9·4 in.

Broadside : 4—12 in., 4—9·4 in.

Machinery : 2 sets 4 cylinder vertical triple expansion.   2 screws.   Boilers : 12 Yarrow.   Designed H.P. 20,000 = 20 kts.   Coal : *normal* 750 tons ; *maximum* 1580 tons + 166 tons oil fuel.

Armour Notes.—Main belt is 285¼ feet long l y 7½ feet deep, 5 feet of it below water.   6″ bulkheads.   Upper belt same length.   Battery, etc., 180 feet long.

Gunnery Notes.—Big guns have arcs of fire 290°.   Bow ones 29½ feet above normal waterline, after, 26 feet. Manœuvred electrically.   9·4 average 24½ feet above water.   Battery guns 16 feet above water.   These have arcs of fire 130°—100°.   The 12 inch are extremely powerful guns, but the 9·4's are not a new model.   Two range and fire control towers amidships above upper 3·9 inch battery guns.

Torpedo Notes.—Net defence fitted (Bullivant).   There is also special internal protection against mines and torpedoes, consisting of internal fore and aft bulkheads, built up by two layers of high-tensile steel.

Name	Built and engined at	Laid down	Completed	Trials	Boilers	Best recent speed
Ers. F. Ferdinand	All at Stabilimento Tecnico	Sept., '07	1910	20,600 = 20·68	Yarrow in all	
Zrinyi		Oct., '08	1911	= 20·5		
Radetzky		Dec., '07	1911	= 20·5		

E. F. FERDINAND.   *Photo, Spartali.*

Note.

E. F. FERDINAND interned at Venice.   Reported that, after examination, it has been decided that she is not worth repairing for service in Italian Navy.   RADETZKY and ZRINYI both interned at Spalato.

FULL BROADSIDE DETAIL VIEW OF RADETZKY.   *Photo, Alfieri.*

(E. KARL CLASS—3 SHIPS).

ERZHERZOG KARL (Oct., 1903), **ERZHERZOG FRIEDRICH** (April, 1904), and **ERZHERZOG FERDINAND MAX** (May, 1905).

Displacement, 10,600 metric tons. Complement, 748.

Length (*waterline*), 408 feet. Beam, 71¾ feet. *Mean* draught, 24⅔ feet. Length (*p.p.*), 390½ feet.

Guns (Skoda) :
4—9·4 inch, 40 cal.
12—7·5 inch, 42 cal.
12—11 pdr., 45 cal.
(Some anti-aircraft)
(2—9 pdr., landing)
8—3 pdr.
3 machine
Torpedo tubes (17.7 inch) :
2 *submerged*

Armour (Krupp) :
8¼"—6" Belt (amidships)
9" Bulkheads........ ......
2" Belt (bow).............
3" Deck (flat on belt) ...
2¾" Deck (at ends) ......
9½" Barbettes............
9½" Turrets ....
9½" Turret bases ......
5" Lower deck (side)......
6¾"   ,,   ,, (bulkhead)
6" Battery (N.C.) ......
6" Small Turrets (N.C.)
8½" Conning tower ......
(Total weight 2922 tons).

Ahead :
2—9·4 in.
4—7·5 in.

ERZHERZOG KARL

Astern :
2—9·4 in.
4—7·5 in.

Broadside : 4—9·4 in., 6—7·5 in.

Machinery : 2 sets 4 cylinder triple expansion. 2 screws. Boilers : 12 Yarrow. Designed H.P. 18,000 = 19 kts. Coal : *normal* 550 tons ; *maximum* 1315 tons. (*E. F. Max* also carries a small amount of oil fuel, about 35 tons).

Armour Notes.—Belt is 8¼ feet wide by 225 feet long ; 3½ feet of it below waterline ; lower edge is about 6" thick.

Gunnery Notes.—Loading positions, big guns : all round. Hoists, electric. Big guns manœuvred electrically, secondary guns electrically. Big guns with 20° elevation have a range of 17,000 yards.
Arcs of fire : Big guns, 260°.
Height of guns above water : Bow turret, 20½ feet. After turret, 20 feet. Main deck battery, 13 feet.

Torpedo Notes.—6 searchlights.

Engineering Notes.—On the average 126 revs. = 19 kts. ; 128 = 19.5 kts. ; 138 = 20.5 kts.

General Notes.—The double bottom extends 240 feet amidships only. Average cost per ship £912,500.

ERZHERZOG KARL.

Note :—All interned at Cattaro.

Small fire controls now fitted high up on foremast of all ships as *E. Karl* above.

Name	Builder	Machinery	Laid down	Com-pleted	Last Refit	Trials : n.d.	f.d.	Boilers	Recent best speed
E. Karl	Triest	All by Stabilimento Tecnico	1901	Feb. '05		13,180 = 19·16	17,926 = 20·36	Yarrow in all	
E. Friedrich	Triest		1902	Oct. '06		14,100 = 19·01	18,130 = 20·57		
E. Ferdinand Max	Triest		1903	Apr. '07		14,390 = 19·57	18,600 = 20·76		

490

Note.—Appearance after reconstruction is shown *approximately* by plans below.

HABSBURG (Sept., 1900), **ARPAD** (Sept., 1901), **BABENBERG** (Oct., 1902).
Displacement, 8300 metric tons. Complement, 623.

Length (*p.p.*), 354⅓ feet. Beam, 65 feet. { *Maximum* draught, 24 feet. } Length (*w.l.*), 408 feet.
{ *Mean* ,, 23¾ ,, }

Guns: (*See General Notes.*)
3—9·4 inch, 40 cal. (A). ⎱ ?
12—5·9 inch, 40 cal. ⎰ ?
10—11 pdr.
(2—9 pdr. landing).
8—3 pdr.
2 machine.
Torpedo tubes (17·7 inch):
2 *submerged.*

Armour (Krupp):
8⅔″ Belt (amidships) ...... ▨
2″ Belt (bow) (N.C.) ...... ▦
2½″ Armour deck (flat amidships)
7¾″ Bulkheads ....
8¼″ Barbettes (N.C.)...... ▨
6″ Turrets to these (N.C.) ▨
4″ Lower deck side ...... ▥
5″ Casemates (12) (N.C.) ▨
8″ Conning tower (N.C.) ▨
(Total weight 2250 tons).

Ahead:
2—9·4 in.
4—5·9 in.

Astern:
1—9·4 in.
4—5·9 in.

Broadside: 3—9·4 in., 6—5·9 in.

Machinery: 2 sets triple expansion, 4 cylinder. 2 screws. Boilers: 16 Belleville (model, 1900).
Designed H.P. 15000 = 18·5 kts. Coal: *normal* 500 tons, *maximum* 840 tons.

General Notes.—First two built at Triest, last at Pola. Machinery by Stab. Tecnico, in all. Made 19·6 kts. on first trials. *Habsburg* reconstructed and partly reboilered 1911. *Arpad* reconstructed in 1912 and *Babenberg* in 1913. Superstructures were greatly reduced, funnels shortened, fore bridges and charthouse rebuilt arc of fore-turret enlarged. About 70-80 tons removed from each ship. May now have 20·8 tubes. 9·4 inch guns Skoda in *Babenberg*, Krupp in other ships.

Photo, Laroux.

MONARCH (May, 1895). Displacement, 5600 metric tons. Complement, 433. Length (*waterline*), 318 feet. Beam, 55¾ feet. *Mean* draught, 21 feet. Length *over all*, 323 feet. Guns (Krupp M. '86): 4—9·4 inch, 40 cal.; 6—5·9 inch, 40 cal.; (2—9 pdr. landing), 12—3 pdr., 2 machine. Torpedo tubes (17·7 inch): 2 *submerged*. Armour (Harvey): 10½″ Belt (amidships), 4¾″ Belt (bow), 2½″ Armour deck (aft), 2⅓″ Deck flat on belt, 9¾″ Bulkhead (aft), 10½″ Barbettes, 8″—5″ Hoods to these, 3″ Lower deck redoubt, 3″ Battery redoubt, 8″ Conning tower, 4″ Conning tower (aft). **Machinery:** 2 sets vertical triple expansion. 2 screws. Boilers: 8 cylindrical. Designed H.P. 8500 = 17 kts. Coal; *normal* 300 tons; *maximum* 500 tons.

BUDAPEST, sometimes referred to as **OFENPEST,** launched April, 1896. Sister ship to *Monarch* described above, but has 16 Belleville boilers without economisers. *Wien,* the third unit of the class, was sunk in Triest Harbour by Captain Rizzo of the Italian Navy. *Budapest* was also torpedoed on this occasion. She did not sink, but was so heavily damaged, it appears she was deemed unfit for full repairs. According to report, all her guns were removed, she was roughly repaired and is now only used as a floating Barracks or Harbour Depot Ship.

There are also two other old battleships, *Kronprinz Erherzog Rudolf* and *Mars.* The former is Port Defence Ship at Cattaro; the latter is now a Training Ship. Both are described with other Miscellaneous Ships on a later page.

(To distinguish from *K. K. VI* note *cranes*, *no* ventilators and position of searchlight on foremast).

SANKT GEORG (December, 1903).

Displacement, 7300 metric tons.   Complement, 628.
Length (*waterline*), $383\frac{5}{6}$ feet.   Beam, $61\frac{1}{2}$ feet.   *Max.* draught, $21\frac{1}{3}$ feet.

Guns (Skoda) (M. '01):
2—9·4 inch, 40 cal.
5—7·5 inch, 42 cal.
4—5·9 inch, 40 cal.
9—11 pdr.
(2—7 pdr. landing).
10—3 pdr.
2 machine.
Torpedo tubes (17·7 inch):
2 *submerged.*

Armour (Krupp):
$8\frac{1}{4}''$ Belt (amidships) ...
2" Belt (forward) ......
$2\frac{1}{2}''$ Armour deck.. ...
$7\frac{1}{2}''$ Bulkheads ......
$8\frac{1}{4}''$ Lower deck side...
8" Barbette..............
5" Turret (aft).........
5" Double casemates (4)

Ahead:
2—9·4 in.
2—7·5 in.
2—5·9 in.

Astern:
3—7·5 in.
2—5·9 in.

Broadside: 2—9·4 in., 3—7·5 in., 2—5·9 in.

Machinery: 2 sets triple expansion. 2 screws. Boilers: 16 Yarrow. Designed H.P. *natural* draught.
12,300 = 21 knots; *forced*, 14,000 = 21. Coal: *normal* 600 tons; *maximum* 1000 tons.
Gunnery Notes.—Loading positions, big guns all round. Hoists: electric and hand. Big guns manœuvred
electrically; 7·5 in. guns, electric; 6 in. guns, hand. Arcs of fire: Big guns 240°.

Name	Builder	Machinery	Laid down	Com-pleted	Trials		Boilers	Best recent speed
S. Georg	Pola	Stab. Tecnico	1903	1906	13,095 = 21·3	15,270 = 22	Yarrow	22·3

General Notes.—Cost £581,583.   Ventilators shown in above elevation by error.

KAISER KARL VI (Oct., 1898). Displacement, 6300 metric tons. Complement, 546. Length (*waterline*),
$390\frac{1}{2}$ feet. Beam, $56\frac{1}{2}$ feet. *Mean* draught, $20\frac{1}{3}$ feet. Guns (Krupp and Skoda): 2—9·4 inch, 40 cal. (*A*), 8—
5·9 inch, 40 cal. (2—7 pdr. landing), 16—3 pdr., 2 machine guns; torpedo tubes, 17·7 inch, (2 *above
water* behind 3" armour).   Armour (Harvey-nickel): $8\frac{2}{3}''$ Belt (amidships); 8" Fore bulkhead; 7" After
bulkhead; 4" Engine hatches; $2\frac{1}{2}''$ Armour deck (ends); $1\frac{1}{4}''$ Armour deck (amidships); 8" Barbettes;
$3\frac{1}{4}''$ Lower deck redoubt; 3" Double casemates (4). Machinery: 2 sets 4-cylinder triple expansion. 2 screws.
Boilers: 18 Belleville. Designed H.P. 12,000 = 20 kts. Coal: *normal* 500 tons; *maximum* 820 tons.
Laid down by Stab. Tecnico, Triest, 1896; completed 1899. Trials: H.P. 12,900 = 20·83 kts.

Note.

SANKT GEORG interned at Cattaro.

KAISER KARL VI interned at Sebenico.

All now have small crow's nest high on foremast, and short mainmast.
SAIDA.   (IMPROVED SPAUN CLASS).   *Official Photo.*

SAIDA (Oct., 1912), **HELGOLAND** (Nov., 1912), **NOVARA** (Feb., 1913).

Normal displacement, 3500 metric tons.   Complement, 318.

Length (*w.l.*), 410¾ feet.   Beam, 42 feet.   *Mean* draught, 15 feet.   Length *over all*, 428½ feet.

Saida —
Guns :
9—4·1 inch.
1—3 inch (anti-aircraft).
1 machine.
1 landing.
Torpedo tubes (in all) 6—17·7 inch :
3 pairs *above water*.

Other 2 —
Guns :
8—3·9 inch (50 cal. semi-auto).
1 machine.
1 landing.

Armour (steel) :
2½″ Belt (amidships).........
2″ Bulkheads ....
¾″ Deck.......................

Machinery : Turbine (*see Notes*). 4 screws. Boilers : 16 Yarrow. Designed H.P. 25,000=27 kts.
Coal : *normal*, 450 tons ; *maximum*, 750 tons.   Radius of action as *Ad. Spaun.*

Name	Builder	Machinery	Laid down	Completed	Trials	Turbines	Boilers	Best recent speed
Saida	Monfalcone	Prager Masch.	Sep.'11	May, '11		Pfenniger	Yarrow	29·2
Helgoland	Fiume	Danubius	Oct.'11	Oct., '14		A.E.G.	Yarrow	
Novara	Fiume	Danubius	Feb.'12	Oct., '14		A.E.G.	Yarrow	

Now has short mainmast.

ADMIRAL SPAUN (October, 1909).

Normal displacement, 3500 metric tons.   Complement, 320.

Length (*w.l.*), 410¾ feet.   Beam 42 feet.   *Mean* draught, 15 feet.   Length *over all*, 428½ feet.

Guns :
7—3·9 inch (50 cal., semi-auto.)
1 Machine.
Torpedo tubes (17·7 inch) :
8 *above water*, in 4 pairs.

Armour :
2½″ Belt ......
2″ Bulkheads
¾″ Deck .. ...

ADMIRAL SPAUN

Machinery : Parsons turbine. 4 screws. Boilers : 16 Yarrow. Designed H.P. 20,000=26 kts.
Coal : *normal* 450, *maximum* 780 (with oil fuel). Radii of action : 860 miles at *full power* (27 kts.), 1600 miles at 24 kts.

Name	Builder	Machinery	Laid down	Completed	First Trials	Boilers	Present best speed
A. Spaun ?	Pola	Stab Tecnico	Jan.'08	1910	25,000=27·02	Yarrow	29

Note.—SAIDA and ADMIRAL SPAUN interned at Venice, both reported refitting for service in Italian Navy. HELGOLAND and NOVARA interned at Cattaro.

Interned at Pola.

Photo, Spartali.

KAISERIN-UND-KÖNIGIN-MARIA-THERESIA (1893, rebuilt 1909). 5200 metric tons. Complement, 468. Length (*p.p.*), 351 feet. Beam, 52½ feet. *Mean* draught, 21½ feet. Length *over all,* 374 feet. Guns: 2—7·5 inch, 42 cal.; 8—5·9 inch, 35 cal.; (2—7 pdr. landing), 16—3 pdr., 1 Machine. Torpedo tubes (17·7 inch): 4 *above water.* Armour (steel): 4″ Belt (amidships); 2¼ ″Armour deck, 4″ Lower deck (redoubt); 4″ Barbettes; 4″ Sponsons; 4″ Conning tower; 4″ Bulkheads; 4″ Hoods to barbettes; 4″ Shields to upper deck guns. Machinery: 2 sets horizontal triple expansion. 2 screws. Boilers: 10 cylindrical. Designed H.P. *natural* 5880=17 kts.; *forced* 9500=19 kts. Coal: *normal* 600 tons; *maximum* 740 tons.

Interned at Cattaro.

*****KAISER-FRANZ-JOSEF** (1889, rebuilt 1905). 4000 metric tons. Complement, 441. Length (*waterline*), 321½ feet. Beam, 48¼ feet. *Mean* draught, 19 feet. Guns (re-armed 1905-06): 2—5·9 inch, 40 cal.; and 6—5·9 inch, 35 cal.; (2—7 pdr. landing), 16—3 pdr., 1 Machine. Torpedo tubes (14 inch): 3 *above water.* Armour (steel): 2¼″ Armour deck; 3½″ Barbettes, 3½″ Hoods to these; 4″ Conning tower. Machinery: 2 sets horizontal triple expansion. 2 screws. Boilers: 4 cylindrical, double-ended. Designed H.P.: *natural* 6400=18 kts.; *forced* 8000=19 kts. Coal: *normal* 400 tons; *maximum* 720 tons.

*Reported, October 1919, to have foundered at Cattaro.

Both interned at Pola.
Now carry a small crow's nest high on the foremast.

ASPERN (May, 1898), 2400 tons. **SZIGETVAR** (October, 1900), 2300 tons. Complement, 305. Length (*w.l.*), 315¾ feet. Beam 39⅓ feet. *Maximum* draught, 17 feet (varies a little). Guns: 8—4·7 inch (40 cal.(, 10—3 pdr., 1 machine. Torpedo tubes (17·7 inch) (2 *submerged*). Armour: 2″ deck amidships. Machinery: 2 sets triple expansion, by Stab. Tecnico. 2 screws. Boilers: 8 Yarrow. Designed H.P. 7800=20 kts. Coal: *normal* 300 tons; *maximum* 480 tons. Both built at Pola. *Zenta* of this class lost in the war.

***

Old "Torpedo Cruisers."

No photo available.
See silhouettes and "Lakroma" (on Miscellaneous page)
which they resemble.

LEOPARD (Elswick, 1885), **PANTER** (Elswick, 1885). 1530 tons. Complement, 202 *average.* Dimensions: 226⅓ (*w.l.*) × 32¾ × 14 feet (*mean* draught). Guns (new): 4—9 pdr., 10—3 pdr. Torpedo tubes: 4—14 inch (*submerged*). Armour: 2″ deck over engines. Machinery: Vertical inverted triple expansion. 2 screws. Boilers were cylindrical but may have been replaced by new Yarrow. Designed H.P. 6000=18 kts. Coal: *normal* 200 tons; *maximum* 300 tons.

Note.

These two old ships have been reconstructed at an unknown date. They are still officially classed with the Austro-Hungarian "Active Fleet," but may only be used now for subsidiary service. A later ship of this type, *Lakroma* (ex-*Tiger*) was converted to an Admiralty yacht. Her photo and details will be found among Miscellaneous Ships at end of this section. Disposal of these ships, 1919, not known.

MAGNET.

MAGNET (Schichau, 1896). 510 tons.
Complement, 80.

Guns :
  6—3 pdr.
  1 machine.
Torpedo tubes (T) :
  3 above water.

Armour :
  $\frac{3}{4}''$ over engines.

Machinery : 2 sets triple expansion. 2 screws. Boilers : Thornycroft. Designed H.P. 6000 = 23 kts. Coal : 105 tons.

Has three funnels now. See Silhouettes.

SATELLIT (Schichau, 1892). 540 tons. Complement, 84.

Guns :
  1—9 pdr.
  8—3 pdr.
  1 machine.
Torpedo tubes :
  2 above water.

Armour :
  $\frac{3}{4}''$ over engines.

Machinery : 2 sets triple expansion. 2 screws. Boilers : 2 Yarrow. Designed H.P. 4000 = 23 kts. (trial in bad weather 4600 = 21·87 kts).

TRABANT (Triest, 1890). 540 tons. Complement, 84. Guns : 2—9 pdr., 8—3 pdr., 1 machine. Torpedo tubes (T) : 2 above water. Armour : $\frac{3}{4}''$ over engines. Machinery : 2 sets triple expansion. 2 screws. Boilers : 4 locomotive. Designed H.P. 3500 = 20 kts. Coal : 150 tons.

PLANET (1889, Jarrow). 480 tons. Complement, 84. Guns : 2—9 pdr., 8—3 pdr., 1 machine. Torpedo tubes (T) : 3 above water. Armour : $\frac{3}{4}''$ over engines. Machinery : 2 sets triple expansion. 2 screws. Boilers : locomotive. Designed H.P. 3500 = 20 kts.

No photo available. See Silhouettes.

BLITZ (Schichau, 1888), **KOMET** (Schichau, 1888). 360 tons.
Complement, 61.

Guns :
  8—3 pdr.
Torpedo tubes :
  3 above water.

Armour :
  $\frac{3}{4}''$ over engines.

Machinery : 1 set triple expansion. 1 screw. Boilers : Blitz, locomotive ; Komet, Yarrow (new in 1912). Designed H.P., 2600 = 21 kts. Coal capacity : 120 tons.

No photo available. See Silhouettes.

METEOR (Schichau, 1887). 350 tons. Complement, 61.

Guns :
  8—3 pdr.
  1 machine.
Torpedo tubes :
  3 above water.

Armour :
  $\frac{3}{4}''$ over engines.

Machinery : 1 set triple expansion. 1 screw. Boilers : locomotive. Designed H.P. 2600 = 21 kts. Coal : 120 tons.

Note.

The torpedo-gunboats described on page preceding this, are listed in the Austro-Hungarian "Almanach für die K. und K. Kriegsmarine" as (and with) destroyers.

(20 + 1) Destroyers

No.	Type	Date	Displacement	H.P.	Max. speed	Fuel	Complement	T. Tubes	Max draug't
			tons		kts.	tons			
1	*Honved*	Bldg.	} 386	17,000 (t)	32·5	95 coal & oil	102	4	...
5	*Dukla*	'14-'17							
1	*Varasdinier*	'13-'15	400	6000 (t)	28	80 coal	...	4	...
4	*Tatra* type	'11-'13	850	17,000 (t)	32·5	95 coal & oil	102	2	9
6		'07-'10							
2	} *Huszar* type (Y)	'07-'09	} 400	6000	28	**90 coal**	65	2	8
1		'06-'08							
1		'05-'07							

(Y) = Yarrow type.   (t) = Turbines.

Disposal of Destroyers, 1919.

At Cattaro : *Dukla, Lika,* * *Triglav,* * *Uszok, Reka, Pandur.*

At Pola : *Balaton, Csepel, Orjen, Tatra, Varasdinier, Dinara. Huszar, Velebit. Csikos, Turul, Scharfschutze, Ulan, Uskoke.*

At Porto Ré (near Fiume) : *Honved* (unfinished).

*Not to be confused with T.B D. of same name and type, sunk during the War.

Varasdinier (ex-Chinese *Lung Tuan*, 1913). 400 tons.   Dimensions: 219·8 × 20·3 × 8 feet.   Yarrow boilers. Armament : 6—11 pdr. (2 of 45 calibre length and remainder 30 calibre length), 4– 17·7 inch tubes in two twin deck mountings.

(8 + 1) Tatra Class.

ORJEN.

9 *Tatra* class, named ***Honved*** (not finished), ***Dukla, Lika, Triglav, Uszok*** (built·1914-17), and ***Tatra, Balaton, Csepel*** (1912), ***Orjen*** (1913).   All built by Danubius Co., Fiume.   Armament : 2—3·9 inch, 4—11 pdr., 2—11 pda. AA., 1 machine, 4—20·8 inch tubes.   A.E.G. turbines.   5 Yarrow boilers.   Dimensions: 274 × 25½ × 8¼ feet. Oil fuel, also coal.   All made 32·5 to 33 kts. on trials.   Tenth boat of class, *Lovcen*, reported not begun.

(10) Huszar Class.

LATER SIX HUSZARS.

Photo. Spartiali.

EARLIER FIVE HUSZARS.

Photo, Spartiali.

10 *Huszar* class named : ***Huszar*** (1905), ***Ulan*** (1906), ***Uskoke, Scharfschütze*** (1907), and later boats, ***Pandur, Turul*** 1908), ***Csikos, Dinara, Reka, Velebit*** (1909).   Yarrow type. 400 tons.   Dimensions: 219·8 × 20·3 × 6 feet.   Armament : 6—11 pdr., 1 machine, 2—17·7 inch tubes.   Designed H.P. 6000 = 28 kts.   4 Yarrow boilers.   Coal : 90 tons.   *Huszar* built by Yarrow ; rest by Stab. Tecnico.

50 Sea-going, **34** Coastal (= total of **84**) **Torpedo Boats.**

No. & Type		Date	Dis-place-ment	I.H.P.	*Max.* speed	Coal and Oil	Com-ple-ment	Tubes
Sea-going—								
27	74 T—81 T / 82 F—97 F / 98 M—100 M	1913-'15	250	5000	28 (t)	..	41	3
23	64 F—73 F / 52 T—63 T / 50 E	1905-'09	200	3000	25	47	29	2
Coastal—								
9 oil fuel	1—6 / 9—10 & 12	1909 / 1910	110	2600 / 2400	26 / 28	22	20	2
6	4 Nos. 13—16 (Y) / 1 No. 17 (Y) / 1 No. 18 (Y)	'98-'99 / 1896 / 1896	115 / 107 / 134	1800	24	30	21	2—3 / 2 / 2
19	Nos. 31—40 / Nos. 19—30	'86-'92 / '87-'91	78	1000 / 900	19	18—28	16	2

(Y) = Yarrow. (S) = Schichau.

(**Note.**—Two of these have been sunk, but no details as to which have been published).

Short mast now, stepped before forebridge
9 boats: Nos. *1—10* and *12* (1909-10). Armament: 2—3 pdr., 2—17·7 inch tubes. Oil fuel only. First six, Yarrow boilers. Last six, White Forster boilers. *No. 11* now in service in Italian Navy as *Francesco Rismondo*.
Note.—Nos. *3* and *7* captured by French, 1918.

---

74 T—81 T, 98 M—100 M, one funnel, one mast aft, high bridges.

82 F—97 F, 2 funnels (fore raised) and one mast aft of funnels.

27 "*Standard design*" boats, Nos. **74 T—81 T** (Trieste), **82 F—97 F**, (Fiume), **98 M—100 M** (Monfalcone). 250 tons. Oil fuel and coal-burning Yarrow boilers. Armament: 2—11 pdr. (one of these AA.), 1 machine, 4—17·7 inch torpedo tubes in 2 twin deck mountings. Dimensions: 178·3 × 18·7 × 4·9 feet.

Nos. 13—16 have short mast stepped against fore funnel.
6 *Yarrow*: Nos. **13—18** (1898-99). Guns: 2—3 pdr. 2 or 3—17·7 inch tubes. All Yarrow boilers, except No. 18, Schulz-Thornycroft.

23 boats (ex *Kaiman* class), No. **50 E** (Yarrow, Poplar, 1905), Nos. **52 T—63 T** (Trieste, 1906-7), **64 F—73 F** (Fiume, 1908-9). 200 tons. Guns: 4—3 pdr., 1 machine, 3 tubes. Dimensions: 180 × 18 × 4¼ feet. *51 T* lost during the war.

19 old boats: **31—40, 19—25, 27, 29, 30,** Armament: 2—1 pdr., 2—14 inch tubes. (All reconstructed as above photo). Yarrow boilers. Nos. *22* and *26* War Losses.

Tabulated Details.

No.	Type	First begun	Com-pleted	Displace-ment tons	H.P. above below	Speed. kts.	Endurance in miles. at (kts.)	Tubes or Gear	Comp-lement
4	{XL, XLI, XLII, XVLII}	1917	1918	$\frac{516}{730}$	$\frac{1100}{760}$	$\frac{13\cdot5}{7\cdot5}$	$\frac{8500\,(6)}{55\,(4)}$	5	35
5	{XXVII, XXIX, XXXI, XXXII}	1916	1917	$\frac{263}{324}$	$\frac{280}{280}$	$\frac{9}{5\cdot8}$	$\frac{6500\,(5)}{55\,(4)}$	2	21
2	XXI, XXII	1916	1917	...	...	$\frac{15}{9}$	...	2	11
2	XVII, XI	1914	1915	$\frac{127}{166}$	$\frac{60}{120}$	$\frac{6\cdot5}{5\cdot5}$	$\frac{1600\,(5)}{40\,(5)}$	2	...
1	XV	1913	1914	...	...	...	...	...	...
1	V	1908	1910	$\frac{236}{273}$	$\frac{500}{230}$	$\frac{11\frac{1}{4}}{9}$	$\frac{1000\,(11)}{27\frac{1}{4}\,(9)}$	3	14
1	IV	1908	1909	$\frac{240}{300}$	$\frac{600}{320}$	$\frac{12}{8\cdot5}$	$\frac{1200\,(9)}{60\,(6)}$	3	16
2	II, I	1908	1910	$\frac{230}{270}$	$\frac{640}{200}$	$\frac{12\cdot2}{7\cdot3}$	$\frac{}{25\,(7)}$	3	14

Note.

Disposal of above boats as follows :—

Interned at Cattaro :—XXII, XXIX, XXI, XLI, XLIII, XLVII.

Interned at Pola :—I, II, XI, XV, XVII, XXVII, XXXII.

Interned at Venice :—V, XXI, XXVIII, XL.   These boats may be taken over for Italian Navy.

Interned at Fiume :—IV.

Incomplete Boats.

At Pola :—5 boats.

At Fiume :—5 boats (2 nearly ready).

At Monfalcone :—3 boats.

Above may have been dismantled or broken up under Allied supervision.   Not included in Table.

No photo available.

See Silhouettes.

4 boats : **XL, XLI, XLIII, XLVII.**   Built 1917-18.   Details of first two uncertain, but *XLIII* and *XLVII* believed to be ex-German *UB 43* and *UB 47*, sold to Austria.   Probably all four boats are alike.   Dimensions: 142 × 19 × 12 feet.   Periscope depth : 42 feet.   Armament : 1—4·1 inch or 22 pdr., 5—19·7 inch tubes (4 bow, 1 stern).   Diesel engines : 2 sets M.A.N. 4-cycle.   2 screws.   Oil : *normal*, 35 tons ; *maximum*, 71 tons.   Lubricating oil : 7 tons.   Diving depth : 245 feet limit.   Dive to 30 feet in 40 secs.   Complement, *about* 35.   Other details as Table.

5 boats : **XXVII, XXVIII, XXIX, XXXI** and **XXXII.**   Details not certain ; but from view of *XXVIII* at Venice, it appears that these boats are of the German *UB 18—47* type, re-erected or built by Whiteheads, of Fiume.   Dimensions : 118 × 14¼ × 11¾ feet.   Armament : 1—11 pdr. AA,, 2 (bow)—19·7 or 20·8 inch tubes.   Machinery : 2—140 B.H.P. Diesel motors.   2 screws.   Oil : *normal*, 22 tons ; *maximum*, 28 tons.   3 tons lubricating oil.   *Maximum* diving depth : 163 feet.   Dive to 30 feet in 40 secs.   Complement, *about* 21.   Other details as Table.

Similar to Danish *Ægir* Class,
but with steel bridge screen.

2 boats : **XXI, XXII.**   Built by Whitehead, Fiume, 1916-17.   From view of *XXI* at Venice, these boats are much the same type as the Hay-Whitehead boats *Ægir, Galathea, Neptune,* &c., built for Danish Navy.   Armed with 1—11 pdr. AA. and 2 bow tubes.

(Continued on next page.)

2 boats: *XVII* (built by Weser Co., and erected at Pola, 1915), *XI* (built by Krupp, Germania 1914—15, and re-erected at Pola). Dimensions: 92 × 10·3 × 9¾ feet. Armament: 1—11 pdr. AA. and 2 (bow)—17·7 inch tubes. One 60 B.H.P. heavy oil engine. Can make 8·5 kts. for short periods *on surface* by using oil and electric motors together, but only 6·5 with oil motor. Oil: 3·5 tons and 5 tons lubricating oil. Diving depth: 163 feet. Submerge to 30 feet in 30 secs. Complement, 16. Other details as Table; are same as German *UB 1—17* class.

Appearance unknown.

1 boat: *XV* (built 1913-14). No details known.

1 *Whitehead-Holland* type: *V.* Built at Fiume in 1909. Dimensions: 105 × 13¾ × feet. Dive in 3¼ minutes. Can make 10¼ kts. awash. 3—17·7 inch tubes. *U 6* has been sunk during the war. Practically identical with the U.S. "C" class submarines.

1 *Krupp-Germania* type: *IV* (1908). Dimensions: 141¾ × 12·3 × 9¾ feet. 2 sets of 300 H.P. Körting motors. Armed with 1—11 pdr. AA. gun and 3—17·7 inch tubes. Cost *about* £62,500. This boat is badly over-engined and suffers from excessive vibration. The *maximum* surface speed cannot be kept up for any length of time.

No Photo Available.

2 *Lake* type: *II, I* (1908). Built at Pola. Dimensions: 100 × 11½ × feet. 3—17·7 inch tubes: 2 in bow and 1 in stern. Can make 10¼ knots awash. Dive in 2¼ minutes. Cost, £60,320 each. Are badly over-engined and cannot make designed speed on surface without excessive vibration.

Subsidiary Local Defence.

(At Cattaro.)

KRONPRINZ ERZHERZOG RUDOLF (1887). 6900 tons. Guns: 3 old 12 inch, 6—4·7 inch, 12—11 pdr. (old), 16 smaller. Probably disarmed now and only a hulk. Belt, 12 inch steel amidships. Original speed, 16 kts. Complement 454.

Submarine Depot Ships.
(Vorattsschiffe für Unterseeboote.)

GAA (1891), *ex Moskva* (Russian), *ex Furst Bismark* (German liner), 13,000 tons. Armament, 4—4·7 inch, 4—11 pdr. H.P. 16,000 = 19 kts. Complement 331.

No photo available.

LUSSIN (1883, 1914). 1000 tons. Guns: 4—3 pdr. Machinery: (1914), 1800 h.p. Diesel motors = 14 kts. Complement 154.

Submarine Depot Ships *(continued.)*

PELIKAN (1891). 2430 tons. Guns: 2—9 pdr., 8—3 pdr., and carries 30 torpedoes. H.P. 4000 = 14 kts. Coal: 400 tons. Complement 196.

(A special salvage ship, Herkules, is described on the next page.)

Mine Layers *(Minenleger)*

No photo available.

CHAMÄLEON (1913). 1100 tons. Dimensions: $288\frac{3}{4} \times 30 \times 9$ feet. Guns: 4—14 pdr. (2 are AA). Designed H.P. 5500 = 21 kts. Yarrow boilers. Carries 300 mines.

No photo available.

BASILISK (1902). 314 tons. Armament: 2—3 pdr., 4 machine. Speed 11 kts. Complement 40. Carries about 150 mines.

CARNIOL (No. V.) of Austrian Lloyd line. 2812 tons gross. About 200 mines carried.

Mining Ships *(continued)*.

SALAMANDER (1891). 268 tons. Armament: 2—3 pdr. Speed, 10 kts. Complement 20. Carries about 90 mines.

DROMEDAR (1891). 175 tons. Guns: 3—3 pdr. Speed, 10 kts. Complement 20. Carries about 50 mines.

There are two other old ships **Delta** and **Aurora** (1871-3). 1340 tons. 11 knots, *nominal* speed, used as mine depot ships. They are practically non-effective. Also **Gastein (No. IV.)** of Austrian Lloyd line, 3815 tons gross. Depot for about 700 mines.

Mine Sweepers.

10 Old Torpedo boats, *Nos. 27, 29, 30, 33—38 & 40,* all about 80 tons displacement, were fitted as mine-sweepers before the war. There are also a large number of requisitioned craft used for this service.

Fuel Ships *(Kohlendampfer)*.

Photo wanted.

POLA (1914), **TEODO** (1915). Colliers. 13,200 tons. Dimensions: $429\frac{3}{4} \times 57 \times 25\frac{1}{4}$ feet. Designed H.P., 6200 = 14 kts. Yarrow boilers. Guns: not known. Carry 7000 tons coal as cargo.

Fuel Ships (*continued*).

Photo wanted.

VESTA (1892). Oil tanker. 2130 tons. Designed H.P., 1200 = 10 kts.

Repair Ship (*Werkstättenschiff*).

For appearance, v. Silhouettes.

CYCLOP (1871). 2150 tons. Designed H.P., 850 = 11 kts. Guns: 2—11 pdr. Complement, 93.

Salvage Ship (*Bergungsdampfer*).

Photo wanted.

HERKULES (1910). 1500 tons. Dimensions: 210 × 33¾ × 13 feet. Designed H.P., 2500 = 10 kts. Yarrow boilers. Complement, 81.

Subsidiary Service Vessels.

Elevation by courtesy of Messrs. G. L. Watson & Co., Glasgow.

TAURUS (ex-*Nirvana*, 1904). 1300 tons. Dimensions: 220 × 30 × 13 feet. Designed H.P., 2000 = 15 kts. Guns: 2—3 pdr., 2—1 pdr. Coal, 230 tons.

(Interned at Constantinople.)

Subsidiary Service Vessels (*continued*).

LAKROMA (ex-*Tiger*, 1887). Old "Torpedo Cruiser" used as Admiralty Yacht. 1680 tons. Designed H.P., 6000 = 18 kts. Guns: 6—3 pdr. Complement, 177.

(For appearance, v. Silhouettes.)

MIRAMAR (1872). Used as Imperial Yacht. 1830 tons. Designed H.P., 2000 = 17 kts. (Paddle-wheel steamer). Guns: 2—3 pdr., 2—1 pdr. Complement, 159.

also

Dalmat (1896). Yacht. 260 tons. Designed H.P., 325 = 12 kts. Guns: one or two small Q.F. and machine.

Training Ships.

Old battleship **MONARCH** used for this duty before the war; she is described on a previous page.

MARS (ex *Tegetthof*) (1878, 1893). 7500 tons. Guns: 6—old 9·4 inch Krupp, 5—old 5·9 inch, 2—old 11 pdr., 15 smaller. Belt, 14½″ iron. Original speed (re-engined 1892), 16 kts. Complement 574.

Training Ships (*continued*).

(**Note.**—The following three gunboats were used before the war as sea-going Gunnery Training Ships—hence their mixed armaments. They have been kept in good repair, re-boilered, and are said to be capable of still making their designed speeds).

SEBENICO (Pola, 1882). 890 tons. H.P., 800 = 14 kts. Coal: 200 tons. Guns: 1—5·9 inch, 1—4·7 inch, 1—11 pdr., 8—3 pdr., 2—1 pdr., 2 machine. 2 *submerged* 14 inch tubes.

SPALATO (Triest, 1879). **ZARA** (Pola, 1879). 840 tons. H.P., 800 = 14 kts. Guns: *Spalato*, 2—4·7 inch, 1—3·9 inch, 1—7 pdr., 8—3 pdr., 1—1 pdr., 1 machine; 1 *submerged* 14 inch tube. *Zara*: 2—3·4 inch (14 pdr.), 1—7 pdr., 4—3 pdr., 3 machine; 2 *submerged* 14 inch tubes.

(Tenders to "Mars.")

Albatros and ***Nautilus***. Each was built in 1873, displaces 570 tons, and is armed with 1—11 pdr. and 2—3 pdr. guns. H.P., 400 = kts. speed.

(Late) BULGARIAN NAVY.

RECOGNITION SILHOUETTES.

Scale : 1 inch = 160 feet.

ENSIGN

MERCANTILE

NADEZHDA.

Torpedo boats.

Scale : 1 inch = 80 feet.

XVIII. (Submarine).

Torpedo Gunboat.

(Used as a Royal Yacht and Training Ship.)

Photo, Geiser.

Interned at Sevastopol.

NADEZHDA (Bordeaux, 1898). 715 tons. Dimensions : 220 × 27¼ × 10 feet. Guns (Creusot) : 2—3·9 in., 2—9 pdr., 2—3 pdr. Torpedo tubes : 2 *above water*. Armour : *Nil.* Designed H.P. 2600 = 17 kts. (18·85 trial.) Boilers : Lagrafel d'Allest. Complement 97.

Miscellaneous Ships, interned at Varna.

SIMEON VELIKI. 600 tons. Guns : 2—12 pdr., 4—3 pdr. 70 H.P. **ASJEN.** 400 tons. Guns : 4—3 pdr. 70 H.P. **ALEXANDER I.** No details known.

4 Torpedo Boats.

All taken over by Allies.

4 *Creusot* boats : **Smyeli, Khrabry, Deraki, Strogi** (built in sections in France ; reassembled at Varna, 1907-8). 100 tons. Dimensions : 126½ × 13¼ × 8¾ feet. Armament : 3—3 pdr., 3—18 inch tubes. Designed H.P. 2000 = 26 kts. 1 screw. Du Temple boilers. Complement, 23.

Vedette Boats.

Botef, Levski. Small craft of 12 tons, armed with spar torpedoes. Interned at Varna. *Boris, Liuben Karavelor, Raina, Rakovski, Voivode, Stefan Karajo, Hadji Lemeter*, all small motor Vedette boats. Six taken over by Allies, disposal of other boat not known.

Submarine.

Probably Austrian " XVIII " ceded to Bulgaria.

Same appearance as Austrian *XVII* and *XI* on a preceding page.

Taken over by French Navy.

1 boat : **XVIII** (1916). 127/166 tons. Dimensions : 92 × 10¼ × 9¾ feet. Armament : 1—1 pdr. or M.G., 2—17·7 inch torpedo tubes. H.P. 60 = 6·5 *on surface* with oil engine only (8·4 with electric motors for short periods). 120 H.P. = 5¼ kts. *submerged*. Endurance : 1600 miles at 5 kts. *on surface*, 50 miles at 2¼ kts. *submerged*. Complement, 16. Oil : 3·5 tons.

GERMAN FLEET.

INCLUDING SHIPS SALVED AT SCAPA FLOW AND THOSE TO BE SURRENDERED UNDER PEACE TREATY.

WILHELMSHAVEN to		miles.
	Cherbourg	510
	Dover	330
	Gibraltar...	1565
	Havre	450
	Heligoland	48
	Hull	330
	Kiao-chau	11100
	Malta...	2555
	New York...	3570
	Port Said	3530
	Portsmouth	440
	Rio de Janeiro	5470
	Rosyth	450
	Sheerness	280

KIEL to		miles.
	Copenhagen	160
	Danzig	280
	Libau	360
	Memel	330
	Kronstadt	670
	Skaw	240

DANZIG to		
	Libau...	120
	Memel	113
	Kiel	280

Wilhelmshaven to *Kiel*, 80 miles (by canal much of the way).
" " 530 " (via Great Belt).

MAP OF GERMAN COAST, SHOWING NAVAL AND PRIVATE YARDS, &c.

Fortifications to be Dismantled.

HELIGOLAND.—West Mole, 1950 feet long; East Mole, 1290 feet long. Of very little worth for large ships, owing to insufficient depth of water. Harbour can be used by torpedo craft, gunboats and small light cruisers. Naval hospital, barracks, and W/T. station. Admiralty Chart No. 126.

	Miles
To Cuxhaven	40
„ Wilhelmshaven	48
„ Yarmouth	260

Flags.

Reported new National Ensign has black, gold and red horizontal and equal stripes. Naval flags not known.

Mercantile Marine.

June, 1919, 3,427,000 tons *gross* but a large amount must be handed over to the Allies and United States.

Coinage.

Mark (100 pfennige) *nominal* value = 11¾d. British, 24 cents U.S.A., but rate of exchange has depreciated.

Colour of Ships.

Big ships : light grey all over.
Torpedo craft : varies from black to dull brown.

Active Naval *Personnel.*

Floating Docks.

Note :—Several of these have been sold, though such sales are reported to be contrary to the Treaty of Peace.

503

WILHELMSHAVEN. Fleet base; also base for torpedo craft, and seaplanes. Two large basins. Harbour for torpedo craft inside yard.

Docks (Graving): Nos. (1), (2) and (3), 625 × 99½ × 36 feet; No. (4), 584 × 101 × 35 feet; No. (5), 584 × 101 × 35 feet; No. (6), 584 × 94 × 35 feet; No. (7), 822 × 131 × 34 feet; No. (8), 822 × 114¾ × 34 feet. Five floating docks and 4 pontoons for torpedo boats. One 35,000 ton floating dock. Four building slips, (1) 600 feet, (2) 345 feet, (3) 300 feet, (4) about 600 feet. **Men** employed, *about* 11,500. Machinery: 38 of 9300 H.P. Admiralty Chart No. 3346. Rise of Spring Tide, 11¼ feet. Harbour has to be dredged continually on account of the sand which silts up very badly. Wangeroog (at mouth of Jade) is a minor Naval Station.

BREMERHAVEN. Port for Bremen, which is 50 miles inland of river mouth, and about 28 miles from Bremerhaven. At Bremen are the headquarters of the N. Deutscher Lloyd, and the big shipbuilding firm, Weser Act-Gesellschaft. Trade of the district (Bremerhaven, Vegesack, etc. included) was 2,750,000 tons of shipping cleared annually before the war. Kaiser Dry Dock No. 1, 741 × 98 × 35 feet, can take ships up to 50,000 tons. Another (N.D.L. floating) 450 × 58 × 19½ feet. At Bremerhaven, Seebeck Co. has one dock (No. 1) 550 × 65 × 21 feet, and three smaller. At Geestemünde, the same firm has two docks, each 547 × 80 × 18 feet. Also at Geestemünde, two smaller dry docks; and at Hammelwarden, one small dry dock. At Bremen, one floating dock, 490 × 90 × 23 feet (12,000 tons), and another smaller (3000 tons). Geestemünde, Bremen, and Bremerhaven are minor Naval Stations. Naval Hospital, Barracks, &c., at Lehe, near Bremerhaven.

Admiralty Chart No. 3346. Rise of Spring Tide, 10¾ feet.

GERMAN HARBOURS.—NORTH SEA (*Continued*).

(Divided into 2000 yard squares.   Uniform scale.   Soundings in fathoms.)

CUXHAVEN (and North Sea entrance to Kiel Canal).

CUXHAVEN.   Port for Hamburg, which is 65 miles from the sea, and headquarters of the H.A.P.A.G. (Hamburg-American Line).   Mine and Torpedo Station at Groden.   Ammunition Stores; Naval Airship and Seaplane Base; Naval Hospital and Barracks; W/T. Station.   Before the war, trade of Hamburg and Cuxhaven amounted to about 9,500,000 tons of shipping cleared per. annum.   Very strongly fortified.   A dredged channel for Destroyers is believed to exist north of Medem Sand.   Brunsbüttel coaling basin 1700 × 680 feet area.   Naval Airship Station at Fuhlsbüttel, near Hamburg.   Admiralty Chart No. 3261.   Rise of Spring Tide, 10¼ feet.

GERMAN HARBOURS:—NORTH SEA (*Continued.*)

(To Special Scale.   Divided into 4000 yard squares.   Soundings in fathoms).

Map is to Special Scale : see Note inset.

EMDEN. New and large W/T. Station. One floating dock (Inner Harbour) $284\frac{1}{2} \times 59\frac{1}{2} \times 17\frac{3}{4}$ feet (3500 tons). 1 smaller (2500 tons). Lock between Inner Harbour and Ems River $853 \times 131 \times 43$ feet. Inner and Outer Harbours 37 feet deep connected by dredged channel 40 feet deep. There is a small canal (Ems-Jade) between this port and Wilhelmshaven, which was only suitable for small vessels of shallow draught in 1914. The Borkum is fortified. **Big Naval W/T.** Station at Norddeich. Admiralty Chart No. 3761.

Note.—Channel along Wybelsumer Plate from Ems River into Port said to be dredged now to 5 fathoms. Channel out to Borkum may also be dredged.

GERMAN NAVY.

KIEL CANAL.

Length : 61¾ miles. Width at surface : 394 feet and 144 feet at bottom. New double locks : 1082 × 147 × 36 feet. Old locks (at Holtenau and Brunsbüttel) : 482 × 82 × 29½ feet. Sidings : 4 of 3600 × 540 feet, 11 other bays of 984 feet for turning. Speed of ships : 10 kts. for large, 15 kts. for small. Time of passage : 7 to 10 hours, according to size of ships ; but 16 battleships can, in emergency, pass in 6 hours.

Naval Airship Stations.

AHLHORN	NORDHOLZ
FRIEDRICHSHAVEN	STOLP (in Pommern)
KÖNIGSBERG (Seerappen)	WITTMUNDHAFEN
NIEDERGORSDORF	

NORTH SEA—Seaplane Bases.

BORKUM	NORDENEY
HELIGOLAND	WILHELMSHAVEN
LIST	

BALTIC—Seaplane Bases.

APENRADE	KIEL
BUG (Rügen Island)	PUTZIG
DANZIG	SEERAPPEN
FLENSBURG	SEDDIN
HOLTENAU	WIEK (Rügen Island)
NEST	WARNEMÜNDE

Note.

The following details of Principal Private Yards in North Sea and Baltic relate to conditions up to August, 1914.

NORTH SEA (*Nordsee*).

Principal Private Yards :

BLOHM & VOSS (HAMBURG). Ten *Slips* (four 600 feet long, five each about 500 feet long, and one slip 328 feet). Five *Docks* (floating). (1) 320 × 52 × 18. (2) 355 × 52 × 18. (3) 558 × 88 × 25. (4) 595 × 88 × 25. (5) 728 × 123 × 36 feet (46,000 tons). Possibly a sixth (40,000 tons) intended originally for Pola D.Y. (Austria-Hungary). Probably build submarines and destroyers now. *Employees*, 10,000. *Machinery*, 10,000 H.P. Bought Janssen & Schmilinsky Yard for extensions, 1917, with dock 400 × 50 × 16 feet.

A. G. WESER (BREMEN). Five *Slips* (one of 650 feet, one of 490 feet, two of 328 feet, one small). Three *Docks* (floating) of small size. Build submarines. *Employees*, 6000. *Machinery*, 4220 H.P.

BREMER-VULKAN (VEGESACK). Six *Slips* (one of 650 feet, two about 500 feet, three smaller). *Docks*, one floating. Probably build submarines and destroyers now. *Employees*, about 3100. *Machinery*, 2800 H.P.

VULCAN (HAMBURG). Two *Slips*, 650 feet or so. Four floating docks : No. 4, 605 × 85 × 28 feet (17,500 tons) ; No. 3, 610 × 106 × 28 feet (27,000 tons). Another dock, 723¾ × 108½ × 32¾ feet (32,000 tons) may exist. Two smaller floating docks, 433 × 70 ×   feet (6000 tons) and 510 × 82 ×   feet (11,000 tons). *Employees*, about 9000. H.P. 6500.

JOHANN C. TECKLENBORG (GEESTEMUNDE). Six *Slips* (two of 600 feet, two about 500 feet, two smaller). 2600 men. H.P. 2600. Two dry docks.

REIHERSTIEG SCHIFFSWERFTE (HAMBURG). One *Slip* about 550 feet, one about 400, five small. *Docks* : one (floating) 511½ × 97 × 26 feet (20,000 tons), three smaller. *Employees*, about 2000. H.P. about 4000. Bought J. & N. Wichorst Yard, 1917, for extensions.

BALTIC (*Ostsee*).

(A)—Principal Private Yards.

HOWALDT (KIEL). Nine *Slips* (two over 700 feet, one about 500 feet, six smaller). *Docs* : one floating (11,000 tons). *Employees*, about 3500. *Machinery* :

KRUPP'S GERMANIA (KIEL). Nine *Slips* (five of 700 to 520 feet, the rest smaller). Submarines built here for which 10-12 slips were available in 1914. *Employees*, 6400. *Machinery*, 4000 H.P. *Docks* : None.

SCHICHAU (ELBING). Twenty-seven *Slips* (six over 650 feet long, the others all small). Two (six ?) *Docks* (floating) for torpedo craft. *Employees*, about 10,000. *Machinery*, 5000 H.P.

VULCAN (BREDOW-STETTIN). Seven *Slips* (two over 650 feet, two about 500 feet, three about 350 feet or so). Two *Docks* (floating). (1) 416 × 58 × 17 feet. (2) 300 × 37 × 14½ feet. *Employees*, 7000.

(Uniform Scale.   Divided into 2000 yard squares.   Soundings in fathoms).

KIEL (and Baltic entrance to Kiel Canal). Fleet, torpedo craft, and seaplane bases and training stations. Two large basins. Docks: (1) 423 × 71 × 28. (2) 382 × 70 × 25½ (3) 362 × 64½ × 22½ (4) 344 × 67 × 16 (5) 570 × 94 × 30 (6) 570 × 94 × 30. Also one floating dock (40,000 tons), 660 × 96 × 32 feet, and five small floating. Another 36,000 ton floating, and 1 small private floating dock (Swentine). Two building slips. (1) 427 feet. (2) 427 feet. Men employed, *about* 10,500. Machinery: 109 of 23,240 H.P. Admiralty Chart, No. 33.

GERMAN DOCKYARDS.—**BALTIC**—(*Continued*).

(Divided into 2000 yard squares.   Uniform Scale.   Soundings in fathoms).

Other smaller Naval Stations in 1914 in Baltic, were :—

  FRIEDRICHSORT (see Kiel Map).   Torpedo manufactory and range ; munitions and
    mine depots ; naval hospital and barracks.

  DIETRICHSDORF :   Ammunition·depot.

  WARNEMÜNDE :   Seaplane base 1914—19.

  NEUMÜNSTER ı H :   Big naval W/T. station.

  SONDERBURG :   Naval hospital and barracks.

SWINEMUNDE.   Port for Stettin, a smaller naval station, which is 36 miles up the river.
    Trade of Stettin and Swinemunde is about 1,300,000 tons of shipping cleared
    annually, but is much greater at present.   No docks here suitable for large
    warships.

FLENSBURG - MÜRWICK.   Seaplane Station.   Smaller Naval Station in 1914,
    with Gunnery and Torpedo Schools, Naval Hospital and Barracks.   Floating
    Pontoon Dock, 280 × 49 × 19 feet.   2,800 tons.

Note.

*By plebiscite of the population of Slesvig, Flensburg may become a Danish Port in
    the near future.*

ONE FUNNEL.

DELPHIN.

FUCHS

M 1—60 (and 61—138 ?)
(*Mine Sweepers.*)

'Wachtschiffen.''
(*Trawler Mine Sweeper.*)

HAI

NORDSEE (*tender.*)

ZIETEN (D).

TWO FUNNELS. (D = Disarmed.)

DRACHE (*tender*).

BLITZ *class* (D).

PANTHER.

NAUTILUS (*minelayer*). (D)

LORELEY.

(*Surrendered to Allies.*)

ALBATROSS (*mine layer*) (D).

NYMPHE *class* (D) also NIOBE (D).
(*Conning tower and bridge against fore-funnel
"Arkona," "Medusa," has slightly thicker funnels*).

ODIN (D).
BEOWULF—*Icebreaker.*

HOHENZOLLERN.
(*Paid Off*).

NOTE.—(D) Signifies disarmed ships used as Depot and Training Ships, Hulks, &c.

TWO FUNNELS—*continued.*

KAISER FRIEDRICH *class.* (D)
"*K. Barbarossa*" *has cranes between funnels like* "*Hertha*" *class.* " *K. Karl der Grosse*," *resembles* " *Wittlesbach* " *class.* (*Mostly Hulks.*)

HERTHA *class.* (D)
(*Depot and Training Ships.*)

BADEN.
At Scapa Flow, under salvage. . .

PRINZ HEINRICH. (D)

WITTELSBACH *class.*
Turrets removed from 2 ships—others disarmed.

TO BE SURRENDERED?

NASSAU *class.* Guns dismounted.
"*Rhineland*" *dismantled and armour removed.*

THREE FUNNELS.

DEUTSCHLAND *class.* (D)

BRAUNSCHWEIG *class.* (D)
"*Lothringen*" *and* "*Preussen*" *have superstructures for carrying 12 motor boat mine sweepers.*

TO BE SURRENDERED.

OSTFRIESLAND *class.* Guns dismounted.

511

THREE FUNNELS. (D) = Disarmed.

FREYA.
(*Training Ship*).

Kaiserin Augusta.
(*Gunnery School.*)

Graudenz *class* *

* **Now have double searchlight tops on masts, as " Konigsberg " Class.**

BERLIN *class* (D).
(*Bridges against fore funnel.,*

PILLAU (*approximate*).

KÖNIGSBERG *class*.
(*Masts and funnels raking, latter half-cased. Super-firing guns aft.*)

REPORTED THAT LIGHT CRUISERS GIVEN BELOW ARE TO BE SURRENDERED.

LÜBECK and MÜNCHEN as BERLIN class opposite.

DANZIG (D).
(*Bridges round base of foremast.*)

STETTIN *class* (D).
(*Funnels unevenly spaced.*) *Now Seaplane Carriers. Appearance probably much altered.*

KOLBERG *class* (D).
Also STRALSUND (4 funnels) *appearance as* " *Strassburg.*"

FOUR FUNNELS.

STRASSBURG (D).

ROON (D).

FRANKFORT, *at Scapa Flow, being salved.*
Also EMDEN & NÜRNBERG, *under salvage at Scapa Flow. Appearance as* " *Königsberg* " *class.*

Notes.—Majority disarmed, except boats of the " Iron Division " and those engaged in Mine Sweeping. Reported that 42 modern Destroyers and 50 "A" Torpedo Boats are to be given up, numbers not yet known. * Denotes types now with raised fore funnels.

From T 3 to T 81.
Old t.b. now disarmed and used for subsidiary services. Some much shorter than above type.

A 1—25.

A 26—36 and later boats.

G 82—87
G 88 & 89 } **Old t.b.**
Tubes probably removed.

D 10 t.b.

T 42 t.b.
Tubes probably removed.

D 3 —5, D 7—9 t.b.
Mostly disarmed and used for Subsidiary Service.

T 91—101 t.b.d.
Some (or all) disarmed.

T 102—107
T 103 —113
T 114, T 120, T 122—125 } **t.b.d.**
T 126—131
Lengths of forecastles and distances of mast from 2nd funnel vary.

V 108—105 t.b. (ex *Dutch*).

T 132—136 *class* t.b.d.

T 137 t.b.d.

T 139 —149 *class* t.b.d.

(1)   (2)
T 151—161 *class* t.b.d.*

T 163, T 164 t.b.d.*

T 165—168 *class* t.b.d.*

T 174, T 175*
S 176—179 } **t.b.d.**

T 180—185 *class* t.b.d.

T 186, T 189, T 191 t.b.d.*

G 192—197 *class* t.b.d.*
G 169—173 *class* t.b.d.*
(Practically identical with each other).

V 1—6*
G 7—11* } *classes* **t.b.d.**

" War V & S " t.b.d. :—
V 26—V 130, S 51—S 139
Some boats have short mainmasts.   *H types said to be same as V & S types. 17 or 19 of these boats salved at Scapa Flow.*

G 95 t.b.d.*

G 102* (*ex-Argentine boat*). †
(Now has raised forefunnel, with derrick just abaft same and compass platform between third funnel and mainmast.)
† *Salved at Scapa Flow.*

B 97, B 98, †
(Compass platform actually between after tubes.)
† *Seized at Scapa Flow.*

V 100.
(Same appearance, but derrick between first and second funnels, with boom slung forward ; big ventilator between second and third funnels.)

2 K

GERMAN UNIFORMS, GUNS AND TORPEDOES.

INSIGNIA OF RANK ON SLEEVES FOR EXECUTIVES.

Gross-Admiral (= Admiral of the Fleet) as Admiral but 4 upper stripes.

Crowns may have been removed.

Admiral. Vize-Admiral. Kontre-Admiral. Kommodore Kapitän zu See. Korvetten-   Kapitän-   Oberleut z. See. Leutenant z. See
(Vice-Ad.)   (Rear-Ad.)   (Commodore).   (Captain)   Kapitän.   Leutnant.   (Lieut.)   (Sub-Lieut.)
Fregatten-Kapitän &   (Commander)   (Lieut.-Comm.)

Flaggoffiziere.   Stabsoffiziere.   Subalternoffiziere.

Note.—Torpedo officers are without the crown on sleeve, as also are all civilian branches. Engineer officers given same official status as Executive, July, 1908.

Torpedo officers have between the gold stripes, *brown*; Engineers, *black*; Doctors, *blue*; Paymasters, *light blue*; Constructors, *black*.

(The colour of the branch is also worn on the epaulettes, full dress, and worked into the shoulder straps).

Paymasters, constructors and legal officers have silver buttons, badges, &c., as well as epaulette fringes, instead of gold, and cloth instead of velvet between the stripes. They are *officials* and not officers.

Torpedoes (1919).

Note : The following details are understood to be based on very sound information.

Size.	Name or Mark.	Air Pressure.	Charge. (lbs.)	Max. Range. (yds.) } at kts.	Type of Heater.
23·6	H 8	2485	616	16350 at 28 / 5450 at 35	Steam
19·7	G VII.*** (23 feet)	2275	430	11700 at 28 / 5500 at 35	Steam
19 7	G VI. A V **	2275	441	5500 at 27 / 2200 at 40	Dry
17·7	G/125	2133	308	6560 at 24 / 2200 at 36	Dry

Mines (Notes unofficial).

No exact details available. Spherical horned type said to have charge of 220-240 lbs. T.N.T. Pear-shaped "Carbonit" mines said to have charge of 166 lbs. wet guncotton. Marks I and II, soluble safety plugs. Later marks have safety pin attached by rod to sinker. Horns said to be glass tubes (containing battery acid) and covered with lead or soft metal. Bending of horn breaks glass tube and acid runs to battery, which at once becomes active and fires detonator.

Naval Guns (Details unofficial).

Notation.	Calibre.		Usual Naval Designation.	Length in cals.	Date of Model.	Weight of Gun.	Weight of A.P. shot.	Initial Velocity.	Maximum penetration direct impact against K.C at			Danger space against average ships at			Approximate Muzzle Energy.
									9000 yds.	6000 yds.	3000 yds.	10,000	5000	3000	
	inch.	c/m.				tons.	lbs.	foot-secs.	in.	in.	in.	yards.	yards.	yards.	foot tons.
A 9*	15	38·1		45	'13	82½	1675½	2920	16	18½	21	...	...	...	99,000
A 4*	11	28		45	'04	36·3	} 661·4	{ 2920	7	12	15	170	580	950	39,100
A 3*	11	28		40	'01	32·2		2756	6	10	14	150	450	740	31,600
A 2*	9.4	24		40	'99	20·3	} 418·9	{ 2756	4	8	12	130	400	700	22,050
A*	9.4	24		40	'98	20·3		2625	3½	7	10	110	350	620	22,000
A*	8·2	21		40	'01	13·4	275·6	2756	3	6	9	...	...	...	14,735
B*	6·7	17		40	'01	7·5	154·5	2756	...	3	5	80	240	460	8,275
C*	5·9	15		50	...	5·5		{ 3084	...	...	...	...	...	...	6,690
C*	5·9	15		45	'09	5	} 101·4	{ 2920	...	...	5	...	200	420	5,990
E*	5·9	15		40	'01	4·9		{ 2756	...	...	3½	...	140	350	5,335
E*	5·9	15		35	...	4·4		2231	...	...	...	...	...	...	...
F*	4·1	10 5		40	...	1·7	35·2	2756	...	...	...	...	...	...	1,860
F*	4·1	10·5		35	..	1·2	38 2	2000	...	...	...	...	...	...	1,645

* Brass cartridge cases to all guns.

Lesser guns : 3.4 inch (88 m/m) firing 22 lb. projectiles in modern and 15 lb. in old models; also 2 inch (4 pdr.) of 55 and shorter calibres. Also anti-aircraft models, about which no reliable details are available.

Projectiles : Guns of 11 inch and over fire A.P., Ersatz A.P., H.E., and common shell.

The 1899 and later models have the recoil utilized to return the gun to firing position for pieces over 5.9 inch. In 5.9 in. springs are employed. German guns have a lower muzzle pressure than normally obtains, but mountings are arranged to give large degree of elevation.

12 inch, 50 cal. *Helgoland* class.
11 inch, 45 cal. in *Nassaus.*
11 inch, 40 cal., M. '01 in *Deutschland* and *Braunschweig* classes (removed from some).

Under Salvage at Scapa Flow.

(Bayern Class—1 Ship).

BADEN *(30th Oct,, 1915)*.

Displacement, *about* 28,000 tons. Complement, over 1100.

Length, $623\frac{1}{3}$ (*o.a.*) feet. Beam, $99\frac{3}{4}$ feet. *Mean* draught, $28\frac{1}{4}$ feet.

Guns.
8—15 inch, 45 cal.
16—5·9 inch, 45 cal.
4—22 pdr. (anti-aircraft).
Torpedo tubes (23·6 inch).
4 *submerged* (broadside) ?
1 *submerged* (bow) ?

Armour (Krupp):✳
15″ Belt (amidships) ....
8″—6″ Belt (ends) ....
″ Deck ....
10″ Side above Belt...........
″ Turrets ....
8″ Battery ....
$17\frac{1}{2}$″ Conning Tower . ...
✳Details very approximate.

BADEN.

Ahead :
4—15 in.
2—5·9 in.
1—23·6 in. tube.

Astern :
4—15 in
4—5·9 in.

Broadside : 8—15 in., 8—5·9 in., 2—23·6 in. tubes.

Machinery : "Marine-type" (geared ?) turbines. Boilers : Schulz-Thornycroft. 2 or 4 screws.
Designed H.P. 34,000 = 21 kts. Coal : *normal*, 1000 tons ; *maximum*, 4800 tons. Also oil.

Torpedo Notes.—Broadside tubes angle 30° before to 60° abaft beam.

Name	Builder	Machinery	Laid down	Com- pleted	Trials	Turbines	Best recent speed
Baden	Schic'au, D'nz'g	Schichau	Feb. '14 1915	Nov.'16*		} "Marine- type"	

*Approximate date of completion.

General Notes.—Is *Ersatz Worth* of 1912-13 Programme. Was Fleet Flagship, High Sea Fleet. Sister ship *Bayern*
("T"), scuttled at Scapa Flow, 21st June, 1919. *Baden* was interned at Scapa Flow in place of the unfinished
Battle Cruiser *Mackensen* ; an attempt was made to scuttle her on June 21st, 1919, but she sank in shallow water
and is being refloated.

Note : These two Dreadnoughts are lying launched but unfinished in German
Ports. "Sachsen" has turrets 2 and 3 in place with guns ; armour belt
and one funnel in place. "Württemberg" to be Base Ship for Baltic
Minesweepers ; has armour in place.

SACHSEN (Nov., 1916), WÜRTTEMBERG (Aug. 1917).

Displacement, *about* 28,100 tons.

Length, (*o.a.*) $626\frac{2}{3}$ feet. Beam, 100 feet. Draught, 28 feet.

Guns : 8—15 inch as *Baden*, but said to have 18—5·9 inch, with 4 AA. guns. Tubes (23·6 inch).
Number not known.

Armour : As *Baden*, but thinner belt and more horizontal protection. Machinery : As *Baden*, but H.P.
increased to give 23 knots. Fuel : As *Baden*.

Notes.—*Sachsen* is *Ersatz Kaiser Friedrich III* of 1914-15 Programme, begun by Krupp. Germania, 1914. *Wurttemberg*
is *Ersatz Kaiser Wilhelm II*, of 1915-16 Programme, begun by Vulcan, Hamburg, 1915. Believed to be of a modified
Bayern type. Work on these ships said to have been stopped in 1917 and never begun again. *Ersatz Kaiser
Wilhelm der Grosse*, begun by Howaldt, Kiel, 1915, never got beyond framing stage, and was dismantled.

Reported that surrender of all is demanded under Peace Treaty.

(OSTFRIESLAND CLASS).

THÜRINGEN (Nov., 1909), **HELGOLAND** (Sept., 1909), **OSTFRIESLAND** (Sept., 1909),
OLDENBURG (June, 1910).

Normal displacement, 22,800 tons. Complement, 1097 to 1106.
Length (*waterline*), 546¼ feet. Beam, 93¼ feet. { *Maximum* draught, 29½ feet.
{ *Mean*   "   27 feet.

Guns :
12—12 in., 50 cal. (A⁶)
14—5·9 in., 45 cal.
4—22 pdr. anti-aircraft
2 machine.
Torpedo tubes (19·7 inch) :
1 *submerged* (bow)
1 *submerged* (stern)
4 *submerged* (broadside)

All disarmed, but guns on board.

Armour (Krupp) :
11¾″ Belt ....
8″ Belt (bow).........
4″ Belt (aft) ....
1½″ Deck on slopes...
12″ Turrets...........
12″ Turret bases ...
6¼″ Battery...........
12″ Conning tower
(fore) ....
8″ C. T. (aft) ....
(Total weight: 5100 tons).

HELGOLAND.

Note.

OLDENBURG and HELGOLAND laid up at Kiel and OSTFRIESLAND and THURINGEN at Wilhelmshaven.

The four 3·4 inch (22 pdr.) AA. guns are in after superstructure; all other 3·4's on plans have been removed.

Appearance.

Funnels have been raised by about 6 feet.

Ahead :
6—12 in.
2—5·9 in.
1—19·7″ T.

Broadside : 8—12 in., 7—5·9 in , 2—19·7 in. tubes.

Astern :
6—12 in.
4—5·9 in.
1—19·7″ T.

Machinery : Reciprocating. 3 screws. Boilers : 15 Schulz-Thornycroft. Designed H.P. 25,000 = 20·5 kts.
Coal : *normal* 900 tons ; *maximum* 3,000 tons, including oil (200 tons, may be more now).

Engineering Notes.—125 r.p.m.=21 kts. *about.* Have double (athwartship) rudders.

Name	Builder	Machinery	Ordered	Laid down	Began trials	Trials (full power). Mean	Best speed	Finished trials
Thüringen	Weser, Bremen	Weser	June.'08	Jan. '09	July, '11	34,944=21·075	21·2	Sept. '11
Helgoland	Howaldt, Kiel	Howald	May. '08	Dec.,'08	Aug. '11	31,258=20·81	22	Dec. '11
Ostfriesland	W'l'mshaven Y		May, '08	Oct.,'08	Aug. '11	34,944=21·10	21·39	Sept. '11
Oldenburg	Schichau, Danzig	Schichau	Apl. '09	Mar., '09	July, '12	34,394=21·3	22·2	July, '12

General Notes.—All four ships are extremely good sea boats. *Thüringen* (Ers. *Beowulf*), *Helgoland* (Ers. *Siegfried*), and *Ostfriesland* (Ers. *Oldenburg*), 1908 Programme. *Oldenburg* (Ers. *Frithjof*), 1909 Programme.

OSTFRIESLAND.

(NASSAU CLASS.)
WESTFALEN (July, 1908), **NASSAU** (March, 1908), **POSEN** (Dec., 1908) & **RHEINLAND** (Sept., 1908).
Normal displacement, 18,900 tons. Complement, 957 to 966.

Length (*waterline*), 478 feet. Beam, 88¼ feet. { Mean draught, 26½ feet. / Max. „ 27½ feet. } Length (*p.p.*), 451½ feet.

Guns (M '04) :
12—11 inch, 45 cal. (A⁵).
12—5·9 inch, 45 cal.
22 pdr. anti-aircraft.
2 machine.
Torpedo tubes (17·7 inch) :
    6 *submerged* (one bow, one stern, and four broadside).

Armour (Krupp) :
11¾″ Belt (amidships) ...... ▨
8″ Belt (bow) .... ▩
4″ Belt (aft) .... ▥
″ Deck on slopes ....
11″ Barbettes .... ▨
11″ Turrets to these...... = ▨
8″ Lower deck redoubt... ▧
7″ Battery .... ▨
12″ Conning tower ....
        (Total weight: — tons)

Reported that surrender of all is demanded under Peace Treaty

Ahead :
6—11 in.
2—5·9 in.
1—19·7″ T.

Astern :
6—11 in.
2—5·9 in.
1—19·7″ T

Broadside: 8—11 in., 6—5·9 in., 1—19·7 in. tube.

Machinery : 3 sets 3 cylinder triple expansion. 3 screws. Boilers: 12 Schulz Thornycroft or "Marine."
Designed H.P. 20,000 = 19·9 kts. Coal: *normal*, 950 tons ; *maximum*, 2700 tons, also 200 tons oil.
Armour Notes.—Underwater lateral bulkheads, 2″ thick amidships.
Gunnery Notes.—All round loading positions to big guns, but fixed elevation. Electric, hydraulic and hand
    gear. Electric hoists to all guns. Ammunition supply to 6 inch reported unsatisfactory. Spotting
    stations aloft. Controls in each turret. 22—pdr. AA. guns in aft superstructure ; all other 3·4 inch
    removed.
Torpedo Notes.—Net defence fitted to all. Specially large searchlights.
Engineering Notes.—Excellent steamers. *Nominal* radius 5700 miles at economical speed.

Notes.

All disarmed, but guns on board. RHEINLAND lying dismantled at Kiel, with armour removed ; never repaired after being mined, 1918. WESTFALEN lying up at Kiel ; NASSAU and POSEN lying up at Wilhelmshaven.

Name	Builder	Machinery	Ordered	Laid down	Began trials	Trials : (full power) mean	Best speed	Finished trials
Westfalen	Weser, Bremen	Weser	Oct., '06	July, '07	Nov., '09	27,104 = 20·3	20·4	May, '10
Nassau	Wilhelmshaven		May, '06	July, '06	Oct., '09	25,508 = 20	20·8	May, '10
Posen	Germania, Kiel	Krupp	Apl., '07	July, '07	May, '10	27,745 = 20	21·39	Sept., '10
Rheinland	Vulkan, Stettin	Vulkan	Apl., '07	Aug., '07	Apl., '10	26,100 = 20·3	—	Sept., '10

WESTFALEN.

General Notes.—Cost of *Nassaus* £1,838,000 per ship. Keel of *Nassau* laid 1906, but no further progress
    was made on her till July, 1907. As originally designed she was to have carried only eight big guns.
These ships steam well, but they draw more than the designed draught by at least a foot. They are very
    cramped internally and it is difficult to accommodate the crews. Some cabins have to accommodate 4
    officers. Ventilation is very poor. They are only moderately successful, being overgunned for their
    displacement, but they are extremely steady gun platforms. The shooting from these ships always
    averages better than from any others. *Nassau* (*Ers. Bayern*) and *Westfalen* (*Ers. Sachsen*), 1906
    Programme ; *Rheinland* (*Ers. Württemburg*) and *Posen* (*Ers. Baden*), 1907 Programme.

GERMAN BATTLE-CRUISERS.

Note :—All unfinished, very doubtful if any will be completed now.

PRINZ EITEL FRIEDRICH (*Ersatz Vineta*), begun by Wilhelmshaven D.Y., May, 1916 ; *ERSATZ HANSA*,* begun by Blohm & Voss, 1917. Both unlaunched. Nothing known of design of these ships, but unofficially said to be same as *Graf Spee*. Have been abandoned on slips since 1917.

*Reported unofficially that this ship would have been named *Scharnhorst* when launched. The U.S. Bureau of Naval Intelligence says : " *Ersatz Freya* on ways, Blohm and Voss Yard, Hamburg, April, 1919. Work being continued to permit of launching, probably in October." This statement evidently refers to *Ersatz Hansa*, still unlaunched, November, 1919.

GRAF SPEE (September, 1917).

Displacement, *about* 27,000 tons.

Length $\left\{ \begin{array}{l} w.l.\ 715\ feet \\ o.a.\ 740?\ ,, \end{array} \right\}$ Beam, 93 feet. Draught, 27 feet.

Guns :
6—15 inch, 45 cal.
14—5.9 inch, — cal.
4—22 pdr. AA.
2 or 4 M.G.
Torpedo tubes 6 (23.6 inch ?) :
(positions unknown)

Armour :
6¾″ Belt . . . .
10″ Barbettes . . . .
(Decks thick) . . . .
Splinter-proof screens to
5.9 inch guns . . . .

Launched : half armour in place ; half turret armour in place ; boilers on board.

Machinery : Turbine. Boilers : Schulz-Thornycroft. Designed S.H.P. 85,000 = 28 kts. also reported as 100,000 S.H.P. = 28.5 kts. Fuel : *max.* 4800 tons (oil only ?).

Notes.—Begun as *Ersatz Freya*, of 1916-17 Programme. Design is of interest, as it was intended to be an imitation of the British *Repulse* class. Begun by Schichau, Danzig, 1916. Work stopped eighteen months after laying down and never resumed. General build as *Hindenburg*, but *without* fore superfiring turret.

MACKENSEN (April, 1917).

Normal displacement, 27,000 tons. Complement, 1125.

Length (*waterline*), 700 feet. Beam, 95⅛ feet. *Mean* draught, 27¼ feet.

Guns :
8—12 inch, 50 cal. (A⁵)
14—5.9 inch, 45 cal.
4—22 pdr. (anti-aircraft)
2 M.G.
Torpedo tubes (23.6 inch ?) :
2 or 4 *submerged* (broadside)
1 *submerged* (bow)
1 *submerged* (stern ?)

Armour :
12″ Belt (amidships) . . .
5″ Belt (ends) . . . .
4″ Deck (flat) amidships
3″ Deck (slopes) below it
10″ Turrets . . . .
10½″ Barbettes . . . .
7″ Battery . . . .
15″ C.T. (fore) . . . .
8″ C.T. (aft) . . . .

Launched : hull only with part of armour belt.

Machinery : " Marine Type " turbines. 4 screws. Boilers : 18 Schulz-Thornycroft. Designed H.P. 85,000 = 28 kts. Coal : *normal*, 1000 tons ; *maximum*, 3380 tons + 320-570 tons oil fuel.

Notes.—Begun 1915, by Blohm & Voss, Hamburg. Intended that she should be interned at Scapa Flow in 1918, with other German ships. When the Allied Naval Commission visited Germany, she was found to be a mere hulk, and in so disgusting a state of filth, the idea of towing her to a British port was given up. *Baden* was interned instead of *Mackensen*.

(ex Greek *Salamis*, November, 1914).

Displacement, 19,500 tons.

Length, 570¾ feet. Beam, 82 feet. Draught, 25¼ feet.

Guns (Bethlehem—see *Notes*) :
8—14 inch, 45 cal.
12—6 inch, 50 cal.
12—12 pdr.
Torpedo tubes (19.7 inch) :
3 *submerged*

Armour (Krupp) :
9¾″ Belt (amidships) . .
4″ Belt (ends) . . . .
6″ Battery . . . .
9¾″ Barbettes . . . .
11¾″ C.T. (fore) . . . .

Launched : hull with armour and part of superstructure in place.

Machinery : A.E.G.-Curtis turbines. 3 screws. Designed S.H.P. 40,000 = 23 kts. Boilers : Fuel : 1200 tons coal and also some oil fuel.

Gunnery Notes.—Bethlehem guns never delivered, the 14-inch being bought by British Admiralty for arming the *Abercrombie* type Monitors.

Notes.—Begun for Greece by Vulkan, Hamburg, July, 1913. A German Naval Annual says this ship was launched under the name of *Vasilefs Giorgios*. Used as a Hulk from 1914 to 1918, and still unfinished. Her condition is said to be as bad as that of *Mackensen*.

OLD GERMAN BATTLESHIPS.

Under The Peace Treaty, Germany is allowed to keep in effective commission ten Battleships of the "Deutschland" or "Braunschweig" Type. Excepting accidental losses, none of these ships may be replaced until they are 20 years old; and any Battleship built to replace them must not exceed 10,000 metric tons. Possible that all nine of the "Deutschland" and "Braunschweig" class Battleships may be re-fitted and re-armed.

(DEUTSCHLAND CLASS—4 SHIPS).

(BRAUNSCHWEIG CLASS—5 SHIPS).

DEUTSCHLAND (Nov., 1904), **HANNOVER** (Sept., 1905), **SCHLESWIG-HOLSTEIN** (Dec., 1906), and **SCHLESIEN** (May, 1906). Displacement, 13,200 tons. Complement, (743 ?). Length (*waterline*), 413 feet. Beam, 72¼ feet. *Mean* draught, 25¼ feet. Length *over all*, 430 feet. *Guns (M. '01): 4—11 inch, 40 cal. (A³), 14—6·7 inch, 40 cal., 20—3·4 inch (22 pdr.). ? 2 Machine. Torpedo tubes (17·7 inch): 6 *submerged* (bow, stern, and broadside). Armour (Krupp): 9½" Belt (amidships), 4" Belt (ends), 3"—1½" Deck, 11" Barbettes, 10" Turrets to these, 8" Lower deck (side), 6¾" Battery, 12" Conning tower (fore), 6" Conning tower (aft). Machinery: 3 sets 3 cylinder vertical triple expansion. 3 screws. Boilers: 12 Schulz Thornycroft, except *Deutschland*: 6 cylindrical + 8 Schultz-T. Designed H.P. 17,000 = 18 kts. Coal: *normal* 800 tons; *maximum* 1750 tons. Also 200 tons oil fuel. *Nominal* radius 5500 kts. at 10 kts.

*Note.—Guns and tubes given above those originally mounted. Present armaments and disposal of ships thus :—

Name			Guns	Service, 1919
Deutschland	..	..	Disarmed ; guns removed.	Accommodation Ship.
Hannover	..	..	Disarmed.	Accommodation Ship.
Schleswig-Holstein	..	..	6—4.1 inch only.	
Schlesien	..	..	Disarmed.	Accommodation Ship.

Name.	Builder.	Machinery.	Laid down.	Completed.	Trials : 22 hrs. at ¾.	6 hrs. full p.	Boilers.	Best recent speed.
Deutschland	Germania, Kiel	Krupp	1903	1906	11,377 = 17·1	16,935 = 15·53	Schulz in all.	18·9
Hannover	Wilhelmsh'vn	...	1904	1907	12,153 = 16·9	17,768 = 18·7		19·16
Schleswig-Holstein	Schichau, D'zig	Schichau	1905	1908		19,868 = 19		
Schlesien	Germania, Kiel	Krupp	1905	1908		19,465 = 18·5		19·03

BRAUNSCHWEIG (Dec., 1902), **ELSASS** (May, 1903), **LOTHRINGEN** (May, 1904), **HESSEN** (Sept., 1903), & **PREUSSEN** (Oct., 1903). Displacement, 13,200 tons. Complement, (743 ?). Length (*waterline*), 413⅓ feet. Beam, 72⅖ feet. *Mean* draught, 25¾ feet. Length *over all*, 430 feet. *Guns (M. '01.): 4—11 inch, 40 cal, (A³), 14—6·7 inch, 40 cal., 18—3·4 inch (22 pdr.) ?, 2 Machine. Torpedo tubes (17·7 inch): 5 *submerged* (bow and broadside), 1 *above water* (stern). Armour (Krupp): 8¾" Belt (amidships), 4" Belt (ends), 3" Deck on slopes, 11" Barbettes to these, 11" Turrets (side), 5" Lower deck, 6" Battery, 6¾" Small turrets, 12" Conning tower, 6" Conning tower (aft). Machinery: 3 sets 3 cylinder vertical inverted triple expansion. 3 screws. Boilers: 8 Schulz-Thornycroft + 6 cylindrical. Designed H.P. 16,000 = 18 kts. Coal: *normal* 700 tons; *maximum* 1670 tons. Also 200 tons of oil (in double bottom). *Nominal* radius: 5500 miles at 10 kts.

*Note.—Guns and tubes given, those originally mounted. Present guns and disposal of ships as follows :—

Name				Guns		Service.
Braunschweig	..	..	Disarmed ; guns removed.			Accommodation Ship.
Elsass	..	..		,,	,,	Accommodation Ship.
Lothringen	..	..	..	,,	,,	Sea-going Parent Ship for Motor Boat Minesweepers.*
Hessen	..	..	..	,,	,,	Accommodation Ship.
Preussen	..	..	..	,,	,,	Sea-going Parent Ship for Motor Boat Minesweepers.*

Name.	Builder.	Machinery.	Laid down.	Completed.	Full power trials : 24 hrs.	6 hrs.	Boilers.	Best recent speed.
Braunschweig	Germania, Kiel		1901	1904	11,382 = 16·3	17,312 = 18·6		18·1
Hessen	Germania, Kiel		1902	1905	11,384 = 16·4	16,900 = 18·23	8 Schulz-T. and 6 cyl. in all.	
Preussen	Vulkan.Stettin	By Builders	1902	1905	11,304 = 16·2	18,374 = 18 69		
Elsass	Schichau, D'zig		1901	1904	11,554 = 16·7	16,812 = 18·7		18·6
Lothringen	Schichau, D'zig		1902	1906	11,573 = 16·5	16,950 = 18·54		

* Each has superstructures for carrying 12 Motor Boat Minesweepers.

OBSOLETE GERMAN BATTLESHIPS.

Note.—K. Karl der Grosse was not reconstructed, and has military masts and high upperworks like Wittelsbach class opposite. K. Barbarossa has small cranes amidships and between funnels.

WITTELSBACH (1900), **WETTIN** (1901), **ZÄHRINGEN** (1901), **MECKLENBURG** (1901), **SCHWABEN** (1901). Displacement, 11,800 tons. Complement was 683. Dimensions : 410¾ (w.l.), 416½ (o.a.) × 68¼ × 28 feet (maximum draught). *Guns (M. '99) : 4—9.4 inch, 40 cal., 18—5·9 inch, 40 cal., 12—3·4 inch (15 pdr.), 2 M.G. *Torpedo tubes (17·7 inch) : 6 submerged (bow, stern and broadside). Armour (Krupp) : 9″ Belt (ends), 3″ Deck on slopes, 10″ Barbettes, 10″ Turrets to them, 5½″ Lower deck (redoubt), 5½″ Battery, 6″ Casemates (4 bow), 6″ Small turrets, 10″ Conning tower. Machinery : 3 sets vertical triple expansion. 3 screws. Boilers : 6 Schulz-Thornycroft and 6 cylindrical. Designed H.P. 15,000 = 18 kts. Coal : normal, 653 tons ; maximum, 1800 tons. Oil : 200 tons.

*Guns and tubes given, those originally mounted. Present armament and disposal of ships as follows :—

Name			Guns	Service
Wittelsbach	..	..	} Disarmed.	Parent Ships for Minesweepers, Wilhelmshaven.
Wettin	..	..		
Zahringen	..	..	{ Turrets removed. 7—5·9 inch.* 4—15 pdr.*	} Training Ship, Danzig.
Mecklenburg	..	..	Disarmed.	Accommodation Ship, Kiel.
Schwaben	..	..	{ Turrets removed. 6—5·9 inch.* 4—15 pdr.*	} Sea-going Parent Ship for Motor Boat Minesweepers, Wilhelmshaven.

*Guns on board, but ships are disarmed.

Brandenburg only a Hulk now. Wörth, Hulk, on Sale List.

KAISER FRIEDRICH III (1896), **K. WILHELM DER GROSSE** (1899). **K. KARL DER GROSSE** (1899). Displacement, 10,790 tons, reconstructed (K. Karl der Grosse) 11,130 tons. Complement was 622-661. Dimensions : 384 × 68 × 27 feet (maximum draught). Guns : Nil. Torpedo tubes (17·7 inch) : 5 submerged (bow and broadside), but may be removed. Armour (Krupp) : 12″ Belt (amidships), 4″ Belt (bow), 8″ Bulkheads (aft), 3″ Deck (flat on belt), 10″ Barbettes, 10″ Turrets to these, 6″ on secondary guns, 10″ Conning tower (N.C.). Machinery : 3 sets vertical 3-cylinder triple expansion. 3 screws. Boilers : 12—cylindrical and Schulz. Designed H.P. 13,500 = 18 kts. Coal : normal, 650 tons ; maximum, 1050 tons ; also 200 tons liquid fuel (double bottom). Kaiser Friedrich III, Depot Ship ; other two, Accommodation Ships : Kaiser Wilhelm II, Kaiser Barbarossa, only Hulks now.

ODIN (1894). Accommodation Ship for 5th Mine Sweeping Flotilla. 4100 tons. Complement was 307. Guns : Nil. Torpedo tubes (17·7 inch) : 3 submerged (may be removed). Armour (Nickel) : 8½″ Belt (amidships only). H.P. 5000 = 15 kts. Boilers : 8 Schulz-Thornycroft. Coal : 600 tons, and small quantity of oil fuel. All others of class sold or for sale.

(Accommodation Ship.)

ROON (June, 1903). Displacement, 9500 tons. Complement (was 633). Dimensions : 417⅔ × 66¼ × 25¾ feet (*maximum* draught). Guns : None. Torpedo tubes (17·7 inch) : 4 *submerged* (1 bow, 1 stern, 2 broadside). Armour (Krupp) : 4″ Belt (amidships), 3″ Belt (ends), 2¾″ Deck (slopes), 6″ Turrets, 4″ Turret bases, 4″ Lower deck redoubt, 4″ battery, etc., 6″ C.T. (fore), 3″ C.T. (aft). Machinery : 3 sets vertical triple expansion. 3 screws. Boilers : 16 Dürr. Designed H.P. 19,000 = 21 kts. Coal : *normal*, 750 tons ; *maximum*, 1600 tons ; also 200 tons of oil. Built by Kiel D.Y., 1902-5.

(Stokers' Training Ship.)

PRINZ HEINRICH (March, 1900). Displacement, 8900 tons. Complement (was 567). Dimensions : 409¾ × 64¼ × 25½ feet (*maximum* draught). Guns : None. Torpedo tubes 18 inch) : 1 *submerged* (bow), 2 *submerged* (broadside), 1 *above water* (stern), all probably removed. Armour (Krupp) : 4″ Belt (amidships), 3″ Belt (ends), 2″ Deck, 6″ Turrets, 4″ Turret bases, 4″ Lower deck side, 4″ Battery. Machinery : 3 sets triple expansion 4-cylinder. 3 screws. Boilers : 14 Dürr. Designed H.P. 15,000 = 20·5 kts. Coal : *normal*, 750 tons ; *maximum*, 1500 tons. Also 200 tons liquid fuel.

Note: Fürst Bismarck sold 1919.

(" Hertha " still Cadets' Training Ship ; others Depot Ships.)
(Freya has three funnels—For appearance, v. silhouettes.)

FREYA (1897), **HERTHA** (1897), 5660 tons, **HANSA** (1898), and **VINETA** (1897), 5890 tons. Complement, 465. Dimensions : 358-360¼ × 57-57¾ × 23 feet (*maximum* draught). Guns : *Hansa*, 1—5·9 inch, 4—4·1 inch, 14—3·4 inch. Torpedo tubes (17·7 inch) : 3 *submerged* (1 in bow), *Hansa* only—all others, no guns or tubes. Armour (Krupp) : 4″ Deck, 4″ Turrets and Casemates. Machinery : 3 sets 4-cylinder triple expansion. 3 screws. Designed H.P. 10,000 = 18·5 kts. Coal : *normal*, 900 tons ; *maximum*, 900-920 tons. Are Depot Ships. *Victoria Luise*, Hulk now.

(Gunnery School Ship.)

KAISERIN AUGUSTA (1892). Displacement, 6060 tons. Complement (was 439). Dimensions : 401 × 51 × 25½ feet. Guns : 1—5·9 inch, 4—4·1 inch, 10—3·4 inch (22 and 15 pdr.). Torpedo tubes (13·8 inch) : 1 *submerged* (bow), 2 *above water* (broadside). Armour : 3½″ Deck (amidships), 1½″ at ends. Machinery : 3 sets vertical triple expansion. 3 screws. Boilers : 8 two-ended cylindrical. Designed H.P. *forced* draught 12,000 = 21·5 kts. (much less now). Coal : 810 tons.

GERMAN LIGHT CRUISERS.

Under the Treaty of Versailles, Germany may only keep 6 Light Cruisers in commission.   Excepting accidental losses, none of these six ships may be replaced until they are 20 years old.

Any types of Cruisers or Light Cruisers built by Germany in future must not exceed 6,000 metric tons in displacement.

Not Completed.

Name	*Builder*	*Begun*	*Launched*	*Condition*
FRAUENLOB	Kiel D.Y.	1916	1918	Hull only ; work stopped.
ROSTOCK	Kiel D.Y.	1916	(yes).	Not known.
WIESBADEN*	Kiel D.Y.	1916	(yes).	Not known.
(Name Unknown).	Kiel D.Y.	—	(no).	On slip ; one quarter built.
LEIPZIG	Weser, Bremen.	1916	Jan., 1918.	Hull only.
ERSATZ EMDEN	Weser, Bremen.	1917	No ?	Nearly ready for launching.
ERSATZ KÖLN	Weser, Bremen.	1917	No ?	One stopped. Work was proceeding on other in April, 1919, to keep hands employed.
MAGDEBURG	Howaldt, Kiel.	1916	1918	Part of engines in place. Work stopped.

* No details known of above ships.

*Selected for internment at Scapa Flow, but Light Cruiser *Dresden* took her place. Not certain if *Wiesbaden* is finished or not. Reported that she was torpedoed in Baltic in November, 1918, by a German " Red " Destroyer, but reached Kiel. Whether completing or under repair, all work on her has stopped.

GERMAN LIGHT CRUISERS.

(All are officially rated as "Kleine Geschützte Kreuzer" or "Small Protected Cruisers.")

KÖNIGSBERG CLASS.

Following two under salvage at Scapa Flow.

EMDEN (February, 1916). **NÜRNBERG** (January, 1916).

Following ship now in German Navy.

KÖNIGSBERG (December, 1915).

Displacement, *about* 4,200 tons.   Complement, —.

Length, 450 feet.   Beam, 43½ feet.   Draught, 16 feet.

Photo by courtesy of Dr. J. A. Prendergast.

Guns :
8—5·9 inch, 50 cal. (semi-auto.)
2 or 3—22 pdr. anti-aircraft
Torpedo tubes (19·7 inch) :
2 *above water*
2 *submerged*.

Armour :
″ Belt (amidships) ....
″ Belt (ends) ....
″ Deck (amidships) ....
″ Gun Shields ....
″ Conning Tower (fore)·
″ Conning Tower (aft)...

Ahead :
4—5·9 in.   Broadside : 5—5·9 in.   Astern :
4—5·9 in.

Machinery : "Marine type," but some may have geared turbines.   screws. Boilers: Schulz-Thornycroft. Designed H.P.   = 28·5 kts.   Coal : *normal,*   tons ; *maximum,* 1240 tons (+500 tons oil fuel).

Gunnery Notes.—In Karlsruhe class, the 5·9 inch guns under fore bridges are a deck higher than in *Frankfurt* ; that is, on same level as the forecastle 5·9's.

Name	Builder	Machinery	Laid down	Completed	Trials	Turbines
Emden	Weser, Bremen	Weser, Bremen	1915	Aug.'15		
Nürnberg	Howaldt, Kiel	Howaldt	1915	Nov.'16		
Königsberg	Weser Co., Bremen	Weser Co.	1914	Aug.'16		

General Notes.—Emden begun as *Ersatz Nymphe*, Nurnberg as *Ersatz Thetis*, both under 1915-16 Programme. *Königsberg* begun as *Ersatz Gazelle*, 1914-15 Programme.
Scuttled at Scapa Flow, June 21st, 1919.—Dresden (*Ersatz Amazone.* of 1916-17 Programme), launched by Howaldt. Kiel, November, 1916, and delivered 1918 ; *Koln* (*Ersatz Ariadne*, of 1916-17 Programme), launched by Blohm & Voss, Hamburg, October, 1916, and finished 1917 ; *Karlsruhe* (*Ersatz Niobe*, of 1914-15 Programme), launched at Kiel D.Y., February, 1916, and completed November, 1916. Two Minelaying Cruisers, *Bremse* and *Brummer* (not of *Königsberg* class), also scuttled at Scapa Flow.

Photo, C.N.

FRANKFURT.

Salved at Scapa Flow.
FRANKFURT (March, 1915).

Displacement, 5120 tons.   Complement,
Length, 465 feet.   Beam, 45½ feet.   Draught, 17 feet.
Note to Plans.—Delete 5·9 inch as dotted ; above water tubes
are in these positions, and *not* guns.

Guns :
8—5·9 inch, 50 cal., S.A.
2—22 pdr. anti-aircraft.
Torpedo tubes (19·7 inch) :
2 *above water.*
2 *submerged.*
Can carry 120 mines.

Armour :
6″ Belt ....
4—3″ Ends ....
1½″ Deck ....
" Gun shields ....
" C.T. (fore) ....
" C.T. (aft) ....

Ahead :
4—5·9 in.

Broadside : 5—5·9 in.

Astern :
4—5·9 in.

Machinery.—"Marine type" turbines, but may have geared turbines. Boilers : Schulz-Thornycroft.
Designed H.P.   = 28 kts.   Coal : *normal,*   tons ; *maximum,* 1500 tons (+oil fuel ?).

Name.	Builder.	Machinery.	Laid down.	Com-pleted.	First trials.	Turbines.	Best recent speed.
Frankfurt	Kiel D.Y.		Dec. '13	Aug. '15			

Notes.—Begun under 1913-14 Programme as *Ersatz Hela.*   Note that her second funnel is plain and wholly cased up to top, instead of being half-cased like first and third funnels. The half-casing to second funnel in above view is not correct.

No photo available—see Silhouettes.

**Plans show design with original Russian armament of 8—5·1 inch guns.
Now has raised fore funnel. Only has 2—22 pdr. anti-aircraft guns
mounted now ; armour belt and tubes removed.**

PILLAU (ex-Russian *Muraviev Amurski*, April, 1914).
Displacement, 4350 tons.   Complement, 372.

Length (*p.p.*), 403 feet. Beam, 46 feet. { *Mean* draught, 16 feet. { Length (*o.a.*), 441 feet.
                                            { *Max.*   „   19 feet. {

Guns :
8—5·9 inch, 50 cal., S.A.
2—22 pdr. anti-aircraft
Torpedo tubes (19·7 inch) :
2 *above water.*

Armour :
1½″ Deck (on slopes)......
¾″ Deck (bow)   ....
3″ Deck (over rudder) ...
3″ Conning tower ....

Machinery : Schichau (Melms & Pfenninger) turbines. 3 screws. Designed H.P. 27,400 = 27½ kts.
Boilers : Yarrow (may be altered to Schulz Thornycroft). Coal : *normal* 500 tons ; *maximum* 1000 tons,
and 250 tons oil fuel.

Name	Builder	Machinery	Laid down	Com-pleted	Trials : F. P.	Boilers	Best recent speed
Pillau	Schichau,Danzig	Schichau	Apl., '13	Dec. '15			

General Notes.—Design is based on *Kolberg* class. A sister ship, *Elbing*, sunk in the Battle of Jutland. Both vessels were seized by Germany on outbreak of war with Russia, for whom they were originally laid down.

Differ in build : REGENSBURG has thick funnels.

REGENSBURG (April, 1914), GRAUDENZ (October, 1913).

Normal displacement 4900 tons. Complement 364.

Length (*waterline*) 456 feet. Beam 45 feet. *Mean* draught 16 feet. (*Max.* 17 feet).

Plans as before being re-armed.

Guns :
7—5·9 inch, 50 cal.
2—22 pdr. anti-aircraft
2″ machine
Torpedo tubes (19·7 inch) :
2 *submerged*

Carry 120 mines each.

Armour :
4″ Belt (amidships)
2½″ Belt (ends) ..
2″ Deck (amidships)
4″ Conning tower

Machinery : "Marine Type" Turbine. 4 screws. Boilers : 14 Schulz-Thornycroft. Designed H.P. 26,000 = 27.25 kts. Coal : *normal* 470 tons ; *maximum* 1300 tons. Oil : 220 tons.

Gunnery Notes.—Originally had 2—5·9 inch and 8—4·1 inch, as plans above.

Armour Notes.—Belt is rather deeper than in *Stralsund* and *Strassburg.*

General Notes.—Belong to 1912 Programme. *Regensburg* built and engined by Weser, Bremen ; *Graudenz* built by Kiel D.Y. Both laid down 1912 and completed 1914. Radius of action about 5,500 to 6,000 miles at cruising speed. Most of the notes for *Breslau* class apply to these ships. Two other light cruisers (*Karlsruhe* and *Rostock*) intermediate between this class and *Stralsund* and *Strassburg* have been lost during the war.

STRALSUND (Nov., 1911), STRASSBURG (Aug., 1911).

Normal displacement, 4550 tons ; 5100 tons, *full load.* Complement, 370-373.
Length (*w.l.*), 446¼ feet. Beam, 43·6 feet. *Mean* draught, 16¾ feet.

Plans as before being re-armed. "Stralsund" to be surrendered ? "Strassburg" Leader, Baltic Sweepers ; has only 1 gun.

Guns :
7—5·9 inch, 50 cal.
2—22 pdr. anti-aircraft
2 machine
Torpedo tubes (19·7 in.) :
2 *submerged*
2 *above water.*

Carry 120 mines.

Armour :
3½″ Belt (amidships)
2¼″ Belt (ends)......
2″ Deck (amidships)
4″ Conning tower...

Machinery : Turbine. 4 screws. Boilers : 16 Schulz-Thornycroft. Designed H.P. : *Stralsund* 24,200, 26·75 kts. *Strassburg* 26,000, 27 kts. Coal : *normal* 750 tons ; *maximum* 1200 tons. Oil : 130 tons.

Armour Notes.—Belt is very narrow, and at full load practically submerged.
Engineering Notes.—4 boilers are oil burning.

Name	Builder	Machinery	Laid down	Completed	Trials (mean)		Turbines	Best speed
					6 hours	Best hour		
Stralsund	Weser, Bremen	Weser.	Ap. '10	June '12	27,032 = 26·9	35.515 = 28·27	Bergmann	...
Strassburg	W'l'mshaven Y.	...	Ap. '10	Dec.'12	25,647 = 26·9	35,742 = 28·28	Parsons	...

Belong to the 1910 Programme. *Magdeburg* of this class sunk 1914 in the Baltic. *Breslau* mined and sunk off Imbros, 1918. They are very fast ships, but vibrate greatly over 22 kts. Proved bad sea boats on first trials, and large bilge-keels were fitted to lessen rolling. All were heavily forced on trials. Very lightly built, extensive use being made of steel castings and aluminium. Engine-rooms very cramped. Double-bottom shallow, and only carried up amidships to under side of protective deck. Above protective deck are coal-bunkers, about 12 feet wide.

Both to be surrendered ? Both disarmed.

(Kolberg Class).

KOLBERG (Nov. 1908), & **AUGSBURG** (July, 1909).

Normal displacement, 4350 tons.   Complement, 379.

Length (*waterline*), 426½ feet.   Beam 46 feet.   *Maximum* draught, 17¾ feet.

Guns :
  6—5·9 inch.
  2—22 pdr. anti-aircraft
  2 Machine.
Torpedo tubes (17·7 in.)
  2 *submerged*.

Carry 120 Mines.

Armour (Krupp) :
  2″ Deck (amidships)
  ¾″ Deck (ends) ......
  4″ Conning tower...

Plans as before being re-armed.

Machinery : Turbines : *Kolberg*, Melms & Pfenninger ; *Augsburg*, Parsons.   4 screws.   Boilers : 15 Schulz-Thornycroft.   Designed H.P. 19,600 = 25 kts.   Coal : *normal* 400 tons ; *maximum* 900 tons, and some oil fuel.

Name	Builder	Machinery	Laid down	Completed	Trials	Turbines	Best recent speed
Kolberg	Schichau Kiel Yard.	Schichau	Mar.,'07	Dec. '09	30,400 = 26·3	Melms & P.	
Augsburg		...	Sept.'08	Oct. '10	31,340 = 27	Parsons	

**Appearance probably altered as both Seaplane carriers now.   Are disarmed.
To be surrendered ?**

(Stettin Class.)

STUTTGART (Sept., 1906), **STETTIN** (March, 1907).

Normal Displacement, *Stuttgart* 3470 tons ; *Stettin* 3550 tons.   Complement, 328 (350 war).
Length (*waterline*), 389¼ feet.   Beam, 43⅔ feet.   *Maximum* draught, 17½ feet.

Guns :
  10—4·1 inch, 40 cal.
  (1 anti-aircraft ?)
  2 Machine.
Torpedo tubes (17·7 in.) :
  2 *submerged*.

Carry 108 Mines.

Armour (Krupp) :
  2″ Deck ....
  ¾″ Deck (at ends) ......
  4″ Conning tower

Machinery : *Stuttgart* 2 sets 4 cylinder triple expansion, 2 screws.   *Stettin*, Turbine (Parsons), 4 screws.   Boilers : 10 Schulz-Thornycroft.   Designed H.P. 13,000 *Stuttgart* and 13,400 *Stettin* = 23 kts.   Coal : *normal* 400 tons ; *maximum* 880 tons.

Name	Builder	Machinery	Laid down	Completed	Refit	Trial on sea course of 170 miles.	Boilers	Best speed
Stuttgart (r)	Danzig Yard	Vulcan Co.	1905	1908		13,745 = 23·7	Schulz-	...
Stettin (t)	Vulcan		1905	1908		15,448 = 24*	Thornycroft	...

Maximum was 19,768 = 24·9.   She once touched 21,400 = 25·7.

DANZIG. Has bridges round foremast.

HAMBURG, &c., as above.

DANZIG (September, 1905), **HAMBURG** (July, 1903), **BERLIN** (September, 1903), **LÜBECK** (March, 1904), and **MÜNCHEN** (April, 1904). *Normal* displacement, 3250 tons. Complement, 303. Dimensions : 362.9 × 43.3 × 17½ feet (*maximum* draught). Guns : As noted below. Torpedo tubes (17.7 inch) : 2 *submerged*. Armour (Krupp) : 2″ Deck, ¾″ Deck (at ends), 4″ C.T. Machinery : 2 sets 4-cylinder triple expansion. 2 screws. *Lübeck*, turbine (Parsons), 8 screws on 4 shafts. Boilers : 10 Shulz-Thornycroft. Designed H.P. 10,000 (*Lübeck* 11,200 S.H.P.) = 22 kts. Coal : *normal*, 400 tons ; *maximum*, 860 tons. *Nominal* radius, 5900 at 10 kts. *Danzig* begun 1904, completed 1907 ; others begun 1902-3, completed 1904-5.

Notes.

Reported that DANZIG, MÜNCHEN and LÜBECK are named for surrender in Peace Treaty.

Name	Armament	Mines	Present Service	Station
Danzig ..	10—4.1 inch, 2 M.G.	108	Paid off.	Danzig.
Hamburg ..	,, ,,	,,	,,	Wilhelmshaven
Berlin ..	,, ,,	,,	Headquarters S.N.O. Baltic.	Kiel.
München ..	,, ,,	,,	Paid off.	Kiel.
Lübeck ..	2—5.9 inch, 6—4.1 inch, 2 M.G.	,,	,,	Kiel.

ARKONA (April, 1902). Displacement, 2700 tons (sheathed). Complement, 281. Dimensions : 342·4 × 40·3 × 17¼ feet (*maximum* draught). Guns : 10—4·1 inch, 2 M.G. Torpedo tubes (17·7 inch) : 2 *submerged*. Can carry 400 mines. Armour (Krupp) : 2″ Deck, 4″ C.T. Machinery : 2 sets 4-cylinder triple expansion. 2 screws. Designed H.P. 8000 = 21·5 kts. Coal : *normal*, 450 tons ; *maximum*, 710 tons. Boilers : 9 Schulz-Thornycroft.

Condition of all Ships named on this page.

Arkona :—Guns on board. Sea-going Parent Ship for Motor Boat Minesweepers (*UZ* boats), North Sea.

Nymphe :—Disarmed. Depot Ship.

Thetis :—Disarmed.

Amazone :—Disarmed.

Medusa :—Guns on board. Sea-going Parent Ship for North Sea Motor Boat Minesweepers (*UZ* boats).

Niobe :—Disarmed and paid off.

(*Gazelle :*—Only Mine Hulk. Is deleted.)

(*Gefion :*—Hulk. Is deleted.)

MEDUSA.   *Photo, Abrahams, Devonport.*

NYMPHE (1899), **THETIS** (1900), **AMAZONE** (1900), & **MEDUSA** (1900). *Normal* displacement, 2650 tons. (Sheathed and Muntz metalled.) Complement, 275. Dimensions : 324·4 × 38·7 × 17¼ feet (*maximum* draught). Guns : 6—4·1 inch, 2 M.G. Torpedo tubes (17·7 inch) : 2 *submerged*. Armour (Krupp) : 2″ Deck (amidships), ¾″ Deck (at ends), 3½″ Glacis to engine room hatches, 3″ C.T. Cofferdam and cellulose amidships. Machinery : 2 sets 4-cylinder triple expansion. 2 screws. Boilers : 9 Schulz-Thornycroft. Designed H.P. 8000 = 21 kts. Coal : *normal*, 380 tons ; *maximum*, 580 tons.

As *Medusa.*

NIOBE (1899). *Normal* displacement, 2600 tons. (Sheathed and Muntz metalled.) Complement, 268. Dimensions : 342·5 × 38·7 × 17¼ feet (*maximum* draught). Guns : 10—4·1 inch, 40 cal., 2 M.G. Torpedo tubes (17·7 inch) : 2 *submerged*. Armour (Krupp) : 2″ Deck (amidships), ¾″ Deck (at ends), 3½″ Glacis to hatches, &c., 3″ C.T., Cofferdam and cellulose amidships. Machinery : 2 sets 4-cylinder triple expansion. 2 screws. Boilers : 5 Thornycroft in *Niobe*. Designed H.P. 8000 = 21·5 kts. Coal : *normal*, 300 tons ; *maximum*, 600 tons.

90 (a) Modern
88 (b) Older } **Destroyers = 178.**

(a) *About* 45 of these unfinished.   (b) *About* 12—15 of these quite useless.

Totals.	Class.	Begun.	Completed.	Displacement.	*Nominal* H.P.	*Nominal* Speed.	T. Tubes.	Coal/*Oil*.†	Complement.
				tons		kts.		tons	
35	G 148—H 190	1917	..	..	..	..	..	..	..
10	S 115—B 124	1916	1919 ?	1400	..	35—38	4	..	..
13	V 125—H 147	1916	1918 }	750—800	..	34—35	4 or 6	..	..
9	S 53—G 95	1915	1916 }						
1	V 100	1915	1916	1300	..	34	6	..	..
2	B 97, 98 }								
4	V 43—S 51	1914	1915	700—750	23,000*t*	34	6	*300*	..
1	G 102	1913	1915	1250	24,000*t*	32	6	*345*	9½
2	V 26, V 28	1913	1915	650	20,000*t*	32·5	6	*290*	..
4	S 18—24	1912	1914	570	15,000*t*	32·5	4	*135/55*	..
9	{ G 11—7 V 6—1 }	1911	1912	564	15,000*t*	32·5	4	*140/60*	73
8	{ T 197—192 T 191—186 }	1910	1911	648—656	16,000*t*	32·5	4*	*165/55*	83—93
11	{ T 185—180 T 179—176 T 175—174 }	1909	1910	636—654	16,000*t*	31·5—32.5	4*	*170/45*	83
7	{ T 173—169 T 168—165 T 164—163 }	1908	1909	613—636	14,000*t*	30—32	3*	*160/40*	83
11	T 161—151	1907	1908	554	10,250	30	3*	160	83
11	T 149—139	1906	1907	530	10,000	30	3*	190	72
1	T 137	1905	1907	572	10,800*t*	32	3*	170	80
6	T 136—132	1905	1907	487	6500	27	3*	135	60
10	{ T 131—125 T 122—120 T 114	1904 1903 1902	1906 1905 1904	485 470 420	6500 6500 6200	27 27 26 }	3*	116	60—56
6	T 113—108	1901	1903	400	5600	27 }			
6	T 107—102	1900	1902	400	5400	26 }	3*	92-116	56
11	T 101—91	1899	1900	400	5400	26 }			

*Tubes removed from nearly all these boats.
†An additional deck load of coal can be carried as follows :—+ 10 tons up to T 114, + 15 tons from T 120 up to T 149, *about* 20 tons up to V 28, *about* 25 tons in later boats.

Notes.

Under the Peace Treaty, Germany may not keep more than 12 Destroyers in commission, and, excepting accidental losses, no boat may be replaced until 15 years old. Any future Destroyers built by Germany must not exceed 800 metric tons in displacement.

Reported that Germany has still to surrender 42 modern Destroyers. Not yet known which boats Germany will retain and which she will hand over.

With the exception of boats engaged in Minesweeping, Germany has only the "Iron Flotilla" in effective condition now. The "Iron Flotilla" consists of H 147, H 146, S 139, S 135, S 134, S 133, V 130, S 116, S 113, B 97.

Majority of boats with "T" index letter have had armament removed and are fitted for Minesweeping.

General Notes to Table.

B boats built by Blohm & Voss (Hamburg), G boats at Krupp's Germania Yard, H boats by Howaldt (Kiel), S boats by Schichau, V boats by Vulkan (Stettin). All are officially rated as "*Grosse Torpedoboote*," or "Big Torpedo Boats," and *not* as Destroyers ("*Torpedoboote-Zerstorer*"). Unless otherwise noted, all boats have Schulz-Thornycroft (or "Marine Type") boilers. The details tabulated are generally simplified to the average design of each group.

GERMAN DESTROYERS (*Grosse Torpedoboote*).

1917-19 (majority unfinished).

Not finished,

2 *Krupp-Germania* : **G 148, G 149.**
6 *Howaldt* : **H 166—H ;69, H 188—H 190.**
15 *Schichau* : **S 152--S 157, S 179—S 187.**
12 *Vulkan* : **V 158—V 165, V 140—V 144.**

Launched 1918-19, but all work now stopped.   No details available, but said to be about 750 to 800 tons.
Believed that *G150* and *151* were never begun, and boats numbered *170* to *178* were never contracted for.

1917-19 (majority unfinished).

Photo wanted.

3 *Blohm & Voss* : **B 122—B 124.**
1 *Krupp-Germania* : **G 119.**
3 *Schichau* : **S 113—S 115.**
3 *Vulkan* : **V 116—118.**

Launched 1917-18, but only a few finished.   *G 120, G 121* abandoned.   *About* 1400 tons.   Armed with 4—5.9 inch and
    4—23.6 inch tubes.   Speed : 35-38 kts.   No other details known.

1917-18.

Photo wanted.

2 *Howaldt* : **H 146, H 147.**

Photo wanted.

6 *Schichau* : **S 132—S 135, S 137, S 139.**

Photo wanted.

5 *Vulkan* : **V 125—V 128, V 130.**

Launched 1917-18.   *About* 750-800 tons.   Dimensions : *about* 270 × 27 × 10½ feet.   Armament : 3—4.1 inch, 2 M.G.,
    4 or 6 tubes (size unknown).   Speed : *about* 35 kts.
Notes.—All above *H, S* and *V* boats believed to be same in build as boats numbered *S 51* to *G 95.*
Scuttled at Scapa Flow.—*H 145, S 131, S 132* (salved), *S 136, S 137* (salved), *S 138, V 125—127* (all salved).
War Losses.—None.

1915-16.

From the " Illustrirte Zeitung."

4 *Schichau* : **S53,* S54,⊕ S60,* S63** ⎱ Launched 1915-16.
4 *Vulkan* : **V71, V79, V80,* V81*** ⎰

*Salved at Scapa Flow.

(Raised fore funnel now).

1 *Krupp-Germania* : **G 95** (1916).

Photo, Newspaper Illustrations Co.

V84-67. S66-58. S57-49.

G 96-86.

Displacement *about* 750 tons. **Approximate** dimensions : 270 to 272 × 27 × feet. S.H.P. 23,000. Designed speed : 34 kts. Armament : 3—4·1 inch 2 machine, may also have a small automatic (or semi-auto.) anti-aircraft gun. Torpedo tubes : 6—19·7 inch, in 2 single and 2 twin deck mountings. Complement, 96 to 100. Oil only 330 tons.

Note to boats in preceding column :—

War Losses.—*S 57, S 58, S 59, S 61, S 62, S 64, S 66, V 67, V 68, V 72, V 74, V 75, V 76, V 77, V 84, G 85, G 87, G 88, G 90, G 93, G 94, G 96.*

Scuttled at Scapa Flow (not salved).—*S 55, S 56, S 65, V 70, V 78, V 82, V 83, G 86, G 89, G 91, G 92.*

1915.

No Photo available.

Appearance as B 98 below, but derrick is before *second* funnel with boom slung *forward*. Very big ventilator between 2nd and 3rd funnels. Searchlight on aft bridge is not raised on tower.

Under salvage at Scapa Flow.

1 *Vulkan* : **V 100** (probably built 1915-16). Displacement : *About* 1300 tons. Dimensions : *about* 328 × 32 × 10 feet (*mean* draught). Designed speed : 34 kts. A.E.G.-Curtis or " Marine type " turbines. Armament : 4—4.1 inch, 2 M.G. May also have an automatic (or semi-auto.) AA. gun. May carry some mines. Torpedo tubes : 6—19.7 inch. Complement, *about* 140-160. Oil fuel only. *V 99* lost during War.

1915.

2 *Blohm & Voss* : **B 98** and **B 97.** Launched, 1915.

Displacement about 1300 tons. Approximate dimensions 325×32×10 feet (*mean* draught). Designed speed : 34 kts. Turbine engines, Armament : 4—4·1 inch, 2 machine—may also have a small automatic or semi-auto. anti-aircraft gun and carry mines. Torpedo tubes : 6—19·7 inch. Complement, about 140-160. Oil fuel only.

Note.—B 98 arrived at Scapa Flow with German Fleet mails just after German Fleet (and B 108—112) had been scuttled. She was seized at once. Probably boats begun in 1914 for Chinese Navy.

2 L 2

1915.

As illustration of *S* & *V* types on preceding page.

1 *Schichau* : **S 51***
3 *Vulkan* : **V 43,*** **V 44,*** **V 46*** } Launched 1915.

About 700-750 tons. Dimensions : 262-270 × 26-27 × 10-11 feet. Guns : 3—3·4 inch (22 pdr.), 2 M.G. Torpedo tubes : 6—19·7 inch (2 twin, 2 single mountings). Designed S.H.P. *about* 23,000 = 34 kts. Oil fuel only : *about* 300 tons. *V 46* last of pre-war (1914-15) Programme boats.

*Salved at Scapa Flow. *S 50, S 52, V 45* not salved.

V 47, V 48 (special type), both War Losses.

G 37 War Loss. *G 38, G 39, G 40,* not salved at Scapa Flow. *G 37—40* class therefore extinct.

1914 *(ex-Argentine)*.

1 ex-*Argentine* boat : **G 102** (Krupp-Germania, 1914). Displacement : *normal*, 1250 tons ; *full load*, 1460 tons. Dimensions : 312¾ × 30 × 8⅝ feet (*mean* draught). *Max.* draught, 9½ feet. Armament : 4—4·1 inch guns, 2 M.G. ; may also have a small automatic (or semi-auto.) AA. gun. Torpedo tubes : 6—19·7 inch. Machinery : Turbines and 5 double-ended boilers. Designed H.P. 24,000 = 32 kts. Fuel : (oil only) 345 tons.

Note.—*G 102* salved at Scapa Flow. *G 101, G 103, G 104,* not salved. These were originally the destroyers *San Luis, Santa Fé, Santiago,* and *Tucuman,* laid down for the Argentine in 1913-14 and appropriated for German Navy after outbreak of war.

1913—14.

S 31—36 class has been totally destroyed, viz.:—*S 31, 33, 35,* War Losses ; *S 32, 36,* scuttled at Scapa Flow and **not** salved.

Photo wanted.

2 *Vulkan* : **V 26, V 28.** Launched 1914. *About* 650 tons. Armament : 3—3·4 inch (22 pdr.), 2 M.G. Torpedo tubes : 6—19·7 inch. S.H.P. 20,000 = 32·5 kts. Oil only : *about* 290 tons. Complement, 90.

War Losses.—*V 25, V 27, V 29. V 30* sunk November 20th, 1918.

1912—13.

Illustration on next page

4 *Schichau* : **S 18, S 19, S 23, S 24.** Launched 1913. *About* 570 tons. Dimensions : 234⅜ × 24½ × 10 feet Armament : 2—4·1 inch, 1—3·4 inch (22 pdr.). Torpedo tubes : 4—19·7 inch. Designed S.H.P. 15,000 = 32·5 kts. Melms-Pfenninger turbines. Fuel : 135 tons coal + 55 tons oil. Complement, 75.

War Losses.—*S 13, S 14, S 15, S 16, S 17, S 20, S 21, S 22.*

GERMAN DESTROYERS.

1911–1912 (and 2 **1913** Replace Boats).

G 7, 9, 8, 10.

Photo by courtesy of S. Anderson, Esq.

Note.– All have raised fore funnels now.

G 9.

4 *Krupp-Germania* : **G 7, G 8, G 10, G 11** (launched 1911-12).

5 *Vulkan* : **V 1—V 3** (1911), **V 5, V 6** (1913).

Displacement 564 to 570 tons *normal* ; 700 tons *full load ?* Dimensions : $233 \times 25 \times 9\frac{5}{8}$ feet (*mean* draught). Armament : 2 –3·4 inch (22 pdr.) 30 cal.,2 machine. Torpedo tubes : 4 –19·7 inch. Machinery : turbines, Parsons in Germania boats, A.E.G.-Curtis in Vulkan boats. Designed H.P., 15,000=32·5 kts. *S 23* made 37 kts. on trials, other boats all exceeded designed speeds. Fuel : 140 tons coal, 60 tons oil. 4 Schulz-Thornycroft boilers (1 oil burning). Complement, 73.

Appearance Notes.—Raking stem. Rise of turtle-back strongly marked. Gun on forecastle, large ventilator between bow tubes. W/T. cabin immediately abaft fore-funnel. Mainmast well aft of 2nd funnel.

Notes.—*V 5* and *V 6* built to replace original *V 5* and *V 6* sold to Greece, and now Greek *Keravnos* and *Neagenea*. *V 4*, *G 9*, *G 12*, lost during war. *V 2*, *V 3*, *V 5*, non-effective.

From the " Illustrirte Zeitung."

S—
   S 21.

S 22.
S 20.

S 19.

For description of above T.B.D. see previous page.

1910.

V Boats (V 186). Ventilator between bow tubes *low.*

V186-191
G192-197.
650 TONS.

Notes.

Nearly all the Destroyers listed on this and succeeding pages have had their tubes removed and fitted for minesweeping.

About a dozen of them have been mined or otherwise injured during the War and not repaired; they are entirely non-effective for fighting purposes. Boilers and engines of many are in a very poor condition, and the *maximum* speeds given must be taken with reserve.

All these boats were built with the usual *G*, *S* and *V* builders' index letters, but were given letter *T* to avoid duplication of numbers, with the later boats numbered from *V 1* up to *H 190*, described on preceding pages. In description of *T* boats, *G* refers to Krupp-Germania boats, *S* to Schichau boats, and *V* to Vulkan boats.

Note:— All have raised fore funnel now.

G Boats (G 196). Ventilator between bow tubes *high.*
5 *Krupp Germania,* **T 192, T 193, T 195—T 197.** } launched 1910-11.
3 *Vulkan,* **T 190, T 189** and **T 186.**

Displacements: *G* boats 648 tons, *V* boats 656 tons *normal* (750 tons *full load* ?). Dimensions: 213 × 26 × 10½ feet. Armament: 2—3·4 inch (22 pdr.) 30 cal., 2 machine guns. Torpedo tubes: 4—19·7 inch. Machinery: Parsons turbines in *G* boats, A. E. G.—Curtis in *V* boats. Designed H.P. 16.000 = 32·5 kts. Fuel: 160-170 tons coal, 55 tons oil. 4 Schulz-Thornycroft boilers (1 oil burning). Complement **83** (93 War Complement).

Appearance Notes.—Break between forecastle and bridges small, the space for working bow (beam) tubes being extremely cramped. Heights of bow ventilators vary, see note to illustrations above. Gun on forecastle, W/T. cabin immediately abaft forefunnel. Mainmast well aft of funnels in *G* boats, but not so far in *V* boats.

War Losses: V 187, V 188, V 191, G 194. At present *T 190* and *T 196* are quite useless.

GERMAN DESTROYERS (*Grosse Torpedoboote*).

1909-10.

G174-175
S176-179
V180-185
640-670 TONS

Photo wanted of *T 174, 175* and *T 176—179.*

Now have tall foremasts.

6 *Vulkan,* **T 185—180**
3 *Schichau,* **T 179, T 178,** * **T 176** ⎫ launched 1909-10.
2 *Krupp-Germania,* **G 175** and **G 174** ⎭

Displacements: *V* boats 637 tons, *S* boats 636 tons, *G* boats 654 tons *normal* (760 tons *full load?*). Dimensions *about* 243 × 26 × 10 feet. Armament: 2—3·4 inch (22 pdr.) 30 cal., 4 or 2 machine guns. Torpedo tubes: 4—19·7 inch. Machinery: A. E. G-Curtis turbines in *V* boats, Schichau (Melms and Pfenninger) in *S* boats, Parsons in *G* boats. Designed H.P. 16,000 = 31·5 to 32·5 kts. Fuel: *S* and *V* boats, 150 tons coal and 40 tons oil ; *G* boats, 190 tons coal and 50 tons oil. Complement 83.

Appearance Notes.—Break between forecastle and bridges very small. In *G* and *S* boats forecastle is *short,* with big, tall ventilator just abaft. In *V* boats forecastle is *long,* and *small* ventilator (or *none?*) abaft of same. *G* and *S* boats *very big and tall* funnels, standard compass is *on* after bridge, and derrick *abaft* of mast. Note that beam torpedo tubes are *not* between forecastle and bridges but *abaft* of bridges and forefunnel. In this type, ventilators between funnels are near to second funnel. Gun mounted on forecastle. *G* boats have big ventilator close to and abeam of mainmast on *port* side only. Boat in davits on port beam and abeam of after funnel may also be a distinguishing feature.
* *S 178* sunk by *Yorck* in 1913. She was salved. *S 177* War Loss. *T 174, T 185,* both useless.

1908-9.

Fore funnels of all now raised.

3 *Krupp Germania,* **T 169, T 170, T 173.**
4 *Schichau,* **T 168—165.**
2 *Vulkan,* **T 164, T 163.**

V162-164
S165-168
G169-173
615-640 TONS

All launched 1908—9. Displacements: *G* boats, 636 tons, *S* boats 615 tons, *V* boats 613 tons *normal* (750 tons *full load?*) Dimensions: *about* 243 × 26 × 10 feet. Armament: 2—3·4 inch (22 pdr.) 30 cal., 4 or 2 machine guns. Torpedo tubes, 3—17·7 inch. Machinery: Turbines: Parsons in *G* boats (*G 173* Zoelly turbines), Schichau (Melms & Pfenninger) in *S* boats and A. E. G.-Curtis in *V* boats. Designed H.P. 14,000 = 30 to 32 kts. Fuel: 160 tons coal, 40 tons oil. Complement 83.

Appearance Notes.— *G 169—173* almost same as *G 192—197* Class. *V* and *S* boats have slightly longer forecastles, higher funnels and derrick *abaft* mast. Ventilators differently arranged (see Silhouettes).
G 171 lost by collision in 1912. *V 162, T 172,* War Losses. *T 168- 170,* quite useless. Original *S 165—168* sold to Turkey.

1907-08.

554 TONS

T 156—T 161 as above photo, and plan.

No Photo available.

Two tubes between funnels, with ventilator between same. Ventilator in space between 2nd funnel and mainmast, closer to funnel than to mainmast.

T 151—T 155.

11 *Vulkan,* **T 161—151,** launched 1907-8. Displacement: 554 tons. *normal* (670 tons *full load?*) Dimensions: 236½ × 25¾ × 10 feet (*mean* draught). Guns: 2—3·4 inch (15 pdr.), 35 cal., 2 machine. Torpedo tubes: 3—17·7 inch. Machinery: *T 161* has A.E.G.-Curtis turbines, the remainder reciprocating engines. Designed H.P. 10,250 = 30 kts. Coal: 160 tons ; *T 161,* 170 tons. Complement, 83.

Appearance Notes.—Very big funnels ; short and high forecastle, with gun mounted on same. Derrick abaft mainmast. Standard compass not on after bridge, but just before it.

War Losses.— *V 150.*

535

GERMAN DESTROYERS (*Grosse Torpedoboote*).

1906.

T 138.   T 146.   T 147.   T 141.   T 144.

S138-149
530 TONS

Note : Fore bridges and chart house, now raised.

War Loss : T 138.

T 144.   (Now has gun on fo'xle).

11 *Schichau :* **T 149—139,** launched 1906-7. Displacement: 530 tons. Dimensions: $231 \times 25\frac{5}{8} \times 8\frac{5}{8}$ feet (*mean draught.*) Armament: 1—3·4 inch (15 pdr.), 35 cal., 3—4 pdr., 55 cal., 2 machine. Torpedo tubes: 3—17·7 inch. Machinery, reciprocating. Designed H.P. 10,000 = 30 kts. Coal: 190 tons. Complement, 80.

Appearance Notes.—Break between forecastle and bridges fairly long. Bridges run well aft of forefunnel. Funnels large and tall. Mainmast well aft of second funnel with single large ventilator centrally in space between second funnel and mainmast. 4 pdr. gun between mainmast and this ventilator. Compass on raised platform immediately abaft mainmast.

1905-6.

G137
570 TONS

1 *Krupp-Germania* special boat : **T 137** (launched 1907). Displacement: 565 tons. Dimensions: $234\frac{5}{8} \times 25 \times 9\frac{5}{8}$ feet. Armament: 1—3·4 inch (15 pdr.), 35 cal., 3—4 pdr., 55 cal., 2 machine. Torpedo tubes: 3—17·7 inch. Machinery: Parsons turbine. Designed H.P. 10,000 = 32 kts., made 33·9 on trials. Coal: 170 tons. Complement, 80.

Appearance Notes.—Raised forecastle short. Raised steam-pipe to fore funnel. Ventilators between funnels close to fore funnel and mast well aft of second funnel—compare these details with boats below. Distinctive features are the guns on raised platforms, between second funnel and aft as shown in above photo. Steam-pipe to fore funnel *raised*, as boats below.

G132-136
490 TONS

6 *Krupp-Germania :* **T 136—132** (launched 1905-06).

Displacement: 487 tons. Dimensions: $207 \times 23 \times 7\frac{1}{2}$ feet. Armament: 4—4 pdr., 55 cal., 2 machine. But *T 135* (illustrated above) has special armament of 1—3·4 inch (15 pdr.), 35 cal., 2—4 pdr., 55 cal., 2 machine. Torpedo tubes: 3—17·7 inch. Machinery, reciprocating. Designed H.P. 6500 = 27 kts. Coal: 135 tons. Complement, 68.

Appearance Notes.—Raised forecastle very short, no gun mounted on same. Space between forecastle and bridges long. Steam-pipe raised above forefunnel. Funnels spaced wide apart. Mainmast close to second funnel, with derrick on after side. *Two* guns abaft mainmast.

536

OLD GERMAN DESTROYERS (*Grosse Torpedoboote*).

1904-2.

T 130. Note rudder under forefoot, which is fitted to all German Destroyers.

T 121 OFF THE MOUTH OF THE EMS.

1917 War Photo.

10 *Schichau* : { **T 131, T 130,** * **T 128 —125** (launched 1904-5). 485 tons. }
{ **T 122—120** (launched 1904). 470 tons. } *Plans as given in next column with 1901-1898 boats.*
{ **T 114** * (launched 1902). 420 tons. }

Armament: 3—4 pdr., 40 cal., 2 machine, 3—17·7 inch tubes. Designed H.P. 6500=27 kts. (T 114, 6200=26 kts.) Coal : 116 tons. Complement, 60.

Appearance Notes.—Low in water. Long forecastle without any gun, long space between forecastle and bridges. Tall funnels, with raised steam pipe to fore funnel.

* T 129, T 124, T 123, 119, 118, 117, 116 and 115 have been sunk. T 125 useless.

1901-1898.

G108-113
S114-119
S120-131
420-475 TONS

6 *Krupp-Germania* : **T 113—108** (1901-2). 400 tons. Armament: 3—4 pdr., 2 machine. 3—17·7 inch tubes. H.P. 6000 = 26 kts. Coal : about 110 tons. Complement, 56.

Appearance Notes.—Much the same as *T 131—114* class, but shorter forecastle, no raised steam pipe to forefunnel, mainmast rather more aft.

No Photo available.

Plan as given above for *T 113—108* boats, but only *one* tube midway between funnels, the third tube being *abaft mainmast.*

6 *Schichau* : **T 107—102** (1900-01). As *T 113-108* above, but coal 95 tons and H.P. 5400 = 26 kts. *T 107* useless.

Appearance Notes.—Long fo'xle, funnels and mainmast set well towards stern. Big after funnel.

No Photo available.

See Silhouettes : Also Appearance Notes below.

9 *Schichau* : **T 100, T 98—91** (1899—1900). 400 tons. Armament: 3—4 pdr., 2 M.G. 3—17·7 inch tubes (probably removed from majority). H.P. 5400 = 26 kts. Coal : 95 tons.

2 *Schichau* : **T 101, T 99.** As above boats, but tubes removed and perhaps guns. Both were Submarine Tenders before war.

Appearance Notes.—Much as *T 131—114* boats on this page, but have *large and tall* funnels. Single and fairly large ventilator midway between funnels ; a similar ventilator before and at foot of mainmast. *High sterns.*

* T 91 bears name **Sleipner**.

GERMAN TORPEDO BOATS (*Torpedoboote*).

74* Modern }
60† Old } **Torpedo Boats = 124§**

*11 of these interned.   †Majority are useless.

§Peace Treaty limits Germany to 12 Torpedo Boats. Not to be replaced unless 15 years old or lost by accident.
New boats not to be over 200 tons.

Totals.	Name or Number.	Date.	Displacement.	I.H.P.	Max. Speed.	*Torpedo Tubes.	Coal.	Complement.
			tons.		kts.		tons.	
3	V 105—108	1914-15	320	5300t	32	4	..	..
1	D 10	1897-99	355	5500	28	2	80	60
1	D 9	1893-94	380	4040	24½		105	59
2	D 8, D 7	1890-92	350	4000	23	3	75	49
2	D 6, D 5	1888-90	320	3600	23		90	49
2	D 4, D 3	1887-89	300	2500	21		65	49
30	A 59—95	1916-17	200	..	24	1	35	..
27	A 26—55	1915-16		..	15	2	29	..
14	A 1—25	1915	80	..				
2	T 88 & 89	1898	160	1800	25	2	36	24
6	T 87—82							
7	T 81—74	1889—	180—150	1500	25—22	3	30	24—16
5	T 73—69	1897						
6	T 63—55							
2	T 53, T 49	1889—	150	1500	25—22	3	30	16
2	T 45, T 42	1897		1350				
22	T 40—T 3	1885-7	85	1000	20	3	30	16

***Note.**—Many have been converted into Mine Sweepers and have no tubes now.

1914 Appropriated Boats.

No Photo available : for appearance as originally designed, r. Silhouettes.

3 *ex-Dutch* boats : **V 108, V 106, V 105** (Vulkan, 1913-14). 320 tons. Dimensions : 201 × 20½ × 6 feet (**mean** draught).
    Armed with 2—13 pdr. guns and 4—17·7 inch tubes. Designed H.P. 5,300 = 27 kts. Turbines.
Note.—The above were originally the Dutch *Z 1—Z 4*, and were appropriated for German Navy after the outbreak of war.
War Loss.—*V 107.*

"Divisional Boats."

1 *Thornycroft* : **D 10** (1895). 355 tons. Armament : 5—4 pdr., 2—17·7 inch tubes. Speed (originally) 28 kts. Boilers : Yarrow.

D 7, with guns and tubes removed, used for Subsidiary Service.   *Photo, Seward, Weymouth.*

7 *Schichau*. **D 9** (1894), **D 8, D 7** (1891), **D 6, D 5** (1888-89), **D 4, D 3** (1887). For details, see Destroyer Tables on a preceding page. Armament : 3—4 pdrs., 3—17·7 inch tubes, one *submerged* in bow. Tubes probably removed from all now. Reconstructed and given two funnels 1907-09.
Note.—D 3 had tubes removed and was used for Fisheries Protection before war, being armed with 4—4 pdr. guns. D 5 also had tubes removed and was Tender to Submarine Depot Ships. D 1 and D 2 still exist, but are quite useless.

538

GERMAN FIRST-CLASS TORPEDO BOATS.

1915-17

A 26—36 (later boats similar, but longer fo'xle).

From the " Illustrirte Zeitung."

30 boats, by various yards : **A 59, A 61—A 66, A 68—A 70, A 74—A 76, A 78, A 80—A 95.** Built about 1916-17.

27* boats, by various yards : **A 26—A 31,* A 33—A 36, A 37—A 49,* A 52 - A 55.** Built about 1915-16.

*A 30, A 40, A 42, A 43, A 47, interned in Holland on German evacuation of Belgium. Present disposal not known.
If deducted, total is 22 boats.

General Notes.—Displace *about* 200-250 tons. Dimensions : *about* 170 × 16¾ × 5-7 feet. Guns : 2—3.4 inch (22 pdr.),
1 M.G. Torpedo tubes (17.7 inch) : 1 (removed from sweeping boats). Speed : 24 kts. Fuel : Oil only. Complement, 35.

War Losses.—A 32, A 50, A 56, A 57, A 58, A 60, A 71, A 72, A 73, A 77, A 79.   A 57 and A 67 do not seem to exist now,
but are not reported as War Losses.

1915

A 1—25 TYPE.

Photo, L. N. A.

14* boats, by various yards (several sent in sections to Antwerp and assembled there) : **A 1, A 5,* A 8,* A 9,* A 11,*
A 16,* A 17, A 18, A 20,* A 21- 25.** Built about 1915.

*Interned in Holland after German evacuation of Belgium.   Present disposal not known.   If deducted, total is 12 boats.

About 80 tons. Dimensions : 140 × 19½ × 8½ feet. Guns : 1—4 pdr., 1 M.G. Torpedo tubes (17.7 inch) : 1 or 2
(removed from sweepers). Speed : 15 kts. Coal : *about* 30 tons. Complement, 29.

War Losses.—A 2, A 3, A 6, A 7, A 10, A 13, A 15, A 19.   A 4, A 12, A 14, abandoned in Flanders and now units of
Belgian Navy.

OLD GERMAN TORPEDO BOATS (*Kleine Torpedoboote*).

Above-water tubes probably removed. Now used as Minesweepers, Tenders, &c.

2 *Krupp-Germania,* **T 89** and **T 88** (1897-8). 1—4 pdr., 2—17·7 inch tubes.

6 *Schichau:* **T 87—T 82** (1898). 1—4 pdr., 3—17·7 inch tubes (1 bow *submerged*, 2 deck).

5 *Schichau:* **T 81—74** (1893-4). Armed as *T 87—T 82* above.
* Less *T 78* War Loss.

T 42 (1887). Appearance after being re-boilered and re-engined.

16 *Schichau:* **T 73—69, T 63—59, T 55, T 53, T 49, T 45, T 42** (1889-1897). 1—4 pdr, 3—13·8 inch tubes (1 bow *submerged*, 2 deck).

War Losses: T 43, 46, 47, 50, 51, 52, 54, 56, 58, 58, 64, 65, 66, 68.

2nd & 3rd CLASS.

Like *T 81—74* but shorter and with big funnel.

22 *old boats :* **T 40—33, T 31—27, T 25, T 24, T 21—20, T 16, T 15—13, T 11, T 3** (1885-1889). 85 tons. Speed: 17 kts. (probably much less now). Armament: 1—4 pdr., 3 torpedo tubes (2 deck and 1 *submerged* bow). Guns and tubes may have been removed from some. Complement, 16.

Appearance: Similar to *T 81—74* opposite, but much shorter in length.

Notes.—*T 36, 35, 31—27* and *25* converted to Mine sweepers, tubes being removed ; some (or all) of the other boats may also have been altered for this service. *T 25 War Loss.*

Motor Launches.

No photo available.

49 boats: **F**...—**F**... (built 1917-18). 23 tons. About 55 feet long.

No photo available.

Total Number uncertain : **UZ 1—50** (built 1916-17). About 60 tons. Length, 85 feet. Speed, 15 kts.

Note.—UZ = Unterseeboote-Zerstorer (Submarine Destroyer). All *UZ* and *F* boats fitted as Anti-Submarine craft and Minesweepers.

"Controlled Torpedoes."

These craft were used off the Belgian Coast, and are simply a modern development of the old Brennan and Lay torpedoes. The "controlled torpedo" is a small boat with twin petrol motors, partly covered in. The crew leave after it has been started. About 30-50 miles of single-core insulated electric cable connect the boat's steering and control gears with the shore directing station. A seaplane, escorted by a strong escort of fighting 'planes, "spots" for the "controlled torpedo," sending instructions by W/T. on course, speed, etc., to the shore controlling station. About 300-500 lbs. of high-explosive are contained in the bows of the "torpedo," being exploded on impact with the target.

(Submarines).

Under the Peace Treaty, Germany is absolutely prohibited from building (or maintaining in service) any Submarines, whether of Naval or Mercantile types.

All unfinished German Submarines—of which there were a considerable number at the end of 1918—have been dismantled, broken up, scuttled outside German ports or otherwise disposed of.

German Submarines, divided among the Allied Navies for investigation and trials noted in each Allied (and U.S.) Navy Section.

Mine Layers (are disarmed).

ALBATROSS after naval action of 1/7/15 ; foremast partly shot away.
(Was Mining School Ship before the war.)

ALBATROSS (October, 1907). 2200 tons. Complement, 197. Length, 295 feet. Beam, 42⅔ feet. *Maximum* draught, *about* 13 feet. Armament : 8—3·4 inch (15 pdr.), 35 cal. Boilers : Schulz-Thornycroft. Designed H.P. 6000 = 20 kts. Coal, 450 tons. **Carries 600 mines.**

Note.—Was disabled and driven ashore near Ostergarm Lighthouse, Gothland Island (Baltic), by Russian Cruisers on July 1st, 1915. Above illustration shows her being towed to internment at Viborg. Released from internment by Sweden in 1918.

S.M.S. "Nautilus," Minenleger.

NAUTILUS (1906). 1950 tons. Complement, 198. Length, 305 feet. Beam, 42⅔ feet. Draught, 13¼ feet. Armament : 8—3·4 inch, 15 pdr. Boilers : Schulz-Thornycroft. Machinery : reciprocating. Designed H.P. 6000 = 20 kts. Coal, 415 tons. **Carries 200 mines.**

Appearance unknown.

F.M. 1—36 (Built 1917-18.) 175 tons. *About* 139½ × 19⅔ × 4½ feet. Guns: 1—3·4 inch 22 pdr. I.H.P. 600 = 13·5 kts. Coal, 38 tons. Fitted to carry mines.

Notes.—Shallow draught sweepers. Proved of little worth owing to inadequate fuel supply and dangerous instability.

M 28—30, M 32—35, M 37, M 38, M 42—46, M 48, M 50—54, M 57—62, M 65, M 66, M 68—82, M 84—90, M 93—94, M 96—122, M 125, M 129, M 137, M 138. (Built 1915-18.) *About* 480 tons. *About* 192 × 24 × 8½ feet. Guns: see next column. I.H.P. 1600 = 17 kts. 2 screws. Coal: 150 tons and 12 tons oil. Complement 40. Can carry 30 mines.

War Losses: M 31, M 36, M 39, M 40, M 41, M 47, M 49, M 55, M 56, M 63, M 64, M 67, M 83, M 91, M 92, M 95.

Not finished?—M 123, M 124, 126—128, 130—136.

Similar to boats below.

M 19, M 20, M 21, M 25. (Built 1915.) *About* 400 tons. *About* 164 × 20 × 9 feet. Guns: see below. I.H.P. 1500 = 16 kts. Complement, 40. Can carry 30 mines.

War Losses: M 22, M 23, M 24, M 26, M 27.

M 1—5, M 7, M 8, M 10, M 13, M 17, M 18. (Built 1915.) *About* 350 tons. *About* 106 × 23 × 9 feet. Guns: see below. I.H.P. 1500 = 16 kts. Complement, 40. Carry 30 mines.

War Losses: M 6, M 9, M 11, M 12, M 14, M 15, M 16.

Armaments for all "M" Types.

(a) 3—4·1 inch, *or* (b) 2—4·1 inch, *or* (c) 1—4·1 inch, *or* (d) 2—3·4 inch, 22 pdr. Also 2 machine.

GERMAN GUNBOATS (*Kanonenboote*).

DELPHIN.

DELPHIN (Meyer, Papenburg, 1906). 450 tons. Complement 41. Armament: 4—3·4 inch (22 pdr.), 2—4 pdr., 4 M.G. Speed: 9·5 kts. Coal: 55 tons.

PANTHER (April, 1901). Displacement, 1000 tons. Dimensions: 210·3 × 31·8 × 10·2 feet. Complement, 130. Guns: 2—4·1 inch, 40 cal., 6—1 pdr., 2 Machine. Machinery: Triple expansion. 2 screws. Boilers: 4 Schulz-Thornycroft. Designed H.P. 1300 = 14 kts. Coal: 275 tons.

Perhaps never begun.

METEOR ? (Danzig Yard, 1914 or 1915 ?). 1150 tons. Dimensions: 219⅘ × 33½ × 10½ feet. Guns: 4—4·1 inch, 2—1 pdr., 2 machine. Machinery: 2 sets triple expansion. 2 screws. Boilers: 4 Schulz-Thornycroft. Designed H.P. 1550 = 14 kts. Coal: tons. Was intended for "surveying service" on East African Coast.

DRACHE (Germania, 1908). 790 tons. Complement 64. Guns: 4—3·4 inch (22 pdr.), 4—4 pdr. Speed: 15 kts. Coal: 150 tons.

FUCHS

HAI (Geestemünde, 1907). 640 tons. Complement 51. Armament: 8—4 pdr. Speed: 12·5 kts. Coal: 75 tons.

FUCHS (Meyer, Papenburg, 1905). 640 tons. Complement 51. Armament: 2—4·1 inch, 2—3·4 inch (15 pdr.). Speed: 12·5 kts. Coal: 75 tons.

Photo, S. Anderson, Esq.

BLITZ & **PFEIL** (1882). 1388 tons. Dimensions: 246 × 34½ × 13¾ feet. Complement, 134. Guns: 6—3·4 inch (15 pdr.), 4 machine. Tubes: 2 *above water* (probably removed), 1 *submerged*. Designed H.P. 2700 = 15 kts. Coal: 250 tons.

(Continued on next page.)

Gunboats—(continued).

ZIETEN (1876). 1006 tons. Complement, 108. Guns : 6—4 pdr. Tubes (13·8 inch) : 2 *submerged* (bow and stern). Speed : under 13 kts. Coal : 140 tons.

No Photo available.

GREIF. No details known.

No Photo available.

PRIMULA. Sea-going Parent Ship, 5th Minesweeping Flotilla.

No Photo available.

SPERBER. No details known.

Also :

Grille (1857). 350 tons. Speed : 13 kts. Guns : 2—3·4 inch. *Condor* (Mine Hulk), *Schwalbe* (Target Hulk).

River Gunboats.
(All on Vistula.)

No Photo available.

MÖWE. Ex Shallow Draught River Steamer, armed with 1—1 pdr. and 1 M.G.

No Photo available.

LIEBE. Ex Shallow Draught Tug. Guns : 1—3·4 inch (22 pdr.) 1—1 pdr.

No Photo available.

GARDENGO. Ex Shallow Draught Tug. Guns : 1—3·4 inch (22 pdr.), 1 M.G.

Submarine Depot and Salvage Ship.

No Photo available.

(Surrendered.)

CYCLOP (Danzig, 1914). Dock and Salvage Ship for Submarines, designed for raising 1200 tons deadweight. 2800 tons. Dimensions : 295 × 64 × 13 feet. Guns : None. Machinery : Reported to be Diesel engines. Speed : 9 kts.

Fleet Tender.

NORDSEE (Atlas Werfte, Bremen, 1914). 790 tons. Dimensions : 175¾ × 30¾ × feet. Armed with 2—3·4 inch (22 pdr.) guns. H.P. 1700 = kts. Serves as Leader of North Sea Patrols.

Yachts (*Jachten*).

Not finished.

(ex *Ersatz Hohenzollern*, Vulkan, Stettin, 1915). 7300 tons. Complement, 455. Dimensions: $528\frac{1}{4} \times 62\frac{1}{3} \times 20$ feet. (Guns: Not known, but is capable of mounting about 12—5·9 inch. Machinery: Turbines. 3 screws. Boilers: 10 Schulz-Thornycroft (2 oil burning). Designed H.P. 25,000 = 24 kts. Coal: 1000 tons + 500 tons oil.

Royal Yacht.

HOHENZOLLERN. (Vulkan, Stettin, 1892; re-constructed 1907). 4200 tons. Complement, 348. Dimensions: $380\frac{1}{2} \times 46 \times 19\frac{1}{4}$ feet. Armament: 2—4.pdr. Boilers (1907): Schulz-Thornycroft. Designed H.P. 9500 = 21·5 kts. Coal: 510 tons.

(Surrendered.)

LORELEY (ex *Mohican*, Henderson, Glasgow, 1885). 925 tons. Dimensions: $207\cdot4 \times 27\cdot1 \times 13\frac{1}{2}$ feet. Guns: 2—4 pdr. Speed: Made 13.4 kts. on trials; now about 12 kts. Coal: 165 tons. Complement, 60.

Admiralty Trawlers.

("Wachtschiffen.")

About 250 tons *gross*. H.P. 450 = 10 kts. Guns: 1 or 2 small.

These are Trawler Mine-Sweepers, of which a large number were built by the smaller German Shipyards during the War. The majority have been sold to private owners for fisheries purposes, but a few may still remain for Mine Clearance duties. About 100 were built during the War and 30 were sunk.

Fleet Auxiliaries.

Various Oilers, Colliers, &c., including a few ships used as Auxiliary Mine Layers. Believed that all have reverted to mercantile service, including German Mercantile and Fishing Vessels used as Submarine Decoy Ships (" Q-boats ").

Surveying Ships (*Vermessungsfahrzuge*).

No Photo available.

HYÄNE (1878). 493 tons. Complement, 85. Guns: 1—3.4 inch (15 pdr.), 1—4 pdr., 3—1 pdr. H.P. 340 = 8 kts. Coal: 110 tons.

No Photo available.

TRITON. No details known. May be the ex-Russian Surveying Ship, launched at and during German occupation of Reval, 1918. If so, her details are :—270 tons. Dimensions: $127\frac{3}{4} \times 20 \times 10$ feet.

Training Ships.

For Gunnery :—

KAISERIN AUGUSTA. Old Cruiser, previously described on an earlier page.

Sea-going Torpedo School Ship :—

WÜRTTEMBERG, (old) (1878). 7300 tons. I.H.P. 6000 = 15 kts. Guns: 2—3·4 inch (22 pdr.), 8—1 pdr., 4 M.G. Torpedo tubes: 2—19·7 inch, *submerged* ; 2—13·7 inch, *submerged* ; 1—13.7 inch, *above water*. Coal: 650 tons. Is serving temporarily as Sea-going Tender to Minesweepers.

HUNGARIAN DANUBE FLOTILLA.

Note.

All ships transferred to the Hungarian Government from the late Austro-Hungarian Navy in October, 1918.

Flags.

Details wanted.

Minister of Defence :—

Personnel :—

During the regime of the Bela Kun Government at Buda-Pest, a Danube Monitor was re-named **POSZONY.** Identity of this ship not known.

RECOGNITION SILHOUETTES.

Scale: 1 inch = 160 feet.

Patrol Boats.   Szamos.   Maros *class* monitors.

Körös.   Almos & Enns type.
(*As re-built.*)   (*Approximate.*)

Monitors.

For *Temes*, see next page. Has been so largely reconstructed, she might be regarded as a new Monitor, launched in 1915.

> Photo wanted.

ALMOS (1915), **SAVA** (1915), **BOSNIA** (1915), **RAGUSA** (1915). All completed 1916. Reported to be identical with *Enns* and *Inn* below. *Bosnia* and *Sava* built under 1914-15 Austro-Hungarian Naval Programme. All surrendered. *Bosnia* and *Sava* taken over by British and Serbs.

> Photo wanted.

ENNS* (1913), **INN*** (1913). 528 tons. Dimensions : 190 × 33¾ × 4¼ feet. Designed H.P. 1500 = 13 kts. Boilers : Yarrow. Armament : 2—4.7 inch + 3—4.7 inch howitzers, 2—11 pdr., 6 M.G. Armour : 1½″ Belt and Bulkheads, 1″ Deck, 2″ C.T. and Turrets (2). Complement, 86. Fuel : Oil only. Belong to 1912 Austro-Hungarian Naval Programme.

* *Inn* mined and sunk in the Danube River, Sept. 22nd, 1917. Subsequently salved, repaired and returned to active service. *Enns* taken over by British and Serbs.

> Photo wanted.

TEMES. Originally sister to *Bodrog,** and launched 1904. Sunk, October, 1914 ; raised, June, 1916. Has been so largely rebuilt, she is now practically a new Monitor. Present armament said to be : 2—4.7 inch, 4—11 pdr., 6 M.G. Other details not known.

* *Bodrog,* Serbian prize.

***KÖRÖS** (1892), ***SZAMOS** (1892). 440 tons. Dimensions : 177⅙ × 29½ × 4 feet. Designed H.P. 1200 = 10 kts. Boilers : Yarrow. Guns : 2—4.7 inch (35 cal.), 2—9 pdr., 2 M.G. Armour : 2″ Belt, ¾″ Deck, 3″ Turret, 2″ C.T. Complement, 79-80. Coal : 80 tons.

*KÖRÖS sunk, April 1915, but subsequently raised, repaired, and returned to active service.

***LEITHA** (1871), ***MAROS** (1871). Both reconstructed, 1894. 305 tons. Dimensions : 164 × 20¼ × 3½ feet. H.P. 700 = 8 kts. Guns : 1—4.7 inch (35 cal.), 2 or 3 —11pdr., 3 M.G. Armour : 1¾″ Belt, 1″ Deck, 2″ Turret. Complement, 57. Coal : 20 tons.

*Taken over by British and Serbs.

Torpedo Vessel.

Photo wanted.

VEKSEL. (——) No details known, but said to be armed with 1—3.9 inch, 1 M.G. and 2 torpedo tubes.

Mining Craft.

No Photo available.

MINELAYER (NAME UNKNOWN). No exact details available, but said to be armed with 2—11 pdr. and 2—3 pdr. guns and to carry 30 mines.

No Photo available.

TULIN. Barge, propelled by motor engines and carrying 140 mines.

HUNGARIAN DANUBE FLOTILLA.

Scouts.

Barsch,* Borsto, Fogos,* Isuka,* Kompo, Vels,* Visa. Guns : 1 or 2—3 pdr.

* Taken over by British and Serbs.

Patrol Boats.

2 *boats* (numbers not known), **g, h** (1909), 18 tons, 22 kts., 1 M.G. ; **f** (1907), 12 tons, 22 kts., 1 M.G. ; **b, d** (1906-9), 40 tons, 14 kts. Guns : 1 or 2 small. Complement 13.

Also several motor launches.

Miscellaneous.

Elina
Samarna } Armed Steamers, each having 2—11 pdrs.
Val. 594 tons *gross*
Hebe. Armed Yacht.
Bayo }
Boski } Armed Trawlers.

RUSSIAN FLEET.

FLAGS.—Not known. A new National Ensign is reported to have been adopted, with the Russian words, "The Soviets of the Federal Republics," on a red ground.

UNIFORMS.—Shoulder markings abolished, and rank is now indicated by stripes on cuff, as in British Navy. *All* ranks now have gold buttons. Officers' caps have an anchor badge, on a red ground, and encircled by a wreath, much the same as in the British Navy. Ranks are distinguished thus:—

Admiral : $\frac{3}{4}$-inch top stripe with curl and three stars round curl; two 1-inch lower stripes.

Vice-Admiral : Same as Admiral but only *two* stars.

Kontre-Admiral : Same as Admiral but only *one* star, above curl.

Kapitan (*I Ranga*) : Same as Admiral but *no* stars.

Kapitan (*II Ranga*) : Two 1-inch gold stripes, top with curl.

Starchi Leitenant : One 1-inch or $\frac{3}{4}$-inch top stripe with curl, and *three* $\frac{1}{2}$-inch gold stripes below.

Lietenant : Same as above but only *two* $\frac{1}{2}$-inch gold stripes below.

Mitchman : Same as above but only *one* $\frac{1}{2}$-inch gold stripe below.

Pra'porchi : This is a temporary rank, about equivalent to Sub-Lieut., R.N.R. in British Navy. One $\frac{1}{2}$-inch gold stripe *without* curl.

Note.—The above particulars relate to changes introduced by the Kerensky Government. Under the Bolshevist Administration it is said that all marks of rank in the Fleet and Army have been abolished.

SEVASTOPOL to	miles.
Batum	400
Bizerta	1300
Constantinople	298
Gibraltar	2000
Kertch	175
Malta	1000
Nikolaieff	200
Novorossisk	200
Odessa	165
Piræus	660
Salonika	643
Toulon	1654

(LIBAU)* to	miles.
Brest	1430
Cherbourg	1220
Copenhagen	465
Danzig	360
Gibraltar	2330
Kiel	550
Memel	230
Reval	50
Rosyth	1010
Vladivostok	12,405
Windau	50

KRONSTADT to	miles.
Abö	250
Bornholm	627
Brest	1680
Cherbourg	1470
Copenhagen	715
Danzig	558
Gibraltar	2580
Helsingfors	150
Kiel	800
Libau	250
Memel	480
Reval	150
Rosyth	1345
Petrograd	21
(By sea canal)	
Vladivostok	12,655
Windau	200

VLADIVOSTOK to	miles.
Hong Kong	1740
Kiao-chau	1150
Maitsuru	470
Manila	2080
Matsumai	380
Nagasaki	620
Port Arthur	1170
Sassebo	600
Wei-hai-wei	950

Note.

The present boundaries of Russia are so indeterminate, it has been deemed advisable to suspend the General Maps.

Modern Naval Guns (Obukhoff).

Notation.	Designation.	Length in Calibres.	Weight of Guns.	Weight of A.P. Shot.	Initial Velocity (approximate).	*Maximum* Penetration with A.P. Capped Shell against K.C. Armour. 8000 yds.	5000 yds.	3000 yds.	Danger Space against average warship at 10,000 yards.	5000 yards.	3000 yards.	Usual Rounds per minute.
	inch.	calibres.	tons.	lbs.	f.s.	in.	in.	in.	yards.	yards.	yards.	
A⁷	14	45	82·6	1486	2525	...	...	22½	...	...	...	...
A⁶	12	50	48·2	714	3000	...	14½	20	...	...	...	...
A⁴	12	40	43·5	714	2600	6½	14	18	150	460	750	0·30
A A	12	35	56	714	2200	4½	8	11	120	380	580	0·25
A³	10 (V)	50	35	497	3000	6	12¾	15½	...	...	...	...
A³	10	45	32	490	2500	5	10½	13	130	450	700	0·45
A	8 (V)	50	17	216	3300	...	7½	10½	...	...	...	...
A	8	45	15½	188	2800	...	6	9½	105	430	625	1
D*	6	45	7½	89	2900	...	4¼	6	60	250	485	3
E*	6	45	7	89	2600	...	3¼	5	50	200	430	3
F*	5·1	55	...	...	...	...	...	...	...	...	...	...
F*	4·7	45	2¼	46	2600	...	...	...	...	...	...	about 4
F*	3	60	14 cwt.	13½	2700	...	...	...	...	...	...	...
F*	3	35	12 ,,	13½	2600	...	...	...	...	...	...	...

* = Brass cartridge cases. V = Vickers. *Maximum* rates of 10 inch and 8 inch are 3 and 6 rounds per minute. These guns are in the *Rurik*.

Guns.

Baltic Ships.

14″45 in *Kinburn* class (4 ships) not yet completed.
12″50 in *Gangoot* class (4 ships).
12″40 in *Respublika* class (2 ships), *Slava.*
12″35 in *Tchesma.*
10″50 in *Rurik.*

8″50 in *Respublika* class (2 ships), *Petr Veliki* and *Rurik.*
8″45 in *Bayan* class (2 ships), *Saria Svobodi*, *Gromoboi* and *Rossiya.*
6″45 in *Slava*, *Grajdanin*, *Petr Veliki*, *Bayan*, and all cruisers.
5·1″55 in *Kinburn* class (4 ships) and *Admiral Butakoff* class (4 ships).

Black Sea Ships.

12″50 in *Volia.*
12″40 in *Evstafi* class (2 ships) and *Boretz za Svobodu.*
10″45 in *Rostislav.*

8″50 in *Evstafi* class (2 ships).
6″45 in *Evstafi* class (2 ships), *Boretz za Svobodu*, *Rostislav*, *Tri Sviatitelia.*
5·1″55 in *Admiral Nakhimov* class (4 ships) and *Gen. Korniloff.*

Note.—A considerable number of guns have been dismounted from Russian warships for service on various land fronts.

RUSSIAN BALTIC AND PACIFIC DOCKYARDS, Etc.

Divided into squares of 2000 yards.   Uniform scale.   Soundings in fathoms.   Heights in feet.

Merchant Fleet.

This, exclusive of vessels on the Caspian, consists of 788 steamers of 1,016,547 tons *gross;* and 3068 sailing vessels, of 625,239 tons *gross.* In view of the Revolutions, of the requisitioning of tonnage by the Allied Governments, and extensive seizures by the enemy, these totals had best be regarded as purely nominal figures.

Chief Trade Ports.

Petrograd, Vladivostok,

COINAGE:

Colour of Ships.

Big Ships: Light grey.   *Destroyers & Submarines:* Not known.

Personnel.

Before the War exceeded 60,000 (including Reserves?) During the War, *active* personnel, excluding mobilised Reserves, is said to have been 51,670 officers and men (inclusive of Coastguards and Marines). Owing to numerous desertions present strength is entirely unknown.

Overseas Possessions: None.

Naval Arsenals, Etc.

KRONSTADT.   Fitting out and repairing yard for Baltic Fleet. No slips. Four large dry docks; (*a*) $600 \times 85 \times 29\frac{1}{2}$ feet; (*b*) $490 \times 85 \times 29$ feet; (*c*) and (*d*) smaller, but both able to take most Russian ships except the big cruisers.

Kronstadt is fed from the shipbuilding yards at Petrograd, the New Admiralty (2 slips), Galernii Ostrov (3 slips), Baltic works (3 slips), and torpedo-boat yards at Izhora (on the Neva). The channel above Kronstadt is now about 35 feet deep. Admiralty Chart No. 2215.

(White Sea).

Murmansk, on the Kola Inlet, reported to have been used as a subsidiary base for torpedo craft, mine-sweepers and ice-breakers.

Commercial harbours at Kronstadt and Petrograd.

Private yards at Petrograd: Putilov Works, Nevski Shipbuilding and Mechanical Works.

KRONSTADT.   (Fort Peter was blown up in Dec., 1917.)

(In the Pacific).

VLADIVOSTOK.   Small dockyard. Government wharf 1500 feet long, 27 feet depth of water alongside. Two docks, each $618\frac{1}{2} \times 90 \times 34\frac{1}{2}$ feet, and a third $572 \times 90 \times 30$. One small floating dock 300 feet long. Two small basins. Some repairing shops. Three floating cranes, 50, 75 and 100 tons. Water shallow. Good *tideless* protected harbour. Harbour is frozen in January and February, but passage is cleared by ice-breakers. Strongly fortified (high-site batteries with 10 in. disappearing guns). Admiralty Chart No. 1011. Allied troops landed here during 1918.

Commercial harbours: Vladivostok, Nikolaievsk.

VLADIVOSTOK.

(Map of Sevastopol is transferred to Black Sea Section.)

Summer, 1919.

C-in-C. (Army, Navy, &c.): Vatzetis.
Baltic Naval Forces: (not known).
Black Sea: (not known).
Volga and Caspian: Saks.

BALTIC SECTION

(INCLUSIVE OF SHIPS IN THE WHITE SEA, AT VLADIVOSTOK AND ON AMUR RIVER).

The Baltic Fleet is completely disorganised. Owing to desertion of *personnel*, executions of naval officers, looting and mishandling of ships, very few ships can now be deemed effective. During 1919, the Bolshevist Active Fleet was reported to consist of **PETROPAVLOVSK, ANDREI PERVOSVANNI, OLEG,** the Destroyers *Gavriil, Azard, Konstantin, Svoboda* (First Flotilla), *Vsadnik, Gaidamak, Amuretz, Ussurietz* (Second Flotilla), and three or seven Submarines. First two ships named are out of action and **OLEG** is sunk.

As regards ships listed as building and completing: all work ceased in June, 1917, and practically nothing further has been done to advance construction during the past two years.

It is not worth while dividing the Russian Navy pages into Bolshevist and Anti-Bolshevist sections. On the next page a list is given of ships in the White Sea and at Vladivostok—that is, *not* under Bolshevist control. Vessels named in heavy type are listed on following pages; those in small type cannot be described for lack of details. Ships not included in the White Sea, Vladivostok or Amur River lists may be taken as under Bolshevist control.

It must be added that details of the White Sea ships refer to conditions before the Allied evacuation of Northern Russia. It is probable that many vessels were brought to Allied Ports in the autumn of 1919, while those left in the White Sea or Dvina River may have been scuttled or disabled.

Various ex-Russian Baltic Warships have been transferred to the Esthonian and Finnish Navy Sections (*q.v.*).

RUSSIAN (NON-BOLSHEVIST) WARSHIPS, FLEET AUXILIARIES, &c.

WHITE SEA (Summer, 1919).

Old Battleship :—
TCHESMA

Cruisers :—
VARYAG
GLORY VI. (British, *alias* Russian *Askold*)*

Destroyers :—
Leit. Sergieff
Kapt. Yurassovski
Bestrashni
Beshumni
Grosovoi
Vlastni

Submarines :—
Sviatoi Georg
Delfin

Trawlers :—
About 30-40 (about 15 of *Axe* class with British crews).

Yachts :—
Alvina
Josephine
(Above reported to have U.S. crews now.)
Yaroslavni

Auxiliaries :—
TAIMYR
VAIGATCH
BAKAN
Ludmilla
Kolguieff

Miscellaneous :—
PAHKTUSOV
XENIA
Advance
Antony
Cheviot
Inei
Kingfisher
Koupava
Olen
Orlik
Sniedzhinka
Strepet

* *Glory IV* now laid up in the Gareloch, Firth of Clyde.

Ice Breakers :—
KANADA (reported returned to Canada, listed in Canadian Section as *Earl Grey*).
SVIATOGOR (paid off at Devonport, Sept., 1919. Is listed in British Navy Section).
Ilya Mourometz
Mikula Salianinovich
(Both above with French Personnel.)
Kniaz Pojarski
Kozma Minin

Tugs and Ice Breakers :—
About 10.

Motor Patrol Boats :—
About 8 or 10.

Dvina Flotilla :—
Advokat } Gunboats.
Gorodoff ∫
Razlyff (may be Armed Yacht *Rasviet*).
Various Armed Barges.

VLADIVOSTOCK.

Destroyers :—
Besposhtchadni
Bravi
Boiki*
Bodri
Grosni
Leit. Maleieff
Insh. Mech. Anastassoff
Tverdi
Totchni
Trevoshni
Smyell
Serditi
Statni
Skori

Gunboat :—
MANDJUR (Minelayer)

Mine Layers :—
DIOMID
PATROKL
ULIS
MONGUGAI

Miscellaneous :—
Alèut
Kamchadal
Okhtosk
Orel
SHILKA
TOBOL†
Takut

* Destroyer *Boiki* now in Mediterranean as French Destroyer *Quentin Roosevelt*.

† Said to have been sunk 1916, as a Mercantile Vessel.

AMUR RIVER FLOTILLA.

GROSA
SHKWAL
SHTORM
SMERTCH
TYFUN
URAGAN
VIKHR
VYUGA
OROKANIN
MONGOL
BURIAT
VOGUL
SIBIRIAK
KOREL
KIRGIZ
KALMUIK
SIRIANIN
VOTYAK
Kopya
Palash
Pika
Pistolet
Pulya
Shtik

ONE AND TWO FUNNELS.   **(For Two Funnel Battleship types, see next page).**

MINREP *class*.
(2 may be Finnish now)
(*Mine sweepers.*)

KHRABRI.   GROZIASTCHI.

Gunboats; appearance may be altered now.

BUG.

NAROVA & ONEGA (*Minelayers*).

PETSHORA.

VOLGA (*Mine layer*).
(KHABAROVSK similar).

ANADYR

BAKAN.
(May be Finnish now).

BORGA & LAKHTA.⁂
(*May be Finnish now).

EVROPA.

RIGA

AFRICA.

MANDJUR (*Vladivostock*).

VOIN (*Training Ship*).

NIKOLAIEFF.

ERMAK (*Ice breaker*).

KHIVINETZ.

AMUR (*Mine layer*).

RUSSIAN WARSHIPS RECOGNITION SILHOUETTES.

TWO FUNNELS (continued).

Petr Veliki (Ice Breaker).

Saria Svobodi (Reported Sunk).

Tchesma (White Sea).

Grajdanin.

Gangut class (4 ships).

Respublika class (2 ships).

Ex-Shtandart and Kretchet. (Yachts).

THREE FUNNELS.

Bogatyr (Reported Sunk).

Avrora class (2 ships, Scuttled as Block Ships?).

Okean (Training Ship).

FOUR FUNNELS.

Rurik.

Angara (Repair or Depot Ship).

Variag (White Sea).

FIVE FUNNELS.

British Glory IV (Russian Askold) Laid up in the Clyde.

Rossia & Gromoboi.

Bayan class (2 ships).

Leit. Sergieff, Vnimatelni &
Bestrashni *classes* (12) t.b.d.*

Normand type (6) t.b.*

Amuretz type (4) t.b.d.

E. Bukharski type (6) t.b.d.

K. Liebknecht type (2).†

Kondratenko *class* t.b.d. (3) †

Notes.

Silhouette for Liet. Ilyin *class* t.b.d. is based on that given in a German Naval Annual. Its accuracy cannot be guaranteed.

Destroyers of classes marked * taken over by Allies or now units of Finnish and Esthonian Navies, or attached to Denikin's Army.

Destroyers and Submarines of classes marked † Bolshevist Volga and Caspian Flotilla.

Ukräina type t.b.d. (7).
(Fore funnel now raised).

Isyaslav *class* (2 or 4) t.b.d.*

Leit. Ilyin type ? (Of Gavriil *class*`.

Lovki *class* t.b.d.† (8), also
Grosovoi *class* (2) without main mast.*

Dyelni,† Bravi, Tverdi,* Smyeli* and
Pritki t.b.d.*† *classes* (26).

Novik t.b.d.

BYELUGA *class* (4 ?)

ALLIGATOR *class* (4)

Believed captured by Germans, 19.8.

All Bubnov type ; appearance not known.

KATASKA *class* (2).　　MAKREL *class* (2).*　MINOGA.*

VOLGA & CASPIAN.

SVIATOI GEORG.

(*White Sea.*)

" Improved Bubnov " type.

(Silhouette only approximate ; may be boats of
EDINOROG, TIGR and VOLK *classes*).

BORODINO (1917?) **ISMAIL** (June, 1915), **KINBURN** (Oct., 1915), **NAVARIN** (1917?).

Normal displacement, *about* 32,500 tons.   Complement,

Length, *about* 728¼ feet.   Beam, 98 feet.   Draught, 28¾ feet.

Guns :
12—14 inch, 45 cal. (A⁷)
24—5·1 inch, 55 cal.
4—4 inch (anti-aircraft)
4 machine
Torpedo tubes :
6 *submerged.*

Armour :
12″ Belt ....
 ″ Belt (bow) ....
 ″ Belt (aft) ....
 ″ Deck ....
 ″ Turrets ....
 ″ Battery ....

Notes.

Owing to lack of materials and labour, work was stopped on these ships in 1917. It is very doubtful if they will ever be completed now.

Plans are based on information and sketches furnished by the Naval Attache of the Russian Embassy, 1917.

Machinery   Parsons turbines.   screws.   Boilers : 25 Yarrow.   Designed H.P. = 68,000 = 26½ kts.
Coal : *normal*   tons ; *maximum* 1,950 tons + 1575 tons oil fuel.

Name	Builder	Machinery	Laid down	Com-pleted	Trials	Turbines	Boilers	Best recent speed
Borodino	Galernii	{ All by Franco- Russian Co. }	Dec.'12	**?**			{ All Yarrow }	
Ismail	Baltic Works		Dec.'12					
Kinburn	Baltic Works		Dec.'12					
Navarin	Galernii		Dec.'12					

GANGŪT (Oct., 1911), **POLTAVA** (July, 1911), **PETROPAVLOVSK** (Sept., 1911), **SEVASTOPOL** (June, 1911).

Normal displacement, 23,370 metric tons.   Complement, 1125.

Length *over all*, 594 feet.   Beam, 87 feet.   *Mean* draught, 27½ feet.

Guns
12—12 inch, 50 cal. (A⁶).
16—4·7 inch, 50 cal.
2—9 pdr. (anti-aircraft).*
1—3 pdr.
8 Machine.
Torpedo tubes (18 inch):
  4 *submerged.*
  *2—11 pdr. AA.
   in *Poltava*

Armour (Krupp):
8¾″ Belt (amidships) …
5″-2″ Belt (ends)
3″-4″ Internal belt (*see notes*)
3″ Deck…………
12″-10″ Turrets…
8″ Turret bases………
6″ Battery …………
10″ Conning tower……

Ahead :
3—12 in.
2 to 4—4·7 in.

Astern :
3—12 in.
2 to 4—4·7 in.

Broadside, 12—12 in., 8—4·7 in.

Machinery : Parsons turbine. 4 screws. Boilers: 25 Yarrow. Designed H.P. 42,000 = 23 kts. Coal : *normal*, 1000 tons ; *maximum*, 3000 tons. Also 1170 tons oil.

Gunnery Notes.—The port plate above each gun is in the form of a hinged flap, allowing each 12-inch gun to elevate to 30—40° *maximum*. Arcs of fire : End triple 12-inch barbettes, 310° ; central barbettes, 130° *each beam* ; aft group of 4—4·7 inch, 90° ; other 4·7 inch, 85°.

Armour Notes.—Belt is about 15 feet wide, 5 feet of it below water, uniform thickness. There is a *secondary* 3″-4″ internal belt 11 feet inboard above protective deck, extending between the end barbettes. The space between main belt and internal belts is divided up into w.t. compartments.

Name	Builder	Machinery	Laid down	Completed	Trials : Full power		Boilers	Best recent speed
Gangūt	Galernii I.	Franco-Rus.Wks.	June,'09	Jan. '14	About 50,000	=23	Yarrow	
Poltava	Galernii I.	Franco-Rus.Wks.	June,'09	Jan. '15		=23	Yarrow	
Petropavlorsk	Baltic Works	Baltic Works	June,'09	Jan. '14		=23	Yarrow	
Sevastopol	Baltic Works	Baltic Works	June,'09	Jan. '15		=23·4	Yarrow	

General Notes.—The late Gen. Vittorio Cuniberti prepared the original designs for this class—compare general resemblance to his Italian *Dante Alighieri*. The Ministry of Marine afterwards altered the plans to include Russian ideas of armouring, ice-breaking bows and other special features. The design of these ships has been very severely criticised, but, although abnormal in many details, they may have proved quite successful in service.

Poltava.

Note : PETROPAVLOVSK, after being torpedoed by British C. M. B., sank in shallow water and on an even keel at Kronstadt. She can easily be raised and is therefore not deleted. POLTAVA aground. GANGUT laid up at Petrograd. Condition of SEVASTOPOL unknown.

Gangūt.

(RESPUBLIKA CLASS—2 SHIPS).

RESPUBLIKA (ex-*Imperator Pavel Pervi*, Sept., 1907) & **ANDREI PERVOSVANNI*** (Oct., 1906).

Normal displacement, 17,680 metric tons.   Complement, 933.

Length (*waterline*), 454 feet.   Beam, 80 feet.   *Mean* draught, 27 feet.   Length *over all*, 460 feet.

Guns :
4—12 inch, 40 cal. (A^4).
14—8 inch, 50 cal. (*A*).
12—4·7 inch, 50 cal.
2—3 pdr.
8 Machine.

Torpedo tubes (18 inch) :
2 *submerged* (broadside).

*Docked, Aug. 1909, after being torpedoed by British C.M.G.

Armour (Krupp) :
8½″ Belt (amidships) ....
5″ Belt (bow) ....
4″ Belt (aft) ....
3″ Deck ......
2″ Splinter deck ....
10″ Big turrets (N.C.) ....
5″ Turret bases (*see notes*) ...
7″ Small turrets ....
4″ Bases (*see notes*) ....
5″—3″ Main deck side
5″ Battery (N.C.)
3″ Q.F. Battery (amidships)...
8″ Conning tower (N.C.) ..
6″ After C.T. (N.C.) ....
(Total weight 4400 tons).

A. PERVOSVANNI.   (Note derricks.)

Photo, Seward, Weymouth.

Note.—Both ships now rigged as Silhouette.

Ahead :
2—12 in.
6—8 in.

Astern :
2—12 in.
6—8 in.

Broadside : 4—12 in., 7—8 in.

Machinery : 2 sets triple expansion.   2 screws.   Boilers : 25 Belleville.   Designed H.P. 17,600 = 18 kts. (*c.f.* trials).   Coal : *normal* — tons ; *maximum. Respublika* 1,325 tons, *A.P.* 1,500 tons.

Armour Notes.—Belt is 7½ feet wide, 5 feet of it below waterline ; lower edge is 3″ thick.   Turret bases 5″—4″ according to the side armour forming additional protection to them.   3″ floor to batteries.   2″ lateral " anti-torpedo " bulkheads.

Gunnery Notes.—Loading positions, big guns : all round.   Hoists : electric.   Big guns manœuvred electrically ; secondary turrets, electrically.   Arcs of fire : Big guns, 270° ; secondary guns, 150°.

Torpedo Notes —6 searchlights.

Name	Builder	Machinery	Laid down	Completed	Last refit	Trials	Boilers	Best recent speed
A. Pervosvanni	Galernii Island	Baltic Works	Jan., '03	Aug.'10		18,596 = 17	Belleville	14*
Respublika	Baltic Works	Baltic Works	Sept.,'03	Sept.'10		17,775 = 17·7	Belleville	

*Full speed, 1918.

General Notes.—Design altered during construction in order to embody Japanese war lessons : armour thinned and extended to cover hull, Q.F. battery increased, etc., etc.   Hulls unpierced ; all ventilation through decks.

RESPUBLIKA.   (Note cranes.)

GRAJDANIN (ex-*Tsesarevitch*) (Feb., 1901).   *Photo. Abrahams, Devonport.*

Normal displacement, 13,210 metric tons.   Complement, 803.

Length (*over all*), 388¾ feet.   Beam, 76 feet.   *Maximum* draught, 28¼ feet.

Guns :
4—12 inch, 40 cal. (A^4)
12—6 inch, 45 cal.
10—11 pdr.
4—6 pdr.
2—1 pdr., AA.
6 Machine
Torpedo tubes (18 inch) :
removed.

Armour (Krupp) :
10″ Belt (amidships) ...... ▪▪▪▪
6″ Belt (ends) .... ▨▨▨
4″ Deck (slopes) ....
8″—6″ Lower deck side { ▨▨▨ ▨▨▨
2″ Main deck ....
10″ Turrets (NC) .... ▨▨▨
10—8″ Turret bases (NC) ▨▨▨
6″ Small turrets (**6**) ... ▨▨▨
6″ Bases to these .... ▨▨▨
10″ Conning tower (NC)... ▨▨▨
5″ Tube to it .... ▨▨▨
(Total weight 4000 tons)

Ahead :
2—12 in.
8—6 in.

Astern :
2—12 in.
8—6 in.

Broadside :—4—12 in., 6—6 in.

Machinery : 2 sets triple expansion. 2 screws. Boilers : 20 Belleville, without economisers. Designed H.P. 16,300=18 kts. Coal : *normal* 800 tons ; *maximum* 1350 tons. Laid down at La Seyne, Toulon, 1899, completed 1903.

(In White Sea).

TCHESMA (ex-*Tango*, ex-*Poltava*) (Nov., 1894).   Displacement 10,960 tons.   Complement, 700. Length, 369 feet.   Beam, 72½ feet.   *Maximum* draught, 27 feet.   Guns (Obukhoff) : 4—12 inch, 40 cal. (*AA*), 12—6 inch, 45 cal., and 8—12 pdr.   Armour (compound) : Belt 15″ (partial).   Turrets (steel) 10″, small turrets 5″.   Designed H.P. 11,000=17 kts.   Boilers : 16 Miyabara.   Coal : *maximum* 1050 tons. Sunk at Port Arthur in the Russo-Japanese War 1904 ; salved in 1905 by the Japanese and re-named *Tango*.   Retroceded to Russia by Japan, March, 1916.

Notes.

Two other very old battleships, *Saria Svobodi* and *Petr Veliki*, will be found on pages immediately preceding Black Sea Section. Both possess little military value at present beyond use on subsidiary duties or for coastal defence and attack. *Saria Svobodi* reported sunk at Kronstadt. *Petr Veliki* an Icebreaker in 1919.

Has F.C. top on foremast now.   *Photo, Abrahams, Devonport.*

Disabled, but may be repaired and in commission.
RURIK (Nov., 1906).
Normal displacement, 15,190 tons. Complement, 899.
Length *over all*, 529 feet. Beam, 75 feet. *Mean* draught, 26 feet. Length (*p.p.*), 490 feet.

Guns (Vickers) :	Armour (Krupp) :
4—10 inch, 50 cal. (A³)	6″ Belt (amid.) (K.C.) ...
8—8 inch, 50 cal. (A)	4″ Belt (bow) (N.C.)
20—4·7 inch, 50 cal.	3″ Belt (stern) (N.C.) ...
2—3 pdr.	1½″ Armour deck ... ...
2—1 pdr., AA.	8″ Turrets (K.C.) ....
2 machine.	6″ Turret bases ....
Torpedo tubes (18 inch) :	7″ Secondary turrets .....
2 *submerged* (broadside).	3″ Redoubt (N.C.) ...
	3″ Battery (N.C. ......
	8″ Conning tower (N.C.)

Ahead :
2—10 in.
4—8 in.   Broadside : 4—10 in., 4—8 in.   Astern :
                                                                       2—10 in.
                                                                       4—8 in.

Machinery : 2 sets 4 cylinder quadruple expansion. 2 screws. Boilers : 28 Belleville.
Designed H.P., with ¾ power, 19,700 = 21 kts., full power not specified. Coal : *normal* 1200 tons ;
maximum 1916 tons.
General Notes.—Built and engined by Vickers, Ltd. Laid down September, 1905, completed September, 1908.
On trials : Mean for ten hours was 20,675 H.P. = 21·5 kts. ; has made 22·4 kts. Big guns 35° elevation.
Armoured magazines and special anti-torpedo protection.

(Officially rated as " Cruisers.")   *Photo, Abrahams, Devonport.*
ADMIRAL MAKAROV (May 1906, re-fitted 1916). **BAYAN** (August, 1907).
Displacement, 7900 metric tons. Complement, 568—593.
Length (*o.a*), 449⅔ feet, Beam, 57·5 feet, *Mean* draught, 21·3 feet.

Guns :	Armour (Krupp) :
3—8 inch, 45 cal. (A).	8″ Belt (amidships)
12—6 inch, 45 cal.	4″ Belt (forward)
2—11 pdr. (A.M).	2″ Armour deck...
1—1 pdr., AA. (Bayan.)	2½″ deck (aft) .....
2—3 pdr.	6″ bulkhead (aft)...
Torpedo tubes (18 inch) :	3¼″-9½″ Upper belt
2 *submerged.*	6″ Turrets ....
	″ Turret bases ...
	2⅓″ Battery........
	5½″ Conning tower

Note.

Re-armed during War. Extra 8 inch mounted
without shield between 4th funnel and mainmast.
4—6 inch added—positions unknown.

Machinery : 2 sets vertical triple expansion. 2 screws. Boilers : 26 Belleville. Designed H.P. 16,500 =
21 kts. Coal : *normal* 750 tons ; *maximum Bayan* 950 tons, A.M. 1050 tons.
Notes.—*Bayan* laid down at New Admiralty Yard, Petrograd, 1905, and completed 1910. Machinery by Franco-
Russian Co. *Admiral Makarov* begun by La Seyne, Co., Toulon, 1905, completed 1908. Machinery by builders.
Pallada sunk by *U 26*, in Finnish Gulf, October 1914.

Photo, Abraham & Sons, Devonport.

Громобой. **GROMOBOI** (May, 1899).

Displacement, 13,430 metric tons. Sheathed and coppered. Complement, 868.

Length (*waterline*), 472½ feet. Beam, 68½ feet. *Mean* draught, 27¾ feet.

Guns (as re-armed) :
  6—8 inch, 45 cal. (*A*).
  20—6 inch, 45 cal.
  2—9 pdr. A A.
  2—3 pdr.
Torpedo tubes :
  2 *submerged.*
  (broadside).

Armour (Harvey-nickel) :
  6″ Belt ....
  2″ Deck ....
  6″ Bulkheads ....
  4″ Lower deck (amidships)
  6″ Casemates (14) ....
  2″ Hoists.........
  10″ Conning tower ....
  (Total *about* 2100 tons.)

Note.
Re-armed during war.
Present gun positions not known.

Россія **ROSSIYA** (May, 1896).

Displacement, 12,195 tons (sheathed and coppered). Complement, 833.

Length (*over all*), 480 feet. Beam, 68½ feet. *Mean* draught, 26 feet.

Guns (as re-armed) :
  4—8 in., 45 cal. (*A*)
  14—6 in., 45 cal.
  2—3 pdr.
  2—M.G.
Torpedo tubes :
  removed

Armour (Harvey) :
  8″–5″ Belt
  4″ Belt (aft) ....
  2½″ Deck ....
  [Deck flat on belt].
  6″ Bulkheads .....
  4″ Lower deck
    (amidships)
  6″ Battery bulkh'ds
  2″ Casements to 8″)
  2″ Screens in battery

Note.
8—6 inch removed during war.
Present best speed 17—17½ kts.

Machinery : 3 sets triple expansion. 3 screws Boilers :——————— Designed H.P. 14,500 = 19 kts. Coal : *normal* 800 tons ; *maximum* 2300 tons.

Armour Notes.—Belt is 7 feet wide by about 330 feet long.

General Notes.—Laid down at Baltic Works, 1898 ; completed 1901 ; re-fitted 1907, when 2 above water tubes were removed, and upper deck guns casemated in. Made 20·1 kts. on first trials, with 15,499 H.P., but best recent speed known of is 18·5 kts.

Machinery : 3 sets vertical triple expansion. 3 screws. Boilers (fitted 1907) : 32 Belleville in 4 groups. Designed H.P. : 14,500 = 19 kts. Coal : *normal* 1000 tons ; *maximum* 2500 tons.

Armour Notes.—Belt is carried right aft, but incomplete forward. It is *about* 7 feet wide. 4″ armour in wake of engines. 6″ bulkheads protect battery from raking fire.

General Notes.—Laid down at Baltic Works, 1893 ; completed 1898 ; re-fitted 1907, when all torpedo tubes were removed. Made 20·25 kts. on first trials, with 18,446 H.P.

Note.

Plans given below are based on those published in an Enemy Naval Annual. Their accuracy cannot be guaranteed.

ADMIRAL BUTAKOFF (*not launched*). **ADMIRAL GREIG** (Dec. 1916), *ADMIRAL SPIRIDOFF* (*not launched*), and **SVIETLANA** (June, 1915).

Displacement, 6800 metric tons. Complement,
Length, 507¾ feet. Beam, 50⅓ feet. Draught, 18⅓ feet.

Guns :
15—5·1 inch, 55 cal.
4—4 in. (anti-aircraft)
4—3 in. .
4 machine
Torpedo Tubes :
2 *submerged*
Carry 100 mines

Armour :
3″ Belt...... ....
1″ Deck ....
3″ Gun shields ....
″ Conning tower ......

Machinery : Brown Curtis or Parsons turbines.   Boilers : 25 Yarrow.   H.P. 50,000 = 29·5 kts.   Coal : *normal*, tons; *maximum*, 1170 (with oil fuel).

Name	Builder and Machinery.	Laid down	Completed	Trials	Turbines.	Best recent speed.
Ad. Butakoff	Putilov Yard, Petrograd	Nov. '13				
Ad. Greig	Baltic Works, Reval*	Dec. '13	?			
Ad. Spiridoff	Putilov Yard, Petrograd	Nov. '13				
Svietlana	Baltic Works, Reval *	Dec. '13				

General Notes.—Built under 1912 Naval Programme.   Are equipped for carrying seaplanes.   *Ad. Butakoff* and *Ad. Spiridoff* were originally intended for Siberian Fleet in Pacific.   Four sister ships of the *Admiral Nakhimoff* class building in Black Sea.

* Towed to Petrograd, 1918.

2 s

Laid up in the Gareloch, Firth of Clyde, 1919.

British **GLORY IV,** *alias* Russian **ASKOLD** (April, 1900). 6000 metric tons. Complement, 600. Dimensions : 430¼ (*o.a.*) × 55½ × 20¾ feet (*mean* draught). Armament : 12—6 inch, 45 cal.; 10—11 pdr., 2—3 pdr. AA., 2 M.G. Torpedo tubes (18 inch) : 2 *submerged* (broadside), 2 *above water*. Fitted for Minelaying. Armour : 3″ Deck, 4″ Funnel bases, 6″ C.T Machinery : 3 sets triple expansion. 3 screws. Boilers : 18 Schulz-Thornycroft. Designed H.P. 19,500 = 23 kts. Coal : *normal,* 720 tons ; *maximum,* 1050 tons. Was in Far East, 1914, and served with Allied Fleets during the War.

(*White Sea—dismantled at Liverpool,* 1917.)

VARIAG (ex *Soya,* ex *Variag*) (Oct., 1899). 6600 tons. Complement, ——. Dimensions : 416 (*w.l.*) × 52 × 21 feet (*max.* draught). Armament : 2—12 pdr. Armour : 3″ Deck, 6″ C.T. Machinery : 2 sets 4-cylinder inverted triple expansion. Designed H.P. 20,000 = 23 kts. Coal : *normal,* 770 tons ; *maximum,* 1300 tons. Sunk at Chemulpo (Korea), Feb., 1904, during Russo-Japanese War. Salved, Aug., 1905, repaired by Japanese and re-named *Soya.* Retroceded to Russia by Japan, March, 1916.

Present existence of these 3 Cruisers very doubtful.

Reported sunk at Kronstadt by British C.M.B., August, 1919.

BOGATYR (January, 1901). 6650 tons. Complement, 565. Dimensions : 433 (*w.l.*) × 54½ × 20⅔ feet (*max.* draught). Length *over all,* 440 feet. Armament : 16—5.1 inch, 55 cal., 4 M.G. Torpedo tubes (18 inch) : 2 *submerged* (broadside). Armour : 3″ Deck, 3″ Turrets, 3″ Casemates (4). Machinery : 2 screws. Boilers : Normand-Sigaudy. Designed H.P. 19,500 = 23 kts. Coal : *normal,* 900 tons ; *maximum,* 1270 tons. Fitted for Minelaying. *Oleg* sunk by British C.M.B., June, 1919.

Reported scuttled as Block Ships.

(Діана : АВрора.) **DIANA** (October, 1899) & **AVRORA** (May, 1900). 6830 metric tons. Complement, 573. Dimensions : 410 (*w.l.*) × 55 × 21¼ feet (*mean* draught). Armament : *Aurora,* 10—6 inch, 45 cal., 5—6 pdr. AA., 2 M.G. ; *Diana,* 10—5.1 inch, 4—6 pdr., 4—6 pdr. AA. Carries 125 mines. Torpedo tubes (18 inch), no tubes in *Diana ;* 2 *submerged* (broadside) in *Avrora.* She is also fitted for Minelaying. Machinery : 3 sets horizontal 3-cylinder. Designed H.P. 11,600 = 20 kts. 3 screws. Boilers : 24 Belleville. Coal : *normal,* 960 tons ; *maximum,* 970 tons. Looted by Bolshevist crews, 1917, and abandoned in the Neva, 1918 ; said to have been scuttled there as Blockships.

RUSSIAN GUNBOATS AND DESPATCH VESSELS.

For Amur River Monitors of the *Grosa* type, and the Caspian Sea gunboats *Ardahan* and *Kars*, see later pages.

Armoured Gunboat.

KHRABRI (1895). 1740 tons. Complement, 197. Guns : 1—6 inch, 45 cal. ; 5—5.1 inch, 55 cal. ; 2—1 pdr., 1—1 pdr. AA., 2 M.G. Armour : 5″ Harvey, waterline belt amidships, 3″ ditto aft. Designed H.P. 2000 = 14 kts. Niclausse boilers. Coal : *maximum*, 160 tons.

Note.—Re-fitted and re-armed, 1916. Appearance may be altered.

Gunboats.

(*Disarmed, April,* 1919.)

KHIVINETZ (1905). Displacement, 1340 tons. Complement, 161. Guns : 4—4.7 inch, 2—3 pdr. AA. Machinery : Triple expansion. 2 screws. Boilers : 8 Belleville. Designed H.P. 1400 = 13½ kts. Coal : *normal*, 100 tons ; *maximum*, 190 tons.

Gunboats (Mine Layers).

Photo, Capt. Alan Burgoyne, M.P.
(*Disarmed.*)

GROZIASTCHI (1890). 1640 tons. Complement, 176. Guns : 4—6 inch, 2—11 pdr. Armour : 5″ Belt amidships, 3″ Aft, with 3¾″ Bulkhead forward. Designed H.P. 2000 = 14 kts. Coal : 150 tons. Belleville boilers. Carries 20-30 mines.

Note.—Re-fitted and re-armed, 1916. May now be of different appearance.

(*At Vladivostok.*)

MANDJUR (1886). 1440 tons. Guns (old) : 2—8 inch, 1—6 inch, 4—9 pdr. Torpedo tubes : 1—14 inch (in bow). Designed speed : 13 kts. Coal : 250 tons. Complement, 160.

Fitted as Minelayer. Carries *about* 50 mines.

River Gunboats—Location unknown.

8 *Gunboats* : (Names or Numbers unknown, built 1915-17). —— tons. Dimensions : 66 × 19 × 2½ feet. Guns : 2—3 inch (mountain type), 2 M.G. Speed : 12½ kts.

Despatch Vessels.

No Photos.

Lastotchka (Yarrow, 1904). 120 tons. Speed 18 kts. Turbine engines.

Razvyedchik and *Dozorni* (both 1904). 100 tons. Complement 23 Guns : 1—1 pdr., 1 machine. Speed, 16 kts. Both re-fitted 1915-1916.

(*May be in Finnish Navy.*)

BAKAN (1896). 883 tons. Guns : 2—11 pdr., 4—3 pdr. H.P. 800 = 11 kts. Coal : 130 tons. Complement, 98.

Note.—Re-fitted and re-armed, 1916. Appearance may be changed.

Also :—

Porashayustchi (ex-Destroyer of *Pritki* type).
Petrol T. B. No. 1.

Abrek, Berkut, Harpun, Kitobol, Kondor, Konvoir, Namet, Nived, Ozilya, Periskop, Rognieda, Sputnik, Yakor.

2 N 2

RUSSIAN DESTROYERS (*Eskadrenny Minonossetz* if over 400 tons, *Minonossetz* if under).

$\left.\begin{array}{l} \textit{21 Building?} \\ \textbf{92* Completed.} \end{array}\right\} = \textbf{113}^{*} \textbf{ Destroyers.}$

*Gavriil and 2 other T.B.D. reported sunk ; if so totals are 89 completed and 110 total T.B.D.

No.	Type	Date	Displacement	H.P.	Max. speed	Coal or Oil	Complement	Tubes / Mines	Max. Draught
4	" Hogland type "	1916–?	1550	34,000	32t	tons 300	..	12/80	11
3	Zabiaka	1912–15	1610	32,000	35t	400	110	12/80	9¼
4	Isyaslav	1912–?	1350	32,700	35t	150	110	12/80	9⅔
27	Gavryil	1912–?	1260	30,000	35t	150	110	12/80	9¾
1	Novik	1910–12	1200	33,000	32t	400	140	8/80	10½
3	Kondratenko class (K)	1904–06	625	7300	25	190	98	3/50	9½
6	E. Bukharski class (K)	1904–07	580	6500	25	150–205	94	3/25	8½
7	Ukräina class	1903–07	500	6200	25	130	85	3/16	8
2	Leit. Sergieff (S)	1903–05	350	6000	29	95	64	3	7½
10	Vnimatelni (S) 1904–07 / Bestrashni (S) 1899–01		355	6000	27	125	64	3/16	6
8	Lovki class (N)	1904–05	330	5700	27	60	65	2/15	7
2	Grosovoi class (N)*	1899–01	310	5700	26	80	59	2/6	8
10	Dyelni class (Y) 1904–06 / Bravi class (Y) 1902–06		350	5700	26	100	64	2/14	6
4									
5	Tverdi class (Y)*	1905–06	300	3800	25	60	59	2	6
4	Smyeli class (Y)*	1899–03	380	3800	26½	70	52	1/18	6½
3	Pritki class (Y)*	1895–01	220	3800	27	60	52	1/18	7½

*These are officially rated with torpedo boats.

Types :—(K)=Krupp. (S)=Schichau. (N)=Normand. (Y)=Yarrow.

4 Hogland type (Mine Layers).

Work stopped.

4 *boats* (not named), begun 1916, by Petrograd Metal Works. 1550 tons. Dimensions : 324¾ × 31¼ × 11 feet. Guns : 5—4 inch, 2—9 pdr. AA., 4 M.G. Torpedo tubes (18 inch) : 12 in 4 triples. To carry 80 mines each. S.H.P. 34,000 = 32 kts. Turbines. Oil : *about* 300 tons.

3 Zabiaka type (Mine Layers).

Photo wanted.

3 *Petrograd Metal Works* : **Orphei, Pobieditel, Zabiaka** (all 1914). 1610 tons. Dimensions : 321½ × 30¼ × 9¼ feet. Guns : 4—4 inch, 1—2 pdr. AA. pom-pom, 2 M.G. Torpedo tubes (18 inch) : 12 in 4 triples. Carry 80 mines. Designed S.H.P. 32,000 = 35 kts. Oil : 400 tons. Complement, 110.

RUSSIAN DESTROYERS.

2 (+ 2) Isyaslav type (Mine Layers).

4 *Reval Shipbuilding Co.:* **Briatshislav, Feodor Stratilat, Isyaslav, Priamislav,** 1350 tons.
Dimensions : 344½ × 31¼ × 9⅜ feet. Designed H.P. 32,700 = 35 kts. Parsons turbines and Normand boilers.
Armament : 4—4 inch, 1—9 pdr. AA., 2 M.G. Torpedo tubes (18 inch) : 12, in 4 triple deck mountings. Oil :
150 tons. Builders are sometimes referred to as Lange & Becker, Böcker & Co., or Chantiers de Nord-Ouest.

Note.—*Azard* captured by British, now Esthonian *Lennuk*. *Feodor-Stratilat* towed to Petrograd 1918, not yet finished.
Briatshislav not finished.

12 (+ 15 ?) Gavryil type (Mine Layers.)

No Photo available.

4 *Petrograd Metal Works :* **Azard, Desna** (*Desna* reported sunk at Petrograd, July, 1919), **Lieutun, Samsun.**

7 *Putilov Works, Petrograd :* **Kapitan 2r. Isyimettlev, Kapitan 2r. Kern°, Kapitan 2r. Konon
Zotov,* Kapitan 2r. Kroun°, Kapitan-Leit. Belli,* Leit. Dubassov,° Leit. Ilyin.**

7 *Russo-Baltic S.B. Co. (Reval) :* **Gavryil,§ Konstantin, Mietshislav, Mikhail,*† Sokol,*† Svoboda,
Vladimir*†.**

9 *Ziese Yard, Riga :* **Hogland,*‡ Grengamn,*‡ Khios,*‡ Kulm,*‡ Patras,*‡ Rymnik,*‡ Smolensk,*‡
Stirsuden,°‡ Tenedos*‡.**

* Not finished, 1919. Towed from Reval (†) or Riga (‡) to Petrograd, February, 1918. § Reported sunk 1919 but
not deleted from totals.

Displacement : 1260 tons. Dimensions : 314¾ × 30½ × 9¾ feet. Designed H.P. 30,000 = 35 kts. All have turbines
and oil fuel only. Armament : 4—4 inch, 1—2 pdr. AA., 2 M.G. Torpedo tubes (18 inch) : 12, in 4 triple deck
mountings. Carry 80 mines. Complement, 110. Oil : 150 tons.

Note.—Bolshevist *Spartak*, ex Kerensky *Mikula Maklej*, ex Czarist *Kapitan Kingsbergen*, captured by British and now
Esthonian *Wambola*.

1911 Special Boat (Mine Layer.)

1 *Putilov-Vulkan* boat : **Novik** (Putilov Yard, Petrograd, 1911). 1200 tons. Dimensions : 336 × 31.2 × 9.8 feet.
Designed H.P. 33,000 = 32 kts. A. E. G.-Curtis turbines and 400 tons oil fuel only. Complement, 112 (60 now).
Trials : 42,800 = 36.3 kts. Armament : 4—4 inch, 1—2 pdr. AA., 4 M.G., 8—18 inch tubes in 4 twin deck mountings.
Carries 80 mines.

Note.—Built at the expense of the Putilov Co., as an experiment, and taken over for the Russian Navy.

3 Gen. Kondratenko type (Mine Layers.)

3 " *Kondratenko* " *class,* named **Gen. Kondratenko, Sibirski-Strelok** (Helsingfors, 1906), **Pogranitchnik,**
(Crichton Yard, Abö, 1905). 625 tons. Dimensions : 246.7 × 26.9 × 8.5 feet. Designed H.P. 7300 = 25 kts.
Coal : 215 tons. Complement, 101–98. All armed with 3—4 inch, 2—3 pdr., 3 M.G., and 3—18" deck tubes, in
one twin and one single mounting. Carry 50 mines.

Notes.—Much the same build as *Amuretz* class, (next page), but have a raised poop. *Okhotnik* lost during the war.

6 Emir Bukharski type (Mine Layers).

4 Later boats, named **Gaidamak, Vsadnik,** (Krupp-Germania Yard, Kiel, 1905), **Amuretz,** (Riga, 1905), **Ussurietz** (Helsingfors, 1907), the last two being built from materials supplied by Krupps. 570 tons. Dimensions: *Gaidamak* and *Vsadnik,* 233 × 24.2 × 7.5 feet. *Amuretz* and *Ussurietz,* 233 × 23.6 × 7.8 feet. Designed H.P. 6500 in first two, 6200 in second two = 25 kts. Coal: 205 tons. Complement, 97–94. All armed with 2—4 inch, 1—3 pdr., 1—1 pdr. AA., 4 M.G., and 3—18 inch deck tubes. Carry 25 mines.

(With Bolshevist Volga Flotilla).

2 Earlier boats, named **Yakob Sverdlov** (ex *Emir Bukharski*), **Karl Liebknecht** (ex *Finn*), (Helsingfors, 1905-4.) 580 tons. Dimensions: 237.8 × 26.9 × 7.7 feet. Designed H.P. 6200 = 25 kts. Machinery of *Y. Sverdlov* by Schichau. Coal: 150 tons. Complement: 97–94. Armament: 2—4 inch, 2 or 1—1 pdr., 4 M.G., and 3 deck torpedo tubes. Carry 25 mines. *Moskvityanin* sunk in Caspian Sea, 1919.

7 Ukraina type (Mine Layers).

Fore funnel now raised.

7 *"Ukraina" class,* named **Donskoi-Kasack** (1907), **Stereguchi Strashni** (all 1905), **Turkmenetz-Stavropolski,** * **Ukraina, Voiskovoi** (all 1904), **Zabaikaletz** (1907.) All built by Lange's Yard, Riga. 500 tons. Dimensions: 240 × 23½ × 7½ feet. Designed H.P. 6200 = 25 kts. Boilers: 4 Normand. Coal: 50 tons *normal,* 135 tons *full load.* Complement, 88–85. Armament: 3—4 inch, 1—1 pdr., 2 M.G., and 2 torpedo tubes (18″). Carry 16 mines.

*Bolshevist Volga Flotilla.

2 Leit. Sergieff type.
10 Vnimatelni type (Mine Layers).

2 *Schichau, Danzig.* **Leit. Sergieff,*** **Kapitan Yurassovski*** (both launched 1905). 350 tons. Dimensions: 202½ × 22⅓ × 7½ feet. Designed H.P. 6000 = 29 kts. 4 Thornycroft boilers. Coal: 95 tons. Complement, 64. All armed with 2—11 pdr., 5—3 pdr., and 3 tubes.

3 *Schichau, Elbing.* **Bestrashni,*** **Besposhtchadni,†** **Beshumni*** (all launched 1899).

Also :—

7 *Schichau, Danzig.* **Boyevoi, Burni, Insh. Mech. Svereff, Insh. Mech. Dmitrieff, Vnimatelni, Vnushitelni, Vuinoslivi.** (All built by Schichau, Danzig, and launched 1905–6). 355 tons. Dimensions: 208½ × 23 × 6 feet. Designed H.P. 6000 = 27 kts. 4 Schichau Boilers. Coal: 125 tons. Complement, 64. All armed with 2—11 pdr., 6 M.G., and 3—18″ tubes. Carry 16 mines.

*In White Sea. †At Vladivostok.

8 Lovki type (Mine Layers).

8 "*Lovki*" class, named **Lovki, Likoi,** (Normand Le Havre, 1905), **Legki, Iskusni, Krepki** (La Seyne, 1905), **Metki,** **Molodetski, Mostchni** (F. & C. de la Med. Havre, 1905). 330 tons. Dimensions : 185⅜ × 21 × 5¾ feet. Designed H.P. 5700=27 kts. Boilers : 4 Normand. Coal : 100—110 tons. Complement, 65. All armed with 2—11 pdr., 2 M.G., and 2 deck tubes (18"). Carry 15 mines.

*Bolshevist Volga Flotilla.

2 Grosovoi type (1 boat Mine Layer).

(*Are officially rated as Torpedo Boats.* Both in White Sea.)

2 "*Grosovoi*" class, named **Grosovoi, Vlastni.** (F. et C. de la Med., Le Havre, 1900). 310 tons. Dimensions : 185¾ × 19½ × 6½ feet. Designed H.P. 5700=26 kts. Boilers : 4 Normand. Coal : 60 tons. Complement, 59. Both armed with 2—11 pdr., 1 M.G., and 2 deck tubes (18"). *Vlastni* carries 6 mines.

26 Yarrow or Modified Yarrow type (1907-1894.)

10 "*Dyelni*" class, named **Dyelni,*** **Dostoini,*** **Dieyatelni,*** **Rastoropni,*** **Razyastchi, Silni, Stroini,*** **Storoshevoi,*** (launched 1906-5). **Gremyastchi, Vidni** (1905-4). Re-armed with 2—4 in., 2 M.G. Tubes : 2—18". Carry 14 mines.

*Bolshevist Volga Flotilla

4 "*Bravi*" class, named **Bravi,†** **Boiki,§** **Bodri,†** **Grosni†** launched 1905-2.) No mainmast.

†At Vladivostok, disarmed. §*Boiki* now in Mediterranean as French T.B.D. *Quentin Roosevelt*.

Above T.B.D. all built by Nevski Works, Petrograd, and displace 350 tons. Dimensions : 210 × 21 × 6½ feet. Designed H.P. 5,700=26 kts. Boilers : 4 Normand in *Dyelni* class, 4 Yarrow in *Bravi* class. Coal : 80 tons. Complement, 64. *Bravi* class armed with 1—11 pdr., 5—3 pdr., and 2 deck torpedo tubes, but *Bravi, Boiki, Bodri* have stem tube.

As above photo but *Smyeli* class no mainmast and straight stems, and *Pritki* class straight stems with mainmast.

Following Boats officially rated as Torpedo Boats :—

5 "*Tverdi*" class, named **Leit.†** **Maleieff,†** **Insh. Mech. Anastassoff,†** **Tverdi,†** **Totchni,†** **Trevoshni†** (Okhta Works, Petrograd, 1906 ; re-erected at Vladivostok).

4 "*Smyeli*" class, named **Smyeli,†** **Serditi,†** **Statni,†** **Skori,†** (Nevski Works, Petrograd, 1901, re-erected at Port Arthur).

3 "*Pritki*" class, named **Pritki*** (ex *Sokol*, Yarrow, Poplar, 1895), **Protchni*** (Izhora Works, Petrograd, 1900–1899). **Retivi*** (Nevski Works Petrograd, 1901).

Above T.B.D. displace 380–220 tons (see Summary Table). Dimensions : *about* 190 × 18½ × 5½—6 feet. H.P. 3800=27-25 kts. (4000=29 kts. in *Pritki*). Boilers : 4 locomotive in *Tverdi* class, 4 Yarrow in others. Coal : 65 tons. Complement, 59-52. All armed with 2—11 pdr., 2 M.G., 2—18" tubes in *Tverdi* class : others 1—15" tube and 18 mines.

*Bolshevist Volga Flotilla. †At Vladivostok, disarmed.

RUSSIAN (BALTIC) TORPEDO BOATS.

No.	Type	Date	Displacement	H.P.	Max. speed	Fuel	Complement	T. Tubes	Max. draug't
5	*Nos. 220—214* (N)	1902–04	150	5700	29	30	25	2	5
1	*No. 213* (N)	1902	190	3800	24	60	26	2	5
3	*Nos. 142, 129, 128*	1894–98	120	2000	21	20	20	3	$6\frac{3}{4}$
1	*Petrol T.B. No. 1*	1904	..	..	..	..	..	..	..

(N)=Normand type.

5 *Normand* type. **Nos. 214, 216, 217, 219, 220,** (1902-4.). Guns: 2—3 pdr. and 2—15 in. tubes, (double mounted). Other and older t.b. have 2—1 pdr. and 3 tubes.

2 pole masts.
No funnel.

1 ——— type. **Petrol T.B. No. 1.** 3 small guns. 1 tube. Used now as a despatch vessel.

28 { *20 building?* / **14** modern / **14** old } **Submarines** (*Podvodnija Lodki.*)

(Inclusive of Baltic and Siberian flotillas.)

No.	Type	Date	Displacement	H.P.	Max. speed kts.	Fuel tons	Tubes and Gear.	Complement	Max. draug't
10	*G 1—10* (H)	?	$\frac{960}{1260}$	$\frac{2200}{700}$	$\frac{16}{9}$	60	16*	..	14
10	*B 1—10* (B)	?	$\frac{970}{1265}$	$\frac{3150}{700}$	$\frac{17}{9}$	58	16*	..	13
1	*Sviatoi Georg* (LA)	1916–17	$\frac{250}{370}$	$\frac{700}{500}$	$\frac{13}{8\cdot5}$	For 1500 miles / For 70-80 miles	2	..	..
1	*Forel* (B)	1912–17	$\frac{650}{784}$	$\frac{840}{900}$	$\frac{11}{9}$	40	4*	..	$12\frac{1}{2}$
2	*Edinorog* (B)	1912–17	Do.	$\frac{2640}{900}$	$\frac{16}{9}$	40	12	..	$12\frac{1}{2}$
2	*Volk* (B)	1912–16	Do.	$\frac{500}{840}$	$\frac{10}{9}$	40	12	52	$12\frac{1}{2}$
7	*Tigr* (B)	1912–17	Do.	$\frac{500}{900}$	$\frac{10}{9}$	40	8	..	$12\frac{2}{3}$
4	*Alligator* (L)	1908	$\frac{450}{500}$	$\frac{400}{400}$	$\frac{8}{7}$	15	4	23	16
1	*Moinga* (B)	1908	$\frac{117}{177}$	$\frac{480}{140}$	$\frac{11}{5\cdot5}$	5	2	20	9
2	*Makrel* (B)	1907	$\frac{150}{200}$	$\frac{100}{100}$	$\frac{7\cdot5}{5}$	$2\frac{3}{4}$	4	16	$9\frac{1}{2}$
4	*Byeluga* (H)	1904	$\frac{110}{120}$	$\frac{160}{60}$	$\frac{8\cdot5}{6}$	2	1	16	10
2	*Kataska* (B)	1904	$\frac{150}{200}$	$\frac{120}{100}$	$\frac{9}{7}$	3	4	20	$9\frac{1}{2}$
1	*Delfin* (B)	1903	115	..	$\frac{10}{8}$	..	2	12	..

(B)=Bubnov type.   (LA)=Laurenti-Ansaldo type.   (L)=Lake type.   (H)=Holland type.

* Mine Layers.

10 ? Holland Type (Mine-layers).

> Doubtful if ever begun.

10 *Holland* boats: *G 1—10*, ordered from Nobel & Lessner, 1916. 262×22½×14 feet. Guns: 2—12 or 14 pdr., 2 M.G. Tubes: 10. Dropping gears: 6. Mines: 10. Other details as Table.

10 ? Bubnov Type (Mine-layers).

> Doubtful if ever begun.

10 *Bubnov* boats: *B 1—4* (Baltic Works, Petrograd), *B 5—10* (Russo-Baltic Works, Reval). 264×23×14 feet. Guns, tubes, dropping gears, mines, as *G 1—10* above. Other details as table.

1 Laurenti Boat.

Photo by courtesy of Messrs. Ansaldo-San Giorgio.
(In White Sea.)

1 *Laurenti-Ansaldo* type: **Sviatoi Georg** (Ansaldo-San Giorgio, Spezia, 1916 or 1917). Dimensions: *about* 150 × 14 × 10 feet. Machinery: 2 sets of 350 H.P., 6-cyl. 2-cycle Fiat Diesel engines *on surface*. Radius of action: *about* 1500 miles at cruising speed *on surface*, 70 or 80 miles at a low speed *submerged*. Armament: 1 small Q.F. and 2 bow 18-inch torpedo tubes. Is generally similar to Spanish *Monturiol* and Brazilian *F* classes. Arrived at Archangel, Sept., 1917.

12 "Improved Bubnov" Type (1 boat Mine-layer).

> Photo Wanted.

1 *Special* boat: **Forel,** (Baltic Works, Petrograd, 1912—17) Mine-layer. Different H.P. and speeds to other boats,— see Table. Guns: 1—6 pdr., 1—1 pdr., AA. 1 M.G. 4 Tubes. Carries 40—50 Mines.

> Photo Wanted.

2 *Edinorog* type: **Smaya, Yasy,** (Nobel & Lessner, Reval, 1912—17). Guns: 2 or 1—6 pdr., 1—1 pdr. AA., 1 M.G. Tubes: 4. Dropping Gears: 8.

> Photo Wanted.

2 *Volk* type: **Vyepr, Volk** (Baltic Works, Petrograd, 1912—16). Guns: 2—6 pdr., 1—1 pdr. AA. Tubes: 4. Dropping Gears: 8. Have Diesel engines removed from Amur River Gunboats.

> Photo Wanted.

7 *Tigr* type: **Kuguar, Leopard, Pantera, Ryss, Tigr, Tur, Yaguar** (Nobel & Lessner, Reval, 1912-17). Guns: 2—6 pdr., 1—1 pdr. AA., 1 M.G. Tubes: 4. Dropping Gears: 8.

General Notes : All launched 1915-16. Dimensions: 223 × 14⅜ × 12⅔ feet. Other details as Table. *Bars, Gepard, Lvitsa, Ugor* and *Edinorog* war losses. Mine-layer *Ersh* sunk by H.M. ships *Valorous* and *Vancouver*, 1919.

4 Lake Type.

Photo, Lieut.-Col. Alan H. Burgoyne, M.P.

All reported to have been captured by the Germans, 1918.

4 *Lake* type: **Alligator, Drakon, Kaiman, Krokodil** (1908). Dimensions: 133×14×16 feet. Naptha (or light oil) motors for surface. Armament: 1—3 pdr., 1 machine, 4—18 inch tubes, 2 dropping gears for 18 inch torpedoes.

1 Bubnov Type.

No photo available.

Bolshevist Volga Flotilla.

1 *Bubnov* type: **Minoga** (1908, re-built 1915). Dimensions: 197×18⅝×8 feet. Diesel engines. 1—1 pdr. gun. Two 18 inch tubes.

2 Bubnov Type.

No photo Available.

Bolshevist Volga Flotilla.

2 early *Bubnov* type: **Makrel, Okun** (1907). Displacement, 150/200 tons. 4—18 inch dropping gears.

4 Old Holland Type.

No photo available.

Reported that all were captured by Germans, in 1918.

4 early *Holland* type: **Byeluga, Piskar, Sterliad, Tchuka** (1904). 1—1 pdr. gun. 1—15 inch dropping gear.

2 Old Bubnov Type.

No photo available.

Bolshevist Volga Flotilla.

2 early *Bubnov* type: **Ugor** (ex *Graf Sheremetier*), **Kasatka,** (Built about 1904, re-built 1914-15). Similar to *Makrel* and *Okun*, but have 1—1 pdr. and 1 M.G.

1 Old Bubnov Type.

Illustrated in
"Fighting Ships" up to
1915-16.

In White Sea.

1 old *Bubnov* boat **Delfin** (1903). Used to be armed with 2—15 inch dropping gears. Present value almost *nil.*

570

Motor Patrol Boats.

Total number unknown. Some in the Baltic ; others in the White and Black Seas. Builders : chiefly U.S. firms, 1915-16. —— tons. Dimensions : 60 × 10 × 2⅝ feet, but others may be 80-85 feet long. Machinery : Twin or triple sets of petrol motors (12-cyl., Standard, Dusenberg, Van Blerck, &c). H.P. 500-600 = 25-26 kts. designed speed. Some made 30.1 kts. on trials in smooth water, but best sea speed is only about 20 kts. for short periods. Fuel : 4000 galls. petrol = 600 miles at cruising speed. Guns : One (11 pdr., 6 or 3 pdr. ?), and perhaps M.G. Depth charges may also be carried. Crew, about 8-10.

Coast Patrol Boats :—

Barsuk	*Mesen*	*Stvol*
Dulo	*Palash*	*Tumba*
Gornostai	*Pistolet*	*Tzapfa*
Griff	*Pulva*	*Vladimir*
Kobchik*	*Ruslan*	*Voron*
Korsun	*Shaska*	*Vuidra*
Kunitsa	*Sobol*	*Yastreb*

* May be in Finnish Navy now.

Destroyer Depot Ships.

Repair Ships, **ANGARA** and **KAMA** attached to T.B.D. Flotillas.

Submarine Depot Ships.

Cruiser **DIANA** : for details, see preceding pages with other cruisers.

> *No photo available.*
> *(Resembles German " Vulkan.")*

VOLKHOV (Putilov, 1913). 2400 tons. Dimensions : 315 × 69 × 11¾ feet. Diesel engines. H.P. 1200 = 10 kts. Radius 3600 miles. Can raise 1000 tons.

Note.—Carries all essential stores for submarines (oil fuel, reserve accumulators, &c.), and has compressed air, distilling and charging plant, workshops, &c.

> *No photo available.*

(At Vladivostok ?)

TOBOL (1899). 5500 tons. H.P. 2500 = 8 kts. Not certain if this ship, or another of same name, was sunk in 1916. Reported to be Transport at Vladivostok, 1919.

KHABAROVSK (1895). 2800 tons. H.P. 1800 = 12·5 kts. Guns : 2—11 pdr.. 2—3 pdr., 2 M.G. Coal : 390 tons. Complement, 132.

EVROPA (1878). 3200 tons. H.P. 12,000 = 13 kts. Guns : 4—3 pdr.; tubes : 2 *above water*, 1 *submerged*. Coal : 390 tons.

Seaplane Carrier.

> *No photo available.*

ORLITZA (——). 3000 tons. 10 kts. speed. Guns : 8—11 pdr., 2 M.G. Carries 4 seaplanes.

Mine Layers.

> *No photo available.*

(At Vladivostok).

DIOMID, PATROKL, ULIS (1913-14). 600 tons. Complement, 41. Dimensions : 160 × 26½ × feet, Guns : *Not known.* H.P. —— = 12 kts. speed.

AMŪR (1907). 3608 tons. Complement, 318. Dimensions : 320 × 46 × 14½ feet. Armament : 9—4·7 inch, 4 M.G. H.P. 4700 = 17 kts. Boilers : 12 Belleville. Coal : 670 tons. Carries 320 mines. *Yenessei* of this type lost in the war.

(Continued on next page.)

Mine Layers (continued).

VOLGA (1905) 1711 tons. Complement, 266. H.P. 1600 = 13 kts. Babcock boilers. Armament : 4—3 pdr. Carries 236 mines. Coal : 160 tons.

No photo available.

USSURI (1901). 3200 tons. Complement, 210. Dimensions : 236 × 36 × 15 feet. Guns : 3—11 pdr., 4—3 pdr., 2 M.G. H.P. 1056 = 10 kts. Carries 500 mines.

No photo available.

(*Transport, at Vladivostok.*)

SHILKA (Elswick. 1896). 3500 tons. Complement, 205. Dimensions : 278 × 39.4 × 17 feet. Guns : 4—4.7 inch, 8—11 pdr., 4 M.G. H.P. 1650 = 11 kts.

No photo available.

(*At Vladivostok.*)

MONGUGAI (Flensburg, 1891). 2500 tons. Complement, 193. Dimensions : 202 × 30 × 18 feet. Guns : 7—3 pdr. H.P. 6000 = 9 kts.

Mine Layers (continued).

ONEGA (ex *Gertzog Edinburgski*, 1875). 4840 tons ; and **NAROVA** (ex *General Admiral*, 1872). 5030 tons. Speed : 12-13 kts. Guns : 4—11 pdr., 4 M.G. Complete 6″ iron belt. Carry 600 mines.

Also :—
Ilmen,* Lena, Lovat, Luga, Msta,* Svir,* Ural.
*May be in Finnish Navy now.

Mine Sweepers.

No photo available.

ISKRA, PLAMYA, PATRON (Middlesborough, 1913-14). 500 tons. Dimensions : 146 × 24½ × 10 feet. Guns : 2—11 pdr. H.P. 650 = 11 kts.

MINREP. (Now has a main mast.)

FUGAS, MINREP,* PROVODNIK, SAPAL,* VZRUIV (1911). 150 tons. Guns : 2—3 pdr. Speed : 10 kts.
*May be in Finnish Navy now.

Also about 14 other small craft and about 5 Torpedo Boats fitted as Sweepers.

Repair Ships.

No photo available.

OKA (1914), **KAMA** (1911). 2000 tons. Speed : 10 kts.

PETSHORA (1910). 2000 tons. Speed : 10 kts. Coal : 170 tons.

No photo available.

(*In White Sea.*)

XENIA (ex *Cayo Soto*, 1900). 5900 tons. Speed : 11 kts. Guns : 2—11 pdr., 2—3 pdr., 2 M.G. Coal : 400 tons.

Repair Ships—(continued).

ANADYR (1896). 12,000 tons. Speed : 13 kts.

ANGARA (Clydebank, 1898, ex *Anegawa Maru*, ex *Angara*). 5920 tons. H.P. 3000 = 13 kts. (less at present). Belleville boilers. Coal : 800 tons. Captured in the Russo-Japanese War. In 1911, presented to Russia by the Emperor of Japan.

Salvage Ships.

Assistans	*Meteor*	*Silach*
Hero	*Nordmir*	*Solid*
Karin	*Protektor*	

Transports.

32 ships laid up in Baltic. Auxiliary Cruiser *Orel* and 3 or 4 Transports at Vladivostok.

Transports—(continued).

BORGA (1882), 4700 tons, and **LAKHTA** (1889), 5000 tons. Speed : 10 kts.

SAMOYED (1895). 1300 tons. Speed : 12 kts.

PAKHTUSOV (——). 1100 tons. Speed : 9 kts. In White Sea.

TAIMYR (1908), **VAIGATCH** (1908). In White Sea. 1290 tons. Speed : 10 kts. (*Surveying Ships.*)

MURMAN (1912, for White Sea). 500 tons.
(Also other ships, chartered or requisitioned for period of war.)

Hospital Ships.

14 laid up in Baltic.

Oil Tankers.

Aramis	*Olga*	*Tamara*
Elena	*Spinoza*	*Tatiana*
Nina		

Ice Breakers.

Ilya Mourometz, Kniaz Pojarski, Kozma Minin, Mikula Salianinovich, were in White Sea, 1919, under control of Allies.

Gorod Revel and *Herkules* are in the Baltic.

Ice Breakers (continued).

No photo available.

TSAR MIKHAIL FEODOROVITCH (Vulkan, Stettin, 1914). 1391 tons *gross*. Dimensions : 244 × 57 × 27½ feet. H.P. = 10 kts. speed.

(*In the Baltic.*)

ERMAK (Elswick, 1898). 8000 tons. Dimensions : 305 × 71 × 25 feet. 1¼″ Steel belt. H.P. 10,000 = 16 kts. Coal : 3000 tons.

(*In the Baltic.*)

PETR VELIKI (1872, re-constructed 1905). Displacement, 9665 tons. Armament (new in 1905) :* 4—8 inch (50 cal.), 12—6 inch (45 cal.), 12—12 pdr., 4—6 pdr., 8—3 pdr., 2 M.G. H.P. 8260 = 13 kts. Coal : 1200 tons. Present speed : 11 kts.

* All guns probably removed now.

Armed Yachts.

Ex-SHTANDART (1895). 5557 tons. Guns: 8—3 pdr. H.P. 10,600 = 21 kts. Belleville boilers.

(Flagship, Bolshevist C-in-C. Baltic).

KRETCHET (ex-*Polarnaya-Sviedza*, 1890). 3640 tons. Guns: 6—12 pdr. H.P. 5600 = 18·8 kts. Cylindrical boilers.

Ex-ALEXANDRIA (1903). 500 tons. 14·5 kts. Paddle-wheel Yacht. There are also 9 small Yachts of from 800—180 tons.

Gunnery School Ships.

Reported sunk at Kronstadt.

SARIA SVOBODI (ex-*Imperator Aleksandr II*, 1887, re-constructed 1905). Displacement 9390 metric tons. Complement, 648. Armament: 2—12 inch (30 cal.); 6—6 inch (45 cal.); 4—4·7 inch, 2—3 pdr., 1 machine, 2—3 inch AA. Armour (Compound): Belt 14″ 6″, Barbette 12″. Designed H.P. 8500 = 15 kts. Coal: 1080 tons.

(And Transport.)   Photo, Seward, Weymouth.

RIGA (ex *Belgravia*), (Blohm & Voss, 1899). 14,500 tons. Complement, 273. Guns: 2—6 inch, 8—4·7 inch, 8—12 pdr., 4—6 pdr., 4—3 pdr., 18 machine. H.P. 4000 = 12 kts. An Enemy Naval Annual refers to a sister ship, *Argun*, of which nothing is known in this country. Also *Vyemi*.

Diving School.

Old *Afrika* (1877), 2600 tons.

Engineers' Training Ships.

(And Transport.)

OKEAN (Howaldt, 1902). 11,900 tons. H.P. 11,000 = 18 kts. Coal: 1600 tons. Boilers: 6 Belleville, 6 Niclausse, 3 Yarrow, 2 Thornycroft. Complement, 700.

Also Despatch vessels *Lastotchka*, *Petrol T.B. No. 1.*, Auxiliaries *Nicolai Pogolski Buksir*, *Byelomor*, *Kotka*, *Samoyed*.

Mine and Torpedo School Ships.

NIKOLAIEFF (ex-*Palatia*) (1894). 13,500 tons. Complement, 272. H.P. 4200 = 13 kts. Guns: 2—11 pdr., 4—3 pdr. Tubes: 4 *above water.*

Also *Aziya*. *Osvoboditelni*, *Khoper*,* *Terek*,* Motor boat *No. 5.*
*Mine-layer.

Old Training Ship.

VOIN (1893). 1280 tons. Guns: 4—12 pdr. Speed, 9 kts.

DVINA RIVER FLOTILLA.

Gunboats.

ADVOKAT.

GORODOFF.

RAZLYFF.

Note.—Above three gunboats were under the White Ensign during the British operations in Northern Russia.

Supposed that there is the usual extemporised Fleet of River Steamers and Armed Barges, &c., used by the Allies and Bolshevists in Northern Russia. British Aircraft have attacked Bolshevist Craft of this kind on various occasions. But no details are available of these ships.

AMUR RIVER FLOTILLA.

Scale : **1 inch = 160 feet.**

NO FUNNELS.

GROSA *class* (8 ships).

River Monitors & Gunboats.

Photo: "Motor Ship & Motor Boat."

GROSA, SHKWAL, SHTORM, SMERTCH, TYFUN, URAGAN, VIKHR, VYUGA (——1910). Displacement, 950 tons. Complement, . Length (*waterline*), 233 feet. Beam, $42\frac{1}{3}$ feet. Draught, $4\frac{1}{2}$ feet. Guns : 2—6 inch (one forward, one aft), 4—4·7 inch in pairs in midship turrets, 4 machine. Armour: $4\frac{1}{2}''$ turrets. Machinery : Nobel-Lessner Diesel motors. 1000 h.p. = 11 kts.

Note.—The machinery has been removed from all of the above ships to provide engines for new Submarines built during the War. Their 6-inch guns have been removed for shore service.

River Monitors & Gunboats (*continued*).

No photo available.

OROKANIN, MONGOL, BURIAT, VOGUL, SIBIRIAK, KOREL and **KIRGIZ, KALMUIK, SIRIANIN, VOTYAK** (1909). 190 tons. Complement, 40. Dimensions : 164 × 27 × 2 feet. Guns : 2—11 pdr.,* 2 machine,* but last four have 1—4·7 inch* and 1 machine gun.* Designed H.P., 500 = 11 kts. Coal : 145 tons.

* The Bolshevists removed all guns from these ships.

No photo available.

Kopyo, Palash, Pika, Pistolet, Pulya, Shtik.

These are motor patrol-boats (1908) of 24 tons, 16 kts. speed, each armed with 1—3 inch mountain gun and a M.G.

Note.—Kinjal, Rapira, Sablya, Shashka, transported to Black Sea and Danube during the War.

BLACK SEA SECTION

(INCLUSIVE OF CASPIAN SEA AND VOLGA RIVER FLOTILLAS.)

The Russian Black Sea Fleet no longer exists. The following account gives a summary of this Fleet's dissolution.

When the Austro-German Armies were advancing, in 1918, on the Crimean Naval Ports, the Destroyer *Gnievni* was blown up at Sebastopol. When the fall of Sebastopol was imminent, the two Dreadnoughts **SVOBODNAYA ROSSIA** and **VOLYA** proceeded to Novorossisk in company with Destroyers and various Auxiliaries. Other ships took refuge in the Sea of Azov. **SVOBODNAYA ROSSIA** was torpedoed and sunk by the Russian Destroyer *Kertch.* The Destroyers *Feodnissi, Gadjibey, Kaliaklya, Kertch, Pronsitelni, Gromki, Leit. Shestakov, Kap. Leit. Baranoff, Smietlivi* and *Stremitelni* were partially destroyed and scuttled in 1918.

When the Allied Fleet entered the Black Sea, the Dreadnought **VOLYA** was taken over by the British. Destroyers were divided thus: *Derski* (British), *Schastlivi* (British, wrecked at Mudros), *Bespokolni, Kapitan Saken* (France), **ZORKI** (Italy), *Zvonki* (Greece). Seaplane Carrier, **ALMAZ,** taken over by France.

In April, 1919, Bolshevist Armies were advancing on Odessa and Sebastopol, and it became necessary to scuttle or disable Russian Warships at those ports. The Submarines *AG 1, Gagara, Orlan, Morsh, Kashalot, Kit, Narval, Krab* (minelayer), *Karp, Karas* were scuttled and other Submarines removed. The machinery of the following ships was completely destroyed by explosives: **EVSTAFI, IOANN ZLATOUST, BORETZ ZA SVOBODU, ROSTISLAV, TRIA SVIATITELIA, SINOP, PAMIAT MERKURIYA,** *Buistri, Jeevoi, Jootki, Zavidni,* **ZAVETNI, BERESAN.**

The "Denikin Volunteer Fleet" consists of **GENERAL KORNILOFF,** *Pospyeschni, Puilki, Jarki, Strogi, Svirepi, Burevestnik, Utka, Lebed, Pelikan, Nerpa, Tyulen,* **DONETZ, KUBANETZ, TERETZ** and various Armed River Barges, Auxiliaries, etc.

RUSSIAN BLACK SEA FLEET.—RECOGNITION SILHOUETTES.

ONE FUNNEL.

Teretz *class* (3 ships).
(*Denikin*).

Albatross *class* (2 ships).

Kasarki.
(*Disarmed*).

Dunai & Beshtau.

TWO FUNNELS.

Machinery of Ships below destroyed :—

Sinop.

Rostislav.

Volya.
(*Taken over by British.*)

Tri Sviatitelia.
(*Has been reconstructed. Present appearance
probably differs from above*).

Berezan.

Almaz.
(*Seaplane Carrier taken over by France.*)

Machinery of all destroyed.

THREE FUNNELS.

Evstafi *class* (2 ships).

Boretz Za Svobodu.

Gen. Korniloff (*Denikin*.)
P. Merkuria (**Machinery destroyed**).
(*Turrets now removed and replaced by guns in shields.*)

2 o

RUSSIAN BLACK SEA SILHOUETTES.

Scale: 1inch = 1 foot.

DESTROYERS.

KAP. SAKEN
(France).

BESPOKOINI (France).
DERSKI (British).
BISTRI (engines destroyed).
POSPYESHNI ⎫
PUILKI ⎭ Denikin.

ZAVIDNI ⎫
ZAVETNI ⎪ Engines
JEEVOI ⎬ destroyed.
JOOTKI ⎪
JARKI (Denikin).
ZVONKI (Greek).
ZORKI (Italy).

SVIREPI ⎫
STROGI ⎭ Denikin.

Scale : 1" = 80 feet.

AG 2—6 (Submarines)
(*If completed*).

SEVASTOPOL. Two slips. Two large docks (487 ×
85 × 32 and 445 × 85 × 28). One basin.
Admiralty Chart No. 963.

NIKOLAIEFF. Building yard only. Floating dock,
558 × 136 × 30 feet (30,000 tons), *building*. Strongly
fortified approaches. Too shallow water for use as a
base, channel only navigable for ships of 25 feet
maximum draught. A private yard exists here.

NOVORISSISK. Used as Base by General Denikin's
Warships.

Other fortified Black Sea bases without yards or docks;
Batûm, Kinburn, Otchakoff, Azov, Kertch, Yenakali,
Poti (all well fortified).

Commercial harbours at Odessa, Batûm.

SEVASTOPOL.

BLACK SEA PORT.

Stanford's Geog¹ Estab.ᵗ London

ODESSA. One Private Floating Dock (Russian Steam Navigation and Trading Co.) 381 × 63
(clear between sides) × 19½ feet (on blocks). Patent slip for vessels up to 1000 tons.
Admiralty Chart No. 603.

VOLYA (April, 1914), and **DEMOKRATIYA** (18th Oct., 1916).

	Length. (o.a.)	Beam.	Draught.	Displacement.
Volya	551 feet 2 inches	× 89 feet 8 inches	× 27 feet 4 inches (*max.*)	= 22,600 tons
Demokratiya	597 feet 1 inch	× 95 feet 1 inch	× 29 feet 5 inches	= 27,300 tons

Complement.—1252 (*Volya*).

Guns : (*Volya*).
12—12 inch, 50 cal. (A⁶)
18—5·1 inch, 55 cal.⁕
8—11 pdr.⁕
4—9 pdr. (anti-aircraft)⁕
4—3 pdr.⁕
4 machine⁕
Torpedo tubes (18.)
    4 *submerged.*
⁕*Demokratiya* :
   20—5·1 inch.
   4—4 inch AA.
   4—M.G.

Corrections to Plans : Fore funnel should be close to foremast, mainmast should be much further aft with C.T. abaft same. Also have overhanging or "yacht" stems. Two foremost 5·1 inch removed from *Volya*.

Armour :
12″–8″ Belt (amidships)
5″–4″ Belt (bow)
4″ Belt (stern)
3″ Deck
9″–8″ Upper Belt
12″ Turrets and Bases
5″ Battery
12″ Conning tower (fore)
8″ Conning tower (aft)

Svobodnaya Rossiya (has been sunk).

Machinery : Parsons or Brown-Curtis. 4 screws. Boilers : 20 Yarrow. Designed H.P., *Volya*, 26,500 ; H.P. *Demokratiya* 27,900. Speed of both, 21 kts. *Volya*, 2,300 tons *maximum*. Oil 720 tons. (Fuel for *Demokratiya* unknown).

Name.	Builder.	Machinery.	Laid down.	Completed.	Trials.	Turbines.	Boilers.	Best recent speed.
Volya	Nikolaieff (B)		Aug.'11	June,'17	{29040 = 21·4		Yarrow	
Demokratiya	Nikolaieff (B)		July'14	?			Yarrow	

B = Bunge & Ivanoff—Brown (Clydebank)

General Notes.—Design generally resembles *Gangut* class. Original names were *Imperator Aleksandr Treti* (now *Volya*), and *Imperator Nikolai Vtoroi* (now *Demokratiya*). Completion of first two ships *Imp. Maria* and *Imp. Ekaterina Vtoroi* (latter re-named *Svobodnaya Rossia*), was accelerated after the beginning of the war. *Imp. Maria*, the first ship of this class, destroyed by explosion at Sebastopol during the war.

Volya.

Notes.

VOLYA taken over by British.
DEMOKRATIYA not finished. All work stopped on her two years ago.
Imperatritza Maria salved 1919. Funnels, masts, barbettes, C.T., &c., removed. She has been docked *upside down* at Nicolaieff.

IOANN ZLATOUST (AND EVSTAFI).

Photo by favour of Kapitan Ketlinsky.

EVSTAFI CLASS—(2 SHIPS).

EVSTAFI (Nov., 1906) & IOANN ZLATOUST (May, 1906).

Displacement, 13,000 metric tons. Complement, 879.

Length (*over all*), 385¾ feet. Beam, 74 feet. *Maximum* draught, 27 feet.

Guns :
4—12 in., 40 cal. (A⁴).
4—8 in., 50 cal. (A).
12—6 in., 45 cal.
Torpedo tubes (18 inch) :
  2 *submerged* (broadside).

Armour (Krupp) :
9″—7″ Belt (amidships)
2″—Belt (bow) .. ..
7″ Bulkheads ....
2¼″ Armour deck (behind belt)
3″ Deck (forward and aft)...
10″ Turrets (N.C.) and bases...
6″ Lower deck side ....
5″ Battery (N.C.) ......
9″ Conning tower ....
  (5″ Tube to it.)

Ahead :
2—12 in.
2—8 in.
2—6 in.

Astern :
2—12 in.
2—8 in.
2—6 in.

Machinery : **Destroyed** 25/4/19. Coal : *normal* 670 tons, *maximum* 1000 tons. *Evstafi* built at Nikolaieff, *I. Zlatoust* at Sevastopol. Both laid down 1903. Completed 1910.

BORETZ ZA SVOBODU (ex *Pantelimon*, ex *Kniaz. P. Tavritcheski*) (Oct., 1900).

Displacement, 12,840 metric tons. Complement, 741.

Length (*over all*), 378⅓ feet. Beam, 73 feet. Draught, 27 feet *maximum*.

Guns :
4—12 in., 40 cal. (A⁴).
12—6 in., 45 cal.
(Other guns and tubes removed during war).

Armour (Krupp) :
9″—7″ Belt (amidships)
2″—Belt (bow) ....
7″ Bulkheads ....
2¼″ Armour deck (behind belt)
3″ Deck (forward and aft) ...
10″ Turrets (N.C.) ....
10″ Turret bases ....
6″ Lower deck side ....
5″ Battery (N.C.) ......
9″ Conning tower ....
  (5″ Tube to it.)

Ahead :
2—12 in.
4—6 in.

Astern :
2—12 in.
4—6 in.

Broadside : 4—12 in., 8—6 in.

Machinery : **Destroyed** 25/4/19. Coal : *normal* 670 tons, *maximum* 1100 tons. Laid down at Nikolaieff 1898, completed 1903.

Ростиславъ ROSTISLAV (Sept. 1896).

Displacement, 9020 metric tons. Complement, 641.

Length (*waterline*), 341 feet. Beam, 69 feet. *Mean draught*, 25 feet. Length *over all*, 348 feet.

Guns (Obukhoff) :
- 4—10 inch, 45 cal. (A³).
- 8—6 inch, 45 cal.
- 18—11 pdr.
- 6—9 pdr. AA.
- 3 machine

Armour (Harvey) :
- 15″—8″ Belt (amidships)
- 3″ Deck (flat on belt) ....
- 12″ Fore turret ....
- 9″ After turret ....
- 6″ Turret bases..........)
- 6″ Lower deck redoubt......
- 6″ Small turrets ...
- 6″ Small turret bases ......)
- 10″ Conning tower.............
- (Total weight 2400 tons).

Ahead :
2—10 in.
4—6 in.

Astern :
2—10 in.
4—6 in.

Machinery : **Destroyed** 25/4/19. Coal : *normal* 500 tons ; *maximum* 800 tons. Liquid fuel also carried.
General Notes.—Laid down at Nikolaieff, 1895, and completed for sea, 1898. Cost about £850,000.

(Before reconstruction). *Photo by favour of H.I.H. Grand Duke Alexander.*

TRI SVIATITELIA. (Nov., 1893, reconstructed, 1912). 13,530 tons. Complement, 744.
Guns : 4—12 inch (40 cal.) ; 14—6 inch, 2—6 pdr. AA., 2—1 pdr., 3 M.G. Tubes : 2—18 inch *submerged.* Armour (Creusot special) : 16″ Belt (incomplete) with 12″ bulkheads and 3″ deck flat on top edge of belt. 16″ lower deck redoubt and 5″ battery redoubt over. 16″ turrets with 12″ bases. 12″ (fore) C.T. Machinery : **Destroyed** 25/4/19. Coal : *normal* 750 tons ; *maximum* 900 tons.

SINOP (1887, re-constructed, 1910). 11,230 tons. Complement, 656. Dimensions : 339 × 69 × 29 feet.
Armament : 4—8 inch, 12—6 inch, 2—3 pdr., 4 M.G. Armour (compound) : 16″—10″ Belt, 12″ Redoubt. Machinery : **Destroyed** 24/5/19. Coal : *max.* 850 tons.

Note.—Another old battleship, *Georgi Pobiedonosetz*, similar to above, is in service still. Only a Port Guardship, and is disarmed.

Note.

The Plans given below are based on those published in an Enemy Naval Annual. Their accuracy cannot be guaranteed in any way. Last two ships may never be completed.

ADMIRAL NAKHIMOFF (Oct., 1915),* **ADMIRAL LAZAREFF** (June 1916),
ADMIRAL KORNILOFF (not launched). *ADMIRAL ISTOMIN* (not launched).

* Almost finished, May 1918.

Displacement, 6750 metric tons. Complement

Length (*waterline*), 507 feet. Beam, 49⅝ feet. Draught, 18½ feet. Length (*over all*), 519¾ feet.

Guns :
15—5·1 inch (55 cal.)
4—9 pdr. (anti-aero)
4 machine
Torpedo tubes (18″)
2 *submerged.*
Carry 100 mines.

Armour :
3″ Belt ....
1″ Deck ....
3″ Gun Shields ....

Machinery : Curtis turbine. Boilers : 13 Yarrow. Designed H.P. 55,000 = 29·75 kts. Coal (*or oil only*): *normal* tons ; *maximum* tons.

Name	Builders	Machinery	Laid down	Completed	Trials	Boilers	Best recent speed
Ad. Nakhimoff	Nikolaieff†		Nov. '13			Yarrow	
Ad. Lazareff	Nikolaieff†		Nov. '13			Yarrow	
Ad. Korniloff	Nikolaieff†		Sept. '14	?			
Ad. Istomin	Nikolaieff†		Sept. '14	?			

General Notes.—Sister ships to *Admiral Butakoff* class, described on a previous page in Baltic Section.
Are equipped for carrying seaplanes.

† Begun by Russian S.B. Co., Nicolaieff, to be completed by Nicolaieff S.B. & Engineering Co.

Protected Cruisers.

GENERAL KORNILOFF October, 1902), **PAMIAT MERKURIA** (*ex Kagul*), (June, 1903).
6750 tons. Complement, 573. Dimensions : 436×54×20½ feet. Armament : *Gen. Korniloff* 16—5·1 inch, *P. Merkuria* 16—6 inch, 2—11 pdr. Tubes (18 inch) : 2 torpedo tubes *submerged.* Armour : 3″ Deck, Turrets and Casemates (4). Machinery : 2 sets 4 cylinder triple expansion. 2 screws. Boilers : 16 Normand. Designed H.P. 19500 = 23 kts.* Coal : *normal* 700 tons ; *maximum* 1100 tons.

* Machinery of *P. Merkuria* destroyed 25/4/19.

Notes : *Gen. Korniloff* with Gen. Denikin's Naval forces. Turrets fore and aft shown in above photo now removed and replaced by 5·1 inch in shields. This ship has borne the names of *Kagul* and *Otchakoff* five times since 1902, viz.:—*Kagul* (1902), *Otchakoff* (1902-6), *Kagul* 1906-17, *Otchakoff* (1917-18), *Kagul* (1918-19).

15 + 4 ?) Black Sea Destroyers.

No.	Type	Date	Displacement	H.P.	Speed	Fuel	Complement	T. tubes	Max. draug't
4	*Cerigo*	'14—'?	tons 1325	29.000	kts. 33 (*t*)	tons 390 *oil only*	121	12	10½
2	*Derski*	'11—'14	1088	25,500	34 (*t*)	270 ,,	141	12	9
3	*Bistri*	'11—'14	1110	23,000	34 (*t*)	350 ,,	110	10	9½
1	*Kap.-Sakem*	'05—'09	800	6500	25	200 *coal*	91	3	9
7	*Zavidni* (L)	'03—'06	350	5700	26	90	71	2	7⅓
2	*Strogi* (Y)	'00—'02	376	3800	26·5	70	56	2	6½

(L) = Laird type. (Y) = Yarrow type. (*t*) Turbines.

Completing at Nicolaieff.

---

4 boats : **Cerigo, Korfu, Levkos, Zante :** 1325 tons. Dimensions : 303½ × 29½ × 9 feet. Armament : 4—4 inch, 1—2 pdr., (anti-aircraft), 12 tubes in 4 triple deck mountings. Turbine engines. Oil fuel only : 390 tons.

No Photo available.

---

2 boats **Bespokoini,**° **Derski** † (1914), 1088 tons.   307½ × 29½ × 9 feet. Armed as *Bistri* type below but carry no mines. S.H.P. 25,500 = 34 kts. Oil, 255—280 tons.

° Taken over by French.
† Taken over by British.

No photo available — see Silhouettes.
2 masts, 3 funnels.

---

3 boats (1913-14), named : **Bistri,*** **Pospyeshni,**† **Pulki,**† 1110 tons. Dimensions : 321½ × 30½ × 9½ feet. Armament : 4—4 inch, 2—3 pdr.,(anti-aircraft), 5-twin 18 inch tubes. Carry 80 mines. H.P. 25,500 = 34 kts. Parsons turbine. 5 boilers. Oil fuel only. 351 tons.

* Engines destroyed, April 27th, 1919.
† Attached to Gen. Denikin's Army

1 boat (1907) : **Kapitan Saken** * (ex *Pushkin*). 800 tons. Dimensions : 242¾ × 27¼ × 8 feet. H.P. 6500 = 26 kts. Armament : 2—4.7 inch (30 cal.). 2—3 pdr. AA., 3 M.G., 3—18 inch tubes. Carries 80 mines. Normand Boilers. Coal : 200 tons.

*Taken over by French.

7 boats (*Laird* type) **Zavidni,*** **Zavetni,*** **Jeevoi,*** **Jootki,*** **Jarki,**† **Zvonki,**‡ **Zorki**‖ (1905). 350 tons. Dimensions : 210 × 21 × 6½ feet (*normal* draught). *Maximum* draught : 7½ feet. H.P. 5700 = 26 kts. Boilers : 4 Yarrow. Carry 90 tons coal or coal + oil. Armament : 2—11 pdr., 2 M.G., 2—18 inch tubes. 18 mines.
*Engines destroyed. †Denikin's Army. ‡To Greece. ‖To Italy.

2 boats (early *Yarrow* type) : **Strogi,*** **Svirepi*** (1901). 376 tons. Dimensions : 190 × 18½ × 5 feet. H.P. 3800 = 26 kts. Boilers : Yarrow. Carry 70 tons, coal. Armament : 2—11 pdr., 2 M.G., 2—15 inch tubes. 12 mines. *Maximum* draught : 6½ feet.

*Denikin's Army.

6 (+ *5 ?*) **Submarines** (*Podvodnija Lodki.*)

No.	Type	Date	Dis-place-ment	H.P.	Max. speed	Fuel	Com-ple-ment	Tubes and Gear.	Max. draught
			tons		kts.	tons			
5 ?	*AG 2—6* (H)	'18 — ?	$\frac{355}{457}$	$\frac{480}{320}$	$\frac{13}{11}$	30	...	4	15¼
4 {	*Lebed, &c.* (B)	'15—'18	$\frac{650}{784}$	$\frac{500}{900}$	$\frac{10}{9}$	40	52	8	12⅔
	Utka, only. (B)	'15—'16		$\frac{2640}{900}$	$\frac{16}{9}$	40	52	12	12⅔
2	*Tyulen.* (B)	'11—'15	$\frac{650}{784}$	$\frac{500}{1400}$	$\frac{10}{11·7}$	21	52	12	12⅔

(H)=Holland type. (B)=Bubnov type.

No photo available.

No photo available.

5 *Holland* type : *AG 4—6* (were still in packing cases, at Nicolaieff, March, 1918), **AG 2, AG 3** (almost finished, March, 1918). Dimensions : 150¼ × 15¾ × 12¼ feet. 4—18 inch bow tubes. Nlseco Diesel engines. Same type as Chilean *H* Submarines. Other details as Table.

No photo available.

4 *Improved Bubnov* type : **Burevestnik,* Utka,* Lebed*** (1916), **Pelikan*** (1917). Dimensions : 223 × 14¾ × 12⅔ feet. Guns : *Burevestnik, Lebed*, 1—11 pdr.; *Utka*, 2—11 pdr., 1—1 pdr., 1 M.G. ; *Pelikan*, 1—11 pdr., 1—1 pdr., 1 M.G. Have 4 tubes and 4 dropping gears (8 gears in *Utka*). B.H.P. and speeds vary, see Table. Have Diesel engines taken from Amur River Gunboats. Other details as Table.

*Gen. Denikin's Army.

2 *Improved Bubnov* type (*Volk* class) : **Nerpa,* Tyulen*** (1913), built at Nikolaieff. Dimensions : 220 × 14½ × 12⅔ feet. Guns : 1—11 pdr., 1—6 pdr. Tubes : 4. Dropping gears : 8. Have Diesel engines taken from Amur River Gunboats. *Are faster submerged than on surface.* Other details as Table.

*Gen. Denikin's Army.

Gunboats.

Fore and mizzen masts now removed.

TERETZ (1887), **DONETZ** (1887), **KUBANETZ** (1887). 1280-1295 tons. Complement, 135. Guns (new in 1904-06): 2—6 inch (45 cal.); 1—4.7 inch (45 cal.); (2—11 pdr. in *Donetz*), 4—3 pdr., 2—1 pdr. H.P. *Donetz* 2000 = 12 kts., *Teretz* 1500 = 11 kts., *Kubanetz* 1500 = 13.5 kts. Boilers (new in 1904-06): Belleville. Coal : 220-237 tons.

Note.—All three attached to Gen. Denikin's Army.

Patrol Boats.

ALBATROSS, BAKLAN (1909). 100 tons. Guns : 6—1 pdr. Speed : 9½ kts. Identical with *Minrep* class in Baltic Section.

Chaika (1910). 25 tons. 1—1 pdr.

Also : *Ledorez, Lidia, Pantikopela.*

Anti-Submarine Patrols.

16 Motor Launches.

Danube Motor Patrol Boats.

Kinjal, Shaska, Sablya, Rapira (1910). 24 tons. 1—3 inch mountain gun, 1 M.G. B.H.P. 200=16 kts. Transported from Amur River during War.

Armed Barges.

K 12, K 15. Guns : 2—6 inch.
K 1, 3, 5, 7, 10, 11, 17. Guns : 1—6 inch.
K 2, 4, 6, 8, 14, 16, 19. Guns : 2—3 inch.
K 9. Guns : 1—3 inch.

Note.—In Sea of Azov and Don River, in support of General Denikin's Armies.

Submarine Depot Ships.

BERESAN (1870). 3050 tons. Guns : 6—3 pdr. or 2—1 pdr. Machinery destroyed, April 28th, 1919.

Also : *Dneprovetz* and *Voz.*

Seaplane Carrier.

ALMAZ* (1903). 3300 tons. Complement, 294. Dimensions : 363 × 43½ × 17½ feet. Guns : 7—4.7 inch. Armour : 3″ Deck over machinery. Designed H.P. 7500 = 19 kts. Belleville boilers. Coal : 650 tons. Carries 4 seaplanes.

*Taken over by France.

Mine Layers.

BESHTAU, DUNAI (1891). 1620 tons. Complement, 234. Guns : 2—6 pdr., 4—3 pdr., 2 M.G. Speed : 13⅓ kts. Coal 130 tons. Carry 350 mines.

Despatch Vessel.

(*Disarmed.*)

KASARSKI (1889, ex Torpedo Gunboat). 400 tons. Complement, 64. Armament : 2—11 pdr., 2 M.G. Designed H.P. 3500 = 21 kts. Coal : 55 tons.

Salvage Ship.

Chernomor.

BOLSHEVIST

VOLGA FLOTILLA.

These ships have access to the Caspian Sea, provided that there is free passage to the delta of the Volga. The Bolshevist Naval Base at Stato Terechnaya on the Caspian Sea, was destroyed during British naval operations in the summer of 1919.

Destroyers :—

Karl Liebknecht
Yakob Sverdlov
Turkhmenetz-Stavropolski
Dostoini
Rastoropni
Dyatelni
Dyelni
Storoshevoi
Mietki
Prytki
Proschni
Retyvi

Submarines :—

Yaguar
Minoga
Makrel
Okun
Kataska

CASPIAN SEA FLOTILLA.

Taken over by British Government, March--Autumn, 1919.

Scale : 1 inch = 160 feet.

KARS & ARDAGAN.

Gunboats.

Photo: "Motor Ship & Motor Boat."

ARDAGAN (1909) & **KARS** (1909). 630 tons. Armament : 1—4.7 inch, 2—4 inch, 1—3 inch. Machinery : Nobel-Lessner Diesel motors. 1000 H.P. = 14 kts.

Despatch Vessels.

Photo wanted.

ASTRABAD (1900). 325 tons. Guns : 5—3 pdr. Speed : 11 kts.

Despatch Vessels —*continued.*

Photo wanted.

GEOK TEPE (1883). 1010 tons. Guns : 4—4 pdr., 4 M.G. Speed : 11 kts.

Surveying Ship.

Photo wanted.

ARAKS (1900). 745 tons. Guns : 4—3 pdr. Designed H.P. 800 = 12½ kts.

Hospital Ship.

Skobelev.

Miscellaneous.

Asia	*Kruger*	*Venture*
Caspia*	*Sergie*	*Windsor Castle*
Emile Nobel	*Slava*	*Zoraster*
Leila*		

*Reported captured from Bolshevists. Above Armed Vessels (under White Ensign) in action with Bolshevist warships, May 21st, 1919, when Ammunition Carrier, *Caspia*, and the *Lelia* were captured. No details known of these ships.

TURKISH FLEET. (INTERNED).

RED ▨▨▨▨ WHITE ☐

| ENSIGN & JACK. | MINISTER OF MARINE. | ADMIRAL OF FLEET. | ADMIRAL. |
| VICE ADMIRAL. | REAR ADMIRAL | COMMODORE. | IMPERIAL STANDARD. |

Note:

All ships interned at the Golden Horn, in the Bosphorous and Gulf of Ismid, under Allied supervision.

Uniforms.

| ADMIRAL OF FLEET. | ADMIRAL. | VICE ADMIRAL. | REAR ADMIRAL. | COMMODORE. | CAPTAIN. | LIEUT. CAPTAIN. |
| COMMANDER. | LIEUT COMMANDER. | LIEUTENANT. | SUB-LIEUTENANT. |

INSIGNIA OF RANK, AUTHORISED 1910.

Other branches.—Without the curl.
Doctors.—Crimson.
Engineers.—Scarlet.
Constructors.—Blue.
Paymasters.—White.

BRITISH OR U.S.A.		TURKEY.
Admiral of the Fleet	=	Buyuk Amiral.
Admiral	=	Amiral
Vice-Ad.	=	Vice-Amiral
Rear-Ad.	=	Liva-Amiral.
Commodore	=	Commodore.
Captain	=	Galion Capitani.
Commander	=	Fregate Capitani.
,,	=	Corvette Capitani.
Lieut. Commander	=	Birindji Yuzbachi.
Lieutenant	=	Yuzbachi.
Sub-Lieut.	=	Mulazim.
Midshipman	=	Mehendis.

Arsenal: Constantinople (*see next page*).

Mercantile Marine: Latest available totals are, 95 steamers of 74,396 tons *gross*, and 963 sailing ships of 205,029 tons *gross*. Many of these, however, have been lost in convoys destroyed by the Russian Black Sea Fleet and through the operations of Allied submarines in the Sea of Marmora. Captured vessels were probably been recovered, on occupation of Sebastopol, Odessa, Batum and other Black Sea Ports.

Minister of Marine:

Colour of ships: Large ships, light grey; ships smaller than (and including) *Muin-i-Zaffer*, khaki; destroyers, black.

Principal Ports: Trebizond, Sinope, Samsoun, Smyrna, Alexandretta,* Beyrût,° Basrah,† Jaffa,† Hodieda,† Djeddah.

  *Occupied by Allied Forces.   †Occupied by Anglo-Indian Expeditionary Force.

Coinage: Lira (Medjidié) of 100 piastres = 18*s*. British, $4·28 U.S.A. One piastre (4 cents U.S.A.) = *about* 2*d*. British. These are *nominal* values. Rate of exchange has depreciated owing to the war.

Personnel: about 6000-8000 all ranks.

Tables of Distances.

(A) CONSTANTINOPLE to (*Mediterranean Ports.*)

	miles.
Alexandria	722
Alexandretta	810
Beyrout	810
Brindisi	786
Cattaro	880
Corfu	682
Gibraltar	1800
Malta	830
Mudros Bay	190
Piraeus	344
Pola (*a*)	996
,, (*b*)	1098
Port Said	786
Salonika	333
Smyrna	273
Toulon	1343
Triest (*a*)	1050
,, (*b*)	1152
Wilhelmshaven (*c*)	3355
,, (*d*)	3893
Zeebrugge (*c*)	3089
,, (*d*)	3905

(*a*) By Canal of Corinth.
(*b*) By Cape Matapan.
(*c*) By English Channel.
(*d*) By north of Scotland & west of Ireland.

(B) CONSTANTINOPLE to (*Black Sea Ports.*)

	miles.
Batoum	586
Burgas	126
Nicolaieff	394
Odessa	342
Sulina (mouth of Danube River.)	254
Trebizond	496
Varna	146

SMYRNA to

	miles.
Alexandretta	623
Beyrout	623
Corfu	529
Cattaro	727
Gibraltar	1641
Malta	677
Mudros Bay	133
Piraeus	196
Pola (*a*)	848
,, (*b*)	945
Salonika	254

(*a*) By Canal of Corinth.
(*b*) By Cape Matapan.

ONE FUNNEL.

MUIN-I-ZAFFER.

MALATIA
(*Gunboat.*)

KEMAL REIS *class* (3)
(*Gunboats*).

AIDAN REIS *class* (4)
(*Gunboats*).

RESCHID PACHA.
(*Transport*).

TIRI-MUJGHIAN.
(*Training Ship*).

TWO FUNNELS.

BERC-I-SATVET *class* (2)
(*Torpedo Gunboats*).

TOORGOOD REIS.

SULTAN SELIM.

THREE FUNNELS.

ERTOGRUL.
(*Royal Yacht.*)

MEDJIDIEH (*is dismantled*).

HAMIDIEH.

TORPEDO CRAFT.

Drach *class* (2) t.b.

Muvanet-i-Milet *class* (2) t.b.d.

Sivri-Hissar *class* (2) t.b.

Samsoun *class* (2) t.b.d.

Ack Hissar *class* (2) t.b.

SULTAN SELIM (ex German *Goeben*, March, 1911).
Displacement, 22,640 tons. Complement, 1013.
Length (*w.l.*), 610¼ feet. Beam, 96 ft. 10 in. Draught (*max. load*), 26 ft. 11 in.

Guns (*see Notes*):
10—11 in. 50 cal. } **Dir. Con.**
12—5·9 in. 45 cal. }
12—3·4 in. 22 pdr.
2 M.G.
(1 landing)
Torpedo tubes (19·7 in.):
1 bow }
2 broadside } all
1 stern } *submerged*

Anti-Torp. Pro.:—

2″—1″ deep H.T. Steel B.H., between extreme
barbettes : Minute internal subdivision.

Armour (Krupp):
11″ Belt (amidships) ......
5″—4″ Belt (bow) ....
4″ Belt (stern) ....
9″—8″ Barbettes ....
10″—8″ Gunhouses ......
·5″ Battery ....
10″ Fore C.T. ....
8″—3″ Double Com.Tube .
8″ After C.T. ....
6″—3″ Com. Tube..... ..
″— ″ R.F. Towers ....
3¼″—1″ Decks ....
″ Roofs to Gunhouses...
3″ Roof, Fore C.T. ......

Photo, Topical.

Note.—In above illustration, the fourth 5·9 inch gun from bows does not appear to be mounted ; it may
have been destroyed when this ship was mined in 1914, and never replaced. Figures and positions
on plan opposite for 5·9 inch guns are those originally mounted.

MOLTKE

Ahead :
6—11 in.
2—5·9 in.
1—19·7 in. T.T.

Astern :
6—11 in.
2—5·9 in.
1—19·7 in. T.T.

Broadside: 10—11 in., 6—5·9 in., 2—19·7 in. T.T. (angling 30°
before to 30° abaft beam).

Name	Builder	Machinery	Ordered Begun	Began Trials	Trials (mean) H.P. kts.	Completed
Sultan Selim	Blohm & Voss, Hamburg	Blohm & Voss, Hamburg	Dec.7, '08 April, 1909	May, 1912	71,275 = 27.2*	July.7 '12†

*Stated to have developed 85,661 H.P. = 27.9 kts. on trials, but this must be *max.* H.P. and best run on mile.
†Extra trials run up to Oct., 1912.

Machinery : Parsons turbine, 4 shaft, direct drive. Boilers : 24 Schulz-Thornycroft = German
"Marine Type." Designed H.P. nominally 52,000 for 25 kts., but when new she could develop 70,000
H.P. = 27 kts. Coal : *normal* about 1000 tons ; *maximum* 3050 tons. Oil fuel : 200 tons.

Gunnery Notes.—All guns German Navy Models, with German Navy type of fire-controls, R.F., &c. 11-inch have large
degree of elevation, and range is only limited by maximum visibility. 5.9 inch range up to 16,500 yards. Two
R.F. towers are sunk into the deck, near amidships (echelon) barbettes.

Torpedo Notes.—Torpedoes and torpedo tubes, German Navy type. Torpedoes probably German G VII*** (23-ft.
steam heater) type with 430 lbs. charge and *max.* ranges of (*a*) 11,700 yards at 28 kts., (*b*) 5,500 yards at 35 kts.
Stern *submerged* torpedo tube is on starboard quarter. 8—60″ controlled S.L. Torpedo nets removed during
War.

Armour and Protection Notes.—Like all other German Battle Cruisers, this ship is heavily armoured and minutely sub-
divided. Main belt between extreme barbettes is *about* 350 feet long, 11″ at w.l. tapering to about 8″ on upper
edge, and 6″ on lower edge. Barbette bases only 1″ where covered by belt.

Engineering Notes.—Endurance is (*a*) 5,350 miles at 10 kts., (*b*) 2,370 miles at a continuous *max.* sea-going speed of 23
kts.

General Notes.—Built under 1909 German Navy Programme as "H," as a sister to German *Moltke.* Proceeded to
Mediterranean about 1913, with Cruiser *Breslau*, it being intended that these two ships should operate from
Austro-Hungarian naval bases. With *Breslau*, this Battle Cruiser escaped from Messina to Constantinople in the
first days of War, and was nominally transferred to the Turkish Navy as the *Sultan Selim*, the *Breslau* (now sunk)
was also becoming the pseudo-Turkish *Midillu*. On November 18th, 1914, *Goeben* fought an indecisive action with
the three Russian pre-Dreadnoughts of the *Evstafi* type. During this action, or shortly afterwards, *Goeben* was
heavily injured by a double mine explosion. The first mine struck the starboard bows over the provision store
rooms, shattering the hull from the belt to the docking keel ; the second mine exploded on the port side over a coal
bunker, disabling the third barbette. It took three months to effect repairs at Constantinople by means of cofferdams.
Goeben appears to have been again mined on another date during 1915 or 1916. During 1917 she was again injured
by bombs dropped from a British Handley-Page aeroplane during a raid on Constantinople. In January, 1918,
Goeben and *Breslau* sank the British Monitors *Raglan* and *M 28* at Imbros, but both ships were mined. *Breslau*
sank, and *Goeben* was beached near Nagara Point, where she was repeatedly attacked by bombing 'planes. An
unsuccessful attempt was also made by submarines against her. She was towed off, and after the capture of
Sebastopol she was taken there to be docked, re-fitted, overhauled, and to have her boilers re-tubed. *Goeben* has
probably had more narrow escapes from destruction than any other Dreadnought or Battle Cruiser in existence :
she certainly is a remarkable testimonial to the thorough under-water protection of German Dreadnoughts and
Battle Cruisers. She is also known to the Turkish Navy by the unofficial name of *Yavuz.* Interned in Gulf of
Ismid with other Turkish warships at end of War.

OLD TURKISH COAST DEFENCE BATTLESHIPS (*Haty-harb-Zırchlıssı*).

(*May be Depot or Special Service Ships now.*)

(*Training Ship.*)

TURKISH PROTECTED CRUISERS

TOORGOOD REIS (1891, rebuilt 1903). 9901 tons. Complement, 579. Dimensions : $379\frac{2}{3}$ × 64 × $24\frac{2}{3}$ feet (*maximum* draught). Guns : 4—11 inch, 40 cal. + 2—11 inch, 35 cal. (all probably removed), 8—4.1 inch, 35 cal. ; 8—3.4 inch (15 pdr.), 2 landing, 2 AA. guns, 4 M.G. Torpedo tubes (18 inch) : 2 *submerged* (broadside). Armour (compound) : $15\frac{3}{4}''$ Belt amidships, 12″ Belt at ends, $2\frac{1}{2}''$ Deck, flat on belt, $11\frac{3}{4}''$ Barbettes, with 5″ shields, 3″ Battery, 12″ C.T. Machinery : 2 sets vertical triple expansion. Boilers : 12 cylindrical return flame (new in 1909). Designed H.P. 9000=17 kts. ; present speed much less. Coal : *normal*, 600 tons ; *maximum*, 812 tons + 98 tons oil. Endurance : 5300 miles at 10 kts., 2600 miles at $15\frac{1}{4}$ kts. Originally was German battleship *Weissenburg*. Purchased 1910. Reported to be practically worn out.

HAMIDIEH (ex *Abdul Hamid*, Elswick, Spet., 1903). 3830 tons. Complement, 302. Dimensions : 368 × $47\frac{1}{2}$ × 16 feet (*mean* draught). Guns : 2—5.9 inch, 45 cal. Torpedo tubes (18 inch) : 2 *above water.* Armour : 4″ Deck. Machinery : 2 sets 4-cylinder triple expansion. 2 screws. Boilers : cylindrical. Designed H.P. 12,000 = 22 kts. (*forced draught*). Coal : *normal*, 275 tons ; *maximum*, 750 tons. Endurance : 5550 miles at 10 kts.

(*Dismantled ; only 1 mast and 1 funnel now.*)

MUIN-I-ZAFFER (1869). Rebuilt by Ansaldo, 1904-7. 2362 tons. Complement, 220. Guns (Krupp, M. '06) : 4—5.9 inch, 40 cal. ; 6—3 inch (12 pdr.), 2—3 pdr. Torpedo tubes (14 inch) : 1. Armour (old, iron) : 6″—3″ Battery, 6″ Battery, 5″ Bulkheads. Machinery : Horizontal compound. 1 screw. Boilers (new in 1906) : cylindrical. Designed H.P. 6500 = 15.5 kts. Coal (*max.*) : 220 tons.

Note.—Old *Idjlalieh* still exists but is utterly useless.

MEDJIDIEH (ex Russian *Prut*, ex Turkish *Medjidieh*, launched 1903). Mined and sunk in Black Sea, 1915. Salved, repaired and re-fitted at Nocilaieff for Russian Navy, 1915-16. Seized by Austro-German Armies at Sebastopol, 1918, and returned to Turkish Navy. 3300 tons. Complement, 365. Dimensions : 225 × 40 × $17\frac{1}{2}$ feet. Guns (as re-armed for Russian Navy) : 4—5.1 inch (Vickers 1914), 4 M.G. Deck 1″. H.P. 12,000 = 22 kts. Niclausse boilers, but may have another type now. Coal : 600 tons. Endurance : 4700 miles at 10 kts. Built by Cramps, Philadelphia.

Old Sloop.

No photo available.

ZUHAF (Germania, 1894). 632 tons. Dimensions : 190 × 24 × 11½ feet. Guns : 4—6 pdr., 2—1 pdr. Torpedo tubes (14 inch) : 2 *above water*. Designed H.P. 650 = 11 kts. Coal : 120 tons. Complement, 82.
Note.—Reported to have been fitted out as a Mine Layer.

Gunboats (*Ganbot*).

4 *St. Nazaire* type : **AIDAN REIS** (June, 1912), **BURACK REIS** (May, 1912), **SAKIZ** (Feb., 1912), and **PREVESAH** (Jan., 1912). 502 tons. Dimensions : 178½ × 27⅔ × 8 feet. H.P. 1025 = 14 kts. Guns : 2—3.9 inch (50 cal.), 2—6 pdr., 4 M.G.

3 *La Seyne* type : **KEMAL REIS** (ex *Durack Reis*, Feb., 1912), **HIZIR REIS** (Feb., 1912) and **ISSA REIS** (Dec., 1911). 413 tons. Dimensions : 154¼ × 25⅜ × 4¼ feet. Guns : 3—3 inch (12 pdr.), 2—3 pdr., 2 M.G. H.P. 850 = 14 kts.

Gunboats—*Continued.*

1 *Creusot* type : **MALATIA** (1907). 210 tons. Dimensions : 154¼ × 19⅔ × 6⅔ feet. Guns : 2—3 pdr. Torpedo tubes : 1 *above water*. H.P. 350 = 12½ kts. Coal : 44 tons. Complement, 30.

Note.—This class originally consisted of eight vessels, viz., *Aintab, Baffra, Malatia, Ordu, Gudjedag, Refadie, Tachkeupru, Nev Shihir.* Five of the class (including *Refadie*) were sunk in the Turco-Italian War, 1912. The others were destroyed in the late war.

No photo available.

BARIK - I - ZAFFER (Constantinople, 1908). 198 tons. Dimensions : 121½ × 18 × 5½ feet. Guns : 4—12 pdr., 2 M.G. Torpedo tubes (14 inch) : 2 *above water*.

Note.—Various sister ships of *Barik-i-Zaffer* believed to have been destroyed during the War, but their names cannot be ascertained exactly.

Gunboats—Existence Doubtful.

Yozgad and *Timsah* reported to have been seen at Constantinople in June, 1919. *Timsah* mined and injured beyond repair. *Yozgad*—if she exists—is utterly useless.

Torpedo Gunboats (*Torpedo Muhribi*).

BERC-I-SATVET (Dec., 1906) and **PEIK-I-SHEVKET** (Nov., 1906). Both built at Krupps' Germania Yard, Kiel. 1014 tons. Dimensions : 262½ × 27⅞ × 9½ feet. Guns : 2—3.9 inch, 4—6 pdr., 2—1 pdr., 2 M.G. Torpedo tubes : 3. Designed H.P. 5100 = 22 kts. Coal : 240 tons.

Note.—*Berc-i-Satvet* torpedoed by British Submarine *E 2*, and *Peik-i-Shevket* by *E 14*, both during 1915. Either boat (or both boats) beached and salved. They have not been sunk, as was believed during the War.

6 Destroyers (*Torpedo Muhriby*).

No.	Type	Date	Dis-place-ment	H.P.	Max. speed	Fuel Coal/Oil.	Com-plement	T. tubes	Max. draug't
			tons		kts.	tons			feet
2	*Muvanet-i-Milet* (S)	'09-'10	607	10,250*t*	33	145/30	87	3	10½
3	*Samsoun*	'07-'10	290	6000	29	70	67	2	10
1	*Berk-Efsan* (K)	1894	270	3400	25	75	...	2	9

(S)=Schichau.   (L)=Chantiers de la Loire.   (K)=Krupp.

Note.

6 New Destroyers were reported to have been begun in 1917 at Constantinople, to German designs, £T1,190,000 being voted for their construction. No report has been received of their launching. If begun, it is very doubtful if they will ever be finished now.

2 *Schichau* boats: **Muvanet-i-Milet** and **Noumouné-i-Hamiyet.** Both 1909. 607 tons. Dimensions: 233½ × 25⅗ × 10¼ feet. Armament: 2—3·4 in. (22 pdr.), 2 machine, 3—18 in. tubes. Schulz-Thornycroft boilers and Schichau (Melms and Pfenninger) turbines. On trials from 36·2 to 34·5 kts., but can only make about 27 now. Endurance: 1200 miles at 15 kts. Were originally built for the German Navy as *S 165—S 168*, and sold to Turkey in 1910. *Yadighiar-i-Milet* and another boat (called *Mahabet-i-Milet* or *Gairet-i-Vatanié*), both sunk during the War.

Destroyers—(*continued*).

3 *French type* boats: **Samsoun, Bassra,** both launched at Bordeaux (1907), and **Tasnoz** launched by Creusot, Chalons, (1907). 290 tons. Dimensions: 185 × 21 × 9½ feet. Armament: 1—12 pdr., 6—3 pdr., 2—18 inch tubes. Endurance: 975 miles at 15 kts. Are practically the same as French *Durandal* class:

(*No photo available*).

(A view of this boat's model was published in "Fighting Ships" up to 1910).

1 *Krupp* boat: **Berk-Efsan** (1894). 270 tons. Dimensions: 187 × 21¼ × 8 feet. Armament: 6—6 pdr., 2—14 in. tubes.

6 Torpedo Boats.

No.	Type	Date	Displacement tons	H.P.	Max. speed	Fuel	Complement	T tubes	Max. draug't
			tons		kts.	tons			feet
2	*Sivri-Hissar* (C)	'06-'07	98	1900	26	15 coal	18	3	5
2	*Drach* (A)	'04-'07	160	2700	24	60 ,,	20	2	7
2	*Younous* (A)	1901	145	2400	27	60 ,,	20	2	6

(C)=Creusot.   (A)=Ansaldo.

2 *Creusot* boats: **Sultan-Hissar, Sivri-Hissar** (1906). Dimensions : 124×14×1½ feet. Armament : 2—1 pdr., 3—18 inch tubes (1 bow, 2 deck). For other details *v.* Table. **Timur** (or **Demir**) *Hissar* lost in present war, and *Hamid-Abad* in Italian War, 1911—12.

2 *Ansaldo* boats : **Drach** (1905) and **Moussoul** (1905). Dimensions : 167×18×4½ feet. Armament : 2—1 pdr., 2—14 in. tubes. For other details *v.* Table. *Kutaya* and *Urfa* of this class lost during the war. *Anatolia* of this class, captured during Balkan war, now Greek *Nikopolis*. *Alpagot* (or *Eliagot*), *Tocad* and *Angora* were sunk during the Balkan and Italian Wars, 1911-12.

Torpedo Boats—(continued).

2 *Ansaldo* boats : **Ack-Hissar** (1904) and **Younous** (1902). Dimensions : 165⅝×18½×5¼ feet. Armament : 2—1 pdr., 2—18 inch tubes. Endurance : 2000 miles at 14 kts. For other details *v.* Table.

During the War, the Germans and Turks attempted to refit and overhaul two old derelict Nordenfeldt Submarines, built about 1889. One of these boats, ex-*Abdul Hamid*, was re-named with the Turkish equivalent of "Porpoise." It is believed that the re-construction of these curiosities proved an absolute failure.

9 Motor Launches.

No photo available.

4 boats of 15 kts. speed, built about 1912-13. No other details known.

Photo, Messrs. J. I. Thornycroft & Co.

5 boats : *Names or numbers not known.* Are Thornycroft type motor patrol boats, built 1911, for customs, police and coast-guard duties. Dimensions : × × 2½ feet. Guns : 2 M.G. or 1 small Q.F. 140 H.P. Thornycroft petrol motor = 11 kts. Bullet-proof steel over conning position and engines.

Note.—Originally 20 of these boats were built. Two were captured during the Turco-Italian War. One captured during the war on the Tigris river and served for a time as H.M.S. *Flycatcher*, but was transferred later to British Army.

Depot Ship.

No photo available.

NEJDMI SHEVKET. No details known.

Transports.

RESCHID PASHA (ex *Port Antonio*). 4458 tons.

OURLA. No details known.

Bezzmi-Alem exists still. Was seen at Constantinople, June, 1919, but has probably gone on Mercantile Service.

Mine-Layers.

Photo Wanted.

NUSRAT (Germania, 1912). 364 tons. Dimensions : 131¼ × 24½ × 8¼ feet. Guns : 2 M.G. H.P. 1200 = 15 kts. Carries 25 mines.

KIRESUND (1877). 3056 tons *gross*. 10 kts.

INTIBAH. No details known.

Mine Sweepers.

No photo available.

CASTOR, POLLUX. No details known.

Yachts.

(Royal Yacht.)

ERTOGRUL (Elswick, 1903). 900 tons. Dimensions : 260 (p.p.) × 27⅘ × 11½ feet. Guns : 8—3 pdr. H.P. 2500 = 21 kts. Machinery : Hawthorn Leslie. Boilers : Cylindrical.

(There is also another small Royal Yacht, **Senguedlu** built at Elswick in 1903, of 180 tons, and 14 kts. speed.)

Yachts—*continued*.

IZZEDIN (——, 1865). 1075 tons. Guns : 2—3.5 inch, 2 M.G. H.P. 350 = 12 kts.

STAMBOUL (——, 1865, 1888). 910 tons. Guns : 2—4.7 inch, 2 M.G. H.P. 350 = 17 kts. *nominal.* Real speed much less now.

GALATA
SUGUTLI } No details known.

Another small yacht, *Aintab*, exists.

Training Ships.

Cruiser **HAMIDIEH** described on an earlier page.

TIRI-MUJGHIAN (ex *Pembroke Castle*, 1883). 4052 tons. Dimensions : 400¼ × 42½ × 21⅓ feet. Guns : 8—3 pdr. Speed : 14 kts.

EXPLANATORY NOTES TO BRITISH NAVY SECTION.

DISPLACEMENTS.

THE figures given are, in all cases, "Navy List Displacement" at *normal* load. Where figures are available, full sea-going displacements at deep load (exclusive of oil fuel) are added. It must be pointed out that these statistics may under-estimate the present displacements of British warships. Additions made during the War have greatly increased displacements. After the Battle of Jutland, about 2000-3000 tons of extra weights were added to British capital ships (a) by the re-inforcement of barbette crowns and strengthening of decks round magazines and shell rooms ; (b) by the provision of flash-tight doors to ammunition trunks and magazines. Dreadnoughts and Battle Cruisers completed before the War were also burdened with director fire controls and enlarged searchlight equipment. Capital Ships and Light Cruisers also received paravanes, aeroplanes (with small flying-off platforms), kite-balloon winches, &c.

In the case of Light Cruisers, these additions resulted in displacement being increased by 500-800 tons. Pre-War types of Destroyers had as much as 100 tons added, in the shape of depth charges and depth charge throwers, paravanes, extra oil fuel and anti-aircraft guns. Such increases of displacement naturally resulted in deeper draughts and loss of *maximum* speed. In the case of armoured ships, the thickest section of waterline armouring is sometimes *submerged* at deep load draught.

COMPLEMENTS.

Figures given are those now ruling, but during the War complements were greatly increased. The *Renown*, for example, is said to have had a complement of 1500 towards the end of the War.

GUNNERY NOTES.

Throughout all classes, the War has resulted in increased and improved systems of gunnery controls (which, in recent forms, are allied to wireless telegraphy), by the installation or addition of director controls, large base range-finders, &c. Range-finders for anti-aircraft guns are also mounted. Rather noticeable additions are the provision of range-clocks at prominent points on the fore or after ends of large ships, and the painting of deflection scales on barbette shields.

Before the War, the tendency of British gunnery was towards flat trajectories with big danger zones and moderately efficient range-taking. The present trend is towards high-angle fire and rather abnormal ranges. High-angle fire gives decreased danger zones, but this drawback can be surmounted by high-efficiency range-finders and controls. A very large number of lighter guns were removed from British Warships, to provide armaments for Defensively Armed Merchant Ships, Submarine Decoy Vessels, Fleet Auxiliaries, Mine Sweepers, Patrols, Small Monitors, &c., &c. Many of the guns so surrendered have not yet been remounted in the Warships from which they were removed, and it is doubtful if they will ever be replaced now.

The only new heavy calibres introduced were the 18-inch and 14-inch guns, but numerous marks of guns from 7.5-inch calibre downwards have been added, including new types of 5.5, 4.7 and 4-inch guns. Anti-aircraft guns are, of course, distributed among all classes. It is projected that all Capital Ships should have a uniform armament of 2—4 inch AA. guns. Examination of armaments will show that the mono-calibre system has become more or less standard, guns of 15 to 12 inch calibre being mounted in Capital Ships, 7.5 to 5.5 inch marks in Light Cruisers, and 4.7 to 4 inch guns in Destroyers. In the earlier "C" Class Cruisers, the mixed 6 inch and 4 inch armament was gradually altered to a uniform 6 inch on the centre-line, the single bigger calibre gun amidships on the flying deck replacing 6—4 inch in the waist.

TORPEDO NOTES.

The increase of tubes in Light Cruiser types has been remarkable. In the case of the "D" type Light Cruisers, as many as 12 tubes are mounted in triple revolving deck mountings. The new British type of triple tube, it may be remarked, weighs *less* than the preceding type of twin tube. It has been suggested that older types of Destroyers should be re-armed with triple tubes, but motives of economy have prevented the suggestion being carried out. Destroyers of the Dover Patrol and Harwich Force each received two extra 14 inch tubes for night actions with enemy Destroyers, but these extra tubes have now been removed. Submerged stern tubes were removed from all Dreadnoughts and Battle-Cruisers during the War.

The *submerged* tubes in the *Renown* Class of Battle-Cruisers, *Courageous* type of Cruisers, and "C" Light Cruisers, have proved very unsatisfactory, as the bars bend when attempting to launch torpedoes at high speeds. These *submerged* tubes will probably be removed and replaced by *above water* positions. Modern Destroyers have hydro-pneumatic firing gear, which allows torpedoes to be fired from the navigating bridges.

SEARCHLIGHTS.

Controls have been devised for these, by which searchlights are controlled on target in conjunction with the guns. Battle-ships and Light Cruisers usually mount 8 to 4—36 inch searchlights, with a pair of 24-inch searchlights for signalling purposes, both by day and by night. The cramped bridges of Dreadnoughts and Battle-Cruisers proved very inconvenient to the signalling staff ; there was also difficulty in bringing signal halyards inboard to the narrow bridges. Accordingly, searchlights were adopted for day signalling, and their use is very prevalent now.

Curiosity may be aroused by the peculiar searchlight towers, added to masts and funnels of British ships, usually called "coffee boxes" It was found that the intense, white glare of the arc was most troublesome to the searchlight operatives and very injurious to the eyes. Accordingly, the "coffee box" tower was devised. In this, the searchlight parties are located *within* the tower, and *below* the searchlights, vision being given by sighting slits, while the searchlights themselves are worked by small motors.

Flotilla Leaders have usually 1 or 2—24 inch searchlights, and Destroyers 1—20 inch searchlight, both types being controlled in conjunction with guns. In the "Modified R" and "S" Destroyers, the searchlight is mounted on and revolves with the after pair of tubes—a detail which has been added to some of the "M" Classes of T.B.D.

AIRCRAFT NOTES.

One of the remarkable features of the War has been the way in which all classes of ships (excepting Destroyers) have been equipped to carry and fly off small aeroplanes from barbette crowns in big ships, and from small platforms in Light Cruisers. In the *Carlisle* and "D" types of Light Cruisers, a high "Arc de Triomphe" hangar has been combined with the fore bridges, the fore portion of which can be closed by wind screens or roller shutters. The reason for this huge erection may be stated in some detail. The small Sopwith "Camels" and "Deck Pups" carried in our Warships have to attain their flying speed with a remarkably short run, on account of the limited length of flying-off platform. So anxious are they to get into the air, they tend to rise by themselves when the carrying ship is steaming into a head wind. Lashing down the 'planes resulted in straining.

Accordingly, small wind screens have sometimes to be rigged round the aeroplanes. But wind screens are a nuisance to rig or unfurl in a rising wind—hence the permanent structures adopted in new Light Cruisers. Kite-balloon winches were added to practically all types of ships from Dreadnoughts to Trawlers, but, of course, excepting Submarines. In the last months of the War, it was the custom for the Grand Fleet to go to sea with about 50 aeroplanes and 30 kite-balloons. A somewhat experimental addition has been made to our British Navy Illustrations in the form of "Aircraft Recognition Views" of various types of Warships. It is proposed that this form of ship illustration should be developed into a regular feature of the book, so far as facilities for obtaining the aerial photographs permit.

MINE LAYING.

Before the War, this duty was considered the *metier* of specially-constructed ships. At the end of hostilities, practically all types of ships from Cruisers down to Trawlers and C.M.B's. were engaged in sowing of "eggs." Mine laying by Destroyers proved extremely successful, and the mine-laying Submarine has fully justified its adoption. If asked to indicate two of the most remarkable developments of the War, we would be inclined to single out (a) the conjoint use of aircraft and warships, and (b) the general adoption of mine laying for all types of war vessels.

MINE SWEEPING.

The invention of the paravane resulted in all classes of ships becoming mine-sweepers of a very efficient type. The pre-war type of sweep, worked by two vessels, was extremely slow in operation and subject to continual breakdowns. The money, time and thought expended on the development of the paravane has been fully justified. In fact, this device is one of the British inventive triumphs of the War, and was adopted by the Navies of all our Allies. Compared with the pre-war form of sweep, it has been said that the " PV " can sweep three times the area in a third of the time required under the old system. Destroyers working PV's. at high speed can sweep great areas in a remarkably short space of time.

Of the types of paravanes used, space forbids description. Roughly, there are two forms, (*a*) high speed for use by Warships, and (*b*) " otter gear," for low speed ships, particularly of the mercantile class. In the Prize Court, and during the hearing of a claim for the destruction of a German Submarine, it was publicly mentioned that the enemy boat was sunk by the use of the H.S.S.S. of H.M.S. *Melampus.* The initials H.S.S.S. stand for High Speed Submarine Sweep, and in this form of paravane explosive charges are detonated automatically, as soon as the PV grips it's target. H.S.M.S. represents High Speed Mine Sweep.

To those interested in paravanes, we would recommend the articles which appeared in the London " Engineer " during January and February, 1919, and in the " Journal of the United States Naval Institute," July, 1919. As regards methods of towing : Capital Ships and Light Cruisers usually tow PVs. from a skeg or sliding bar affixed to stem. Destroyers, by reason of their light draught, are less liable to hit mines forward, and therefore their PVs. are towed from their sterns. It may be remarked that the streaming of PVs. at high speeds may result in *maximum* speed of the towing ship being reduced by about one or two knots.

ARMOUR PROTECTION.

No notable increases have been made in vertical and external protection. But, in the case of horizontal armour, thickening of protection has taken place. Already there is a tendency to decrease the sections of vertical and external armour and to increase the strength of decks against high-angle fire and aero bombs. Alterations effected to British Dreadnoughts have already been noted under the heading of Displacements. Torpedo and mine attack has produced bulge protection—a device which appears likely to become a standard feature in large British Warships.

No German Dreadnought or Battle Cruiser, during the War, succumbed to an Allied mine or torpedo. The internal protection of German Warships was abnormally strong. The *Seydlitz,* for example, was torpedoed in the opening stages of the Battle of Jutland, but was able to keep her station throughout the greater part of the action. Her internal protection consisted of complete internal and longitudinal screens of 2″—1″ H.T. plating, extending over all magazine, shell room, boiler room, and machinery spaces, the screens being set well inboard. This form of armouring was standard in all large German Warships.

In the British Navy, only the *Royal Sovereign, Queen Elizabeth, St. Vincent* and *Bellerophon* Classes have internal protection over areas equal to those of German Capital Ships.

The use of a *complete* internal citadel, with or without bulge protection, will probably become a standard feature in all battle-line units.

War experience has proved the practical inutility of the conning tower. The cramped internal space, poor vision, and the difficulty of dispersing cordite fumes, have led to the abandonment of the conning tower. In many British Dreadnoughts, it merely serves now to house a large gyroscopic compass. In the Falklands Battle, Admiral Sir Doveton Sturdee declined to use the conning tower, and directed the action from the control top on the fore tripod of H.M.S. *Invincible*—a position which has found much favour as an action station for the chief executive staff, on account of the great visibility given.

MACHINERY NOTES.

In this section, we have few remarks to make, beyond noting the fact that the geared turbine and " all oil " fuel system have secured a distinct success. At present, designed speeds must be taken with much reserve, on account of the large weights added to British ships during the War. On deep load, the units of the *Royal Sovereign* Class fitted with bulge protection cannot get much above 20 kts. The " Town " Classes of Light Cruisers, owing to added weights, are said to be good only for 22-23 kts., while the older Destroyers with modern equipment may be down to 24 kts. In the North Sea, large ships were able to economise weight by reducing their fuel capacities.

On the other hand, Destroyers had to have their fuel capacities enlarged, on account of the necessity for these craft to act as an anti-submarine screen for the Battle Fleet. Until the fuel capacities of the Destroyers were enlarged, the endurance of the large ships was limited, not to the fuel carried in their own bunkers, but to the fuel carried by the tanks and bunkers of the Destroyer anti-submarine screen. If the Destroyers had left the Fleet at sea to return to their bases for fuel, the principal Battle Squadrons would have been naked to submarine attack.

It may be asked why the fuel capacities stated for Destroyers are apparently reversed, the larger capacity being given first, instead of the smaller. The explanation is, Destroyers have " peace " and " war " capacities, the " peace " fuel being carried above the water line in tanks. In war, these above water tanks cannot be used, on account of the danger from fire. However, Destroyers did, during the War, use the " peace tanks," it being arranged that they should first burn off the fuel in these compartments, so that they would be empty by the time Destroyers came into the " danger areas " of the North Sea.

APPEARANCE.

Perhaps the best example to the changes caused by the War may be realised by comparing the 1913-14 views of H.M.S. *Neptune* with views of the same ship as she is to-day. In pre-war types of Capital Ships, extra tops have been added to masts for

the main director tower, control tops have been enlarged, bridges re-built to leave conning towers unhampered, and searchlight towers added to funnels and masts—all changes resulting in a great alteration to appearance.

One of the most hideous excrescences is the addition of a " clinker screen " to the fore funnel—a screen devised to keep hot clinkers and gases from the uptakes fouling the upper bridges in a following wind. In Destroyers, the " woodbine " forefunnel of greater elevation than the other stacks serves the same end. Topmasts were generally reduced to stumps on the early days of war, but now that ships are reverting to oceanic cruises, high topmasts are in favour for securing large W/T. ranges. In some ships, the fore topmast has been completely jettisoned and W/T. aerials rigged to a yard attached to the " starfish " under the control top, or directly to the " starfish " itself. This form of rig has a particularly unartistic look.

Dazzle-painting was used in practically all types of ships. It has been abandoned now, but illustrations are given of dazzle-painted British Warships, so as to place this form of coloration on record in our pages. Two views of H.M.S. *Argus* are given, to show that the patterns of painting were not uniform for each beam of the ship. H.M.S. *Argus,* on account of her weird build, offered unique opportunities to the " dazzle " experts to devise a scheme by which her course would be difficult to estimate. Both sides were treated differently, and the result certainly justified their claim to considerable extent. From the air, " dazzled " ships are far more difficult to identify than those painted a uniform colour, and for this reason alone, variegated colouring will probably become a war-paint feature.

Camouflage painting—that is the use of colours to make an object merge into it's surroundings or background—was used in British Warships, when they were serving in the Adriatic or the Gallipoli Campaign. In these cases, ships inshore were liable to be attacked by Submarines on their seaward beam, and attempts were made to make ships indistinguishable from the high mountains of Gallipoli and the Adriatic Coast.

Another form of camouflage we illustrate is the painting of dummy guns and torpedo tubes on the screens of mine-laying Destroyers. As regards eye-deceiving forms of build, the most interesting examples are the " 24 Class " of Sloops and the " Kil " Gunboats.

THE WAR INTERVAL.

Five years have elapsed since we last illustrated British Warship Types. The photographs we now present show so many changes, compared with the views we gave in 1914, some of our readers outside the Service, or in foreign Navies, will, no doubt, be puzzled by the alterations effected in British ships. Accordingly, these notes have been prepared by way of explanation. They also serve to notify points common to classes and types which cannot be placed on the Ship Pages without an inordinate amount of repetition, and use of valuable space required for ship details and illustrations.

SHIPS LOST IN THE WAR.

FINAL LIST.

Compiled by FRANCIS E. McMURTRIE.

Note.—Every effort has been made to render this list as complete as possible, all known losses up to the end of October, 1919, having been included. It is hoped that omissions are few, and that this section will be of permanent value as a record of casualties in the world's naval tonnage resulting from the War.

SHIPS LOST IN THE WAR.

Compiled by F. E. McMURTRIE.

BRITISH.

13 BATTLESHIPS.

BATTLESHIPS—*continued.*

AUDACIOUS (1912). 23,000 tons. Guns: 10—13.5 in., 16—4 in. Mined off North coast of Ireland, 27th October, 1914. For appearance, see photo of KING GEORGE V, on page 54.

VANGUARD (1909.) 19,250 tons. Guns: 10—12 in., 50 cal.; 18—4 in. Destroyed by internal explosion, at Scapa Flow, 9th July, 1917. For appearance, see photo of ST. VINCENT, on page 58.

TRIUMPH (1903). 11,985 tons. Guns: 4—10 in., 45 cal.; 14—7.5 in. II, 50 cal.; 14—14 pdr., etc. Torpedoed by German Submarine U 51 off Gaba Tepe, Gallipoli peninsula, 25th May, 1915.

KING EDWARD VII (1903). 16,350 tons. Guns: 4—12 in. IX, 40 cal.; 4—9.2 in. X, 45 cal.; 10—6 in. VIII, 45 cal.; 12—12 pdr., etc. Mined off N. Scottish coast, lat. 58.43 N., long. 4 12 W., 6th January, 1916.

RUSSELL (1901). 14,000 tons. Guns: 4—12 in. IX, 40 cal.; 12—6 in. VII, 45 cal.; 12—12 pdr., etc. Mined off Malta, 27th April, 1916.

BRITANNIA (1904). Sister to KING EDWARD VII, above. Torpedoed by a German Submarine off Cape Trafalgar, 9th November, 1918.

CORNWALLIS (1901). Sister to RUSSELL, above. Torpedoed by German Submarine, 60 miles S.E. of Malta, 9th January, 1917.

BATTLESHIPS—*continued.*

BULWARK (1899). 15,000 tons. Guns : 4—12 in. IX, 40 cal. ; 12—6 in. VII, 45 cal. ; 18—12 pdr., etc. Destroyed by internal explosion at Sheerness, 26th November, 1914.

FORMIDABLE (1898). Sister to BULWARK, above. Torpedoed by German Submarine U 24, off Portland Bill, 1st January, 1915.

IRRESISTIBLE (1898). Sister to BULWARK, above. Sunk by torpedo from White Cliffs, in the Dardanelles, 18th March, 1915.

OCEAN (1898). 12,950 tons. Guns : 4—12 in. VIII, 35 cal. ; 12—6 in., 40 cal. ; 12—12 pdr., etc. Sunk by torpedo, from White Cliffs, in the Dardanelles, 18th March, 1915.

GOLIATH (1898). Sister to OCEAN, above. Torpedoed by Turkish Destroyer MUAVENET-I-MILET, off De Tott's Battery, in the Dardanelles, 13th May, 1915.

BATTLESHIPS—*continued.*

MAJESTIC (1895). 14,900 tons. Guns : 4—12 in. VIII, 35 cal. ; 12—6 in., 40 cal. ; 16—12 pdr., etc. Torpedoed by German Submarine U 23, off W. beach, Gallipoli peninsula, 27th May, 1915.

3 BATTLE CRUISERS.

QUEEN MARY (1912). 27,000 tons. Guns : 8—13.5 in., 16—4 in. Blown up by gunfire of German Battle-Cruisers during Battle of Jutland, 31st May, 1916. For appearance, see photo of PRINCESS ROYAL, on page 65.

INDEFATIGABLE (1909). 18,750 tons. Guns : 8—12 in., 50 cal. ; 16—4 in. Blown up by gunfire of German Battle-Cruisers, during Battle of Jutland, 31st May, 1916. For appearance, see photo of NEW ZEALAND, on page 67.

INVINCIBLE (1907). 17,250 tons. Guns : 8—12 in. XI, 45 cal. ; 16—4 in. Blown up by gunfire of German Battle-Cruisers during Battle of Jutland, 31st May, 1916. For appearance, see photo of INFLEXIBLE, on page 68.

15 CRUISERS.

DEFENCE (1907). 14,600 tons. Guns : 4—9.2 in. XI, 50 cal. ; 10—7.5 in., II, 50 cal. ; 16—12 pdr., etc. Blown up by gunfire of German Battle Fleet during Battle of Jutland, 31st May, 1916.

CRUISERS—*continued.*

NATAL (1905). 13,550 tons. Guns: 6—9.2 in. X, 45 cal.; 4—7.5 in. II, 50 cal., etc. Blown up by explosion in after magazine, in Cromarty Firth, 30th December, 1915.

COCHRANE (1905). Sister to NATAL, above. Wrecked in estuary of the Mersey, 14th November, 1918.

WARRIOR (1905). Sister to NATAL, above. Foundered after being disabled by gunfire in the Battle of Jutland, 1st June, 1916.

BLACK PRINCE (1904). 13,550 tons. Guns: 6—9.2 in. X, 45 cal.; 10—6 in. XI, 50 cal., etc. Sunk by gunfire of a German Battleship during Battle of Jutland, 31st May, 1916.

CRUISERS—*continued.*

ARGYLL (1904). 10,850 tons. Guns: 4—7.5 in. I, 45 cal.; 6—6 in. VII, 45 cal., etc. Wrecked on Bell Rock, East Coast of Scotland, 28th October, 1915.

HAMPSHIRE (1903). Sister to ARGYLL, above. Mined 1½ miles W. of the Orkneys, 5th June, 1916.

GOOD HOPE (1901). 14,100 tons. Guns: 2—9.2 in. IX, 45 cal.; 16—6 in. VII, 45 cal.; 12—12 pdr., etc. Sunk by gunfire of German Cruisers, SCHARNHORST and GNEISENAU, off Coronel, Chile, 1st November, 1914.

DRAKE (1901). Sister to GOOD HOPE, above. Torpedoed by German Submarine, in Rathlin Sound, off North Coast of Ireland, 2nd October, 1917.

CRUISERS—*continued.*

CRUISERS—*continued.*

MONMOUTH (1901). 9,800 tons. Guns : 14—6 in. VII, 45 cal. ; 9—12 pdr., etc. Sunk by gunfire of German Cruisers, SCHARNHORST and GNEISENAU, off Coronel, Chile, 1st November, 1914.

ARIADNE (1898). 11,000 tons. Guns : 16—6 in., 40 cal. ; 13—12 pdr. etc. Torpedoed by German Submarine, off Beachy Head, 26th July, 1917. (This vessel was employed as a Minelayer.)

ABOUKIR (1900), HOGUE (1900), CRESSY (1899). 12,000 tons. Guns : 2—9.2 in. VIII, 40 cal. ; 12—6 in. VII, 45 cal. ; 13—12 pdr., etc. All three torpedoed by German Submarine U 9, in North Sea, lat. 52.18 N., long. 3.41 E., 22nd September, 1914.

HAWKE (1891). 7,350 tons. Guns : 2—9.2 in., 30 cal. ; 10—6 in., etc. Torpedoed by German Submarine U 9, off East Coast of Scotland, 15th October, 1914.

14 LIGHT CRUISERS.

CASSANDRA (1916). 4,120 tons. Guns: 5—6 in., 2—3 in. AA. Mined in the Baltic, night of 4-5th December, 1918. For appearance, see photo of C type Light Cruiser, on page 81.

ARETHUSA (1913). 3,520 tons. Guns: 2—6 in., 6—4 in. Mined off Felixstowe, 11th February, 1916. For appearance, see photo of UNDAUNTED. on page 83.

NOTTINGHAM (1913). 5,440 tons. Guns: 9—6 in., etc. Torpedoed by German Submarine in North Sea, lat. 55.34 N., long. 0.12 E., 19th August, 1916. For appearance, see photo of LOWESTOFT, on page 84.

AMPHION (1911). 3,440 tons. Guns: 10—4 in., etc. Mined off Thames estuary, 6th August, 1914. For appearance, see photo of ACTIVE, on page 87.

FALMOUTH (1910). 5,250 tons. Guns: 8—6 in., etc. Foundered in North Sea, lat. 54 N., long 0.2 W., 20th August, 1916, after being torpedoed four times by German Submarines. For appearance, see photo of YARMOUTH, on page 85.

HERMES (1898). 5600 tons, Guns: 11—6 in., 40 cal.; 9—12 pdr., etc. Torpedoed by German Submarine U 27, in Straits of Dover, 31st October, 1914, while employed as a Seaplane Carrier.

PATHFINDER (1904). 2,940 tons. Guns: 9—4 in. Torpedoed by German Submarine U 21, off St. Abb's Head, East Coast of Scotland, 5th September, 1914.

PEGASUS (1897). 2,135 tons. Guns: 8—4 in., etc. Sunk by gunfire of German Cruiser KÖNIGSBERG, at Zanzibar, 20th September, 1914.

LIGHT CRUISERS—*continued.*

The following six obsolete Light Cruisers were blown up and sunk as blockships.

VINDICTIVE (1897), 5,750 tons, at Ostend, 10th May, 1918.

BRILLIANT (1891) and **SIRIUS** (1890), 3,600 tons, at Ostend, 23rd April, 1918.

INTREPID and **IPHIGENIA** (1891), 3600 tons, **THETIS** (1890), 3,400 tons, all three at Zeebrugge, 23rd April, 1918.

8 MONITORS.

Raglan (1915). 6,150 tons. Guns: 2—14 in., 2—6 in., 2—12 pdr., etc. Sunk by gunfire of German Battle-Cruiser GOEBEN, in action off Imbros, 20th January, 1918. For appearance, see photo of ABERCROMBIE class, on page 24a.

Glatton (1914). 5,700 tons. Guns: 2—9.2 in., 4—6 in., etc. Caught fire in Dover Harbour, and torpedoed to avoid magazine explosion, 16th September, 1918. For appearance, see photo of GORGON, on page 90. (This vessel was officially classed as a Coast Defence Ship.)

M 30 (1915). 535 tons. Guns: 2—6 in., etc. Sunk by fire of Turkish batteries in Gulf of Smyrna, 13th May, 1916. For appearance, see photo of M 29, on page 92.

M 28 (1915). 570 tons. Guns: 1—9.2 in., 1—12 pdr., etc. Sunk by gunfire of German Battle-Cruiser GOEBEN, in action off Imbros, 20th January, 1918. For appearance, see photo of M 26, on page 92.

M 27 and **M 25** (1915). Sisters to M 28, above. Both lost during operations in the Dvina River, North Russia, 17th September, 1919.

M 21 (1915). 540 tons. Armament as M 28. Mined off Ostend, 20th October, 1918.

M 15 (1915). Sister to M 21, above. Torpedoed by a German Submarine, off Gaza, 11th November, 1917.

20 SLOOPS.

Anchusa (1917). 1290 tons. Guns: 2—4 in., etc. Torpedoed by a German Submarine, off the North Coast of Ireland, 16th July, 1918. For appearance, see photo of POLYANTHUS, on p. 132.

Arbutus (1917). Sister to ANCHUSA, above, but employed as a Special Service Ship. Foundered in St. George's Channel, during very heavy weather, after being torpedoed by a German Submarine, 16th December, 1917.

Bergamot (1917). Sister to ANCHUSA, above, but employed as a Special Service Ship. Torpedoed by a German Submarine, in the Atlantic, 13th August, 1917.

Candytuft (1917). Sister to ANCHUSA, above, but employed as a Special Service Ship. Torpedoed by a German Submarine, off Bougie, 18th November, 1917.

Cowslip (1917). Sister to ANCHUSA, above. Torpedoed by a German Submarine, off Cape Spartel, 25th April, 1918.

Gaillardia (1917). Sister to ANCHUSA, above. Mined off the Orkneys, night of 22nd-23rd March, 1918.

Rhododendron (1917). Sister to ANCHUSA, above. Torpedoed by a German Submarine, in the North Sea, 5th May, 1918.

Alyssum (1915). 1250 tons. Armament as ANCHUSA. Mined off S.W. Coast of Ireland, 18th March, 1917.

Arabis (1915). Sister to ALYSSUM, above. Torpedoed by German Destroyers, off Dogger Bank, night of 10-11th February, 1916.

Genista (1916). Sister to ALYSSUM, above. Torpedoed by a German Submarine, off West Coast of Ireland, 23rd October, 1916.

Gentian and **Myrtle** (1915). Sisters to ALYSSUM, above. Both mined in the Gulf of Finland, 16th July, 1919.

Mignonette (1916). Sister to ALYSSUM, above. Mined off S. W. Coast of Ireland, 17th March, 1917.

Nasturtium (1915). Sister to ALYSSUM, above. Mined in the Mediterranean, 27th April, 1916.

Primula (1915). Sister to ALYSSUM, above. Torpedoed by German Submarine U 35 in Eastern Mediterranean, 1st March, 1916.

Salvia (1916). Sister to ALYSSUM, above, but employed as a Special Service Ship. Torpedoed by a German Submarine off West Coast of Ireland, 20th June, 1917.

Tulip (1916). Sister to ALYSSUM, above, but employed as a Special Service Ship. Torpedoed by a German Submarine in the Atlantic, 30th April, 1917.

Aster (1915). 1200 tons. Armament as ANCHUSA. Mined in the Mediterranean, 4th July, 1917.

Lavender (1915). Sister to ASTER, above. Torpedoed by a German Submarine in the English Channel, 5th May, 1917.

Begonia (1915). Sister to ASTER, above, but employed as a Special Service Ship. Missing, believed torpedoed by a German Submarine in the Atlantic, October, 1917.

Note.—For appearance of above vessels, see photo of "Flower" class Sloop, on page 133.

26 MINESWEEPERS.

(**Note.**—P. = Paddle ; S. = Screw ; T. = Tunnel.)

Roedean (ex ROEBUCK) (1897). S. 1094 tons (gross). Sunk at Longhope, 13th January, 1915.
St. Seiriol (1914). P. 928 tons (gross). Mined off the Shipwash Light Vessel, 25th April, 1918.
Newmarket (1907). S. 833 tons (gross). Missing, Eastern Mediterranean ; last reported 16th July, 1917.
Clacton (1904). S. 820 tons (gross). Torpedoed by a German Submarine at Chai Aghizi, in the Levant, 3rd August, 1916.
Ascot (1916). P. 810 tons displacement. Guns : 2—12 pdr., etc. Torpedoed by a German Submarine, off Farn Islands, 10th November, 1918.
Ludlow (1916). Sister to ASCOT, above. Mined off the Shipwash, 29th December, 1916.
Plumpton (1916). Sister to ASCOT, above. Mined off Ostend, 19th October, 1918.
Redcar (1916) and **Kempton** (1916). Sisters to ASCOT, above. Both mined off Spindle Buoy, to north of Gravelines, 24th June, 1917.
Cupar (1918). S. 800 tons displacement. Guns : 2—12 pdr., etc. Mined off the Tyne, 5th May, 1919.
Kinross (1918). Sister to CUPAR, above. Mined in the Ægean, 16th June, 1919.
Penarth (1918). Sister to CUPAR, above. Mined off the Yorkshire Coast, 4th February, 1919.
Blackmorevale (1916). S. 750 tons displacement. Guns : 1—12 pdr., etc. Mined off Montrose, 1st May, 1918.
Erin's Isle (1912). P. 633 tons (gross). Mined off the Nore, 7th February, 1919.
Queen of the North (1895). P. 590 tons (gross). Mined off Orfordness, 20th July, 1917.
Brighton Queen (1897). P. 553 tons (gross). Mined off Nieuport, 6th October, 1915.
Duchess of Hamilton (1890). P. 553 tons (gross). Mined off the Longsand, 29th November, 1915.
Hythe (1905). P. 509 tons (gross). Lost by collision with Armed Boarding Steamer SARNIA, off Cape Helles, night of 28-29th October, 1915.
Lady Ismay (1911). P. 495 tons (gross). Mined near the Galloper, 21st December, 1917.
Fair Maid (1915). P. 432 tons (gross). Mined near Cross Sand Buoy, 9th November, 1916.
Nepaulin. (1892). P. 378 tons (gross). Mined near Dyck Light Vessel, 20th April, 1917.
Princess Mary II (1911). P. 326 tons (gross). Mined in the Ægean, 2nd August, 1919.
Duchess of Montrose (1902). P. 322 tons (gross). Mined off Dunkirk, 18th March, 1917.
Marsa (1902). P. 317 tons (gross). Lost by collision at entrance to Harwich Harbour, 18th November, 1917.
Fandango (1918). T. 280 tons displacement. Mined in the Dvina River, North Russia, 3rd July, 1919.
Sword Dance (1918). Sister to FANDANGO, above. Mined in the Dvina River, North Russia, 24th June, 1919.

Note.—For appearance of certain of the above vessels, reference should be made to the illustrations of various types of Minesweepers, on pages 134-137.

5 TORPEDO GUNBOATS.

Hazard (1894). 1070 tons. Guns : 2—4.7 in. Lost by collision off Portland Bill, 28th January, 1918, while employed as a Submarine Depot Vessel.

Speedy (1893). 810 tons. Guns : 2—4.7 in. Mined in North Sea, 30 miles off the Humber, 3rd September, 1914.

Jason (1892). Similar to SPEEDY, above. Employed as a Minesweeper. Mined near Coll Island, West Coast of Scotland, 7th April, 1917.
Niger (1892). Sister to JASON, above. Torpedoed by German Submarine, in the Downs, 11th November, 1914.

Seagull (1889). 735 tons. Guns : 2—4.7 in. Lost by collision with a Merchant Vessel, in the Firth of Clyde, 30th September, 1918.

69 FLOTILLA LEADERS and DESTROYERS.

(**a**) *3 Flotilla Leaders.* (For appearance, see photos of " Scott," " Broke," and " Kempenfelt " types, page 100.)

Scott (1917). 1800 tons. Guns : 5—4.7 in., 1—3 in. AA., etc. Tubes : 6—21 in. Torpedoed by a German Submarine, off the Dutch Coast, 15th August, 1918.
Tipperary (1913). 1737 tons. Guns : 6—4 in., etc. Tubes : 4—21 in. Sunk by gunfire during Battle of Jutland, 1st June, 1916.
Hoste (1916). 1666 tons. Guns : 4—4 in., etc. Tubes : 4—21 in. Foundered after collision with NEGRO, during very bad weather, in the North Sea, 21st December, 1916.

FLOTILLA LEADERS and DESTROYERS—*continued*.

(b) *66 Destroyers.* (For appearance of those not illustrated below, see photos of types " V " to " G," on pages 101—114.)

Vehement (1917). 1367 tons. Guns : 4—4 in., 1—3 in. AA., etc. Tubes : 4—21 in. Mined in the North Sea, 2nd August, 1918.

Verulam (1917). Sister to VEHEMENT, above. Mined off Seskaer Island, Gulf of Finland, night of 3rd-4th September, 1919.

Vittoria (1917). Sister to VEHEMENT, above. Torpedoed by a Russian (Bolshevik) Submarine. in the Gulf of Finland, 1st September, 1919.

Ulysses (1917). 1090 tons. Guns : 3—4 in., etc. Tubes : 4—21 in. Lost by collision with a merchantman in the Firth of Clyde, 29th October, 1918.

Tornado (1917). 1091 tons. Similar to ULYSSES, above. Torpedoed by German Submarine, off the Maas Lightship, night of 22nd-23rd December, 1917.

Torrent (1916). 1069 tons. Similar to ULYSSES, above. Torpedoed by German Submarine, off the Maas Lightship, night of 22nd-23rd December, 1917.

Simoom (1916). 1072 tons. Similar to ULYSSES, above. Blown up by gunfire of German Destroyers, during action off Schouwen Bank, 23rd January, 1917.

Setter (1916). 1040 tons. Similar to ULYSSES, above. Lost by collision with SYLPH, during foggy weather, off Harwich, 17th May, 1917.

Recruit (new) (1916). 1075 tons. Similar to ULYSSES, above. Mined in the North Sea, 9th August, 1917.

Ulleswater (1917). 923 tons. Armament as ULYSSES, above. Torpedoed by a German Submarine, off the Dutch Coast, 15th August, 1918.

Strongbow (1916). 898 tons. Armament as ULYSSES, above. Sunk by gunfire of three German Light Cruisers, in convoy action, off Norwegian Coast, 17th October, 1917.

Surprise (1916). 910 tons. Armament as ULYSSES, above. Torpedoed by a German Submarine, off the Maas Lightship, night of 22nd-23rd December, 1917.

Pheasant (1916). 1025 tons. Armament as ULYSSES, above. Mined off the Orkneys, 1st March, 1917.

Partridge (1916). 1016 tons. Sister to PHEASANT, above. Sunk by gunfire of four German Destroyers, in convoy action, off Norwegian Coast, 12th December, 1917.

Narbrough (1916), 1010 tons. **Opal** (1915), 1000 tons. Sisters to PHEASANT, above. Both wrecked outside Scapa Flow, during a violent gale and snowstorm, 12th January, 1918.

Negro (1916). 1025 tons. Sister to PHEASANT, above. Lost by collision with HOSTE, during very bad weather, in the North Sea, 21st December, 1916.

North Star (1916). 1042 tons. Sister to PHEASANT, above. Sunk by fire of German batteries, at Zeebrugge, 23rd April, 1918.

Nomad (1916) and **Nestor** (1915). 1025 tons. Sisters to PHEASANT, above. Sunk by gunfire of German Battle Fleet, in Battle of Jutland, 31st May, 1916.

Nessus (1915). 1022 tons. Sister to PHEASANT, above. Lost by collision with AMPHITRITE, during foggy weather, in the North Sea, 8th September, 1918.

Marmion (1915). 1029 tons. Sister to PHEASANT, above. Lost by collision in the North Sea, 21st October, 1917.

Mary Rose (1915). 1017 tons. Sister to PHEASANT, above. Sunk by gunfire of three German Light Cruisers, in convoy action, off the Norwegian Coast, 17th October, 1917.

Turbulent (1916). 1080 tons. Guns : 5—4 in. Tubes : 4—21 in. Rammed by a large German warship, in the Battle of Jutland, 1st June, 1916.

Medusa (1915). 1007 tons. Guns : 3—4 in., etc. Tubes : 4—21 in. Foundered, after collision with LAVEROCK, off Schleswig Coast, 25th March, 1916.

Lassoo (1915). 1010 tons. Armament as MEDUSA, above. Torpedoed by a German Submarine, off the Maas Lightship, 13th August, 1916.

Laforey (1913). 995 tons. Sister to LASSOO, above. Mined in the English Channel, 23rd March, 1917.

Louis (1913). 965 tons. Sister to LASSOO, above. Wrecked in Suvla Bay, 31st October, 1915.

Fortune (1913). 1000 tons. Similar to LASSOO, above. Sunk by gunfire of German Battle Fleet, in Battle of Jutland, about midnight, 31st May-1st June, 1916.

FLOTILLA LEADERS and DESTROYERS—*continued*.

Ardent (1913). 981 tons. Armament as MEDUSA. Sunk by gunfire of German Battle Fleet, in Battle of Jutland, 1st June, 1916.

Contest (1913). 957 tons. Similar to ARDENT, above. Torpedoed by a German Submarine, in the approaches to the English Channel, 18th September, 1917.

Lynx (1913). 935 tons. Sister to CONTEST, above. Mined off Moray Firth, 9th August, 1915.

Paragon (1913). 917 tons. Sister to CONTEST, above. Torpedoed in action with German Destroyers, in the Straits of Dover, 18th March, 1917.

Shark (1912). 935 tons. Sister to CONTEST, above. Disabled by gunfire of German Light Cruisers, and subsequently torpedoed, in Battle of Jutland, 31st May, 1916.

Sparrowhawk (1912). 935 tons. Sister to CONTEST, above. Disabled by collision with BROKE, in Battle of Jutland, and sunk by MARKSMAN, to avoid falling into enemy hands, 1st June, 1916.

Arno (1914). 550 tons. Guns : 4—12 pdr. Tubes : 3—18 in. Lost by collision, off the Dardanelles, 23rd March, 1918.

Ariel (1911). 763 tons. Guns : 2—4 in., 2—12 pdr. Tubes : 2—21 in. Mined in the North Sea, 2nd August, 1918.

Attack (1911). 785 tons. Sister to ARIEL, above. Torpedoed by a German Submarine, 11 miles off Alexandria, 30th December, 1917.

Phœnix (1911). 765 tons. Sister to ARIEL, above. Torpedoed by an enemy Submarine, in the Adriatic, 14th May, 1918.

Comet (1910). 747 tons. Guns : 2—4 in., 2—12 pdr. Tubes : 2—21 in. Torpedoed by an enemy Submarine, in the Mediterranean, 6th August, 1918.

Goldfinch (1910). Sister to COMET, above. Wrecked on Start Point, Sanday Island, Orkneys, during a fog, night of 18-19th February, 1915.

Staunch (1910). Sister to COMET, above. Torpedoed by a German Submarine, off Gaza, 11th November, 1917.

Pincher (1910). 975 tons. Guns : 1—4 in., 3—12 pdr. Tubes : 2—21 in. Wrecked on the Seven Stones, 24th July, 1918.

Racoon (1910). 913 tons. Sister to PINCHER, above. Wrecked on the North Coast of Ireland, in a snowstorm, 9th January, 1918.

Wolverine (1910). 986 tons. Sister to PINCHER, above. Lost by collision off North West Coast of Ireland, 12th December, 1917.

DESTROYERS—*continued.*

Maori (1909). 1035 tons. Guns : 2—4 in. Tubes : 2—18 in. Mined 2 miles N.W. of Weilingen Lightship, near Zeebrugge, 7th May, 1915.

Nubian (1909). 1062 tons. Armament as MAORI, above. Torpedoed by German Destroyers, in action off Folkestone, 27th October, 1916.

Zulu (1909). 1027 tons. Armament as MAORI, above. Mined in action, in Dover area, 27th October, 1916.

N.B.—The undamaged portions of NUBIAN and ZULU were united to form one Destroyer, named ZUBIAN, and the casualty resulting is therefore counted as the loss of one unit

Ghurka (1907). 880 tons. Guns : 5—12 pdr. Tubes : 2—18 in. Mined 4 miles S.E. of Dungeness buoy, 8th February, 1917.

Derwent (1903). 555 tons. Guns : 1—12 pdr. (12 cwt.), 3—12 pdr. (8 cwt.). Tubes : 2—18 in. Mined off Havre, 2nd May, 1917.
Kale (1904). 545 tons. Sister to DERWENT, above. Mined in the North Sea, 27th March, 1918.
Eden (1903). 540 tons. Sister to DERWENT, above. Lost by collision in the English Channel, 17th June, 1916.

Foyle (1903). 550 tons. Armament as DERWENT, above. Mined in the Straits of Dover, 15th March, 1917.
Itchen (1903). Sister to FOYLE, above. Torpedoed by a German Submarine, in the North Sea, 6th July, 1917.

Erne (1903). 550 tons. Armament as DERWENT, above. Wrecked off Rattray Head, Aberdeen Coast, 6th February, 1915.

DESTROYERS—*continued.*

Velox (1902). 420 tons. Guns : 1—12 pdr., 5—6 pdr. Tubes : 2—18 in. Mined off the Nab Light Vessel, 25th October, 1915.
Success (1901). 385 tons. Armament as VELOX, above. Wrecked off Fife Ness, 27th December, 1914.

Myrmidon (1900). 370 tons. Similar to SUCCESS, above. Lost by collision with s.s. HAMBOURNE, in the English Channel, 26th March, 1917.

Coquette (1897). 355 tons. Armament as VELOX, above. Mined off the East Coast, 7th March, 1916.

Falcon (1899). 408 tons. Armament as VELOX. Lost by collision in the North Sea, 1st April, 1918.
Fairy (1897). 380 tons. Similar to FALCON, above. Sunk through damage sustained in ramming German Submarine UC 75, in the North Sea, 31st May, 1918.

Cheerful (1897). 370 tons. Armament as VELOX. Mined off the Shetlands, 30th June, 1917.
Bittern (1897). 360 tons. Similar to CHEER-FUL, above. Lost by collision with s.s. KENILWORTH, off Portland Bill, 4th April, 1918.

Flirt as above, with different funnel tops and searchlight.

Flirt (1897). 380 tons. Armament as VELOX. Torpedoed by German Destroyers, in the Straits of Dover, 27th October, 1916.

Recruit (1896). 385 tons. Armament as VELOX. Torpedoed by a German Submarine, near the Galloper Lightship, 1st May, 1915.

Lightning (1895).   320 tons.   Armament as VELOX.   Mined off the East Coast, 30th June, 1915.

No. 10 (1907).   245 tons.   Armament as No. 24, above.   Torpedoed by a German Submarine in the North Sea, 10th June, 1915.

No. 9 (1907).   Sister to No. 10, above.   Lost by collision in the North Sea, 26th July, 1916.

Boxer (1894).   280 tons.   Guns : 1—12 pdr., 5—6 pdr.   Tube : 1—18 in.   Lost by collision, in the English Channel, 8th February, 1918.

2 PATROL BOATS.

P 26 (1915).   613 tons.   Guns : 1—4 in., etc.   Mined off Havre, 10th April, 1917.   For appearance, see photo of P boat on page 115.

P 12 (1915).   Sister to P 26, above.   Lost by collision, in English Channel, 4th November, 1918.

11 TORPEDO BOATS.

No. 24 (1908).   319 tons.   Guns : 2—12 pdr.   Tubes : 3—18 in.   Wrecked off Dover breakwater, 28th January, 1917.   For appearance, see photo of No. 36, on page 115.

No. 13 (1907).   270 tons.   Armament as No. 24.   Lost by collision in the North Sea, 26th January, 1916.   For appearance, see photo of No. 28, on page 116.

No. 117 (1904).   197 tons.   Guns : 3—3 pdr.   Tubes : 3—14 in.   Lost by collision in the English Channel, 10th June, 1917.

No. 12 (1907).   263 tons.   Armament as No. 24, above.   Torpedoed by a German Submarine in the North Sea, 10th June, 1915.

No. 11 (1907).   Sister to No. 12, above.   Mined off the East Coast, 7th March, 1916.

No. 96 (1894).   130 tons.   Armament as No. 117, above.   Lost by collision with a Mercantile Fleet Auxiliary in the Straits of Gibraltar, 1st November, 1915.

No. 90 (1895).   Sister to No. 96, above.   Capsized during heavy weather, in the Straits of Gibraltar, 25th April, 1918.

2 Q

TORPEDO BOATS—*continued.*

No. 064 (1886). 87 tons. Guns: 2—1 in. Nordenfelt Tubes: 5—14 in. Wrecked in the Ægean Sea, 21st March, 1915.

No. 046 (1886). 79 tons. Similar to No. 064 above, but only 4 tubes. Foundered during heavy weather in the Eastern Mediterranean, 27th December, 1915.

58 SUBMARINES.

L 55 (1918). 1070 tons. Guns: 1—4 in. Tubes: 6—18 in. Sunk by gunfire of Bolshevik Destroyers in the Gulf of Finland, 4th June, 1919. For appearance, see photo of L type Submarine, on page 119.

L 10 (1918). Sister to L 22, above. Sunk in action with German Destroyer S 33, off Texel, night of 3rd-4th October, 1918.

K 17 (1917). 2650 tons. Guns: 1—4 in., 1—3 in. AA. Tubes: 8—18 in. Rammed by FEARLESS during tactical exercises in the North Sea, 31st January, 1918. For appearance, see photo of K type Submarine, on page 121.

K 4 (1916). Sister to K 17, above. Rammed by INFLEXIBLE, during tactical exercises in the North Sea, 31st January, 1918.

K 1 (1916). Sister to K 17, above. Lost by collision with K 4 in the North Sea, 18th November, 1917.

J 6 (1915). 1900 tons. Guns: 1—4 in. Tubes: 6—18 in. Sunk by gunfire of a Special Service Ship in mistake for an enemy Submarine, 15th October, 1918.

H 10 (1915). 434 tons. Tubes: 4—21 in. Lost in the North Sea, 19th January, 1918.

H 6 (1915). Sister to H 10, above. Stranded on Schiermonnikoog, 18th January, 1916, and acquired by Dutch Navy (now Dutch O 8).

H 5 (1915). Sister to H 10, above. Lost by collision in the Irish Sea, 6th March, 1918.

H 3 (1915). Sister to H 10, above. Sunk in the Adriatic, 15th July, 1916.

G 11 (1916). 975 tons. Guns: 1—12 pdr., etc. Tubes: 1—21 in., 4—18 in. Wrecked off Howick, 22nd November, 1918. For appearance, see photo of G type Submarine, on page 122.

G 9 (1916). 965 tons. Otherwise as G 11. Sunk by PETARD, off Norwegian Coast, in mistake for an enemy Submarine, 16th September, 1917.

G 8 (1916). Sister to G 9, above. Lost in the North Sea, 14th January, 1918.

G 7 (1916). Sister to G 9, above. Lost in the North Sea, 1st November, 1918.

E 50 (1916). 807 tons. Guns: 1—12 pdr. Tubes: 5—18 in. Lost in the North Sea, 31st January, 1918. For appearance, see photo of E type Submarine, on page 122.

E 49 (1916). Sister to E 50, above. Mined off the Shetlands, 12th March, 1917.

E 47 (1916). Sister to E 50, above. Lost in the North Sea, 20th August, 1917.

E 37 (1915). Sister to E 50, above. Lost in the North Sea, 1st December, 1916.

E 36 (1916). Sister to E 50, above. Lost in the North Sea, 19th January, 1917.

E 34 (1917). Sister to E 50, above. Mined in Heligoland Bight, 20th July, 1918.

E 30 (1915). Sister to E 50, above. Lost in the North Sea, 22nd November, 1916.

E 28 (1915). Sister to E 50, above. Lost, date and details unknown.

E 26 (1915). Sister to E 50, above. Lost in the North Sea, 6th July, 1916.

E 24 (1915). Sister to E 50, above. Mined in Heligoland Bight, 24th March, 1916.

E 22 (1913). Sister to E 50, above. Sunk by a German Submarine in the Southern part of the North Sea, 25th April, 1916.

E 20 (1915). Sister to E 50, above. Sunk by the enemy in the Dardanelles, 6th November, 1915.

TORPEDO BOATS—*continued.*

E 19 (1915). Sister to E 50. Blown up in Helsingfors Bay to avoid capture by the enemy, 3rd April, 1918.

E 18 (1915). 805 tons. Similar to E 50. Lost in the Baltic, 24th May, 1916.

E 17 (1915). Sister to E 18, above. Wrecked off Texel, 6th January, 1916.

E 16 (1914). Sister to E 18, above. Mined in Heligoland Bight, 22nd August, 1916.

E 15 (1914). Sister to E 18, above. Stranded on Kephez Point, in the Dardanelles, and torpedoed by picket boats of H.M.S. TRIUMPH and MAJESTIC, to prevent the enemy salving her, 18th April, 1915.

E 14 (1914). 795 tons. Similar to E 18, above. Sunk by enemy gunfire, off Kum Kale, Dardanelles, 28th January, 1918.

E 13 (1914). 791 tons. Similar to E 18, above. Damaged by gunfire of German Destroyers while stranded on Island of Saltholm, 18th August, 1915; interned at Copenhagen, 3rd September, 1915; sold to Danish shipbreakers in March, 1919.

E 10 (1913). 805 tons. Sister to E 18, above. Lost in the North Sea, 18th January, 1915.

E 9 (1913). 807 tons. Similar to E 18, above. Blown up in Helsingfors Bay, to avoid capture by the enemy, 3rd April, 1918.

E 8 (1913). 795 tons. Sister to E 14, above. Blown up in Helsingfors Bay, to avoid capture by the enemy, 4th April, 1918.

E 7 (1913). 791 tons. Sister to E 13, above. Sunk by the enemy, in the Dardanelles, 4th September, 1915.

E 6 (1912). Sister to E 7, above. Mined in the North Sea, 26th December, 1915.

E 5 (1912). Sister to E 7, above. Lost in the North Sea, 7th March, 1916.

E 3 (1912). Sister to E 7, above. Sunk by German Cruiser STRASSBURG, in Heligoland Bight, 18th October, 1914.

E 1 (1912). 795 tons. Similar to E 3, above. Blown up in Helsingfors Bay, to avoid capture by the enemy, 3rd April, 1918.

AE 2 (1913). 791 tons. Similar to E 7, above. Sunk by gunfire of Turkish vessels, in the Sea of Marmora, 30th April, 1915.

AE 1 (1913). Sister to AE 2, above. Foundered off the Bismarck Archipelago, Pacific, 14th September, 1914.

D 6 (1911). 620 tons. Guns: 2—12 pdr. Tubes: 3—18 in. Sunk by a German Submarine, off the North Coast of Ireland, 28th June, 1918.

D 5 (1911). Sister to D 6, above. Mined off Great Yarmouth, 3rd November, 1914.

D 3 (1910). Sister to D 6, above. Sunk by a French airship, in the English Channel, in mistake for an enemy Submarine, 15th March, 1918.

D 2 (1910). 600 tons. Similar to D 6, above. Lost in the North Sea, 1st December, 1914.

SUBMARINES—*continued.*

C 35 (1909). 321 tons. Tubes : 2—18 in. Blown up in Helsingfors Bay, to avoid capture by the enemy, 5th April, 1918.

C 34 (1910). Sister to C 35, above. Sunk by a German Submarine, off the Shetlands, 21st July, 1917.

C 33 (1910). Sister to C 35, above. Lost in the North Sea, 4th August, 1915.

C 32 (1909). Sister to C 35, above. Ran ashore and blown up, in the Gulf of Riga, 17th October, 1917.

C 31 (1909). Sister to C 35, above. Lost off the Belgian Coast, 4th January, 1915.

C 29 (1909). Sister to C 35, above. Mined in the North Sea, 29th August, 1915.

C 27 (1909). Sister to C 35, above. Blown up in Helsingfors Bay, to avoid capture by the enemy, 5th April, 1918.

C 26 (1909). Sister to C 35, above. Blown up in Helsingfors Bay, to avoid capture by the enemy, 4th April, 1918.

C 16 (1908). 316 tons. Similar to C 35, above. Accidentally rammed by a Destroyer of MEDEA type, subsequently salved, but found too badly damaged to be worth repairing.

C 3 (1906). Sister to C 16, above. Blown up at Zeebrugge Mole, 23rd April, 1918.

B 10 (1906). 316 tons. Tubes : 2—18 in. Destroyed by bombs from an Austrian Aeroplane, while under repair, at Venice, 9th August, 1916.

81 AUXILIARIES.

(a) 17 Armed Merchant Cruisers (Gross tonnage in each case).

Calgarian (1914). 17,515 tons. Torpedoed by a German Submarine, off North Coast of Ireland, 1st March, 1918.

Oceanic (1899). 17,274 tons. Wrecked on Foula Island, Shetlands, 8th September, 1914.

Alcantara (1913). 15,300 tons. Torpedoed in action with German Armed Merchant Cruiser GREIF, in the North Sea, lat. 61.48 N., long. 1.40 E., 29th February, 1916.

Avenger (1915). 15,000 tons. Torpedoed by a German Submarine, in the North Atlantic, 14th June, 1917.

Laurentic (1908). 14,892 tons. Torpedoed by a German Submarine, off the North West Coast of Ireland, 23rd January, 1917.

Orama (1911). 12,927 tons. Torpedoed by a German Submarine, in the Atlantic, 19th October, 1917.

Otranto (1909). 12,124 tons. Stranded on Island of Islay, in heavy weather, after being severely damaged by collision with s.s. KASHMIR, 6th October, 1918.

Otway (1909). 12,077 tons. Torpedoed by a German Submarine, in the North Atlantic, 23rd July, 1917.

Marmora (1903). 10,509 tons. Torpedoed by a German Submarine, off the South Coast of Ireland, 23rd July, 1918.

Moldavia (1903). 9500 tons. Torpedoed by a German Submarine, in the English Channel, 23rd May, 1918.

India (1896). 7940 tons. Torpedoed by a German Submarine, off Bodo, West Fjord, 8th August, 1915.

Hilary (1908). 6329 tons. Torpedoed by a German Submarine, in the Atlantic, 25th May, 1917.

Patia (1913). 6103 tons. Torpedoed by a German Submarine, in the Bristol Channel, 13th June, 1918.

Bayano (1913). 5948 tons. Torpedoed by a German Submarine, off Corsewall Point, Galloway, 11th March, 1915.

Viknor (1888). 5386 tons. Mined off the North Coast of Ireland, 13th January, 1915.

Champagne (1895). 5360 tons. Torpedoed by a German Submarine, in the Atlantic, 9th October, 1917.

Clan MacNaughton (1911). 4985 tons. Foundered in a heavy gale, off the North Coast of Ireland, 3rd February, 1915.

(b) 3 Commissioned Escort Ships (Gross tonnage in each case).

Mechanician (1900). 9044 tons. Torpedoed by a German Submarine, 8 miles West of St. Catherine's Point, 20th January, 1918.

Quernmore (1898). 7302 tons. Torpedoed by a German Submarine, 160 miles W. by N. $\frac{3}{4}$N. from Tory Island, 31st July, 1917.

Bostonian (1915). 5736 tons. Torpedoed by a German Submarine, 34 miles S. by E. $\frac{1}{2}$E. from Start Point, 10th October, 1917.

(c) 12 Armed Boarding Steamers (Gross tonnage in each case).

Tithonus (ex TITANIA, 1908). 3463 tons. Torpedoed by a German Submarine, in the North Sea, 28th March, 1918.

Fauvette (1912). 2644 tons. Mined off the East Coast, 9th March, 1916.

Dundee (1911). 2187 tons. Torpedoed by a German Submarine, in the approaches to the English Channel, 3rd September, 1917.

Grive (1905). 2037 tons. Foundered in bad weather, off the Shetlands, 24th December, 1917, after being torpedoed by a German Submarine.

Duke of Albany (1907). 1997 tons. Torpedoed by a German Submarine, 20 miles East of Pentland Skerries, 25th August, 1916.

Tara (ex HIBERNIA, 1900). 1862 tons. Torpedoed by German Submarine U 35, in Solum Bay, Western Egypt, 5th November, 1915.

Louvain (1897). 1830 tons. Torpedoed by a German Submarine, in the Eastern Mediterranean, 20th January, 1918.

Stephen Furness (1910). 1712 tons. Torpedoed by a German Submarine, in the Irish Sea, 13th December, 1917.

Fiona (1905). 1611 tons. Wrecked off Pentland Skerries, 6th September, 1917.

Sarnia (1910). 1498 tons. Torpedoed by a German Submarine, in the Mediterranean, 12th September, 1918.

Ramsey (1895). 1443 tons. Torpedoed by German Auxiliary Minelayer METEOR, in the North Sea, to South East of Pentland Firth, 8th August, 1915.

Snaefell (1910). 1368 tons. Torpedoed by a German Submarine, in the Mediterranean, 5th June, 1918.

SHIPS LOST IN THE WAR—BRITISH *continued.*

(d)   16 Special Service Ships ("Q Boats"). (Gross tonnage in each case.)

Perugia (1901).   4348 tons.   Torpedoed by a German Submarine, in the Gulf of Genoa, 3rd December, 1916.

Bradford City (1910).   3683 tons.   Torpedoed by a German Submarine, in the Straits of Messina, 16th August, 1917.

Remembrance (1910).   3660 tons.   Torpedoed by a German Submarine, in the Mediterranean, 14th August, 1916.

Willow Branch (1892).   3314 tons.   Torpedoed by a German Submarine, off the West Coast of Africa, to East of Cape Verde Islands, 25th April, 1918.

Dunraven (1910).   3117 tons.   Foundered at entrance to English Channel, 10th August, 1917, after being torpedoed by a German Submarine.

Zylpha (1894).   2917 tons.   Torpedoed by a German Submarine, to the South West of Ireland, 15th June, 1917.

Bracondale (1903).   2095 tons.   Torpedoed by a German Submarine, in the Atlantic, 7th August, 1917.

Glenfoyle (1913).   1680 tons.   Torpedoed by a German Submarine, in the Atlantic, 18th September, 1917.

Westphalia (1913).   1467 tons.   Torpedoed by a German Submarine, in the Irish Sea, 11th February, 1918.

Peveril (1904).   1459 tons.   Torpedoed by a German Submarine, outside the Straits of Gibraltar, 6th November, 1917.

Lady Patricia (1916).   1372 tons.   Torpedoed by a German Submarine, in the Atlantic, 20th May, 1917.

Warner (1911).   1273 tons.   Torpedoed by a German Submarine, off West Coast of Ireland, 13th March, 1917.

Penshurst (1906).   1191 tons.   Torpedoed by a German Submarine, off the Bristol Channel, 25th December, 1917.

Vala (1894).   1016 tons.   Believed to have been torpedoed by a German Submarine ; last reported in lat. 47 N., long. 9.32 W., 21st August, 1917.

Lady Olive (1913).   701 tons.   Torpedoed by a German Submarine, in the English Channel, 19th February, 1917.

Stock Force (1917).   732 tons.   Torpedoed by a German Submarine, in the English Channel, 30th July, 1918.

Note.—More than a dozen other Special Service Vessels, of under 500 tons gross, were also lost.

(e)   5 Fleet Messengers (Gross tonnage in each case).

Osmanieh (1906).   4041 tons.   Mined in the Eastern Mediterranean, 31st December, 1917.

Ermine (1912).   1777 tons.   Torpedoed by a German Submarine, in the Ægean, 2nd August, 1917.

Princess Alberta (1905).   1586 tons.   Mined between Stavros and Mudros, 21st February, 1917.

Redbreast (1908).   1313 tons.   Torpedoed by a German Submarine, in the Mediterranean, 15th July, 1917.

Chesterfield (1913).   1013 tons.   Torpedoed by a German Submarine, 42 miles N.E. by E. ½E. from Malta, 18th May, 1918.

Note.—Four Fleet Messengers, of under 500 tons gross, were also lost.

(f)   17 Armed Yachts. (Tonnage by yacht measurement in each case.)

Ægusa (ex ERIN, 1896).   1242 tons.   Mined near Malta, 28th April, 1916.

Goissa (1893).   1023 tons.   Mined in the Dardanelles, 15th November, 1918.

Resource II (ex ENCHANTRESS).   1000 tons.   Destroyed by fire, in Southampton Harbour, 12th November, 1915.

Iolaire (1902).   999 tons.   Wrecked off Stornoway, 1st January, 1919.

Mekong (1906).   899 tons.   Wrecked on Christthorpe Cliff, 12th March, 1916.

Clementina (1887).   625 tons.   Beached after collision, off Tor Cor Point, 5th August, 1915.

Kethailes (1903).   611 tons.   Lost by collision, off Blackwater Lightship, 11th October, 1917.

Conqueror II (1889).   526 tons.   Torpedoed by a German Submarine, in Fair Island Channel, 26th September, 1916.

Irene (1890).   543 tons.   Mined off North Foreland, lat. 51.29 N., long. 1.27 E., 9th November, 1915.

Hersilia (1895).   454 tons.   Wrecked on Eilean Chuai, Hebrides, 6th January, 1916.

Verona (1890).   437 tons.   Mined off Portmahomack, 24th February, 1917.

Sanda (1906).   351 tons.   Sunk by fire of German batteries, off Belgian Coast, 25th September, 1915.

Zaida (1900).   350 tons.   Sunk by a German Submarine, in the Gulf of Alexandretta, 17th August, 1916.

Zarefah (1905).   279 tons.   Mined off Mull Head, Deer Ness, 8th May, 1917.

Aries (1880).   268 tons.   Mined off Leathercoat, 31st October, 1915.

Rhiannon (1914).   138 tons.   Mined off Longsand, 20th July, 1915.

Marcella (1887).   127 tons.   Lost by collision in the Downs, 24th March, 1916.

(g)   11 Miscellaneous Auxiliaries.

Campania (1893).   18,000 tons displacement.   Guns : 6—4.7 in., 1—3 in. AA.   Aircraft Carrier.   Lost by collision with GLORIOUS, during a gale, in the Firth of Forth, 5th November, 1918.

Princess Irene (1914).   5934 tons gross.   Minelayer.   Destroyed by internal explosion, at Sheerness, 27th May, 1915.

Fisgard II (1869).   6010 tons displacement.   Repair Ship.   Foundered in bad weather, off Portland Bill, 17th September, 1914.

Lowtyne (1892).   3231 tons gross.   Not classified.   Torpedoed by a German Submarine, 3½ miles E.S.E. from Whitby, 10th June, 1918.

Ben-My-Chree (1908).   3888 tons displacement.   Aircraft Carrier.   Sunk by fire of Turkish batteries, in Kastelorizo Harbour, 11th January, 1917.

White Head (1880).   1172 tons gross.   Not classified.   Torpedoed by a German Submarine, 40 miles N.N.E. of Suda Bay, 15th October, 1917.

Dalkeith (ex DALHOUSIE, 1889).   741 tons gross.   Salvage Vessel.   Sunk by a German Submarine, during salvage operations, at San Pietro Island, Sardinia, 29th March, 1917.

Thrush (1889).   805 tons displacement.   Salvage Vessel.   Wrecked near Glenarm, County Antrim, 11th April, 1917.

Majestic II (1901).   408 tons gross.   Patrol Paddler.   Foundered, near Oran, 28th July, 1916.

Duchess of Richmond (1910).   354 tons gross.   Patrol Paddler.   Mined, 28th June, 1919.

Stirling Castle (1899).   271 tons gross.   Patrol Paddler.   Blown up, from unknown cause, off West Coast of Malta, 26th September, 1916.

General Note.—The following small craft were lost during the War, but space does not permit of particulars being given :—

29 Motor Launches (M.L. 566, 561, 541, 540, 534, 474, 431, 424, 421, 403, 356, 278, 255, 254, 253, 247, 230, 197, 191, 149, 121, 110, 64, 62, 55, 52, 40, 19, 18).

17 Coastal Motor Boats (Nos. 79 A, 71 A, 67 A, 62 BD, 50, 47, 42, 40, 39 B, 33 A, 18 A, 11, 10, 8, 2, 1).

AMERICAN.

ARMOURED CRUISER.

SAN DIEGO (1904). 13,680 tons. Guns : 4—8 in., 45 cal. ; 14—6 in., 50 cal. ; 20—3 in., etc. Mined, 10 miles off Fire Island, N.Y., 19th July, 1918. For appearance, see photo of HUNTINGTON, on page 198.

2 DESTROYERS.

Jacob Jones (1915). 1150 tons. Guns : 4—4 in., 50 cal. Tubes : 8—21 in. Torpedoed by German Submarine, off the Scillies, 6th December, 1917. No photo available.

Chauncey (1901). 420 tons. Guns : 2—3 in., etc. Tubes : 2—18 in. Lost by collision with U.S.S. CAYA, in the Straits of Gibraltar, 19th November, 1917. For appearance, see photo of STEWART, on page 216.

2 SUBMARINES.

G 2 (1914). 700 tons. Guns : 1—3 in. AA. Tubes : 5—21 in. Foundered in Long Island Sound, off New London, 27th July, 1919. For appearance, see photo of G 1, on page 223.

F 1 (1911). 350 tons. Tubes : 4—21 in. Lost by collision with F 3 during a fog, in American waters, 17th December, 1917. No photo available.

7 AUXILIARIES.

Cyclops (1910). 19,360 tons. Fleet Collier. Missing, supposed foundered in bad weather in the Western Atlantic, end of March, 1918. For appearance, see photo of JUPITER, on page 230.

McCulloch (1898). 1280 tons. Coastguard Cruising Cutter. Lost by collision, in the Pacific, October, 1917.

Tampa (1912). 118i tons. Coastguard Cruising Cutter. Torpedoed by German Submarine, while employed on convoy duty in English Channel, 26th September, 1918. No photo available.

Alcedo (1895). 981 tons gross. Armed Yacht. Torpedoed by German Submarine, in Bay of Biscay, 15th November, 1917.

Mohawk (1902). 980 tons. Coastguard Cruising Cutter. Lost by collision, off New York, 1st October, 1917.

Wakiva II (1907). 852 tons gross. Armed Yacht. Lost by collision, in the Bay of Biscay, 22nd May, 1918.

Guinevere (1908). 499 tons gross. Armed Yacht. Wrecked on French Atlantic Coast, 25th January, 1918.

Note.—The Sloop SCHURZ (lost by collision, 21st June, 1918) is not listed here, as she already appears in the German Losses as the GEIER.

JAPANESE.

BATTLESHIP.

KAWACHI (1910). 21,420 tons. Guns : 12—12 in., 45 and 50 cal. ; 10—6 in., 50 cal. ; 8—4.7 in. ; 12—12 pdr. Destroyed by internal explosion, in Tokuyama Bay, 12th July, 1918.

BATTLE CRUISER.

TSUKUBA (1905). 13,750 tons. Guns : 4—12 in., 45 cal. ; 12—6 in., 45 cal. ; 12—4.7 in. ; 2—14 pdr., etc. Destroyed by internal explosion, at Yokosuka, 14th January, 1917.

2 LIGHT CRUISERS.

OTOWA (1903). 3000 tons. Guns : 2—6 in., 50 cal. ; 6—4.7 in. ; 4—12 pdr. Wrecked near Damio Point, Shima Prefecture, 1st August, 1917.
KASAGI (1898). 4760 tons. Guns : 2—8 in., 10—4.7 in., 12—12 pdr., etc. Wrecked in Tsugaru Straits, July, 1916. For appearance, see photo of CHITOSE, on page 267.

COAST DEFENCE SHIP.

TAKACHIHO (1885). Old Cruiser, of 3700 tons, re-employed as a Minelayer. Guns : 8—6 in. Torpedoed by German Destroyer S 90, 60 miles south of Kiao Chau Bay, night of 17th-18th October, 1914.

DESTROYER.

Shirotaye (1906). 380 tons. Guns : 6—12 pdr. Tubes : 2—18 in. Wrecked during engagement with German Gunboat JAGUAR, in Kiao-Chau Bay, 4th September, 1914. For appearance, see photo of ARARE type, on page 272. (This vessel was subsequently raised, but found to be beyond repair.)

TORPEDO BOAT.

No. 33 (1901). 84 tons. Guns : 2—3 pdr. Tubes : 3—18 in. Mined at entrance to Kiao-Chau Bay, 11th November, 1914.

AUXILIARY.

Shijiki (1916). Fleet oiler. 5300 tons. Lost in a typhoon off Tanegashima, 15th August, 1919.

FRENCH.

4 BATTLESHIPS.

DANTON (1909). 18,400 tons. Guns : 4—12 in., 50 cal. ; 12—9.4 in. : 16—12 dpr., etc. Torpedoed by German Submarine U 64, 20 miles from Coast of Sardinia, 19th March, 1917. For appearance, see DANTON class on page 295.

SUFFREN (1899). 12,750 tons. Guns : 4—12 in., 45 cal. ; 10—6.4 in. : 8—3.9 in., etc. Torpedoed by German Submarine; 50 miles N.W. of Lisbon, 26th November, 1916.

BATTLESHIPS—*continued.*

BOUVET (1896). 12,000 tons. Guns: 2—12 in., 2—10.8 in., 8—5.5 in., 8—3.9 in., etc. Sunk by torpedo from White Cliffs, in the Dardanelles, 18th March, 1915.

GAULOIS (1896). 11,260 tons. Guns: 4—12 in., 10—5.5 in., 8—3.9 in., etc. Torpedoed by German Submarine, in the Ægean Sea, 27th December, 1916. For appearance, see photo of ST. LOUIS, on page 297.

5 CRUISERS.

LÉON GAMBETTA (1901). 12,300 tons. Guns: 4—7.6 in., 16—6.4 in., etc. Torpedoed by Austrian Submarine U5, in Straits of Otranto, 20 miles off Cape Leuca, night of 26-27th April, 1915.

DUPETIT-THOUARS (1901). 9500 tons. Guns: 2—7.6 in., 8—6.4 in., 4—3.9 in., etc. Torpedoed by German Submarine, while on convoy duty in North Atlantic, 7th August, 1918. For appearance, see photo of MONTCALM, on page 300.

KLÉBER (1902). 7700 tons. Guns: 8—6.4 in., 4—3.9 in., etc. Mined, off Cap St. Mathieu, Brest, 27th June, 1917. For appearance, see photo of DESAIX, on page 299.

BATTLESHIPS—*continued.*

CHATEAURENAULT (1898). 8000 tons. Guns: 2—6.4 in., 6—5.5 in., etc. Torpedoed by enemy Submarine, in the Ionian Sea, 14th December, 1917.

AMIRAL CHARNER (1893). 4750 tons. Guns: 2—7.6 in., 6—5.5 in., etc. Torpedoed by German Submarine, off Syrian Coast, 8th February, 1916. For appearance, see photo of BRUIX on page 300.

2 SLOOPS.

Rigel (1915). 1200 tons. Guns: 2—5.5 in., etc. Torpedoed by German Submarine U 35, off Algiers, 2nd October, 1916. For appearance, see photo of ETOILE type Sloop, on page 305.

Kersaint (1897). 1243 tons. Guns: 1—5.5 in., 5—3.9 in. Wrecked near Papeete, Tahiti, 5th March, 1919.

2 MINELAYING GUNBOATS.

Casabianca (1895). 1000 tons. Guns: 1—3.9 in., etc. Lost, by explosion of own mines, near Smyrna, night of 3rd-4th June, 1915.

Cassini (1894). Sister to CASABIANCA, above, but without mainmast. Torpedoed by enemy Submarine, in Mediterranean, 28th February, 1917.

3 GUNBOATS.

Zelee (1899). 650 tons. Guns: 2—3.9 in., etc. (Disarmed at time of loss.) Sunk by gunfire of German Cruisers, SCHARNHORST and GNEISENAU, at Papeete, Tahiti, 22nd September, 1914.

Decidee (1899). Sister to ZELEE. Lost during 1919, details not advised.
Surprise (1895). Similar to ZELEE. Torpedoed by German Submarine U·38, at Funchal, 3rd December, 1916.

13 DESTROYERS.

Renaudin (1913). 756 tons. Guns: 2—3.9 in., 4—9 pdr. Tubes: 4—18 in. Torpedoed by Austrian Submarine U6, off Durazzo, 18th March, 1916. For appearance, see photo of BISSON, on page 312.

Faulx (1911). 745 tons. Armament as RENAUDIN. Lost by collision in Straits of Otranto, 10th March, 1918.
Fourché (1910). Sister to FAULX, above. Torpedoed by Austrian Submarine U 15, in Straits of Otranto, 23rd June, 1916.
Dague (1910). Sister to FAULX, above. Mined, off Antivari, 24th February, 1915.
Boutefeu (1911). 700 tons. Armament as RENAUDIN. Mined in the Straits of Otranto, 15th May, 1917. For appearance, see photo of COMMANDANT BORY, on page 313.

Fantassin (1909). 450 tons. Guns: 6—9 pdr. Tubes: 3—18 in. Lost by collision with MAMELUK, near Corfu, 5th June, 1916.
Carabinier (1908). 416 tons. Armament as FANTASSIN. Wrecked on Syrian Coast, 13th November, 1918. For appearance, see photo of MAMELUK, on page 315.
Etendard (1908). 335 tons. Guns: 1—9 pdr., etc. Tubes: 2—18 in. Torpedoed by German Destroyers, off Dunkirk, 25th April, 1917. For appearance, see photo of CLAYMORE, on page 315.
Branlebas (1907). 330 tons. Guns: 1—9 pdr., etc. Tubes: 2—18 in. Mined, off Dunkirk, 9th November, 1915. For appearance, see photo of FANFARE, on page 315.
Mousquet (1902). 300 tons. Guns: 1—9 pdr., etc. Tubes: 2—15 in. Sunk by gunfire of German Cruiser EMDEN, at Penang, 28th October, 1914. For appearance, see photo of MOUSQUETON, on page 316.
Carabine (1903). Sister to MOUSQUET, above. Lost by accident, date not advised.
Catapulte (1902). Sister to MOUSQUET, above. Lost by collision, near Bizerta, 18th May, 1918.

Yatagan (1900). 300 tons. Guns: 1—9 pdr., etc. Tubes: 2—15 in. Lost by collision with s.s. TEVIOT, off Dieppe, 3rd December, 1916.

9 TORPEDO BOATS.

Nos. 348 and **347** (1906). 97 tons. Guns: 2—1 pdr. Tubes: 3—18 in. Lost by collision, off Toulon, 9th October, 1914. For appearance, see photo of No. 361, page 317.

No. 333 (1906). Sister to No. 348, above. Lost by collision in the Western Mediterranean, 12th March, 1918.

No. 331 (1906). Sister to No. 348, above. Lost by collision, off Cape Barfleur, 17th June, 1915.

No. 325 (1906). Sister to No. 348, above. Mined, off the Coast of Tunis, 22nd January, 1919.

No. 319 (1905). Sister to No. 348, above. Mined, off Nieuport, 15th January, 1915.

No. 317 (1905). Sister to No. 348, above. Mined, off Calais, night of 28th-29th December, 1916.

No. 300 (1905). Similar to No. 348, above, but with 14 in. tubes. Mined, off Havre, 1st February, 1916.

No. 251 (1901). 88 tons. Guns: 2—1 pdr. Tubes: 2—14 in. Lost by collision, in the English Channel, date not reported. For appearance, see photo of No. 176, on page 317.

12 SUBMARINES.

Diane (1914). 630 tons. Tubes, etc.: 10. Lost in English Channel, about 10th March, 1918. No photo available.

Mariotte (1911). 530 tons. Tubes: 7—18 in. Sunk, by German Submarine, in the Dardanelles, 26th July, 1915.

Ariane (1914). 410 tons. Tubes: 8—18 in. Torpedoed by German Submarine, off entrance to Gulf of Bizerta, 19th June, 1917. No photo available.

Foucault (1910). 392 tons. Tubes: 6—18 in. Sunk by bombs from Austrian Seaplane, in Lower Adriatic, 15th September, 1916. For appearance, see photo of COULOMB, on page 321.

Floreal (1908). Sister to FOUCAULT, above. Lost by collision, off Salonika, 2nd August, 1918.

Prairial (1908). Sister to FOUCAULT, above. Lost by collision with merchantman, off Havre, night of April 28th-29th, 1918.

Fresnel (1908). Similar to FOUCAULT, above. Stranded on Albanian Coast, in a fog, and destroyed by gunfire of Austrian Destroyer VARASDINIER, 5th December, 1915.

Bernouilli (1911). Similar to FOUCAULT, above. Sunk by Austrian Submarine, in the Adriatic, about 13th February, 1918.

Joule (1910). Sister to BERNOUILLI, above. Mined in Sea of Marmora, 1st May, 1915.

Monge (1909). Sister to BERNOUILLI, above. Rammed and sunk by Austrian Cruiser HELGOLAND, off Cattaro, 29th December, 1915.

Saphir (1908). 390 tons. Tubes: 2—18 in. Wrecked in avoiding minefield in the Dardanelles, 17th January, 1915. For appearance, see photo of EMERAUDE, on page 322.

Circe (1907). 350 tons. Torpedoed by Austrian Submarine, off Cattaro, 20th September, 1918.

The two following losses are not counted in the total given above :—

Curie (1910). Similar to FOUCAULT, above. Sunk by fire of Austrian batteries, at Pola, 23rd December, 1914. Subsequently salved, and now Austrian U 14. Restored to France, November, 1918.

Turquoise (1908). Sister to SAPHIR, above. Sunk by gunfire of Turkish vessels, in the Sea of Marmora, 31st October, 1915. Salved on 3rd November, and re-named MUSTEDIEH-OMBASHI by Turks. Restored to France, December, 1918.

12 AUXILIARIES.

Gallia (1913). 14,966 tons (gross). Armed Cruiser. Torpedoed by German Submarine U 35, to South of Sardinia, 4th October, 1916.

Provence II (1914). 13,752 tons (gross). Armed Cruiser. Torpedoed by German Submarine U 35. in the Mediterranean, 26th February, 1916.

Burdigala (1897). 12,009 tons (gross). Armed Cruiser. Torpedoed by German Submarine, in the Mediterranean, 14th November, 1916.

Sant'Anna (1910). 9350 tons (gross). Armed Cruiser. Torpedoed by German Submarine, in the Mediterranean, 10th May, 1918.

Himalaya (1902). 5620 tons (gross). Armed Cruiser. Torpedoed by German Submarine, off Algerian Coast, 22nd June, 1917.

Carthage (1910). 5601 tons (gross). Armed Cruiser. Torpedoed by German Submarine, off Cape Helles, Gallipoli, 4th July, 1915.

France IV (1896). 4025 tons (gross). Armed Cruiser. Torpedoed by German Submarine, in Western Mediterranean, November, 1915.

Kanguroo (1912). 2493 tons (gross). Submarine Depot Vessel. Torpedoed by German Submarine U 38, at Funchal, 3rd December, 1916.

Drome (1887). 2200 tons displacement. Fleet Auxiliary. Mined in Gulf of Lions, January, 1918.

Golo II (1905). 1380 tons (gross). Armed Boarding Steamer. Torpedoed by German Submarine, near Corfu, 22nd August, 1917.

Italia (1904). 1305 tons (gross) } Armed Boarding Steamers. Lost through enemy action,
Corse (No particulars available) } date not reported.

ITALIAN.

4 BATTLESHIPS.

LEONARDO DA VINCI (1911). 22,380 tons. Guns: 13—12 in., 46 cal.; 18—4.7 in.; 14—14 pdr., etc. Sunk by fire and explosion, at Taranto, 2nd August, 1916; since salved, but believed to be beyond repair. For appearance, see photos of CONTE DI CAVOUR and GIULIO CESARE, on page 338.

AMALFI (1908). 10,000 tons. Guns: 4—10 in., 45 cal.; 8—7.5 in,, 45 cal.; 16—14 pdr., etc. Torpedoed by Austrian Submarine, in Upper Adriatic, 7th July, 1915. For appearance, see photo of PISA, on page 344.

BATTLESHIPS—*continued*

BENEDETTO BRIN (1901). 13,215 tons. Guns: 4—12 in., 40 cal.; 4—8 in.; 12—6 in.; 20—14 pdr., etc. Destroyed by internal explosion, at Brindisi, 27th September, 1915.

REGINA MARGHERITA (1901). Sister to B. BRIN, above, but armed with 4 extra 6 inch in place of 8 inch guns. Mined off Valona, 11th December, 1916.

ARMOURED CRUISER.

GIUSEPPE GARIBALDI (1899). 7234 tons. Guns: 1—10 in., 45 cal.; 2—8 in., 45 cal.; 14—6 in.; 10—14 pdr., etc. Torpedoed by Austrian Submarine, off Cattaro, 18th July, 1915.

2 LIGHT CRUISERS.

BASILICATA (1914). 2560 tons. Guns: 6—4.7 in., 6—14 pdr., etc. Sunk by an internal explosion, at Port Said, 13th August, 1919. No photo available.

ETRURIA (1891). 2280 tons. Guns: 6—4.7 in., etc. Blown up in Leghorn Harbour, 13th August, 1918. For appearance, see photo of PUGLIA, on page 348.

MONITOR.

Alfriedo Capellini (1916). Guns: 2—15 in., 40 cal.; 2—14 pdr. Capsized off Ancona, 14th November, 1918.

MINELAYING GUNBOAT.

Partenope (1889). 900 tons. Guns: 2—14 pdr., etc. Torpedoed by enemy Submarine, off Bizerta, 24th March, 1918. For appearance, see photo of MINERVA, on page 366.

9 DESTROYERS.

Cesare Rossarol (1915). 1030 tons. Guns: 6—4 in. Tubes: 4—21 in. Mined near Pola, 18th November, 1918. For appearance, see photo of A. POERIO, on page 351.

Benedetto Cairoli (1917). 770 tons. Guns: 4—4 in., 2—14 pdr. Tubes: 4—18 in. Lost by collision, 10th April, 1918. No photo available.

Impetuoso (1913). 680 tons. Guns: 1—4.7 in., 4—14 pdr., etc. Tubes: 2—18 in. Torpedoed by Austrian Submarine U 17, in Straits of Otranto, 10th July, 1916. For appearance, see photo of INDOMITO, on page 353.

Intrepido (1912). Sister to IMPETUOSO, above. Mined off Valona, 4th December, 1915.

Audace (1912). Similar to IMPETUOSO, above. Lost by collision, off Cape Colonna, 29th August, 1916.

Garibaldino (1910). 388 tons. Guns: 4—14 pdr. Tubes: 3—18 in. Lost by collision, 16th July, 1918.

Turbine (1901). 320 tons. Guns: 1—14 pdr., etc. Tubes: 4—18 in. Sunk by gunfire of Austrian Destroyers CSEPEL, LIKA and TATRA, off Barletta, 24th May, 1915. For appearance, see photo of AQUILONE type, on page 354.

Nembo (1901). Sister to TURBINE, above. Torpedoed by Austrian Submarine, in Adriatic, 17th October, 1916.

Borea (1901). Sister to TURBINE, above. Sunk by an Austrian Light Cruiser, 15th May, 1917.

6 TORPEDO BOATS.

Perseo (1905). 210 tons. Guns : 3—3 pdr. Tubes : 3—18 in. Lost by collision, March, 1917. For appearance, see photo of " P " type Torpedo Boat, on page 356.

Scorpione (1905). Similar to PERSEO, above, but armament disposed differently. Lost by collision, 15th May, 1917. For appearance, see photo of " S " class Torpedo Boat, on page 356.

Serpente (1905). Sister to SCORPIONE, above. Mined in the Adriatic, June, 1916.

No. 36 PN (1913). 120 tons. Guns : 1—6 pdr. Tubes : 2—18 in. Mined in the Adriatic, 10th November, 1918.

No. 17 OS (1912). Sister to No. 36 PN, above. Mined in the Upper Adriatic, 2nd July, 1915.

No. 5 PN (1911). Similar to No. 17 OS, above. Torpedoed by an Austrian Submarine, in the Upper Adriatic, 26th June, 1915.

7 SUBMARINES.

Balilla (1914). 680 tons. Guns : 2—14 pdr., AA. Tubes : 5—18 in. Sunk in Cattaro Bay, night of 14th-15th July, 1916.

Alberto Guglielmotti (1914). Similar to BALILLA, above. Accidentally sunk by a British Destroyer, in Sardinian waters, 10th March, 1917. For appearance, see photo of ANGELO EMO, on page 359.

H 5 (1916). 356 tons. Tubes : 4—18 in. Accidentally sunk by a British Submarine, 16th April, 1918. For appearance, see photo of " H " type Submarine, on page 360.

W 4 (1914). 320 tons. Tubes, etc. : 5—18 in. Lost in the Adriatic, about 8th August, 1917. For appearance, see photo of " W " type Submarine, on page 362.

Jalea (1913). 245 tons. Tubes : 2—18 in. Mined, in the Gulf of Trieste, 10th August, 1916. For appearance, see photo of ARGO, on page 363.

Medusa (1911). Sister to JALEA, above. Torpedoed by an Austrian Submarine, in the Adriatic, 9th June, 1915.

Nereide (1912). 225 tons. Tubes : 2—18 in. Torpedoed by an Austrian Submarine, off Pelagosa, 5th August, 1915. For appearance, see photo of NAUTILUS, on page 360.

Note.—The loss of the Submarine GIACINTO PULLINO, captured by the Austrians, in August, 1916, is not counted here, as she is understood to have been restored to Italian hands.

8 AUXILIARIES.

Sterope (1905). Fleet Collier. 9460 tons displacement. Guns : 4—6 pdr. Torpedoed by a German Submarine, off Lisbon, 7th April, 1918. For appearance, see photo of BRONTE, on page 367.

Caprera (1904). Armed Merchant Cruiser. 5040 tons (gross). Torpedoed by an enemy Submarine, 5th February, 1918.

Prometeo (1906). Armed Merchant Cruiser. 4450 tons (gross). Torpedoed by an enemy Submarine, 18th March, 1918.

Citta di Messina (1910). Armed Merchant Cruiser. 3495 tons (gross). Torpedoed by an Austrian Submarine, in the Straits of Otranto, 23rd June, 1916.

Citta di Palermo (1910). Armed Merchant Cruiser. 3415 tons (gross). Mined, in the Lower Adriatic, 8th January, 1916.

Verbano (1908). Armed Boarding Steamer. 2700 tons displacement. Guns : 4—6 pdr. Mined, 13th November, 1918.

Citta di Sassari (1910). Armed Boarding Steamer. 2167 tons (gross). Torpedoed by an enemy Submarine, 2nd December, 1917.

Citta di Milano (1886). Cable Ship. 2123 tons displacement. Guns : 2—6 pdr. Wrecked on Tremiti Islands, in the Adriatic, end of June, 1919.

RUSSIAN.

(B.S. = BLACK SEA.)

6 BATTLESHIPS.

(B.S.) **SVOBODNAYA ROSSIYA** (1914). 24,000 tons. Guns : 10—12 in., 50 cal. ; 20—5.1 in., etc. Destroyed at Novorossisk, to avoid internment, 18th June, 1918. For appearance, see photo, on page 579.

(B.S.) **IMPERATRITSA MARIA** (1913). 22,435 tons. Similar to SVOBODNAYA ROSSIA, above. Sunk by fire and explosion, at Sevastopol, 20th October, 1916 ; since salved, but doubtful if worth repairing.

PETROPAVLOVSK (1911). 23,000 tons. Guns : 12—12 in., 50 cal. ; 16—4.7 in., etc. Torpedoed by British C.M.Bs., at Kronstadt, 18th August, 1919. For appearance, see photo of POLTAVA, on page 556.

BATTLESHIPS—*continued*.

SLAVA (1903). 15,000 tons. Guns : 4—12 in., 40 cal. ; 12—6 in., 45 cal. ; 20—12 pdr., etc. Sunk by gunfire of German Squadron, in Gulf of Riga, 17th October, 1917.

PERESVIET (1898). 13,500 tons. Guns : 4—10 in., 45 cal. ; 10—6 in., 45 cal. ; 16—12 pdr., etc., Mined near Port Said, 4th January, 1917.

BATTLESHIPS—*continued*.

SARIA SVOBODI (1887). 9200 tons. Guns : 2—12 in., 30 cal. ; 5—8 in., 45 cal. ; 8—6 in.,45 cal. ; 4—4.7 in., etc. Sunk, at Kronstadt, in August, 1919. (Possibly torpedoed in British attack on 18th August).

5 CRUISERS.

PALLADA (1906). 7775 tons. Guns : 2—8 in., 45 cal. ; 8—6 in., 45 cal. ; 22—12 pdr., etc. Torpedoed by German Submarine U 26, in Gulf of Finland, 11th October, 1914. For appearance, see photo of BAYAN, on page 559.

OLEG (1903). 6770 tons. Guns : 12—6 in., 45 cal. ; 8—11 pdr., etc. Torpedoed by a British C.M.B., in the Gulf of Finland, 17th June, 1919.
BOGATYR (1901). Similar to OLEG, above. Torpedoed by British C.M.Bs., at Kronstadt, 18th August, 1919.

AVRORA (1900) and **DIANA** (1899). 6700 tons. Guns : 10—6 in., 45 cal. ; 20—11 pdr., etc. Both scuttled by Bolsheviki, for use as blockships, in Gulf of Finland, 1919.

LIGHT CRUISER.

JEMTCHUG (1903). 3130 tons. Guns: 8—4.7 in. Torpedoed by German Cruiser EMDEN, at Penang, 28th October, 1914.

SUBMARINE DEPOT SHIP.

Pamiat Azova (1888). 6700 tons. Guns: 12—6 in., 45 cal.; 2—11 pdr. (may not have mounted all these at time of loss). Torpedoed by British C.M.Bs., at Kronstadt, 18th August, 1919.

3 GUNBOATS.

Sivuch (1907). 875 tons. Guns: 2—4.7 in., 4—12 pdr. Sunk by gunfire of German Cruiser, in Gulf of Riga, 19th August, 1915. For appearance, see photo of GILYAK, on page 375.

Bobr (1908). Sister to SIVUCH, above. Captured by Germans, at Abo, April, 1918; since acquired by Esthonian Government, and renamed LEMBIT.

(B.S.) **Kubanetz** (1887). 1200 tons. Guns: 2—6 in., 45 cal.; 1—4.7 in.; 2—12 pdr. Scuttled, to avoid capture, at Odessa, 29th October, 1914. For appearance, see photo of TERETZ, on page 585.

24 DESTROYERS.

(B.S.) **Feodonissi, Gadjibey, Kaliakrya, Kertch** (1914-15). 1325 tons. Guns: 3—4 in., 1—9 pdr. Tubes: 15—17.7 in. All irreparably damaged, to avoid falling into enemy hands, at Novorossisk, 18th June, 1918. No photo available.

Desna (1915). Similar to FEODONISSI, etc., above. Sunk in Neva, 17th July, 1919.

Grom (1915). Similar to FEODONISSI, etc., above. Sunk by gunfire of German Squadron, near Oesel Island, Gulf of Riga, 14th October, 1917.

Gavryil (1915), and another, unidentified. Similar to GROM, above. Sunk in action with British Destroyers, in Kuporia Bay, Gulf of Finland, 21st October, 1919. at Sevastopol, May, 1918. No photo available.

(B.S.) **Gnievni** (1913). 1100 tons. Guns: 3—4 in., 1—9 pdr. Tubes: 5—17.7 in. Blown np,

(B.S.) **Shastlivi** (1913). Sister to GNIEVNI, above. Foundered, off Mudros, 1919.

(B.S.) **Pronsitelni** (1913). Sister to GNIEVNI, above. Irreparably damaged, to avoid falling into enemy hands, at Novorossisk, 18th June, 1918.

Okhotnik (1906). 600 tons. Guns: 2—4.7 in., etc. Tubes: 3—17.7 in. Mined, near Oesel Island, Gulf of Riga, 26th September, 1917. For appearance, see photo of KONDRATENKO, on page 565.

(B.S.) **Leitenant Zatzarennyi** (1907). 615 tons. Guns: 1—4.7 in., 5—11 pdr. Tubes: 3—17.7 in. Mined, off Sulina, 1st July, 1917. For appearance, see photo of KAPITAN SAKEN, on page 583.

(B.S.) **Leitenant Shestakoff** and **Kapitan-Leitenant Baranoff** (1907). Sisters to LEIT. ZATZARENNYI, above. Both irreparably damaged, to avoid falling into enemy hands, at Novorossisk, 18th June, 1918.

Dobrovoletz (1905). 570 tons. Guns: 2—4 in. Tubes: 3—17.7 in. Mined, at Swalferort, Gulf of Riga, 21st August, 1916. For appearance, see photo of EMIR BUKHARSKI, on page 566.

Kasanetz (1905). 500 tons. Armament as DOBROVOLETZ. Torpedoed by a German Submarine, off Odensholm, 28th October, 1916. For appearance, see photo of STRASHNI-type, on page 566.

Bditelni (1906). 355 tons. Guns: 2—11 pdr. Tubes: 3—17.7 in. Mined, off Mantyluoto, Finnish Coast, 27th November, 1917. For appearance, see photo of Destroyer of this type, on page 566.

(B.S.) **Zhivuchi** (1905). 350 tons. Guns: 1—11 pdr. Tubes: 2—17.7 in. Mined, off Sevastopol, 28th April, 1916. For appearance, see photo of ZAVIDNI type, on page 583.

(B.S.) **Leitenant Pushtchin** (1904). Sister to ZHIVUCHI, above. Torpedoed by an enemy Submarine, off Varna, 9th March, 1916.

Leitenant Burakoff (1904). 330 tons. Guns: 2—11 pdr. Tubes: 2—17.7 in. Mined, off Mariehamn, Aland Islands, 13th August, 1917. For appearance, see photo of LOVKI type, on page 567.

Ispolnitelni (1905) and **Letutchi** (1905). Sisters to LEIT. BURAKOFF, above. Foundered in the Gulf of Finland, 16th December, 1914.

(B.S.) **Stremitelni** (1901). 240 tons. Guns: 1—11 pdr., etc. Tubes: 2—14 in. Irreparably damaged, to avoid falling into enemy hands, at Novorossisk, 18th June, 1918.

29 SUBMARINES.

Bars (1915). 650 tons. Tubes: 6—17.7 in. Sunk by the enemy, in the Baltic, 21st May, 1917; reported to have been salved, by Germans, but ultimate fate uncertain. No photo available.

Ersh (1915). Sister to BARS, above. Sunk by British Destroyers, VALOROUS and VANCOUVER, in Gulf of Finland, 7th August, 1919.

Livitza (1915). Sister to BARS, above. Lost in the Baltic, July, 1917.

Gepard (1915). Sister to BARS, above. Lost in the Baltic, October, 1917.

Edinorog (1915). Similar to BARS, above. Scuttled, to avoid falling into enemy hands, at Reval, February, 1918.

Igor (1915). Similar to BARS, above. Lost in the ice, off Reval, February, 1918.

(B.S.) **Gagara** and **Orlan** (1916). Similar to BARS, above. Scuttled, to avoid falling into Bolshevik hands, April, 1919.

(B.S.) **Morsh** (1913). 460 tons. Tubes, etc.: 8—17.7 in. Lost in the Black Sea, June, 1917 (also reported to have been scuttled, to avoid falling into Bolshevik hands, in April, 1919). No photo available.

(B.S.) **Kashalot, Kit, Narval** (1913). Sisters to MORSH, above. All three scuttled, to avoid falling into Bolshevik hands, April, 1919.

AG 14 (1916). 350 tons. Tubes: 4—18 in. Lost in the Baltic, September, 1917. No photo available.

AG 15, 13, 12, 11 (1916). Sisters to AG 14, above. Blown up or scuttled, to avoid falling into enemy hands, at Hango, April, 1918.

Akula (1909). 360 tons. Tubes: 2—17.7 in. Destroyed by bombs from German Aircraft, off Gothland, November, 1915.

Alligator, Drakon, Kaiman, Krokodil (1908).   450 tons.   Tubes : 4—18 in.   Believed to have been captured by the Germans, at Reval, in March, 1918 ; ultimate fate uncertain.
(B.S.) **Krab** (1912).   500 tons.   Tubes : 2—17.7 in.   Scuttled, to avoid falling into Bolshevik hands, April, 1919.   No photo available.

(B.S.) **Karp** and **Karas** (1907).   200 tons.   Tubes : 1—17.7 in.   Scuttled, to avoid falling into Bolshevik hands, April, 1919.
Byeluga, Piskar, Sterliad (1904).   110 tons.   Tubes : 1—17.7 in.   Believed to have been captured by the Germans, at Reval, in March, 1918 ; ultimate fate uncertain.   No photo available.
Tchuka (1904).   105 tons.   Otherwise as Byeluga, etc., above.   Believed to have been captured by Germans, at Reval, March, 1918 ; ultimate fate uncertain.

4 MINELAYERS.

Yenesei (1906).   3600 tons.   Guns : 5—4.7 in., 2—11 pdr.   Torpedoed by German Submarine U 26, in the Baltic, 4th June, 1915.   For appearance, see photo of Amur, on page 571.
(B.S.) **Prut** (1879).   4900 tons.   Scuttled, to avoid capture, at Sevastopol, 29th October, 1914.   No photo available.
Ladoga (no details available).   Torpedoed by a German Submarine, at the entrance to the Gulf of Finland, 15th August, 1915.
Vassili Veliki (no details available).   Lost in Vaida Bay, White Sea, April, 1916.

General Note: It is probable that other vessels have been lost in addition to the foregoing, but in the present state of Russia, reliable information is extremely difficult to obtain.

GREEK.

DESTROYER.

Doxa (1906).   350 tons.   Guns : 2—12 pdr., etc.   Tubes : 2—18 in.   Torpedoed by a German Submarine, in the Mediterranean, 27th June, 1917.   For appearance, see photo of Aspis type, on page 444.

PORTUGUESE.

RIVER GUNBOAT.

Tete (1903).   70 tons.   Guns : 2—1 pdr.   Destroyed by boiler explosion, in Zambesi, February, 1917.   No photo available.

ROUMANIAN.

TORPEDO BOAT.

Smeul (1888).   55 tons.   Guns : 1—1 pdr.   Tubes : 2—14 in.   Capsized and sank in the Black Sea, 17th May, 1917.   For appearance, see photo of Naluca on page 418.

GERMAN.

11 BATTLESHIPS.

BAYERN (1915).   28,000 tons.   Guns : 8—15 in. ; 16—5.9 in., 50 cal. ; 4—3.4 in. AA.   For appearance, see photo of Baden, on page 515.

KRONPRINZ WILHELM (1914), **MARKGRAF** (1913), **GROSSER KURFÜRST** (1913,) and **KÖNIG** (1913).   25,390 tons.   Guns : 10—12 in., 50 cal. ; 14—5.9 in., 50 cal. ; 4—3.4 in. AA.

KÖNIG ALBERT (1912), **PRINZREGENT LUITPOLD** (1912), **KAISERIN** (1911), **FRIEDRICH DER GROSSE** (1911), and **KAISER.**   24,700 tons.   Guns : 10—12 in., 50 cal. ; 14—5.9 in., 50 cal. ; 2—3.4 in.
The above ten Battleships were scuttled by their crews at Scapa Flow, on 21st June, 1919, to avoid surrender under the Peace Terms.

POMMERN (1905).   13,200 tons   Guns : 4—11 in., 40 cal. ; 14—6.7 in., 40 cal. ; 20—22 pdr.   Torpedoed by British Destroyers in Battle of Jutland, about midnight, 31st May-1st June, 1916.   For appearance, see photo of Deutschland type, on page 519.

6 BATTLE CRUISERS.

HINDENBURG (1915).   26,600 tons.   Guns : 8—12 in., 50 cal. ;   16—5.9 in., 50 cal. ; 8—
3.4 in. AA.

DERFFLINGER (1913).   26,300 tons.   Guns : 8—12 in., 50 cal. ;   14—5.9 in., 50 cal. ;
8—3.4 in. AA.

Both above ships scuttled by their crews at Scapa Flow, 21st June, 1919.

LÜTZOW (1913).   Generally similar to DERFFLINGER, above.   Sunk by gunfire of British
Battle Cruisers, during Battle of Jutland, 31st May, 1916.

MOLTKE (1910).   23,000 tons.   Guns : 10—11 in., 50 cal. ;   12—5.9 in., 45 cal ;   2—3.4 in.
Scuttled by her crew at Scapa Flow, 21st June, 1919.

SEYDLITZ (1912).   25,000 tons.   Guns : 10—11 in., 50 cal. ;   12—5.9 in., 45 cal. ;   2—3.4 in.
Scuttled by her crew at Scapa Flow, 21st June, 1919.

VON DER TANN (1909).   19,400 tons.   Guns : 8—11 in., 50 cal. ;   10—5.9 in., 45 cal. ;   4—
3.4 in.
Scuttled by her crew at Scapa Flow, 21st June, 1919.

6 ARMOURED CRUISERS.

BLÜCHER (1908). 15,500 tons. Guns : 12—8.2 in., 45 cal. ; 8—5.9 in., 45 cal. ; 16—22 pdr. Disabled by gunfire of British Battle Cruiser squadron, and afterwards torpedoed by Destroyer METEOR, near the Dogger Bank, 24th January, 1915.

SCHARNHORST and **GNEISENAU** (1906). 11,600 tons. Guns : 8—8.2 in., 40 cal. ; 6—5.9 in., 40 cal. ; 20—22 pdr. Sunk by gunfire of INVINCIBLE, INFLEXIBLE and CARNARVON, off the Falklands, 8th December, 1914.

YORCK (1904). 9050 tons. Guns : 4—8.2 in., 40 cal. ; 10—5.9 in., 40 cal. ; 14—22 pdr. Mined in Jade Bay, 4th November, 1914. For appearance, see photo of ROON, on page 521.

ARMOURED CRUISERS—*continued.*

FRIEDRICH KARL (1902). 9000 tons. Guns : 4—8.2 in., 40 cal. ; 10—5.9 in., 40 cal. ; 10—15 pdr. Mined in the Baltic, night of 25th-26th November, 1914.

PRINZ ADALBERT (1901). Sister to FRIEDRICH KARL, above. Torpedoed by British Submarine E 8, 20 miles W. of Libau, 23rd October, 1915.

22 LIGHT CRUISERS.

DRESDEN (new) (1916), **KARLSRÜHE** (new) (1916), and **KÖLN** (new) (1916). 5000 tons. Guns : 7—5.9 in., 50 cal. ; 3—3.4 in. AA. All three scuttled by their crews at Scapa Flow, 21st June, 1919. For appearance, see photo of EMDEN, on page 523.

WIESBADEN (1915). Similar to DRESDEN, above. Sunk by gunfire of British Battleships, at Battle of Jutland, 31st May, 1916.

BREMSE (1915) and **BRUMMER** (1915). 4000 tons. Guns : 4—5.9 in., 50 cal. ; 2—3.4 in. AA. Both scuttled by their crews at Scapa Flow, 21st June, 1919. (These vessels were specially fitted for minelaying.)

ELBING (1915). 4500 tons. Guns : 8—5.9 in. Rammed and sunk by a German Battleship, in Battle of Jutland, 1st June, 1916. For appearance, see photo of PILLAU, on page 524.

ROSTOCK (1912). 4900 tons. Guns : 12—4.1 in. Torpedoed by British Destroyers, during Battle of Jutland, 1st June, 1916.

KARLSRÜHE (1912). Sister to ROSTOCK, above. Destroyed by internal explosion, off Trinidad (B.W.I.), in lat. 10.7 N., long. 55.25 W., 4th November, 1914.

SHIPS LOST IN THE WAR--GERMAN *continued.*

LIGHT CRUISERS—*continued.*

MAGDEBURG (1911). 4500 tons. Guns : 12—4.1 in. Driven ashore on Odensholm Island by gunfire of Russian Cruisers BOGATYR and PALLADA, 27th August, 1914, and subsequently became a total loss. For appearance, see photo of STRALSUND, on page 525.

KÖLN (1909) and **MAINZ** (1909). 4300 tons. Guns : 12—4.1 in. Both sunk during action in Heligoland Bight, 28th August, 1914, KÖLN by gunfire of British Battle Cruisers, and MAINZ by a torpedo from Destroyer LAERTES. For appearance, see photo of KOLBERG, on page 526.

EMDEN (1908). 3600 tons. Guns : 10—4.1 in. Driven ashore by gunfire of Australian Cruiser SYDNEY, at North Keeling, Cocos Islands, 9th November, 1914.

DRESDEN (1907). Sister to EMDEN, above. Disabled by gunfire of British Cruisers, KENT and GLASGOW, and scuttled to avoid capture, at Juan Fernandez, 14th March, 1915.

NURNBERG (1906). 3400 tons. Guns : 10—4.1 in. Sunk by gunfire of British Cruiser KENT, off the Falklands, 8th December, 1914.

S.M.S. „Königsberg"

wurde im Juli 1915 in Ost-Afrika durch große englische Übermacht vernichtet, nachdem der Kreuzer bereits längere Zeit im Rufidje-Fluß eingeschlossen war.

KÖNIGSBERG (1905). 3500 tons. Guns : 10—4.1 in. Destroyed by gunfire of British Monitors, SEVERN and MERSEY, in Rufiji estuary, East Africa, 11th July, 1915.

LEIPZIG (1905). 3200 tons. Guns : 10—4.1 in. Sunk by gunfire of British Cruisers CORNWALL and GLASGOW, off the Falklands, 8th December, 1914. For appearance, see photo of DANZIG, on page 527.

BREMEN (1903). Sister to LEIPZIG, above. Torpedoed by British Submarine, in the Eastern Baltic, 17th December, 1915.

UNDINE (1902). 2700 tons. Guns : 10—4.1 in. Torpedoed by British Submarine E 19, 22 miles off Trelleborg, Sweden, 7th November, 1915. For appearance, see photo of ARKONA, on page 528.

FRAUENLOB (1902). Sister to UNDINE, above. Sunk by gunfire of British 2nd Light Cruiser Squadron, during the Battle of Jutland, 31st May, 1916.

ARIADNE (1900). 2650 tons. Guns : 10—4.1 in. Sunk by gunfire of LION during action in Heligoland Bight, 28th August, 1914. For appearance, see photo of MEDUSA, on page 528.

HELA (1895). 2000 tons. Guns : 4—15 pdr. Torpedoed by British Submarine E 9, six miles S. of Heligoland, 13th September, 1914.

2 R

SUBMARINE DEPOT SHIP.

Vulkan (1908). 1200 tons. Lost in North Sea, on passage from Germany to Harwich, 1919.

3 SLOOPS.

Kormoran (1892). 1600 tons. Guns : 8—4.1 in. (Disarmed at time of loss.) Sunk by Japanese gunfire at Tsingtao, October, 1914.

Geier (1894). Sister to Kormoran, above. Interned at Honolulu, 9th November, 1914, and seized by American authorities, March, 1917. Renamed Schurz, and lost by collision with s.s. Florida, off N. Carolina coast, 21st June, 1918.

Seeadler (1892). Sister to Kormoran, above. Blown up at Wilhelmshaven, April, 1917.

5 GUNBOATS.

Eber (1903). 1000 tons. (Disarmed.) Interned at Bahia, 5th September, 1914, and destroyed by fire, to avoid seizure by Brazil, 26th October, 1917. For appearance, see photo of Panther, on page 543.

Luchs (1899), **Tiger** (1899). 900 tons. Guns : 2—4.1 in. Found scuttled on surrender of Tsingtao, 6th November, 1914.

Jaguar (1899), **Iltis** (1898). 900 tons. Guns: 4—15 pdr. Found scuttled on surrender of Tsingtao, 6th November, 1914.

3 SURVEYING VESSELS.

Komet (1911). 980 tons. Guns : 4—22 pdr. Captured by Australian Auxiliary Vessel Nusa, near Cape Wilson, on N.E. coast of Papua, 14th October, 1914. Now Australian Sloop Una. No photo available.

Möwe (1906). 650 tons. Guns : 3—1 pdr. Scuttled at Dar-es-Salaam, 9th August, 1914.

Planet (1905). Sister to Mowe, above. Found scuttled at Yap, Caroline Islands, on occupation by Japanese, 7th October, 1914.

6 RIVER AND LAKE GUNBOATS.

Otter (1909). 260 tons. Guns : 2—4 pdr. Interned in a Chinese port, 1914. Seized in 1917, and now Chinese Gunboat Li-Sui. For appearance, see photo on page 479.

Tsingtau and **Vaterland** (1903). 168 tons. Guns : 1—15 pdr. Tsingtau interned in Whampoa River, 17th August, 1914, and blown up to avoid seizure, March, 1917. Vaterland interned at Nankin, August, 1914, and seized by China in 1917. Now named Li-Chieh. For appearance, see photo on page 479.

Hermann von Wissmann. (No photo available.) Sunk in action with British Gunboat Gwendolen, at Sphinxhaven, East shore of Lake Nyasa, 30th May, 1915.

Hedwig von Wissmann. ·165 tons. (No photo available.) Sunk by gunfire of British Vessels Fifi, Mimi and Toutou, on Lake Tanganyika, 9th February, 1916.

Kingani. 50 tons. (No photo available.) Sunk by gunfire of British Motor Launches Mimi and Toutou, on Lake Tanganyika, 26th December, 1915. Salved and re-named Fifi.

33 MINESWEEPERS.

FM 3 (1918). Foundered, 1918 or 1919.
M 95 (1917). Mined, April, 1918.
M 92, M 83 (1917). Mined, 1st August, 1918.
M 91 (1917). Mined, 10th March, 1918.
M 67, M 64 (1917). Sunk in the North Sea, April, 1918.
M 63 (1917). Mined, 28th June, 1917.
M 62 (1917). Mined, July or August, 1918.
M 57 (1916). Reported lost, date uncertain.
M 56 (1916). Mined, off mouth of Ems, previous to July, 1917
M 55 (1916). Wrecked, 29th October, 1917.
M 49 (1916). Mined, off Schleswig Coast, previous to June, 1917.
M 47 (1916). Sunk, 11th June, 1917.
M 41 (1916). Mined, 6th September, 1918.
M 40, M 36 (1916). Mined in the North Sea, March, 1918.
M 39 (1916). Mined, in the North Sea, April, 1918.
M 38 (1916). Reported lost, date uncertain.
M 31 (1916). Mined, in the Eastern Baltic, 18th June, 1917.
M 27 (1916). Sunk, in the Baltic, March, 1917.
M 26 (1916). Mined, off Schleswig Coast, May, 1917.
M 24 (1916). Mined, off Schleswig Coast, previous to May, 1917.
M 23 (1916). Mined, off mouth of Ems, June, 1917.
M 22 (1916). Mined, 14th October, 1918.
M 18 (1915). Reported lost, date uncertain.
M 16 (1915). Mined, off Schleswig Coast, previous to June, 1917.
M 15, M 14 (1915). Mined, off Schleswig Coast, previous to July, 1917.
M 12 (1915). Mined, about September, 1917.
M 11 (1915). Mined, 29th December, 1917.
M 9 (1915). Mined, off mouth of Ems, previous to July, 1917.
M 6 (1915). Mined, July or August, 1918.

(For appearance and details of vessels of above classes, see pages 542.)

102 DESTROYERS.

(For appearance of most of these vessels, see photos of corresponding types, pages 531 & 537.)

H 145 (1917). Details uncertain ; probably enlarged edition of B 112, below. Scuttled at Scapa Flow, 21st June, 1919.

S 138, S 136, S 131 (1917). Probably similar to H 145, above. Scuttled at Scapa Flow, 21st June, 1919.

V 129 (1917). Probably similar to H 145, above. Scuttled at Scapa Flow, 21st June, 1919.

B 112, B 111, B 110, B 109 (1917). 1300 tons. Guns : 4—4.1 in. Tubes : 6. Scuttled at Scapa Flow, 21st June, 1919.

V 107 (1914). 320 tons. Guns : 2—13 pdr. (?). Tubes : 4. Lost, date and circumstances unknown.

G 104, G 103, G 101 (1916). 1250 tons. Guns : 4—4.1 in. Tubes : 6. Scuttled at Scapa Flow, 21st June, 1919.

V 99 (1914). 1300 tons. Armament as G 104, etc., above. Sunk by gunfire of Russian Gunboat SIVUCH, in Gulf of Riga, 19th August, 1915.

G 96 (1915). 1000 tons. Guns : 3—4.1 in. Tubes : 6. Mined off Ostend, 26th June, 1917.

G 94, G 93, G 87 (1915). Sisters to G 96, above. Sunk at the mouth of the Jade, 30th March, 1918.

G 92, G 91, G 89, G 86 (1915). Sisters to G 96, above. Scuttled at Scapa Flow, 21st June, 1919.

G 90 (1915). Sister to G 96, above. Sunk in the Baltic, 11th November, 1916.

G 88 (1915). Torpedoed by a British C.M.B., off Zeebrugge, night of 7th-8th April, 1917.

G 85 (1915). Sister to G 96, above. Torpedoed by British Destroyer BROKE, off Goodwin Sands, 21st April, 1917.

V 84 (1915). Similar to G 96, above. Sunk, off the mouth of the Ems, previous to June, 1917.

V 83, V 82, V 78, V 70 (1915). Sisters to V 84, above. Scuttled at Scapa Flow, 21st June, 1919.

V 77, V 67 (1915). Sisters to V 84, above. Sunk in Flanders, 7th July, 1918.

V 76, V 75 (1915). Sisters to V 84, above. Mined in the Gulf of Finland, 16th November, 1916.

V 74 (1915). Sister to V 84, above. Blown up at Bruges during evacuation of Flanders, October, 1918.

V 72 (1915). Sister to V 84, above. Sunk in the Baltic, 11th November, 1916.

V 68 (1915). Sister to V 84, above. Sunk in the North Sea, 6th August, 1918.

S 66, S 62 (1915). Similar to G 96, above. Mined off the West Coast of Jutland, July, 1918.

S 65, S 56, S 55, S 53, S 52, S 50, S 49 (1914-15). Sisters to S 66, above. Scuttled at Scapa Flow, 21st June, 1919.

S 64 (1915). Sister to S 66, above. Mined in the Southern portion of the Sound, October, 1917.

S 61 (1915). Sister to S 66, above. Sunk in Flanders, 7th July, 1918.

S 59 (1915). Sister to S 66, above. Sunk in the North Sea, 11th November, 1916.

S 58, S 57 (1915). Sisters to S 66, above. Mined in the Gulf of Finland, 16th November, 1916.

V 48 (1915). 900 tons. Guns : 2—4.1 in., 1—3.4 in. Tubes : 6—19.7 in. Sunk, during Battle of Jutland, 31st May, 1916. (It is believed this was the Destroyer sunk by H.M.S. OBEDIENT, MARVEL, MINDFUL and ONSLAUGHT.)

V 47 (1915). Sister to V 48, above. Sunk in Flanders, 7th July, 1918.

V 45 (1915). Sister to V 48, above. Scuttled at Scapa Flow, 21st June, 1919.

G 42 (1914). Similar to V 48, above. Rammed and sunk by British Flotilla Leader SWIFT, off Goodwin Sands, 21st April, 1917.

G 41 (1914). Sister to G 42, above. Blown up at Bruges, during evacuation of Flanders, October, 1918.

G 40, G 39, G 38 (1914). Sisters to G 42, above. Scuttled at Scapa Flow, 21st June, 1919.

G 37 (1914). Sister to G 42, above. Mined off Walcheren, November, 1917.

S 36, S 32 (1914). Similar to V 48, above. Scuttled at Scapa Flow, 21st June, 1919.

S 35 (1914). Sister to S 36, above. Sunk during Battle of Jutland, 31st May, 1916 (probably by Light Cruisers SOUTHAMPTON and DUBLIN).

S 34 (1914). Sister to S 36, above. Sunk in the North Sea, 3rd October, 1918.

S 33 (1914). Sister to S 36, above. Torpedoed in action with British Submarine L 10, in Heligoland Bight, 3rd October, 1918.

S 31 (1914). Sister to S 36, above. Driven ashore by gunfire of Russian Destroyer NOVIK, in Gulf of Riga, 19th August, 1915.

V 30 (1914). Similar to V 48, above. Mined on voyage from Germany to surrender, 20th November, 1918.

V 29, V 27 (1914). Sisters to V 30, above. Sunk by gunfire of British Battleships, during Battle of Jutland, 31st May, 1916.

V 25 (1914). Sister to V 30, above. Lost during February, 1915.

S 22 (1913). 570 tons. Guns : 2—3.4 in. Tubes : 4—19.7 in. Sunk 25th March, 1916.

S 21 (1913). Sister to S 22, above. Lost early in the War, date uncertain.

S 20 (1913). Sister to S 22, above. Sunk by gunfire of British Light Cruiser CENTAUR, off Belgian Coast, 5th June, 1917.

S 17 (1913). Sister to S 22, above. Mined during May, 1917.

S 16 (1913). Sister to S 22, above. Sunk in the North Sea, January, 1918.

S 15 (1913). Sister to S 22, above. Laid up after being badly damaged in action of 5th June, 1917, and abandoned on evacuation of Bruges, October, 1918.

S 14 (1913). Sister to S 22, above. Lost during February, 1915.

S 13 (1913). Sister to S 22, above. Lost during January, 1916.

G 12 (1912). Similar to S 22, above. Sunk in the North Sea, 8th September, 1915.

V 4 (1911). Similar to S 22, above. Sunk (probably by British Destroyers) during Battle of Jutland, 31st May, 1916.

G 194 (1911). 648 tons. Guns : 2—3.4 in. Tubes : 4—17.7 in. Rammed and sunk by British Light Cruiser CLEOPATRA, near Sylt, 25th March, 1916.

Another (unidentified) of G 194 type. Torpedoed by British Submarine E 9, between Windau and Gothland, 4th June, 1915.

V 191 (1910). 656 tons., otherwise similar to G 194, above. Torpedoed by British Submarine E9, in the Baltic, 17th December, 1915.

V 188 (1910). Sister to V 191, above. Torpedoed by British Submarine E 16, in the North Sea, near the German Coast, 26th July, 1915.

V 187 (1910). Sister to V 191, above. Sunk by gunfire of British Destroyer DEFENDER, during action in Heligoland Bight, 28th August, 1914.

S 177 (1909). 636 tons. Guns : 2—3.4 in. Tubes : 4—17.7 in. Mined off Libau, latter part of 1915.

T 172 (1909). 636 tons. Guns : 2—3.4 in. Tubes : 3—17.7 in. Sunk in the North Sea, 7th July, 1918.

V 162 (1908). 613 tons. otherwise similar to T 172, above. Lost about August, 1916.

V 150 (1907). 554 tons. Guns : 2—3.4 in. Tubes : 3—17.7 in. Lost by collision, in May, 1915.

T 138 (1906). 530 tons. Guns : 1—3.4 in., 3—4 pdr. Tubes : 3—17.7 in. Sunk in the North Sea, 7th July, 1918.

T 129 (1905). 485 tons. Guns : 4—3 pdr. Tubes : 3—17.7 in. Sunk off mouth of Elbe, 1st May, 1917.

T 124 (1904). 470 tons, otherwise similar to T 129, above. Lost by collision with Danish s.s. ANGLO-DANE, at entrance to the Sound, 23rd November, 1914.

T 123 (1904). Sister to T 124, above. Sunk in the North Sea, 1st May, 1917.

T 122 (1904). Sister to T 124, above. Mined near Heligoland, October, 1918.

T 119, T 118, T 117, T 115 (1903). 420 tons, otherwise similar to T 124, above. Sunk by gunfire of British Light Cruiser UNDAUNTED and Destroyers LANCE, LEGION, LENNOX and LOYAL, off Dutch Coast, 17th October, 1914.

T 116 (1903). Sister to T 119, etc., above. Torpedoed by British Submarine E 9, off the mouth of the Ems, 6th October, 1914.

T 100 (1900). 400 tons. Guns : 3—4 pdr. Tubes : 3—17.7 in. Sunk in the Baltic, 15th October, 1918.

T 90 (1899). Sister to T 100, above Wrecked in course of attack on Japanese Cruiser TAKACHIHO, 60 miles South of Kiao-Chau Bay, night of 17th-18th October, 1914.

DESTROYERS—*continued.*

Taku (1898). 280 tons. Guns : 2—4 pdr. Tubes : 2—17.7 in Found scuttled on surrender of Tsingtao, 6th November, 1914.

53 TORPEDO BOATS.

A 79 (1917). About 250 tons. Guns : 1—3.4 in. *or* 2—4 pdr. Tubes : 2. Sunk off West Coast of Jutland, 10th July, 1918.

A 77, A 73 (1917). Sisters to A 79, above. Mined off West Coast of Jutland, 60 miles from Heligoland, 19th January, 1918.

A 72, A 71 (1917). Sisters to A 79, above. Mined during May, 1918.

A 60 (1916). About 200 tons, otherwise similar to A 79, above. Mined off Zeebrugge, 27th November, 1917.

A 58 (1916). Sister to A 60, above. Sunk in the North Sea, 16th August, 1918.

A 57 (1916). Sister to A 60, above. Mined 1st March, 1918.

A 56 (1916). Sister to A 60, above. Mined during March, 1918.

A 50 (1916). Sister to A 60, above. Sunk off the Belgian Coast, previous to April, 1918 (possibly as a result of damage sustained in action with British Destroyers, BOTHA and MORRIS, 21st March, 1918).

A 47, A 43, A 42, A 40, A 30, A 20, A 16, A 11, A 9, A 8, A 5 (1915-16). Some similar to A 60, above, others of about 100 tons or less, with only 1—4 pdr. gun and 2 tubes. All took refuge in Holland on evacuation of Belgium, and were interned there, November, 1918. Since handed over to Belgians (?).

A 45, A 15, A 13 (1915-16). Of same types as A 47, etc., above All three destroyed on evacuation of Flanders, November, 1918.

A 32 (1916). Probably similar to A 60, above. Sunk in the Baltic, 25th October, 1917.

A 19, A 7 (1915). About 100 tons. Guns 1—4 pdr. Tubes : 2. Sunk in action with British Destroyers BOTHA and MORRIS, and French Destroyers MAGON, MEHL and BOUCLIER, off Dunkirk, 21st March, 1918.

A 14, A 12, A 4 (1915). Similar to A 19, etc., above. Abandoned in Flanders, November, 1918, and taken over by the Belgians.

A 10 (1915). Similar to A 19, etc., above. Mined off the Belgian Coast, 6th February, 1918.

A 6, A 2 (1915). Similar to A 19, etc., above. Sunk by gunfire of British Destroyers, LAFOREY, LARK, LAWFORD and LEONIDAS, off Noord Hinder Light, 1st May, 1915.

A 3 (1915). Similar to A 19, etc., above. Sunk in the Baltic, date uncertain.

Another of A type (unidentified). Sunk by gunfire and torpedoes of French Destroyers, BRANLEBAS and ORIFLAMME, in the English Channel, 22nd August, 1915.

T 78 (1894). 153 tons. Guns : 1—4 pdr. Tubes : 3—14 in. Sunk in May or June, 1917.

T 68 (1892). 145 tons, otherwise similar to T 78, above. Sunk in the North Sea, 1st June, 1918.

T 66 (1891). Sister to T 68, above Sunk in the Gulf of Riga, 18th October, 1917.

T 65 (1890). 150 tons, otherwise similar to T 78, above. Sunk in the Gulf of Riga, 27th Oct., 1917.

T 64 (1890). Sister to T 65, above. Sunk in the North Sea, 23rd October, 1916.

T 58, T 52 (1889). Sisters to T 65, above Sunk in the North Sea, 8th August, 1915.

T 57, T 50 (1889). Sisters to T 65, above. Lost, probably before June, 1916.

T 56 (1889). Sister to T 65, above. Wrecked in the Baltic, October, 1917.

T 54 (1889). Sister to T 65, above. Mined in the Baltic, 6th October, 1917.

T 51, T 47 (1888-9). Sisters to T 65, above. Sunk in the North Sea, 29th May, 1915.

T 46 (1887). 130 tons, otherwise similar to T 65, above. Sunk in North Sea, 16th Aug., 1915.

T 44 (1887). Sister to T 46, above. Reported to have been lost by collision, in the North Sea, during February, 1916.

T 43 (1887). Sister to T 46, above. Sunk off Schleswig Coast, before July, 1917.

T 32 (1886). 85 tons. Armament as T 78, above. Sunk in the Baltic, previous to Dec., 1917.

T 25 (1886). Sister to T 32, above. Lost probably before June, 1916.

(For appearance of these Torpedo Boats, see illustrations of corresponding types on pages 539 & 540.)

203 SUBMARINES.

(For convenience of reference, boats surrendered or otherwise disposed of are noted below, though not included in above total.)

(U 1, U 2, U 4, all broken up in Germany ; **U 3** surrendered.)

U 5. Sunk in the North Sea, December, 1914.

U 6. Destroyed by Submarine E 16, in the North Sea, 15th September, 1915.

U 7. Sunk in the North Sea, January, 1915.

U 8. Sunk by Destroyers MAORI and GHURKA, in Straits of Dover, 4th March, 1915.

(U 9. Surrendered.)

U 10. Sunk in the North Sea, May, 1916.

U 11. Sunk in the North Sea, December, 1914.

U 12. Rammed by Destroyer ARIEL, off Aberdeen Coast, 10th March, 1915.

U 13. Sunk in the North Sea, 12th September, 1914.

U 14. Rammed by Trawler HAWK, after being disabled by gunfire, off Peterhead (lat. 57.15 N., long. 0.32 E.), 5th June, 1915.

U 15. Rammed by Light Cruiser BIRMINGHAM, off the Orkneys, 9th August, 1914.

U 16. Foundered, in the Elbe, on voyage to England to surrender, 22nd February, 1919.

(U 17. Broken up in Germany.)

U 18. Rammed by Minesweeping Trawler 96, one mile off Hoxa entrance to Scapa Flow, 24th November, 1914.

(U 19. Surrendered.)

U 20. Stranded at Harbooere, West Coast of Jutland, 4th November, 1916, and blown up by her crew the following day.

U 21. Sunk in the North Sea, on voyage to England to surrender, 22nd February, 1919.

(U 22. Surrendered.)

U 23. Torpedoed by Submarine C 27, working in conjunction with Trawler PRINCESS LOUISE, in the North Sea, 20th July, 1915.

(U 24, U 25, both surrendered.)

U 26. Lost in the Baltic, August, 1915.

U 27. Sunk off the South of Ireland, 19th August, 1915.

U 28. Destroyed in the White Sea, 2nd September, 1917.

U 29. Rammed by Battleship DREADNOUGHT, about lat. 58.21 N., long. 1.12 E., 18th March, 1915.

(U 30. Surrendered.)

U 31. Destroyed, January, 1915.

U 32. Destroyed in the Mediterranean, 8th May, 1918.

(U 33. Surrendered.)

U 34. Sunk in the Mediterranean, 9th November, 1918.

(U 35. Interned at Ferrol, and surrendered to the French in 1919.)

U 36. Sunk by gunfire of Special Service Vessel PRINCE CHARLES, near North Rona, 24th July, 1915

U 37. Lost in the North Sea, about June, 1915.

(**U 38,** surrendered ; **U 39,** interned at Cartagena, 18th May, 1918, and surrendered to the French, 17th March, 1919.)

U 40. Sunk by Submarine C 24, working in conjunction with a Trawler, 50 miles S.E. by S. of Girdle Ness, 23rd June, 1915.

U 41. Sunk by Armed Merchant Cruiser BARALONG, off South of Ireland, 24th September, 1915.

(**U 42** was to have been number of a Submarine ordered in Italy before the War ; this vessel was completed for the Italian Navy under the name of BALILLA—vide Italian losses.)

(**U 43.** Surrendered.)

U 44. Destroyed in the North Sea, 12th August, 1917.

U 45. Torpedoed by Submarine D 7, off North of Ireland, 12th September, 1917.

(**U 46.** Surrendered.)

U 47. Blown up at Pola or Cattaro, end of October, 1918.

U 48. Destroyed by gunfire of Destroyer GIPSY and five Drifters, while stranded on Goodwins, 24th November, 1917.

U 49. Rammed by P 61, in the Atlantic, 11th September, 1917.

U 50. Lost in the North Sea, between 1st and 11th October, 1917.

U 51. Torpedoed by Submarine H 5, in Heligoland Bight, 14th July, 1916.

(**U 52, U 53, U 54, U 55.** All surrendered.)

U 56. Destroyed in the Arctic Sea, 2nd November, 1916.

(**U 57.** Surrendered.)

U 58. Sunk by U.S. Destroyers FANNING and NICHOLSON, off South of Ireland, 17th November, 1917.

U 59. Destroyed in the North Sea, 14th May, 1917.

(**U 60.** Surrendered and subsequently foundered 9 miles S.E. of Berry Head, 12th June, 1919.)

U 61. Sunk in St. George's Channel, 26th March, 1918.

(**U 62, U 63.** Both surrendered.)

U 64. Destroyed in the Mediterranean, 17th June, 1918.

U 65. Blown up at Pola or Cattaro, end of October, 1918.

U 66. Lost in the North Sea, between 1st and 11th October, 1917.

(**U 67.** Surrendered.)

U 68. Sunk off the South of Ireland, 22nd March, 1916.

U 69. Sunk by Destroyer PATRIOT, in the North Sea, 12th July, 1917.

(**U 70, U 71.** Both surrendered.)

U 72. Blown up at Pola or Cattaro, end of October, 1918.

U 73. Blown up at Pola or Cattaro, end of October, 1918.

U 74. Sunk in the North Sea, 27th May, 1916.

U 75. Sunk in the North Sea, 13th December, 1917.

U 76. Sunk in the Arctic Sea, 26th January, 1917.

U 77. Lost in the North Sea, 7th July, 1916.

U 78. Destroyed by Submarine G 2, in the North Sea, 28th October, 1918.

(**U 79, U 80, U 82.** All surrendered.)

U 81. Destroyed in the Atlantic, 1st May, 1917.

U 83. Sunk off S.W. of Ireland, 17th February, 1917.

U 84. Sunk in St. George's Channel, 26th January, 1918.

U 85. Sunk in English Channel, 12th March, 1917.

(**U 86.** Surrendered.)

U 87. Sunk in the Irish Sea, 25th December, 1917.

U 88. Sunk in the Atlantic, 17th September, 1917.

U 89. Rammed by Cruiser ROXBURGH, off N.E. of Ireland, 12th February, 1918.

(**U 90, U 91.** Both surrendered.)

U 92. Sunk in the North Sea, 9th September, 1918.

U 93. Sunk by Special Service Vessel PRIZE, in English Channel, 7th January, 1918.

(**U 94.** Surrendered to the French.)

U 95. Lost about January, 1918.

(**U 96, U 98.** Both surrendered.)

U 97. Foundered on voyage to England to surrender, 21st November, 1918.

U 99. Sunk off the West of Ireland, 20th June, 1917.

(**U 100, U 101.** Both surrendered.)

U 102. Lost, probably in the North Sea, September, 1918.

U 103. Rammed by s.s. OLYMPIC, in English Channel, 12th May, 1918.

U 104. Sunk by Sloop JESSAMINE, off South of Ireland, lat. 51·59 N., long. 6.26 W., 25th April, 1918.

(**U 105.** Surrendered to the French.)

U 106. Lost in the North Sea, between 5th and 9th October, 1917.

(**U 107, U 108.** Both surrendered, latter to the French.)

U 109. Destroyed in Dover area, 26th January, 1918.

U 110. Sunk off North of Ireland, 15th March, 1918.

(**U 111, U 112, U 113, U 114.** All surrendered.)

(**U 115, U 116.** Both unfinished, and destroyed on stocks, at Schichau Yard, Elbing.)

(**U 117, U 118, U 119, U 120, U 121, U 122, U 123, U 124, U 125, U 126.** All surrendered.)

(**U 127** to **U 134,** inclusive, were never completed.)

(**U 135, U 136,** both surrendered ; **U 137, U 138,** were not built ; **U 139, U 140, U 141,** all surrendered.)

(**U 142** to **U 150,** inclusive, were never completed.)

(**U 151, U 152, U 153.** All surrendered.)

U 154. Torpedoed by Submarine E 35, in the Atlantic, in latitude of Cape St. Vincent, 11th May, 1918.

(**U 155.** Surrendered.)

U 156. Sunk in the North Sea, 25th September, 1918.

(**U 157.** Interned 11th November, 1918, and subsequently surrendered.)

(**U 158, U 159.** Were not built.)

(**U 160, U 161, U 162, U 163, U 164.** All surrendered.)

(**U 165** was never completed ; **U 166, U 167,** both surrendered.)

(**UA** was surrendered.)

UB 1. Lost in the Mediterranean, about August, 1915.

(**UB 2.** Broken up in Germany.)

UB 3. Sunk in the North Sea, 24th April, 1916.

UB 4. Sunk in the North Sea, 11th August, 1915.

(**UB 5.** Broken up in Germany.)

(**UB 6.** Stranded on Voorne Island, off Hellevoetsluis, 13th March, 1917, interned by Dutch Government, and surrendered at Harwich, 25th February, 1919.)

UB 7. Destroyed by Russians, in Black Sea, October, 1916.

(**UB 8.** Surrendered. **UB 9,** broken up in Germany.)

UB 10. Destroyed on evacuation of Flanders, October, 1918.

(**UB 11.** Broken up in Germany.)

UB 12. Lost in the North Sea, about August, 1918.

UB 13. Lost, March, 1916.

(**UB 14.** Surrendered.)

UB 15. Lost in the Mediterranean, about May, 1916.

UB 16. Sunk by Submarine E 34, in the North Sea, 10th May, 1918.

UB 17. Sunk in English Channel, 25th February, 1918.

UB 18. Sunk in English Channel, 17th November, 1917.

UB 19. Sunk by Special Service Ship PENSHURST, in English Channel, lat. 50 N., long. 2.48 W., 30th November, 1916.

UB 20. Destroyed by seaplanes 8676 and 8862, in the North Sea, 29th July, 1917.

(**UB 21.** Surrendered.)

UB 22. Sunk in the North Sea, 19th January, 1918.

(**UB 23.** Interned at Coruna, 29th July, 1917, and surrendered to the French after Armistice.)

(**UB 24, UB 25.** Both surrendered, former to the French.)

UB 26. Sunk in the English Channel, 5th April, 1916 ; subsequently salved by the French, and commissioned as ROLAND MOULLOT.

UB 27. Sunk in the North Sea, 29th July, 1917.

(**UB 28.** Surrendered.)

UB 29. Sunk by Destroyer ARIEL 12 miles S.W. of Bishop Rock Lighthouse, 6th December, 1916.

UB 30. Sunk in the North Sea, 13th August, 1918.

UB 31. Destroyed in Dover area, 2nd May, 1918.

UB 32. Destroyed by Seaplane 9860, 27 miles North of Cape Barfleur, 18th August, 1917.

UB 33. Mined in Dover area, 11th April, 1918.

(**UB 34.** Surrendered.)

UB 35. Destroyed in Dover area, 26th January, 1918.

UB 36. Lost in June, 1917.

UB 37. Sunk by Special Service Ship PENSHURST, in English Channel, 14th January, 1917.
UB 38. Destroyed in Dover area, 8th February, 1918.
UB 39. Sunk in English Channel, 17th May, 1917.
UB 40. Destroyed on evacuation of Flanders, October, 1918.
UB 41. Sunk in the North Sea, 5th October, 1917.
(UB 42. Surrendered.)
(UB 43. Sold to Austria.)
UB 44. Destroyed in the Mediterranean, 30th July, 1916.
UB 45. Sunk in the Black Sea, 30th October, 1916.
UB 46. Sunk in the Dardanelles, 16th December, 1916.
(UB 47. Sold to Austria.)
UB 48. Blown up at Pola or Cattaro, end of October, 1918.
(UB 49, UB 50, UB 51. All surrendered.)
UB 52. Torpedoed by Submarine H 4, in the Adriatic, lat. 41.46 N., long. 18.35 E., 23rd May, 1918.
UB 53. Sunk in the Adriatic, 3rd August, 1918.
UB 54. Sunk in the North Sea, 11th March, 1918.
UB 55. Sunk in Dover area, 22nd April, 1918.
UB 56. Sunk in Dover area, 19th December, 1917.
UB 57. Sunk in the North Sea, 14th August, 1918.
UB 58. Sunk in Dover area, 10th March, 1918.
UB 59. Found scuttled at Bruges, October, 1918.
(UB 60, UB 62, UB 64. All surrendered.)
UB 61. Sunk in the North Sea, 29th November, 1917.
UB 63. Sunk in the North Sea, 28th January, 1918.
UB 65. Destroyed by explosion of own torpedo, in action with U.S. Submarine L2, off S.W. of Ireland, 10th July, 1918.
UB 66. Sunk in the Mediterranean, 18th January, 1918.
(UB 67. Surrendered.)
UB 68. Sunk by own crew, after being disabled by gunfire of Sloop SNAPDRAGON and Trawler CRADOSIN, 60 miles N.E. of Malta, 4th October, 1918.
UB 69. Sunk in the Mediterranean, 8th January, 1918.
UB 70. Sunk in the Mediterranean, by British Destroyer BASILISK and U.S.S. SYDONIA, 8th May, 1918.
UB 71. Sunk in Straits of Gibraltar, 21st April, 1918.
UB 72. Torpedoed in English Channel, 12th May, 1918.
(UB 73. Surrendered to the French.)
UB 74. Rammed and depth charged, by Armed Yacht LORNA, off Portland Bill, 26th May, 1918.
UB 75. Sunk in the North Sea, 10th December, 1917.
(UB 76, UB 77, UB 79, UB 80. All surrendered.)
UB 78. Sunk in English Channel, 9th May, 1918.
UB 81. Sunk in English Channel, 2nd December, 1917.
UB 82. Sunk off North of Ireland, 17th April, 1918.
UB 83. Sunk in the North Sea, 10th September, 1918.
(UB 84. Surrendered to the French.)
UB 85. Sunk in the Irish Sea, 30th April, 1918.
(UB 86, UB 87, UB 88. All surrendered.)
UB 89. Foundered, on voyage to England to surrender.
UB 90. Sunk in action with Submarine L 12, off Norwegian Coast, 16th October, 1918.
(UB 91, UB 92, UB 93, UB 94, UB 95, UB 96, UB 97, UB 98, UB 99, UB 100, UB 101, UB 102. All surrendered.)
UB 103. Destroyed in Dover area, 16th September, 1918.
UB 104. Sunk in the North Sea, 19th September, 1918.
(UB 105, UB 106. Both surrendered.)
UB 107. Sunk in the North Sea, 27th July, 1918.
UB 108. Lost about July, 1918.
UB 109. Destroyed in Dover area, 29th August, 1918.
UB 110. Rammed by Destroyer GARRY, off Roker, lat. 54.39 N., long. 0.55 W., 19th July, 1918, and subsequently raised by British.
(UB 111, UB 112, UB 114. All surrendered.)
UB 113. Lost, probably in the North Sea, September, 1918.

UB 115. Sunk in the North Sea, 29th September, 1918.
UB 116. Sunk in the North Sea, 28th October, 1918.
(UB 117, UB 118. Both surrendered.)
UB 119. Lost about May, 1918.
(UB 120, UB 121, UB 122. All surrendered.)
UB 123. Sunk in the North Sea, 19th October, 1918.
UB 124. Sunk off North of Ireland, 20th July, 1918.
(UB 125, UB 126, UB 128. All surrendered.)
UB 127. Lost, probably in the North Sea, September, 1918.
UB 129. Blown up at Pola or Cattaro, end of October, 1918.
(UB 130, UB 131, UB 132, UB 133 all surrendered ; **UB 134, UB 135,** never completed ; **UB 136,** surrendered ; **UB 137** to **UB 141,** inclusive, never completed ; **UB 142, UB 143, UB 144, UB 145,** all surrendered ; **UB 146, UB 147,** never completed ; **UB 148, UB 149, UB 150,** all surrendered ; **UB 151, UB 152, UB 153,** never completed ; **UB 154, UB 155,** both surrendered.)
UC 1. Sunk in the North Sea, 24th July, 1917.
UC 2. Sunk in the North Sea, 2nd July, 1915.
UC 3. Sunk in the North Sea, 23rd April, 1916.
UC 4. Destroyed on evacuation of Flanders, October, 1918.
UC 5. Captured while stranded on Shipwash Shoal, 27th April, 1916.
UC 6. Sunk in the North Sea, 28th September, 1917.
UC 7. Sunk in the North Sea, 21st August, 1916.
UC 8. Stranded on Terschelling, 6th November, 1915, and acquired by Dutch Navy as M 1.
UC 9. Sunk in the North Sea, about October, 1915.
UC 10. Sunk in the North Sea, 6th July, 1916.
UC 11. Sunk in the North Sea, 26th June, 1918.
UC 12. Sunk in the Mediterranean, 17th March, 1916 ; subsequently salved by Italians.
UC 13. Sunk by Russians, in Black Sea, about November, 1916.
UC 14. Sunk in the North Sea, about October, 1917.
UC 15. Sunk in the Black Sea, November, 1916.
UC 16. Destroyed by paravanes and depth charges of Destroyer MELAMPUS, off Selsea Bill, 23rd October, 1917.
(UC 17. Surrendered.)
UC 18. Sunk in the North Sea, 12th March, 1917.
UC 19. Destroyed by depth charges of Destroyer LLEWELLYN, in Straits of Dover, 4th December, 1916.
(UC 20, UC 22, UC 23. All surrendered.)
UC 21. Sunk in the North Sea, 27th September, 1917.
UC 24. Sunk off Cattaro, 24th May, 1917.
UC 25. Blown up at Cattaro or Pola, end of October, 1918.
UC 26. Rammed by Destroyer MILNE, off mouth of Thames, lat. 51.4 N., long. 1.40 E., 9th May, 1917.
(UC 27, UC 28, UC 31. All surrendered.)
UC 29. Sunk off S.W. of Ireland, 7th June, 1917.
UC 30. Sunk in the North Sea, 19th April, 1917.
UC 32. Sunk in the North Sea, 23rd February, 1917.
UC 33. Sunk in the Irish Sea, 26th September, 1917.
UC 34. Blown up at Pola or Cattaro, end of October, 1918.
UC 35. Sunk by French Patrol Vessel AILLY, off Sardinian Coast, 16th May, 1918.
UC 36. Destroyed by bombs of Seaplane 8663, 20 miles E.N.E. of Noord Hinder Lightship, 20th May, 1917.
(UC 37. Surrendered.)
UC 38. Sunk in the Mediterranean, 14th December, 1917.
UC 39. Sunk in the North Sea, 8th February, 1917.
UC 40. Foundered on voyage to England to surrender, 21st February, 1919.
UC 41. Sunk in the North Sea, 21st August, 1917.
UC 42. Sunk off South of Ireland, 10th September, 1917.
UC 43. Torpedoed by Submarine G 13, about 9 miles N.W. of Muckle Flugga Lighthouse, 10th March, 1917.
UC 44. Mined off South of Ireland, 4th August, 1917.
(UC 45. Surrendered.)
UC 46. Rammed by Destroyer LIBERTY, in Straits of Dover, 8th February, 1917.

SUBMARINES—*continued.*

UC 47. Rammed and depth charged, by P 57, in the North Sea, 18th November, 1917.

UC 48. Interned at Ferrol, 23rd March, 1918, and scuttled by her crew, off Coruna, 15th March, 1919.

UC 49. Sunk in the North Sea, 31st May, 1918.

UC 50. Destroyed by depth charges of Destroyer ZUBIAN, in English Channel, Dover area, 4th February, 1918.

UC 51. Sunk by Destroyer FIREDRAKE, in the North Sea, 13th November, 1917.

(UC 52. Surrendered.)

UC 53. Blown up at Pola or Cattaro, end of October, 1918.

UC 54. Blown up at Pola or Cattaro, end of October, 1918.

UC 55. Sunk in the North Sea, 29th September, 1917.

(UC 56. Interned at Santander, 24th May, 1918, and surrendered to French after Armistice.)

UC 57. Lost in the Baltic, between 19th and 22nd November, 1917.

(UC 58, UC 59, UC 60. All surrendered.)

UC 61. Stranded in Dover area, and blown up by crew, 26th July, 1917.

UC 62. Lost in the North Sea, about October, 1917.

UC 63. Sunk by Submarine E 52, near Straits of Dover, 1st November, 1917.

UC 64. Destroyed in Dover area, 20th June, 1918.

UC 65. Torpedoed by Submarine C 15, 3rd November, 1917.

UC 66. Sunk in English Channel, 12th June, 1917.

(UC 67. Surrendered.)

UC 68. Sunk by Submarine C 7, in the North Sea, 5th April, 1917.

UC 69. Sunk in English Channel, 6th December, 1917.

UC 70. Sunk in the North Sea, 28th August, 1918.

UC 71. Sunk off Heligoland, 20th February, 1919.

UC 72. Sunk in the North Sea, 22nd September, 1917.

(UC 73, surrendered ; **UC 74,** interned at Barcelona, 21st November, 1918, and since surrendered.)

UC 75. Rammed by Destroyer FAIRY, in the North Sea, 31st May, 1918.

(UC 76. Surrendered.)

UC 77. Destroyed in Dover area, 10th July, 1918.

UC 78. Destroyed in Dover area, 2nd May, 1918.

UC 79. Sunk by Submarine E 45, in the North Sea, 19th October, 1917.

(UC 80 to **UC 85,** at the Imperial Yard, Danzig, and **UC 86** to **UC 89,** at the Weser Yard, Bremen, were destroyed on the stocks.)

(UC 90. Surrendered.)

UC 91. Foundered in the North Sea, on voyage to England to surrender, 10th February, 1919.

(UC 92, UC 93, UC 94, UC 95, UC 96, UC 97, UC 98, UC 99, UC 100, UC 101, UC 102, UC 103, UC 104, UC 105, UC 106, UC 107, UC 108, UC 109, UC 110, UC 111, UC 112, UC 113, UC 114. All surrendered.)

(Full details of various types comprised above, will be found under German Navy Surrendered Section.)

57 AUXILIARIES.

(Gross Tonnage given in each case.)

(a) 13 Armed Merchant Cruisers.

Cap Trafalgar (1913). 18,710 tons. Sunk by gunfire of British Armed Merchant Cruiser CARMANIA, in action off Brazilian Island of Trinidad, South Atlantic, 14th September, 1914.

Berlin (1908). 17,324 tons. Interned at Trondhjem, 16th November, 1914, and surrendered after Armistice.

Kronprinz Wilhelm (1901). 14,908 tons. Interned at Newport News, 29th April, 1915. Seized by U.S. Government in 1917, and renamed VON STEUBEN.

AUXILIARIES—*continued.*

Kaiser Wilhelm der Grosse (1897). 13,952 tons. Disabled, by gunfire of British Light Cruiser HIGHFLYER, and scuttled, to avoid capture, off Rio de Oro, 27th August, 1914.

Yorck (1906). 8909 tons. Interned at Valparaiso, December, 1914, and seized by Chile in September, 1918.

Lützow (1908). 8826 tons. Captured by British Cruiser BLACK PRINCE, off Port Said, August, 1914. Now s.s. HUNTSEND.

Prinz Eitel Friedrich (1904). 8797 tons. Interned at Newport News, 7th April, 1915. Seized by U.S. Government, in 1917, and renamed DE KALB.

Greif (ex GUBEN) (1914). 4963 tons. Sunk, by gunfire of British Armed Cruisers ALCANTARA and ANDES, and Light Cruiser COMUS, in North Sea, lat. 61.48 N., long. 1.40 E., 29th February, 1916. (Ship was disguised as Norwegian s.s. RENA.)

Schwarzwald (1911). 4892 tons. Lost (probably mined), about February, 1917.

Sao Paulo (1896). 4724 tons. Lost off Schleswig Coast, before July, 1917.

Pallanza (1891). 4606 tons. Lost off mouth of Ems, before July, 1917.

Niederwald (1904). 3490 tons. Lost early in 1918.

Another (unidentified). Torpedoed by British Submarine E 5, off Borkum, December, 1915.

(b) 27 Fleet Auxiliaries.

Moltke (1901). 12,335 tons. Seized by Italian Government and renamed PESARO.

König Albert (1894). 10,484 tons. Seized by Italian Government, renamed FERNANDO PALASCIANO, and employed as a Hospital Ship.

Tabora (1912). 8022 tons. Sunk by gunfire of British Light Cruiser HYACINTH, in inner harbour of Dar-es-Salaam, 23rd March, 1916. (TABORA was disguised as a Hospital Ship.)

Seydlitz (1902). 8008 tons. Interned at Bahia Blanca, 22nd January, 1915, and surrendered after Armistice.

Baden (1913). 7676 tons. Sunk by gunfire of British Light Cruiser BRISTOL and Armed Cruiser MACEDONIA, off the Falklands, 8th December, 1914.

Bethania (1899). 7548 tons. Captured by British Cruiser ESSEX, 300 miles off Cape Hatteras, 7th September, 1914. Now s.s. PARISIAN.

Karnak (1912). 7044 tons. Interned at Antofagasta, November, 1914, and seized by Chile, in September, 1918.

Leda (1914). 6766 tons. Captured by British Cruiser SUFFOLK, 200 miles South of Bermuda, in August, 1914. Subsequently released to Standard Oil Co., as an act of grace, and now American s.s. MATINICOCK.

Rhenania (1904). 6455 tons. Seized by Italian Government and renamed FELTRE.

Navarra (1905). 5794 tons. Set on fire and sunk by her crew, to avoid capture by British Armed Cruiser ORAMA, off Rio de la Plata, 12th November, 1914.

Holger (1906). 5555 tons. Interned at Buenos Aires, 20th February, 1915, and surrendered after Armistice.

Tannenfels (1899). 5341 tons. Captured, in Basilan Straits, Southern Philippines, 8th October, 1914. Now s.s. HUNSLET.

Santa Isabel (1914). 5199 tons. Sunk by gunfire of British Light Cruiser BRISTOL and Armed Cruiser MACEDONIA, off the Falklands, 8th December, 1914.

Sudmark (1913). 5113 tons. Captured by British Cruiser BLACK PRINCE, off Port Said, 15th August, 1914. Now s.s. HUNTSCRAFT.

Eleonore Woermann (1902). 4624 tons. Sunk by gunfire of Commonwealth Battle Cruiser AUSTRALIA, off Patagonian Coast, 6th January, 1915.

Max Brock (1907). 4579 tons. Captured by British Cruiser CUMBERLAND, at Duala, Cameroons, 30th September, 1914. Now s.s. POLICASTRIA.

Markomannia (1911). 4505 tons. Sunk by gunfire of British Light Cruiser YARMOUTH, off Coast of Sumatra, 12th October, 1914.

AUXILIARIES—*continued.*

Macedonia (1900). 4347 tons. Captured by British Light Cruiser GLOUCESTER, in the South Atlantic, on the Equator, March, 1915. Now s.s. POLGOWAN.

Spreewald (1907). 3899 tons. Captured by British Cruiser BERWICK, off the Windward Islands, 12th September, 1914. Now H.M.S. LUCIA.

Graecia (1890). 2753 tons. Captured by British Cruiser ARGONAUT and taken to Gibraltar, 10th October, 1914. Renamed s.s. POLLOKSHIELDS, and wrecked in September, 1915.

Somali (1890). 2550 tons. Captured off Mafia, and scuttled at mouth of Rufiji river, to block exit of KÖNIGSBERG, December, 1914.

Anna Woermann (1893). 2335 tons. Sunk by gunfire of a British Cruiser (probably CUMBERLAND) in September, 1914.

Sui Mow (1907). 1857 tons. Captured by a Japanese Destroyer, off Tamoshima, 15th September, 1914. Now s.s. TAMOSHIMA MARU.

Locksun (1902). 1657 tons. Interned at Honolulu, 8th November, 1914. Seized by U.S. Government, in 1917, and renamed GULFPORT.

Elsbeth (1905). 1651 tons. Sunk by gunfire of British Cruiser HAMPSHIRE, in China Sea, October, 1914.

Ophelia (1912). 1153 tons. Captured by British Destroyer METEOR, in the North Sea, disguised as a Hospital Ship, 17th October, 1914. Renamed s.s. HUNTLY, and sunk by a German Submarine, at midnight, 20th-21st December, 1915.

Another (unidentified). Mined, in the Baltic, December, 1917.

(c) 5 Minelayers.

Königin Luise (1913). 2163 tons. Sunk by gunfire of British Light Cruiser AMPHION and Destroyers LANCE, LARK and LINNET, 40 miles off mouth of Scheldt, 5th August, 1914.

Hermann (1901). 2030 tons. Blown up by gunfire of a Russian Flotilla, in Nörrkoping Bay, 13th June, 1916.

Another (unidentified). Torpedoed by Russian Destroyers, off Windau, November, 1915.

Another (unidentified). Torpedoed by British Submarine E 16, in Heligoland Bight, 22nd December, 1915.

Another (unidentified). Mined off Falsterbo, May, 1916.

(d) 3 Minesweepers.

Marie (1905). 1866 tons. Sunk by gunfire of British Light Cruisers and Destroyers, in the Kattegat, 2nd November, 1917.

Bunz. (No details available.) Mined in Langeland Belt, 15th December, 1915.

Ander. (No details available.) Wrecked in Little Belt, January, 1916.

(e) 9 Miscellaneous.

Santa Fè (1901). Seaplane Carrier. 5342 tons. Interned at Rotterdam, November, 1918, and surrendered after Armistice.

Hindenburg. Icebreaker. About 1000 tons. Mined off Aland Islands, April, 1918.

Graf von Götzen (1915). Armed Lake Steamer. 800 tons. Guns : 1—4.1 in. Scuttled off Kigoma, Lake Tanganyika, July, 1916.

Kuka (1905). Armed Tender. 602 tons. Sunk by a British Cruiser, at Duala, Cameroons, September, 1914.

Buka. Armed Colonial Yacht. Scuttled to avoid capture, at Kieta, Solomon Islands, November, 1914.

Itolo (1903). Armed Tender. 299 tons. Sunk by French Gunboat SURPRISE, in Corisco Bay, 21st September, 1914.

Adjutant. Armed Tug. 250 tons. Scuttled off Kigoma, Lake Tanganyika, July, 1916.

Nachtigal (1895). Armed River Steamer. 249 tons. Blown up by gunfire of British Gunboat DWARF, in Bimbia River, Cameroons, 16th September, 1914.

Mwanza. Armed Lake Steamer. Scuttled in Smith Sound, Victoria Nyanza, June, 1916.

AUXILIARIES—*continued.*

Note.—The following 6 vessels are not counted as German losses, as they originally flew Allied flags :—

Meteor (ex British s.s. VIENNA). Employed as Minelayer. Blown up and sunk, to avoid capture by a British Light Cruiser Squadron, 50 miles N.W. of Horns Reef, 9th August, 1915.

Libau (ex British s.s. CASTRO). Disguised as Norwegian s.s. AUD, and employed to land Casement's party in Ireland. Sunk by gunfire of British Sloop BLUEBELL, off West Coast of Ireland, 20th April, 1916.

Leopard (ex British s.s. YARROWDALE). Sunk, by gunfire of British Cruiser ACHILLES and Armed Boarding Steamer DUNDEE, 16th March, 1917.

Kormoran II (ex Russian Volunteer Fleet s.s. RYAZAN). Interned at Guam, 14th December, 1914, partially blown up, and seized by U.S. Government in 1917.

Seeadler (ex British Sailing Ship PASS OF BALMAHA). Wrecked on Mopeha Island, Lord Howe Group, and completely gutted by fire, 23rd August, 1917.

Bothnia (ex-Russian.) Mined S.W. of Lillegrund, 5th December, 1917.

AUSTRIAN.

3 BATTLESHIPS.

SZENT ISTVAN (1914). 20,000 tons. Guns : 12—12 in., 45 cal. ; 12—5.9 in., 50 cal. ; 18—11 pdr., etc. Torpedoed by Italian Motor Torpedo Boats M.A.S. 15 and 21, off Premuda Island, 30 miles south of Pola, 10th June, 1918. For appearance, see photo of PRINZ EUGEN, on page 488.

VIRIBUS UNITIS (1911). Sister to SZENT ISTVAN, above. Sunk by fixed torpedo, in Pola Harbour, by Italian C.M.B. LOCUSTA, night of 31st October—1st November, 1918.

WIEN (1895). 5600 tons. Guns : 4—9.4 in., 40 cal. ; 6—5.9 in., etc. Torpedoed by Italian Motor Launch, at Trieste, night of 9th-10th December, 1917. For appearance, see photo of MONARCH, on page 491.

3 LIGHT CRUISERS.

KAISERIN ELISABETH (1890). 4000 tons. Guns : 8—5.9 in. Blown up and sunk, off Chiposan, Kiao-Chau Bay, 3rd November, 1914.

KAISER FRANZ JOSEF (1889). Similar to KAISERIN ELIZABETH, above. Lost during heavy weather, off Dalmatian Coast, October, 1919. (This vessel had been allotted to the Yugo-Slav Fleet.)

ZENTA (1897).   2300 tons.   Guns : 8—4.7 in.   Sunk by gunfire of French Squadron, off Antivari, 16th August, 1914.

N.B.—Two or more Light Cruisers which were building at Monfalcone were destroyed when that place was evacuated by the Austrians, in June, 1915, and the shipyard set on fire.

6 DESTROYERS.

Lika and **Triglav** (1913).   800 tons.   Guns : 2—3.9 in., 6—11 pdr.   Tubes : 4—20.8 in.   LIKA mined, and TRIGLAV sunk by gunfire of French Destroyer CASQUE, off Durazzo, 29th December, 1915.   For appearance, see photo of ORJEN, on page 496.

Wildfang (1906).   400 tons.   Guns : 6—11 pdr.   Tubes : 2—17.7 in.   Mined, in Upper Adriatic, middle of June, 1917.
Streiter (1906).   Sister to WILDFANG, above.   Sunk by British Aircraft, at Durazzo, 27th May, 1918.
Dinara (1909) and **Scharfschutze** (1907).   Similar to WILDFANG, above.   Sunk at Durazzo, 2nd October, 1918.   One was torpedoed by an Italian Flotilla of four M.A.S. Torpedo Boats, the other sunk by two British Destroyers in endeavouring to escape.

8 TORPEDO BOATS.

No. 87 (1914).   250 tons.   Guns : 2—11 pdr.   Tubes : 4—17.7 in.   Driven ashore after being torpedoed by Italian Torpedo Boats of M.A.S. type, at Durazzo, 2nd October, 1918.
No. 11 (1910).   110 tons.   Guns : 2—3 pdr.   Tubes : 2.   Delivered by crew into Italian hands, at Porto Recanati, near Ancona, 5th October, 1917.   For appearance, see photo on page 497.
No. 7 and **No. 3** (1910).   Sisters to No. 11, above.   Captured by the French, in the Adriatic, October, 1918.
No. 26 (1886).   78 tons.   Guns : 2—1 pdr.   Tubes : 2.   Mined near Pola, 23rd August, 1914.   For appearance, see photo of No. 20 type, on page 497.
No. 22 (1886).   Sister to No. 26, above.   Torpedoed by French Submarine BERNOUILLI, off Cape Planka, March, 1916.
One. (Unidentified.)   Torpedoed by Italian Motor Launch, off Durazzo, 13th May, 1918.
One. (Unidentified.)   Sunk in action, in Gulf of Drin, 5th September, 1918.

SUBMARINES.

(Number uncertain, probably over 20.)

U 31 (1917).   Details uncertain.   Destroyed by depth charges of British and American Light Craft, at Durazzo, 2nd October, 1918.
U 30 (1917).   Details uncertain.   Sunk in the Adriatic, April, 1917.
U 23 (1916).   450 tons.   Guns : 1—3.4 in.   Tubes : 4—19.7 in.   Sunk by Italian Torpedo Boat AIRONE, in the Adriatic, 21st February, 1918.
U 20 (1916).   Sister to U 23, above.   Sunk in the Adriatic, 17th December, 1916.
U 16 (1915).   190 tons.   Sunk by Italian Destroyer NEMBO, off Taranto, 16th October, 1916.
U 12 (1914).   236 tons.   Tubes : 2—17.7 in.   Torpedoed by Italian Submarine, in Gulf of Venice, 11th August, 1915.   Subsequently salved, and now in Italian hands.
U 6 (1909).   Similar to U 12, above.   Sunk by gunfire of Drifters DULCIE DORIS and EVENING STAR II, in the Adriatic, 13th May, 1916.   For appearance, see photo of U 5, on page 499.
U 4 (1908).   240 tons.   Tubes : 2—17.7 in.   Sunk by French Cruiser WALDECK ROUSSEAU, off Cattaro, October, 1914.
U 3 (1908).   Sister to U 4, above.   Sunk by gunfire of French Destroyer BISSON and an Italian Armed Cruiser, off coast of Montenegro, 12th August, 1915.
One (number unknown),   Sunk in action with Italian Submarine MEDUSA, 10th June, 1915.
One (number unknown).   Destroyed by bombs from Italian Aircraft, in mid-Adriatic, 18th August, 1917.
One (number unknown).   Torpedoed by French Submarine CIRCE, off Cattaro, 26th May, 1917.
One (number unknown).   Rammed by an Italian Destroyer, in Lower Adriatic, December, 1915.
One (number unknown).   Destroyed by bombs from an Italian Aeroplane (officially announced in August, 1918).
One (number unknown).   Sunk in action with Italian Submarine F 12 (officially announced in August, 1918).

N.B.—The Italian Ministry of Marine stated, in October, 1917, that eleven enemy Submarines had been destroyed in the Adriatic since the beginning of that year.   Five were lost in the summer of 1918.

2 AUXILIARIES.

Bathori (1892).   2223 tons.   Sunk by gunfire of British Cruiser MINERVA, off Mediterranean Coast of Spain, 3rd September, 1914.
Beethoven (Cadets' Training Ship).   Mined near Trieste, 17th December, 1914.

TURKISH.

2 BATTLESHIPS.

KHEIREDIN BARBAROSSA (1891). 10,000 tons. Guns: 4—11 in., 40 cal.; 2—11 in., 35 cal.; 8—4.1in., 35 cal.; 8—15½ pdr. Torpedoed by British Submarine E 11. in Sea of Marmora, 5 miles from Constantinople, 8th August, 1915. For appearance, see photo of TORGUD REIS, on page 590.

MESSUDIEH (1874). 10,000 tons. Guns: 2—9.2 in., 40 cal.; 12—6 in., 45 cal.; 14—12 pdr. Torpedoed by British Submarine B 11, off Chanak, in the Dardanelles, 13th December, 1914.

LIGHT CRUISER.

MIDILLI (1911) (ex German BRESLAU). 4500 tons. Guns: 12—4.1 in. Mined during action with British Destroyers LIZARD and TIGRESS, South of Imbros, 20th January, 1918. For appearance, see photo of STRALSUND on page 525.

Note.—The Light Cruiser MEDJIDIEH was mined in the Black Sea, 3rd April, 1915, salved by the Russians and renamed PRUT, but was recaptured by the Turks in May, 1918.

7 (or more) GUNBOATS.

Giassia Reis ? (1912). (Identity not positive.) 500 tons. Guns: 2—4 in. Scuttled, to avoid capture, at Tchesma, 31st October, 1914. For appearance, see photo of this type, on page 591.

Tachkeupru (1908). 210 tons. Guns: 2—3 pdr. Sunk by gunfire of three Russian Destroyers, in the Black Sea, to East of Bosphorus, 10th December, 1915. For appearance, see photo of MALATIA, on page 591.

Marmaris (1907). 490 tons. Guns: 4—9 pdr., etc. Destroyed by fire, after being disabled by gunfire of British Sloop ODIN, in the Tigris, 2nd June, 1915.

Nurelbahr (1903). 200 tons. Guns: 2—3 pdr. Torpedoed by British Submarine E 14, in Sea of Marmora, 1st May, 1915. (No photo available.)

Kastamuni (1906). 185 tons. Guns: 2—3 pdr. Sunk by gunfire of three Russian Destroyers, in Black Sea, to East of Bosphorus, 10th December, 1915. No photo available.

Timsah (1899). 120 tons. Guns: 2—3 pdr. Irreparably damaged by mine, during 1918. (No photo available.)

Pelenk-i-Deria (1890). 880 tons. Guns: 2—4.1 in., etc. Torpedoed by British Submarine E 11, S.W. of Seraglio Point, Constantinople, 22nd May, 1915.

3 DESTROYERS.

Yadighiar-i-Milet (1909). 620 tons. Guns: 2—15 pdr. Tubes: 3—18 in. Irreparably damaged by bombs from British Aircraft, 1917. For appearance, see photo of MUAVENET-I-MILET, on page 592.

Gairet-i-Vatanieh (ex MAHABET-I-MILET) (1909). Sister to YADIGHIAR-I-MILET, above. Wrecked, off Baljik, in Black Sea, May, 1917.

Yar Hissar (1908). 290 tons. Guns: 1—12 pdr., etc. Tubes: 2—18 in. Torpedoed by British Submarine E 11, in Gulf of Ismid, Sea of Marmora, 3rd December, 1915. For appearance, see photo of SAMSOUN, on page 592.

3 (or more) TORPEDO BOATS.

Kutahiya (1906).   175 tons.   Guns : 2—3 pdr.   Tubes : 2—14 in.   Blown up in the Bosphorus, September, 1916.   For appearance, see photo of URFA, on page 593.

Timur Hissar (1906).   97 tons.   Guns : 2—1 pdr., etc.   Tubes : 2—18 in.   Driven ashore in Kalamuti Bay, Khios, by British Destroyers, JED, KENNET and WEAR, 17th April, 1915.   For appearance, see photo of SULTAN HISSAR, on page 593.

Hamidabad (1906).   Sister to TIMUR HISSAR, above.   Sunk by gunfire of Russian Destroyers BISTRI and PULKI, in Inda Bay, Black Sea, 20th October, 1917.

N.B.—Other Turkish Gunboats and Torpedo Craft have been lost, but particulars for identification are not available.   Missing units, which have doubtless been sunk, include the Gunboats KILID-EL-BAHR, SED-EL-BAHR and RESHANIEH, Torpedo Boat URFA, Motor Boats 1 to 8 and 12 to 16.   Some Submarines have also been destroyed, but these were probably German.

---

11 MERCANTILE AUXILIARIES.

Gul-Djemal (1874).   5071 tons.   Torpedoed by British Submarine E 14, in the Sea of Marmora, 3rd May, 1915.

Also the following, lost on various dates in 1915, the exact circumstances being uncertain :—

Midhat Pasha (1901). 4455 tons.	**On-Temmuz** (1892). 2162 tons.
Carmen (ex Austrian Steamer). (1911.) 4424 tons.	**Kizil Irmak** (1890). 1945 tons.
Bahr-i-Amer (1893). 3603 tons.	**Zunguldak** (1884). 1545 tons.
Sabah (1896). 3013 tons.	**Nedjat** (1870). 1523 tons.
Mahmud Shevket Pasha (1886). 2690 tons.	**Hilal** (1877). 1502 tons.
	(Besides others of smaller size.)

BULGARIAN.

TORPEDO BOAT.

Letyastchi (1907).   100 tons.   Guns : 3—3 pdr.   Tubes : 3—18 in.   Lost in 1918, after being handed over to the French.   For appearance, see photo of SMYELI type, on page 502.